FEATURES AND BENEFITS

Algebra, Structure and Method, Book 1

■ The lessons and exercises were written by **Dr. Mary P. Dolciani** and the other experienced authors to ensure that students receive the first-year algebra concepts needed for further study of mathematics. See pp. iii – x (Table of Contents).

■ Algebra concepts and skills are developed using these time-tested and effective varieties of **exercises:**

Oral Exercises check students' understanding of basic lesson ideas. See p. 209.

Graded A, B, and C Written Exercises teach and review algebra concepts presented in the lesson. See pp. 209 – 210.

Numerous **tests and reviews** check students' mastery of algebra skills. See pp. 232 – 237.

Problems give students a chance to apply the problem solving methods discussed in the lessons. See pp. 26, 118 – 121.

NEW optional **Computer Exercises** following selected sections enable students to use a computer to help them learn algebra. See p. 210.

NEW end-of-chapter **Mixed Reviews** test students' ability to solve problems encountered out of context. See p. 274.

■ **NEW** student learning aids:

More **worked-out examples** in the lessons and exercise sets help students apply lesson concepts to solve exercises and problems. See pp. 208 – 210.

Reading Algebra features help students read mathematical explanations more effectively. See p. 142.

Preparing for College Entrance Exams gives students opportunities to practice on test items like those on college entrance exams. See pp. 275, 660.

■ **Calculator Key-Ins** and **Computer Key-Ins** extend algebra lesson concepts. See p. 322.

■ Teaching aids include the following:

Comprehensive **Teacher's Edition** provides teacher's commentary followed by annotated pupil book pages with side-column notes. See Contents, p. T3.

Resource Book includes extra tests, practice exercises, enrichment activities, and problem solving worksheets.

Tests on duplicating masters provide quizzes, chapter tests, and cumulative tests (different from Resource Book tests).

Practice Masters offer concentrated practice on fundamental concepts and skills (different from Resource Book practice exercises).

Solution Key contains worked solutions to pupil book exercises.

Algebra Action: Courseware for Algebra 1 contains disks to supplement or enrich first-year algebra instruction, and a Teacher's Manual.

ALGEBRA

Structure and Method

Book 1

Teacher's Edition

Mary P. Dolciani
Richard G. Brown
William L. Cole

EDITORIAL ADVISER
Robert H. Sorgenfrey

TEACHER CONSULTANTS
Gail H. Clark
Allen C. Demmin
James F. Dudley
Donald Field
Lois A. Martin
Sister Patricia Supple, CSJ

HOUGHTON MIFFLIN COMPANY · BOSTON

Atlanta Dallas Geneva, Ill. Lawrenceville, N.J. Palo Alto Toronto

THE AUTHORS

Mary P. Dolciani, formerly Professor of Mathematical Sciences, Hunter College of the City University of New York.

Richard G. Brown, Mathematics Teacher, The Phillips Exeter Academy, Exeter, New Hampshire.

William L. Cole, Associate Professor of Mathematics Education, Michigan State University.

EDITORIAL ADVISER

Robert H. Sorgenfrey, Professor of Mathematics, University of California, Los Angeles.

TEACHER CONSULTANTS

Gail H. Clark, Mathematics Teacher, Johnson High School, Gainesville, Georgia.

Allen C. Demmin, Mathematics Coordinator, Middleton High School, Middleton, Wisconsin.

James F. Dudley, Mathematics Teacher, Rio Grande High School, Albuquerque, New Mexico.

Donald Field, Mathematics Teacher, Niles West High School, Skokie, Illinois.

Lois A. Martin, Mathematics Teacher, Downingtown High School, Downingtown, Pennsylvania.

Sister Patricia Supple, CSJ, Mathematics Teacher, Daniel Murphy Catholic High School, Los Angeles, California.

The authors of ALGEBRA, Structure and Method, Book 1 wish to thank Robert J. McMurray for his valuable contribution to this Teacher's Edition.

Printed in U.S.A.

ISBN: 0-395-43053-4

ABCDEFGHIJ-D-943210/8987

Contents

Teaching the Course

The Teacher's Edition, Resource Book, and Solution Key have been designed to help you teach algebra. For each chapter in the textbook, the Teacher's Edition provides Lesson Commentary and slightly reduced reproductions of student pages with annotated answers. Side columns next to the student pages present additional teaching aids. The Teacher's Edition also includes extra tests and reviews, an assignment guide, a guide to supplementary materials, and special Reading Algebra, Learning Strategies, Problem Solving Strategies, and Error Analysis sections.

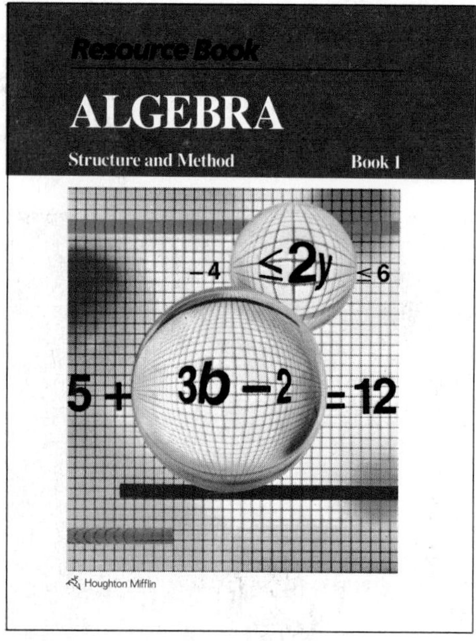

The Resource Book offers extra test, practice, review, and enrichment material—all keyed to the student textbook—in blackline master format. Worksheets designed to help students who are having difficulty solving word problems are also included. The diagram masters help make classroom presentations easier.

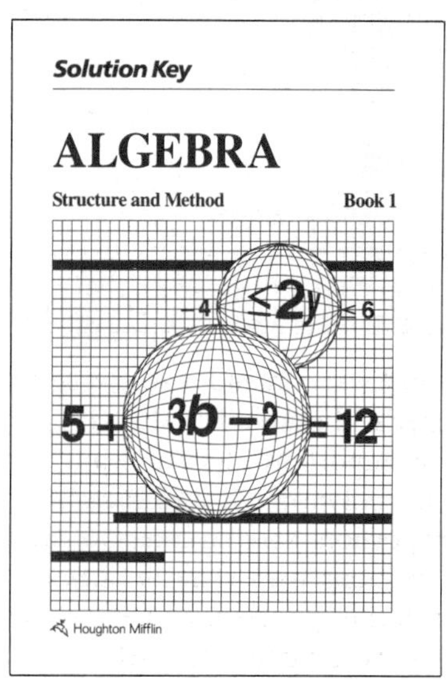

The Solution Key provides step-by-step solutions, including diagrams, for all written exercises in the student book.

Supplementary Materials

The supplementary materials on duplicating masters include Tests and Practice Masters. Each set of masters is keyed to the student textbook and has a separate Answer Key with answers annotated on reduced facsimiles of the masters. *Houghton Mifflin Algebra Action: Courseware for Algebra 1* presents algebra topics in an interesting manner that takes full advantage of the unique capabilities of the computer.

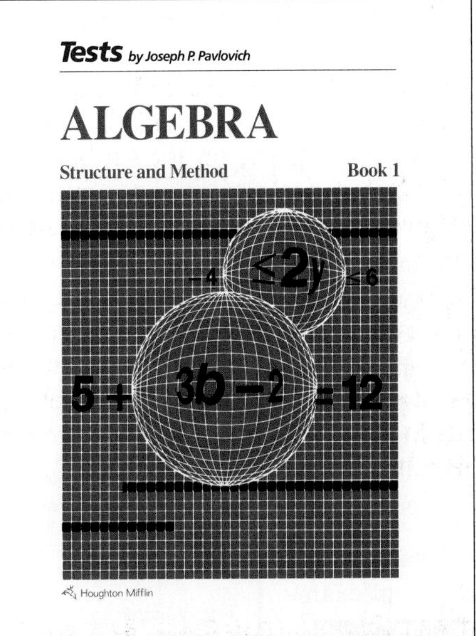

The Tests contain quizzes on small portions of material, chapter tests, and cumulative tests.

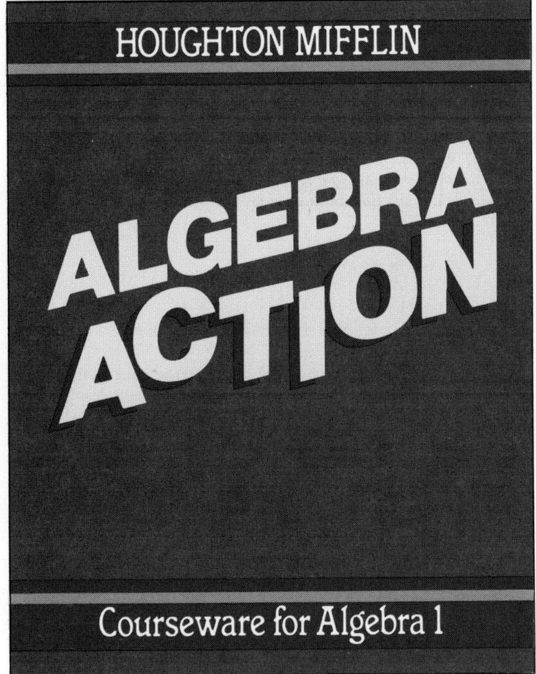

This courseware includes four diskettes and a Teacher's Manual. The diskette lessons focus on important algebra topics, including variables, polynomials and factoring, ratio and proportion, solving linear equations, and operations with radicals. Lessons include tutorial, practice, and enrichment components. Students can select the lessons and the components that they wish to do. The Teacher's Manual includes a chart keying the diskette lessons to the textbook.

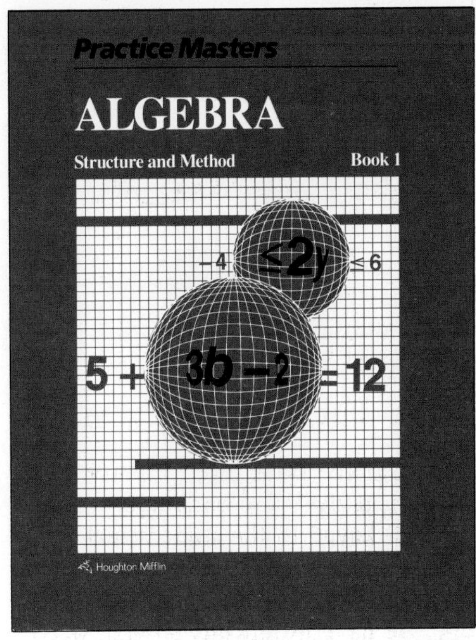

The Practice Masters offer concentrated practice on small portions of material in worksheet format. Periodic cumulative reviews are included.

Using the Teacher's Edition

This Teacher's Edition includes nearly full-sized textbook pages annotated with answers. Time-saving references, suggestions, and extra examples and exercises appear in the adjacent side-columns, where they will be most useful. The simulated Teacher's Edition pages below illustrate the material in the side columns.

For each section in the textbook, page references are given for the corresponding **Teaching Suggestions** and **Suggested Extensions** in the Lesson Commentary at the front of the Teacher's Edition.

Chalkboard Examples provide additional examples to use in presenting the lesson to your students.

The **Common Error** sections alert you to errors that students often make and suggest how you can help your students avoid these errors.

Supplementary Materials include references to the Tests, Practice Masters, and Resource Book that accompany the textbook.

Suggested Assignments for minimum, average, and maximum courses are given with each lesson and also in the **Assignment Guide** at the front of the Teacher's Edition.

Teaching Suggestions
p. T81

Suggested Extensions
p. T82

Chalkboard Examples

1. An integer is represented by d. Write the next four integers in natural order after d. $d + 1, d + 2, d + 3, d + 4$
2. Write an equation to represent the given sentence.

   The sum of three consecutive integers is 15.
   $x + (x + 1) + (x + 2) = 15$

Common Error

Students often represent three consecutive odd integers in natural order as n, $n + 1$, and $n + 3$ because 1 and 3 are odd integers. Remind them that the difference between any two consecutive odd integers, like the difference between any two consecutive even integers, is 2.

Supplementary Materials

Test 5
Resource Book, p. 72

Suggested Assignments

74/1–12
R 75/*Self-Test 2*

Average
74/1–11 odd, 13–16, 18
R 75/*Self-Test 2*

Maximum
74/1–11 odd, 13–17, 20, 21
R 75/*Self-Test 2*

2-7 Solving Problems; Consecutive Integers

Objective To write equations to represent relationships among integers.

SIMULATED PAGE

When you count by ones from any number in the set of integers

$$\ldots, -4, -3, -2, -1, 0, 1, 2, 3, 4, \ldots$$

you obtain **consecutive integers.** For example, $-3, -2, -1, 0, 1$, and 2 are six consecutive integers. Those integers are listed in **natural order,** that is, in order from least to greatest.

Example 1 An integer is represented by m.

a. Write the next three integers in natural order after m.
b. Write in decreasing order the three integers that immediately precede m.
c. Write an equation that states that the sum of seven consecutive integers is 63.

Solution

a. $m + 1, m + 2, m + 3$
b. $m - 1, m - 2, m - 3$
c. $(m - 3) + (m - 2) + (m - 1) + m + (m + 1) + (m + 2) + (m + 3) = 63$

Ten is called an *even* integer because $10 = 2 \times 5$. The integers that are the products of 2 and any integer are the **even integers.** In natural order, they are:

$$\ldots, -4, -2, 0, 2, 4, 6, 8, \ldots$$

An **odd integer** is an integer that is not even. In natural order, the odd integers are:

$$\ldots, -5, -3, -1, 1, 3, 5, \ldots$$

If you count by *twos* from any even integer, you obtain **consecutive even integers.** For example:

Three consecutive even integers: 8; $8 + 2$, or 10; $10 + 2$, or 12

If you count by *twos* from any odd integer, you obtain **consecutive odd integers.** For example:

Three consecutive odd integers: 9; $9 + 2$, or 11; $11 + 2$, or 13

Thus, in natural order,

$$m, m + 2, m + 4$$

are consecutive even integers if m is even, and consecutive odd integers if m is odd.

Features of the Teacher's Edition not illustrated here include **Problem Solving Strategies** and **About the Photo** descriptions (see pp. 1 and xiv). **Permission-to-reproduce tests** and **reviews** and a number of other useful features are located in the front of the Teacher's Edition. See Contents, p. T3, for a complete listing.

Oral Exercises

SIMULATED PAGE

1. If $k = 3$, what are $k + 1$, $k + 2$, and $k + 3$? 4, 5, 6
2. If $r = 1$, what are $r - 1$, $r - 2$, and $r - 3$? 0, −1, −2
3. The least of four consecutive integers is −1. What are the other three integers? 0, 1, 2
4. The greatest of four consecutive integers is 20. What are the other three integers? 19, 18, 17
5. If $x = 15$, represent 14 and 16 in terms of x. $14 = x - 1$, $16 = x + 1$
6. If $p = 20$, represent 18 and 22 in terms of p. $18 = p - 2$, $22 = p + 2$
7. If $d = 7$, represent 3, 5, and 9 in terms of d. $3 = d - 4$, $5 = d - 2$, $9 = d + 2$
8. If $e = 12$, represent 8, 10, 14, and 16 in terms of e. $8 = e - 4$, $10 = e - 2$, $14 = e + 2$, $16 = e + 4$

Written Exercises

Write an equation to represent the stated relationship among integers.

A

1. The sum of two consecutive integers is 87. $x + (x + 1) = 87$
2. The sum of three consecutive integers is 69. $x + (x + 1) + (x + 2) = 69$
3. The sum of four consecutive integers is −106. $x + (x + 1) + (x + 2) + (x + 3) = -106$
4. The sum of four consecutive integers is −42. $x + (x + 1) + (x + 2) + (x + 3) = -42$
5. The sum of three consecutive odd integers is 81. $x + (x + 2) + (x + 4) = 81$
6. The sum of three consecutive odd integers is 147. $x + (x + 2) + (x + 4) = 147$
7. The product of two consecutive even integers is 168. $x(x + 2) = 168$
8. The sum of four consecutive even integers is −100. $x + (x + 2) + (x + 4) + (x + 6) = -100$
9. The greater of two consecutive even integers is six less than twice the smaller. $x + 2 = 2(x) - 6$
10. The smaller of two consecutive even integers is five more than one half of the greater. $x = \frac{1}{2}(x + 2) + 5$
11. The four Smith children were born at two-year intervals. The sum of their ages is 36. $x + (x + 2) + (x + 4) + (x + 6) = 36$
12. A rectangle has a perimeter of 62 cm. The lengths in centimeters of its adjacent sides are consecutive integers. $2x + 2(x + 1) = 62$

B

13. There are four consecutive integers. Their sum is 100 decreased by twice the difference between the greatest and twice the least. $x + (x + 1) + (x + 2) + (x + 3) = 100 - 2[(x + 3) - 2(x)]$
14. There are four consecutive integers. Three times the greatest is 6 more than the sum of the other three. $3(x + 3) = 6 + [x + (x + 1) + (x + 2)]$

Additional A Exercises

Write an equation to represent the stated relationship among integers.

1. The sum of two consecutive integers is 93. $x + (x + 1) = 93$
2. The product of two consecutive even integers is 120. $x(x + 2) = 120$
3. The largest of three consecutive integers is three times the smallest. $x + 2 = 3x$

Mixed Review Exercises

Simplify.

1. $-6 + 13 + (-8)$ −1
2. $m - 18 - (m - 9)$ −9
3. $(-3)(-12) - (9)(-5)$ 81
4. Find the solution over the set of real numbers: $|m| = -2$ no sol.

Additional Answers Written Exercises

13. $x + (x + 1) + (x + 2) + (x + 3) = 100 - 2[(x + 3) - 2(x)]$

Quick Quiz

Simplify.

1. $-4t + 9t - 3$ $5t - 3$
2. $5(y + 5) - 10$ $5y + 15$
3. $8(1 - m) - 2$ $6 - 8m$
4. If $x = 27$, then in terms of x, $26 = \underline{?}$ and $28 = \underline{?}$. $x - 1$; $x + 1$

You can use the **Additional A Exercises** to check whether your students are ready to start the Written Exercises on their own.

Mixed Review Exercises practice skills taught in previous lessons and help keep these skills alive.

Computer Key-In Commentary (not shown) discusses BASIC programming methods and style and common student errors.

Answers that cannot be annotated on the textbook page appear in the side column.

For each Self-Test in the textbook, there is a corresponding **Quick Quiz**.

Organization of the Textbook

Each of the 12 chapters in the textbook has been divided into several groups of related lessons. For example, *Applications and Problem Solving* is one of the three groups of lessons in Chapter 1. This group includes Sections 1-4 through 1-6.

The **objective** of each lesson is stated at the start of the lesson.

Worked-out examples illustrate and reinforce the concepts and skills presented in the text. These examples occur frequently throughout the book. **Graded exercises** follow each lesson.

Applications and Problem Solving

1-4 Words into Symbols: Expressions

Objective To represent numerical relationships stated in words by mathematical expressions.

To solve problems using algebra, you must often translate word phrases about numbers into numerical or variable expressions.

Suppose you think of two numbers, one nine more than the other. If x stands for the smaller number, then the greater number is represented by

$$x + 9.$$

Example 1 Represent each word phrase by a variable expression.

a. Nine less than a number x
b. Nine times a number x
c. One ninth of a number x
d. Nine divided by a number x

Solution **a.** $x - 9$ **b.** $9x$ **c.** $\frac{1}{9}x$ **d.** $\frac{9}{x}$

Each group of lessons is followed by a **Self-Test.** Questions are keyed to lesson objectives. Answers to Self-Tests appear at the back of the book.

Self-Test 2

Vocabulary formula (p. 13)

1. A variable expression for nine times the difference of the number n and one is __?__. **Obj. 1-4, p. 13**

Ample review and test material is included at the ends of chapters. Each chapter has a **Chapter Summary, Chapter Review, Chapter Test,** and **Cumulative Review.** Each chapter except the last has a **Maintaining Skills** page that reviews arithmetic and algebra skills needed for succeeding chapters. Six **Mixed Review** sets test students' ability to solve exercises when they are encountered out of context. The six **Preparing for College Entrance Exams** pages review algebra concepts and help students develop test-taking skills.

Chapter Summary

Chapter Review

Chapter Test

Cumulative Review (Chapters 1–10)

Maintaining Skills

Mixed Review

Preparing for College Entrance Exams

Oral Exercises

Written Exercises

Simplify.

A **1. a.** $(x^4)^3$ **b.** $(x^3)^4$ **c.** $x^3 \cdot x^4$ **2. a.** $(a^7)^2$ **b.** $(a^2)^7$ **c.** $a^2 \cdot a^7$

3. a. $a^n \cdot a^n$ **b.** $(a^n)^2$ **c.** $a^2 \cdot a^n$ **4. a.** $b^t \cdot b^t \cdot b^t$ **b.** $(b^t)^3$ **c.** $b^t \cdot b^3$

Problems

Write an equation based on the facts of each problem. Then solve the equation and answer the question posed in the problem.

A **1.** Negative eight times a number is 376. What is the number?

The different types of material within the textbook have been **color-coded** to emphasize their function. **Exercises** and **problem sets** are preceded by a blue bar.

Calculator Key-In

Computer Key-In

The following program will find the LCD for two denominators.

```
10  PRINT "TO FIND THE LEAST"
20  PRINT "COMMON DENOMINATOR;"
```

Green bars signal the technology strand. The **Calculator** and **Computer Key-In** features indicate ways of using calculators or computers to enhance an algebra course.

Challenge

Extra / *Quadratic Inequalities*

Reading Algebra / *Symbols*

Close attention is needed to read mathematics because mathematical materials usually involve special symbols as well as words. And, often, those symbols can be read in several ways. Here are some examples.

Special features closely related to the mathematical content of the course are **Challenge** problems and **Reading Algebra** and **Extra** sections. Red bars identify these features.

Application / *Consumer Credit*

Historical Note / *The Sieve of Eratosthenes*

Career Note / *Nutritionist*

Biographical Note / *Juan de la Cierva*

Applications and **Career Notes** (yellow bars) relate algebra to everyday life. **Historical** and **Biographical Notes** (gold bars) provide historical background and human interest.

Chapter Tests

Chapter 1 Test

1. Evaluate if $x = 5$, $y = 8$, $z = 1$, $r = 6$, and $s = 2$: **a.** $(x + y)(s + z)$ **b.** $\frac{y + rs}{x - z}$

2. Simplify: **a.** $3 + 9 \cdot 7 - 8 \div 2$ **b.** $\frac{15 \times 4 + 9}{(2 + 1)(2 - 1)}$ **c.** $\frac{15 \times (4 + 9)}{(2 + 1)2 - 1}$

3. Solve if $x \in \{0, 1, 2, 3, 4, 5, 6, 7\}$: **a.** $8x - 6 = 10$ **b.** $\frac{2}{3}x = 4$

4. A bag of peanuts costs c cents. A box of granola bars costs 15¢ more than a bag of peanuts. Represent (a) the cost of 3 boxes of granola bars and (b) the change you would receive after buying a bag of peanuts and a box of granola bars if you gave the salesperson $2.00.

5. Write an equation that represents the given information: Pedro is four times as old as his nephew, Carlos. Carlos is c years old. Five years ago, the sum of their ages was 25.

6. Use the five-step plan to solve the following problem: The number of international units (I.U.) of vitamin A in a cup of skim milk is one ninth the number in a stalk of cooked broccoli. A person who has both the skim milk and the broccoli has received the recommended daily allowance of 5000 I.U. of vitamin A. How many I.U.'s of vitamin A are contained in a cup of skim milk?

7. Graph the given numbers on a number line: $^-2$, $\frac{^-1}{2}$, 0, $\frac{3}{2}$.

8. On a number line, point P has coordinate $^-4$. Write the coordinate of the point halfway between the origin and P.

9. Simplify: **a.** $|-8.5| + |-5.8|$ **b.** $-|-(-\frac{2}{3})|$ **c.** $|-7| + [-(-1)]$

Tell how many solutions each equation has.

10. $|m| = 9$ 11. $|n| = -9$ 12. $|-q| = \frac{1}{9}$

13. Translate into symbols: The absolute value of negative two is greater than the opposite of seven.

Replace each _?_ with < or > to make a true statement.

14. $-\frac{2}{3}$ _?_ $-\frac{3}{2}$ 15. $-|-1|$ _?_ $|-(-1)|$ 16. -0 _?_ $-(5 + 6)$

Chapter 2 Test

Simplify each expression.

1. $1.7 + 0.5 + 8.5 + 4.3$

2. $2 \times 9 \times 50 \times 11$

3. $a + 6 + b + 2$

4. $(-7 + 2) + 5$

5. $[-3 + (-4)] + (-9)$

6. $-\frac{5}{4} + 2 + \frac{1}{4} + (-8)$

7. Solve the equation $-20 + x = -10$.

8. Simplify: $-39 + 18 + 53 + (-72) + (-6) + 75$.

9. Evaluate $-x + y + (-3)$ if $x = -2$ and $y = -4$.

10. Oxygen has a melting point of $-218.4°C$. If the boiling point is $35.4°C$ higher than the melting point, find the boiling point of oxygen.

Simplify.

11. $51 - (7 - 104)$

12. $-3.6 - (-9.15)$

13. $-(r - 4) - (-r)$

14. Find the difference in the latitudes of Athens, Greece, latitude 38°N, and Sydney, Australia, latitude 34°S.

Simplify.

15. $(17 \times 19) + (3 \times 19)$

16. $3(a - 2) + 5(a + 6)$

17. $-9 + (-5)j + 3 + (-2)j$

18. $(-2)(-3)(-5)$

19. $-7(-2a + b) - (-3b)$

20. $(-9)(-8) - 9(-8)$

21. Write an equation to represent the following: The lengths in centimeters of the sides of a triangle are consecutive odd integers. The perimeter of the triangle is 45 cm.

22. If $x \neq 0$, what is the reciprocal of $-\frac{2}{x}$?

Simplify.

23. $\left(-\frac{1}{2}\right)(-72)\left(-\frac{t}{9}\right)$

24. $\left(-\frac{1}{11}\right)(-132x + 66y - 110)$

25. $8\left(-\frac{1}{2}a - \frac{1}{8}b\right) - 75\left(-\frac{1}{3}a\right)$

26. $-27 \div \left(-\frac{1}{3}\right)$

27. $\frac{-j}{12}(-24)\left(\frac{k}{-2}\right)$

28. $\frac{266z}{-14z}$, $z \neq 0$

29. Evaluate $\frac{b - 7c}{a - c}$ if $a = -3$, $b = -1$, and $c = 2$.

Chapter 3 Test

Solve.

1. $r + 115 = -27$

2. $-9 + j = |-8 + 2|$

3. $11 - (t - 7) = 0$

4. $-\frac{v}{4} = -8$

5. $\frac{2a}{15} = -12$

6. $-29d = 377$

7. $-15x - 5x = -40$

8. $1 - 9y = 100$

9. $-\frac{1}{3}z + 7 = -5$

10. $6b - 2(b - 1) = -14$

11. $h + 21 - 2h = 12$

12. The Chans' electric bill for September was \$40.70, which included a tax of \$1.98. If the Chans used 320 kW·h of electricity that month, find the cost per kilowatt-hour.

Solve. If the equation is an identity or if it has no root, state that fact.

13. $7 - 5x = 3x + 31$

14. $3r - 1 + r = -2(1 - 2r)$

15. $\frac{3}{4}(8k - 4) = -3 + 6k$

16. $6(n - 8) = 7(n + 8)$

17. The sum of two numbers is -2. If twice the smaller number is added to three times the larger, the result is 1. Find the numbers.

18. The ages in years of Ben and Barb are consecutive odd integers. In six years, the sum of their ages will be four times Ben's present age. How old is each now if Barb is older than Ben?

19. The manager of the Craft Shoppe bought some rug kits for \$16 each, sold all but 6 of them for \$22 each, and made a total profit of \$168. How many kits were originally bought?

20. Write the missing reasons.

If $a + b = 0$, then $a = -b$.

1. $a + b = 0$	1. ?
2. $(a + b) + (-b) = 0 + (-b)$	2. ?
3. $a + [b + (-b)] = 0 + (-b)$	3. ?
4. $a + 0 = 0 + (-b)$	4. ?
5. $a = -b$	5. ?

Chapter 4 Test

1. Write in exponential form: the cube of three more than x.
2. Simplify: $(1 - 3^2) \div (1 - 3)^2 \times (-6)$.
3. Evaluate $\frac{-x^3 - 1}{(x + 1)^3}$ when $x = -2$.

Simplify.

4. $(3r^2 - 5r - 2) + (-3r^2 + 6r - 8)$
5. $(2a - 9ab + b) - (8b - ab + 7a)$

6. Find three consecutive odd integers such that the sum of the two least integers is 11 more than the greatest integer.

Simplify.

7. $(-4a^2b)\left(\frac{5}{2}b^2c\right)$
8. $5^k \cdot 5 \cdot 5^{k-1}$
9. $7t^3(-t^3) + 5t(3t^5)$
10. $\left(\frac{1}{3}x^3y\right)^3$
11. $-8z(-2z^3)^4$
12. $(3n^x)^2 \cdot (n^4)^x$

13. Multiply: $4y^2(y^3 - 7y - 1)$
14. Simplify: $-2j[7 - j(3j - 5) + j^2]$
15. Solve: $\frac{3}{4}(12n - 20) + 2n^2 = 2n(n + 3)$

Multiply.

16. $(x + 2)(3x^2 + 2x - 1)$
17. $(3c - d)(2c - 5d)$
18. $(7x - 2y)(3x^2 + 4xy)$

19. Solve $P = R(1 + bt)$: **a.** for R **b.** for t
20. The Ortiz family drove from Dawson to Linbury in 1.75 h. The return trip in the rain took 15 min more. If the average speed on the first part of the trip was 10 km/h faster than the speed on the return trip, find the distance from Dawson to Linbury.
21. A rectangular park was 15 m longer than it was wide. When a border of bushes 0.5 m wide was planted around the edges of the park, the area of the park increased by 56 m^2. Find the original dimensions of the park.
22. Show that the following problem has no solution: Marla has 3 dimes and half as many nickels as pennies. If her coins are worth 50¢ in all, how many nickels does she have?

Chapter 5 Test

1. List all the pairs of integral factors of -66.
2. Give the prime factorization of 504.

Simplify. Assume that no denominator equals zero.

3. $\dfrac{(-3xy^2)^3}{36x^2y^6}$
4. $\dfrac{4a^4b \cdot 25abc^4}{10ab^2c^3}$
5. $\dfrac{-3(ab + c)^3}{-9(ab + c)}$
6. $\dfrac{16g^5h^2 - 8g^6h + 4g^7}{4g^5}$
7. $\dfrac{21t + 49}{7} - \dfrac{5t^3 - 9t}{t}$

8. Find the greatest common factor of $252r^2(r + 1)^3$ and $392(r + 1)^4$.
9. Express $3x^4y^2 - 6x^2y^4 + 9y^6$ as the product of its greatest monomial factor and another polynomial.

Express each product as a polynomial.

10. $(3m - 2)(m - 1)$
11. $c(4c + 5)(2c - 3)$
12. $(5e - f)(7e + 4f)$
13. $(z^2 + 7)(z^2 - 7)$
14. $(5a - 8b)(5a + 8b)$
15. $(r - 3)^2$
16. $(s + 6t)^2$
17. $(-2j^3 + k)^2$
18. $(mn^2 - p)^2$

Factor completely. If the polynomial is not factorable, write "prime."

19. $289x^2 - 36y^2$
20. $4v^6 - 9$
21. $25u^2 - 10u + 1$
22. $49h^2 - 28hk + k^2$
23. $n^2 - 17n + 60$
24. $y^2 - 20yz + 56z^2$
25. $r^2 + 18r - 63$
26. $1 - 11ab - 12a^2b^2$
27. $4j^2 - 13j - 10$
28. $7x^2 - 11xy - 6y^2$
29. $3g^5 - 7g^4 + 6g - 14$
30. $9 - (a + 2b)^2$
31. $-6c^3 + 8c^2 + 8c$
32. $m^4 - 24m^2 - 25$
33. $x^2 + 2xy + y^2 - z^4$

Solve.

34. $27x^3 = 3x$
35. $18y^2 + 8 = 24y$
36. $z^3 + 10z^2 = 24z$

37. The sum of two integers is 8, and the sum of their squares is 19 more than their product. Find the integers.
38. The base of a triangle is 3 cm shorter than the altitude. If the area is 20 cm^2, find the length of the base.

Chapter 6 Test

Express in simplest form, noting any restrictions on the variables.

1. $\frac{6a^2 + 4ab}{6a^2 + 13ab + 6b^2}$

2. $\frac{m^2 - 2m + 1}{5 - m - 4m^2}$

3. $\frac{2x^2 - 98}{28x^2 + 4x^3}$

4. $\frac{9c^4d}{7de^2} \cdot \frac{14ce^3}{27c^6}$

5. $\left(-\frac{3x}{y^2}\right)^4 \cdot \frac{xy^6}{18}$

6. $\frac{(a - 5)^3}{3a^3} \cdot \frac{6a^6}{5 - a}$

7. $\left(-\frac{2a}{3b}\right)^3 \div 6a^2b$

8. $\frac{4r^2 + 4s^2}{8rs} \div \frac{8r + 8s}{4r^2s^2}$

9. $\frac{t^4 - 1}{t^3 + t} \div \left(\frac{t - 1}{t}\right)^2$

10. $\frac{x^2 + 2x - 3}{x^2 + 5x + 6} \cdot \frac{4 - x^2}{x^2 - x}$

11. $-12yz^2 \div 4y^2z \div 9z$

12. Find the missing numerator: $\frac{2}{c - 3d} = \frac{?}{c^2 - cd - 6d^2}$

Find the LCD for each group of fractions.

13. $\frac{x + 1}{8}, \frac{x - 1}{28}$

14. $\frac{1}{3a - 9}, \frac{8}{21 - 7a}$

15. $\frac{5}{4bc^2}, \frac{7}{10c^3}, \frac{4}{b^2c}$

Write each expression as a fraction in simplest form.

16. $\frac{2ab}{a - 2b} + \frac{a^2}{2b - a}$

17. $\frac{1}{6n^2} - \frac{5}{4n}$

18. $\frac{7}{9} + \frac{8x}{45} - \frac{x}{15}$

19. $\frac{y}{x + y} - \frac{x}{x + y}$

20. $\frac{z + 3}{z^2 + 2z} - \frac{z + 4}{z^2 - 4}$

21. $h - \frac{2}{h - 1}$

22. $\frac{2c + 1}{3c - 1} + 2$

23. $\frac{t}{2t - 1} + \frac{1}{2t + 1} - 1$

24. $\left(x - \frac{2}{x}\right)\left(2 - \frac{x}{2}\right)$

Divide. Write your answer as a polynomial or mixed expression.

25. $\frac{2 + 4x + 6x^2}{3x - 1}$

26. $\frac{6a^3 - 11a^2 + 1}{3a - 1}$

27. $\frac{b^2 + 5bc + 4c^2}{b + 2c}$

28. Factor $6x^3 - 23x^2 - 5x + 4$ completely given that $2x + 1$ is a factor.

Chapter 7 Test

State each ratio in simplest form.

1. 72 s:0.5 h

2. The ratio of (a) the perimeters and (b) the areas of a rectangle with sides 60 cm and 2.2 m and a square with sides of length 80 cm.

3. Sue and Lois live 13.5 km apart. At 10:00 A.M. each girl leaves her house and jogs toward the other. The ratio of Sue's speed to Lois's speed is 5:4. If the girls meet at 11:15 A.M., how fast does each jog?

Solve.

4. $\frac{3x + 2}{8} = 4$

5. $\frac{5n - 9}{2} = \frac{5n + 4}{3}$

6. $\frac{4}{2a + 5} = \frac{7}{10a - 1}$

7. $\frac{3x + 5}{2} - \frac{8x + 1}{6} = 3$

8. $3y - \frac{2y}{3} = \frac{3y}{2} + 10$

9. $\frac{5}{6}(z + 2) - 8 = \frac{3}{8}(z - 1)$

10. $\frac{9r - 30}{17r + 2} = \frac{2}{5}$

11. $\frac{b + 4}{6b} = \frac{b}{b + 8}$

12. $\frac{9}{x^2 - 3x} + \frac{x}{3 - x} = 1$

13. The sum of a number and twice its reciprocal is 3. Find the number.

14. Express (a) $8\frac{1}{4}\%$ and (b) 320% as fractions in simplest form.

15. Find (a) 5.7% of 80 and (b) 108% of 5.

16. 5.6 is 42% of what number?

17. The number of hospital volunteers recently increased from 25 to 30. What was the percent increase?

18. The Hills estimated that the use of energy-efficient appliances has reduced their monthly electricity usage by 6%. If they now use 366.6 kW·h per month, find the original number of kilowatt-hours used per month.

19. A chemist mixed a 20% acid solution with a 60% acid solution to form 10 L of a 30% solution. How many liters of each solution were used?

20. Emily can paint her fence in 6 h. If she does the job with her son, it takes 2.5 h less. How long would it take her son working alone?

21. Express 0.0059 in (a) scientific notation and (b) expanded notation.

22. Evaluate: **a.** $\frac{5^{-3}}{5^0 \cdot 5^{-5}}$ **b.** $(7 \cdot 2^{-3})^{-2}$

Simplify. Give answers in terms of positive exponents.

23. $(a^0b^{-1})^2$

24. $\frac{e^{-3}}{e^3}$

25. $\left(\frac{g}{g^{-2}}\right)^{-1}$

26. $x^{-2} \cdot x^2$

Chapter 8 Test

1. State whether each ordered pair is a solution of $3x + 4y = 1$.

   a. $(-5, 4)$ b. $\left(-3, \frac{3}{2}\right)$ c. $\left(\frac{2}{3}, -\frac{3}{4}\right)$

2. Solve $\frac{3}{x-1} = \frac{4}{y+2}$ for y in terms of x.
3. Solve $x^2 + y = 4$ if x and y represent whole numbers.
4. Plot the points $A(-4, 2)$, $B(0, -4)$, $C(3, 0)$ and $D(-5, -1)$ in a coordinate plane.

Graph each equation.

5. $4x - 2y = 8$
6. $y = 3x - 4$

7. Solve by the graphic method: $y = \frac{2}{3}x + 3$
   $2x - 3y = -9$
8. Solve by the substitution method: $7x + 3y = 11$
   $3x - y = 23$

Solve by the addition-or-subtraction method.

9. $3a - 5b = 9$
   $4a + 5b = -23$
10. $7x - 3y = 37$
    $5x - 6y = 11$
11. $4r + 2s = 7$
    $3r - 5s = 2$

Solve by using a system of two equations in two variables.

12. Blake paid $2.80 for 16 ten-cent and twenty-cent stamps. How many ten-cent stamps did he buy?
13. Kate is three years less than twice as old as her brother, Brett. Next year Brett's age will be three-fourths Kate's age. How old is each now?
14. A canoeist paddles 21 km downstream in 3 h. The return trip takes 1.2 h longer. What is the rate of the current?
15. A two-digit number is three times the sum of its digits. When the number is subtracted from the number obtained by reversing the digits, the result is 45. Find the original number.
16. If the numerator of a fraction is increased by 1, the value of the resulting fraction is $\frac{2}{3}$. If the numerator and the denominator are both increased by 5, the value of the resulting fraction is $\frac{7}{10}$. Find the original fraction.

Chapter 9 Test

1. Find the slope of the line through the points $(-8, 1)$ and $(-5, -8)$. If $(-1, b)$ lies on the line, find the value of b.
2. Find the slope of the line with equation $7x + 5y = -7$.
3. Write an equation in standard form of the line that has a slope of $\frac{3}{2}$ and a y-intercept of $-\frac{1}{4}$. Draw the graph of the equation.

Write an equation in standard form for each line described.

4. parallel to the graph of $y = -x + 7$ and with y-intercept 0
5. with slope 3 and passing through point $(2, -1)$
6. passing through points $(5, 5)$ and $(0, 5)$

Find the range of each function.

7. $f\colon x \to \frac{1}{2x - 1}$, $D = \{-1, 0, 1\}$
8. $g(x) = x^2 + x$, $D = \{-2, -1, 0\}$
9. Use the functions in Exercises 7 and 8 to find $f(2) \cdot g(2)$.
10. The table at the right shows a function based on consumer prices in 1967.
    a. State the domain and range of the function.
    b. Make a broken-line graph of the function.

Average Purchasing Power of Dollar

Year	1967	1972	1977	1982
Value	$1.00	$0.84	$0.55	$0.35

11. Draw the graph of the function $r(x) = \frac{x + 3}{2}$.
12. Graph the equation $y = 1 - 2x - x^2$ and label the vertex.
13. Find the least value of the function $G\colon x \to 5 + 4x^2$.
14. Given: $x_1 = 6$, $x_2 = 2.5$, and $y_1 = 2.4$. Find y_2 if (x_1, y_1) and (x_2, y_2) are ordered pairs of (a) the same direct variation and (b) the same inverse variation.
15. An employee's wages are directly proportional to the time worked. If Shelli received $114 for 30 hours of work, how much will she receive for 40 hours of work?
16. The brightness of the illumination of an object varies inversely as the square of the distance from the object to the source of light. How far from a bulb does an object receive four times as much illumination as it does when it is 8 m from the bulb?
17. If z varies directly as x and inversely as the cube of y, and $z = 12$ when $x = 3$ and $y = 0.5$, find x when $z = 16$ and $y = 0.75$.

Chapter 10 Test

Solve each inequality if $x \in \{-4, -3, -2, -1, 0, 1, 2, 3, 4\}$.

1. $4 - 3x \geq 1$ **2.** $x^2 > 3x$ **3.** $|x| \leq 1.5$

4. Draw the graph of $2 \geq m > -1$ over the domain {the real numbers}.

Solve each inequality and draw its graph.

5. $-7j > -35$

6. $4 + \frac{5}{3}k \leq k$

7. $3(3a + 1) < -2(1 - 5a)$

8. $2\left(2b + \frac{1}{4}\right) \geq \frac{5}{4}(b - 15)$

9. A bus and a car leave Mundelein at 9:15 A.M., and travel in opposite directions. If the bus travels 10 km/h faster than the car and the distance between them is at least 400 km at 11:45 A.M., what is the least possible speed of the bus?

Solve each open sentence.

10. $-8 \leq c - 3 \leq -1$

11. $5x + 8 > 3$ or $7x - 9 \leq 5$

12. $8 > -2 - 3d > -8$

13. $4f > -24$ or $f + 5 \leq -1$

14. $|g + 7| \geq 2$

15. $|9 - h| = 0$

16. $11 - 8|n| > -13$

17. $-\frac{1}{2}(5 + 3|t|) = -7$

Draw the graph of each open sentence.

18. $|2y - 13| \leq 3$

19. $\left|1 - \frac{3z}{2}\right| > 2$

20. $|4q - (3 - 2q)| = 1$

21. $9|5w + 4| - 7 > 29$

Graph each inequality in a coordinate plane.

22. $2x - y < -6$ **23.** $x + 1 \geq -2$ **24.** $6x + 2y > 8 - 2x$

Graph the solution set of each system.

25. $y \geq x - 3$
$y < 3x + 1$

26. $y < -2x$
$y > -3 - 2x$

27. $2x - y \geq 5$
$x + 2y \leq 7$

Chapter 11 Test

1. Arrange $-\frac{59}{24}$, $-\frac{89}{36}$, and -2.5 in order from least to greatest.

2. If $x \in \{0, 1, 2, 3\}$, state whether $\frac{4}{5 - x}$ increases or decreases in value as x increases in value.

3. Find the rational number halfway between $\frac{3}{5}$ and $\frac{2}{3}$.

4. Express (a) $\frac{7}{45}$ and (b) $\frac{19}{16}$ as decimals.

5. Express (a) 0.725 and (b) $0.3\overline{45}$ as fractions in simplest form.

Simplify.

6. $\sqrt{\frac{100}{9}}$ 7. $\sqrt{0.0121}$ 8. $\sqrt{1225}$ 9. $-\frac{\sqrt{98}}{\sqrt{8}}$

10. $\sqrt{72}$ 11. $3\sqrt{112}$ 12. $\sqrt{\frac{3r^7s}{27rs^3}}$ 13. $\sqrt{z^2 + 2z + 1}$

Find both roots of each equation to the nearest tenth. You may use the Table of Squares Roots on page 650.

14. $m^2 - 81 = 0$ 15. $12a^2 = 75$ 16. $x^2 = 320$

17. A rectangle has width 10 and diagonals of length 26. Find its length.

18. The hypotenuse of a right triangle is 3 cm longer than the second side. If the third side is 9 cm long, find the perimeter of the triangle.

Express in simplest form. Assume that $x > 0$.

19. $\frac{6\sqrt{2}}{\sqrt{15}}$ 20. $\sqrt{\frac{8}{3}} \cdot \sqrt{\frac{45}{32}}$ 21. $\sqrt{x}(\sqrt{x^5} - \sqrt{4x})$

22. $\sqrt{75} - \sqrt{48}$ 23. $\sqrt{\frac{21}{2}} + \sqrt{\frac{3}{14}}$ 24. $\sqrt{6}\left(\sqrt{18} - \sqrt{\frac{1}{2}}\right)$

25. $(\sqrt{3} + 3\sqrt{2})^2$ 26. $(1 + \sqrt{5})(1 - 2\sqrt{5})$ 27. $(\sqrt{2} + \sqrt{7})(\sqrt{2} - \sqrt{7})$

28. Rationalize the denominator of $\frac{4}{1 - \sqrt{3}}$.

Solve.

29. $\sqrt{\frac{a}{3}} - 2 = 2$ 30. $\sqrt{4x - 1} = \frac{1}{2}$ 31. $\sqrt{2s^2 - 3} = 1$

Chapter 12 Test

Solve. If the equation has no solution, so state.

1. $(2x - 1)^2 = 49$

2. $4y^2 + 169 = 0$

3. $\frac{1}{3}z^2 - \frac{1}{2} = 1$

Solve by completing the square. Give irrational roots in simplest radical form and then approximate them to the nearest tenth.

4. $a^2 - 8a = 2$

5. $3b^2 - 12b = 15$

6. $c^2 - 3c = -1$

Solve by the quadratic formula.

7. $r^2 + 2r = 1$

8. $3s^2 - 5s + 1 = 0$

9. $6t^2 + t - 15 = 0$

Solve.

10. $m^2 - 1 = -\frac{3}{2}m$

11. $2v^2 + 0.5 = 5v$

12. $7n^2 + 15n = 0$

13. $\frac{1}{2}(h + 3)^2 = 8$

14. $\frac{x + 1}{3x + 2} = \frac{x + 2}{2x - 1}$

15. $p^2 - 12p = 28$

State the number of real roots.

16. $9d^2 - 6d + 1 = 0$

17. $3e^2 + 7e - 3 = 0$

18. $f^2 + 6f + 10 = 0$

19. How many points does the graph of the parabola with equation $y = 2 - 3x + 4x^2$ have in common with the x-axis? Does its vertex lie above, below, or on the x-axis?

20. The sum of a number and twice its square is 6. Find the number.

21. A picture that is 5 inches by 7 inches is placed in a frame of uniform width. Framing the picture increases the area by 20 square inches. Find the width of the frame.

Cumulative Reviews

Review for Chapters 1–3

Simplify.

1. $\dfrac{30 \div 5 - 2}{2(5 - 3)}$

2. $|-7.2| - |-2.7|$

3. $-1 + 7 + (-13) + 4$

4. $-4 - (-1) - 6$

5. $3(2a - b) + b - 7a$

6. $-\frac{2}{3}(-9x + 3y)$

7. $(-360)\left(-\frac{1}{18}\right)\left(-\frac{1}{4}\right)$

8. $\dfrac{-222t}{6t}, t \neq 0$

9. $\dfrac{-30}{-\frac{1}{2}}$

10. $56 \div 8 - 6 \div 2$

11. $56 \div (8 - 6) \div 2$

12. $0.9 - 1.02 + 0.54$

13. $-7(-5r - 1) + 2(4 - 3r)$

14. $3j - 2k - 3k(5 - j)$

15. $|3 - 1| - |1 - 3|$

Evaluate each expression if $r = -2$, $s = |-3|$, $t = \frac{1}{3}$, and $v = 6$.

16. $-4r(t + v)$

17. $\dfrac{st + 4v}{r - 3}$

18. $\dfrac{(v + r)(v - r)}{t(s + r)}$

Solve each equation over the domain $\{-3, -2, -1, 0, 1, 2, 3\}$.

19. $(x + 1)(x - 2) = 0$

20. $x = -x$

21. $2 - (-x) = 1$

22. Graph the given numbers on one number line: 2, −5, −1.5, 3.5

23. True or false: $-(3 - 7)(-2) < \dfrac{-|-27|}{3}$

24. Laura is twice as old as Bob, who is b years old. Write an expression for Laura's age 7 years ago.

25. Write an equation to represent the following: I have 9 dimes and quarters worth $2.85.

26. Write an equation to represent the following: A rectangle has a perimeter of 64 cm. The lengths in centimeters of its adjacent sides are consecutive odd integers.

Solve. If the equation is an identity or has no solution, state that fact.

27. $|a| = 8$

28. $|b| = -1$

29. $-10 = -3 + k$

30. $15 - (5 - n) = 1$

31. $100 - d = 0$

32. $24 = \dfrac{c}{-2}$

33. $-12j = -84$

34. $2m - 8m + 1 = 55$

35. $4 + \frac{5}{2}(t - 3) = 24$

36. $-5(2h - 1) - 8 = 7$

37. $\frac{2}{5}x + 16 = 0$

38. $-2(3 - b) = 2b + 6$

39. $2y - 17 = 7y + 13$

40. $3\left(2g - \frac{1}{3}\right) = 2\left(3g - \frac{1}{2}\right)$

41. $\frac{5}{6}(7r - 15) = 4r + 4$

42. By increasing the speed of the car by 5 km/h, Alice was able to drive 12 km in 0.2 h. How fast was she driving originally?

43. Six times a number, decreased by 5, is -14. Find the number.

44. Pedro bought five more 20¢ stamps than his friend George. If the average amount of money spent was \$1.70, how many stamps did each buy?

45. The ages of Sam and Pam are consecutive integers. Three years ago, the sum of their ages was 15. How old is each now if Pam is older than Sam?

46. When Kate worked 10 hours overtime she earned \$8 more than one third the amount she earns for 40 hours of work at her usual rate. If her overtime rate is \$2.40 per hour more than her usual rate, find her overtime rate.

47. On a number line, point R has coordinate -7 and point S has coordinate -13. Find the coordinate of the point one third of the way from R to S.

Write the missing reasons. Assume that each variable represents any real number.

48. Prove: If $7x + 1 = 15$, then $x = 2$.

Proof:

	Statement	Reason
1.	$7x + 1 = 15$	1. ?
2.	$(7x + 1) + (-1) = 15 + (-1)$	2. ?
3.	$7x + [1 + (-1)] = 15 + (-1)$	3. ?
4.	$7x + 0 = 15 + (-1)$	4. ?
5.	$7x = 15 + (-1)$	5. ?
6.	$7x = 14$	6. Substitution principle
7.	$\frac{1}{7}(7x) = \frac{1}{7}(14)$	7. ?
8.	$\left(\frac{1}{7} \cdot 7\right)x = \frac{1}{7}(14)$	8. ?
9.	$1 \cdot x = \frac{1}{7}(14)$	9. ?
10.	$x = 2$	10. ?

49. Prove: $-(-a + b) = a - b$

Proof:

	Statement	Reason
1.	$-(-a + b) = -(-a) + (-b)$	1. ?
2.	$= a + (-b)$	2. ?
3.	$= a - b$	3. ?

50. Write a proof including statements and reasons.
Prove: If $a + b = 0$, then $a = -b$.

Review for Chapters 4–6

Perform the indicated operations. Express the answers in simplest form. Assume that no denominator equals zero.

1. $(3 - 5)^2 - (5 - 3)^3$
2. $(5r^2 - 3r + 1) + (-6r^2 + 3r - 7)$
3. $(2x^2 + xy - 3y^2) - (x^2 + 5xy - 4y^2)$
4. $\left(-\frac{20}{3}a^5b^2c\right)\left(\frac{21}{8}ac^3\right)$
5. $5^x \cdot 5^{x-1} \cdot 5$
6. $(-3c^2d)^3\left(\frac{2}{3}cd^2\right)^2$
7. $7h(1 - 2h) - 3h(4h + 2)$
8. $-5d^2(-2 + 3d - 4d^2)$
9. $(5x + y)(2x^2 + 4xy - 5y^2)$
10. $\frac{(2n)^3(-n)^3}{(-4n)^2}$
11. $\frac{36r^3s^4 - 8r^4s^3 - 2r^5s^2}{4r^2s}$
12. $2t(3t - 1)(t + 4)$
13. $(5d^2 - 2e)(d^2 + 3e)$
14. $(11m - 4)(11m + 4)$
15. $(9k + 4)^2$
16. $(-3ab + 2c)^2$

17. Solve the formula $S = \frac{a}{1 - r}$ for r.
18. Give the prime factorization of 504.
19. Find the greatest common factor of $60x^3yz^2$ and $84y^3z^2$.

Factor completely. If the polynomial cannot be factored, write "prime."

20. $-16r^3s + 8r^2s - 32rs$
21. $9a^2 - 121b^2$
22. $16c - c^9$
23. $d^2 - 10d + 100$
24. $4m^2 + 20mn + 25n^2$
25. $z^2 - 12z + 35$
26. $x^2 - 2xy - 63y^2$
27. $j^2 + 10j - 28$
28. $4t^2 + 19t + 12$
29. $15k^2 - 7k - 4$
30. $3 + 2x^3 - x^2 - 6x$
31. $(x - 1)^2 - 4y^2$
32. $g^4 - 22g^2 - 25$
33. $-30q^3 + 65q^2 - 30q$
34. $4r^3s^2 - 28r^2s^3 + 49rs^4$

Solve.

35. $(2k - 7) - (3k + 5) = 5(k - 3)$
36. $(2r + 5)(r - 6) = (2r + 3)(r - 4)$
37. $9x^2 + 3x = 2$
38. $a^3 = 81a$
39. $4y^4 - 4y^3 + y^2 = 0$
40. $8z^2 = 11z - 3$

Solve each problem if it has a solution. If a problem has no solution, explain why.

41. Paul walked to school at 6 km/h and rode home from school at a speed 6 times as fast. If his total traveling time was 56 min, how many minutes did he spend walking?

42. A rectangular garden is 8 m long and 4 m wide. When the garden is widened on all four sides by x meters, the area is tripled. Find the value of x.

43. Find three consecutive odd integers whose sum is 10 less than 4 times the least integer.

44. The sum of two integers is 15. Their product is 9 more than the difference of their squares. Find the integers.

45. Tickets to the basketball game are \$2.50 each for students and \$4.00 each for adults. If \$2800 was collected in all, how many student tickets were sold?

Express in simplest form.

46. $\frac{3x^2 + 7x + 2}{3x^2 + 8x + 4}$

47. $\frac{9r^3 - 4rs^2}{2s^2 - 5sr + 3r^2}$

48. $\frac{b^2 + b}{1 - b} \cdot \frac{1 + b}{b^3 - b}$

49. $\left(\frac{3x}{2}\right)^4 \cdot \left(\frac{4}{x}\right)^3$

50. $(4n)^2 \div \left(\frac{n}{2}\right)^5$

51. $\frac{a^4 - 81}{3 + a} \div (7a - 21)$

Find the LCD for each group of fractions.

52. $\frac{29}{36}, \frac{29}{30}, \frac{15}{16}$

53. $\frac{1}{b^2 + 2b}, \frac{1}{3b + 6}$

54. $\frac{1}{m + n}, \frac{1}{m - n}, \frac{1}{(m + n)^2}$

Write as a polynomial or a fraction in simplest form.

55. $\frac{p}{p - 3} - \frac{2}{3 - p} - \frac{2p - 1}{p - 3}$

56. $\frac{2x - 7}{12} + \frac{5(x - 2)}{18}$

57. $\frac{3}{g - 3} - \frac{2}{g + 2}$

58. $\frac{3}{9t^2 + 6t + 1} - \frac{1}{3t^2 + t}$

59. $\frac{1}{m + 1} + \frac{9}{5m^2 + m - 4}$

60. $\frac{y}{y - 4} - 1$

61. $\frac{1}{x} + 3 + \frac{2}{x - 1}$

62. $\left(\frac{3y^2}{z^2} - 3\right) \div \left(\frac{y}{z} + 1\right)$

63. Express the square of $3d^2 + 2d - 5$ as a polynomial.

64. Find (a) the perimeter and (b) the area of the rectangle shown at the right in terms of x.

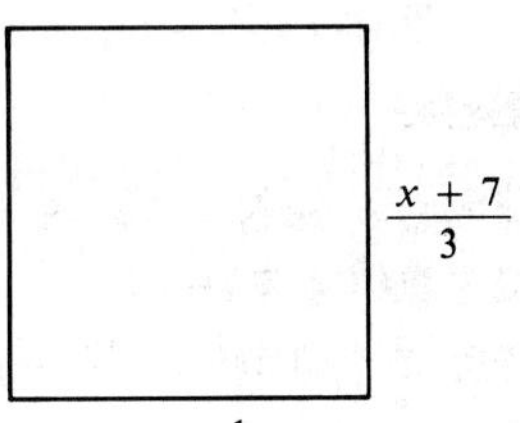

Divide. Write your answer as a polynomial or a mixed expression.

65. $\frac{6c^3 - c^2 + c + 9}{2c + 3}$

66. $\frac{n^3 - 11n + 6}{n - 3}$

67. $\frac{3x^3 - 10x^2y + 9xy^2 - 2y^3}{x - 2y}$

68. Factor $5z^3 + 34z^2 + 53z - 12$ given that $z + 3$ is a factor.

Review for Chapters 7–9

1. State the ratio of 9 months to 2 years in simplest form.
2. Find the ratio of x to y if $5(x + 2y) = 7(y - x)$.

Solve.

3. $\frac{4x + 3}{5} = \frac{9x + 5}{11}$
4. $\frac{8}{y - 2} = 3$
5. $\frac{z}{z + 4} = \frac{z - 2}{z}$
6. $\frac{a + 1}{4} - \frac{a - 3}{5} = \frac{1}{2}$
7. $b + \frac{1}{3}b = 2 - \frac{7b}{6}$
8. $\frac{1}{4}(c - 7) = \frac{1}{10}(c - 4)$
9. $\frac{5r - 1}{8r} + \frac{1}{3} = 1$
10. $\frac{s - 7}{4} = \frac{5}{s + 1}$
11. $\frac{1}{t - 2} - \frac{4}{t^2 - 4} = 0$
12. Express as a fraction in simplest form: **a.** 15.6% **b.** 240%
13. Find $7\frac{1}{2}\%$ of 32.
14. Find 79% of 800.
15. 49 is 35% of what number?
16. What percent of 30 is 75?
17. Express 531,000 in scientific notation and in expanded notation.
18. Evaluate: **a.** $\left(\frac{2^{-3} \cdot 2}{2^{-5}}\right)^{-1}$ **b.** $(3^{-1} - 2^0)^{-2}$

Simplify. Give answers in terms of positive exponents.

19. $(5x^{-1})^{-3}$
20. $(-2y^{-3})^2$
21. $\left(\frac{t}{t^{-2}}\right)^{-1}$
22. The ratio of Jim's age to Ann's age is 3:2, but two years ago it was 5:3. How old is Jim now?
23. A poll of 500 voters found that 320 favored a tax reform proposal. Find (a) the percent in favor of the proposal and (b) the approximate number of voters in favor of it, if there are 15,600 voters.
24. The numerator of a fraction is 3 less than the denominator. The sum of twice the fraction and the reciprocal of the fraction is $\frac{57}{20}$. Find the fraction.
25. Leon spent \$20.25 for a camera lens that had been marked down 10%. What was the original price?
26. How many grams of acid must be added to 80 g of a 25% acid solution in order to produce a 40% acid solution?
27. Carmen can retile the kitchen floor in 8 hours, but if Joe helps her, the job will take only $3\frac{1}{2}$ hours. How long would it take Joe to do the job alone?

28. Is $(-2, -6)$ a solution of $3x^2 - 4xy + y^2 = 0$?

29. Solve $x + 3y = 8$ if x and y are whole numbers.

30. Plot the graphs of $A(4, -2)$, $B(-1, 5)$, and $C(0, -3)$.

31. Graph $4x - y = -8$ in a coordinate plane.

32. Solve by the graphic method: $3x + y = 1$
$x - y = -5$

33. Solve by the substitution method: $\frac{a}{2} = b - 3$
$3b - 2a = 12$

34. Determine the number of solutions of the system: $y = -4x + 2$
$8x + 2y = 5$

35. Solve, using two equations in two variables: Samantha invested \$2000, part at $5\frac{1}{2}\%$ and part at $9\frac{1}{2}\%$. If her annual income from the investments is \$170, how much is invested at each rate?

Solve by the addition-or-subtraction method.

36. $5c - 2d = 1$
$3c + 2d = -9$

37. $2s + 3t = 20$
$4s - 5t = 18$

38. $7j - 2k = -11$
$3j - 5k = 16$

39. A motorboat traveled a certain distance upstream in exactly 2 h. The return trip took 40 min less. During both trips the rate of the current was 4 km/h. How far upstream did the boat travel? How long would this trip have taken if the river had been calm?

40. A two-digit number is two more than three times the sum of its digits. If the digits are reversed, the number is increased by 36. Find the original number.

41. Find the slope of the line through $(-7, -1)$ and $(2, -7)$.

42. Graph the line through $(2, -4)$ with slope $\frac{3}{2}$.

Write an equation in standard form of the line described.

43. slope $\frac{1}{4}$ and y-intercept $-\frac{1}{2}$

44. y-intercept 0 and parallel to the graph of $5x + 2y = 10$

45. slope -3 and through point $(2, 0)$

46. through points $(0, 5)$ and $(8, 11)$

47. Given that $f(t) = t^2 - t + 3$ and t has domain $\{-2, -1, 0, 1, 2\}$, find the range of $f(t)$.

48. Draw the graph of $g: x \rightarrow \frac{1}{2}x^2 + 2x$. Find the least value of the function.

49. Given: $x_1 = 18$, $y_1 = 6$, and $y_2 = 4$. Find x_2 if (x_1, y_1) and (x_2, y_2) are ordered pairs of (a) the same direct variation and (b) the same inverse variation.

50. If a 9 g mass is 20 cm from the fulcrum of a lever, find the mass of an object, 24 cm from the fulcrum, that balances it.

51. The surface area of a cube varies directly as the square of the length of a side. If a cube with sides of length 3 has a surface area of 54, find the surface area of a cube with sides of length 5.

52. The gravitational attraction, G, between two objects is directly proportional to the product of the masses, m and n, and inversely proportional to the square of the distance, d, between their centers of gravity. Translate this statement into a formula.

Review for Chapters 10–12

Classify each statement as true or false.

1. $|-3.5| < |-3.4|$
2. $-2 \geq -5 > -4$
3. $2^{-3} > 3^{-2}$
4. Solve $2y \leq 10$ if the domain of y is {the positive integers}.

Solve each open sentence.

5. $7x + 5 < 3x - 11$
6. $\frac{3}{4}m - 2 \geq 2(m - 6)$
7. $\frac{5}{2}(4 + k) \leq \frac{2}{3}(7k + 2)$

Graph the solution set of each open sentence.

8. $3 > -2 - x > -4$
9. $3 < 2y + 1$ or $\frac{1}{2}y + 1 < -3$
10. $-5z \leq -15$ or $2(1 - z) > -4$
11. $|2 + v| = \frac{3}{2}$
12. $|-4 - m| \geq 4$
13. $9 - 5|j| > -1$
14. $|3 - 2k| < 5$
15. $\left|\frac{1}{2}a + 1\right| \geq 2$
16. $3q - 7 < -4$ and $3q - 7 > 4$
17. $0 = |(d + 3) - (5d + 1)|$
18. A wallet contains nickels and dimes worth more than \$1.05. If the ratio of the number of dimes to the number of nickels is 2:3, find the minimum number of nickels.
19. A scientist has 50 mL of a 40% ammonia solution. At least how much water should she add to produce a solution that is no more than 32% ammonia?

Graph each inequality or system of inequalities.

20. $3x - y > 5$

21. $4(x + 2y) \leq 5y - 12$

22. $3x > -6$
$y \leq x + 5$

23. $3x + 4y \leq 0$
$x + 2y > 3$

24. Arrange this group of numbers in order from least to greatest: $\frac{4}{5}, \frac{13}{18}, \frac{53}{66}, \frac{23}{29}$

25. Find the number one third of the way from $-\frac{5}{6}$ to $\frac{1}{4}$.

26. Express as a decimal: **a.** $4\frac{7}{16}$ **b.** $-\frac{2}{27}$

27. Express $0.\overline{72}$ and 1.98 as fractions in simplest form. Then find their product.

Simplify.

28. $-\sqrt{676}$

29. $\sqrt{\frac{49}{900}}$

30. $\pm\sqrt{0.0256}$

31. $\sqrt{\frac{35}{140}}$

32. $4\sqrt{150}$

33. $\frac{2}{3}\sqrt{243}$

34. $-\sqrt{45a^3b^4}$

35. $\sqrt{1.21x^2}$

36. $\sqrt{g^2 - 4g + 4}$

37. $\sqrt{\frac{m^{10}}{16n^8}}$

38. $\sqrt{3388}$

39. $\sqrt{32k^5}$

40. Use the Table of Square Roots on page 650 to approximate $\sqrt{2511}$ to the nearest tenth.

41. A circle has area 1386 cm^2. Find the diameter of the circle. $\left(\text{Use } \pi \approx \frac{22}{7}.\right)$

42. Is a triangle with sides of lengths 10, 15, and 18 a right triangle?

43. A triangle has three sides of length 8. Find the length of an altitude to the nearest hundredth. (*Hint:* The altitude of this triangle divides the base into two equal parts.)

Simplify.

44. $\sqrt{\frac{14}{27}} \cdot \sqrt{\frac{6}{7}}$

45. $\sqrt{\frac{20}{7}}$

46. $\sqrt{15} \cdot 3\sqrt{40}$

47. $(x\sqrt{3x})^2$

48. $3\sqrt{18} - \sqrt{8} + 2\sqrt{64}$

49. $4\sqrt{12} - \sqrt{\frac{100}{3}} - \sqrt{\frac{1}{75}}$

50. $7\sqrt{5}(\sqrt{15} + 2\sqrt{125})$

51. $(\sqrt{19} + 2\sqrt{3})(\sqrt{19} - 2\sqrt{3})$

52. $(5\sqrt{6} + \sqrt{3})^2$

53. $(2\sqrt{2} - \sqrt{11})(3\sqrt{2} + 5\sqrt{11})$

54. Rationalize the denominator: $\frac{6}{2\sqrt{3} - 3}$

Solve. If the equation has no solution, write "no solution."

55. $\sqrt{x - 7} = 5$ **56.** $\sqrt{y} - 2 = \frac{3}{4}$ **57.** $\sqrt{z + 2} = z$

58. $7p^2 - 10 = 46$ **59.** $(2j - 1)^2 = -4$ **60.** $\frac{1}{5}k^2 - 1 = \frac{1}{4}$

Solve by completing the square.

61. $t^2 + 4t = 21$ **62.** $3n^2 - 24n = 1$ **63.** $x = \frac{x + 3}{x - 5}$

Solve by the quadratic formula.

64. $2y^2 - 8y + 3 = 0$ **65.** $4m^2 + 7m = 1$ **66.** $25s^2 + 0.04 = -2s$

Find (a) the value of the discriminant and (b) the number of different real-number roots that each equation has.

67. $4c^2 - c + 2 = 0$ **68.** $5x^2 + 7x = 6$ **69.** $\frac{1}{6}d^2 + \frac{27}{2} = 3d$

Solve by the easiest method.

70. $2h^2 = 2h + 3$ **71.** $x^2 + 4x = 1$ **72.** $\frac{1}{r} = \frac{r - 1}{r + 3}$

Solve. Approximate irrational roots to the nearest tenth.

73. The sum of a number and its reciprocal is 3. Find the number.

74. If the area of the region inside the rectangle and outside the square is 720, find the value of x.

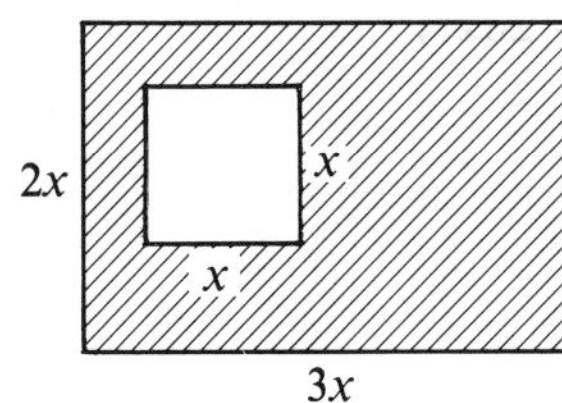

Topical Reviews

Review of Factoring Polynomials

Factor completely.

1. $x^2 + 13x - 14$
2. $3p^2 - 12q^2$
3. $m^2 + 16m - 192$
4. $-4p^2 + 25q^2$
5. $22x^2 - 7x - 2$
6. $36r^2 - 16$
7. $4cx + 6cy - 3ay - 2ax$
8. $6x^2 - 73x + 12$
9. $1 - 81w^8x^4$
10. $4acz - 4bcz + 3ay - 3by$
11. $6x^2 + 15x - 21$
12. $200c^2 + 80c + 8$
13. $9 + 18y - 16y^2$
14. $3 + 20x^2 - 16x$
15. $76x^2y - 19y^5$
16. $4x^2 + 8x - 12$
17. $0.16ax^4 - 0.09ay^2$
18. $4 - 4x - 3x^2$
19. $12x^2 + 57xy - 21y^2$
20. $6(3 - x) + y(x - 3)$
21. $32x^2 - 44x + 5$
22. $14a^3 - 29a^2 - 15a$
23. $30fg - 5fk + 12gh - 2hk$
24. $14x^4 + 21x^3 - 35x^2$
25. $-x^2 - x + 2$
26. $2p^3 - 3p^2 - 8p + 12$
27. $(a - b)^2 + 4ab$
28. $32x^4 - 32x^2 + 2$
29. $2(c - d)^2 - 8$
30. $5c^2d^2 + 30cd + 45$
31. $9 - (a + b)^2$
32. $-p^2 - q^2 - 2pq$
33. $m^4 - 23m^2 - 50$
34. $63x^2y - 28x^2y^3$
35. $-30x^2 - 61x - 30$
36. $4ax - 5mx + 12am - 15m^2$
37. $2a^3 + 2a^2 + a + 1$
38. $(3x - 5)(x + 3) - 4(x + 3)$
39. $(x + 1)(x + 2) - 12$
40. $2x^3 - 12x^2 + x - 6$
41. $(x - 2)(x^2 - 7) + 3(x - 2)$
42. $a^{14} + 4a^{13} - 5a^{12}$
43. $4c^2 - 4c + 1 - 9d^2$
44. $x^4 - 2x^2 + 1$
45. $(x + 1)^2 + 6(x + 1) + 8$
46. $m^2 - n^2 - (m - n)^2$
47. $a(b - c) - (b - c)^2$
48. $x^2 - 6xy + 9y^2 - 1$

Challenge Problems

49. $2a^2 + a - 2 - a^3$
50. $x^4 - (x - 1)^4$

Review of Simplifying Expressions

Simplify. Rationalize denominators where appropriate. Assume that no denominator equals zero.

1. $(5x^7)(-23x^{17})$
2. $(4\sqrt{18})(-2\sqrt{20})$
3. $\frac{3x^2 - 12}{x^2 - 2x - 8}$
4. $\frac{a^2 - b^2}{2a^3} \div \frac{4b - 4a}{a^3 + a^2b}$
5. $\frac{4a - 7}{12} + \frac{a + 1}{9} - \frac{a + 2}{6}$
6. $\frac{2^5 \div 8 + 3}{4 + 3}$

Simplify. Rationalize denominators where appropriate. Assume that no denominator equals zero.

7. $\sqrt{\frac{14}{5}} \cdot \sqrt{\frac{35}{2}}$

8. $\frac{2x^3 + 7x^2 + 16}{x + 4}$

9. $\left(\frac{3x}{7}\right)^2$

10. $\left(1 + \frac{3}{x}\right)\left(1 + \frac{4}{x - 4}\right)$

11. $5\sqrt{8}(8\sqrt{3} - 6\sqrt{2})$

12. $\frac{-32x^7y^4z^9}{18xy^{10}z^{10}}$

13. $\frac{cd}{c^2 - 4cd + 4d^2} + \frac{c}{3c - 6d}$

14. $\left(\frac{a}{-6c^2}\right)^3$

15. $3^4 - 3^2 \div 3^2 - 3$

16. $(y - 5)(2y^2 + 4y - 3)$

17. $\frac{2}{3 - \sqrt{5}}$

18. $(4a)^2\left(\frac{1}{2}a\right)(-a)^3$

19. $\frac{4x - 1}{x^2 - 9} \cdot \frac{x^2 - 3x}{2 - 8x}$

20. $\frac{m - 3}{m^2 + 7m} - \frac{m + 7}{m^2 - 3m}$

21. $\frac{p^3 - 4p^2}{4p^4} \div \frac{48 - 3p^2}{6p^2 + 24p}$

22. $(-3x^2)^4$

23. $\frac{6x^2 + x - 2}{2x^2 + 9x - 5}$

24. $\frac{4ab^2}{4a - 2b} \cdot \frac{4a^2 - b^2}{4a^3 + 4a^2b + ab^2}$

25. $\left(\frac{4a^2}{3b}\right)^2$

26. $\frac{1}{a + 4} + 2 - \frac{1}{a - 4}$

27. $\frac{15x^4 - 4x^3 + 13x + 4}{3x + 1}$

28. $(5 - 7\sqrt{2})^2$

29. $-2(x^6)^4$

30. $18 \div 2 \times 3 - 5 - 20$

31. $\frac{(-6a)^3}{-6a^3}$

32. $(4x + 7)(x + 1)(x + 2)$

33. $\frac{x^2 + 3x - 28}{2x - 4x^2} \div \frac{2x^2 - 7x - 4}{1 - 4x^2}$

34. $\frac{xy^2 - x^3}{2x^2 - 9xy + 7y^2}$

35. $3\sqrt{\frac{4}{7}} + \frac{2}{3}\sqrt{28}$

36. $\frac{5 - 2x}{2x^2 + 5x + 3} + \frac{7x}{4x^2 + 16x + 15}$

37. $\frac{3}{4x^2 + 4x + 1} - \frac{2}{2x^2 - x - 1}$

38. $\left(x - 5 + \frac{6}{x}\right) \div \left(x - \frac{9}{x}\right)$

39. $\frac{(x + 3y)^3}{3x^2 + xy - 24y^2} \cdot \frac{8xy - 3x^2}{x^2 + 6xy + 9y^2}$

40. $(4\sqrt{3x})^2\sqrt{9x}$

41. $\frac{2a^3 + a^2 - 17a + 5}{2a - 5}$

42. $\left(\frac{5c}{2d^5}\right)^4$

43. $(12a^2 - 2a) \div \frac{108a^3 - 3a}{6a^2 - 35a - 6}$

44. $\frac{a}{2a - 3} + \frac{a + 1}{a + 2}$

45. $c^{2n}(c^{3n})^2c^4$

46. $(2x^3 - 3y)^2$

47. $(-4p^2q^3)(3pq^5)(3p^7q)^2$

48. $\frac{2}{3p + 1} - \frac{1}{3p + 2} - 4$

49. $\frac{(4x^3)^3x^2y^2}{22x^7y^5}$

50. $7\sqrt{\frac{27}{8}}$

51. $\frac{8}{4 - 3x} + \frac{6x}{3x - 4}$

52. $a^{m+6} \cdot a^m \cdot a^{2m-1}$

53. $\frac{4x^4 - 14x^2 + 3x^3 - 9x + 6}{4x^2 + 3x - 2}$

54. $\frac{a^2 - ab - ac + bc}{a^2 - 2ab + b^2}$

55. $\left(\frac{3a^2c}{2d}\right)^3$

56. $\frac{5\sqrt{6}}{1 - \sqrt{2}}$

57. $\frac{4x^2 - 21x - 18}{2x^2 - 72} \div \frac{12x^2 - 7x - 12}{x^2 + 7x + 6}$

58. $(3xy^2)^3 \cdot 2(x^2y)^2$

59. $\frac{12x - 3}{x^3 - 5x^2} \cdot \frac{2x^2 - 10x}{2 - 32x^2}$

60. $4\sqrt{32} - 5\sqrt{98} + \sqrt{162}$

61. $(a - 5)^3$

62. $\frac{x - 5}{10 - 2x} + \frac{5}{3x + 15}$

63. $\frac{(7x^2y^5z^7)^5}{(7x^2y^5z^7)^3}$

64. $\frac{4a-4c}{6c^3} \cdot \frac{a^2c+4ac^2+4c^3}{a^2+ac-2c^2}$

65. $\left(\frac{4x}{7y}\right)^2 \div \frac{(3x^2)^2}{-7y^3}$

66. $3c(4c^2c)^3\left(\frac{1}{2}c^3\right)^2$

67. $\left(a-\frac{4}{a+3}\right) \div \left(2a+\frac{a+3}{a-3}\right)$

68. $\frac{4-x^2}{x^2+3x-10} \cdot \frac{2x^2-9x+7}{2x^2-3x-14}$

69. $\frac{3}{p^2-6p+5}+\frac{4}{p^2-25}$

70. $3(2+3\sqrt{2})^2$

71. $\frac{4x+2y}{6y} \div \frac{2x^2+xy}{4}$

72. $\frac{15x^3+38x-14-41x^2}{7-5x}$

73. $(\sqrt{2x^3})(5\sqrt{8x^6})$

74. $\frac{2x-7}{3x^2+4x+1}+\frac{x+4}{9x^2-1}$

75. $\frac{16x^3-36x}{-4x^2-12x-9} \div (6-4x)$

76. $\left(\frac{x^2}{3}-x\right)\left(1+\frac{7}{x}\right)$

77. $\frac{3\sqrt{2}-7}{3\sqrt{2}+7}$

78. $\frac{4x-y}{8xy+2y^2} \cdot \frac{16x^2+8xy+y^2}{y^2-16x^2}$

79. $\frac{3x}{x^2-1}-\frac{1}{5-5x}$

80. $\frac{3\sqrt{2}-\sqrt{3}}{\sqrt{8}}-\sqrt{\frac{3}{2}}$

81. $5^{2n} \cdot 5^{4n+2} \cdot 5$

82. $(2\sqrt{6}+3\sqrt{7})(2\sqrt{6}-3\sqrt{7})$

83. $\sqrt{\frac{6}{5}}+\sqrt{\frac{5}{6}}-\frac{\sqrt{120}}{15}$

84. $(3a)^2(2a^2b^4)^3-(-3a^4b)^2(b^2)^5$

85. $8y^{-3}$

86. $c^{-3}d^4e^0$

87. $(x^{-1}y^2)^{-1}$

88. $\frac{3a^{-1}b^{-2}}{2^{-1}c^{-1}}$

89. $\frac{3^{-1}u^{-1}v^2}{2u^3v^{-4}}$

90. $\frac{p^{-4}q^5r^{-6}}{pq^{-2}r^3}$

Challenge Problems

91. $\frac{\frac{1}{a^2}+\frac{1}{ab}}{\frac{1}{ab}+\frac{1}{b^2}}$

92. $\frac{\frac{c}{d}-3+\frac{2d}{c}}{\frac{4d}{c}-\frac{c}{d}}$

93. $\frac{x^3-y^3}{x^4+xy^3} \cdot \frac{6x^3-6xy^2}{4x^2+4xy+4y^2}$

Review of Solving Equations, Inequalities, and Systems

Solve the following equations and inequalities. If a problem has no solution, write "no solution."

1. $4y-1=31$

2. $-2n+9n-343=0$

3. $3y+82=58-y$

4. $7n-6=9n-114$

5. $2(2x-1)+4=26$

6. $3(y+4)+y=20$

7. $5a-1-3(a+7)=2(a-6)$

8. $4+6(2x-3) \leq (1-3x)2+x$

9. $\frac{3}{x^2-7x+6}+\frac{1}{x^2-1}=\frac{x+3}{x^2-5x-6}$

10. $4\left(\frac{1}{2}x+7\right)-3x=\frac{1}{3}(9-6x)+23$

11. $2x+\frac{2}{3}(4-x)=\frac{1}{6}(4x+5)+\frac{9}{2}$

12. $\frac{5}{2}(1-4a) \leq \frac{3}{2}-\frac{7}{5}(6a+5)$

Solve the following equations, inequalities, and systems. If a problem has no solution, write "no solution." Graph the solution sets for Exercises 14, 31, 46, 64, and 75, which are marked with a g.

13. $\sqrt{3x - 2} = x - 2$

g14. $|3x - 8| \geq 4$

15. $0.5y + 0.1 = y^2$

16. $4x - y = 7$
$x - 5y = -3$

17. $0.1y - 0.02x = 0.02$
$0.1x - 0.16y = 0.24$

18. $y = 6 - 3x$
$5x - 4y = 10$

19. $\frac{3}{x^2 - 9} + \frac{2}{x + 3} = \frac{7}{x - 3}$

20. $\frac{a + b}{c} = d$ (Solve for a.)

21. $3 - \frac{2}{3x} = x$

22. $\frac{7x + 2}{4} = \frac{5}{x - 3}$

23. $\frac{5}{4a - 4} + \frac{3}{6a - 6} - 2 = \frac{1}{a - 1}$

24. $\sqrt{\frac{5a + 4}{2}} = 4$

25. $x - 4x^2 = 1 - 7x$

26. $3|x - 2| = 6$

27. $3 + 5(x - 7) > 3x + 7$

28. $\frac{3(2x - 7)}{11} - \frac{2 - 3x}{3} = \frac{17}{33}$

29. $\frac{x + 1}{x^2 - x} - \frac{13}{2x} = 2$

30. $\frac{3}{a + 5} - \frac{2}{2a + 3} = 0$

g31. $|-3 - 2a| \leq 11$

32. $3cx - a = c(5 - x)$
(Solve for x.)

33. $7 - 2x^2 = 0$

34. $x^2 + 6x - 2 = 0$

35. $\sqrt{2w^2 + 7} = 6$

36. $6\left(5 - \frac{1}{3}x\right) \leq 3 - x$

37. $\frac{4x - 5}{x + 2} = \frac{1 - 5x}{x + 6}$

38. $\frac{x}{x - 1} + \frac{12}{x + 1} = \frac{2}{x^2 - 1}$

39. $\frac{9}{4x + 1} - \frac{2}{2x - 3} = -1$

40. $m^3 + 4m^2 - 9m - 36 = 0$

41. $(a - 5)(2a + 3) = -11$

42. $2\sqrt{x - 3} = 5$

43. $\frac{m - n}{3} = 5$
$\frac{m + n}{3} = -1$

44. $4a + 4 = 7b$
$\frac{a}{3} + b + 2 = 0$

45. $y = -\frac{5}{2}x + 3$
$x = -\frac{2}{5}y + 1$

g46. $|2x + 1| < 7$

47. $2x^2 - 4x = 3$

48. $81p^4 - 18p^2 + 1 = 0$

49. $\frac{5}{2x} - \frac{4}{3x} = \frac{7}{12}$

50. $\frac{3}{5x + 3} = \frac{1}{3x - 7}$

51. $\frac{1}{x + 3} + \frac{2}{x^2(x + 3)} = \frac{2}{x^2}$

52. $\frac{cx - a}{2c} = d$ (Solve for x.)

53. $3 - 2(c + 1) + 3c = 28 - 8c$

54. $\frac{x^2}{3x - 2} = -2$

55. $2\sqrt{t} = 2\sqrt{3} - 6$

56. $|5x - 2| = 0$

57. $10x^2 - 6 = 7x$

58. $-\frac{3x - 1}{8} \geq \frac{x}{3} + \frac{71}{24}$

59. $\frac{4}{x} = \frac{x}{3}$

60. $\frac{3}{x - 4} + \frac{1}{2x - 8} = -1$

61. $\frac{x}{3} - \frac{3}{x} = 3$

62. $\frac{2x}{x - 2} - \frac{3}{x + 2} = \frac{7}{x^2 - 4}$

63. $\frac{1}{x - 4} - \frac{1}{x} = 2$

g64. $|4 - y| > |-2 - 4|$

65. $0.02x^2 + 0.2x - 2 = 0$

66. $\sqrt{3x^2 + 4x} = 8$

67. $s = vt - \frac{1}{2}gt^2$ (Solve for v.)

68. $\frac{3w - 1}{7} + \frac{5 - 2w}{2} = -\frac{15}{14}$

69. $\frac{4}{3} - \frac{3c + 1}{2} > 12$

70. $t = \frac{1 - 6s}{5}$

$s = \frac{2 - 6t}{7}$

71. $\frac{1}{5}(3x - 5y) = 5$

$x = -2y - 10$

72. $y = \frac{1}{6}(x - 5)$

$3x - 18y = 15$

73. $3c^3 + 48c = 24c^2$

74. $\sqrt{2x + 3} = \sqrt{x^2 - 5}$

[g]**75.** $\left|-\frac{4x}{7}\right| \leq 3$

Challenge Problems

76. $\frac{4x + 1}{3x^2 - 12x} + \frac{x}{16 - 4x} = \frac{1}{12x} - \frac{1}{4}$

77. $\frac{8}{2x^2 + 9x - 5} + \frac{3x - 1}{1 - 4x^2} = \frac{x + 1}{2x^2 + 11x + 5}$

78. $\sqrt{3x - 5} = \sqrt{x - 2} + 1$

79. $\sqrt{2x - 2} = \sqrt{x} + 1$

Review of Solving Word Problems

Use the Table of Square Roots on page 650 where applicable.

1. Four brothers decided to buy a color television set that cost \$392. Their contributions were in the ratio 4:2:3:5. How much did each contribute?

2. Marie and Tony went shopping together. Marie bought 2 L of milk and 10 oranges for \$3.44. Tony bought 3 L of milk and 8 oranges for \$3.69. What was the cost of one liter of milk? of one orange?

3. The hypotenuse of a right triangle is 3 cm longer than twice the length of the shorter side. The longer side measures 12 cm. Find the lengths of the shorter side and the hypotenuse.

4. Card reader *A* can read decks of punched cards in half the time it takes card reader *B*. Together they can read a certain deck in eight minutes. How long would it take each reader alone to read the deck?

5. How many grams of a 5% antiseptic solution must be added to 300 g of a 10% solution to produce an 8% solution?

6. Anthony has \$6.10 in coins. He has six more quarters than nickels and half as many dimes as quarters. He also has three half dollars. How many coins of each type does he have?

7. John Kennedy's picture appears on 8% of Pedro's collection of presidential campaign buttons. If he has 34 Kennedy buttons, how many buttons has he in all?

8. Two years ago Seth was one third as old as his father. If he is now 22 years younger than his father, how old is Seth now?

9. A square and a rectangle have the same area. If the length of the rectangle is 4 cm greater and the width is 3 cm less than the length of a side of the square, what are the dimensions of the rectangle?

10. Colin and Maureen receive \$3.50 per hour and \$4.00 per hour respectively for working in Brendan's garden. Colin works on Saturdays and Maureen works on Sundays. How much money did each one earn if they received \$42 between them for a total of 11 hours' work one weekend?

11. The ratio of the lengths of the sides of two squares is 3:7. The sum of their areas is 522 cm^2. Find the area of each square.

12. Find the three smallest consecutive odd integers whose sum is at least 99.

13. The volume of a cylinder varies directly as the square of the radius of the base. If the volume is 18 cm^3 when the radius is 3 cm, find the volume when the radius is 4 cm.

14. Heather paid \$650 for some stock in Newcar, Inc. If she sold the stock for \$728, what was the percent gain on her original investment?

15. The width of a rectangle is 5 cm less than half its length. Its area is 72 cm^2. Find the length and the width of the rectangle.

16. The denominator of a fraction is 1 more than twice the numerator. If 1 is subtracted from the numerator, the resulting fraction is equivalent to $\frac{1}{3}$. Find the original fraction.

17. The first cyclist in a two-leg relay race rode at a speed of 40 km/h. The second cyclist rode at 30 km/h. If they completed the 170 km course in 4 h 50 min, how far did each cyclist ride?

18. A doll's quilt is made from 150 small squares. It is possible to make a quilt of the same size using 100 squares, 1 cm longer on each side than the smaller squares. What is the length of a side of each smaller square?

19. Inge invested part of her \$6000 savings in common stock and the rest in rare stamps. At the end of the year, she realized a gain of 9% on the stock and 12% on the stamps. If her savings now amount to \$6615, how much did she invest in stamps?

20. A 3 m by 5 m rectangular wall hanging is hung in the center of a wall. The uncovered part of the wall is a border strip of uniform width. How wide is the border strip if the area of the wall hanging is three sevenths of the area of the entire wall?

21. A tea merchant prepares a blend of 30 kg of tea to sell at \$2.95 per kilogram. The merchant blends two types of tea, one selling at \$2.70 per kilogram, the other at \$3.00 per kilogram. How much of each type should the merchant use?

22. The sum of the digits of a two-digit number is 11. If the digits are reversed, the new number is 7 more than twice the original number. Find the original number.

23. Paula leaves her house at 1:20 P.M. to get to the ball park by 2:00 P.M. Malcolm, who is to meet her there, leaves his house at 1:30 P.M. Paula lives 2 km farther away from the ball park than Malcolm, but can walk 2 km/h faster. How fast can Paula walk?

24. A boat can travel 6 km downstream in 40 min. The return trip takes one hour. Find the rate of the boat in still water and the rate of the current.

25. Flying with the wind, a small airplane can travel 1080 miles in 6 hours. Flying against the wind, the plane can travel only 720 miles in 6 hours. Find the speed of the plane in still air and the speed of the wind.

Challenge Problems

26. Louise can trim the shrubbery in 6 h working alone. Her father can do it in 5 h. They worked together until dinner but trimmed only $\frac{11}{15}$ of the shrubbery. How long did they work?

27. On their way to a campsite, Edie and Wilma walked 5 km west and 8 km north. After lunch they walked 3 more km west and 7 km north, arriving at the campsite at 5 P.M. How far would they have walked had they taken the more dangerous, straight-line route through the forest?

Review of Lines and Graphing

Solve each system by the graphic method.

1. $x - y = 6$
   $x + y = -2$

2. $y = 3x - 6$
   $2x + y = 4$

3. $y = -\frac{2}{3}x + 3$
   $4x + 6y = 18$

Write in standard form an equation of the line that passes through the given points.

4. $(-3, 6), (4, -1)$
5. $(0, 3), (-2, -2)$
6. $(7, -4), (11, -10)$
7. $(4, -3), (4, 0)$
8. $(1, 8), (4, 7)$
9. $(-5, -1), (7, -1)$
10. $(6, -2), (2, -6)$
11. $(-4, 5), (-6, 1)$

Solve each open sentence and graph each solution set that is not empty.

12. $4 < 2x \leq 8$
13. $-2x \leq 4$ and $x < 3.5$
14. $-4x > 2$ and $x + 1 > 6$
15. $2 - 3x < 5$ or $2x - 5 < -3$
16. $5a - 1 \leq 9$ or $7 - 3a \geq -2$
17. $|1 - 2x| > 3$

Write an equation for each line whose graph is shown.

18. 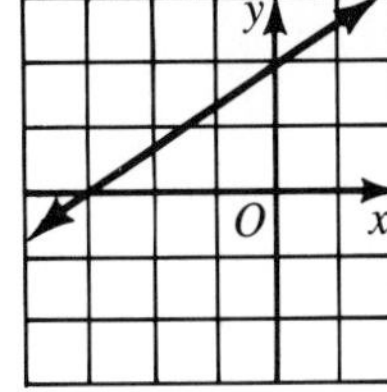

19. 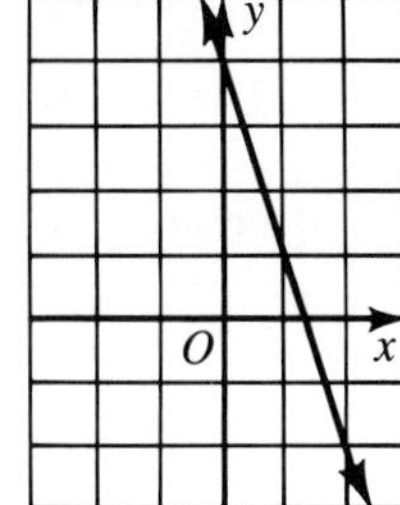

20. 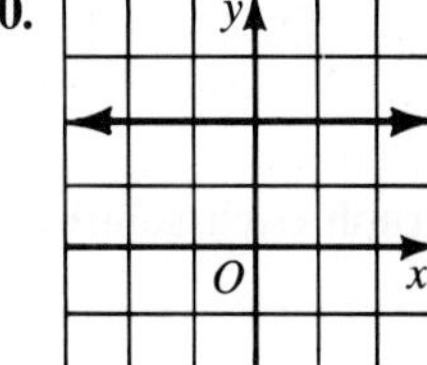

21. 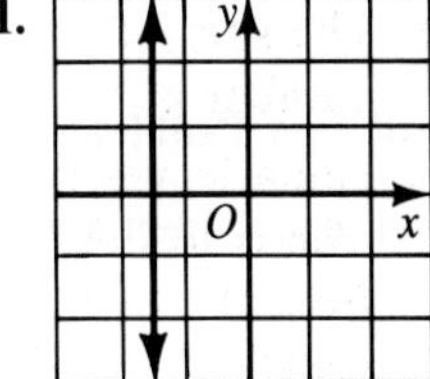

Find the coordinates of the vertex of the graph of each equation. Use the vertex and four other points to graph each equation on a separate coordinate plane.

22. $y = x^2 - 2x$ **23.** $y = -2x^2 + 5x - 3$ **24.** $y = x^2 + 4x + 1$

Graph each pair of inequalities and indicate the solution set of the system with cross-hatching or shading.

25. $y \geq x + 3$
$y > -2x - 1$

26. $x + 2y > 4$
$x \geq 3$

27. $3x - 5y < 5$
$x - 3y \geq 0$

Write in standard form an equation of the line that has the given slope and passes through the given point.

28. $m = \frac{4}{3}$; $(0, 4)$ **29.** $m = \frac{2}{3}$; $(-3, -3)$

30. $m = -\frac{1}{4}$; $(6, 0)$ **31.** $m = \frac{3}{8}$; $(1, -3)$

32. $m = -5$; $(5, -2)$ **33.** $m = 0$; $(6, 4)$

34. The points $(3, -4)$ and $(-2, a)$ lie on a line with slope $\frac{3}{5}$. Find the value of a.

Write an equation in standard form for the line that passes through the given point and has the slope described.

35. $(2, 3)$; the same slope as the graph of $3x - y = 2$

36. $(-1, 4)$; the same slope as the graph of $x + 2y = 5$

Graph the line whose equation or slope and y-intercept is given.

37. $m = -\frac{3}{4}$, $b = -1$ **38.** $\frac{x}{2} + \frac{y}{4} = 1$ **39.** $x = 2\frac{1}{2}$

40. $y = \frac{1}{2}x + 3$ **41.** $m = -\frac{2}{3}$, $b = 3$ **42.** $4y - 3x = 4$

Use slope to determine whether the points lie on the same line.

43. $(4, 7)$, $(2, -1)$, $(-6, -33)$, $(-1, -13)$ **44.** $(3, -7)$, $(-1, -4)$, $(6, -10)$, $(-9, 2)$

Challenge Problems

Solve each open sentence and graph each solution set that is not empty.

45. $-1 \leq t \leq 3$ and $|t| \geq 2$ **46.** $\frac{1}{2}|3x - 6| + 3 < 2$

47. $x > 3\frac{1}{2}$ or x is an integer.

Answers

Chapter Tests

Chapter 1 Test

1. a. 39 **b.** 5 **2. a.** 62 **b.** 23 **c.** 39 **3. a.** {2} **b.** {6} **4. a.** $3(c + 15)$, or $3c + 45$ **b.** $200 - (2c + 15)$, or $185 - 2c$ **5.** $(4c - 5) + (c - 5) = 25$, or $5c - 10 = 25$ **6.** 500 I.U.
7. 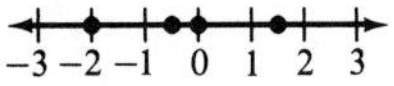

8. -2 **9. a.** 14.3 **b.** $-\frac{2}{3}$ **c.** 8 **10.** 2 **11.** none **12.** 2
13. $|-2| > -7$ **14.** $>$ **15.** $<$ **16.** $>$

Chapter 2 Test

1. 15 **2.** 9900 **3.** $a + b + 8$ **4.** 0 **5.** -16 **6.** -7 **7.** 10 **8.** 29 **9.** -5 **10.** $-183\,°\text{C}$ **11.** 148 **12.** 5.55 **13.** 4 **14.** 72° **15.** 380 **16.** $8a + 24$ **17.** $-6 - 7j$ **18.** -30 **19.** $14a - 4b$ **20.** 144 **21.** $x + (x + 2) + (x + 4) = 45$, or $3x + 6 = 45$ **22.** $-\frac{x}{2}$ **23.** $-4t$ **24.** $12x - 6y + 10$ **25.** $21a - b$ **26.** 81 **27.** $-jk$ **28.** -19 **29.** 3

Chapter 3 Test

1. -142 **2.** 15 **3.** 18 **4.** 32 **5.** -90 **6.** -13 **7.** 2 **8.** -11 **9.** 36 **10.** -4 **11.** 9 **12.** 12.1¢ **13.** -3 **14.** no root **15.** identity **16.** -104 **17.** -7 and 5 **18.** Ben is 7; Barb is 9. **19.** 50 **20.** (1) Given (2) Add. prop. of equality (3) Assoc. axiom for addition (4) Axiom of opposites (5) Identity axiom for addition

Chapter 4 Test

1. $(x + 3)^3$ **2.** 12 **3.** -7 **4.** $r - 10$ **5.** $-5a - 8ab - 7b$ **6.** 13, 15, 17 **7.** $-10a^2b^3c$ **8.** 5^{2k}, or 25^k **9.** $8t^6$ **10.** $\frac{1}{27}x^9y^3$ **11.** $-128z^{13}$ **12.** $9n^{6x}$ **13.** $4y^5 - 28y^3 - 4y^2$ **14.** $-14j + 4j^3 - 10j^2$ **15.** 5 **16.** $3x^3 + 8x^2 + 3x - 2$ **17.** $6c^2 - 17cd + 5d^2$ **18.** $21x^3 + 22x^2y - 8xy^2$ **19. a.** $R = \frac{P}{1 + bt}$ **b.** $t = \frac{P - R}{Rb}$ **20.** 140 km **21.** 20 m by 35 m **22.** Marla would have to have $5\frac{5}{7}$ pennies, which is not possible.

Chapter 5 Test

1. $(1)(-66)$, $(2)(-33)$, $(3)(-22)$, $(6)(-11)$, $(11)(-6)$, $(22)(-3)$, $(33)(-2)$, $(66)(-1)$ **2.** $2^3 \cdot 3^2 \cdot 7$ **3.** $-\frac{3x}{4}$ **4.** $10a^4c$ **5.** $\frac{(ab + c)^2}{3}$ **6.** $4h^2 - 2gh + g^2$ **7.** $3t - 5t^2 + 16$ **8.** $28(r + 1)^3$ **9.** $3y^2(x^4 - 2x^2y^2 + 3y^4)$ **10.** $3m^2 - 5m + 2$ **11.** $8c^3 - 2c^2 - 15c$ **12.** $35e^2 + 13ef - 4f^2$ **13.** $z^4 - 49$ **14.** $25a^2 - 64b^2$ **15.** $r^2 - 6r + 9$ **16.** $s^2 + 12st + 36t^2$ **17.** $4j^6 - 4j^3k + k^2$ **18.** $m^2n^4 - 2mn^2p + p^2$ **19.** $(17x - 6y)(17x + 6y)$ **20.** $(2v^3 - 3)(2v^3 + 3)$ **21.** $(5u - 1)^2$ **22.** prime **23.** $(n - 12)(n - 5)$ **24.** prime **25.** $(r + 21)(r - 3)$ **26.** $(1 - 12ab)(1 + ab)$ **27.** prime **28.** $(7x + 3y)(x - 2y)$ **29.** $(g^4 + 2)(3g - 7)$ **30.** $(3 - a - 2b)(3 + a + 2b)$ **31.** $-2c(3c + 2)(c - 2)$ **32.** $(m - 5)(m + 5)(m^2 + 1)$ **33.** $(x + y - z^2)(x + y + z^2)$ **34.** $\left\{0, \frac{1}{3}, -\frac{1}{3}\right\}$ **35.** $\frac{2}{3}$ **36.** $\{0, 2, -12\}$ **37.** 3 and 5 **38.** 5 cm

Chapter 6 Test

1. $\frac{2a}{2a + 3b}$; $a \neq -\frac{2}{3}b$, $a \neq -\frac{3}{2}b$
2. $-\frac{m - 1}{4m + 5}$; $m \neq 1$, $m \neq -\frac{5}{4}$

3. $\frac{(x-7)}{2x^2}$; $x \neq 0, x \neq -7$ 4. $\frac{2e}{3c}$; $c \neq 0, d \neq 0, e \neq 0$

5. $\frac{9x^5}{2y^2}$; $y \neq 0$ 6. $-2a^3(a-5)^2$; $a \neq 0, a \neq 5$

7. $-\frac{4a}{81b^4}$; $a \neq 0, b \neq 0$ 8. $\frac{rs(r^2+s^2)}{4(r+s)}$; $r \neq 0, s \neq 0, r \neq -s$ 9. $\frac{t(t+1)}{t-1}$; $t \neq 1, t \neq 0$

10. $\frac{2-x}{x}$; $x \neq 0, x \neq 1, x \neq -2, x \neq -3$

11. $-\frac{1}{3y}$; $y \neq 0, z \neq 0$ 12. $2(c+2d)$ 13. 56

14. $-21(a-3)$ 15. $20b^2c^3$ 16. $-a$

17. $\frac{2-15n}{12n^2}$ 18. $\frac{7+x}{9}$ 19. $\frac{y-x}{x+y}$

20. $-\frac{3}{z(z-2)}$ 21. $\frac{(h-2)(h+1)}{h-1}$ 22. $\frac{8c-1}{3c-1}$

23. $\frac{-t(2t-3)}{(2t-1)(2t+1)}$ 24. $\frac{4x^2-x^3-8+2x}{2x}$

25. $2x+2+\frac{4}{3x-1}$ 26. $2a^2-3a-1$

27. $b+3c-\frac{2c^2}{b+2c}$ 28. $(2x+1)(3x-1)(x-4)$

Chapter 7 Test

1. 1 : 25 2. a. 7 : 4 b. 33 : 16 3. Sue: 6 km/h, Lois: 4.8 km/h 4. 10 5. 7 6. $\frac{3}{2}$ 7. 4

8. 12 9. 13 10. 14 11. $\left\{4, -\frac{8}{5}\right\}$

12. $-\frac{3}{2}$ 13. 1 or 2 14. a. $\frac{33}{400}$ b. $\frac{16}{5}$

15. a. 4.56 b. 5.4 16. $\frac{40}{3}$ 17. 20%

18. 390 kW · h 19. 7.5 L of 20%, 2.5 L of 60%
20. 8.4 h 21. a. 5.9×10^{-3} b. $0 \times 10^{-1} + 0 \times 10^{-2} + 5 \times 10^{-3} + 9 \times 10^{-4}$ 22. a. 25
b. $\frac{64}{49}$ 23. $\frac{1}{b^2}$ 24. $\frac{1}{e^6}$ 25. $\frac{1}{g^3}$ 26. 1

Chapter 8 Test

1. a. yes b. no c. no 2. $y = \frac{4x-10}{3}$

3. $\{(2, 0), (0, 4), (1, 3)\}$

4. 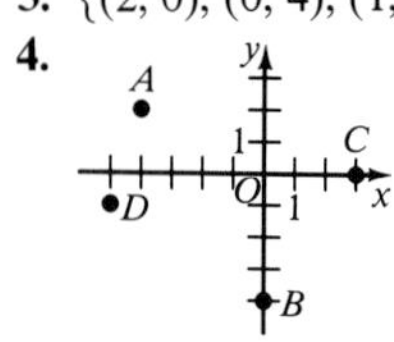

5. 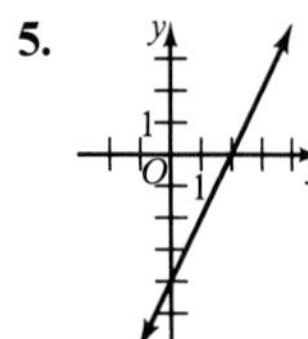

6.

7. 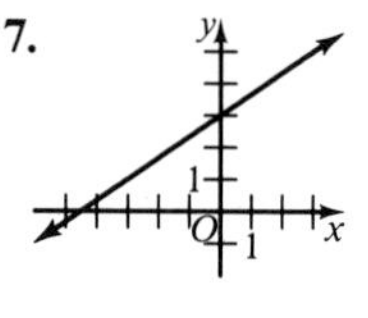

8. $(5, -8)$
9. $(-2, -3)$

10. $(7, 4)$ 11. $\left(\frac{3}{2}, \frac{1}{2}\right)$ 12. 4 ten-cent stamps
13. Kate is 7; Brett is 5. 14. 1 km/h
15. 27 16. $\frac{9}{15}$

Chapter 9 Test

1. -3; -20 2. $-\frac{7}{5}$

3. $-6x + 4y = -1$; see graph at right 4. $x + y = 0$
5. $-3x + y = -7$ 6. $y = 5$

7. $\left\{-\frac{1}{3}, -1, 1\right\}$ 8. $\{2, 0\}$ 9. 2

10. a. $D = \{1967, 1972, 1977, 1982\}$, $R = \{\$1.00, \$.84, \$.55, \$.35\}$ b. 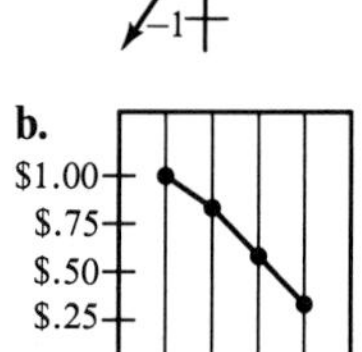

11. 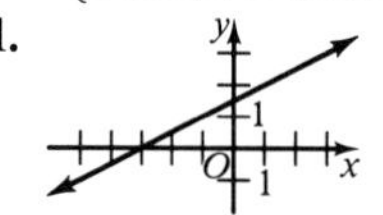

12. 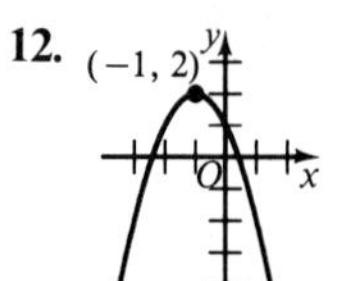

13. 5 14. a. 1 b. 5.76
15. $152 16. 4 m
17. 13.5

Chapter 10 Test

1. $\{-4, -3, -2, -1, 0, 1\}$
2. $\{-4, -3, -2, -1, 4\}$ 3. $\{-1, 0, 1\}$
4.

5. {the real numbers less than 5} 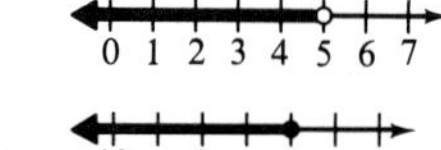

6. $\{-6$, and the real numbers less than $-6\}$ 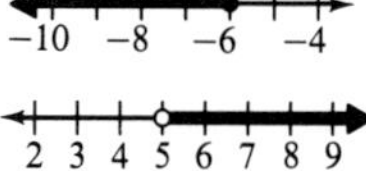

7. {the real numbers greater than 5} 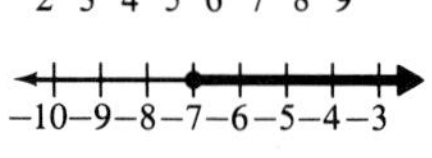

8. $\{-7$, and the real numbers greater than $-7\}$ 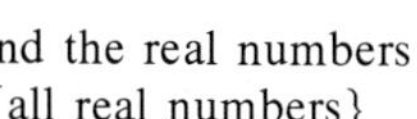

9. 85 km/h 10. $\{-5, 2$, and the real numbers between -5 and $2\}$ 11. {all real numbers}

12. $\left\{\text{the real numbers between } -\frac{10}{3} \text{ and } 2\right\}$

13. {all real numbers} 14. $\{-5, -9,$ and the real numbers greater than -5 or less than $-9\}$ 15. {9}

16. $\{$the real numbers between -3 and $3\}$

17. $\{3, -3\}$

18. 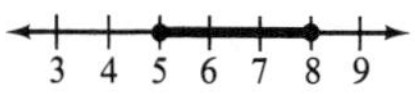

19. 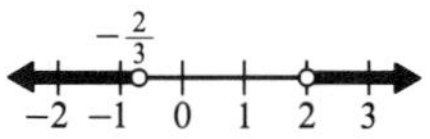

20. 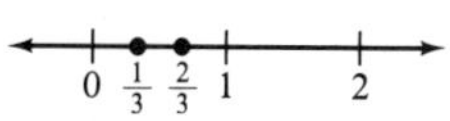

21. 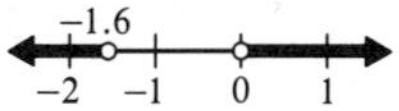

22. 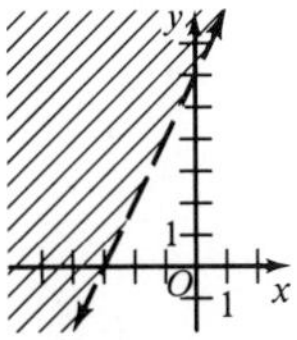

23. 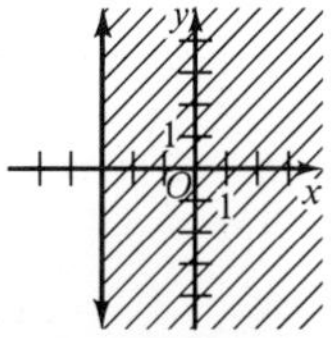

24. 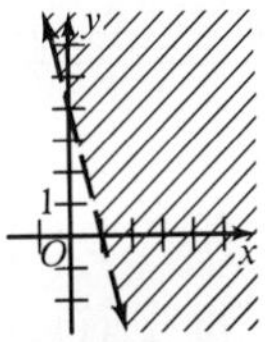

25. 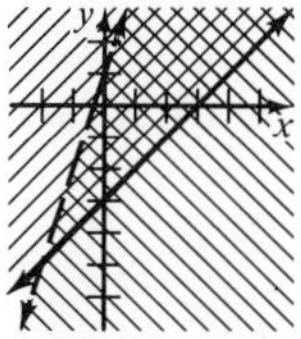

26. 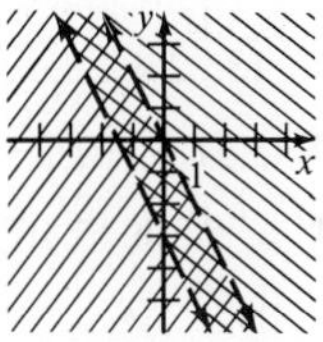

27. 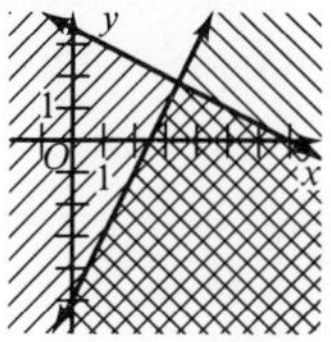

Chapter 11 Test

1. $-2.5, -\frac{89}{36}, -\frac{59}{24}$ 2. increases 3. $\frac{19}{30}$

4. a. $0.1\overline{5}$ b. 1.1875 5. a. $\frac{29}{40}$ b. $\frac{19}{55}$

6. $\frac{10}{3}$ 7. 0.11 8. 35 9. -3.5 10. $6\sqrt{2}$

11. $12\sqrt{7}$ 12. $\frac{1}{3}\left|\frac{r^3}{s}\right|$ 13. $|z+1|$ 14. $\{9, -9\}$

15. $\{2.5, -2.5\}$ 16. $\{17.9, -17.9\}$

17. 24 18. 36 cm 19. $\frac{2\sqrt{30}}{5}$ 20. $\frac{\sqrt{15}}{2}$

21. $x^3 - 2x$ 22. $\sqrt{3}$ 23. $\frac{4}{7}\sqrt{42}$ 24. $5\sqrt{3}$

25. $21 + 6\sqrt{6}$ 26. $-9 - \sqrt{5}$ 27. -5

28. $-2(1 + \sqrt{3})$ 29. 48 30. $\frac{5}{16}$

31. $\{\sqrt{2}, -\sqrt{2}\}$

Chapter 12 Test

1. $\{4, -3\}$ 2. no solution 3. $\left\{\frac{3\sqrt{2}}{2}, -\frac{3\sqrt{2}}{2}\right\}$

4. $\{4 + 3\sqrt{2}, 4 - 3\sqrt{2}\}$; $\{8.2, -0.2\}$ 5. $\{5, -1\}$

6. $\left\{\frac{3+\sqrt{5}}{2}, \frac{3-\sqrt{5}}{2}\right\}$; $\{2.6, 0.4\}$

7. $\{-1 + \sqrt{2}, -1 - \sqrt{2}\}$ 8. $\left\{\frac{5+\sqrt{13}}{6}, \frac{5-\sqrt{13}}{6}\right\}$

9. $\left\{-\frac{5}{3}, \frac{3}{2}\right\}$ 10. $\left\{-2, \frac{1}{2}\right\}$

11. $\left\{\frac{5+\sqrt{21}}{4}, \frac{5-\sqrt{21}}{4}\right\}$ 12. $\left\{0, -\frac{15}{7}\right\}$

13. $\{-7, 1\}$ 14. $\left\{\frac{-7+\sqrt{29}}{2}, \frac{-7-\sqrt{29}}{2}\right\}$

15. $\{-2, 14\}$ 16. one 17. two

18. no real roots 19. none; above

20. -2 or $\frac{3}{2}$ 21. 0.74 in.

Cumulative Reviews

Review for Chapters 1–3

1. 1 2. 4.5 3. -3 4. -9 5. $-a - 2b$

6. $6x - 2y$ 7. -5 8. -37 9. 60 10. 4

11. 14 12. 0.42 13. $29r + 15$

14. $3j - 17k + 3jk$ 15. 0 16. $\frac{152}{3}$ 17. -5

18. 96 19. $\{-1, 2\}$ 20. $\{0\}$ 21. $\{-1\}$

22. 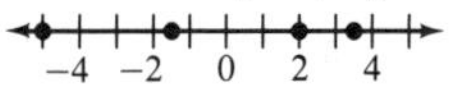 23. F 24. $2b - 7$

25. $10d + 25(9 - d) = 285$ 26. $2x + 2(x + 2) = 64$, or $4x + 4 = 64$ 27. $\{8, -8\}$ 28. no solution

29. -7 30. -9 31. 100 32. -48

33. 7 34. -9 35. 11 36. -1 37. -40

38. no solution 39. -6 40. identity

41. 9 42. 55 km/h 43. $-\frac{3}{2}$ 44. George bought 6 stamps; Pedro bought 11. 45. Sam is 10; Pam is 11. 46. \$7.20 per hour 47. -9

48. (1) Given (2) Addition prop. of equality (3) Associative axiom for add. (4) Axiom of opposites (5) Identity axiom for add. (7) Mult. prop. of equality (8) Associative axiom for mult. (9) Axiom of reciprocals (10) Substitution principle **49.** (1) Prop. of Opp. of a Sum (2) Definition of opposite (3) Definition of subtraction

50.

Statements	Reasons
1. $a + b = 0$	1. Given
2. $a + b + (-b) = 0 + (-b)$	2. Addition prop. of equality
3. $a + [b + (-b)] = 0 + (-b)$	3. Assoc. axiom for add.
4. $a + 0 = 0 + (-b)$	4. Axiom of opposites
5. $a = -b$	5. Identity axiom for add.

Review for Chapters 4–6

1. -4 **2.** $-r^2 - 6$ **3.** $x^2 - 4xy + y^2$
4. $-\frac{35}{2}a^6b^2c^4$ **5.** 5^{2x} **6.** $-12c^8d^7$
7. $-26h^2 + h$ **8.** $10d^2 - 15d^3 + 20d^4$
9. $10x^3 + 22x^2y - 21xy^2 - 5y^3$ **10.** $-\frac{n^4}{2}$
11. $9rs^2 - 2r^2s^2 - \frac{1}{2}r^3s$ **12.** $6t^3 + 22t^2 - 8t$
13. $5d^4 + 13d^2e - 6e^2$ **14.** $121m^2 - 16$
15. $81k^2 + 72k + 16$ **16.** $9a^2b^2 - 12abc + 4c^2$
17. $\frac{S - a}{S} = r$ **18.** $2^3 \cdot 3^2 \cdot 7$ **19.** $12yz^2$
20. $-8rs(2r^2 - r + 4)$ **21.** $(3a - 11b)(3a + 11b)$
22. $c(2 - c^2)(2 + c^2)(4 + c^4)$ **23.** prime
24. $(2m + 5n)^2$ **25.** $(z - 5)(z - 7)$
26. $(x - 9y)(x + 7y)$ **27.** prime
28. $(4t + 3)(t + 4)$ **29.** $(3k + 1)(5k - 4)$
30. $(x^2 - 3)(2x - 1)$ **31.** $(x - 1 + 2y)(x - 1 - 2y)$
32. prime **33.** $-5q(3q - 2)(2q - 3)$
34. $rs^2(2r - 7s)^2$ **35.** $\frac{1}{2}$ **36.** -9
37. $\left\{\frac{1}{3}, -\frac{2}{3}\right\}$ **38.** $\{0, 9, -9\}$ **39.** $\left\{0, \frac{1}{2}\right\}$
40. $\left\{\frac{3}{8}, 1\right\}$ **41.** 48 min **42.** 2 m
43. no solution; The only possible integers are 16, 18, and 20, which are even. **44.** 6 and 9 or 39 and -24 **45.** no solution; We need to know the total number of tickets sold. **46.** $\frac{3x + 1}{3x + 2}$

47. $\frac{r(3r + 2s)}{r - s}$ **48.** $-\frac{1 + b}{(b - 1)^2}$ **49.** $324x$
50. $\frac{512}{n^3}$ **51.** $\frac{a^2 + 9}{7}$ **52.** 720 **53.** $3b(b + 2)$
54. $(m + n)^2(m - n)$ **55.** -1 **56.** $\frac{16x - 41}{36}$
57. $\frac{g + 12}{(g - 3)(g + 2)}$ **58.** $-\frac{1}{t(3t + 1)^2}$
59. $\frac{5}{5m - 4}$ **60.** $\frac{4}{y - 4}$ **61.** $\frac{3x^2 - 1}{x(x - 1)}$
62. $\frac{3(y - z)}{z}$ **63.** $9d^4 + 12d^3 - 26d^2 - 20d + 25$
64. $\frac{8x + 11}{3}$; $\frac{2x^2 + 13x - 7}{6}$ **65.** $3c^2 - 5c + 8 - \frac{15}{2c + 3}$
66. $n^2 + 3n - 2$ **67.** $3x^2 - 4xy + y^2$
68. $(z + 3)(5z - 1)(z + 4)$

Review for Chapters 7–9

1. 3 : 8 **2.** $-1 : 4$ **3.** 8 **4.** $\frac{14}{3}$ **5.** 4
6. -7 **7.** $\frac{4}{5}$ **8.** 9 **9.** -3 **10.** $\{9, -3\}$
11. no solution **12. a.** $\frac{39}{250}$ **b.** $\frac{12}{5}$ **13.** 2.4
14. 632 **15.** 140 **16.** 250% **17.** 5.31×10^5; $5 \times 10^5 + 3 \times 10^4 + 1 \times 10^3 + 0 \times 10^2 + 0 \times 10^1 + 0 \times 10^0$ **18. a.** $\frac{1}{8}$ **b.** $\frac{9}{4}$ **19.** $\frac{x^3}{125}$ **20.** $\frac{4}{y^6}$
21. $\frac{1}{t^3}$ **22.** 12 years old **23. a.** 64% **b.** 9984
24. $\frac{12}{15}$ or $\frac{5}{8}$ **25.** \$22.50 **26.** 20 g
27. $6\frac{2}{9}$ hours **28.** yes **29.** $\{(8, 0), (2, 2), (5, 1)\}$
30. **31.** **32.**

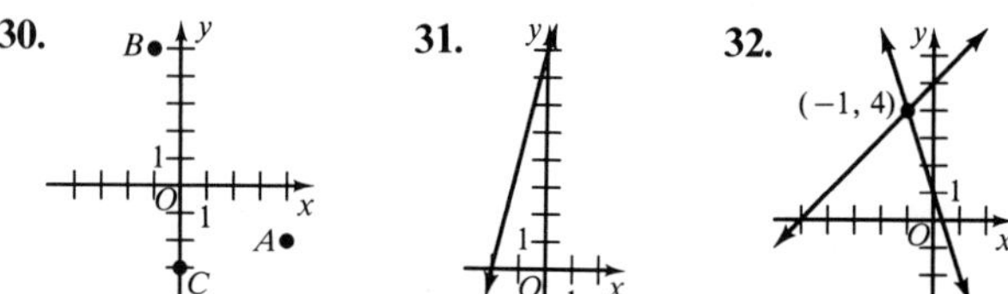

33. $(-6, 0)$ **34.** none **35.** \$500 at 5.5%, \$1500 at 9.5% **36.** $(-1, -3)$ **37.** $(7, 2)$ **38.** $(-3, -5)$
39. 32 km; 1.6 h **40.** 26 **41.** $-\frac{2}{3}$
42.

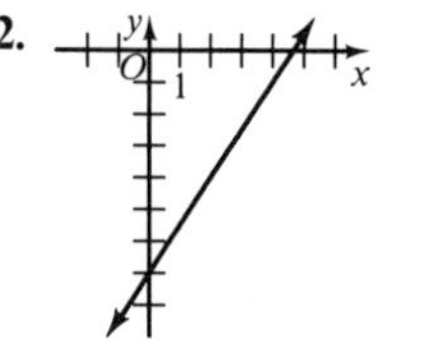

43. $-x + 4y = -2$
44. $5x + 2y = 0$
45. $3x + y = 6$
46. $-3x + 4y = 20$
47. $\{9, 5, 3\}$

48. −2

49. a. 12 b. 27
50. 7.5 g 51. 150
52. $G = \frac{kmn}{d^2}$

23.

24. $\frac{13}{18}, \frac{23}{29}, \frac{4}{5}, \frac{53}{66}$ 25. $-\frac{17}{36}$
26. a. 4.4375 b. $-0.\overline{074}$
27. $\frac{8}{11}; \frac{99}{50}; \frac{36}{25}$ 28. −26

Review for Chapters 10–12

1. F 2. F 3. T 4. {1, 2, 3, 4, 5}
5. {the real numbers less than −4} 6. {8, and the real numbers less than 8} 7. {4, and the real numbers greater than 4}

8. 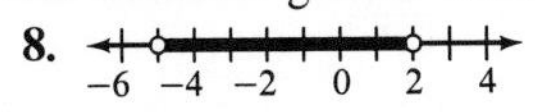

9. 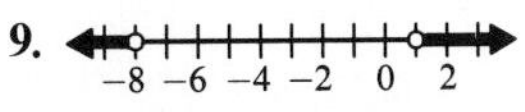

10.
11.
12.
13.
14.
15.
16.
17.

18. 9 nickels 19. 12.5 mL

20. 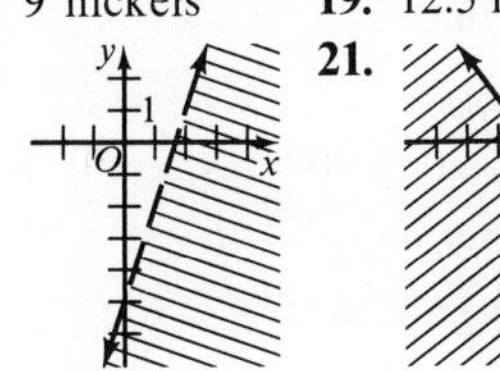

21. 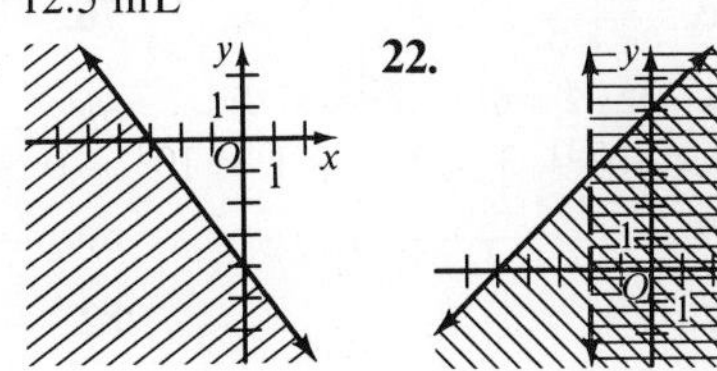

22.

29. $\frac{7}{30}$ 30. ± 0.16 31. $\frac{1}{2}$ 32. $20\sqrt{6}$ 33. $6\sqrt{3}$
34. $-3|a|b^2\sqrt{5a}$ 35. $1.1|x|$ 36. $|g - 2|$
37. $\frac{|m^5|}{4n^4}$ 38. $22\sqrt{7}$ 39. $4k^2\sqrt{2k}$ 40. 50.1
41. 42 cm 42. no 43. 6.93 44. $\frac{2}{3}$
45. $\frac{2\sqrt{35}}{7}$ 46. $30\sqrt{6}$ 47. $3x^3$ 48. $16 + 7\sqrt{2}$
49. $\frac{23\sqrt{3}}{5}$ 50. $35\sqrt{3} + 350$ 51. 7
52. $153 + 30\sqrt{2}$ 53. $-43 + 7\sqrt{22}$
54. $4\sqrt{3} + 6$ 55. 32 56. $\frac{121}{16}$ 57. 2
58. $\{2\sqrt{2}, -2\sqrt{2}\}$ 59. no solution 60. $\left\{\frac{5}{2}, -\frac{5}{2}\right\}$
61. $\{-7, 3\}$ 62. $\left\{\frac{12 + 7\sqrt{3}}{3}, \frac{12 - 7\sqrt{3}}{3}\right\}$
63. $\{3 + 2\sqrt{3}, 3 - 2\sqrt{3}\}$ 64. $\left\{\frac{4 + \sqrt{10}}{2}, \frac{4 - \sqrt{10}}{2}\right\}$
65. $\left\{\frac{-7 + \sqrt{65}}{8}, \frac{-7 - \sqrt{65}}{8}\right\}$ 66. $-\frac{1}{25}$
67. a. −31 b. none 68. a. 169 b. two
69. a. 0 b. one 70. $\left\{\frac{1 + \sqrt{7}}{2}, \frac{1 - \sqrt{7}}{2}\right\}$
71. $\{-2 + \sqrt{5}, -2 - \sqrt{5}\}$ 72. $\{3, -1\}$
73. $\{2.6, 0.4\}$ 74. 12

Topical Reviews

Review of Factoring Polynomials

1. $(x + 14)(x - 1)$ 2. $3(p + 2q)(p - 2q)$
3. $(m + 24)(m - 8)$ 4. $(5q + 2p)(5q - 2p)$
5. $(11x + 2)(2x - 1)$ 6. $4(3r + 2)(3r - 2)$
7. $(2x + 3y)(2c - a)$ 8. $(6x - 1)(x - 12)$
9. $(1 + 9w^4x^2)(1 + 3w^2x)(1 - 3w^2x)$
10. $(a - b)(4cz + 3y)$
11. $3(2x + 7)(x - 1)$ 12. $8(5c + 1)^2$
13. $(3 + 8y)(3 - 2y)$ 14. $(10x - 3)(2x - 1)$
15. $19y(2x + y^2)(2x - y^2)$ 16. $4(x + 3)(x - 1)$
17. $a(0.4x^2 + 0.3y)(0.4x^2 - 0.3y)$
18. $(2 - 3x)(2 + x)$
19. $3(4x^2 + 19xy - 7y^2)$ 20. $(x - 3)(y - 6)$
21. $(4x - 5)(8x - 1)$ 22. $a(7a + 3)(2a - 5)$
23. $(6g - k)(5f + 2h)$ 24. $7x^2(2x + 5)(x - 1)$
25. $(x + 2)(1 - x)$
26. $(2p - 3)(p + 2)(p - 2)$
27. $(a + b)^2$ 28. $2(16x^4 - 16x^2 + 1)$
29. $2(c - d + 2)(c - d - 2)$ 30. $5(cd + 3)^2$
31. $(3 + a + b)(3 - a - b)$ 32. $-(p + q)^2$
33. $(m + 5)(m - 5)(m^2 + 2)$ 34. $7x^2y(3 + 2y)(3 - 2y)$
35. $-(6x + 5)(5x + 6)$ 36. $(4a - 5m)(x + 3m)$
37. $(2a^2 + 1)(a + 1)$ 38. $3(x + 3)(x - 3)$
39. $(x + 5)(x - 2)$ 40. $(x - 6)(2x^2 + 1)$
41. $(x - 2)^2(x + 2)$ 42. $a^{12}(a + 5)(a - 1)$

43. $(2c + 3d - 1)(2c - 3d - 1)$
44. $(x - 1)^2(x + 1)^2$
45. $(x + 3)(x + 5)$ 46. $2n(m - n)$
47. $(b - c)(a - b + c)$
48. $(x - 3y + 1)(x - 3y - 1)$
49. $(a + 1)(a - 2)(1 - a)$
50. $(2x^2 - 2x + 1)(2x - 1)$

Review of Simplifying Expressions

1. $-115x^{24}$ 2. $-48\sqrt{10}$
3. $\frac{3x - 6}{x - 4}$ 4. $-\frac{(a + b)^2}{8a}$
5. $\frac{10a - 29}{36}$ 6. 1
7. 7 8. $2x^2 - x + 4$
9. $\frac{9x^2}{49}$ 10. $\frac{x + 3}{x - 4}$
11. $80\sqrt{6} - 120$ 12. $-\frac{16x^6}{9y^6z}$
13. $\frac{c^2 + cd}{3(c - 2d)^2}$ 14. $-\frac{a^3}{216c^6}$
15. 77 16. $2y^3 - 6y^2 - 23y + 15$
17. $\frac{3 + \sqrt{5}}{2}$ 18. $-8a^6$
19. $-\frac{x}{2x + 6}$ 20. $\frac{-20m - 40}{m(m + 7)(m - 3)}$
21. $-\frac{1}{2p}$ 22. $81x^8$
23. $\frac{3x + 2}{x + 5}$ 24. $\frac{2b^2}{2a + b}$
25. $\frac{16a^4}{9b^2}$ 26. $\frac{2a^2 - 40}{(a + 4)(a - 4)}$
27. $5x^3 - 3x^2 + x + 4$ 28. $123 - 70\sqrt{2}$
29. $-2x^{24}$ 30. 2
31. 36
32. $4x^3 + 19x^2 + 29x + 14$
33. $\frac{x + 7}{2x}$ 34. $\frac{-x(y + x)}{2x - 7y}$
35. $\frac{46\sqrt{7}}{21}$ 36. $\frac{3x^2 + 7x + 25}{(2x + 3)(x + 1)(2x + 5)}$
37. $\frac{-x - 5}{(2x + 1)^2(x - 1)}$ 38. $\frac{x - 2}{x + 3}$
39. $-x$ 40. $144x\sqrt{x}$
41. $a^2 + 3a - 1$ 42. $\frac{625c^4}{16d^{20}}$
43. $\frac{2(a - 6)}{3}$ 44. $\frac{3a^2 + a - 3}{(2a - 3)(a + 2)}$
45. c^{8n+4} 46. $4x^6 - 12x^3y + 9y^2$
47. $-108p^{17}q^{10}$ 48. $\frac{-36p^2 - 33p - 5}{(3p + 1)(3p + 2)}$
49. $\frac{32x^4}{11y^3}$ 50. $\frac{21\sqrt{6}}{4}$
51. 2 52. a^{4m+5}
53. $x^2 - 3$ 54. $\frac{a - c}{a - b}$
55. $\frac{27a^6c^3}{8d^3}$ 56. $-5\sqrt{6} - 10\sqrt{3}$
57. $\frac{x + 1}{2(3x - 4)}$ 58. $54x^7y^8$
59. $-\frac{3}{x(4x + 1)}$ 60. $-10\sqrt{2}$
61. $a^3 - 15a^2 + 75a - 125$ 62. $\frac{-3x - 5}{6(x + 5)}$
63. $49x^4y^{10}z^{14}$ 64. $\frac{2(a + 2c)}{3c^2}$
65. $\frac{-16y}{63x^2}$ 66. $48c^{16}$
67. $\frac{(a + 4)(a - 3)}{(2a - 3)(a + 3)}$ 68. $\frac{1 - x}{x + 5}$
69. $\frac{7p + 11}{(p - 1)(p + 5)(p - 5)}$ 70. $66 + 36\sqrt{2}$
71. $\frac{4}{3xy}$ 72. $-3x^2 + 4x - 2$
73. $20x^4\sqrt{x}$ 74. $\frac{7x^2 - 18x + 11}{(3x + 1)(3x - 1)(x + 1)}$
75. $\frac{2x}{2x + 3}$ 76. $\frac{(x - 3)(x + 7)}{3}$
77. $\frac{42\sqrt{2} - 67}{31}$ 78. $-\frac{1}{2y}$
79. $\frac{16x + 1}{5(x + 1)(x - 1)}$ 80. $\frac{6 - 3\sqrt{6}}{4}$
81. 5^{6n+3} 82. -39
83. $\frac{7\sqrt{30}}{30}$ 84. $63a^8b^{12}$
85. $\frac{8}{y^3}$ 86. $\frac{d^4}{c^3}$
87. $\frac{x}{y^2}$ 88. $\frac{6c}{ab^2}$
89. $\frac{v^6}{6u^4}$ 90. $\frac{q^7}{p^5r^9}$
91. $\frac{b}{a}$ 92. $\frac{d - c}{2d + c}$
93. $\frac{3(x - y)^2}{2(x^2 - xy + y^2)}$

Review of Solving Equations, Inequalities, and Systems

1. 8 2. 49 3. −6 4. 54 5. 6 6. 2
7. no solution 8. $\left\{\text{the real numbers less than or equal to } \frac{16}{17}\right\}$ 9. $\{0, 2\}$ 10. −2 11. 4

12. {the real numbers greater than or equal to 5} **13.** 6 **14.** $\left\{\text{the real numbers greater than or equal to 4 or less than or equal to } \frac{4}{3}\right\}$

15. $\left\{\frac{5+\sqrt{65}}{20}, \frac{5-\sqrt{65}}{20}\right\}$ **16.** (2, 1)

17. (4, 1) **18.** (2, 0) **19.** $\frac{-24}{5}$ **20.** $cd - b$

21. $\left\{\frac{9+\sqrt{57}}{6}, \frac{9-\sqrt{57}}{6}\right\}$ **22.** $\left\{-1, \frac{26}{7}\right\}$

23. $\frac{11}{8}$ **24.** $\frac{28}{5}$ **25.** $\left\{\frac{2+\sqrt{3}}{2}, \frac{2-\sqrt{3}}{2}\right\}$

26. {0, 4} **27.** $\left\{\text{the real numbers greater than } \frac{39}{2}\right\}$

28. 2 **29.** $\left\{-3, \frac{5}{4}\right\}$ **30.** $\frac{1}{4}$ **31.** {−7, 4, and the real numbers between −7 and 4} **32.** $\frac{5c+a}{4c}$

33. $\left\{\frac{\sqrt{14}}{2}, -\frac{\sqrt{14}}{2}\right\}$ **34.** $\{-3+\sqrt{11}, -3-\sqrt{11}\}$

35. $\left\{\frac{\sqrt{58}}{2}, -\frac{\sqrt{58}}{2}\right\}$ **36.** {the real numbers greater than or equal to 27} **37.** $\left\{-4, \frac{8}{9}\right\}$

38. −14 **39.** {2, −2} **40.** {−4, −3, 3}

41. $\left\{4, -\frac{1}{2}\right\}$ **42.** $\frac{37}{4}$ **43.** (6, −9)

44. $\left(-\frac{54}{19}, -\frac{20}{19}\right)$ **45.** no solution

46. {the real numbers between −4 and 3}

47. $\left\{\frac{2+\sqrt{10}}{2}, \frac{2-\sqrt{10}}{2}\right\}$ **48.** $\left\{-\frac{1}{3}, \frac{1}{3}\right\}$ **49.** 2

50. 6 **51.** $\{1+\sqrt{5}, 1-\sqrt{5}\}$

52. $\frac{2cd+a}{c}$ **53.** 3 **54.** $\{-3+\sqrt{13}, -3-\sqrt{13}\}$

55. $12 - 6\sqrt{3}$ **56.** $\frac{2}{5}$ **57.** $\left\{\frac{6}{5}, -\frac{1}{2}\right\}$

58. {the real numbers less than or equal to −4}

59. $\{2\sqrt{3}, -2\sqrt{3}\}$ **60.** $\frac{1}{2}$

61. $\left\{\frac{9+3\sqrt{13}}{2}, \frac{9-3\sqrt{13}}{2}\right\}$ **62.** $\left\{-1, \frac{1}{2}\right\}$

63. $\{2+\sqrt{6}, 2-\sqrt{6}\}$

64. {the real numbers greater than 10 or less than −2}

65. $\{-5+5\sqrt{5}, -5-5\sqrt{5}\}$ **66.** $\left\{4, -\frac{16}{3}\right\}$

67. $\frac{2s+gt^2}{2t}$ **68.** 6 **69.** $\left\{\text{the real numbers less than } -\frac{67}{9}\right\}$ **70.** (−4, 5) **71.** (0, −5)

72. Infinite set of solutions **73.** {0, 4}

74. 4 **75.** $\left\{-\frac{21}{4}, \frac{21}{4}, \text{ and the real numbers between } -\frac{21}{4} \text{ and } \frac{21}{4}\right\}$ **76.** $-\frac{8}{3}$

77. $\left\{\frac{1+\sqrt{281}}{10}, \frac{1-\sqrt{281}}{10}\right\}$ **78.** {2, 3} **79.** 9

Review of Solving Word Problems

1. \$112, \$56, \$84, \$140
2. 1 L milk, \$.67; 1 orange, \$.21
3. side = 5 cm, hyp. = 13 cm
4. Reader *A*, 12 min; Reader *B*, 24 min
5. 200 g
6. 8 nickels, 14 quarters, 7 dimes, 3 half dollars
7. 425 buttons
8. 13 years
9. 9 cm by 16 cm
10. Colin, \$14.00; Maureen, \$28.00
11. 81 cm^2, 441 cm^2
12. 31, 33, 35 (Divide 99 by 3 to find the middle number)
13. 32 cm^3
14. 12%
15. 4 cm by 18 cm
16. $\frac{4}{9}$
17. first cyclist, 100 km; second cyclist, 70 km
18. about 4.45 cm
19. \$2500
20. 1 m
21. 5 kg at \$2.70, 25 kg at \$3.00
22. 38
23. 6 km/h
24. boat: 7.5 km/h; current: 1.5 km/h
25. airplane: 150 mph; wind: 30 mph
26. 2 h
27. 17 km

Review of Lines and Graphing

1.

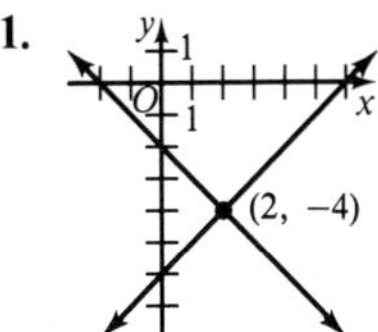

2.

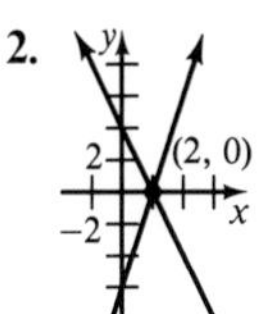

3.

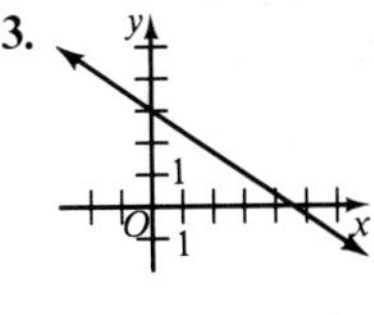

4. $x + y = 3$ **5.** $5x - 2y = -6$ **6.** $3x + 2y = 13$

7. $x = 4$ **8.** $x + 3y = 25$ **9.** $y = -1$

10. $x - y = 8$ 11. $2x - y = -13$

12. {4, and the real numbers between 2 and 4}

13. {-2, and the real numbers between -2 and 3.5}

14. no solution 15. {all real numbers}

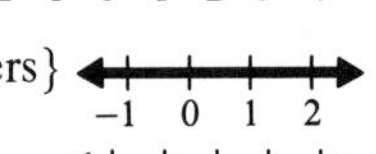

16. {the real numbers less than or equal to 3}

17. {the real numbers greater than 2 or less than -1}

18. $2x - 3y = -6$ 19. $3x + y = 4$ 20. $y = 2$

21. $x = -\frac{3}{2}$ 22.

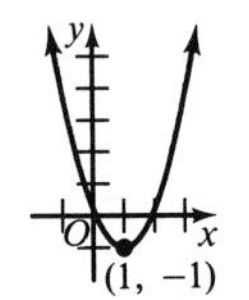

23. $(\frac{5}{4}, \frac{1}{8})$

24. (−2, −3)

25.

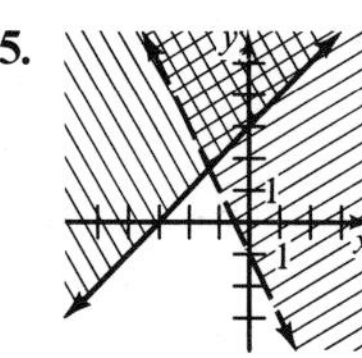

26.

27.

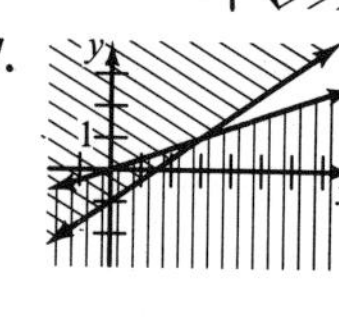

28. $4x - 3y = 12$ 29. $2x - 3y = 3$ 30. $x + 4y = 6$

31. $3x - 8y = 27$ 32. $5x + y = 23$ 33. $y = 4$

34. -7 35. $3x - y = 3$ 36. $x + 2y = 7$

37. 38. 39.

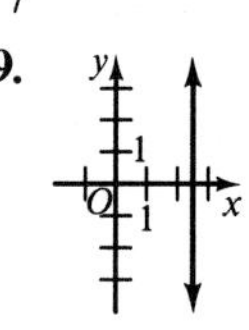

40.

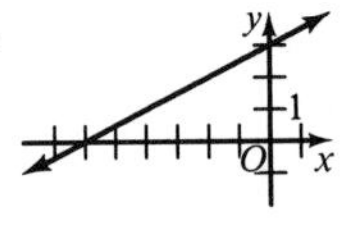

41.

42.

43. Yes; $m = 4$ 44. No

45. {2, 3, and the real numbers between 2 and 3}

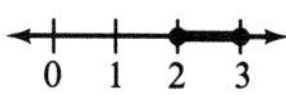

46. no solution

47. {the real numbers greater than 3.5 or all integers less than or equal to 3}

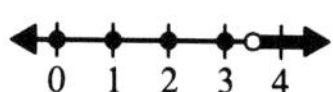

Reading Algebra

Suggestions for helping your students learn how to read an algebra textbook

The question is sometimes asked, "Why do we need to teach reading in an algebra class?" A study of reading algebra reveals that it is integrally tied to the learning of algebra. Difficulties that students encounter in algebra are often the result of difficulties in reading. To improve reading algebra is to improve algebra. To improve reading is to increase the chance of making the student a more independent learner since reading is a learning-to-learn skill. Once a student learns to read proficiently, doors are opened that were previously closed.

The ideas of algebra are expressed in compact form, with extensive use of mathematical symbols, and are applied in the solution of a wide variety of problems. Exposition and examples are illustrated with diagrams that must be read and understood along with the text. Following through the solution of an equation often requires up-and-down eye movements as well as the familiar left-to-right motion, together with pauses to consider how successive steps in the solution are related. For all these reasons, even students who can read other material proficiently may have trouble in reading algebra. Throughout the course, students will profit from the teacher's specific suggestions for improving their reading skills.

Many familiar words—for example, *power, variation, imaginary*—take on specialized meanings in algebra. These meanings need to be pointed out to students, and the importance of learning definitions and using mathematical terms correctly needs to be emphasized.

Diagrams are of great value in almost all branches of mathematics. Their importance in algebra should not be overlooked. Students need to realize that diagrams are essential parts of the discussion, the examples, and often the exercises, and that the diagrams must be read along with the words of the text. Identifying and interpreting the information provided by diagrams, graphs, and charts is a skill that has to be learned. Without adequate preparation, students are likely to become frustrated as they attempt to cope with material presented in this way.

All the learning activities that have been mentioned are essentially reading activities. Clearly, successful reading calls for practice and patience on the part of both teacher and students. Consistent work on reading that is to be integrated into the content of the course seems to be the method most likely to lead to success. To help the learner, this textbook has been organized in a way that is easy to follow, with important material highlighted. Six major reading objectives are stressed throughout. These objectives are interrelated; it is hardly possible to teach one without the others. Practical ways of accomplishing these objectives are presented in appropriate sections of the Lesson Commentary. We encourage you to practice the objectives at every opportunity throughout the year, as the particular needs of your own students may suggest.

Objective 1

Reading and Communicating Orally

This first objective is to ensure that students have a basic understanding of the relationship between what is spoken and what is written. A mathematics textbook contains many symbols, figures, charts, and graphs that are not commonly used in other books. It is not always possible to express their content in words. Further, the interrelationship between symbols is often complex, and the method of verbalizing may be unclear. It is not uncommon for a set of symbols to be verbalized in several ways within one class lesson. For example, a^2 may be called the square of a, the second power of a, a squared, or a to the second power. Practice is necessary if the relationship between the spoken and the written is to be understood.

Math teachers need to stress the use of oral language by having students verbalize in sentences, summarize, repeat, say another way, read aloud, work together, and perform other tasks that enhance both their own understanding and their ability to communicate the meaning of algebraic expressions.

Objective 2

Reading Silently

This second objective is to provide students with the necessary skills to be able to read silently, recognizing that one's purpose determines the speed and type of reading. When students read silently it is often beneficial if they do so with a purpose—to find the main idea, to look for a specific detail, to summarize, to answer a question, to study an example.

Different purposes demand different types of reading. For previewing or reviewing a lesson, skimming (rapid reading) is used. By contrast, slow reading is used when the student is trying to learn the main ideas and important details of a lesson. For slow reading, it is beneficial for teachers to provide questions in advance that will be discussed upon completion of the reading. When beginning a section, students may be directed first to skim the page to find new ideas and symbols, then to read carefully, and finally to answer questions or work exercises.

Objective 3

Using Symbols

The third objective is to assist students in recognizing symbols and in associating symbols with words and figures. As was suggested earlier, the verbalization of symbols creates a reading problem for many students. The word forms of symbols often are not obvious to students. Once learned, they must be reinforced to ensure retention. Other difficulties introduced by the use of symbols are their conciseness, the order in which they are read, and their association with concepts not actually stated.

The compact symbolism used in algebra has the advantage of showing the structure of a complex reasoning process. Consider the following example:

Symbols

1. $7(x + 8) - 4x = (-2 + x)(-5)$
2. $7x + 56 - 4x = 10 - 5x$
3. $3x + 56 = 10 - 5x$
4. $8x = -46$
5. $x = -\frac{46}{8}$
6. $x = -\frac{23}{4}$

Some principles involved

2. Distributive axiom
3. Combination of similar terms
4. Addition prop. of equality
5. Multiplication prop. of equality
6. Cancellation rule for fractions

Reading expressions of this kind demands a slow pace, concentration, and the ability to recognize elements that are implied rather than explicitly stated. One way to recognize the conciseness of the symbolism is to write out in words the ideas that appear in symbolic form. If students are asked to perform this kind of exercise occasionally, they soon come to appreciate the economy of using symbols.

Students will benefit from the teacher's explicit demonstration of the appropriate choice and ordering of symbols in the solution of equations and word problems. When several different symbolic forms can be used to represent the same idea, comparisons of these forms will help students recognize the flexibility of algebraic symbolism.

Objective 4

Using Mathematical Words

This fourth objective is to stress the mathematical meaning of words. A mathematics page contains words of everyday language (and, when, the), words that are unique to mathematics (monomial, abscissa, secant), and familiar words with specialized meanings in mathematics (prime, variable, complex). The most commonly used words are primarily *structure* words, whereas most of the *content* words are mathematical. This implies that the meaning of the content words needs to be taught in the mathematics classroom.

You can help students find clues for words within the words themselves and from content clues on the page, such as charts, figures, and symbols. Call attention to prefixes such as *bi-* and *quadr-* that students may know already and that they can use in figuring out the meaning of new words. Point out also that certain important words—*equivalent,* for example—are used without change of meaning in combination with many other words. You should be aware that students may have been exposed to several different names for the same concept—distributive rule, distributive axiom, distributive property, for instance—and that they may therefore be confused.

Understanding definitions of terms is of primary importance. Use of the glossary and the index should be encouraged. It is not out of place to have a spelling quiz from time to time.

Objective 5

Reading Charts, Graphs, and Diagrams

This fifth objective is to make sure that students can relate the reading of charts, graphs, and diagrams to the rest of the exposition and exercises. Tables and graphs play an integral role in the development of many lessons in algebra. Geometric diagrams are used in problems throughout the textbook, and the discussion of a number of important concepts is illustrated by diagrams. Many students fail to use these visual aids to their advantage. Through oral reading and questioning you can assist students in relating these aids to the words and symbols on the page.

Many students may need a good deal of help in understanding how a table or chart is organized and in relating a table to the graphic representation of the data. Construction of a chart on the chalkboard, with a discussion of the procedure, will help to make the structure clearer to students. The best way to check students' understanding is to involve them in constructing and explaining charts and diagrams.

Objective 6

Reading Word Problems

This sixth objective is to give students confidence in attacking word problems independently and to help them develop their reasoning power in a variety of situations.

If teachers or students were asked how reading skills are used in algebra, they would probably say, "In word problems." Few mathematics teachers would question the importance of careful reading as the first step in solving a problem, but one needs to do more than say, "Read the problem carefully." How does the student "read carefully"? More specific help is needed.

One learns to read carefully by having some specific questions to ask oneself while reading, by taking advantage of all available resources that aid in comprehension, and by thinking about the problem in a well-organized way. The teacher can help students by working with them through the solution of a variety of problems, following the plan of attack suggested in the textbook on page 26. You may need to point out that many problems that *look* very different are basically alike and can be solved by the same method.

Learning Strategies

Suggestions for helping students learn mathematics successfully

A teacher's job is to help students become independent thinkers, not to make them dependent on the teacher's guidance. The purpose of this section is to provide some suggestions for teachers when their students need help in learning mathematics. When a student comes to you for help in studying for a test, when a student just can't seem to do the homework problems, or when a student seems to be disorganized in approaching mathematics, you must avoid both the extreme of helping too much and thereby making the student dependent and the other extreme of saying something like, "You have to figure it out yourself." No doubt students have often come to you with questions and statements of frustration like those quoted below. The numbered suggestions that follow each of these quotations are intended to help you respond in a way that will encourage independent thinking.

"I don't understand the book when I try to read it. What should I do?"

1. Be an active reader; when you read an example from the book, write out the solution in your notebook as you study it. In that way you will understand why certain things are done because you will be doing them as the authors explain them.
2. Learn the boldface words and their meanings. If a paragraph talks about factors, for example, and you don't know what a factor is, then the paragraph will not make any sense. Look up the words you don't know in the Glossary or in the Index at the back of the book. Finally, use the words when describing for someone else how you did a mathematics problem.

"When you explain it in class I understand it, but when I try to do it for homework my mind just goes blank and I forget how to do the problems."

1. If you *think* that you can do a problem, then you are ahead of the game. By saying "I can't do this problem," you are defeating yourself and giving yourself an excuse to stop trying.
2. Your teacher thinks you can do the problem; otherwise he or she would not have assigned it to you. Look again at the discussion preceding the exercises in the textbook and at the notes you made in class. Be sure to review the examples that are worked out in the book.
3. Before your teacher or another student explains a problem in class, write the problem in your notebook. Then listen to the explanation of the solution. Try not to take notes while the explanation is going on, but listen carefully to get a feel for the direction of the solution and the order of the steps. When the explanation is finished, write up the solution in your notebook. If there's any confusion or if you have forgotten any step in the solution, ask about it right then and there. Perhaps several others are stuck at the same place you are; someone had better clear up the confusion, and it might as well be you.
4. Each day before doing your homework it's a good idea to look at the assignment from the previous day because part of your homework is probably review. Pay particular attention to those exercises you thought you could solve but couldn't. Can you do them now?
5. Finally, remember that there can be more than one way to do a mathematics problem. If the first method you try doesn't work, look for another way.

"How do I begin work on a problem? When I'm stuck on a problem I don't know what to do."

Here are some questions to ask yourself:

1. What is the problem asking for? What do you have to find or to do? Do you understand all the words? Can you rewrite the question in another way? Have you seen a problem like this before? What does this problem have in common with others you've seen before?
2. What is known? What are the conditions within which you must work? Can you rewrite the given items or the conditions in another way? Can you guess an answer?
3. Once you've solved a problem you can use the same procedure to solve others like it. Can you solve it a different way? Find out whether another student has solved it in a different way.

"I can't seem to organize my solutions to word problems. What do I write down first?"

1. Usually you can begin by using x or another letter to represent the quantity you are asked to find. Then see if you can express other quantities and relationships in terms of x. As the book suggests, it is often helpful to set up a chart, as in the rate-time-distance problems.
2. Read the problem carefully to find the relationships that are involved. Look for phrases such as "is twice" or "are equal to," for some form of the verb "to be" usually indicates where the equals sign in an equation will be located.
3. Sometimes it is helpful to guess an answer and then test your guess to see whether or not it is correct. The process you go through in testing your guess is usually the same process that is used to set up an equation to solve the problem.

"My friend and I work together on our homework a lot. It's helpful to have someone to work with, but most of the time she ends up doing the problem before I'm even started."

It's fun to work with someone so you can share ideas and feel a sense of cooperation. Be sure to take turns in talking through the problems; one person should not do all the explaining. When one person is talking through the problem, the other has to listen carefully to what is being said in order to understand each step. If you are doing the talking, just think out loud so your friend can hear the answers to all the questions you are asking yourself. Listen carefully if your friend makes a suggestion because she is thinking just as hard about the problem as you and she may say something that turns out to be the missing link you need.

Sometimes the two of you may want to work independently for a while. If you do manage to solve the problem alone, then remember to explain in detail what it was that led you to the solution and why you did what you did. What did you see that gave you a start? Why did you take a particular step? What prompted you to do what you did?

When you have finished with a problem, review what the two of you did to see whether or not you can go through the problem from start to finish with no unnecessary steps.

"How should I study for the next test?"

Most studying for tests actually takes place through your daily homework assignments and class work. Therefore do not think that the only preparation for a test should take place the night before.

Here are some study suggestions:

1. Review the meanings of the boldface words in the book.
2. Review the examples worked out in the book by covering up each solution, writing out your solution, and then seeing if you have the right answer.
3. Review the problems done in class that are in your notebook.
4. Do the chapter review exercises.
5. Pick out the problems from your homework that you tried and did not get. Can you do them now?
6. Have a friend make up a problem for you to do. Then make up one for your friend.

Implications for Teachers and Teaching

Textbooks present the material of the course in a clear, orderly fashion, and your students can learn a lot by reading the text carefully and closely. A textbook, however, is a concise and carefully edited document from which all false starts and fumbling for correct answers have necessarily been omitted. You can help your students by pointing out that a great deal of human learning takes place by means of trial and error, and that the neat and orderly presentation in the textbook is the final result. When you sense that your students are having difficulty with some section of the course, explain that real learning takes place through asking questions, trying guesses, starting down false paths, and trying new methods of approach. The following specific suggestions may help you as you encourage your students to become better problem solvers.

1. Before showing your students how to do a problem, spend some time in asking and answering the questions given in the section on problem solving. (See pages 24–26.) You will then be doing things with a purpose, and your students will not think that doing mathematics is akin to doing magic tricks.
2. Have your students make up their own problems. You will get a sense of the sophistication of their understanding of the material and you may get some good test questions!
3. Take some time in class for your students to work together. Encourage cooperation and sharing.
4. There is often more than one way to do a mathematics problem. Help your students see these various ways. For example, one student will let x represent the time in a motion problem, and a second student will let x represent the distance. The two equations will not yield the same solution, but the problem question will eventually be answered.
5. A common theme that runs throughout algebra is that of rewriting. Factoring is a technique used to rewrite an expression so a quadratic equation can be solved or a fraction can be simplified; multiplying out factors is used to rewrite an expression in order to combine like terms. Rewriting is used to change an expression into an equivalent form that is more useful for a particular purpose.
6. Insist that your students use the correct word for a concept or procedure. "The number in front of this thing combines with those, and the whole thing cancels." Sound familiar? Using words like *coefficient, term, factor, root, evaluate,* and *function* will keep your students aware of important and subtle differences in meaning.
7. Finally, give your students plenty of time in class to write in their notebooks and to think about a question before attempting to answer it. Too often we are in a hurry to get on to the next question, and we fail to realize how much time it takes for a student to listen, understand, and respond. Giving a student that time will make the learning process an enjoyable and profitable experience.

Problem Solving Strategies

Some strategies that your students can use to become better problem solvers

A problem solving strategy is simply a plan or technique for solving a problem. There are a number of well-known problem solving strategies that relate specifically to algebra. For example, transforming an equation into an equivalent equation whose solution is obvious is a strategy for solving linear equations, and applying the quadratic formula is a strategy for solving quadratic equations. One of the goals of an algebra course is to familiarize students with these standard techniques and to give students enough practice with these techniques so that they can use them confidently and successfully to solve algebra problems.

These rather specific strategies are not the only ones that students can use in solving algebra problems, however. Other, more general, strategies, such as looking for a pattern or drawing a diagram, can be very effective problem solving tools. These general strategies can help not only with algebra problems but also with problems in other branches of mathematics and in other subject areas. Since these general strategies provide an *approach* to solving a problem rather than a specific method of solution, they are particularly useful for attacking a problem when the method of solution is not obvious.

For example, suppose several algebra students are confronted with a word problem that they do not know how to solve. One student might ask, "Is this problem similar to any of the types of problems I have seen before?" Another student might try to organize information in a table or a chart or a diagram. Still another might guess an answer and by checking it with the words of the problem discover a general method of solution. Each of these approaches can be a useful strategy.

Below is a list of general problem solving strategies and skills that are helpful in an Algebra 1 course. Each of these strategies is used in the textbook in several different contexts. By using strategies such as these, students can become better problem solvers and may also grow to enjoy problem solving more.

- look for a pattern in the data
- use a table or a chart
- draw a diagram
- generalize from specific examples
- write and solve an equation, an inequality, or a system of equations or inequalities
- use the 5-step problem solving plan discussed on page 26
- apply a standard formula
- recognize a problem as a standard type
- solve a simpler, related problem
- use trial and error and the process of elimination
- reason backward
- make a deductive argument
- recognize the possibility of no solution

In the side column at the beginning of each chapter (see, for example, page 1), there is a short list of problem solving strategies related to topics presented in the chapter, together with references to places in the chapter where these strategies might profitably be used and discussed.

Error Analysis

Anticipating common errors and helping students avoid them

Since mathematics builds on previously learned symbols, concepts, and skills, error patterns that are left uncorrected will impede students' progress. Of course, there are many different reasons for errors, but certain types of errors are more common than others. If you are aware of these common errors, you can help students avoid them and you can be better prepared to help students overcome them if they do occur. Throughout the book, in the side columns next to the textbook pages, common errors have been identified and suggestions for avoiding them have been provided. (See, for example, "Common Errors" on pages 94, 123, and 184.) The errors discussed in the side columns are fairly specific. However, many of them can be grouped into one or more of the following categories:

Errors in Reading and Translating

(See, for example, pp. 14, 25, 164, 278, and 469.)

Students often have difficulty in translating English phrases and sentences into mathematical expressions and sentences. For example, students may translate the expression "five less than a number" as $5 - n$. Not reading word problems carefully, with concentration on their meaning, is another frequent cause of difficulty. Students may make mistakes because they do not fully understand the meanings of mathematical terms—for example, "maximum value of a function." Words such as *or*, which have a different meaning in mathematics than in everyday speech, may cause confusion.

Failure to Understand Symbols

(See, for example, pp. 138, 203, 324, and 454.)

Students often do not fully understand the meanings of mathematical symbols. As a result, they may make the following errors:

$\frac{6}{0} = 0$ $\quad -x^2 = (-x)^2$ $\quad b^n = nb$

$2^{-2} = -4$ $\quad (a + b)^2 = a^2 + b^2$ $\quad -2 > x > 3$

$0.\overline{5} = \frac{1}{2}$ $\quad 2\sqrt{3} = \sqrt{6}$ $\quad \sqrt{x^2} = x$

Misunderstanding of Properties

(See, for example, pp. 65, 223, 283, 290, and 454.)

Recurring errors often stem from students' misapplying properties in the ways shown below.

Addition property of equality: $x + 2 = 6$
$x = 8$

Multiplication property of equality: $\frac{x}{2} + \frac{x}{3} = 5$
$3x + 2x = 5$

Division property of equality: $3x(x + 2) = 0$
$x + 2 = 0$

Multiplication axiom of order: $2x > -8$
$x < -4$

Distributive axiom: $-4(x + 1) = 9$
$-4x + 1 = 9$

Zero-product property: $(x - 3)(x + 2) = 14$
$x - 3 = 14$ or $x + 2 = 14$

Cancellation rule for fractions: $\frac{x}{\cancel{3}_1} = \frac{\cancel{6}^2}{5}$

Errors in Using Standard Forms

(See, for example, pp. 397, 523, and 553.)

Although students may have memorized the Pythagorean theorem or the quadratic formula, they may not understand the importance of using the standard form when they apply these formulas.

Consequently, they often try to work with an expression or an equation without first putting it into standard form. This means that they may substitute incorrect values in the formula $a^2 + b^2 = c^2$ or try to solve an equation by the quadratic formula before transforming it so that one side is 0. Other errors that students are liable to make are illustrated below.

$2x + 3y = 6$ $\quad$ $y = 1 - 3x$

slope $= 2$ $\quad$ slope $= 1$

y-intercept $= -3$

$x^2 + 1 - 2x = 0$

$a = 1, b = 1, c = -2$

Use of Incorrect Formulas

(See, for example, pp. 109, 393, and 559.)

Many errors are the result of students' using formulas that are incorrect. Some of the more common "impostors" are shown below.

$p = l + w$ $\quad$ $C = \pi r^2$ $\quad$ slope $= \dfrac{x_2 - x_1}{y_2 - y_1}$

$x = -b \pm \dfrac{\sqrt{b^2 - 4ac}}{2a}$ $\quad$ discriminant $= \sqrt{b^2 - 4ac}$

Errors in Simplifying

(See, for example, pp. 6, 191, 245, 256, and 511.)

In addition to some of the reasons already given, students may make errors in simplifying expressions because of incorrect assumptions such as $\sqrt{a^2 - b^2} = \sqrt{a^2} - \sqrt{b^2}$. They may also make errors because they do not take notice of grouping symbols such as the fraction bar or because they do not follow the prescribed order of operations or because they add unlike terms. Students sometimes confuse the rules of exponents—multiplying exponents when they are multiplying and dividing exponents when they are dividing. Students may forget to (or not realize that they must) change the sign of every term of a polynomial that they are subtracting. Simplifying fractions seems to be particularly troublesome. Thinking that $\frac{n}{n} = 0$ can lead to errors such as $6x^2 + 8x + 2 = 2(3x^2 + 4x)$.

Errors such as $\dfrac{\cancel{x} + 3}{\cancel{x}} = 3$ and $\dfrac{\overset{3}{\cancel{6}}\cancel{y}(x + 3)}{\underset{1}{\cancel{2}}y^{\cancel{2}}(x + 1)} = \dfrac{3(x + 3)}{2(x + 1)}$ are common.

Errors in Checking

(See, for example, pp. 229, 351, 363, 460, and 535.)

Checking can help students develop self-confidence and alert them to errors. However, a check that is incorrectly performed is not useful. Students often fail to realize that it is not only helpful but necessary to check the roots of fractional and radical equations. The following checking errors may occur: Students may occasionally substitute a value for a variable such as 8 for x, get a true statement such as $4 = 4$, and conclude that the solution is 4. Students may not realize that they must check their answers with the *words* of word problems or that they must check their solutions to systems of linear equations in *both* the *original* equations. Some students may think that they should always discard negative solutions. Students may not think of checking their answers when the method involves, for example, considering whether an answer is reasonable or multiplying to check factoring.

Assignment Guide

The following guide offers suggestions for planning separate minimum, average, and maximum courses that you can adapt as necessary to fit the needs of your particular classes.

Because students' interests and backgrounds differ widely from class to class, most of the optional features are not listed. You will want to choose those features which best suit your individual classes. If you have access to a computer that accepts BASIC, you may wish to allow some time for your students to do the Computer Key-Ins or the Computer Exercises. Please see the note on page x regarding these features.

All the assignments refer to written exercises, with the letter "P" indicating word problems. The letter "S" indicates the spiraled portion of the assignment, which reviews earlier work. The letter "R" indicates a review built into the text. "EP" refers the teacher to the Extra Practice section, which contains extra exercises and problems to be used as needed.

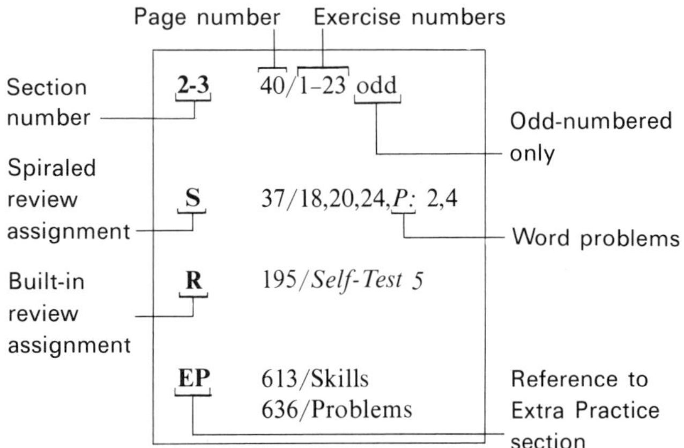

Summary Time Schedule for the Assignments

Chapter	1	2	3	4	5	6	7	8	9	10	11	12	Looking Ahead	Total
Minimum Course	13	12	14	15	19	13	15	15	14	10	14	6	0	160
Average Course	12	11	13	15	20	12	15	14	14	11	13	10	0	160
Maximum Course	10	11	12	14	16	11	14	13	13	10	14	10	12	160

Trimester Semester Trimester

LESSON	MINIMUM COURSE	AVERAGE COURSE	MAXIMUM COURSE
1	**1-1** 3/1–20, 25–31 odd	**1-1** 3/1–26, 29–38	**1-1** 3/1–41 odd **1-2** 7/1–14 odd, 15–17, 23–33
2	**1-2** 7/1–23, 25, 26 **S** 4/21–24	**1-2** 7/1–20, 23–28, 31, 32 **S** 4/27, 28, 39–42	**1-3** 11/2–20 even, 21–33, 35 **S** 8/34–36
3	**1-3** 11/1–25	**1-3** 11/2–20 even, 21–34 **R** 12/*Self-Test 1*	**1-4** 15/2–34 even **R** 12/*Self-Test 1*

LESSON	MINIMUM COURSE	AVERAGE COURSE	MAXIMUM COURSE
4	**1-4** 15/1–17 **R** 12/*Self-Test 1*	**1-4** 15/1–6, 7–31 odd	**1-5** 22/1–31 odd **S** 4/40, 42
5	**1-4** 16/18–26 **1-5** 20/1–15	**1-4** 16/22–30 even **1-5** 20/1–12	**1-6** 26/*P:* 1–8 **S** 23/32–34
6	**1-5** 21/16–27 **S** 11/26–29	**1-5** 21/13–23 odd, 25–28 **S** 16/32, 33	**1-6** 27/*P:* 9–15 **R** 28/*Self-Test 2*
7	**1-6** 26/*P:* 1–7	**1-6** 27/*P:* 1–8 **S** 22/29–32	**1-7** 32/2–22 even, 27–46 **1-8** 36/1–33 odd, 45
8	**1-6** 27/*P:* 7–12 **R** 28/*Self-Test 2*	**1-6** 27/*P:* 9–14 **R** 28/*Self-Test 2*	**1-8** 36/39–44, 46 **1-9** 38/1–55 odd **R** 40/*Self-Test 3*
9	**1-7** 32/2–42 even **S** 27/*P:* 13	**1-7** 32/1–16, 21–24, 31, 34–37, 39–45	*Prepare for Chapter Test* **R** 41/*Chapter Review* **EP** 607/*Skills* 633/*Problems*
10	**1-8** 36/1–28 odd, 35–38 **S** 32/1–13 odd	**1-8** 36/1–41 odd **1-9** 38/1–43 odd **R** 40/*Self-Test 3*	*Administer Chapter 1 Test* 29/*Reading Algebra:* 1–10
11	**1-9** 38/1–32 **R** 40/*Self-Test 3*	*Prepare for Chapter Test* **R** 41/*Chapter Review* **EP** 607/*Skills* 633/*Problems*	**2-1** 48/1–28
12	*Prepare for Chapter Test* **R** 41/*Chapter Review* **EP** 607/*Skills* 633/*Problems*	*Administer Chapter 1 Test* 29/*Reading Algebra:* 1–10	**2-2** 51/1–23 odd, 25–40
13	*Administer Chapter 1 Test* **R** 43/*Maintaining Skills*	**2-1** 48/1–25	**2-3** 55/3–21 odd, 24–38 even; 56/*P:* 9–15
14	**2-1** 48/1–22	**2-2** 51/1–23 odd, 25–38 **S** 48/26–28	**2-4** 60/2–52 even, 53 62/*P:* 2, 3, 5, 8–10 **R** 63/*Self-Test 1*
15	**2-2** 51/1–35 odd **S** 48/23, 24	**2-3** 55/1–19 odd, 24–34 even 56/*P:* 1, 4–6, 11, 13	**2-5** 66/1–29 odd, 31–44, 47–49 **S** 56/35, 37
16	**2-3** 55/1–13, 23–26 56/*P:* 1–5	**2-4** 60/2–40 even, 45–50 62/*P:* 2, 3, 5, 8–10 **R** 63/*Self-Test 1*	**2-6** 70/1–25 odd, 27–44 **S** 61/54 67/50
17	**2-3** 55/14–20, 27–30 57/*P:* 6–10 **2-4** 60/1–12	**2-5** 66/1–29 odd, 31–38, 41–44, 47 **S** 57/*P:* 14	**2-7** 74/1–12 odd, 13–17, 20, 21 **R** 75/*Self-Test 2*

LESSON	MINIMUM COURSE	AVERAGE COURSE	MAXIMUM COURSE
18	**2-4** 61/14–40 even 62/*P:* 1–3, 5, 8	**2-6** 70/1–15 odd, 19–36, 41, 42 **S** 67/39, 40, 45, 46, 48	**2-8** 78/1–27 odd, 29–34
19	**2-5** 66/1–36 **R** 63/*Self-Test 1*	**2-7** 74/1–11 odd, 13–16, 18 **R** 75/*Self-Test 2*	**2-9** 82/1–31 **R** 84/*Self-Test 3*
20	**2-6** 70/1–30 **S** 67/37, 38	**2-8** 78/2–18 even, 19–31 **S** 75/17, 19	*Prepare for Chapter Test* **R** 85/*Chapter Review* **EP** 609/*Skills* 633/*Problems*
21	**2-7** 74/1–12 **R** 75/*Self-Test 2*	**2-9** 82/1–18, 21–27 **S** 78/32–34 **R** 84/*Self-Test 3*	*Administer Chapter 2 Test* **R** 90/*Mixed Review*
22	**2-8** 78/1–24 **S** 74/13, 14	*Prepare for Chapter Test* **R** 85/*Chapter Review* **EP** 609/*Skills* 633/*Problems*	**3-1** 96/1–53 odd 97/*P:* 1–15 odd
23	**2-9** 82/1–26 **R** 84/*Self-Test 3*	*Administer Chapter 2 Test* **R** 90/*Mixed Review*	**3-2** 101/1–29 odd, 30–35, *P:* 9, 10, 13, 14 **S** 96/54–56
24	*Prepare for Chapter Test* **R** 85/*Chapter Review* **EP** 609/*Skills* 633/*Problems*	**3-1** 96/1–23 odd, 25–36 97/*P:* 1, 2, 5, 8	**3-3** 105/10–48 even **S** 102/*P:* 15, 16 **R** 106/*Self-Test 1*
25	*Administer Chapter 2 Test* **R** 89/*Maintaining Skills*	**3-1** 96/37–48 97/*P:* 10, 11, 13, 14 **3-2** 101/1–31 odd	**3-4** 110/*P:* 1–11 odd, 15, 16, 21, 22 **S** 105/49–52
26	**3-1** 96/1–23 odd 97/*P:* 1, 2, 5	**3-2** 101/14–32 even, *P:* 7, 9, 10, 13 **3-3** 105/1–9	**3-4** 111/*P:* 25–33 **S** 101/36
27	**3-1** 96/10–34 even 97/*P:* 6, 8–11	**3-3** 105/10–40 even **S** 102/*P:* 15, 16 **R** 106/*Self-Test 1*	**3-5** 113/2–38 even 114/*P:* 6, 9, 14, 16–18 **R** 116/*Self-Test 2*
28	**3-2** 101/1–31 odd, *P:* 1–11 odd	**3-4** 110/*P:* 1–11 odd, 15, 16, 21, 22 **S** 105/43–46	**3-6** 120/*P:* 3, 7, 9, 10–13 **S** 115/*P:* 19, 20
29	**3-3** 105/2–30 even **S** 101/*P:* 2, 6, 8	**3-4** 111/*P:* 23, 24, 26, 27, 30, 31, 32 **S** 96/53, 54	**3-6** 120/*P:* 15–20 **3-7** 123/*P:* 2, 4–6
30	**3-3** 105/7–37 odd **S** 98/*P:* 12–14	**3-5** 113/2–32 even, 33 114/*P:* 2, 6, 9, 16, 17 **R** 116/*Self-Test 2*	**3-7** 124/*P:* 9, 11, 12, 15, 16 **S** 121/*P:* 21, 22

LESSON	MINIMUM COURSE	AVERAGE COURSE	MAXIMUM COURSE
31	**3-4** 110/*P:* 1–15 odd **S** 105/32–38 even **R** 106/*Self-Test 1*	**3-6** 120/*P:* 1–3, 7, 9, 10, 11 **S** 114/34–37	**3-8** 128/1–11 **R** 131/*Self-Test 3*
32	**3-4** 110/*P:* 2–20 even	**3-6** 120/*P:* 12, 14–17, 19 **3-7** 123/*P:* 2, 4, 5	*Prepare for Chapter Test* **R** 132/*Chapter Review* **EP** 611/*Skills* 634/*Problems*
33	**3-5** 113/1–25 odd **S** 110/*P:* 21–25	**3-7** 123/*P:* 3, 6, 7, 9, 11, 12, 15 **S** 105/49, 50	*Administer Chapter 3 Test* **R** 134/*Cumulative Review*
34	**3-5** 113/10–22 even 114/*P:* 2–14 even	**3-8** 128/1, 2, 4, 5, 7 **R** 131/*Self-Test 3*	**4-1** 140/1–41 odd
35	**3-6** 120/*P:* 1–7 **R** 116/*Self-Test 2*	*Prepare for Chapter Test* **R** 132/*Chapter Review* **EP** 611/*Skills* 634/*Problems*	**4-2** 145/2–48 even 146/*P:* 6–9 **S** 140/40, 42
36	**3-6** 120/*P:* 8–12 **3-7** 123/*P:* 1–5	*Administer Chapter 3 Test* **R** 134/*Cumulative* *Review*	**4-2** 146/35–39 odd, *P:* 10–13 **R** 147/*Self-Test 1*
37	**3-7** 124/*P:* 6–10 **R** 131/*Self-Test 3,* 1–3	**4-1** 140/1–39 odd	**43** 149/1–43 odd
38	*Prepare for Chapter Test* **R** 132/*Chapter Review,* 1–11 **EP** 611/*Skills* 634/*Problems*	**4-2** 145/2–46 even 146/*P:* 2, 4	**4-4** 152/1–23 odd, 25–41 **S** 150/38, 40, 42
39	*Administer Chapter 3 Test* **R** 135/*Maintaining Skills*	**4-2** 146/39–47 odd, *P:* 6, 7, 9, 10 **R** 147/*Self-Test 1*	**4-5** 155/2–38 even, 39–45 **S** 153/42, 43
40	**4-1** 140/1–33 odd	**4-3** 149/1–37 odd **S** 147/*P:* 11	**4-6** 158/1–47 odd **S** 146/49, 50
41	**4-2** 145/2–24 even 146/*P:* 2, 4	**4-4** 152/1–23 odd, 25–38 **S** 149/28, 30, 32	**4-7** 162/1–29 odd **R** 160/*Self-Test 2*
42	**4-2** 146/26–42 even, *P:* 5–8 **4-3** 149/1–10	**4-5** 155/2–28 even, 33–39, 41 **S** 153/39, 40, 41	**4-8** 166/*P:* 1–10 **S** 162/26, 28, 30
43	**4-3** 149/11–30 **R** 147/*Self-Test 1*	**4-6** 158/1–45 odd **R** 160/*Self-Test 2*	**4-8** 167/*P:* 11–15 **4-9** 169/*P:* 1, 2, 4
44	**4-4** 152/1–20 **S** 146/*P:* 9, 10	**4-7** 162/1–23 odd	**4-9** 169/*P:* 5, 7–10 **S** 159/42, 44, 46

LESSON	MINIMUM COURSE	AVERAGE COURSE	MAXIMUM COURSE
45	**4-4** 153/21–33 **4-5** 155/2–14 even	**4-8** 166/*P:* 1–5, 7, 9 **S** 162/24–27	**4-10** 172/*P:* 1–11 odd, 12–16 **S** 170/*P:* 11 **R** 174/*Self-Test 3*
46	**4-5** 155/16–36 even **S** 150/35–37	**4-8** 166/*P:* 6, 8, 11, 12, 13 **S** 159/38–46 even	*Prepare for Chapter Test* **R** 175/*Chapter Review* **EP** 613/*Skills* 636/*Problems*
47	**4-6** 158/1–25 odd **S** 155/33, 35, 37	**4-9** 169/*P:* 1, 2, 4, 5, 8 **S** 150/39, 40	*Administer Chapter 4 Test* **5-1** 185/1–45 odd
48	**4-6** 159/27–41 odd **R** 160/*Self-Test 2*	**4-9** 169/*P:* 3, 6, 7, 9 **S** 167/*P:* 10, 14	**5-2** 189/2–34 even, 35–42 **S** 185/46, 47
49	**4-7** 162/1–15 **S** 159/36, 38, 40	**4-10** 172/*P:* 1, 2, 4, 6, 7, 10, 12 **R** 174/*Self-Test 3*	**5-3** 192/1–49 odd 194/*P:* 2–10 even
50	**4-8** 166/*P:* 1–5, 7 **S** 162/16–18	*Prepare for Chapter Test* **R** 175/*Chapter Review* **EP** 613/*Skills* 636/*Problems*	**5-4** 197/1–41 odd **S** 190/43–46 **R** 195/*Self-Test 1*
51	**4-8** 166/*P:* 6, 8, 9 **4-9** 169/*P:* 1, 2, 4, 5	*Administer Chapter 4 Test* **R** 180/*Mixed Review*	**5-5** 200/2–56 even **S** 198/42–44
52	**4-9** 169/*P:* 3, 6, 9 **4-10** 172/*P:* 1, 3, 4, 7	**5-1** 185/1–45 odd	**5-6** 205/2–60 even **R** 207/*Self-Test 2*
53	*Prepare for Chapter Test* **R** 175/*Chapter Review* **EP** 613/*Skills* 636/*Problems*	**5-2** 189/2–42 even	**5-7** 209/1–49 odd **S** 206/61–63
54	*Administer Chapter 4 Test* **R** 179/*Maintaining Skills*	**5-2** 189/29–41 odd **5-3** 192/1–21 odd, 27–31	**5-8** 212/2–48 even
55	**5-1** 185/1–39 odd	**5-3** 193/33–49 odd 194/*P:* 2, 5, 6 **R** 195/*Self-Test 1*	**5-9** 216/1–43 odd **R** 216/*Self-Test 3*
56	**5-2** 189/1–25 **S** 185/44, 45, 46	**5-4** 197/1–41 odd **S** 195/*P:* 8	**5-10** 219/2–50 even **S** 216/38–44 even
57	**5-2** 189/26–38 even **5-3** 192/1–21 odd	**5-5** 200/2–50 even **S** 198/38, 43	**5-11** 222/8–50 even
58	**5-3** 193/27–36, 45–48 194/*P:* 1–3, 5	**5-6** 205/2–20 even, 21–49 odd **S** 185/44, 46, 47	**5-11** 222/35–51 odd, 52–57 **S** 220/51–55

LESSON	MINIMUM COURSE	AVERAGE COURSE	MAXIMUM COURSE
59	**5-4** 197/1–15 **R** 195/*Self-Test 1*	**5-6** 205/42–60 even **R** 207/*Self-Test 2*	**5-12** 225/1–51 odd
60	**5-4** 197/16–30 **S** 193/37–41	**5-7** 209/1–45 odd	**5-12** 225/36–50 even **5-13** 229/*P:* 4, 5, 9, 10, 12, 13
61	**5-5** 200/1–12, 21–28 **S** 197/34, 35	**5-8** 212/2–40 even, 43 **S** 210/20–38 even	**5-13** 230/*P:* 15, 16, 17–27 odd **R** 232/*Self-Test 4*
62	**5-5** 201/29–34, 41–44 **5-6** 205/1–8	**5-9** 216/1–39 odd **S** 212/17–29 odd	*Prepare for Chapter Test* **R** 233/*Chapter Review* **EP** 615/*Skills* 638/*Problems*
63	**5-6** 205/9–19 odd, 21–29, 42, 43, 44	**5-10** 219/2–34 even **R** 216/*Self-Test 3*	*Administer Chapter 5 Test* 202/*Extra:* 1–7
64	**5-7** 209/1–33 odd **R** 207/*Self-Test 2*	**5-10** 219/35–53 odd **S** 206/59, 61, 62	**6-1** 240/1–53 odd
65	**5-8** 212/2–32 even **S** 210/20–30 even	**5-11** 222/8–40 even **S** 216/37, 40, 41	**6-2** 246/8–50 even **S** 241/55, 56
66	**5-9** 216/1–15 **R** 216/*Self-Test 3*	**5-12** 225/1–15 odd, 16–28	**6-3** 249/5–41 odd **R** 250/*Self-Test 1*
67	**5-9** 216/16–26 **5-10** 219/1–6	**5-12** 225/29–39 odd; 40–51 **S** 222/41–51 odd	**6-4** 253/6–32 even, 34–47 **S** 250/40, 42
68	**5-11** 222/1–8, 10–15, 19–24	**5-13** 229/*P:* 2–14 even, 20, 22	**6-5** 256/1–35 odd **S** 241/52–54
69	**5-12** 225/1–14 **S** 216/27–32	**5-13** 230/*P:* 15–18, 21, 23, 25 **R** 232/*Self-Test 4*	**6-5** 258/38–54 **R** 258/*Self-Test 2*
70	**5-12** 225/15–41 odd	*Prepare for Chapter Test* **R** 233/*Chapter Review* **EP** 615/*Skills* 638/*Problems*	**6-6** 261/1–45 odd **S** 258/56, 57
71	**5-13** 229/*P:* 2–14 even **R** 232/*Self-Test 4*	*Administer Chapter 5 Test* **R** 236/*Cumulative Review*	**6-7** 265/1–23 odd **S** 261/34–46 even
72	*Prepare for Chapter Test* **R** 233/*Chapter Review* **EP** 615/*Skills* 638/*Problems*	**6-1** 240/1–21	**6-7** 265/25–39 odd **R** 266/*Self-Test 3*

LESSON	MINIMUM COURSE	AVERAGE COURSE	MAXIMUM COURSE
73	*Administer Chapter 5 Test* **R** 237/*Maintaining Skills*	**6-1** 240/22–35, 39, 40, 43–50	*Prepare for Chapter Test* **R** 269/*Chapter Review* **EP** 617/*Skills*
74	**6-1** 240/1–17	**6-2** 246/1, 4, 6, 7, 13, 14, 15–33 odd, 35–44	*Administer Chapter 6 Test* 267/*Extra:* 1–27 odd
75	**6-1** 240/22–35, 40, 41	**6-3** 249/1–37 odd **S** 247/46–48 **R** 250/*Self-Test 1*	**7-1** 279/2–28 even 280/*P:* 2–8 even, 9–13
76	**6-2** 246/1–40 **S** 240/18–21	**6-4** 253/2–44 even **S** 250/32–38 even	**7-2** 284/1–43 odd 285/*P:* 3–7 odd, 8–11
77	**6-3** 249/1–27 odd **S** 246/41–44	**6-5** 256/1–35 odd **S** 241/51, 52, 55	**7-3** 289/1–33 odd 290/*P:* 4–8 even, 9, 11 **R** 286/*Self-Test 1*
78	**6-3** 249/2–20 even, 29–32 **R** 250/*Self-Test 1*	**6-5** 257/18, 20, 22, 38–50 **R** 258/*Self-Test 2*	**7-4** 292/7–41 odd 293/*P:* 3, 7, 8 **S** 281/15
79	**6-4** 253/2–36 even	**6-6** 261/1–37 odd **S** 258/51–53	**7-4** 292/36–42 even 293/*P:* 9, 11, 12 **S** 290/*P:* 7, 10, 13
80	**6-5** 256/1–25 odd **S** 254/31–41 odd	**6-6** 261/22–42 even **6-7** 265/1–6	**7-5** 297/1–65 odd 299/*P:* 3–5, 10, 12, 15 **R** 294/*Self-Test 2*
81	**6-5** 257/28, 29, 32–41 **R** 258/*Self-Test 2*	**6-7** 265/9–37 odd **R** 266/*Self-Test 3*	**7-6** 302/1–21 odd 303/*P:* 1–11 odd, 13–16 **S** 293/41, 44 **R** 305/*Self-Test 3*
82	**6-6** 261/1–18 **S** 258/42, 43	*Prepare for Chapter Test* **R** 269/*Chapter Review* **EP** 617/*Skills*	**7-7** 309/*P:* 4–6, 10, 12, 18, 20, 21 **S** 281/*P:* 14, 16
83	**6-6** 261/19–26 **6-7** 265/1–6	*Administer Chapter 6 Test* **R** 274/*Mixed Review*	**7-7** 310/*P:* 22–28 **7-8** 315/*P:* 1–13 odd **S** 289/32, 34
84	**6-7** 265/7–23 odd **R** 266/*Self-Test 3*	**7-1** 279/2–22 even 280/*P:* 1, 3, 5, 6	**7-8** 315/*P:* 10, 15, 16, 18, 19 **R** 316/*Self-Test 4*
85	*Prepare for Chapter Test* **R** 269/*Chapter Review* **EP** 617/*Skills*	**7-1** 280/*P:* 2, 9–13 **7-2** 284/1–23 odd	**7-9** 319/2–32 even 320/*P:* 1–5 odd **S** 316/*P:* 20–22
86	*Administer Chapter 6 Test* **R** 273/*Maintaining Skills*	**7-2** 284/25–35 285/*P:* 1, 5–9 **S** 279/23–25	**7-10** 325/1–57 odd 327/*P:* 2, 4, 5 **R** 327/*Self-Test 4*

LESSON	MINIMUM COURSE	AVERAGE COURSE	MAXIMUM COURSE
87	**7-1** 279/2–20 even 280/*P:* 1, 3, 5	**7-3** 289/1–33 odd, *P:* 1, 3, 4 **R** 286/*Self-Test 1*	*Prepare for Chapter Test* **R** 329/*Chapter Review* **EP** 619/*Skills* 638/*Problems*
88	**7-1** 280/*P:* 2–8 even **7-2** 284/1–15 odd	**7-3** 290/*P:* 4–12 even **7-4** 292/7–29 odd	*Administer Chapter 7 Test* **R** 326/59–63
89	**7-2** 284/16–26 285/*P:* 1–6 **S** 279/11, 13, 15	**7-4** 292/22, 26, 28–38 293/*P:* 4, 6, 7, 9	**8-1** 337/1–37 odd
90	**7-3** 289/1–27 odd, *P:* 1, 3, 4 **R** 286/*Self-Test 1*	**7-5** 297/1–65 odd 299/*P:* 3–5, 10, 12, 15 **R** 294/*Self-Test 2*	**8-2** 343/14–42 even, 43, 44 **R** 344/*Self-Test 1*
91	**7-3** 289/*P:* 2, 5, 7, 8 **7-4** 292/1–6, 7–17 odd	**7-6** 302/1–21 odd 303/*P:* 1–7 odd, 10, 11, 13, 14 **R** 305/*Self-Test 3*	**8-3** 348/1–11 odd, 13–20 **S** 338/38
92	**7-4** 292/18–25 293/*P:* 1–6 **S** 284/27, 28, 31	**7-7** 309/*P:* 4–6, 10, 12, 14, 18 **S** 293/*P:* 8, 10, 11	**8-4** 352/1–39 odd **S** 349/22–24
93	**7-5** 297/1–35 odd, 37–40 **R** 294/*Self-Test 2*	**7-7** 310/*P:* 13, 15, 19–22 **7-8** 315/*P:* 1–9 odd **S** 299/*P:* 13, 14	**8-5** 357/*P:* 1, 5, 9, 12, 15, 17, 20, 21 **S** 353/38, 40, 41
94	**7-5** 298/45–59 odd, 60–65 299/*P:* 1–4 **S** 293/*P:* 7, 9	**7-8** 315/*P:* 11–18 **R** 316/*Self-Test 4*	**8-6** 359/1–25 odd 360/*P:* 2–10 even
95	**7-6** 302/1–21 odd 303/*P:* 1–13 odd **R** 305/*Self-Test 3*	**7-9** 319/2–32 even 320/*P:* 1, 3–5 **S** 316/*P:* 19, 20	**8-7** 364/1–27 odd 367/*P:* 12, 14, 15, 17–19 **S** 360/27–29
96	**7-7** 309/*P:* 2–16 even **S** 298/46–54 even	**7-10** 325/1–49 odd 327/*P:* 2, 4 **R** 327/*Self-Test 5*	**8-7** 365/35, 36 365/10–30 even 367/*P:* 21, 23, 26–28
97	**7-7** 309/*P:* 9–15 odd, 19 **7-8** 315/*P:* 1–4	*Prepare for Chapter Test* **R** 329/*Chapter Review* **EP** 619/*Skills* 638/*Problems*	**8-8** 373/*P:* 1–13 odd **R** 369/*Self-Test 2*
98	**7-8** 315/*P:* 5–10 **S** 304/*P:* 8, 10, 12	*Administer Chapter 7 Test* **R** 332/*Cumulative Review*	**8-8** 374/*P:* 10, 12, 14, 15 **8-9** 378/*P:* 2–16 even
99	**7-9** 319/2–32 even 320/*P:* 1–3 **R** 316/*Self-Test 4*	**8-1** 337/1–33 odd	**8-9** 379/*P:* 19–24, 28 **R** 382/*Self-Test 3*

LESSON	MINIMUM COURSE	AVERAGE COURSE	MAXIMUM COURSE
100	*Prepare for Chapter Test* **R** 329/*Chapter Review,* 1–15 **EP** 619/*Skills* 638/*Problems*	**8-2** 343/14–42 even, 43, 44 **S** 338/30, 32	*Prepare for Chapter Test* **R** 383/*Chapter Review* **EP** 621/*Skills* 643/*Problems*
101	*Administer Chapter 7 Test* **R** 333/*Maintaining Skills*	**8-3** 348/1–15 odd, 17–20 **R** 344/*Self-Test 1*	*Administer Chapter 8 Test* 382/*Extra:* 1–6
102	**8-1** 337/1–21 odd, 29	**8-4** 352/1–27 odd, 28, 29 **S** 349/22, 23	**9-1** 394/1–41 odd **S** 343/37, 39
103	**8-2** 343/1–35 odd **S** 337/10–20 even	**8-4** 352/31–34, 38 **8-5** 357/*P:* 1, 2, 5, 9, 15	**9-2** 399/2–38 even **S** 395/40, 42
104	**8-3** 348/1–14 **R** 344/*Self-Test 1*	**8-5** 357/*P:* 16–20, 22 **S** 353/39, 40	**9-3** 402/2–28 even, 29–35 **S** 400/37, 39
105	**8-4** 352/1–17 odd **S** 348/17, 18	**8-6** 359/1–23 odd 360/*P:* 1, 3–7	**9-4** 406/2–34 even **R** 403/*Self-Test 1*
106	**8-4** 352/8–22 even, 25 **8-5** 357/*P:* 1, 2, 5, 9	**8-7** 364/1–25 odd 366/*P:* 3–11 odd	**9-4** 406/35–46 **9-5** 410/1–7 odd
107	**8-5** 357/*P:* 10–15 **S** 343/25–35 odd	**8-7** 365/10–26 even 367/*P:* 16, 17, 19, 21–23	**9-6** 416/1–31 odd, 32 **S** 407/47, 48
108	**8-6** 359/1–17 360/*P:* 1–4	**8-8** 373/*P:* 1–11 odd **R** 369/*Self-Test 2*	**9-7** 421/1, 2, 5, 7, 10–13, 18–22 even 422/*P:* 3, 5, 8 **R** 417/*Self-Test 2*
109	**8-7** 364/1–19 odd 366/*P:* 1, 3, 5 **S** 360/18–22	**8-8** 374/*P:* 8, 10, 12–14 **8-9** 378/*P:* 2–10 even	**9-7** 423/*P:* 7, 9–14 **9-8** 426/1–7 odd, 10–14
110	**8-7** 365/1–12 366/*P:* 6–12	**8-9** 379/*P:* 16–21 **R** 382/*Self-Test 3*	**9-8** 428/*P:* 3–17 odd **S** 417/33–36
111	**8-8** 373/*P:* 1–5 **R** 369/*Self-Test 2*	*Prepare for Chapter Test* **R** 383/*Chapter Review* **EP** 621/*Skills* 643/*Problems*	**9-9** 432/*P:* 3, 5, 7–11 **S** 422/23, 24
112	**8-8** 373/*P:* 6–10 **S** 364/20, 21, 23, 24	*Administer Chapter 8 Test* **R** 388/*Cumulative Review*	**9-10** 436/1, 4, 6–10, *P:* 2–12 even **R** 438/*Self-Test 3*
113	**8-9** 378/*P:* 1–4, 7–9 **S** 365/13–16	**9-1** 394/1–39 odd **S** 343/25–35 odd	*Prepare for Chapter Test* **R** 442/*Chapter Review* **EP** 622/*Skills* 644/*Problems*

LESSON	MINIMUM COURSE	AVERAGE COURSE	MAXIMUM COURSE
114	**8-9** 378/*P:* 5, 6, 9, 13, 14 **R** 382/*Self-Test 3*	**9-2** 399/2–32 even **S** 395/38, 40	*Administer Chapter 9 Test* 440/*Extra:* 1–24
115	*Prepare for Chapter Test* **R** 383/*Chapter Review* **EP** 621/*Skills* 643/*Problems*	**9-2** 399/25–33 odd, 34, 38 **9-3** 402/2–16 even	**10-1** 451/1–25 odd, 27–38
116	*Administer Chapter 8 Test* **R** 387/*Maintaining Skills*	**9-3** 402/18–28 even, 29–33 **R** 403/*Self-Test 1*	**10-2** 457/9–47 odd, 49–56
117	**9-1** 394/1–35 odd **S** 343/34, 36	**9-4** 406/2–34 even **S** 400/35–37	**10-3** 461/1–17 odd 462/*P:* 2, 4, 10, 13, 17 **S** 457/57–64
118	**9-2** 399/2–24 even **S** 395/36–38	**9-4** 406/35–45 **9-5** 410/1, 5, 7	**10-4** 471/1–37 odd **S** 463/*P:* 16, 20, 22 **R** 464/*Self-Test 1*
119	**9-2** 399/3, 5, 19–25 odd, 26, 27, 31	**9-6** 416/1–27 odd **S** 402/34, 35	**10-5** 475/1–34 **S** 464/*P:* 26
120	**9-3** 402/1–4, 6–28 even **S** 394/16–20 even	**9-7** 421/2–22 even 422/*P:* 1, 3, 5 **R** 417/*Self-Test 2*	**10-6** 477/1–18, 19–23 odd **S** 462/19, 20
121	**9-4** 406/2–30 even **R** 403/*Self-Test 1*	**9-7** 422/*P:* 6–11 **9-8** 426/1–7 odd, 10–13	**10-7** 482/1–4, 9–18, 25–29, 34, 35 **S** 478/25 **R** 478/*Self-Test 2*
122	**9-4** 406/32–44 even **9-5** 410/1, 5	**9-8** 427/*P:* 1–13 odd **S** 416/31, 32	**10-8** 485/1–21 odd, 23–26 **R** 487/*Self-Test 3*
123	**9-6** 416/1–17 odd, 19, 25 **S** 410/2, 7	**9-9** 432/*P:* 3–9 **S** 429/*P:* 14–16	*Prepare for Chapter Test* **R** 492/*Chapter Review* **EP** 626/*Skills* 646/*Problems*
124	**9-7** 421/2–20 even 422/*P:* 1, 3 **R** 417/*Self-Test 2*	**9-10** 436/1–4, 7, *P:* 2, 3, 5, 8, 9, 11 **R** 438/*Self-Test 3*	*Administer Chapter 10 Test* 487/*Extra:* 1–4
125	**9-7** 422/*P:* 2, 4–11 **S** 416/20, 26	*Prepare for Chapter Test* **R** 442/*Chapter Review* **EP** 622/*Skills* 644/*Problems*	**11-1** 501/1–35 odd, 36
126	**9-8** 426/1–15 odd 428/*P:* 2, 8	*Administer Chapter 9 Test* **R** 446/*Cumulative Review*	**11-2** 507/2–40 even, 41, 42

LESSON	MINIMUM COURSE	AVERAGE COURSE	MAXIMUM COURSE
127	**9-8** 427/*P:* 1–11 odd **S** 423/*P:* 12, 13	**10-1** 451/1–34	**11-3** 512/1–49 odd **S** 508/43 **R** 513/*Self-Test 1*
128	**9-9** 432/*P:* 1–6 **R** 438/*Self-Test 3,* 1–3	**10-2** 457/9–55 odd **S** 452/35–38	**11-4** 516/1–31 **S** 503/37–40
129	*Prepare for Chapter Test* **R** 442/*Chapter Review,* 1–14 **EP** 622/*Skills* 644/*Problems*	**10-3** 461/2–18 even 462/*P:* 2, 4, 7, 10, 14	**11-5** 518/2–46 even, *P:* 1, 5, 8, 9
130	*Administer Chapter 9 Test* **R** 447/*Maintaining Skills,* 1–29 odd	**10-4** 471/1–31 odd **S** 462/*P:* 3, 5, 11 **R** 464/*Self-Test 1*	**11-6** 523/1–27 odd 524/*P:* 1–7 odd **S** 518/47–50
131	**10-1** 451/1–28	**10-5** 475/1–25 **S** 471/28–34 even	**11-7** 528/2–36 even **S** 519/*P:* 10, 11 **R** 524/*Self-Test 2*
132	**10-2** 456/1–8, 9–41 odd	**10-6** 477/1–12, 13–17 odd **S** 463/*P:* 6, 12, 16	**11-7** 528/25–43 odd **11-8** 530/1–18
133	**10-3** 461/2–14 even 462/*P:* 1–3, 7, 9, 10	**10-7** 482/1–4, 9–18, 25–29 **R** 478/*Self-Test 2*	**11-8** 530/19–36 **S** 524/*P:* 9
134	**10-4** 470/1–12 **S** 462/*P:* 4, 5, 11, 12 **R** 464/*Self-Test 1*	**10-8** 485/1–12 **S** 478/14–18 even	**11-9** 532/1–35 odd **S** 530/31, 33, 35
135	**10-4** 471/13–22 **10-5** 475/1–6	**10-8** 485/13–22 **R** 487/*Self-Test 3*	**11-10** 535/2–30 even 536/*P:* 3–6, 9, 10 **S** 533/38, 39, 42
136	**10-5** 475/7–20 **10-6** 477/1–12 **S** 471/23–26	*Prepare for Chapter Test* **R** 492/*Chapter Review* **EP** 626/*Skills* 646/*Problems*	**11-10** 535/31–47 odd 536/*P:* 11, 12 **R** 537/*Self-Test 3*
137	**10-7** 482/1–4, 9–18, 25–29 **R** 478/*Self-Test 2*	*Administer Chapter 10 Test* **R** 496/*Mixed Review*	*Prepare for Chapter Test* **R** 542/*Chapter Review* **EP** 628/*Skills* 647/*Problems*
138	**10-7** 483/19–21, 30–33 **10-8** 485/1–11 odd	**11-1** 501/1–33 odd	*Administer Chapter 11 Test* 525/*Extra:* 1–14 537/*Extra:* 1–20
139	*Prepare for Chapter Test* **R** 492/*Chapter Review,* 1–8, 10, 11 **EP** 626/*Skills* 646/*Problems*	**11-2** 507/2–40 even **S** 502/34, 35	**12-1** 549/1–51 odd

LESSON	MINIMUM COURSE	AVERAGE COURSE	MAXIMUM COURSE
140	*Administer Chapter 10 Test* **R** 495/*Maintaining Skills*	**11-3** 512/1–49 odd **S** 507/41	**12-1** 549/52–57 **12-2** 552/2–18 even
141	**11-1** 501/1–29 odd	**11-4** 516/1–28 **R** 513/*Self-Test 1*	**12-2** 552/20–38 even **S** 549/58
142	**11-2** 507/2–40 even **S** 502/28,. 30	**11-5** 518/2–42 even, *P:* 1, 3, 5	**123** 554/1–21 odd, 23–25 **S** 552/37, 39
143	**11-3** 512/1–39 odd, 40–43 **S** 507/19, 21, 27, 29	**11-6** 523/1–23 odd 524/*P:* 1, 4, 5 **S** 519/*P:* 4, 6, 9	**12-4** 559/2–20 even
144	**11-4** 516/1–22 **R** 513/*Self-Test 1*	**11-7** 528/1–24 **S** 524/*P:* 2, 3 **R** 524/*Self-Test 2*	**12-5** 563/1–31 odd **R** 561/*Self-Test 1*
145	**11-5** 518/2–36 even, *P:* 1, 3, 5 **S** 516/26–28	**11-7** 528/25–35 odd **11-8** 530/1–10	**12-6** 566/*P:* 3–5, 8–11 **S** 564/28, 30
146	**11-6** 523/1–21 odd 524/*P:* 1, 3, 4	**11-8** 530/12–30 even **S** 528/26–36 even	**12-6** 566/*P:* 2, 6, 7, 12–15 **R** 568/*Self-Test 2*
147	**11-7** 528/1–20 **R** 524/*Self-Test 2*	**11-9** 532/1–31 odd **S** 530/11–29 odd	*Prepare for Chapter Test* **R** 569/*Chapter Review* **EP** 631/*Skills* 648/*Problems*
148	**11-7** 528/21–31 **S** 518/*P:* 2, 4, 6	**11-10** 535/2–32 even 536/*P:* 1–6, 9 **R** 537/*Self-Test 3*	*Administer Chapter 12 Test* 555/*Extra:* 1–22 567/*Extra:* 1–9
149	**11-8** 530/1–14 **S** 524/*P:* 2, 5, 6	*Prepare for Chapter Test* **R** 542/*Chapter Review* **EP** 628/*Skills* 647/*Problems*	**Looking Ahead** 578/1–20
150	**11-8** 530/15–27 **S** 512/22–28 even	*Administer Chapter 11 Test* **R** 544/*Cumulative Review*	**Looking Ahead** 580/1–10 **S** 578/21, 22
151	**11-9** 532/1–29 odd	**12-1** 549/1–45 odd	**Looking Ahead** 582/1–22 583/*P:* 1–11 odd
152	**11-10** 535/1–23 odd 536/*P:* 1–4 **R** 537/*Self-Test 3*	**12-1** 549/46–53 **12-2** 552/2–12 even	**Looking Ahead** 585/1–6, 7–13 odd 586/*P:* 2, 5–8 **S** 582/23, 24

LESSON	MINIMUM COURSE	AVERAGE COURSE	MAXIMUM COURSE
153	*Prepare for Chapter Test* **R** 542/*Chapter Review* **EP** 628/*Skills* 647/*Problems*	**12-2** 552/14–36 even **S** 549/40, 42, 49, 51	**Looking Ahead** 589/1–16 **S** 583/*P:* 12
154	*Administer Chapter 11 Test* **R** 545/*Maintaining Skills*	**12-3** 554/1–23 odd, 24 **S** 552/31, 33, 35	**Looking Ahead** 591/1–27 odd **S** 586/*P:* 9
155	**12-1** 549/1–37 odd	**12-4** 559/2–20 even **R** 561/*Self-Test 1*	**Looking Ahead** 593/2–18 even 594/*P:* 1, 2, 4, 9–11
156	**12-2** 552/1–10 **S** 549/20–30 even	**12-5** 563/1–27 odd **S** 559/19	**Looking Ahead** 597/1, 2, 5, 7–11 **S** 595/*P:* 12–14
157	**12-2** 552/11–27	**12-5** 563/22–30 even **12-6** 566/*P:* 1, 3, 8–10	**Looking Ahead** 600/2–4, 6, 8 **S** 595/*P:* 15–16
158	**12-3** 554/1–12 **S** 552/28–30	**12-6** 566/*P:* 2, 5, 7, 11–14 **S** 554/20, 22 **R** 568/*Self-Test 2*	**Looking Ahead** 604/1–7 odd, 8, 10–15
159	**12-3** 554/13–15 **R** 561/*Self-Test 1,* 1–6 569/*Chapter Review,* 1–6	*Prepare for Chapter Test* **R** 569/*Chapter Review* **EP** 631/*Skills* 648/*Problems*	*Prepare for Chapter Test* **R** 605/*Review*
160	*Administer Chapter 12 Test* (*through Lesson 12-3*)	*Administer Chapter 12 Test*	*Administer Looking Ahead Test*

Supplementary Materials Guide

For use after Section	Practice Masters	Tests	Resource Book				
			Tests	Practice Exercises	Mixed Review	Enrichment Activities	Problem Solving
1-2				p. 67			
1-3	Sheet 1						
1-5		Test 1					
1-6	Sheet 2			p. 68			
1-9	Sheet 3	Test 2		p. 69			
Chapter 1	Sheet 4	Test 3	pp. 5, 7			p. 146	
2-2	Sheet 5						
2-3				p. 70			
2-4	Sheet 6	Test 4					
2-5				p. 71			
2-6	Sheet 7						
2-7		Test 5		p. 72			
2-9	Sheet 8	Test 6		p. 73			
Chapter 2	Sheet 9	Test 7	pp. 9, 11			p. 147	
Cum. Review Chaps. 1–2	Sheet 10						
3-2	Sheet 11						
3-3		Test 8		p. 74			
3-4	Sheet 12						
3-5				p. 75			
3-6	Sheet 13	Test 9					p. 161
3-7							p. 163
3-8	Sheet 14	Test 10		p. 76			
Chapter 3	Sheet 15	Test 11	pp. 13, 15			p. 149	
Cum. Review Chaps. 1–3	Sheets 16 and 17		p. 17	p. 77	p. 133		
4-2	Sheet 18			p. 79			
4-4	Sheet 19			p. 80			
4-6	Sheet 20	Test 12		p. 81			
4-8	Sheet 21			p. 82			p. 165
4-9							p. 169
4-10	Sheet 22	Test 13		p. 83			
Chapter 4	Sheet 23	Test 14	pp. 19, 21			p. 151	
Cum. Review Chaps. 1–4		Test 15					
5-2	Sheet 24						
5-3				p. 84			
5-4	Sheet 25	Test 16					
5-6	Sheet 26			p. 85			
5-8	Sheet 27						
5-9		Test 17		p. 86			
5-10	Sheet 28						
5-11				p. 87			
5-12	Sheet 29						
5-13	Sheet 30	Test 18		p. 88			

For use after Section	Practice Masters	Tests	Resource Book				
			Tests	Practice Exercises	Mixed Review	Enrichment Activities	Problem Solving
Chapter 5	Sheet 31	Test 19	pp. 23, 25			p. 152	
Cum. Review Chaps. 4–5	Sheet 32						
6-2	Sheet 33			p. 89			
6-3		Test 20					
6-4	Sheet 34			p. 90			
6-6	Sheet 35			p. 91			
6-7	Sheet 36	Test 21		p. 92			
Chapter 6	Sheet 37	Test 22	pp. 27, 29			p. 153	
Cum. Reviews Chaps. 4–6 Chaps. 1–6	Sheets 38 and 39	Test 23	p. 31 p. 33	p. 93 p. 95	p. 135		
7-2	Sheet 40			p. 97			
7-4	Sheet 41			p. 98			
7-5		Test 24					
7-6	Sheet 42			p. 99			
7-7							p. 171
7-8	Sheet 43			p. 100			p. 174
7-10	Sheet 44	Test 25		p. 101			
Chapter 7	Sheet 45	Test 26	pp. 36, 38			p. 154	
8-2	Sheet 46			p. 102			
8-4	Sheet 47			p. 103			
8-5		Test 27					
8-6	Sheet 48						
8-7	Sheet 49			p. 104			
8-8				p. 105			p. 176
8-9	Sheet 50	Test 28		p. 106			p. 179
Chapter 8	Sheet 51	Test 29	pp. 40, 42			p. 155	
Cum. Reviews Chaps. 7–8 Chaps. 5–8	Sheet 52	Test 30					
9-1				p. 107			
9-2	Sheet 53						
9-3		Test 31		p. 108			
9-4	Sheet 54						
9-5				p. 109			
9-6	Sheet 55	Test 32		p. 110			
9-8	Sheet 56						
9-10	Sheet 57	Test 33		p. 111			
Chapter 9	Sheet 58	Test 34	pp. 44, 46			p. 156	
Cum. Reviews Chaps. 7–9 Chaps. 1–9	Sheets 59 and 60		p. 48	p. 112	p. 138		
10-2	Sheet 61			p. 114			
10-3		Test 35		p. 115			
10-4	Sheet 62			p. 116			
10-6	Sheet 63			p. 117			
10-7		Test 36					

For use after Section	Practice Masters	Tests	Resource Book				
			Tests	Practice Exercises	Mixed Review	Enrichment Activities	Problem Solving
10-8	Sheet 64			p. 118			
Chapter 10	Sheet 65	Test 37	pp. 50, 52			p. 158	
11-2	Sheet 66			p. 119			
11-3		Test 38					
11-4	Sheet 67			p. 120			
11-6	Sheet 68	Test 39		p. 121			
11-8	Sheet 69			p. 122			
11-10	Sheet 70	Test 40		p. 123			
Chapter 11	Sheet 71	Test 41	pp. 54, 56			p. 159	
Cum. Review Chaps. 10–11	Sheet 72						
12-2	Sheet 73			p. 124			
12-3		Test 42		p. 125			
12-4	Sheet 74			p. 126			
12-6	Sheet 75	Test 43		p. 127			
Chapter 12	Sheet 76	Test 44	pp. 58, 60			p. 160	
Cum. Reviews Chaps. 10–12	Sheets 77 and 78		p. 62	p. 128			
Chaps. 9–12		Test 45					
Chaps. 7–12		Test 46	p. 64	p. 130			
Chaps. 1–12	Sheets 79 and 80				p. 142		

ALGEBRA ACTION: Courseware for Algebra I

This program develops topics in the same order as *Algebra, Structure and Method, Book 1,* c. 1986. The chart correlates each disk with the textbook chapters covering corresponding material. A more detailed correlation appears in the Teacher's Manual of the courseware.

For use with Chapters	Disk Number	Disk Topics
1–3	1	Variables; evaluating expressions; distributive axiom and combining like terms; word problems; signed number practice; solving linear equations in one variable
4–7	2	Greatest common factor; multiplying and factoring polynomials; simplifying algebraic fractions; adding, subtracting, multiplying, and dividing algebraic fractions; ratios and proportions; percent, mixture, and work problem applications
8–9	3	Coordinate plane; solving systems of linear equations: graphing, substitution, and multiplication with addition or subtraction; slope; functions; direct and inverse variations
10–12	4	Inequalities with one variable; conjunctions and disjunctions; inequalities with two variables; squaring numbers; square roots; Pythagorean theorem; simplifying radicals; quadratic formula

Lesson Commentary

1 Introduction to Algebra

This chapter develops some of the basic symbolism and terminology that students have seen before but have generally not absorbed. The concepts of variables, expressions, and equations are presented in meaningful examples in an intuitive manner. This in turn leads to an introduction to algebraic problem solving that will be the basis for problem solving throughout the course. The chapter concludes with the development of certain important concepts related to the real numbers using the one-to-one correspondence between numbers and points on a number line.

1-1 (pages 1–4)

Key Mathematical Ideas

- simplifying numerical expressions
- using the substitution principle to evaluate variable expressions

Teaching Suggestions

The concept of a variable may be difficult for some students to grasp. You may find it helpful to use the example on page 1 to stress the idea that $0.104 \times n$ is a *general* expression for water pressure, which depends upon how the depth, *n*, *varies.* Ask your students for other examples of variable expressions. Possibilities include the variable expression for the total cost of buying *n* items at a fixed price per item or the variable expression for the perimeter of a square.

You might want to ask your students what the difference between an expression and an equation is, since many students do not realize that there is a distinction.

Students are generally more willing to adopt the convention of omitting the multiplication symbol in variable expressions once they realize how easily a handwritten multiplication symbol could be mistaken for the variable *x* or vice versa.

Point out that the substitution principle (page 2) merely allows us to *substitute* one expression for another of equal value.

Parentheses are used to indicate which calculation comes first in expressions that involve more than one operation. (Other grouping symbols and conventions for order of operations are presented in the next lesson.)

This might be an opportune time to review the meaning of *sum, difference, product,* and *quotient.* When doing Example 1 with your students, be sure to point out that the word *quantity* is a key word used to indicate that parentheses are needed in writing a mathematical expression.

Exercises 41 and 42 on page 4 will give you an opportunity to point out to your more able students that although a variable can represent any number, it can be replaced in a given expression by only one value of the variable at a time.

Students may be interested in reading *Why We Call it "Algebra"* on page 28 and the Historical Note on the development of variables on page 116.

Suggested Extensions

Ask students to simplify each of the following, performing operations in parentheses first and then in order from left to right.

1. $(200 - 20) \div (10 - 4) + 2$ 32
2. $(200 - 20) \div 10 - (4 + 2)$ 12
3. $200 - (20 \div 10) - (4 + 2)$ 192
4. $200 - (20 \div 10) - 4 + 2$ 196

To lead into the next lesson, ask your students if $200 - 20 \div 10 - 4 + 2$ is equal to any of the expressions above. It is equal to the expression in 4.

1-2 (pages 5–8)

Key Mathematical Ideas

- simplifying expressions containing grouping symbols
- using the correct order of operations to simplify expressions in which grouping symbols have been omitted

Teaching Suggestions

Emphasize that mathematics is a language that attempts to express statements as concisely as possible. Thus, multiplication symbols are generally omitted from expressions when grouping symbols are used. Point out that brackets are generally used in expressions or equations that already contain parentheses to make more complicated expressions easier to read.

To show that the fraction bar is a grouping symbol, point out that expressions like

$$\frac{20 + 4}{2 \times 4} \text{ can be written } (20 + 4) \div (2 \times 4)$$

and must be entered in a format very similar to this when using a computer (see the Computer Key-In on page 9).

To introduce the order of operations, ask your students to simplify $20 - 5 \times 2$. Since some students will probably get 30 and others, 10, you can use this opportunity to point out why it was necessary for mathematicians to agree upon an order of operations. Point out that the order of operations is one of many conventions that your students will learn about in this course. In discussing this example, you may note that in the expression $20 - 5n$, it does seem reasonable to consider $5n$ as one number subtracted from 20.

Many teachers use the mnemonic device **M**y **D**ear **A**unt **S**ally to remind students of the agreed-upon order of operations. If you use this device, point out that multiplication and division, and addition and subtraction, may be interchanged depending on which of the two operations appears first in reading an expression from left to right.

You may want to direct your students' attention to the Historical Note about π that appears on page 533 before or after they do Exercises 22 and 23 on page 8.

Suggested Extension

Have students place grouping symbols in the following expressions so that each will have the stated value.

1. $9 + 35 \div 7 - 2$; 16 $9 + 35 \div (7 - 2)$
2. $2 \times 8 - 3 + 6 \div 2$; 13 $2 \times (8 - 3) + (6 \div 2)$
3. $20 - 4 \times 2 + 8 \div 16$; 10
   $(20 - 4) \times (2 + 8) \div 16$

1-3 (pages 10–11)

Key Mathematical Ideas

- using the terminology and symbolism associated with equations
- determining the solution set of an equation over a specified domain

Teaching Suggestions

Students may have learned synonyms for some of the terms introduced in this lesson, such as *element*, rather than *member*, *of a set*, and *member*, rather than *side*, *of an equation*. This text avoids referring to *members* of an equation because of possible confusion with *members* of a set.

To introduce the concept of an open sentence you can ask your students whether each of the following statements is true or false.

$3 + 5 = 8$	true
$10 - 2 \cdot 3 = 24$	false
$x + 9 = 13$	depends on the value of the variable; true for $x = 4$

Emphasize that the members of the solution set of an open sentence must (1) be in the domain of the open sentence and (2) make the open sentence true. Point out that the domain of a variable is sometimes called its replacement set because the members of this set are the only *replacements* for the variable that can be considered for inclusion in the solution set of an open sentence.

If your students have trouble remembering what the symbol $\in$ means, point out that it resembles the letter E and can be thought of as meaning *is an element of.*

After considering the solution set of an equation whose solution set is its domain (see last paragraph, page 11), you may want to challenge your students to find the solution set of an equation such as $3x + 1 = 3x - 2$, which has no solution.

Suggested Extensions

1. Challenge students to write five equations whose solution set is the set of all numbers. For example, $x + 0 = x$, $3 + x = x + 3$, $x = x$, $4x = x \cdot 4$, and so on.
2. Challenge students to write five equations that have no solution. For example, $x + 1 = x + 3$, $x = x - 2$, $0 \cdot x = 15$, and so on.

1-4 (pages 13–17)

Key Mathematical Idea

- translating numerical relationships from words into mathematical expressions

Teaching Suggestions

Remind students that mathematics is a language that people throughout the world use. Have your students think of themselves as translators who will be translating English into mathematical symbols. In preparation for solving word problems in Section 1-6, this lesson provides students with practice translating numerical relationships into mathematical expressions. The next lesson involves translating English sentences into equations.

Students may initially have trouble expressing a number in terms of another number represented by a variable when their sum is known (see Exercises 11 and 12 on page 15). To guide their thinking, ask your students, for example, "What number and 6 have a sum of 14?" Then ask them what they did to the sum to find the unknown number. Once they have found the correct answer to Exercise 11, for example, you may wish to show them that $x + (30 - x)$ really is equal to 30. Some students won't be convinced unless you do.

Suggested Extension

Have students represent their own age as x and write an expression for each of the following in terms of x.

1. their mother's (or father's) age
2. a sibling's age (Have them invent one if necessary.)
3. their own age in five years
4. three times their age
5. twice their age in three years

Have students save these for use in the next two lessons.

Reading Algebra

Sometimes students wonder why they can't write $5 < x$ for "five less than a number." Emphasize that "five less than a number" is a phrase; there is no verb; it does not express a complete thought. $5 < x$, read "5 *is* less than x," on the other hand, is a sentence.

Be sure to point out that the word *of* in a word phrase expressing relationships between numbers indicates multiplication. In fact, it would be helpful at this time to develop a list of various ways the symbols for all four operations can be verbalized. (See *Reading Algebra/Symbols*, page xiii.)

1-5 (pages 18–23)

Key Mathematical Idea

- translating word sentences involving numerical relationships into equations

Teaching Suggestion

This lesson builds upon the foundation laid in the previous lesson. Many students will feel that they are supposed to find an "answer" because that is what they have generally been asked to do. Explain that translating sentences into equations is just part of the problem-solving process and that we will concentrate on finding the answer, or solution, later.

Suggested Extensions

Have students write complete sentences starting with the five expressions for age in the previous Suggested Extension and using "is" or "will be." Have them save these sentences to be used in the next lesson.

Ask students to (a) restate each of the following sentences using the word *is* and (b) write an equation to represent each sentence in terms of the specified variable.

Answers may vary. An example is given.

1. In a class of 25 students there are three more girls than boys. Let $b =$ the number of boys in the class.
   The total number of boys and girls in the class *is* 25; $b + (b + 3) = 25$.
2. Lance and Rita drove 400 miles, or $\frac{2}{3}$ of the way from Kansas City, Missouri, to Denver, Colorado. Let $d =$ the number of miles from Kansas City, Missouri, to Denver, Colorado.
   Two thirds of the distance from Kansas City, Missouri, to Denver, Colorado, *is* 400 miles;
   $\frac{2}{3}d = 400$.
3. Fred has a collection of quarters worth \$18.75. Let $q =$ the number of quarters.
   The value of Fred's collection of quarters *is* \$18.75; $0.25q = 18.75$.
4. Clair bought a tennis racquet for \$60. The frame cost \$16 more than the strings. Let $s =$ the cost of the strings.
   The cost of the strings plus the cost of the frame *is* \$60; $s + (s + 16) = 60$.

Reading Algebra

Emphasize that an English sentence must contain a verb and that in sentences about numerical relationships, that verb will often be some form of the verb *is*. If your students can substitute *is equal to* for *is*, they have identified the part of the sentence that should be represented by the equality symbol when the word sentence is translated into an equation. Be sure to point out that other forms of the verb *is* such as *are*, *was*, and *will be* would also be represented by an equals sign. Sometimes the problem solver will find it helpful to restate the conditions of the given problem to reveal the verb. The last sentence of Example 3 on page 19, for example, can be restated, "The total time for the return trip *is* two minutes less than the time for the trip to school."

1-6 (pages 24–27)

Key Mathematical Idea

- using the five-step plan to solve word problems

Teaching Suggestions

Many of the problems at this stage are so easy to solve that students may be able to find the correct answer using an arithmetic approach or by trial and error. Point out that what you are most interested in at this time is that they learn a problem-solving process that they can use to help them solve more difficult problems as the course proceeds. Because the five-step plan will be used throughout the course, you may wish to post it where students can refer to it when necessary.

Students often have trouble solving word problems. Point out the relevance of this lesson; most problems that anyone has to solve outside the classroom are word problems.

Especially emphasize Steps 1, 2, and 5 of the five-step plan, the three steps students tend to think are unnecessary. Caution your students to read word problems very carefully, since overlooking or misreading even one word affects the rest of their work. To help students choose the quantity to represent by a variable (Step 2), ask them to which quantity other quantities in the problem are compared. For example, if Jared is four years older than Shera, it makes sense to represent Shera's age by the variable. Also, in step 2, require students to identify the variable very specifically. For example, they should write, "Let d = Diana's age now," not "Let d = Diana." They should also represent any other quantities described in the problem in terms of that variable before writing the equation. For example, then $d - 4$ = Diana's age 4 years ago. This may keep students from omitting a portion of the equation needed to represent the information given and helps them answer the question asked correctly. Checking their answers (Step 5) will give them confidence if they have gotten the correct answer or give them a chance to find their own mistake if they have made a careless error. Students should be cautioned to check their answers with the *words* of the problem. Substituting the value they got for the variable into their equation will not help them find their error if their equation does not correctly represent the given information.

Suggested Extensions

Have students write word problems using the sentences they wrote for the last *Suggested Extensions*. Have them exchange papers and use the five-step plan to solve the problems.

Students may also enjoy making up other word problems from their own experience for their classmates to solve.

Example: Our basketball team won three more games this year than it did last year. During the two years it won 27 games. How many games did it win this year?
15 games

1-7 (pages 30–33)

Key Mathematical Idea

- correspondence of the real numbers and points on a number line

Teaching Suggestions

In developing the number line, point out to your students that "0", or the origin, can be placed anywhere on the line and that the unit length is also of their choosing. Emphasize the fact that the location of the origin and the unit distance can vary but only from number line to number line. You may wish to mark the location of several integers on your number line with a compass to stress that once the location of the origin and the unit distance have been determined, every number that your students are familiar with is associated with some point of the line and that every point on the line is associated with some "real" number.

Be sure to point out that the points on a number line are indicated by capital letters. Encourage your students to draw arrowheads on their number lines. Be sure to show them how to graph some positive and negative fractions and mixed numbers. Point out that larger numbers are always to the right of smaller numbers on a horizontal number line. Thus, for example, $^-3$, which is farther from 0, is less than $^-1$. Be sure to graph some infinite sets such as the set of integers and the set of whole numbers. Emphasize that one or both arrowheads of the number line are made very heavy when graphing infinite sets to indicate the members of the set that could not be specifically marked on the number line. Point out that the number line on page 31 is much thicker than the ones on page 30, because it represents the graph of each real number.

If students think the term "real" number strange, point out that they will learn about other kinds of numbers, such as imaginary numbers, in future mathematics courses. For now, all they need to know is that the set of real numbers includes any numbers that they will encounter in this course.

You may wish to introduce other sets of numbers such as the set of counting, or natural, numbers and the set of digits along with the set of integers and the set of whole numbers. If students have trouble remembering that 0 is a member of the set of whole numbers, you can point out that 0, which looks like a *hole*, belongs to the set of *whole* numbers. You should also emphasize that zero is neither negative nor positive.

1-8 (pages 34–36)

Key Mathematical Idea

- opposites and absolute values

Teaching Suggestions

The number line can be very useful in presenting this lesson. Draw a number line on the chalkboard and use a compass to locate the opposite of several numbers. Be sure to include 0 and some positive and negative integers, fractions, and mixed numbers. As you do this, point out that each number and its opposite are the same distance from the origin but are in opposite directions (hence the name "opposite"). The axiom of opposites will be introduced in the next chapter.

Be sure your students understand, for example, that "the opposite of 3," or "-3," and "negative 3," or "$^{-}3$," are the same number. Understanding this now will make subtracting real numbers (Section 2-4) much easier for them.

Emphasize that $-a$, for example, is not necessarily a negative number. Use numerical examples to show students that when a is negative, $-a$ is positive; that when $a = 0$, $-a = 0$; and that when a is positive, $-a$ is negative.

Students will probably have less trouble understanding the notion of absolute value if you emphasize that the absolute value of a number is the distance from the origin to the graph of the number on the number line. Using a compass, show your students that the distance, for example, from the origin to -3 is the same as the distance from the origin to 3, or $|-3| = |3| = 3$. Point out that since distance can never be negative, the absolute value of a number can never be negative.

Suggested Extension

Have students write out each of the following expressions in words. Answers may vary.

1. $7 - [-(-3)]$ seven minus the opposite of negative three
2. $-8 + (-6)$ the sum of the opposite of eight and the opposite of 6
3. $2x - (-5 - x)$ two times x minus the quantity negative five minus x
4. $-|a - b|$ the opposite of the absolute value of the difference of a and b
5. $|-a| + (-a)$ the sum of the absolute value of negative a and the opposite of a

1-9 (pages 37–39)

Key Mathematical Idea

- the order relations of the real numbers

Teaching Suggestions

Point out to your students that the order relations are always read from left to right; the *greater than* symbol points to the right, where the numbers on a number line get progressively larger, and the *less than* symbol points to the left, where the numbers on a number line get progressively smaller.

Be sure to assign exercises that require students to compare numbers between 0 and 1 and numbers between 0 and -1.

The exercises in this lesson allow students to review many concepts learned earlier in the chapter.

Suggested Extension

Ask students to replace each __?__ with one of the symbols $<$ or $>$ to make a true statement. Then write out a general statement about the order of any two numbers compared with the order of their opposites.

1. 5 __?__ 4 $>$
-5 __?__ -4 $<$
2. -6 __?__ -1 $<$
6 __?__ 1 $>$
3. -8 __?__ 3 $<$
8 __?__ -3 $>$
4. 7 __?__ -2 $>$
-7 __?__ 2 $<$
5. 5 __?__ 0 $>$
-5 __?__ 0 $<$
6. 0 __?__ -3 $>$
0 __?__ 3 $<$

The order of any two numbers is the reverse of the order of their opposites.

2 Working with Real Numbers

This chapter focuses on using the four operations and the axioms of real numbers to simplify numerical and algebraic expressions.

The commutative, associative, distributive, and other axioms are introduced to help students simplify numerical and algebraic expressions. Students learn to add real numbers, first by using a number line and then by developing rules consistent with the results suggested by the number line. The concepts of opposites, or additive inverses, and absolute values are also developed using the number line. Subtraction is defined in terms of addition. The rules for multiplication are introduced, and division is defined in terms of multiplication. The properties of real numbers and problem-solving skills are developed further in Section 2-7.

2-1 (pages 45–48)

Key Mathematical Idea

- use of commutative and associative axioms to simplify expressions

Teaching Suggestions

Write the axioms of closure for addition and multiplication on the chalkboard and illustrate both axioms with a variety of numerical examples.

Students may already be familiar with the commutative and associative axioms for addition and multiplication. Present a variety of examples to illustrate each property. Exercises 23–25 on page 48 can be used to point out to students that the commutative and associative axioms do not hold for subtraction and division. Point out that the commutative properties have to do with *order:* no matter what *order* you choose to add or multiply two numbers, you get the same sum or product. Point out that the word *associative* is similar to the word *association,* meaning a *group,* and has to do with *grouping:* no matter how you *group* two numbers to be added or multiplied, you get the same sum or product.

Suggested Extension

Have students identify the property illustrated in each of the following.

1. $2 + (x + 2)3 = 2 + 3(x + 2)$ Comm. ax. for mult.
2. $5 + [3 + (2a + 1)] = (5 + 3) + (2a + 1)$ Assoc. ax. for add.
3. $[(2x + y) + 3x] + (y + 4x) =$ $[(y + 2x) + 3x] + (4x + y)$ Comm. ax. for add.
4. $\frac{1}{2}[6(3m + 2)] = (\frac{1}{2} \cdot 6)(3m + 2)$ Assoc. ax. for mult.

2-2 (pages 49–52)

Key Mathematical Ideas

- addition of real numbers on the number line
- using the identity axiom of addition and the axiom of opposites

Teaching Suggestions

Some students may find it helpful to relate number line addition to adding gains and losses, with the sum being the net gain (positive) or net loss (negative). They are familiar with games that involve gains and losses with the possibility of going "in the hole." Suggest a game in which a person has scores of 30, -80, and 20, and ask the students what the net score would be. (-30)

Reading Algebra

This section provides a good opportunity for you to show how diagrams must be read along with the text discussion. You might draw the first diagram on page 49 on the chalkboard and ask a student to read aloud the paragraph above the figure. Have the reader pause after "at the origin," "2 units to the left," and "5 units to the left" as you show the corresponding moves on the diagram. Then ask students to relate the text and the second diagram in the same way, by moving a finger along the diagram.

Suggested Extension

The first three plays of a football team starting from its own 20-yard line are described below. Using the diagram below, have students draw arrows to represent the sequence of plays. Then have them represent these plays as the sum of three integers and state the net gain or loss as a positive or negative number.

1. gain of 7 yd, loss of 3 yd, loss of 6 yd
   $7 + (-3) + (-6) = -2$
2. loss of 5 yd, loss of 2 yd, gain of 12 yd
   $-5 + (-2) + 12 = 5$
3. gain of 8 yd, loss of 5 yd, gain of 9 yd
   $8 + (-5) + 9 = 12$
4. loss of 1 yd, loss of 4 yd, loss of 10 yd
   $-1 + (-4) + (-10) = -15$
5. loss of 3 yd, no gain or loss, gain of 3 yd
   $-3 + 0 + 3 = 0$

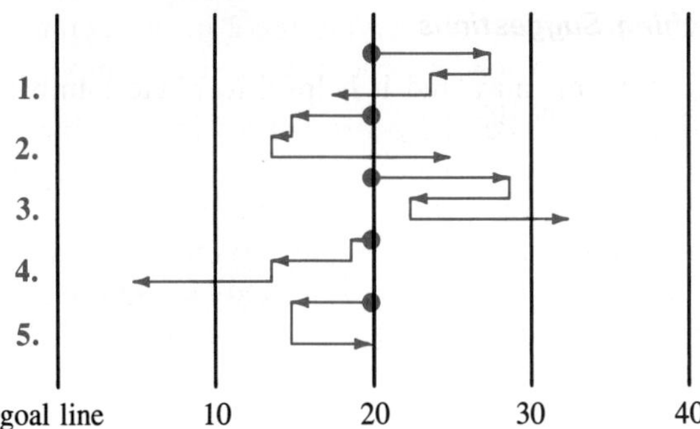

2-3 (pages 53–58)

Key Mathematical Ideas

- general rules for adding real numbers
- using addition to solve word problems

Teaching Suggestions

Your students learned to add real numbers using a number line in the previous lesson. They should be encouraged to use the number line to find sums whenever they become confused about the rules or for checking when they are unsure of an answer. The rules for adding positive and negative numbers given on page 54 merely help us find sums more quickly. Use numerical examples and number lines to find the sums as you go over these rules with your students. If you use several examples such as $2 + (-3)$, $1 + (-10)$, and $25 + (-38)$ to illustrate Rule 4, it should be clear that the sum must be negative and that we must subtract absolute values because the arrows go in opposite directions. A student may ask "But what if a is negative and b is positive?" Point out that Rules 3 and 4 cover all cases when one number is negative and the other is positive because the commutative axiom for addition always allows you to write the positive number first.

Exercises 29–34 on page 56 will require students to think analytically and will help prepare them for the next lesson.

Suggested Extensions

Ask your students to explain why the following statements are true.

1. $|-4 + 3| \neq |-4| + |3|$
2. $|5 + (-6)| \neq |-5| + |-6|$

1. $|-4 + 3| = |-1| = 1;$
   $|-4| + |3| = 4 + 3 = 7;\ 1 \neq 7$
2. $|5 + (-6)| = |-1| = 1;$
   $|-5| + |-6| = 5 + 6 = 11;\ 1 \neq 11$

2-4 (pages 59–63)

Key Mathematical Ideas

- using the definition of subtraction to simplify expressions involving differences
- using subtraction to solve word problems

Teaching Suggestions

This is a difficult lesson for many students. Encourage students to express each difference as a sum and apply the rules they learned in the previous lesson even when the expressions are as easy to simplify as Oral Exercises 1 and 2 on page 60. Stress that what you are most interested in is that they always apply the definition of subtraction so that they will not become confused when one or both of the numbers involved are negative.

To convince students that their answers are correct, have them check their answers using addition. Examples: $7 - 8 = -1$ and $-1 + 8 = 7$; $-5 - (-3) = -2$ and $-2 + (-3) = -5$.

If students still need to be convinced that the correct answer is reasonable, try this approach using the number line. Remind students that when they subtract two positive numbers a and b with $a > b$, the difference, $a - b$, is positive. Point out that this holds for all real numbers a and b. Likewise, if $a < b$, $a - b$ is negative for all real numbers. Thus, the difference of a and b can be found by first finding the distance between a and b on the number line and then determining whether the difference is positive or negative based on whether $a > b$ or $a < b$. Show several examples:

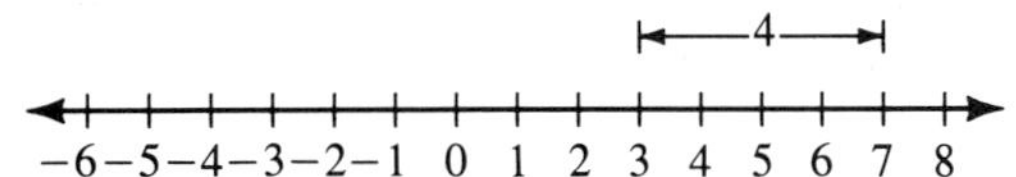

$7 - 3 = 4$ because $7 > 3$.
$3 - 7 = -4$ because $3 < 7$.

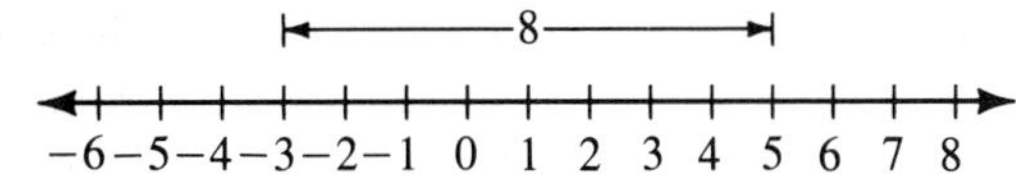

$5 - (-3) = 8$ because $5 > -3$.
$-3 - 5 = -8$ because $-3 < 5$.

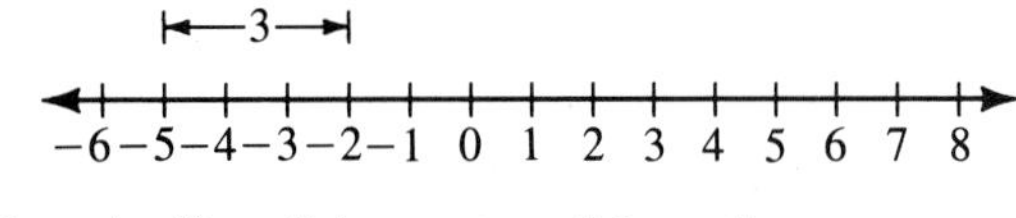

$-2 - (-5) = 3$ because $-2 > -5$.
$-5 - (-2) = -3$ because $-5 < -2$.

Suggested Extension

Have students find the following pairs of differences using a number line (see Teaching Suggestions). Then have them check their answers using addition.

1. a. $6 - 2$ 4
b. $2 - 6$ −4

2. a. $-4 - (-1)$ −3
b. $-1 - (-4)$ 3

3. a. $-3 - 2$ −5
b. $2 - (-3)$ 5

4. a. $8 - 0$ 8
b. $0 - 8$ −8

5. a. $0 - (-5)$ 5
b. $-5 - 0$ −5

6. a. $7 - (-2)$ 9
b. $-2 - 7$ −9

2-5 (pages 64–67)

Key Mathematical Idea

- using the distributive property to simplify expressions

Teaching Suggestions

You can point out to students that they have used the distributive property before, probably without realizing it. Instead of carrying the 2 in the example at the left below, we could write the example as shown at the right.

$$\begin{array}{r} 23 \\ \times\ 7 \\ \hline 161 \end{array} \qquad \begin{array}{rcr} & & 23 \\ & & \times\ 7 \\ \hline (7 \times 3) & = & 21 \\ (7 \times 20) & = & 140 \\ \hline & & 161 \end{array}$$

$$\text{or } 7 \times 23 = 7 \times (20 + 3) = 7 \times 20 + 7 \times 3 = 140 + 21 = 161$$

Emphasize that terms are separated by "+" or "−" and that the distributive axiom helps us combine like terms.

Remind students that each new lesson builds upon what they have learned in previous lessons. For example, although they would use the distributive axiom to simplify Exercises 19 and 20 on page 66, students must also use the correct order of operations learned in Chapter 1.

Reading Algebra

You can check students' understanding of the distributive axiom by having them verbalize some of the expressions in the examples on page 65. For example, one might read Example 1b as follows: "Eight times nine and five tenths is equal to eight times the sum of nine and five tenths, and this is equal to the sum of eight times nine and eight times five tenths, which equals seventy-two plus four, or seventy-six." Ask for other, equally correct, ways of reading the sentence.

Suggested Extension

Ask students which of the following statements would be true for all real numbers. true: 2, 4, 6

1. $3(2a + b) = 6a + b$
2. $2(x + 1) + 4 = 2x + 2 + 4$
3. $\frac{1}{2}[2(4x + 6)] = 2x + 3$
4. $4[(2m + n) + 3] = 4(2m + n) + 12$
5. $5 + 3(4y - 5) = 32y - 40$
6. $\frac{1}{2}[(8x + 6y + 2) + 10x] = (4x + 3y + 1) + 5x$

2-6 (pages 68–71)

Key Mathematical Idea

- using rules and properties to find the products of real numbers

Teaching Suggestions

Students often confuse the new rules for multiplication with the rules for addition. Many students who would have added -5 and -3 correctly before, may now write $(-5) + (-3) = 8$. Do not allow them to make a statement such as "two minuses make a plus." Require precise language as in the following statements.

The product of two negative numbers is positive.
The sum of two negative numbers is negative.
The product of a positive and a negative number is negative.
The sum of a positive and a negative number may be either positive or negative.

You may wish to give these statements on a completion quiz.

You should expect to spend extra time on Exercises 27–40 on page 71. It would be wise to assign the odd-numbered exercises followed by discussion, then the even-numbered exercises.

Suggested Extension

Have your students simplify each of the following.

1. a. $(-8)(-3)$ 24
   b. $(-8) + (-3)$ −11
2. a. $(9)(-2)$ −18
   b. $(9) + (-2)$ 7
3. a. $(4)(-6)$ −24
   b. $(4) + (-6)$ −2
4. a. $(-7)(0)$ 0
   b. $(-7) + (0)$ −7
5. a. $(2)(-3)(-1)(4)(-2)$ −48
   b. $(2) + (-3) + (-1) + (4) + (-2)$ 0
6. a. $(-1)(-2)(-3)(-4)$ 24
   b. $(-1) + (-2) + (-3) + (-4)$ −10

2-7 (pages 72–75)

Key Mathematical Idea

- translating relationships among integers into equations

Teaching Suggestions

This lesson will make students think about the relationships among consecutive, consecutive odd, and consecutive even integers and prepare them to solve word problems involving these relationships. Point out that even integers, which always end in 0, 2, 4, 6, or 8, can be represented by $2n$, where $n \in \{\text{integers}\}$, and that the odd integers, which always end in 1, 3, 5, 7, or 9, can be represented by $2n + 1$.

Use several examples to illustrate that n, $n + 2$, $n + 4$, and so on may represent either consecutive even or consecutive odd integers. Ask a student to select any three consecutive odd integers and find their sum. Then show how the equation $15 + 17 + 19 = 51$, for example, can be written in terms of the smallest integer:

$$15 + (15 + 2) + (15 + 4) = 51$$

Stress that there is more than one correct way to write an equation about consecutive, consecutive even, or consecutive odd integers.

Suggested Extensions

Write the consecutive integers 11, 12, and 13, for example, on the chalkboard. Have the class help you write true statements about these integers and translate them into equations. For example:
The sum of three consecutive integers is 36.
$n + (n + 1) + (n + 2) = 36$
Three times the smallest integer is 8 more than the sum of the two larger integers.
$3n = (n + 1) + (n + 2) + 8$
Twice the sum of the two smaller integers is 19 less than five times the largest.
$2[n + (n + 1)] = 5(n + 2) - 19$

Now have each student select three consecutive integers, complete the following statements about them, and write an equation to represent each statement. Answers will vary.

1. The sum of three consecutive integers is __?__.
2. Three times the smallest integer is __?__ more than the sum of the two larger integers.
3. Twice the sum of the two smaller integers is __?__ less than five times the largest.

2-8 (pages 76–78)

Key Mathematical Idea

- using the axiom of reciprocals to simplify products

Teaching Suggestions

It would be worthwhile to review the axiom of opposites as you introduce the axiom of reciprocals. You can review the relationships between numbers and their opposites using a number line similar to the one shown on page 34 and contrast this with a number line like the one below, which shows some numbers and their reciprocals.

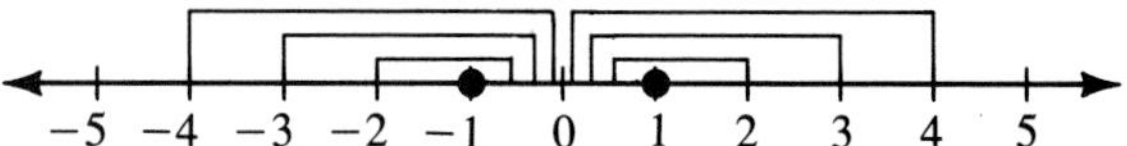

Point out that the sum of opposites, or additive inverses, is 0, the identity element for addition, and that the product of reciprocals, or multiplicative inverses, is 1, or the identity element for multiplication. Using the number line above, also point out the following facts about reciprocals.

1. The numbers 1 and -1 are their own reciprocals.
2. The number 0 has no reciprocal.
3. If $a > 1$, $0 < \frac{1}{a} < 1$; if $a < -1$, $-1 < \frac{1}{a} < 0$.

You will probably have to remind students that the reciprocal of a negative number is also a negative number.

Students may ask why we say, "For every nonzero number a," or "For $a \neq 0$" when we discuss the number $\frac{1}{a}$. Students sometimes think that $\frac{1}{0} = 0$ or that $\frac{1}{0} = 1$. Point out that this is impossible since $0 \times 0 \neq 1$ and $1 \times 0 \neq 1$. Explain that division by 0 has no meaning in the set of real numbers.

Suggested Extension

Have students replace each __?__ with a number to make a true statement.

1. $-8(\underline{?}) = 1$ $-\frac{1}{8}$

2. $-\frac{1}{4}(\underline{?}) = 1$ -4

3. $-\frac{7}{3}(\underline{?}) = 1$ $-\frac{3}{7}$

4. $-150(\underline{?}) = 1$ $-\frac{1}{150}$

5. $-1(\underline{?}) = 1$ -1

6. $0(\underline{?}) = 1$ no solution

7. $5\frac{1}{2}(\underline{?}) = 1$ $\frac{2}{11}$

8. $-\frac{1}{1000}(\underline{?}) = 1$ -1000

9. $\frac{7}{16}(\underline{?}) = 1$ $\frac{16}{7}$

10. $-1\frac{1}{2}(\underline{?}) = 1$ $-\frac{2}{3}$

2-9 (pages 80–83)

Key Mathematical Ideas

- using the definition of division to express quotients as products
- simplifying quotients

Teaching Suggestions

Point out to your students that they used the definition of division whenever they found the quotient of two fractions by inverting the second one and multiplying. Also point out that division is defined in terms of multiplication just as subtraction is defined in terms of addition. Make sure students understand that the rules for dividing real numbers are similar to the rules for multiplying real numbers because the definition of division allows us to replace any quotient by a product.

Suggested Extension

Have students replace each _?_ with a number to make a true statement.

1. If $14 \div (-2) = \underline{?}$, then $\underline{?}\,(-2) = 14$. $-7, -7$
2. If $-8 \div \frac{1}{2} = \underline{?}$, then $\underline{?} \cdot \frac{1}{2} = -8$. $-16, -16$
3. If $\frac{4}{5} \div 3 = \underline{?}$, then $\underline{?} \cdot 3 = \frac{4}{5}$. $\frac{4}{15}, \frac{4}{15}$
4. If $-\frac{1}{2} \div \left(-\frac{1}{4}\right) = \underline{?}$, then $\underline{?}\left(-\frac{1}{4}\right) = -\frac{1}{2}$. $2, 2$

3 Solving Equations and Problems

Algebraic methods of solving equations are developed using the properties of equality. Multistep solutions require the use of many properties from earlier sections. The algebraic method of problem solving is now considered in its entirety. The use of charts is introduced as an aid to organizing information in various types of word problems, including cost and value problems.

An introduction to proofs of algebraic theorems is presented in the last section.

3-1 (pages 93–98)

Key Mathematical Ideas

- using the addition and subtraction properties of equality to solve equations
- solving simple word problems using addition or subtraction

Teaching Suggestions

Begin with some simple examples, emphasizing that the solution of an equation is a number and not another equation. For example, the solution to Example 1 is -5, not $v = -5$.

Some students want to show steps of a solution horizontally as, for example, $x - 4 = 9 = x = 13$. Point out that the equivalence symbol $\leftrightarrow$ can be used for this purpose, but that the equals sign cannot. Stress that the vertical form is conventional and the equals signs should be lined up.

You can establish good equation-solving strategy by reminding students of their primary goal: isolating the variable on one side of the equation.

Suggested Extension

Have your students match each equation on the left with an equivalent equation on the right.

1. $4 - x = 7$	**a.** $4 - x = -7$
2. $-x = 7$	**b.** $x = -7$
3. $x - 4 = 7$	**c.** $x + 4 = -7$
4. $4 + x = 7$	**d.** $x - 4 = -7$
5. $-x = -7$	**e.** $-4 - x = -7$
6. $4 + x = -7$	**f.** $7 - x = 0$

1. d 2. b 3. a 4. e 5. f 6. c

3-2 (pages 99–102)

Key Mathematical Ideas

- using the multiplication and division properties of equality to solve equations
- solving simple word problems using multiplication or division

Teaching Suggestions

Remind students that the goal in solving an equation is to transform it into an equation that has only the variable on one of the sides. Point out that we can solve an equation of the form $ax = b$ $(a \neq 0)$ by multiplying each side by $\frac{1}{a}$ or by dividing each side by a.

Point out that $\frac{1}{3}x$ and $\frac{x}{3}$ represent the same number and that $3\left(\frac{1}{3}x\right)$ and $3 \cdot \frac{x}{3}$ are each equal to $1x$, or x.

Be sure that students understand why zero cannot be used as a multiplier or as a divisor in transforming equations.

Encourage students to use transformation by substitution to check their work.

3-3 (pages 103–107)

Key Mathematical Idea

- using several transformations to solve equations

Teaching Suggestions

Encourage students who obviously have more difficulty to write all intermediate steps as shown in Example 2, page 104, before writing the condensed solution shown below it. The ultimate objective is to be able to produce the condensed solution, but students must earn the right to skip steps. Also, place more emphasis on the check at this stage, particularly for those students who have more difficulty.

Students will frequently "lose" a minus sign in solving equations such as $4 - 3x = 10$ by writing $3x = 6$. Include ample practice with this case.

Discuss the two methods shown below for solving the equation $\frac{1}{2}t - 1 = -8$.

$\frac{1}{2}t - 1 = -8$	$\frac{1}{2}t - 1 = -8$
$\frac{1}{2}t - 1 + 1 = -8 + 1$	$2\left(\frac{1}{2}t - 1\right) = 2(-8)$
$\frac{1}{2}t = -7$	$t - 2 = -16$
$2\left(\frac{1}{2}t\right) = 2(-7)$	$t - 2 + 2 = -16 + 2$
$t = -14$	$t = -14$

Note that it is generally easier to solve equations by adding or subtracting before multiplying or dividing.

Suggested Extension

Write the equation $0.024(x - 50) = -4.8$ on the chalkboard.

1. Ask students to solve the equation by using the distributive property first. -150
2. Ask students to solve the equation by dividing each side by 0.024 first.
3. Ask students to solve the equation by multiplying each side by 1000 first.
4. Ask individual students to discuss why they prefer one method over another.

3-4 (pages 108–111)

Key Mathematical Idea

- using the five-step plan to solve word problems

Teaching Suggestions

You will need to discuss many examples and to stress the importance of organization and neatness. Remind students that accurate problem solving requires slow, careful reading. As in Chapter 1, require that the variable be identified precisely as a number.

Present the following two problems to the class for comparison. The first is an arithmetic problem.

1. Ned is 10 years old. His mother is twice as old as Ned will be in 6 years. How old is his mother?

The arithmetic would be as follows.

$$\begin{array}{r} 10 \\ +\ 6 \\ \hline 16 \end{array} \qquad \begin{array}{r} 16 \\ \times 2 \\ \hline 32 \end{array}$$

$\therefore$ Ned's mother is 32 years old.

If m represents his mother's age, the horizontal form is:

$$m = 2(10 + 6)$$
$$m = 2(16)$$
$$m = 32$$

2. Nancy's mother is 42 years old. She is twice as old as Nancy will be in 6 years. How old is Nancy?

Point out that the sentence to be translated is very similar to the sentence in the arithmetic problem, but the operations must be indicated instead of carried out.

Let n represent Nancy's age now.
Then $42 = 2(n + 6)$

Let students solve the equation (15) and check the answer.

Reading Algebra

As students begin more difficult work with problems, you may want to remind them of the material on reading problems on page 29. Work through the solved examples in this section with students to make sure they understand how to apply the steps outlined on page 26. Emphasize the value of looking for words in problems that suggest the operations involved in the solution. Examples are perimeter of a triangle (addition); area of a rectangle (multiplication); average (addition and division); consecutive even integers (successive additions of 2).

Suggested Extension

Have each student make up a problem with the answer "12." Use the following examples.

1. $$\begin{array}{r} 12 \\ -\ 5 \\ \hline 7 \end{array} \qquad \begin{array}{r} 7 \\ \times 3 \\ \hline 21 \end{array} \qquad \begin{array}{r} 21 \\ +\ 4 \\ \hline 25 \end{array}$$

Cindy is 25 years old. She is 4 years more than 3 times as old as Al was 5 years ago. How old is Al?

2. $8 + 2(10) + 3(12) = 64$

I'm thinking of three consecutive even integers. When I add the smallest, twice the second, and three times the largest, the result is 64. Find the largest integer.

3-5 (pages 112–117)

Key Mathematical Ideas

- solving equations when the variable appears in both sides
- solving problems leading to equations with the variable in both sides

Teaching Suggestions

Review the concept of equivalent equations, equations with the same solution set over a specified domain. Stress that the following transformations produce equivalent equations:

1. simplifying one side or both sides
2. adding the same number to both sides or subtracting the same number from both sides
3. multiplying or dividing both sides by the same *nonzero* number

Suggest that students check each solution to an equation in the *original* equation. If the solution does not check, students should check each step of the solution, beginning at the top, to locate the step in which an error was made.

Point out that while most of the equations in this chapter have one solution, some equations in this section have no solution and others are satisfied by every real number. Students should be aware of the three possibilities that exist for a linear equation in one variable: the equation has a unique root, has no root, or is an identity.

Suggested Extension

Each of the following solutions is incorrect. Have students identify which two consecutive equations are not equivalent and state why.

1. **a.** $2x + 5 = 3(x - 4)$
b. $2x + 5 = 3x - 12$
c. $5 = x - 12$
d. $-7 = x$

2. **a.** $\frac{1}{3}(6x - 12) = 6 + 4(x - 2)$
b. $2x - 4 = 10(x - 2)$
c. $2x - 4 = 10x - 20$
d. $-4 = 8x - 20$
e. $16 = 8x$
f. $2 = x$

3. **a.** $5(x + 4) - x = -6(x - 10)$
b. $5x + 20 - x = -6x + 60$
c. $4x + 20 = -6x + 60$
d. $10x + 20 = 60$
e. $x + 20 = 6$
f. $x = -14$

1. c and d; $5 + 12 = x - 12 + 12$ is equivalent to $17 = x$.
2. a and b; $6 + 4(x - 2) = 6 + 4x - 8 = 4x - 2$; $10(x - 2) = 10x - 20$; $4x - 2 \neq 10x - 20$.
3. d and e; $\frac{1}{10}(10x + 20) = \frac{1}{10}(60)$ gives $x + 2 = 6$.

3-6 (pages 118–121)

Key Mathematical Idea

- using charts to solve word problems

Teaching Suggestions

Point out that a chart is particularly useful in problems involving two or more numbers that we do not know. It helps us represent the different numbers in terms of a single variable before writing the equation.

Many students find that once they have set up a chart and filled it in, they can complete the solution process with little difficulty. The Oral Exercises provide good practice in completing charts. After you discuss some of these, you might help students set up charts for a few of the Written Exercises.

3-7 (pages 122–125)

Key Mathematical Idea

- solving problems involving cost and value

Teaching Suggestions

Present the following arithmetic problem related to the example on page 122:

Roger paid 50 cents each for 75 programs for the football game. He sold all but 15 of them for \$1 each. What was his profit in cents?

75 bought	60
−15	×100
60 sold	6000¢ selling cost
75	6000
×50	−3750
3750¢ buying cost	2250¢ profit

profit in cents = $100(75 - 15) - 50(75)$

Compare this equation with the text equation when the profit is known but the number of programs bought is not.

Next, present the problem stated at the top of the following page and help students develop and complete the chart used in solving the problem.

Eric has 8 nickels, twice as many dimes as nickels, and 4 more quarters than nickels. What is the total value of his coins?

	Number	× Value of Coin	= Total Value
Nickels	8	5	5(8)
Dimes	$2 \cdot 8$	10	$10(2 \cdot 8)$
Quarters	8 + 4	25	25(8 + 4)

The total value is

$$5(8) + 10(2 \cdot 8) + 25(8 + 4) = 40 + 160 + 300 = 500, \text{ or } \$5.00.$$

Now have students make a chart for the following problem by replacing 8 by n.

Erica has some nickels, twice as many dimes as nickels, and 4 more quarters than nickels. The total value of all her coins is \$6.50. How many coins of each type does she have?

	Number	× Value of Coin	= Total Value
Nickels	n	5	$5n$
Dimes	$2n$	10	$10(2n)$
Quarters	$n + 4$	25	$25(n + 4)$

Help students write and solve an equation and answer the question. Discuss why \$6.50 must be expressed in terms of cents.

$$5n + 10(2n) + 25(n + 4) = 650$$
$$5n + 20n + 25n + 100 = 650$$
$$50n = 550$$
$$n = 11 \quad \text{11 nickels}$$
$$2n = 22 \quad \text{22 dimes}$$
$$n + 4 = 15 \quad \text{15 quarters}$$

Emphasize that the various types of problems in this section are variations of this basic type:

(number of units) $\cdot$ (unit value) = total value

When solving problems like these, students should remember the need for uniformity in the choice of units (for example, cents or dollars).

3-8 (pages 126–129)

Key Mathematical Idea

- proving theorems in algebra

Teaching Suggestions

This will probably be the first exposure to proof of any kind for your students. A good way to begin is to review the properties learned thus far. (See the summaries on pages 84 and 85.)

For the most part, students will be asked in this section to provide reasons for proofs, not to write complete proofs. Encourage your students to become familiar with the two-column proof format.

Most students will have little success writing original proofs and some may become discouraged. Tell students that it is important for them to be able to understand a proof.

Discuss the idea that the structure of algebra is based on axioms, theorems, and logical reasoning. Note that each new fact, or theorem, can be justified using definitions, axioms, given facts, and previously proved theorems.

Suggested Extension

Ask your students to provide the missing statements and reason in the following proof of the multiplication property of zero.

Prove: For every real number a, $a \cdot 0 = 0$ and $0 \cdot a = 0$.

Proof:

STATEMENTS	REASONS
1. $0 + 0 = 0$	1. Identity axiom for addition
2. ?	2. Mult. prop. of equality
3. ?	3. Distributive axiom
4. ?	4. Identity axiom for addition
5. $a \cdot 0 = 0$	5. Subtr. prop. of equality
6. $0 \cdot a = 0$	6. ?

2. $a(0 + 0) = a \cdot 0$
3. $a \cdot 0 + a \cdot 0 = a \cdot 0$
4. $a \cdot 0 + a \cdot 0 = 0 + a \cdot 0$
6. Commutative axiom for multiplication

4 Polynomials

The concept of an exponent and the first rules of exponents are introduced. The addition, subtraction, and multiplication of polynomials are developed and applied in conjunction with additional rules of exponents. Previous work with equations is extended to transforming formulas. The chapter concludes with further development of problem solving skills in a variety of new problems including uniform motion and area problems. These problems provide an opportunity to apply the skills developed in the chapter.

4-1 (pages 137–140)

Key Mathematical Idea

- simplifying expressions with exponents

Teaching Suggestions

Write the following expressions on the chalkboard:

$$5^4 \qquad (-3)^5 \qquad -3^5 \qquad (2x)^3 \qquad 2x^3$$

For each expression, ask students to identify the base and the exponent and to write the expression in factored, or expanded, form. Be sure students understand the difference between $(-3)^5$ and -3^5 and between $(2x)^3$ and $2x^3$. The Oral Exercises and A-level exercises provide excellent practice with exponents and help uncover some of the mistakes that students commonly make when working with exponents. Caution students against evaluating b^n as $b \cdot n$. Emphasize that x has the implied exponent 1.

Review the order of operations on page 138. Emphasize the second step, the new one in the list.

Suggested Extensions

Write each expression on the chalkboard and ask students to place grouping symbols so that the expression has the given value.

1. $2 \cdot 1 + 7 - 10^2 \cdot 3 \div (-4) + 2$; -12

2. $2 \cdot 1 + 7 - 10^2 \cdot 3 \div (-4) + 2$; 93

3. $3 \cdot 4 - 3 \cdot 2^4 \div 4^3 \div 2$; -8

4. $3 \cdot 4 - 3 \cdot 2^4 - 4^3 \div 2$; $42{,}592$

1. $2 \cdot (1 + 7 - 10)^2 \cdot 3 \div [(-4) + 2] = -12$
2. $2(1 + 7) - 10^2 \cdot 3 \div (-4) + 2 = 93$
3. $[3(4 - 3 \cdot 2)^4 - 4^3] \div 2 = -8$
4. $[3 \cdot (4 - 3) \cdot 2^4 - 4]^3 \div 2 = 42{,}592$

4-2 (pages 143–147)

Key Mathematical Idea

- addition and subtraction of polynomials

Teaching Suggestions

Assign the Independent Study, page 142, before beginning Section 4-2. Many students open a textbook only to work exercises, believing that their teacher will teach them everything they need to know. Encourage students to develop the habit of studying the text presentation both before and after classroom discussion. Section 4-2 would be a good place to give a quiz before any discussion since the lesson introduces terminology which students should be able to grasp with careful reading and study. Encourage students throughout the course to use the text presentation as a major source of help in the learning process.

Discuss the words *monorail, bicycle,* and *triangle.* Ask students to give other words using the prefixes *mono-*, *bi-*, and *tri-*, and state the meaning of each prefix.

Write the following monomials on the chalkboard: $-5x^2y^3z$, $2^5a^7b^9$, and $9pq^2r^3s^4t^5$. For each monomial, have your students state the degree in each variable and the degree of the monomial. If they have difficulty, ask them to think of the factored form of the monomial. The Oral Exercises provide practice with finding the degree of a polynomial.

Demonstrate both the horizontal and the vertical forms of addition and subtraction of polynomials. Suggest that when students use the vertical form they can include a small operation sign to remind them of the operation to be performed.

Errors in subtraction are very common. Warn students to work carefully and to check their work. Some students may find it helpful to think of a subtraction problem as multiplying the second polynomial by -1 and then finding the sum. Emphasize that $(a + b) - (c + d) = a + b - c - d$ and remind students to combine like terms.

Suggested Extensions

Instruct your students to find the missing polynomial P for each of the following.

1. $3x^2 - 4x + 7 + P = 0$
2. $7y - y^5 + 4y^3 - 3 + y^2 + P = 0$
3. $2z^4 - 9z^2 + z^6 - P = 0$
4. $8ab^2 - a^3 - 9a^2b + b^3 - P = 0$

1. $-3x^2 + 4x - 7$
2. $y^5 - 4y^3 - y^2 - 7y + 3$
3. $z^6 + 2z^4 - 9z^2$
4. $-a^3 - 9a^2b + 8ab^2 + b^3$

4-3 (pages 148–150)

Key Mathematical Ideas

- first rule of exponents
- multiplying monomials

Teaching Suggestions

The rules of exponents often cause difficulty somewhat like the operations with integers. Students will appear to be successful with one rule treated in isolation, but once all the rules are established, students tend to become confused. Therefore, place emphasis on the concept behind the rule. That is, students are likely to be successful if you stress the definition of an exponent, which is the basis of the rules of exponents.

Point out once again that $x = x^1$.

The role of the commutative and associative axioms for multiplication is critical in multiplying monomials as illustrated in Example 1, page 148.

Point out to students that even though these axioms are normally applied mentally, the students should be aware of their application.

Caution students that the rule of exponents on page 148 applies only to powers with the same base. Point out the simplification in Example 2, noting that a sum like $-8a^6b^4 + 3a^4b^6$ cannot be simplified further.

Suggested Extensions

Your students can explore distributive properties by telling whether each statement is true or false. If it is false, students should give an example. If it is true, students should prove it.

1. $a^{m \cdot n} = a^m \cdot a^n$
2. $a^{m+n} = a^m + a^n$
3. $(ab)^m = a^m \cdot b^m$
4. $(a + b)^m = a^m + b^m$

1. False; example: $3^{2 \cdot 3} = 3^6 = 729$;
   $3^2 \cdot 3^3 = 9 \cdot 27 = 243$
2. False; example: $3^{2+3} = 3^5 = 243$;
   $3^2 + 3^3 = 9 + 27 = 36$
3. True; $(ab)^m = ab \cdot ab \cdot ab \cdot \cdots \cdot ab$ (m factors)
   $= (a \cdot a \cdot \cdots \cdot a)(b \cdot b \cdot \cdots \cdot b)$
   (m factors of a, m factors of b)
   $= a^m \cdot b^m$
4. False; example: $(3 + 4)^2 = 7^2 = 49$;
   $3^2 + 4^2 = 9 + 16 = 25$

4-4 (pages 151–153)

Key Mathematical Ideas

- two more rules of exponents
- finding powers of monomials

Teaching Suggestions

Point out that the second rule of exponents in this section, $(ab)^m = a^mb^m$, can easily be generalized to any number of factors by the same reasoning, $(abcd\ldots)^m = a^mb^mc^md^m \ldots$.

The B exercises of this section require students to use all three rules that have been established this far. Caution students to use only one rule at a time until they are experienced enough to skip steps.

Reading Algebra

You will find it worthwhile to focus on the symbolism used in this lesson. Example 1 and the rules of exponents might be read aloud. Point out that an expression such as $(x^3)^2$ can be read in several different ways—for example, "x cubed to the second power," "x cubed [pause] squared," "the square of the cube of x." Any word form that makes the meaning clear is acceptable. Ask students to respond to the Oral Exercises with complete sentences—for example, "The square of the fourth power of x is x to the eighth power."

Suggested Extensions

Ask students to simplify each expression. Assume that each variable represents a positive integer.

1. $(a^n)^2 \cdot (a^2)^n$ 2. $(2x^2y)^n$

3. $[(3a)^m]^n \cdot (3a^m)^n$

1. a^{4n} 2. $2^n x^{2n} y^n$ 3. $3^{mn+n} \cdot a^{2mn}$

4-5 (pages 154–156)

Key Mathematical Idea

- multiplying a polynomial by a monomial

Teaching Suggestions

The new skill introduced in this lesson, multiplying a polynomial by a monomial, is based on the distributive axiom and the rules of exponents. Point out that once the distributive axiom is applied, the resulting expression is of the type found in Lesson 4-4:

$$2t^2(3t^3 - t - 9) = 2t^2(3t^3) + 2t^2(-t) + 2t^2(-9)$$

You can prepare students for the next section by discussing both the horizontal and vertical forms of multiplication.

Caution students that it is easy to confuse signs when multiplying and simplifying expressions. Students should be especially careful when working on Exercises 19–38, page 155.

Suggested Extensions

Show students the following product:

$$\begin{aligned}(ax + b)(cx + d) &= ax(cx + d) + b(cx + d)\\ &= acx^2 + adx + bcx + bd\\ &= acx^2 + (ad + bc)x + bd\end{aligned}$$

Thus,

$$\begin{aligned}(2x + 1)(3x - 4) &= 2x(3x - 4) + 1(3x - 4)\\ &= 6x^2 - 8x + 3x - 4\\ &= 6x^2 - 5x - 4\end{aligned}$$

Have students find each product.

1. $(5x + 2)(2x + 3)$ 2. $(3x - 4)(4x - 3)$

3. $(6x - 1)(x + 5)$ 4. $(2x + 7)(2x - 7)$

1. $10x^2 + 19x + 6$ 2. $12x^2 - 25x + 12$
3. $6x^2 + 29x - 5$ 4. $4x^2 - 49$

4-6 (pages 157–160)

Key Mathematical Idea

- multiplying polynomials

Teaching Suggestions

You can develop the idea of multiplication of polynomials with the following numerical example:

$$\begin{aligned}(27)(13) &= (20 + 7)(10 + 3)\\ &= 20(10 + 3) + 7(10 + 3)\\ &= 20(10) + 20(3) + 7(10) + 7(3)\\ &= 200 + 60 + 70 + 21 = 351\end{aligned}$$

Similarly,

$$\begin{aligned}(2x + 3)(4x + 5) &= 2x(4x + 5) + 3(4x + 5)\\ &= 2x(4x) + 2x(5) + 3(4x) + 15\\ &= 8x^2 + (10 + 12)x + 15\\ &= 8x^2 + 22x + 15\end{aligned}$$

Use the following example and ask the class to discover a short rule for multiplying polynomials.

$$\begin{aligned}&(a + b)(c + d + e)\\ &\quad= (a + b)c + (a + b)d + (a + b)e\\ &\quad= ac + bc + ad + bd + ae + be\end{aligned}$$

Multiply each term of the first polynomial by each term of the second polynomial.

Also ask the class to discover a rule for determining the number of terms, before combining, in a product of two polynomials. Multiply the number of terms in the first by the number of terms in the second.

Stress the fact that simplest form requires that similar terms be combined. However, you need not require students to do this mentally at this point. Note that in Section 5-4 a shortcut method is developed for multiplying binomials.

Suggested Extensions

Ask students to multiply, assuming that each variable in an exponent represents a positive integer.

1. $(x^n + 7)(3x^n - 9)$
2. $(x^n + y^n)(x^n + y^n)$
3. $(t^n - 1)(t^{2n} - 3t^n + 1)$
4. $(x^n + y^n)(x^n - y^n)$

1. $3x^{2n} + 12x^n - 63$ 2. $x^{2n} + 2x^ny^n + y^{2n}$
3. $t^{3n} - 4t^{2n} + 4t^n - 1$ 4. $x^{2n} - y^{2n}$

4-7 (pages 161–162)

Key Mathematical Idea

- solving a formula for one variable in terms of other variables

Teaching Suggestions

Using the formula for the area of a trapezoid in Example 1, page 161, present the following table.

	A	h	b	a
a.	84	7	15	?
b.	66	12	8	?
c.	45	9	1.5	?
d.	28	$\frac{8}{3}$	16	?

Point out that the use of the original formula would require the solution of four separate equations. But if the original formula is solved for a first, then the computation is much simpler.

Use part (a) in the table to illustrate how the steps carried out for specific numbers parallel the steps indicated in the general solution.

$$\begin{aligned} 84 &= \tfrac{1}{2}(7)(a + 15) \\ 2 \cdot 84 &= 7(a + 15) \\ \frac{2 \cdot 84}{7} &= a + 15 \\ \frac{2 \cdot 84}{7} - 15 &= a \end{aligned} \qquad \begin{aligned} A &= \tfrac{1}{2}h(a + b) \\ 2A &= h(a + b) \\ \frac{2A}{h} &= a + b \\ \frac{2A}{h} - b &= a \end{aligned}$$

Suggested Extension

Have students use the original formula to solve for a in parts (b), (c), and (d) in the table. Then have them compute a in each case by the derived formula, $a = \frac{2A}{h} - b$. b. $a = 3$ c. $a = 8.5$ d. $a = 5$

4-8 (pages 163–167)

Key Mathematical Idea

- solving uniform motion problems

Teaching Suggestions

Students are still inexperienced at problem solving. They may wonder how they are supposed to know what to let the variable represent when there is more than one unknown number in the problem. Show them that in Example 1, page 163, we may choose to let x = speed of the eastbound plane. The chart would then be as follows.

	Rate	× Time =	Distance
Westbound	$x - 60$	2.5	$2.5(x - 60)$
Eastbound	x	2.5	$2.5x$

The equation would then be $2.5(x - 60) + 2.5x = 4150$. The last step would be $x = 860$ and $x - 60 = 800$. The answers to the question are the same as the text answers. This approach emphasizes the importance of precisely identifying the variable so we know its significance when we have solved for it. Point out that the choice in the text is made because eastbound speed is given in terms of westbound speed in the problem.

You may want to ask students to solve Example 2, page 164, by letting x = the Costanzas' driving time.

Emphasize the usefulness of preparing a chart and drawing a sketch when solving a uniform motion problem. Also, point out that each example in the text represents a different type of distance problem: motion in opposite directions, motion in the same direction, and round-trip travel. Students should have enough practice to feel comfortable with each of these types.

4-9 (*pages 168–171*)

Key Mathematical Idea

- solving problems related to area

Teaching Suggestions

Some students may see different methods of dissecting the border in the example on page 168 which yield equations equivalent to the text equation.

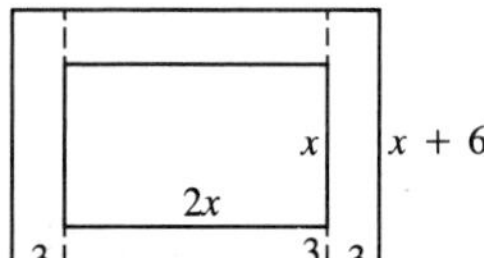

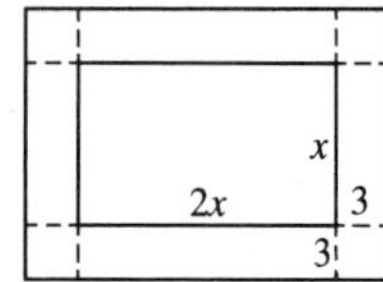

$$2[3(x + 6)] + 2[3(2x)] = 216$$
$$18x + 36 = 216$$

$$2[3(2x)] + 2[3(x)] + 4(3^2) = 216$$
$$18x + 36 = 216$$

You may discuss the acceptability of each of these. Point out, however, that if the picture should tilt in its frame as shown below, only the subtraction equation of the text would still be valid. Of course, most of the area problems of this section involve uniform borders.

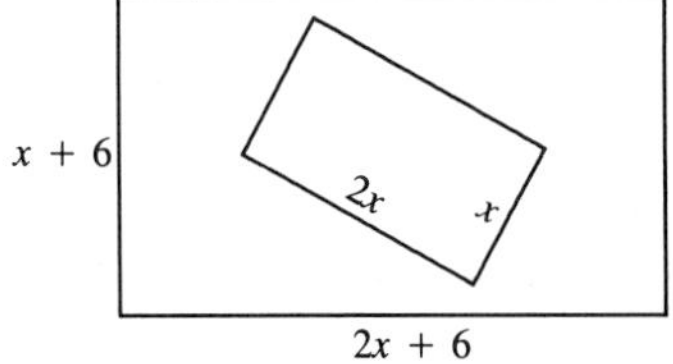

Suggested Extension

Present the following problem to the class:

A hole in the shape of a parallelogram is cut from a piece of cardboard as shown. The base of the parallelogram is 1 cm more than the height. The area of the remaining cardboard is 34 cm^2. Find the base and height of the hole.

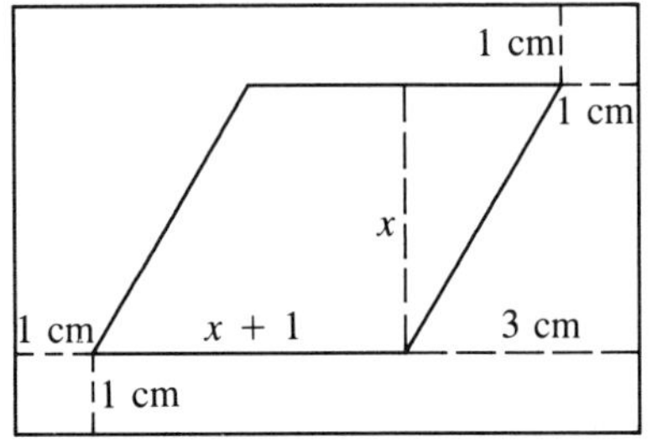

base, 5 cm; height, 4 cm

4-10 (*pages 172–174*)

Key Mathematical Idea

- recognizing problems without solutions

Teaching Suggestions

The example on page 172 illustrates one type of word problem with no solution: a word problem whose associated equation has no solution. Point out that there are two other reasons that a word problem may have no solution. Problem 2, page 173, cannot be solved because there is not enough information to determine a unique solution. Problem 4 has no solution because the solution produced by the associated equation, $26\frac{1}{2}$ and $27\frac{1}{2}$, does not satisfy the requirement of the problem.

Remind students of the definition of the domain of a variable as discussed in Section 1-3. Before discussing Problem 1, page 172, ask students to identify the domain of n if n = number of dimes. natural numbers Then as students solve the equation $10n + 25n = 800$, they will get a solution that is not in the domain of the variable. Point out that this situation is another indication of contradictory information. There are students who would accept $22\frac{6}{7}$ dimes as an answer.

5 Factoring Polynomials

This chapter develops the factorization of composite numbers, monomials, and polynomials. Division of monomials is presented as a related skill along with the rule of exponents for division. Several sections are devoted to the special techniques of factoring polynomials. One section provides practice in multiplying binomials mentally. The last part of the chapter develops the key technique used for solving polynomial equations and applies this technique to problem solving.

5-1 (pages 183-186)

Key Mathematical Ideas

- finding the prime factorization of composite numbers
- finding the greatest common factor of a set of integers

Teaching Suggestions

Use the following example to illustrate the relationship between the factors of a number and the divisors of that number.

Since $3 \cdot 5 = 15$, 3 is a factor of 15 and 5 is a factor of 15.
$15 \div 3 = 5$ and so 3 is a divisor of 15.
$15 \div 5 = 3$ and so 5 is a divisor of 15.
If an integer is a factor of a number, then it is a divisor of that number.
If an integer is a divisor of a number, then it is a factor of that number.

List and illustrate these tests for divisibility:

a. 2 is a factor if the ones' digit is even.
b. 3 is a factor if the sum of the digits is divisible by 3.
c. 5 is a factor if the ones' digit is 0 or 5.

Point out the two special cases involving the GCF. Note that the GCF of two numbers can be 1, for example, GCF (15, 26) = 1. Also, the GCF of two numbers can be the smaller number, for example, GCF (14, 70) = 14.

Reading Algebra

You might use this section to give students practice in skimming (reading quickly) to acquire specific information. Ask them to read the section rapidly, looking for the main ideas and finding out what types of exercises they will be asked to do after studying the section. When they have had time for skimming, list their findings on the chalkboard.
factor integers, find prime factorizations of numbers, find the GCF of two or more numbers

Suggested Extension

Some of your students may enjoy finding all the prime numbers less than a specified number by using the sieve of Eratosthenes, presented on page 213.

5-2 (pages 187-190)

Key Mathematical Ideas

- dividing monomials
- rule of exponents for division
- finding the GCF of two or more monomials

Teaching Suggestions

Stress the fact that in the cancellation rule, only *factors* can be cancelled. $\frac{3x}{3y} = \frac{x}{y}$ because 3 is a common factor, but $\frac{3+x}{3+y}$ cannot be simplified because 3 is not a common *factor.*

Use this opportunity to review the rules for exponents from Sections 4-3 and 4-4 (pages 148 and 151). You can use the cancellation rule for fractions to develop the rule of exponents for division with the following examples:

$$\frac{a^5}{a^2} = \frac{\not{a} \cdot \not{a} \cdot a \cdot a \cdot a}{\not{a} \cdot \not{a}} = a^3 \qquad \frac{a^3}{a^4} = \frac{\not{a} \cdot \not{a} \cdot \not{a} \cdot 1}{\not{a} \cdot \not{a} \cdot \not{a} \cdot a} = \frac{1}{a}$$

Point out the need for the factor 1 in the second example above.

Some students have difficulty finding the GCF of two monomials, so be sure to discuss the method outlined in Example 6. Have students use this method to find the GCF of $12a^3bc^3$ and $10a^2b^3c^4$. Show the class that each monomial can now be expressed as the product of the GCF and another monomial: GCF $= 2a^2bc^3$

$12a^3bc^3 = 2a^2bc^3 \cdot 6a$ and $10a^2b^3c^4 = 2a^2bc^3 \cdot 5b^2c$

Point out that students can check their work by verifying that the other monomials, $6a$ and $5b^2c$, have no common factor greater than 1.

Suggested Extension

Have students find the area of the shaded region in factored form. Then have them evaluate the area using $\pi \approx \frac{22}{7}$ and $r = 14$.

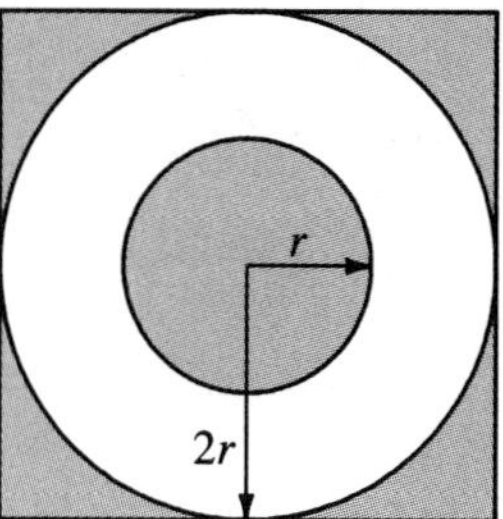

$A = (16 - 3\pi)r^2$
≈ 1288 sq. units

5-3 (pages 191-195)

Key Mathematical Ideas

- dividing a polynomial by a monomial
- finding the greatest monomial factor of a polynomial

Teaching Suggestions

Place strong emphasis on checking division exercises and factoring exercises by multiplication. You might ask students to verify Examples 1 and 2 in this way.

For Example 1: $4x^2(x^2 + 2xy - 3y^2)$

For Example 2: $xy\left(xy + \frac{1}{y} - \frac{1}{x}\right)$

Some students have difficulty factoring when the greatest common monomial factor is one of the terms of the polynomial. For example, $12x^3y^2 + 18x^2y^3 + 6x^2y = 6x^2y(2xy + 3y^2 + 1)$. Such students will fail to write the 1. But if they think in terms of multiplication, they will think "What must I multiply by $6x^2y$ to get $6x^2y$?" Stress the following two points in this type of factoring problem.

1. The polynomial factor in parentheses must have the same number of terms as the original polynomial.
2. The greatest common monomial factor of the terms of the polynomial in parentheses should be 1.

5-4 (pages 196-198)

Key Mathematical Ideas

- finding the product of two binomials mentally
- terminology related to a quadratic polynomial

Teaching Suggestions

The most common memory device used in multiplying two binomials is FOIL (first times first, outside plus inside, last times last). If you do present this device, stress the fact that it is not a "method," but rather a means of remembering the shortcut that allows us to skip the middle step in the following application of the distributive property.

First Last

$$(a + b)(c + d) = a(c + d) + b(c + d)$$

Inside / Outside

F O I L

$$= ac + ad + bc + bd$$

Point out that if the first terms are similar and the last terms are similar, then the outside product and the inside product will always be similar and can be combined. Make the point that the ability to combine these terms mentally will be important later in the chapter when factoring is introduced.

Reading Algebra

This section begins by showing three methods of multiplying binomials. The third of these is a short method that is then expressed as a rule. Students may need help in reading this material with understanding. You might show all three methods on the chalkboard. Point to the expression $4x + 7$ in the vertical form of the example and ask students to find it in each of the other methods. Ask if it has been changed in any way (enclosed in parentheses) and ask what happens to it in each method. Continue to relate other expressions so that students see how the distributive axiom is being used.

5-5 (pages 199–202)

Key Mathematical Ideas

- simplifying products of the form $(a + b)(a - b)$
- factoring the difference of squares

Teaching Suggestions

Both the multiplication and factoring exercises of this section depend upon students' recognition of the specified pattern. Be sure students get enough practice to recognize the pattern even when other patterns are present.

Point out the table of squares on page 649 of the text. You might also encourage students to make and memorize their own tables of squares from $1^2 = 1$ through $15^2 = 225$. Knowing these perfect squares will be helpful throughout the course. Also illustrate the pattern of perfect squares involving exponents.

$$(x^1)^2 = x^2$$
$$(x^2)^2 = x^4$$
$$(x^3)^2 = x^6$$
$$(x^n)^2 = x^{2n},\ n \text{ a positive integer}$$

The two types of exercises can be illustrated and reinforced with numerical examples as follows:

$$\begin{array}{c|c} (8 + 5)(8 - 5) & 8^2 - 5^2 \\ 13 \cdot 3 & 64 - 25 \end{array}$$
$$39 = 39$$

$$\begin{array}{c|c} 15^2 - 7^2 & (15 + 7)(15 - 7) \\ 225 - 49 & 22 \cdot 8 \end{array}$$
$$176 = 176$$

See Exercises 13–20 for additional practice.

Suggested Extension

The Extra on page 202 discusses factoring patterns for the sum and the difference of cubes. This feature provides an interesting extension of the lesson.

5-6 (pages 203–207)

Key Mathematical Ideas

- squaring a binomial
- recognizing and factoring a trinomial square

Teaching Suggestions

Two of the most universal errors that algebra teachers encounter are the two related false statements $(a + b)^2 = a^2 + b^2$ and $a + b = \sqrt{a^2 + b^2}$.

Along with the text development, the concept of the square of a binomial can be reinforced by both arithmetic and geometry. $(3 + 4)^2 = 7^2 = 49$ and $3^2 + 2(3 \cdot 4) + 4^2 = 9 + 24 + 16 = 49$ but $3^2 + 4^2 = 9 + 16 = 25 \neq 49$.

For geometric interpretations of the trinomial square formulas, refer to Example 3 and Exercise 62, page 206.

Emphasize that in both trinomial square patterns, a plus sign precedes the last term. Thus, it should be obvious to students that a polynomial like $9x^2 + 6x - 4$ cannot be a trinomial square.

Suggested Extensions

Ask students to factor each polynomial, assuming that n is a positive integer.

1. $x^{2n} + 2x^ny^{2n} + y^{4n}$ $(x^n + y^{2n})^2$
2. $4x^{6n} - 20x^{3n} + 25$ $(2x^{3n} - 5)^2$
3. $x^{2n} - 2x^n + 1 - y^{2n}$ $(x^n - 1 + y^n)(x^n - 1 - y^n)$
4. $2x^{9n} - 4x^{5n} + 2x^n$ $2x^n(x^{4n} - 1)^2$

5–7 (pages 208–210)

Key Mathematical Idea

- factoring quadratic trinomials of the form $x^2 + bx + c$ with c positive

Teaching Suggestions

Write the following multiplication problems on the chalkboard and call on class members to use the short method to find the products.

$(x + 1)(x + 24) = x^2 + 25x + 24$
$(x - 1)(x - 24) = x^2 - 25x + 24$
$(x + 2)(x + 12) = x^2 + 14x + 24$
$(x - 2)(x - 12) = x^2 - 14x + 24$
$(x + 3)(x + 8) = x^2 + 11x + 24$
$(x - 3)(x - 8) = x^2 - 11x + 24$
$(x + 4)(x + 6) = x^2 + 10x + 24$
$(x - 4)(x - 6) = x^2 - 10x + 24$

Stress the common form of each of these trinomials: x^2 ________ $+ 24$. Then choose one of these eight trinomials, say $x^2 - 14x + 24$. Point out that to factor this trinomial we need to discover what two numbers we used to get the middle term when we multiplied. That is, $x^2 - 14x + 24 = (x - \underline{?})(x - \underline{?})$. Emphasize, then, that factoring is the "reverse process" of multiplying.

Suggested Extensions

Have students find all possible values of r and c such that $x + r$ is a factor of both trinomials.

1. $x^2 - 24x + 143$ and $x^2 - 26x + c$
   $r = -11$ and $c = 165$, or $r = -13$ and $c = 169$
2. $x^2 + 40x + 204$ and $x^2 + 77x + c$
   $r = 34$ and $c = 1462$, or $r = 6$ and $c = 426$

5–8 (pages 211–213)

Key Mathematical Idea

- factoring quadratic trinomials of the form $x^2 + bx + c$ with c negative

Teaching Suggestions

Present the following multiplication problems to the class as in the previous section.

$(x + 1)(x - 54) = x^2 - 53x - 54$
$(x - 1)(x + 54) = x^2 + 53x - 54$
$(x + 2)(x - 27) = x^2 - 25x - 54$
$(x - 2)(x + 27) = x^2 + 25x - 54$
$(x + 3)(x - 18) = x^2 - 15x - 54$
$(x - 3)(x + 18) = x^2 + 15x - 54$
$(x + 6)(x - 9) = x^2 - 3x - 54$
$(x - 6)(x + 9) = x^2 + 3x - 54$

Once again point out the common form of each of these trinomials: x^2 ________ $- 54$. Now discuss the procedure for factoring a trinomial of this form. Emphasize that since the constant term is negative, the required pair of factors of -54 must have opposite signs. Also, remind students that it is important for them to check factors by multiplying.

Suggested Extensions

Ask students to factor each trinomial, assuming that n is a positive integer.

1. $(x^2 - 1)^2 - 3(x^2 - 1) - 40$ (*Hint:* Let $y = x^2 - 1$.) $(x + 3)(x - 3)(x^2 + 4)$
2. $(x^2 + 4x)^2 - 9(x^2 + 4x) - 36$ (*Hint:* Let $z = x^2 + 4x$.) $(x + 1)(x + 3)(x + 6)(x - 2)$
3. $x^{6n} - 2x^{3n} - 35$ $(x^{3n} - 7)(x^{3n} + 5)$
4. $x^{4n} + 2x^{2n}y^{2n} - 3y^{4n}$
   $(x^{2n} + 3y^{2n})(x^n + y^n)(x^n - y^n)$

5–9 (pages 214–217)

Key Mathematical Idea

- factoring trinomials of the form $ax^2 + bx + c$ with $a > 1$

Teaching Suggestions

Explain that the purpose of this lesson is to learn to factor trinomials regardless of the coefficient of the quadratic term. Note that the basic method of factoring is the same as in previous lessons but that there are now more possibilities to try.

Encourage students to use an orderly system of trials so that they will not overlook a possible pair of factors. For example, when factoring $12x^2 + 23x + 10$, students should select a starting point, say $(4x \quad)(3x \quad)$ and consider all factor combinations of 10 before trying $(2x \quad)(6x \quad)$ or $(12x \quad)(x \quad)$.

Remind students that the most important factoring clue is the sign of the constant or last term. The following hints may also be helpful:

1. If the last coefficient is 1, reverse the terms. Example: $2x^2 + 3xy + y^2 = y^2 + 3xy + 2x^2$ $= (y + 2x)(y + x)$
2. If the first coefficient is negative, begin by factoring out a monomial factor of -1. (See Example 4, page 215.)
3. Factor out common factors. Example: $3x^2 + 12x - 15 = 3(x^2 + 4x - 5)$ $= 3(x + 5)(x - 1)$
4. Use your knowledge of even and odd numbers to eliminate some of the possibilities. Example: To factor $12x^2 + 23x + 10$, note that 23 is odd. Therefore $(6x \quad)(2x \quad)$, $(4x + 2)(3x + 5)$, $(12x + 2)(3x + 5)$, $(4x + 10)(3x + 1)$, and $(12x + 10)(3x + 1)$ are among the possibilities that can be mentally discarded. (Each has an even linear term that is the sum of two even addends.) The linear term $23x$ must be the sum of an even and an odd linear term.

Suggested Extensions

Ask students to determine all integral values for k for which the trinomial can be factored.

1. $4t^2 + kt + 2$ **2.** $3x^3 + kx + 10$

3. $2m^2 + km + 9$ **4.** $12y^2 + ky + 5$

1. 6, 9, -6, -9
2. 11, 13, 17, 31, -11, -13, -17, -31
3. 9, 11, 19, -9, -11, -19
4. 16, 17, 19, 23, 32, 61, -16, -17, -19, -23, -32, -61

5-10 (pages 218-220)

Key Mathematical Idea

- factoring polynomials by grouping terms

Teaching Suggestions

Some students may wonder how to decide whether they should group the first two, first three, or last three terms. It is a good time to discuss the exploratory nature of learning mathematics. Encourage students to try grouping any way they can just to see what happens. For example, if they should show the following,

$$x^2 + 10x + 25 - 4y^2 = (x^2 + 10x) + (25 - 4y^2) = x(x + 10) + (5 + 2y)(5 - 2y),$$

point out that they have not made a mistake. They simply tried something that did not lead any farther so they should try again.

$$x^2 + 10x + 25 - 4y^2 = (x^2 + 10x + 25) - 4y^2 = (x + 5)^2 - 4y^2,$$

which can now be factored as the difference of two squares.

Some students will feel that $x(x + 10) + (5 + 2y)(5 - 2y)$ is an appropriate factorization. Point out that $x(x + 10) + (5 + 2y)(5 - 2y)$ is an indicated sum and $(x + 5 + 2y)(x + 5 - 2y)$ is an indicated product. Stress that factoring a polynomial means expressing it as an indicated product.

Suggested Extensions

Have students identify which of these polynomials are prime and factor the ones that are not prime.

1. $x^2 - y^2 + 4y + 4$ **2.** $x^3 + 3x^2 - 2x - 6$

3. $9a^2 - 30a + 25 - b^2$ **4.** $2m^2 + 2mn + 3m + 3$

5. $xy + x + 2y + 4$ **6.** $b^2 - c^2 + 2b - 2c$

1. prime
2. $(x^2 - 2)(x + 3)$
3. $(3a - 5 + b)(3a - 5 - b)$
4. prime
5. prime
6. $(b + c + 2)(b - c)$

5-11 (pages 221-222)

Key Mathematical Idea

- factoring polynomials completely

Teaching Suggestions

This section ties together the various methods for factoring polynomials. Since these methods are applied in the last two sections of the chapter and throughout the course, it is important to spend enough time for each student to master the techniques of factoring. The guidelines on page 221 are an excellent starting point for students having difficulty.

You can point out that students can evaluate a polynomial in expanded and factored form to check their work. For example, to check the answer $30x^3 + 51x^2 + 9x = 3x(5x + 1)(2x + 3)$ on page 221, let $x = 2$:

$30 \cdot 2^3 + 51 \cdot 2^2 + 9 \cdot 2 = 240 + 204 + 18 = 462$ and $3 \cdot 2(5 \cdot 2 + 1)(2 \cdot 2 + 3) = 6 \cdot 11 \cdot 7 = 462$; $462 = 462$. ✓

5-12 (pages 223-227)

Key Mathematical Idea

- solving polynomial equations by using factoring and the zero-product property

Teaching Suggestions

You can use this opportunity to review the meaning of the term "degree of a polynomial." Remind students that a linear equation has degree 1, a quadratic equation has degree 2, and a cubic equation has degree 3. Relate the degree of a polynomial equation to the number of roots it has (the degree gives the maximum number of roots). Emphasize that repeated roots may occur. For example, $4x^2 - 20x + 25 = 0$ is equivalent to $(2x - 5)^2 = 0$; it has a double root, $\frac{5}{2}$.

It is very common for students to apply the zero-product property without expressing the equation in standard form. For example, they will write $x^2 + 2x = 3$, $x(x + 2) = 3$, and so $x = 0$ or $x = -2$. Caution students to check that one side of a polynomial equation is zero before they attempt to factor the polynomial. Discuss the warning at the bottom of page 224; it will help students avoid "losing roots."

Suggest that when students solve polynomial equations they write each factor in a separate column as shown in the examples. Also, encourage students to check their answers by substituting them in the original equations.

Suggested Extensions

Each of the following solutions is wrong. Have students identify the two consecutive steps that are not equivalent.

1. **a.** $x^2 + 70 = 10 - 16x$
b. $x^2 + 16x + 60 = 0$
c. $(x + 6)(x + 10) = 0$
d. $x = 6$ or $x = 10$

c and **d**; $x = -6$ or $x = -10$

2. **a.** $x(2x + 15) = 27$
b. $2x^2 + 15x = 27$
c. $2x^2 + 15x - 27 = 0$
d. $(2x + 3)(x - 9) = 0$
e. $x = -\frac{3}{2}$ or $x = 9$

c and **d**; $x = \frac{3}{2}$ or $x = -9$

3. **a.** $x^2 + 5x - 14 = 10$
b. $(x + 7)(x - 2) = 10$
c. $x + 7 = 0$ or $x - 2 = 0$
d. $x = -7$ or $x = 2$

b and **c**; $x = 3$ or $x = -8$

5-13 (pages 228-233)

Key Mathematical Idea

- solving word problems involving quadratic equations

Teaching Suggestions

It may be helpful to review the five-step method for solving problems. (See Section 1-6.) Remind students to define each variable carefully and to draw a sketch or prepare a chart when possible.

Point out that many quadratic equations have solutions that do not satisfy the requirements of the associated word problems. Example 1, page 228, illustrates this idea. Stress that it is important to check each root with the facts of the problem.

One effective way to handle word problems is to have students work in pairs. Students can often help each other with minor problems and you can concentrate on students with major difficulties.

Suggested Extension

Ask your students to solve the following problem: A bus that can carry 45 people is to be rented for an excursion at the rate of $40 per person if 20 or fewer people go. If more than 20 go, each passenger's fare is reduced 50¢ for each person over 20. How many passengers can go for a rental fee of $1200? Is $1200 the maximum rental fee?

40 passengers; No, when 45 people go, the fee is $1237.50.

6 Fractions

A thorough treatment of algebraic fractions and operations with fractions is presented in this chapter. Simplest form is emphasized throughout and considerable practice in factoring polynomials is provided. Emphasis is placed on writing mixed expressions as fractions in simplest form and on dividing polynomials using the long division form.

6-1 (pages 239–243)

Key Mathematical Idea

- writing algebraic fractions in simplest form

Teaching Suggestions

It will be helpful to begin this lesson with a review of the cancellation rule for fractions (page 187) and greatest common factors (see page 191). Tell students that to simplify a quotient of polynomials they must divide the numerator and the denominator by the greatest factor common to both the numerator and the denominator.

Emphasize the importance of recognizing factors that are opposites of each other. After discussing Example 3, ask students to name the opposite of each expression: $5 + 2t$, $2t - 5$, $5 - 2t$, $-5 - 2t$.

One common error is for students to cancel single terms of binomial factors. Use the following examples to caution students against this mistake:

$$\frac{(\cancel{3x+2}) + 1}{(\cancel{3x+2})(x+5)} \neq \frac{1}{x+5} \qquad \frac{\cancel{2x+1}}{x^2 + \cancel{2x+1}} \neq \frac{1}{x^2}$$

$$\frac{(\cancel{x+5})(x-2) + (\cancel{x-7})(x+1)}{(\cancel{x+5})(\cancel{x-7})} \neq (x-2) + (x+1)$$

When students cancel common factors have them use a line for each prime factor. Do not permit cancellations like

$$\frac{(x+2)(\cancel{2}x + \cancel{5})}{(\cancel{2}x + \cancel{5})(x+4)} = \frac{x+2}{x+4}.$$

6-2 (pages 244–247)

Key Mathematical Idea

- multiplying algebraic fractions

Teaching Suggestions

Some students will want to begin working on a problem like $\frac{2x+2}{x^2+3x+2} \cdot \frac{x^2-3x-10}{x^2-25}$ by multiplying the numerators and multiplying the denominators. Emphasize that the multiplication rule for fractions is the last property that should be used.

Note that our objective is to find the simplest form of the expression. Get the class to agree that the first step in simplifying the expression is to factor each polynomial:

$$\frac{2x+2}{x^2+3x+2} \cdot \frac{x^2-3x-10}{x^2-25}$$
$$= \frac{2(x+1)}{(x+1)(x+2)} \cdot \frac{(x+2)(x-5)}{(x+5)(x-5)} = \frac{2}{x+5}$$

Show students how an arithmetic check may be helpful. Let $x = 3$:

$$\frac{2(3)+2}{3^2+3(3)+2} \cdot \frac{3^2-3(3)-10}{3^2-25} \quad \Big| \quad \frac{2}{3+5}$$
$$\frac{8}{20} \cdot \frac{-10}{-16} \quad \Big| \quad \frac{2}{8}$$
$$\frac{2}{5} \cdot \frac{5}{8} \quad \Big|$$
$$\frac{1}{4} = \frac{1}{4}$$

Point out that if the equation is true for $x = 3$, it is probably, but not necessarily, true for all x in the domain of x. However, if the equation is false for $x = 3$, there is definitely a mistake in the work. You may wish to discuss the concept of a counterexample.

Suggested Extension

Have students check to see whether the following equation is true or false when $x = 3$. Then use algebra to confirm this equation or to find a correct one.

$$\frac{12x^2-3}{2x^2-4x} \cdot \frac{x^2+2x-8}{6x-3} = \frac{2x^2+9x+4}{2x}$$

$\frac{49}{6} = \frac{49}{6}$; $\frac{3(2x+1)(2x-1)}{2x(x-2)} \cdot \frac{(x+4)(x-2)}{3(2x-1)} =$

$\frac{(2x+1)(x+4)}{2x} = \frac{2x^2+9x+4}{2x}$

6-3 (pages 248–250)

Key Mathematical Idea

- dividing algebraic fractions

Teaching Suggestions

Division of real numbers was presented in Section 2-9. Point out that dividing algebraic fractions involves a similar procedure: to divide, multiply by the reciprocal.

You can emphasize the relationship between division and multiplication by reminding students that $a \div b = x$ is equivalent to $bx = a$. Also, have students use this equivalence as follows:

1. Ask students to simplify
$$\frac{6x-6}{x^2+3x+2} \div \frac{2x-2}{x^2-x-6}.$$
$$\frac{6(x-1)}{(x+2)(x+1)} \cdot \frac{(x+2)(x-3)}{2(x-1)} = \frac{3(x-3)}{x+1} = \frac{3x-9}{x+1}$$
2. Have them check their work by multiplying the quotient and the divisor.
$$\frac{3x-9}{x+1} \cdot \frac{2x-2}{x^2-x-6} = \frac{3(x-3)}{x+1} \cdot \frac{2(x-1)}{(x-3)(x+2)}$$
$$= \frac{6(x-1)}{(x+1)(x+2)} = \frac{6x-6}{x^2+3x+2} \checkmark$$

6-4 (pages 251–254)

Key Mathematical Ideas

- finding least common denominators of fractions
- writing fractions with their least common denominator

Teaching Suggestions

Students frequently confuse the GCF and LCM of a set of numbers. Show how the prime factorization can be used to find the GCF and the LCM and emphasize the difference between them. For example, for $60 = 2^2 \cdot 3 \cdot 5$ and $75 = 3 \cdot 5^2$:

$\text{GCF} = 3 \cdot 5 = 15$	$\text{LCM} = 2^2 \cdot 3 \cdot 5^2 = 300$
$60 = 15 \cdot 4$	$300 = 60 \cdot 5$
$75 = 15 \cdot 5$	$300 = 75 \cdot 4$

Also remind students of the two special cases that were referred to in Section 5-1 of this commentary.

$15 = 3 \cdot 5$ $\qquad$ $14 = 2 \cdot 7$
$26 = 2 \cdot 13$ $\qquad$ $70 = 2 \cdot 5 \cdot 7$
$GCF = 1$ $\qquad$ $GCF = 2 \cdot 7$
$LCM = 2 \cdot 3 \cdot 5 \cdot 13$ $\qquad$ $LCM = 2 \cdot 5 \cdot 7$

Generalize these results with the following statements and then point out that both generalizations hold for polynomials.

1. If the GCF of two numbers is 1, the LCM is their product.
2. If the GCF of two numbers is the smaller number, the LCM is the larger number.

If some students have difficulty doing Exercises 1–24, suggest that they leave space in which a multiplier can be written. For example, to do Exercise 14, they can write

$$\frac{4}{a-1} = \frac{4}{a-1} \cdot \frac{\quad}{\quad} = \frac{\quad}{2(a-1)}$$

Then they can go back and fill in the missing multipliers and numerator. This procedure may also be helpful when students are expressing a group of fractions with their LCD.

Suggested Extension

Have students find the LCD of any two fractions and the GCF of their denominators. Ask students to find the LCD by using the GCF. (*Hint:* Numerical examples are simplest to use.)
Multiply the two denominators together and divide the product by the GCF to obtain the LCD.

6–5 (pages 255–259)

Key Mathematical Idea

- adding and subtracting algebraic fractions with like denominators and with unlike denominators

Teaching Suggestions

Adding and subtracting algebraic fractions are among the most difficult skills for beginning algebra students. It might be helpful for students to organize their work in the following way on the more difficult problems.

1. Factor each denominator but leave space for the multiplication.

$$\frac{x^2}{x^2-9} + \frac{1}{x+3} + \frac{x}{2x+6} =$$
$$\frac{x^2 \quad \cdot}{(x+3)(x-3)\cdot} + \frac{1 \quad \cdot}{(x+3)\cdot} + \frac{x \quad \cdot}{2(x+3)\cdot}$$

2. Write the LCD separately in factored form.
$LCD = 2(x+3)(x-3)$

3. Now complete the expression above by writing the necessary factor(s) in the denominators first, checking that each denominator is the LCD.

$$\frac{x^2 \quad \cdot 2}{(x+3)(x-3)\cdot 2} + \frac{1 \quad \cdot 2(x-3)}{(x+3)\cdot 2(x-3)} + \frac{x \quad \cdot (x-3)}{2(x+3)\cdot(x-3)}$$

4. Complete the problem with the students.

It is also necessary once again to stress the fact that a fraction bar is a grouping symbol, particularly in subtraction.

$$\frac{5x-1}{6} - \frac{3x-7}{10} = \frac{25x-5}{6\cdot 5} - \frac{9x-21}{10\cdot 3} =$$
$$\frac{(25x-5)-(9x-21)}{30} = \frac{25x-5-9x+21}{30} =$$
$$\frac{16x+16}{30} = \frac{2(8x+8)}{2\cdot 15} = \frac{8x-8}{15}$$

The use of the parentheses shown in red may help avoid one of the most common errors in this type of problem, forgetting to distribute the minus sign.

Suggested Extension

Have students find the following sum. Tell them *not* to write the LCD as a single number until the last step.

$$\frac{25}{84} + \frac{49}{90} + \frac{2}{105}$$
$$\frac{25\cdot 3\cdot 5}{(2^2\cdot 3\cdot 7)\cdot 3\cdot 5} + \frac{49\cdot 2\cdot 7}{(2\cdot 3^2\cdot 5)\cdot 2\cdot 7} + \frac{2\cdot 2^2\cdot 3}{(2\cdot 5\cdot 7)\cdot 2^2\cdot 3} =$$
$$\frac{375+686+24}{2^2\cdot 3^2\cdot 5\cdot 7} = \frac{1085}{2^2\cdot 3^2\cdot 5\cdot 7} = \frac{5\cdot 7\cdot 31}{2^2\cdot 3^2\cdot 5\cdot 7} = \frac{31}{36}$$

6–6 (pages 260–262)

Key Mathematical Idea

- writing a mixed expression as a single fraction in simplest form

Teaching Suggestions

Although this section is an extension of the previous one, simplifying mixed expressions can be quite troublesome for many students.

Point out that a mixed number has the addition implied: $4\frac{2}{5}$ means $4 + \frac{2}{5}$. A mixed expression, on the other hand, requires a plus sign.

Suggested Extensions

Have students identify each statement as true or false. If a statement is false, have them change the right side to make it true.

1. $2 + \frac{x}{5} = \frac{2 + x}{5}$ false; $2 + \frac{x}{5} = \frac{10 + x}{5}$
2. $x + 2 + \frac{1}{3} = \frac{3(x + 2) + 1}{3}$ true
3. $\frac{x}{3} + 4 + \frac{3}{x} = \frac{x^2 + 12x + 9}{3x}$ true
4. $5 - \frac{x + 2}{2} = \frac{12 - x}{2}$ false; $5 - \frac{x + 2}{2} = \frac{8 - x}{2}$
5. $\frac{x + 2}{2} - 5 = \frac{x - 8}{2}$ true

6–7 (pages 263–268)

Key Mathematical Idea

- dividing a polynomial by another polynomial

Teaching Suggestions

Emphasize the parallels between long division with numbers and with polynomials. Point out that the two examples on page 263 are identical if $x = 10$ except for one minor difference. In Step 1 with numbers the first digit, 2, of the quotient is written over the 8 and in Step 1 with polynomials the first term of the quotient, $2x$, is written over the first term, $6x^2$.

Emphasize the following points:

1. The identity

   dividend = quotient × divisor + remainder

   should be used to check divisions.
2. The terms in the divisor and the dividend should be written in order of decreasing degree in the variable.
3. At each step in a polynomial division, the term of the quotient is determined by dividing the first term of the dividend or partial remainder by the first term of the divisor.

   In Example 1, $3x = \frac{12x^2}{4x}$ and $7 = \frac{28x}{4x}$.

   In Example 2, $3a^2 = \frac{3a^3}{a}$, $6a = \frac{6a^2}{a}$, $12 = \frac{12a}{a}$.
4. If the remainder is zero, then both the divisor and the quotient are factors of the dividend. If the remainder is not zero, the answer should be given as a mixed expression.

Suggested Extensions

1. Ask students to find each quotient.

   a. $\frac{x^3 - y^3}{x - y}$ $x^2 + xy + y^2$

   b. $\frac{x^4 + y^4}{x + y}$ $x^3 - x^2y + xy^2 - y^3 + \frac{2y^4}{x + y}$

   c. $\frac{x^5 - y^5}{x - y}$ $x^4 + x^3y + x^2y^2 + xy^3 + y^4$

   d. $\frac{2x^4 - x^3y + xy^3 - 2y^4}{x^2 - y^2}$ $2x^2 - xy + 2y^2$
2. Assign the Extra on pages 267–268, which introduces complex fractions. This topic requires students to use many of the skills developed in the chapter.

7 Applying Fractions

This chapter presents a wide variety of equations and word problems related to algebraic fractions. Ratios are introduced and proportions are solved as a special case of fractional equations. Extensive treatment is given to solutions of fractional equations. The sections on percent, mixture, and work problems both extend and reinforce problem solving skills. The concluding sections provide further work with both exponents and fractions.

7-1 (pages 277–281)

Key Mathematical Ideas

- meaning of ratio
- forms of expressing a ratio
- solving problems involving ratios

Teaching Suggestions

Make the point that because a ratio can be expressed as a fraction, it has the properties of a fraction. For example, in Oral Exercises 9–11, page 278, we simplify the ratios by applying the rules of exponents as we have done before.

Draw students' attention to the decimal form of a ratio. Many students do not recognize that 1.75 can represent a ratio.

Some students may prefer the following solution to the Example on page 278:

Let a = the number of acres of alfalfa and let $160 - a$ = the number of acres of wheat.

Then $\frac{a}{160 - a} = \frac{3}{5}$. (Solving proportions like this one is covered in Section 7-2.)

Suggested Extension

Ask one of your students to prepare a report about sports statistics, many of which are based on ratios. The sports pages of a newspaper can provide the basis for a class discussion about ratios.

7-2 (pages 282–287)

Key Mathematical Ideas

- solving proportions
- solving problems involving proportions

Teaching Suggestions

Some students confuse the statements $a:b = c:d$ and $a \cdot d = b \cdot c$, thinking of the second as a proportion also.

Many students also tend to reverse the order of the second ratio of a proportion in a word problem. In Example 5, page 283, a student might write the incorrect proportion $\frac{352}{11} = \frac{4}{x}$. Appeal to the common-sense aspect of writing a proportion. Point out that we have a choice in the order of the first ratio, but that the second must "correspond" in the same order. Writing in words may help:

$$\frac{\text{no. of miles}}{\text{no. of gallons}} = \frac{\text{no. of miles}}{\text{no. of gallons}}$$

or

$$\frac{\text{no. of gallons}}{\text{no. of miles}} = \frac{\text{no. of gallons}}{\text{no. of miles}}$$

Suggested Extension

Illustrate the use of an extended proportion by giving the class the following example:

A photo 4 inches wide and 7 inches long is enlarged twice. The length of the first enlargement is 14 inches and the width of the second enlargement is 10 inches. Find the width, x, of the first and the length, y, of the second. $x = 8$; $y = 17.5$

7-3 (pages 288–290)

Key Mathematical Ideas

- solving equations with fractional coefficients
- solving problems involving fractional coefficients

Teaching Suggestions

Let students compare two solutions to the same equation:

$$\frac{1}{2}x + \frac{1}{3}(x - 2) = 11$$
$$\frac{1}{2}x + \frac{1}{3}x - \frac{2}{3} = 11$$
$$\frac{1}{2}x + \frac{1}{3}x = 11 + \frac{2}{3}$$
$$\frac{3}{6}x + \frac{2}{6}x = \frac{33}{3} + \frac{2}{3}$$
$$\frac{5}{6}x = \frac{35}{3}$$
$$x = \frac{35}{3} \cdot \frac{6}{5} = 14$$

$$\frac{1}{2}x + \frac{1}{3}(x - 2) = 11$$
$$6\left[\frac{1}{2}x + \frac{1}{3}(x - 2)\right] = 6 \cdot 11$$
$$3x + 2(x - 2) = 66$$
$$3x + 2x - 4 = 66$$
$$5x - 4 = 66$$
$$5x = 70$$
$$x = 14$$

Point out the need to find the LCD, 6, in both solutions. Stress the desirability of eliminating the fractions as soon as possible.

Challenge your class to find the error in the following solution and then to solve the equation correctly.

$$\frac{2}{3}(2x - 1) + \frac{1}{4}\left(x + \frac{1}{2}\right) = \frac{1}{8}(5x + 34)$$
$$24\left[\frac{2}{3}(2x - 1) + \frac{1}{4}\left(x + \frac{1}{2}\right)\right] = 24\left[\frac{1}{8}\left(5x + 34\right)\right]$$
$$16(2x - 1) + 6(x + 12) = 3(5x + 34)$$
$$32x - 16 + 6x + 72 = 15x + 102$$
$$38x + 56 = 15x + 102$$
$$23x = 46$$
$$x = 2$$

The third step should be $16(2x - 1) + 6\left(x + \frac{1}{2}\right) = 3(5x + 34)$. The solution is 5.

Suggested Extension

Have students solve each equation.

1. $\frac{5x(x - 1)}{4} - \frac{x + 2}{2} = 5$ $x = 3$ or $-\frac{8}{5}$
2. $\frac{y^2}{3} + \frac{y}{12} = \frac{1}{8}$ $y = -\frac{3}{4}$ or $\frac{1}{2}$
3. $\frac{5}{4}z^2 + \frac{1}{5} = z$ $z = \frac{2}{5}$
4. $\frac{(t + 1)(t - 2)}{6} - \frac{5(t + 3)}{8} = \frac{37}{4}$ $t = 11$ or $-\frac{25}{4}$

7-4 (pages 291–294)

Key Mathematical Ideas

- solving fractional equations
- solving problems involving fractional equations

Teaching Suggestions

Some students attempt to solve fractional equations by rewriting each fraction with the LCD as denominator. Point out that it is simpler to solve a fractional equation by multiplying each side by the LCD. Illustrate the difference between simplifying an expression with algebraic fractions and solving a fractional equation having the same LCD.

Emphasize that often an apparent root of a fractional equation does not satisfy the original equation. Suggest that students begin solving fractional equations by listing the values of the variable for which any fractions are meaningless, that is, values that make a denominator equal to zero. Substituting apparent solutions in the original equation is also helpful in eliminating extraneous roots.

Suggested Extension

Ask students to solve each equation.

1. $1 + \frac{9}{x^4} = \frac{10}{x^2}$ $\{1, -1, 3, -3\}$
2. $12 - \frac{13}{t} + \frac{3}{t^2} = 0$ $\left\{\frac{1}{3}, \frac{3}{4}\right\}$

3. $\dfrac{3}{y+1}+\dfrac{y}{y-1}+\dfrac{4}{y-4}=1$ $\left\{\frac{1}{4}, 2\right\}$

4. $\dfrac{a+3}{a^2-1}+\dfrac{a-3}{a^2-a}=\dfrac{2a}{a^2+a}$ no solution

7-5 (pages 295–299)

Key Mathematical Ideas

- working with percents
- solving equations with decimal coefficients
- solving problems involving percents

Teaching Suggestions

Students should know the fraction, decimal, and percent equivalents for all fractions with denominators 2, 3, 4, 5, 8, and 10. It may be helpful to have each student make a table of these equivalents and memorize the entries.

Students frequently have difficulty with percents less than 1% or greater than 100%. Stress that 1% = 0.01 and that 100% = 1.0. You can illustrate these concepts with a diagram representing 100% divided into 100 squares as shown below. Note that $\frac{3}{8}$% = 0.00375 and that 0.5% = 0.005.

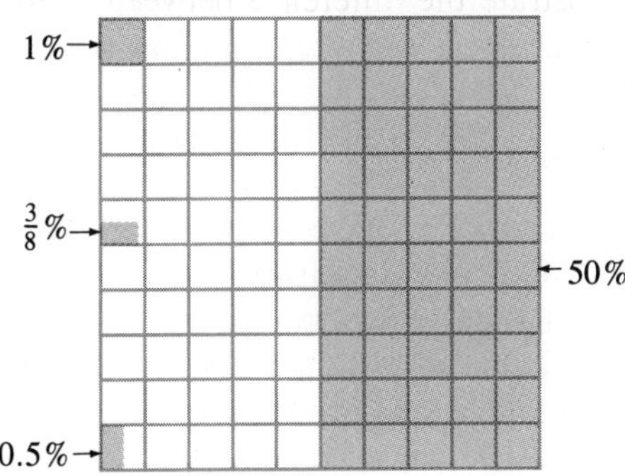

Examples 2, 3, and 4 illustrate the three basic types of percent problems. Written Exercises 13–20 and 25–36, page 297, provide practice with these three types of problems. Pay particular attention to Exercises 17 and 34, which cover the special cases discussed above.

For additional practice in converting from percents to decimals you can have students express each of the following as a decimal: 300%, 30%, 3%, 0.3%, and 0.03%. Then have them express each of the following decimals as a percent: 0.0075, 0.075, 0.75, 7.5, and 75.

Suggested Extension

Assign the Calculator Key-In on page 311 for additional practice with percents.

7-6 (pages 300–305)

Key Mathematical Ideas

- solving problems involving percent of increase or percent of decrease
- solving investment problems

Teaching Suggestions

Percent problems provide good practice with both fractional equations and equations with decimal coefficients. Emphasize the importance of answering the question in a word problem completely, including units in the answer. Point out that some problems, like Problems 8 and 11 on page 304, ask for *two* numbers. Make sure students check each solution with the words of the problem.

Suggested Extension

Have students tell why the answer to the following problem is incorrect:

> The annual membership fee in a club was increased to $40 this year, which was a 20% increase over last year. What was last year's fee?
>
> Let x = last year's fee.
>
> $$\frac{20}{100}=\frac{40-x}{40}$$
> $$800 = 4000 - 100x$$
> $$100x = 3200$$
> $$x = 32$$
>
> $$\frac{20}{100}=\frac{40-32}{40},$$
>
> so last year's fee was $32.

The original equation should be $\frac{20}{100}=\frac{40-x}{x}$ or $\frac{120}{100}=\frac{40}{x}$; so $x = 33\frac{1}{3}$ or about 33.33.

7-7 (pages 306–311)

Key Mathematical Idea

- solving mixture problems

Teaching Suggestions

Some students may find a sketch helpful in visualizing a problem. The sketch below might be used to explain Example 1, page 306. Note that although the nuts and raisins are to be mixed, they can be considered separately in the sketch.

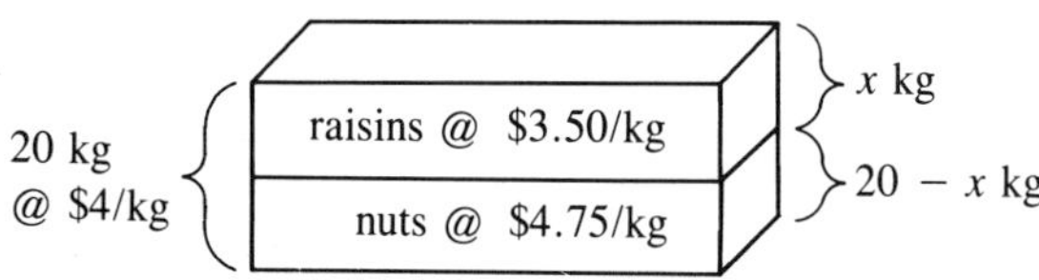

When you discuss Example 1, point out that the problem can be solved by letting x represent the number of kilograms of nuts. Ask students to write and solve an equation using this idea.

Emphasize the value of preparing a chart for a word problem and remind students to read problems carefully.

Reading Algebra

To use charts effectively in the solution of problems, students must understand their organization. Since many students find mixture problems difficult, you may want to spend some time in discussing the charts in Examples 1 and 2. Point out that each of the words in the equation at the top of the chart identifies the quantities in the column below. Thus, in Example 1, under "Cost" we have successively the total cost (in dollars) of the raisins, the total cost of the nuts, and the total cost of the mixture. These quantities can then be used to set up the equation in Step 3.

Suggested Extension

Have students show that each of the following problems has no solution and ask them to explain why.

1. Dan has 100 coins worth $12.50. He has twice as many nickels as quarters, 5 more quarters than dimes, and the rest are pennies. How many pennies does he have?
   Let q = number of quarters. Since
   $25q + 10(q - 5) + 5(2q) +$
   $[100 - (q + q - 5 + 2q)] = 1250$
   gives a nonintegral value for q, there is no solution.
2. Lori Eigenbrode invested a sum of money partly at 8% and partly at 5.5%. If her annual income from these investments was $270, how much did she invest at each rate?
   There is not enough information to write an equation, so there are an infinite number of solutions and thus no unique solution.
3. How many grams of water must be evaporated from 100 g of a 30% acid solution to produce a 25% acid solution?
   Students do *not* need to write an equation. Point out that evaporating water *increases* the acid concentration; the facts of the problem are inconsistent.

7-8 (pages 312–316)

Key Mathematical Idea

- solving problems involving rate of work

Teaching Suggestions

Point out to the class that solutions of work problems require a special strategy. Remind students that the equation written to solve a word problem is the translation of an English sentence that incorporates the facts of the problem. In Example 1, page 312, the required verbal sentence is not as obvious as it may be in some other problems. Emphasize that the verbal equation in Step 3 is a model that can normally be used to solve a work problem.

You may want to present another verbal sentence that can be used to solve Example 1:

fractional part done by *A* in one unit of time	+	fractional part done by *B* in one unit of time	=	fractional part done by *A* and *B* together in one unit of time

An equivalent equation for Example 1 would then be $\frac{1}{4} + \frac{1}{3} = \frac{1}{x}$.

Some students have difficulty identifying the work rate. Oral Exercises 1–4 provide practice with this skill. Oral Exercises 5–7 provide practice in completing charts.

Suggested Extension

Your students may enjoy the challenge of solving the following problem:

At 12:00 P.M. Professor Lopez began to grade a set of test papers. At 1:15 her assistant joined her and together they finished the job at 5:00 P.M. If the assistant would need 2 hours more than the professor to grade the papers working alone, how long would Professor Lopez need to grade all the papers by herself? 8 hours

7-9 (pages 317–322)

Key Mathematical Ideas

- writing numbers in scientific notation
- performing computation with numbers in scientific notation

Teaching Suggestions

You can introduce nonnegative powers of 10 by having students consider the following pattern:

$$1000 = 10^3$$
$$100 = 10^2$$
$$10 = 10^1$$
$$1 = 10^? \quad 0$$
$$\frac{1}{10} = 0.1 = 10^? \quad -1$$
$$\frac{1}{100} = 0.01 = 10^? \quad -2$$

The left sides are obtained by successively dividing by 10. Ask the class what the missing exponents would have to be for the pattern to continue. Zero and negative exponents will be developed further in the next section.

To reinforce the idea of powers of ten, ask students to match equal numbers below.

1. 1,230,000	**a.** 123×10^2
2. 123,000	**b.** 1.23×10^{-3}
3. 12,300	**c.** 1230×10^{-4}
4. 1230	**d.** 1.23×10^6
5. 1.23	**e.** 0.0123×10^7
6. 0.123	**f.** 12.3×10^{-5}
7. 0.00123	**g.** 0.123×10^4
8. 0.000123	**h.** 0.00123×10^3

1. d 2. e 3. a 4. g 5. h 6. c 7. b 8. f

As you define scientific notation and discuss Examples 1 and 2 on page 318, emphasize that a number written in scientific notation with 10 raised to the nth power is equivalent to the number obtained by moving the decimal point n places to the right if n is positive and n places to the left if n is negative.

$2.6 \times 1000 = 2600$ $\quad$ $2.6 \times 0.001 = 0.0026$
$2.6 \times 10^3 = 2600$ $\quad$ $2.6 \times 10^{-3} = 0.0026$

Suggested Extension

If your students use calculators or computers, it is important that they understand how to use scientific notation. The Computer Key-In and the Calculator Key-In on page 322 can be assigned to help students interpret the formats of scientific notation used by computers and by calculators.

7-10 (pages 323–327)

Key Mathematical Ideas

- using negative and zero exponents
- solving problems involving zero and negative exponents

Teaching Suggestions

Explain to the class that many definitions are made in mathematics on the basis of consistency with previously established rules. The rule

$\frac{a^m}{a^n} = a^{m-n}$ was established for positive integral exponents only. The symbol a^{-4} cannot have meaning in terms of the number of factors of a, so we define it to be consistent with the rule above, as developed on page 323.

Stress the fact that all the rules summarized on page 324 now apply to all integral exponents. You may wish to mention the fact that exponents can be fractions and that the same rules will still apply. Refer students to the C-level exercises on page 326.

Emphasize the fact that a positive number raised to *any* power is always positive. Many students confuse the two problems $2^{-3} = \frac{1}{8}$ and $(-2)^3 = -8$.

Suggested Extension

Have students write each of the following without exponents.

1. 5^3 **2.** 5^{-3} **3.** $(-5)^3$ **4.** $(-5)^{-3}$

5. $\left(\frac{1}{5}\right)^3$ **6.** $\left(\frac{1}{5}\right)^{-3}$ **7.** $\left(-\frac{1}{5}\right)^3$ **8.** $\left(-\frac{1}{5}\right)^{-3}$

1. 125 2. $\frac{1}{5^3} = \frac{1}{125}$ 3. $(-5)(-5)(-5) = -125$

4. $\frac{1}{(-5)^3} = -\frac{1}{125}$

5. $\left(\frac{1}{5}\right)\left(\frac{1}{5}\right)\left(\frac{1}{5}\right) = \frac{1}{125}$ 6. $(5^{-1})^{-3} = 5^3 = 125$

7. $\left(-\frac{1}{5}\right)\left(-\frac{1}{5}\right)\left(-\frac{1}{5}\right) = -\frac{1}{125}$

8. $[(-5)^{-1}]^{-3} = (-5)^3 = -125$

8 Linear Equations and Systems

This chapter introduces the basic tools for working with more than one variable in linear equations. By extending the number line to the two-dimensional coordinate plane, problems involving two variables can be represented graphically. Ordered pairs are graphed as points and linear equations in two variables are graphed as lines. Three methods of solving a system of linear equations are presented: the graphic method, the substitution method, and the addition-or-subtraction method. Problem solving skills are extended to include many types of problems associated with systems of linear equations. Applications include wind and water current problems and age, digit, and fraction problems.

8-1 (pages 335–338)

Key Mathematical Ideas

- selecting ordered pairs that are solutions of equations in two variables
- solving equations in two variables over specified domains of the variables

Teaching Suggestions

The material in this section may be completely new to some students, so the idea of an equation in two variables should be explained carefully. Emphasize that if an equation contains two variables, each of its solutions must be an ordered pair of numbers. If the idea of an *ordered* pair is not familiar to students, be sure to point out the importance of giving the numbers in a solution pair in the appropriate order.

Emphasize that a linear equation in two variables usually has many solutions, as illustrated on page 335. Illustrate how substitution is used to determine whether or not a given ordered pair is a solution of a given equation.

When you discuss Examples 2 and 3 on page 336, stress the value of solving for one variable in terms of the other. (Recall that transforming formulas was discussed in Section 4-7.) Point out that it is sometimes easier to solve for a certain variable than to solve for the other. Ask students which variable would be easiest to solve for in Written Exercises 21, 22, and 28.

Suggested Extension

Have students solve for y in terms of x and identify the smallest whole-number value for x such that the value of y is negative.

1. $3x + y = 4$ **2.** $x + 3y = 3$
3. $3x + 2y = 20$ **4.** $7x + 15y = 90$

1. $y = 4 - 3x$; $x = 2$ 2. $y = \frac{3 - x}{3}$; $x = 4$
3. $y = \frac{20 - 3x}{2}$; $x = 7$ 4. $y = \frac{90 - 7x}{15}$; $x = 13$

8-2 (pages 339–345)

Key Mathematical Ideas

- graphing ordered pairs in the coordinate plane
- graphing linear equations in the coordinate plane

Teaching Suggestions

Many students are confused initially when plotting points or reading the coordinates of a given point, so considerable practice is necessary. Be sure to cover all combinations of signs of coordinates and emphasize the two special cases in which the x-coordinate is 0 (points on the y-axis) and the y-coordinate is 0 (points on the x-axis).

Point out that when students graph a line that is neither horizontal nor vertical, they may select any convenient values for x and y and use these values to find two ordered-pair solutions. Frequently the intercepts are convenient values to compute but when the intercepts are not integers, other values may be more convenient. For example, to graph $2x + 3y = 7$ it is helpful to note that $2(2) + 3(1) = 7$ and $2(5) + 3(-1) = 7$ and so the line contains (2, 1) and (5, −1). You may want to define the terms *x-intercept* (the x-coordinate of the point where a line intersects the x-axis) and *y-intercept* (the y-coordinate of the point where a line intersects the y-axis). Point out that the line with equation $ax + by = c$, $a \neq 0$ and $b \neq 0$, has x-intercept $\frac{c}{a}$ and y-intercept $\frac{c}{b}$.

Suggested Extensions

1. Have students graph the equation $y = x$. On the same set of axes have them plot the following points in pairs.

a. (5, 2), (2, 5) **b.** (3, −2), (−2, 3)
c. (−5, 1), (1, −5) **d.** (4, 0), (0, 4)
e. (−6, −2), (−2, −6) **f.** (0, −3), (−3, 0)

2. Ask students to state an observation based on their graph.
The points (x, y) and (y, x) are symmetric with respect to the line $y = x$.

3. Challenge students to complete this statement: The points (x, y) and (_?_, _?_) are symmetric with respect to the line $y = -x$. $(-y, -x)$

8-3 (pages 346–349)

Key Mathematical Idea

- solving a system of linear equations by graphing

Teaching Suggestions

Continue to stress the point that if an ordered pair is on the graph of an equation it *must* be a solution of the equation, but that if a point is not on the graph it *cannot* be a solution.

Emphasize the three diagrams on page 346.

Point out that two lines in a plane may intersect, be parallel, or coincide. Since each solution of a system of linear equations in two variables is a point on both graphs, a system can have either a unique solution, no solution, or an infinite number of solutions. Ask the class if it would be possible for two linear equations to have exactly two ordered pairs as solutions. Ask why or why not.

Reading Algebra

When reading graphs students often fail to perceive important details. A fun activity is to pair students so that one has a graph such as the first diagram on page 346 and the other has a sheet of graph paper with only the x- and y-axes drawn. The first student describes the graph orally, and the second student tries to draw it from the description. After the graph has been completed and checked, the students exchange roles, using another graph. Hints for the first graph on page 346 might be: "There are two lines that intersect at the point $(3, -1)$." "One of the lines passes through the point $(0, 5)$." "The other line passes through $(0, -4)$." "The equations of the lines are $2x + y = 5$ and $x - y = 4$."

Suggested Extension

Have students identify the two equations for which each ordered pair is a solution.

1. $(1, 3)$	**a.** $x - 2y = 2$	1. b, d
2. $(-2, 5)$	**b.** $2x + 3y = 11$	2. b, c
3. $(4, 1)$	**c.** $3x + 2y = 4$	3. a, b
4. $(-4, -3)$	**d.** $6x - 5y = -9$	4. a, d

8-4 (pages 350–353)

Key Mathematical Idea

- solving a system of linear equations by substitution

Teaching Suggestions

Introduce the substitution method as a technique that gives more accurate solutions than the graphic method. For example, the system $\begin{aligned} x + \quad y &= -2 \\ 6x + 10y &= -7 \end{aligned}$ is easily solved by substitution but difficult to solve by graphing. Point out that the substitution method is usually used only when at least one of the four coefficients of the variables is 1 or -1.

A common error is shown in the following example. Caution students against solving for $-y$ or for $-x$.

$$2x - y = 3 \rightarrow -y = 3 - 2x$$
$$3x + 2y = 8$$
$$3x + 2(3 - 2x) = 8$$

Emphasize the importance of solving for just x or just y before substituting.

Suggested Extension

For each of the following systems tell your students to (a) solve by the substitution method, (b) tell whether the graphs of the equations intersect, are parallel, or coincide, and (c) check their answer to part (b) by graphing the equations.

1. $2x - y = 6$
$y = 2x + 6$

2. $x - 3y = -6$
$3x - y = -6$

3. $x + 5y = 0$
$y = -\frac{1}{5}x + 5$

4. $4x + 8y = -16$
$x + 2y = -4$

1. a. $-6 = 6$ b. parallel
2. a. $\left(-\frac{3}{2}, \frac{3}{2}\right)$ b. intersect
3. a. $25 = 0$ b. parallel
4. a. $-16 = -16$ b. coincide

8-5 (pages 354–357)

Key Mathematical Idea

- using systems of linear equations in two variables to solve word problems

Teaching Suggestions

As Example 1 shows, many problems can be solved by using just one equation and one variable or by using a system of equations in two variables. Stress that students should use systems of equations in this section to gain practice in writing and solving systems.

For most students, the chief difficulty in solving the word problems in this section is in identifying two independent relationships on which to base two equations in two variables. The Oral Exercises provide excellent practice in setting up systems of equations.

Notice that the C-level exercises require students to solve systems of three equations in three variables.

Suggested Extension

A variety of word problems are included in the four remaining sections of this chapter. You may wish to help students prepare for this work by assigning the feature on page 370, which discusses problem-solving strategies, with emphasis on the development of reading skills, and gives students additional practice in solving various types of problems.

8-6 (pages 358–361)

Key Mathematical Idea

- solving a system of linear equations by addition-or-subtraction

Teaching Suggestions

The addition-or-subtraction method is based on the addition property of equality. Show the class that there are two versions of the addition property of equality:

If $a = b$, then $a + c = b + c$.
If $a = b$ and $c = d$, then $a + c = b + d$.

You may illustrate the second version with a numerical example:

If $2 + 3 = 5$ and $9 - 2 = 7$,
then $(2 + 3) + (9 - 2) = 5 + 7$.

Instruct students to write equations in standard form before deciding to add or subtract. (See Written Exercises 15–26.) Remind students to write similar terms in the same column to avoid addition or subtraction errors. After the value of one variable is known, that value should be substituted in the simpler equation (if there is one) to find the value of the second variable. For example, to solve the system in Oral Exercise 2, note that $3x = 18$, so $x = 6$; substitute 6 for x in the first equation to find that $y = 1$. Finally recommend that students check each solution by substituting the values in the original equations.

You may want to point out that all the systems in Written Exercises 1–12 have been designed so that the coefficients of one variable are the same or are opposites. In the next section students will learn to solve systems that cannot be solved simply by adding or subtracting.

Suggested Extension

Have students use addition or subtraction to solve each system. (Mention that the solution will be an *ordered triple* (x, y, z).)

1. $x + y - z = 0$
$x - y - z = 10$
$3x - y + z = 8$
(2, −5, −3)

2. $3x - 2y + z = 5$
$2y - z = 7$
$3x - 2y - 5z = 47$
(4, 0, −7)

8-7 (pages 362–369)

Key Mathematical Idea

- using multiplication with the addition-or-subtraction method to solve a system of linear equations

Teaching Suggestions

Some students will attempt to solve a system in this section by adding or subtracting immediately. Point out that this does not help in finding the solution. Stress that we need to eliminate one variable by finding an equivalent system in which the coefficients of one variable are equal or opposites.

It may be helpful to point out that the required coefficients of the variable that is to be eliminated are equal to the LCM of its original coefficients. For example, to eliminate y in the system below, note that $12 \cdot 5 = 60$ and $15 \cdot 4 = 60$.

$$\begin{aligned} 25x + 12y = -2 &\rightarrow \underline{\ ?\ }x + 60y = \underline{\ ?\ } \\ 16x + 15y = 28 &\rightarrow \underline{\ ?\ }x + 60y = \underline{\ ?\ } \\ &\quad 125x + 60y = -10 \\ &\quad 64x + 60y = 112 \end{aligned}$$

The solution is (−2, 4).

Be sure to assign some of the Mixed Practice exercises on pages 365–366 to be sure that students are comfortable with the graphic method, the substitution method, and the addition-or-subtraction method. You may want to ask students to solve the system $\begin{aligned} 5x + 2y &= -4 \\ x - 2y &= -8 \end{aligned}$ by all three methods.

Reading Algebra

This section is a good one for students to study independently before it is discussed in class. You might provide the following key questions to guide students as they read:

What is the addition-or-subtraction method?
Where is it explained in your book?
Why can't you use this method immediately with the given equations?
What must you do before you can use the addition-or-subtraction method?
Can you explain the solution of Example 1 without looking at the directions?
Why are there two multiplication steps in the solution of Example 2?

Suggested Extensions

If students are interested in solving systems of linear equations by using a computer or a calculator, refer them to the Computer Key-In on page 368 or to the Calculator Key-In on page 369.

8-8 (pages 371–374)

Key Mathematical Idea

- solving motion problems involving wind and water currents

Teaching Suggestions

Previous uniform motion problems were solved with one variable only. Point out that the same relationship involving distance, rate, and time still holds, but with the introduction of wind or current, we are required to express the rate in terms of two variables.

Some students fail to notice common factors that occur in equations. Emphasize Step 3 in the example on page 372. Point out that it is considerably easier to solve $\begin{aligned} r + w &= 1000 \\ r - w &= 800 \end{aligned}$ than to solve $\begin{aligned} 6r + 6w &= 6000 \\ 75r - 75w &= 60{,}000 \end{aligned}$.

Suggested Extensions

Give your class the following problem: An airplane takes off to fly north at 120 km/h. The pilot ignores the fact that the wind is blowing from the west at 50 km/h.

1. Use a coordinate plane to represent the motion during the first 6 minutes as follows:
   a. Draw an arrow from the origin to the point (0, 12) to represent the motion due to the engine.
   b. Draw an arrow from (0, 12) to (5, 12) to represent the motion due to the wind.
   c. Draw an arrow from the origin to (5, 12) to represent the actual motion of the plane.
2. Use the edge of a second piece of graph paper as a ruler to measure the length of the arrow drawn in part (c), above. How far will the plane actually travel in 6 minutes? in one hour? 13 km; 130 km
3. How far will the plane be from the expected location at the end of six minutes? at the end of one hour? 5 km east; 50 km east

8-9 (pages 375–380)

Key Mathematical Idea

- solving digit, age, and fraction problems by using systems of equations

Teaching Suggestions

Emphasize the value of making a chart when solving a digit problem or an age problem. Remind students to check their answers to digit, age, and fraction problems by checking each solution with the words of the problem.

When you discuss digit problems, you might caution students not to confuse the sum of the digits of a number with the number itself.

When you discuss fraction problems, you may need to review the procedure for solving proportions.

9 Introduction to Functions

This chapter continues the development of linear equations introduced in Chapter 8. The characteristics and equation forms of lines are presented. Next, functions are introduced and specified by equations, tables, and graphs. Particular attention is given to linear and quadratic functions and their graphs. The chapter concludes with an important application of functions: several types of variation with practical examples of each type.

9-1 (pages 391–395)

Key Mathematical Ideas

- defining slope
- finding the slope of a line

Teaching Suggestions

A simple classroom model can be used to illustrate the concept of slope. Place a stack of books on a desk and prop a ruler up on the books as shown below.

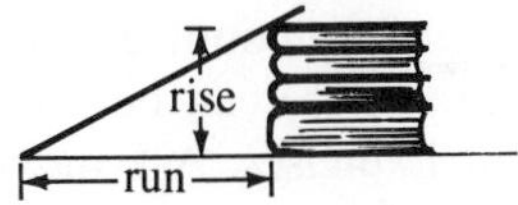

Point out that the steepness of the ruler depends on the number of books in the pile. The speed of a marble rolling down the ruler increases as the number of books increases.

Draw several lines, emphasizing that the slope of a straight line is constant—positive if the line rises from left to right and negative if it falls from left to right.

The difference between zero slope and no slope causes a great deal of difficulty for many students. Stress the significance of a zero numerator or denominator. You may wish to try this approach: Use the line whose equation is $y = x$ with slope 1 as a starting point, pointing out that it makes a 45° angle with both axes. As the steepness decreases, the line approaches the horizontal and the numerical value of the slope approaches 0. (See the figure at the left below.) Therefore the slope of a horizontal line is 0.

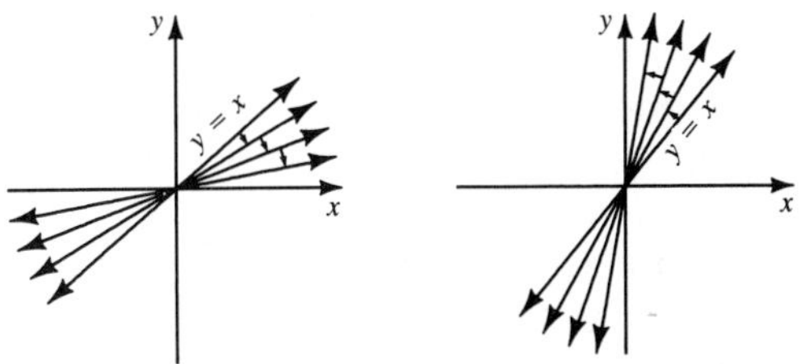

As the steepness increases from 1, the line approaches the vertical and the numerical value of the slope just gets larger and larger without approaching any specific number. (See the figure at the right above.) A line with a slope of 1,000,000 is almost vertical, so it seems reasonable that there is no number that we can assign to the slope of a vertical line.

Suggested Extension

Challenge students to use their answers to Written Exercises 13–24 to find an expression for the slope of the line with equation $ax + by = c$, $b \neq 0$.

slope $= -\frac{a}{b}$

9-2 (pages 396–400)

Key Mathematical Idea

- using the slope-intercept form of a linear equation

Teaching Suggestions

Be sure to discuss the development and the graphs on pages 396 and 397 to give students a thorough understanding of the significance of m and b in the slope-intercept equation of a line.

It will be helpful to emphasize Example 2 on page 397. Some students continue to rely on a table of values when graphing a linear equation. Emphasize the advantage of using the slope and the y-intercept to locate points on the graph. Have students begin the "stair-stepping" process by graphing the point $(0, b)$, which can be found by inspection from $y = mx + b$. For example, to graph $3x - 2y = 8$, have students use $y = \frac{3}{2}x - 4$, graph $(0, -4)$, and then use the slope to locate other points. Suggest that students verify their work by substituting the coordinates of one point in the original equation: $3(4) - 2(2) = 8$, so $(4, 2)$ does lie on the line.

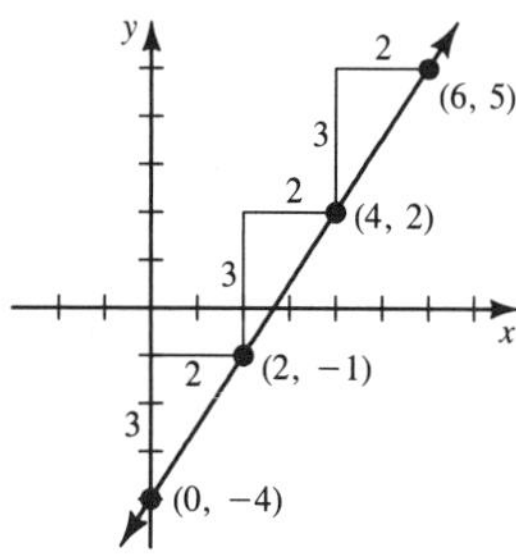

9-3 (pages 401–402)

Key Mathematical Idea

- finding an equation of a line given the slope and one point on the line, or given two points on the line

Teaching Suggestions

Reinforce the idea that every line in the coordinate plane has an equation of the form $Ax + By = C$ where A and B are not both equal to zero. Information that determines a line can be given in various ways; this information can be used to find an equation either in standard form or in slope-intercept form.

Remind students that the coordinates of every point on a line must satisfy the equation of the line. Thus, in the Example on page 401, the value of b can be determined by using *either* point: $y = \frac{3}{2}x + b$; using $(-2, -1)$, $-1 = \frac{3}{2}(-2) + b$; $-1 = -3 + b$; $b = 2$.

9-4 (pages 404–407)

Key Mathematical Ideas

- understanding the concept of function
- finding values of functions

Teaching Suggestions

The foundation of the concept of *function* has already been established with the introduction of ordered pairs. Nonetheless, the formal definition of a function and the related notation cause difficulty for many students. Stress that a function consists of a domain, a range, and a rule that tells how to associate members of the two sets. Be sure students understand that every function assigns each member of the domain to *exactly one* member of the range; also, each member of the range must be assigned to at least one member of the domain.

Discuss the arrow notation and function notation used to specify a function. Note that, for example, $g: x \rightarrow 4 + 3x - x^2$ and $f(y) = 4 + 3y - y^2$ are equivalent functions.

Reading Algebra

The verbalizations of functions given in symbolic form (pages 404 and 405) can be reinforced as students do the Oral Exercises. Ask individual students to read the directions aloud; to read each exercise aloud; to give each answer as a complete sentence.

9-5 (pages 408–411)

Key Mathematical Idea

- defining functions by using tables, bar graphs, and broken-line graphs

Teaching Suggestions

Point out that not every function can be specified by a numerical relationship. For example, the data in the examples on pages 408 and 409 do not follow a quantifiable pattern. These functions can be specified by means of tables, bar graphs, or broken-line graphs.

You can illustrate the idea of a function as an association by pointing out that each student in the class has a particular grade point average (GPA). Stress that this association follows the requirements of a function: no one student will have two GPA's at a given point in time, but two different students may have the same GPA.

It will be helpful to emphasize that any function can be expressed as a set of ordered pairs. For example, (corn, 40) is an ordered pair of the function on page 408 and (1975, 250) is an ordered pair of the function on page 409. Note that a member of the domain of a function is listed as the first coordinate of an ordered pair and the associated member of the range is listed as the second coordinate. Realizing that a function can be specified by ordered pairs will help prepare students for the next section.

Suggested Extension

Students should realize that not every pairing is a function. If time permits, have students read the Extra on page 440 about relations. The exercises provide excellent reinforcement of the idea of a function.

9-6 (pages 412–417)

Key Mathematical Idea

- graphing linear functions and quadratic functions

Teaching Suggestions

Students are already familiar with linear functions from their work with linear equations. Encourage students to think of a linear function in terms of a domain, a rule, and a range. Point out that if the domain is not specified, it is assumed to be the set of real numbers.

Understanding quadratic functions may be difficult for some students. Discuss the quadratic functions developed on pages 412, 413, and 414. Discuss why each graph represents a function. Stress the fact that the coefficient of x^2 determines whether the parabola opens upward or downward, and thus whether the function has a minimum point or a maximum point.

Suggest that students draw in the axis of symmetry when they are graphing parabolas. Remind students that the axis of symmetry always contains the vertex of a parabola.

Reading Algebra

This section gives you a good opportunity to help students understand how equations, tables, and graphs are used together to describe a given function. As an aid in interpreting the tables and graphs, you might give students some specific questions to consider as they read the section. For example, the following questions relate to the table and graph at the bottom of page 412.

What part of the table would be filled in first? (the top row)

Would the numbers under x or those under $x^2 - 2x - 2 = y$ usually be filled in first? (those under x)

Where do the numbers in the left-hand column come from? (They are chosen by the person making the table.)

How do you know what equations to write in the right-hand column? (Substitute the chosen values of x in the equation at the top of the column.)

Where do the ordered pairs shown on the graph come from? (They are the values of x and y from the table.)

9-7 (pages 418–423)

Key Mathematical Idea

- solving problems involving direct variation

Teaching Suggestions

Remind students that the graph of an equation of the form $y = kx$ is a line with slope k. Mention that in most practical situations, the constant k is a positive number.

When you introduce the relationship $\frac{y_1}{x_1} = \frac{y_2}{x_2}$, review the meaning of subscripts. Stress that each variable with a subscript represents a particular value of the variable. Point out that the form $\frac{y_1}{x_1} = \frac{y_2}{x_2}$ indicates that the quotient, or ratio, of the variables is constant. Remind students of the procedure used to solve proportions. (See Section 7-2.)

The following example may appeal to students: Jan worked 7 hours last week and earned \$28. If her wages vary directly as the number of hours worked, find the constant of variation and the amount she will earn if she works 17.5 hours.

$k = \text{hourly rate} = \frac{28}{7} = 4;\ w = 4(17.5) = 70;$

or $\frac{28}{7} = \frac{w}{17.5}$ and $w = \frac{28(17.5)}{7} = 70$

Use these computations to illustrate the general formulas $\frac{y}{x} = k$, $y = kx$, and $\frac{y_1}{x_1} = \frac{y_2}{x_2}$.

9-8 (pages 424–429)

Key Mathematical Idea

- solving problems involving inverse variation

Teaching Suggestions

You can introduce the concept of inverse variation by using the following table showing the values of various coins and the number of each coin needed to equal one dollar. Emphasize that one value increases as the other decreases and that $vn = 100$ for each coin.

Coin	Value in Cents	No. needed for \$1
Penny	1	100
Nickel	5	20
Dime	10	10
Quarter	25	4
Half-dollar	50	2
Dollar	100	1

Be sure students are able to distinguish the formulas for inverse variation from those for direct variation. Oral Exercises 1–12 can serve this purpose.

9-9 (pages 430–433)

Key Mathematical Ideas

- solving problems involving quadratic direct variation
- solving problems involving inverse variation as the square

Teaching Suggestions

The simplest example of quadratic direct variation is given by the formula for the area of a square, $A = s^2$. Show the class that its graph is half the parabola $y = x^2$.

s	$A = s^2$
1	1
2	4
3	9
4	16

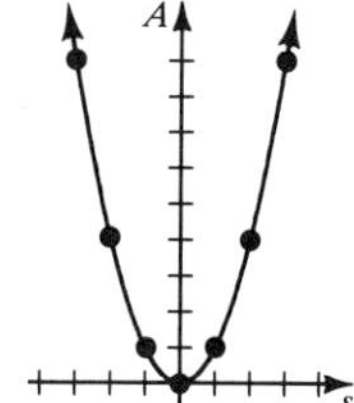

Generalize to any relationship of the form $y = kx^2$. Ask students to identify the value of k in the example above.

It may be helpful to refer back to Written Exercises 7–12 and 32 on pages 416–417 to show the effect that changes in the value of k have on the graph of $y = kx^2$. Point out that the value of k influences the rate at which y changes with respect to x.

A flashlight can be used to show that illumination decreases as the distance between the flashlight and the lit surface increases.

Suggested Extension

Ask your students to use the functions $f: x \rightarrow x^2$ and $g: x \rightarrow \frac{1}{x}$ to answer the questions given at the top of the next page.

1. Find $f[g(x)]$ by finding $g(x)$ first.

$f[g(x)] = \left(\frac{1}{x}\right)^2 = \frac{1}{x^2}$

2. Find $g[f(x)]$. $g[f(x)] = \frac{1}{x^2}$

3. Describe $f[g(x)]$ and $g[f(x)]$ in terms of variation.

The functions are equivalent inverse square variations.

4. Graph $h(x) = \frac{1}{x^2}$.

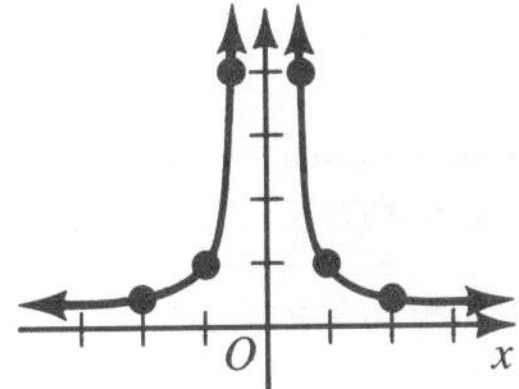

(Note that the Application on page 439 provides an alternative extension of the lesson.)

9-10 (pages 434–438)

Key Mathematical Idea

- solving problems involving joint variation and combined variation

Teaching Suggestions

Joint and combined variations are examples of functions of more than one variable. Be sure students understand that joint variation is always direct variation. In combined variation the words "directly" and "inversely" are specified.

Point out a difference between inverse variation and joint variation: in inverse variation, the constant equals the product ($k = xy$) and in joint variation, the constant is a factor of the product ($z = kxy$).

The text covers the proportion method of solving variation problems. It is equally possible to solve these problems by finding the value of k first.

10 Inequalities

The introduction to inequalities presented in Section 1-9 provides the background for this chapter. The consideration of the order of the real numbers leads to the treatment of inequalities in one variable. Solutions of inequalities are presented and extended to include conjunctions, disjunctions, and absolute value. Problem-solving skills are further developed with applications related to inequalities. Linear inequalities in two variables and systems of linear inequalities are investigated with emphasis on their graphs.

10-1 (pages 449–452)

Key Mathematical Ideas

- reviewing the concept of order of real numbers
- solving inequalities by substitution and by inspection

Teaching Suggestions

It may be helpful to begin the lesson by reviewing the material presented in Sections 1-7 and 1-9 (number lines and comparing real numbers). Remind students of the one-to-one correspondence between points on the number line and the real numbers. Remind students that a dot used as the graph of a number actually represents a point that has no size; also, a segment, no matter how short, is the graph of an infinite set of numbers.

Emphasize the difference between the symbols $<$ and $\leq$, and between $>$ and $\geq$. Also, remind students that a statement such as $x \geq 5$ is equivalent to the statement $5 \leq x$.

The significance of the words "and" and "or" is developed more thoroughly in Section 10-4, but begin to stress the idea of true and false statements using the examples on the next page.

$-5 < -2$ and $-2 < 0$		true	An "and" statement is true only if both parts are true.
$-1 < -3$ and $-3 < 5$		false	
$5 > 2$	or $5 < 9$	true	An "or" statement is true if either part is true.
$7 > 4$	or $7 = 4$	true	
$-2 > 0$	or $-2 < -4$	false	

Suggested Extension

Have students solve each inequality over the domain {the positive integers}. (If they need a hint, suggest that factoring may help.)

1. $x^2 - 4x + 3 \leq 0$ {1, 2, 3}
2. $y^3 - 4y^2 + 4y > 0$ {1, 3, 4, 5, 6, . . .}
3. $z^2 \leq z + 12$ {1, 2, 3, 4}
4. $2t^2 - 3t > 14$ {4, 5, 6, 7, . . .}
5. $4n^2 - 20n + 25 \leq 0$ $\emptyset$
6. $6v^2 + 7v + 2 > 0$ {the positive integers}

10-2 (pages 453–458)

Key Mathematical Idea

- solving inequalities and graphing their solution sets

Teaching Suggestions

Discuss the similarities of solving equations and inequalities and the following important difference. The last step in the solution of an equation may contain the variable in either side without loss of clarity. The last step in the solution of an inequality is often clearer if the variable is on the left side. Consider this example:

$$5 - 3x > 9 - x; \quad -4 > 2x; \quad -2 > x$$

Many students would solve the above inequality correctly but graph its solution set incorrectly. Stress the equivalence $a > b \leftrightarrow b < a$ and write the additional step, $x < -2$.

One of the most common errors students make is that of neglecting to reverse the direction of an inequality after multiplying or dividing each side by a negative number. Emphasize this characteristic unique to inequalities. The Challenge on page 467 highlights the property.

Suggest that students can perform a "reasonable check" of their work by substituting a convenient integer in the original inequality.

Be sure to discuss Written Exercise 3, page 456, to be sure that all students understand how to graph inequality statements involving the symbol $\neq$.

10-3 (pages 459–467)

Key Mathematical Idea

- solving problems involving inequalities

Teaching Suggestions

Discuss the idea with the class that many practical problems involve inequalities. Students make use of phrases such as "at least" and "not more than" frequently in their own experience. The Written Exercises, pages 461–462, allow students to concentrate on the translation of these types of phrases before worrying about solving. Stress the fact that all other aspects of translation are the same as they were in writing equations from word problems.

Emphasize the extra step in the checks of Examples 1 and 2 on pages 459 and 460. Note that it is advisable to check that apparent solutions do check with the facts of the problem and that "adjacent" values do not.

The list at the bottom of page 460 may help students translate word problems into inequalities correctly.

Reading Algebra

Before students begin this section, make sure that they have read the discussion of reading inequalities on page 458. Most students recognize the importance of using a pencil or pen as they think about the solution of a word problem. Fewer students, however, realize the value of making notes as they are *reading* mathematics. You might challenge students to read the solution of Example 2 on their own with pencil and paper at hand to write down any computations, notes, or diagrams that help them understand the solution or remember questions about any of the steps. When they have finished, discuss the solution and point out that writing things down often helps one to remember them.

10-4 (pages 468–471)

Key Mathematical Ideas

- understanding conjunctions and disjunctions
- finding solution sets of combined inequalities

Teaching Suggestions

Discuss the importance of the number line as a means of displaying the solution set of an inequality. Students do not easily grasp the solution sets of conjunctions and disjunctions without using a number line. Encourage students to draw neat, precise graphs with arrowheads and with a clear distinction between open and closed endpoints.

Students sometimes have trouble distinguishing between solution sets of conjunctions and disjunctions. The Oral Exercises provide valuable practice with this.

Suggested Extension

You can relate the ideas of intersection and union to conjunctions and disjunctions. Tell your students that the graph of a conjunction is the *intersection* of the graphs of its parts and that the graph of a disjunction is the *union* of the graph of its parts. Have students work on the Extra, pages 465–466, for an understanding of intersection, union, Venn diagrams, and the distributivity of intersection and of union (see Exercises 27 and 28).

10-5 (pages 472–475)

Key Mathematical Idea

- solving equations and inequalities involving absolute value

Teaching Suggestions

Review the definition of absolute value on page 35. Remind students that the absolute value of any real number is the distance on the number line between the number and the origin.

Emphasize the importance of the words *distance* and *difference* in the statement "The *distance* between the graphs of a and b is the absolute value of the *difference* of a and b." Students often miss the significance of the operation of subtraction in the statement: the distance between a and b is $|a - b|$.

Examples 2, 3, and 4 show two ways to solve inequalities, one graphical and the other algebraic. Tell students that even though they may prefer one method of solution over the other, both are important to their future work in mathematics. Encourage them to use both methods in at least some of the Written Exercises.

Help students understand the following two general statements where k is a positive constant:

$|a - b| > k$ is equivalent to the disjunction
$a - b > k$ or $a - b < -k$.

$|a - b| < k$ is equivalent to the conjunction
$-k < a - b$ and $a - b < k$.

Suggested Extension

Challenge students to graph the solution set of each inequality.

1. $2 \leq |x| \leq 3$

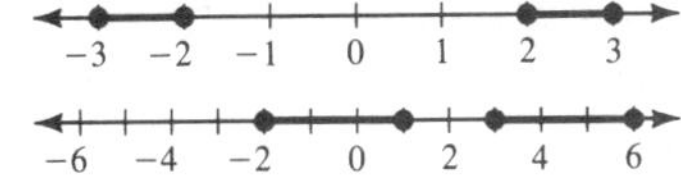

2. $1 \leq |x - 2| \leq 4$

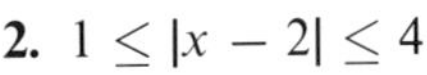

3. $4 < |3 - x| \leq 6$

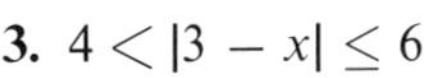

10-6 (pages 476–479)

Key Mathematical Idea

- solving more difficult open sentences involving absolute value

Teaching Suggestions

Explain the statement that the absolute value of a product is the product of the absolute values. Point out that this statement says that if a number is factored from an absolute value quantity, it must be positive. For example, $|3x| = 3|x|$ and $|-3x| = 3|x|$.

Introduce Example 2 by pointing out that since $a - b = -(b - a)$, $|a - b| = |b - a|$. You can illustrate this equality by showing students that $|4 - x| > 7$ and $|x - 4| > 7$ have the same solution set.

10-7 (pages 480–483)

Key Mathematical Idea

- graphing linear inequalities in two variables

Teaching Suggestions

Point out the boxed procedure on page 481 for graphing a linear inequality in the coordinate plane. Remind students that after they transform an inequality so that y is alone on one side, they can use the slope and y-intercept to graph the boundary line. Relate the symbols $\leq$, $\geq$, $<$, and $>$ to the inclusion or exclusion of the boundary line in the graph and remind students to use care in drawing either a solid or a dashed boundary line.

10-8 (pages 484–491)

Key Mathematical Idea

- graphing the solution set of a system of two linear inequalities in two variables

Teaching Suggestions

Point out that graphing is the only simple way to specify the solution set of a system of inequalities. There are no simple transformations for producing equivalent systems of inequalities as there are for systems of equalities. For example, if $a > b$ and $c > d$, it is not always true that $a - c > b - d$. ($2 > -1$ and $-2 > -6$, but $2 - (-2) < -1 - (-6)$.)

Suggested Extension

Students are often curious as to the usefulness of the algebra they are learning. Discuss the theory of linear programming, emphasizing the use of graphs of systems of inequalities. Encourage interested students to investigate linear programming by reading the Extra on pages 487–490 and by trying to solve some of the exercises.

11 Rational and Irrational Numbers

Rational numbers are formally defined and then investigated in decimal form and in square-root form. Irrational numbers are introduced in terms of irrational square roots. Finding the square roots of variable expressions leads to the Pythagorean theorem and its applications.

The last part of the chapter focuses on radical expressions and equations. Operations with radicals and various techniques for simplifying radicals are presented. The chapter concludes with the solution of simple radical equations and of word problems involving radical equations.

11-1 (pages 499–503)

Key Mathematical Ideas

- comparing rational numbers
- understanding the density property for rational numbers

Teaching Suggestions

Point out that integers, mixed numbers, and terminating decimals are all rational since each can be expressed as the quotient of two integers.

You can emphasize the density property by using a number line. Help the class locate the rational number halfway between 0 and $1\frac{1}{2}$, halfway between $\frac{1}{2}$ and $1\frac{3}{4}$, and so on.

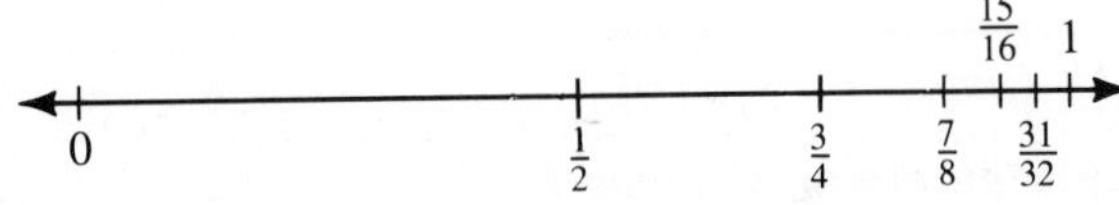

Ask the class how many rational numbers are between $\frac{1}{999}$ and $\frac{1}{1000}$. an infinite number

11-2 (pages 504–509)

Key Mathematical Ideas

- expressing rational numbers as terminating or repeating decimals
- expressing terminating or repeating decimals as common fractions

Teaching Suggestions

It is possible to determine whether a common rational fraction in simplest form can be expressed as a terminating or repeating decimal by the following rules:

1. If the prime factors of the denominator are only twos and/or fives (the prime factors of 10), the decimal is terminating.
2. If the denominator contains a prime factor other than 2 or 5, the decimal is repeating.

Illustrate rule 1 as shown:

$$\frac{23}{80} = \frac{23}{2^4 \cdot 5} \cdot \frac{5^3}{5^3} = \frac{23 \cdot 125}{10^4} = \frac{2875}{10{,}000} = 0.2875$$

Ask students to use these rules to identify whether the decimal representation of the number would terminate (T) or repeat (R).

$\frac{5}{12}$ R $\quad \frac{7}{32}$ T $\quad \frac{6}{625}$ T $\quad \frac{11}{35}$ R $\quad \frac{21}{4000}$ T

Emphasize that students should be familiar with the two definitions of a rational number:

1. any number that can be written as a ratio of two integers with a nonzero denominator
2. any number whose decimal representation is a terminating decimal or a repeating decimal

Most students will not be familiar with the method for converting a repeating decimal to a fraction. Be sure they understand how to determine the power of ten to use as a multiplier.

Reading Algebra

After a brief discussion of this section, you might want to have students read certain portions aloud, both to reinforce the sight-sound relationship and to assist with comprehension. Suggestions follow.

1. Have a student read the boxed generalization on page 505. Follow the reading with a discussion of the meaning of the statement and with some specific examples.
2. Have one student read Example 2 aloud while another student writes it on the board. (A good way to read $0.\overline{285}$ is "zero point two eight five, with two eight five repeating.")
3. Have a student read the material on approximations at the bottom of page 506. Follow the reading with a discussion of why approximations are useful.

Suggested Extension

Students may be surprised by the results they obtain when they express $9.\overline{9}$ and $0.2\overline{9}$ as common fractions. (In lowest terms, the numbers are $\frac{10}{1}$ and $\frac{3}{10}$.) Ask students to show that the value of any repeating decimal of the form $x.\overline{9}$, where x is a whole number, is $x + 1$.

Let $N = x.\overline{9}$. Then $10N = x9.\overline{9}$.

$$10N = x9.\overline{9}$$
$$N = x.\overline{9}$$
$$9N = x9 - x = (x \cdot 10 + 9) - x = 10x + 9 - x$$
$$= 9x + 9 = 9(x + 1);\ N = \frac{9(x + 1)}{9} = x + 1$$

11-3 (Pages 510–513)

Key Mathematical Idea

- finding square roots that are rational

Teaching Suggestions

It was suggested in the Lesson Commentary for Section 5-5 that students prepare a table and memorize the squares of the integers from one to fifteen. If they did so, this is a good time to review the table. Stress the importance of recognizing perfect squares at sight.

Some students tend to write $\sqrt{3^2} = \sqrt{9} = 3$. Emphasize the definition of square root: $\sqrt{x^2} = |x|$. Point out that evaluating 87^2 to evaluate $\sqrt{87^2}$ is a waste of effort.

Many students have difficulty with square roots of decimals. Help them discover that if the radicand is a perfect square, the number of digits to the right of the decimal point must be even. Then the number of digits to the right of the decimal point in the square root is half that number. Elaborate on the text example, page 512, $\sqrt{0.81}$, by pointing out that the denominator in the fraction form, $\sqrt{\frac{81}{100}}$, must be an even power of 10, $\sqrt{\frac{81}{10^2}}$, and the exponent in the square root is half the exponent in the radical, $\frac{9}{10^1}$. For example,

$$\sqrt{0.000121} = \sqrt{\frac{121}{10^6}} = \frac{11}{10^3} = \frac{11}{1000} = 0.011$$

Encourage students to read $\sqrt{x}$ as "the positive square root of x." This will help them remember that the principal square root of a number is nonnegative.

Suggested Extension

Ask students to find the value(s) of x for which the statement is true.

1. $\sqrt{(x - 1)^2} = x - 1$ $x \geq 1$
2. $\sqrt{x + 3} = 0$ $x = -3$
3. $\sqrt{x^2} = -x$ $x \leq 0$
4. $\sqrt{x^2} = -1$ no solution
5. $\sqrt{(x - 4)^2} = 0$ $x = 4$
6. $\sqrt{(x + 1)^2} = 2$ $x = 1$ or $x = -3$

11-4 (pages 514–516)

Key Mathematical Ideas

- defining irrational numbers
- simplifying radicals
- approximating irrational square units

Teaching Suggestions

Write the square roots $\sqrt{16}$, $\sqrt{26}$, and $\sqrt{36}$ on the chalkboard. Point out that $\sqrt{16} = 4$, $\sqrt{36} = 6$, and that 26 is halfway between 16 and 36. Ask students to estimate $\sqrt{26}$. $\frac{1}{2}(4 + 6) = 5$ Ask, "Is 5 too large or too small?" It is too small because $5^2 = 25$. Ask the class to try 5.1 by evaluating $(5.1)^2$. $(5.1)^2 = 26.01$, so $\sqrt{26}$ is close to 5.1. Discuss the proof on pages 514 and 515, emphasizing that since 26 is not the square of an integer, $\sqrt{26}$ cannot be a rational number.

Point out that the symbol $\sqrt{}$ has previously been used to indicate an operation. Now students can think of $\sqrt{x}$ as naming a unique real number. Show students that we can approximate an irrational number like $\sqrt{26}$ to as many decimal places as we choose. Have students refer to the Property of Completeness (page 515) and the Table of Square

Roots (page 650) to approximate $\sqrt{26}$ to three decimal places. $\sqrt{26} \approx 5.099$

Emphasize that every real number is either rational or irrational and that no number can be both rational and irrational. Remind students that of the three decimal terms for real numbers—terminating, infinite repeating, and infinite nonrepeating—only the last is irrational.

When you discuss Oral Exercises 6–10 and Written Exercises 1–15, remind students that for a radical to be in simplest form, the radicand should contain no square integral factor other than 1.

Suggested Extensions

1. Have students identify each number as rational (R) or irrational (I).
   a. $\sqrt{10}$ I **b.** $2\sqrt{9}$ R **c.** 3.14 R **d.** $1.\overline{527}$ R
   e. 0.010010001 . . . I **f.** $\frac{1}{5}\sqrt{5}$ I **g.** $\frac{22}{7}$ R
   h. 4π I **i.** $\frac{\sqrt{98}}{\sqrt{2}}$ R **j.** $(\sqrt{30})^2$ R
2. Ask students to read the Historical Note about π on page 533.

11-5 (pages 517–519)

Key Mathematical Ideas

- finding square roots of variable expressions
- solving equations and problems involving square roots

Teaching Suggestions

Write the chart below on the chalkboard with the first column filled in. Ask the class to help you complete the chart.

a	$\|a\|$	a^2	$\sqrt{a^2}$
1	1	1	1
2	2	4	2
3	3	9	3
−1	1	1	1
−2	2	4	2
−3	3	9	3

Point out that columns 2 and 4 are always equal: $|a| = \sqrt{a^2}$. Now add columns with the headings a^4 and $\sqrt{a^4}$. Help students realize that $\sqrt{a^4} = a^2$ for every real value of a since $a^2 \geq 0$ for every value of a. Generalize so that students understand that absolute values are needed for square roots only if the exponent of the variable in the answer is an odd number.

Many students have difficulty with exercises like Written Exercise 4 on page 518. Point out that for an expression like $\sqrt{x^3}$ to be defined, x must be nonnegative; therefore, $\sqrt{x^3} = \sqrt{x^2} \cdot \sqrt{x} = x\sqrt{x}$. Students should see that absolute values are not needed in this problem.

Some students may need to review the formula for the trinomial square. Refer them to Section 5-6.

Suggested Extensions

1. Ask your students to use a large piece of graph paper to plot the parabola $y = x^2$. Then have them use their graphs to estimate values of x to the nearest half unit for which:
   a. $y = 9$ $x = 3$ or $x = -3$
   b. $y = -1$ no value of x
   c. $y = 5$ $x \approx 2$ or $x \approx -2$
   d. $y = 13$ $x \approx 3\frac{1}{2}$ or $x \approx -3\frac{1}{2}$
   e. $y = 0$ $x = 0$
   f. $y = 6$ $x \approx 2\frac{1}{2}$ or $x \approx -2\frac{1}{2}$
2. Some of your students may be interested in exploring fractional exponents. Refer them to the Extra on pages 537–539.

11-6 (pages 520–526)

Key Mathematical Idea

- applying the Pythagorean theorem and its converse

Teaching Suggestions

Students have probably studied the Pythagorean theorem in previous courses. Nevertheless, some explanation will be helpful. In addition to discussing the proof given on page 520, you can present the following alternate statement of the theorem: "In any right triangle, the area of the square on the hypotenuse equals the sum of the areas of the squares on the legs." Have students count the squares to verify that $c^2 = a^2 + b^2$.

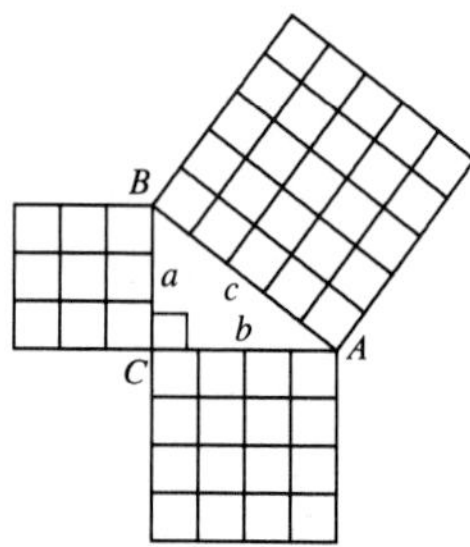

When you discuss Examples 2 and 3 on page 522, discuss the need for rejecting negative solutions when a solution represents a length.

Reading Algebra

Although the terms from geometry used in this section are probably well known to most of your students, you may want to check their understanding. Remind them to use the diagrams to help them understand the technical words.

Suggested Extension

Define Pythagorean triples as three positive integers $\{a, b, c\}$ such that $a^2 + b^2 = c^2$.

a. Ask students to use the equations $a = 2xy$, $b = x^2 - y^2$, and $c = x^2 + y^2$ to verify that $\{2xy, x^2 - y^2, x^2 + y^2\}$ is a Pythagorean triple. $a^2 + b^2 = (2xy)^2 + (x^2 - y^2)^2 = 4x^2y^2 + (x^4 - 2x^2y^2 + y^4) = x^4 + 2x^2y^2 + y^4 = (x^2 + y^2)^2 = c^2$

b. Use the given values of x and y and verify that the resulting values of a, b, and c form a Pythagorean triple.

$x = 2, y = 1$ $4^2 + 3^2 = 5^2$
$x = 3, y = 2$ $12^2 + 5^2 = 13^2$
$x = 4, y = 1$ $8^2 + 15^2 = 17^2$
$x = 5, y = 2$ $20^2 + 21^2 = 29^2$
$x = 8, y = 3$ $48^2 + 55^2 = 73^2$

11-7 (pages 527–528)

Key Mathematical Idea

- simplifying products and quotients of radicals

Teaching Suggestions

Review the product and quotient properties of square roots before introducing the new material.

Emphasize that when students are rationalizing a denominator, they should select the *smallest* multiplier that will produce a perfect square radicand in the denominator. For instance, to simplify $\sqrt{\frac{5}{8}}$ in Example 2, page 527, we use $\sqrt{2}$ as the multiplier, not $\sqrt{8}$. Stress that students can identify the required multiplier by simplifying the numerator and denominator first.

Be sure to discuss Oral Exercises 3, 7, and 8, cautioning students to simplify quotients before rationalizing the denominator. For example, $\frac{\sqrt{18}}{\sqrt{3}} = \sqrt{\frac{18}{3}} = \sqrt{6}$. Multiplying $\frac{\sqrt{18}}{\sqrt{3}}$ by $\frac{\sqrt{3}}{\sqrt{3}}$ merely complicates the process.

Suggested Extension

Present the following problem to your students: A square with sides of length s is inscribed in a circle as shown. Find, in terms of s,

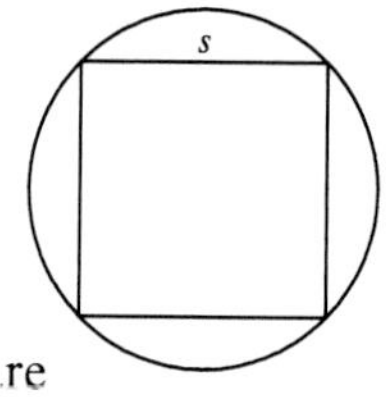

a. the radius of the circle.
b. the circumference of the circle.
c. the area of the circle.
d. the ratio of the perimeter of the square to the circumference.
e. the ratio of the area of the square to the area of the circle.

a. $\frac{1}{2}s\sqrt{2}$ **b.** $\pi s\sqrt{2}$ **c.** $\frac{1}{2}\pi s^2$ **d.** $\frac{2\sqrt{2}}{\pi}$ **e.** $\frac{2}{\pi}$

11-8 (pages 529–530)

Key Mathematical Idea

- simplifying sums and differences of radicals

Teaching Suggestions

To develop the idea of simplifying sums and differences of radicals, draw an analogy with simplifying sums and differences of polynomials:

$$2x + 3x = (2 + 3)x = 5x$$
$$2\sqrt{7} + 3\sqrt{7} = (2 + 3)\sqrt{7} = 5\sqrt{7}$$

Discuss the Example on page 529, emphasizing that each term must be in simplest form before the terms can be combined.

It may be helpful to stress the difference between the addition and multiplication of radicals with the following example:

$$\sqrt{4}\cdot\sqrt{9} \stackrel{?}{=} \sqrt{4\cdot 9} \qquad \sqrt{4} + \sqrt{9} \stackrel{?}{=} \sqrt{4 + 9}$$
$$2\cdot 3 \stackrel{?}{=} \sqrt{36} \qquad 2 + 3 \stackrel{?}{=} \sqrt{13}$$
$$6 = 6 \checkmark \qquad 5 \neq \sqrt{13}$$

You can then generalize: $\sqrt{a}\cdot\sqrt{b} = \sqrt{ab}$ but $\sqrt{a} + \sqrt{b} \neq \sqrt{a + b}$.

Suggested Extensions

1. Have students classify as true or false.
   a. $3\sqrt{2} + 2\sqrt{3} = 5\sqrt{5}$ F
   b. $\sqrt{7}\cdot\sqrt{11} = \sqrt{77}$ T
   c. $\sqrt{15} + \sqrt{30} = (1 + \sqrt{2})\sqrt{15}$ T
   d. $\sqrt{14} + \sqrt{21} = \sqrt{35}$ F
   e. $\sqrt{3} + \sqrt{4} = \sqrt{5}$ F
   f. $\sqrt{9} + \sqrt{25} = \sqrt{64}$ T
   g. $3\cdot\sqrt{10} + \sqrt{10} = 10\sqrt{3}$ F
   h. $\sqrt{2} + \sqrt{8} = \sqrt{18}$ T
2. Ask students to solve each equation.
   a. $x\sqrt{2} - \sqrt{6} = \sqrt{24} - x\sqrt{8}$ $x = \sqrt{3}$
   b. $\sqrt{175} - y\sqrt{63} = y\sqrt{112} - \sqrt{448}$ $y = \frac{13}{7}$
   c. $\sqrt{240z^2} + \sqrt{45} = \sqrt{405} + \sqrt{15z^2}$
   $z = \frac{2\sqrt{3}}{3}$ or $z = -\frac{2\sqrt{3}}{3}$

11-9 (pages 531–533)

Key Mathematical Ideas

- multiplying binomials containing square-root radicals
- using conjugates to rationalize denominators

Teaching Suggestions

It will be helpful to begin the lesson with a review of the product patterns. Emphasize these formulas:

$$(a + b)(a - b) = a^2 - b^2$$
$$(a + b)^2 = a^2 + 2ab + b^2$$
$$(a - b)^2 = a^2 - 2ab + b^2$$

Point out the similarity between simplifying $(a + b)(a - b)$ and $(5 + \sqrt{3})(5 - \sqrt{3})$ in Example 1, page 531.

Sometimes students forget to combine similar terms when multiplying binomials containing square roots. Emphasize that the square of a binomial containing one or two square roots is itself a binomial; the product of two conjugate binomials is always equal to a single rational number.

Develop the idea of rationalizing denominators by asking the class what value of x will produce a rational denominator:

$$\frac{3}{2 + \sqrt{5}}\cdot\frac{x}{x} = \frac{\quad}{\text{rational}}$$

Show that if $x = \sqrt{5}$ or if $x = 2 + \sqrt{5}$ the denominator will still be irrational. Complete the example using the conjugate value, $2 - \sqrt{5}$, for x.

Suggested Extension

Have students select the number from the product list below that is the product of the given binomial and its conjugate.

Binomial	Product	
a. $3 + \sqrt{5}$	2	a. 4
b. $\sqrt{3} + 5$	4	b. −22
c. $\sqrt{3} + \sqrt{5}$	22	c. −2
d. $5 - \sqrt{3}$	−2	d. 22
e. $\sqrt{5} - 3$	−4	e. −4
f. $\sqrt{5} - \sqrt{3}$	−22	f. 2

11-10 (pages 534–536)

Key Mathematical Ideas

- solving simple radical equations
- solving word problems involving square roots

Teaching Suggestions

Review the idea of inverse operations introduced on page 103. Point out that taking a square root and squaring are inverse operations; thus, squaring a radical equation can eliminate the square root.

Stress the Property of Square Roots of Equal Numbers stated on page 517: $r^2 = s^2$ if and only if $r = s$ or $r = -s$. Thus, if we are given $x = 3$ and we square both sides, we obtain $x^2 = 9$. Since $x = 3$ has the solution set $\{3\}$ and $x^2 = 9$ has the solution set $\{3, -3\}$, the equations are not equivalent. Be sure students understand that squaring may introduce extraneous roots so that checking each apparent root is essential.

The solution to Example 2, page 534, shows the importance of isolating the radical before squaring. You may want to emphasize this idea by squaring each side of the original equation:

$$(4x + 1) + 2 \cdot 5\sqrt{4x + 1} + 25 = 64$$

Students should see that this new equation is even more complicated than the original one.

12 Quadratic Functions

This chapter concentrates on various methods of solving quadratic equations. In previous chapters students have learned to solve quadratic equations by factoring and by using the property of square roots of equal numbers. These methods are supplemented by the methods of completing the square and using the quadratic formula. Graphs of quadratic functions are related to solutions of quadratic equations by means of the discriminant.

One section ties together all the methods of solving quadratic equations by listing guidelines for selecting the most appropriate method. These techniques of solution are then applied to a variety of word problems, some of which have irrational solutions.

12-1 (pages 547–549)

Key Mathematical Idea

- solving quadratic equations involving perfect squares

Teaching Suggestions

Emphasize the three possible cases for an equation $x^2 = k$. As noted on page 547, such an equation can have two different real-number solutions, one real-number solution, or no real-number solution depending on the value of k. Write the following equations on the chalkboard and ask the class to tell how many real-number roots each equation has. (Students should not solve the equations.)

$(2x - 1)^2 = 4$ 2 $\qquad (x - 3)^2 + 9 = 0$ 0

$x^2 + 1 = 7$ 2 $\qquad (x - \frac{1}{2})^2 = 0$ 1

Remind students that irrational roots should be written in simplest radical form (see page 527).

Suggested Extensions

1. Challenge students to solve each equation.
   a. $(\sqrt{2y} - 1)^2 = 9$ $\{8\}$
   b. $(\sqrt{x + 1} - 8)^2 = 25$ $\{8, 168\}$
   c. $(\sqrt{z} + 2)^2 = 3$ $\emptyset$
   d. $(4 - \sqrt{t})^2 = 18$ $\{34 + 24\sqrt{2}\}$
2. The Extra on pages 555 and 556 introduces imaginary numbers and solutions of equations of the form $x^2 = k$ where $k < 0$. This material offers excellent preparation for future work.

12-2 (pages 550–552)

Key Mathematical Idea

- solving quadratic equations by completing the square

Teaching Suggestions

Write the equation $(x - 5)^2 = 3$ on the chalkboard and have the class complete the solution. $x = 5 \pm \sqrt{3}$ Then write the following sequence on the chalkboard:

$$(x - 5)^2 = 3$$
$$x^2 - 10x + 25 = 3$$
$$x^2 - 10x + 22 = 0$$

Point out that each of these equations has the solution set $\{5 \pm \sqrt{3}\}$ since all the equations are equivalent. Introduce the method of completing the square as a way of obtaining an equation like $(x - 5)^2 = 3$ from an equation like $x^2 - 10x + 22 = 0$.

The Oral Exercises offer valuable practice in completing the square, the only new skill required for this section. Emphasize that the relationship between a, $2a$, and a^2 in the identities $(x + a)^2 = x^2 + 2ax + a^2$ and $(x - a)^2 = x^2 - 2ax + a^2$ exists only when the coefficient of the quadratic term is 1.

Be sure to discuss Example 3 on page 551, emphasizing the need to divide each side of the equation by 5 and to add $\left(\frac{7}{10}\right)^2$ to *both* sides.

12-3 (pages 553–556)

Key Mathematical Idea

- solving quadratic equations by using the quadratic formula

Teaching Suggestions

The derivation of the quadratic formula on page 553 may be difficult for some students to understand. Nevertheless, it is worthwhile to discuss the derivation step by step. Emphasize that the formula is obtained by completing the square of the general quadratic equation $ax^2 + bx + c = 0$. While students should not be expected to derive the formula, they should memorize it. Encourage students to write out the formula to avoid errors every time they use it.

Students often make errors substituting for a, b, and c. Stress the importance of expressing an equation in the form $ax^2 + bx + c = 0$ before applying the quadratic formula. Students may find it helpful to write a "skeleton form" of the formula as shown below and then to substitute the appropriate values.

$$x = \frac{-(\ \ ) \pm \sqrt{(\ \ )^2 - 4(\ \ )(\ \ )}}{2(\ \ )}$$

If some student should ask about equations for which $b^2 - 4ac < 0$, point out that such an equation has no *real* roots. You may add that the roots of these equations contain *imaginary numbers*. Refer interested students to the optional feature on page 555.

Reading Algebra

To check students' understanding of the symbolism, after they have read through this lesson, you might choose a few of the expressions used in the derivation of the quadratic formula and in the example on page 554 and read them aloud to the class, asking the students to write them down from your dictation. Then ask several students to choose and dictate other expressions from this section.

Suggested Extensions

1. Have students solve each equation, writing roots in simplest radical form.
   a. $2t^2 - 4t\sqrt{3} + 1 = 0$ $\left\{\frac{2\sqrt{3} \pm \sqrt{10}}{2}\right\}$
   b. $\sqrt{2} \cdot y^2 + 5y + 2\sqrt{2} = 0$ $\left\{-\frac{\sqrt{2}}{2}, -2\sqrt{2}\right\}$
   c. $x^2 - 4x\sqrt{3} - 6 = 0$ $\{2\sqrt{3} \pm 3\sqrt{2}\}$
2. Ask students to find the value(s) of k for which the equation has exactly one solution.
   a. $2m^2 - km + 3 = 0$ $k = \pm 2\sqrt{6}$
   b. $kv^2 - 6v + k = 0$ $k = \pm 3$
   c. $(k + 1)r^2 + 2kr + (k + 2) = 0$ $k = -\frac{2}{3}$
   d. $x^2 + (k + 1)x - k = 0$ $k = -3 \pm 2\sqrt{2}$

12-4 (pages 557–561)

Key Mathematical Idea

- using the discriminant to analyze quadratic equations and functions

Teaching Suggestions

Point out that students have spent quite a bit of time studying quadratic equations and quadratic functions. This section shows the strong relationship between the two topics. Emphasize that the value of the discriminant tells us the number of roots that $ax^2 + bx + c = 0$ has and also the number of x-intercepts that the parabola $y = ax^2 + bx + c$ has. Be sure students realize that the discriminant equals $b^2 - 4ac$, not $\sqrt{b^2 - 4ac}$.

Be sure to discuss Example 3, on page 558, which illustrates the case in which the discriminant is negative. You may want to graph a parabola that lies entirely below the x-axis, such as $y = -x^2 + 2x - 7$, pointing out that its discriminant is also negative.

The chart on page 558 provides a helpful summary of the important facts.

When you discuss the Oral Exercises, have a student explain why it is obvious that the equation in Exercise 8 has two real roots. If an equation $ax^2 + bx + c = 0$ has $a > 0$ and $c < 0$, or $a < 0$ and $c > 0$, then $b^2 - 4ac > 0$.

Suggested Extension

This section concentrates on the points of a parabola for which $y = 0$. We can also consider quadratic inequalities, points for which $y > ax^2 + bx + c$ or $y < ax^2 + bx + c$. The Extra, pages 567–568, relates the graph of a quadratic function to quadratic inequalities.

12-5 (pages 562–564)

Key Mathematical Idea

- choosing the most appropriate method for solving a quadratic equation

Teaching Suggestions

Be sure students realize that more than one method may be suitable for solving a particular quadratic equation. However, encourage students to use the guidelines on page 562 to select a method that will simplify the computations.

Be sure students have memorized the quadratic formula and that they realize the formula can be used to solve any quadratic equation.

It will be helpful to assign and/or discuss as many of the A-level and B-level Written Exercises as possible. These exercises provide the full range of forms of quadratic equations, reinforcing the four methods of solution.

12-6 (pages 565–567)

Key Mathematical Idea

- solving problems involving quadratic equations

Teaching Suggestions

Review the five-step method of solving problems if any students have not mastered it by now. Be sure students check their answers to each word problem with the words of the problem so that they can reject inappropriate roots.

Reading Algebra

As you discuss the example on page 565 with your class, point out that we have a solution in simplest radical form halfway through Step 4. Ask why we can't be satisfied with this, as in the preceding lessons. Students need frequent reminders that practical problems require solutions that make sense under the given conditions. In this particular case:

1. An answer in radical form is not useful.
2. Only the positive root makes sense.
3. The answers must be rounded to usable approximations.
4. The check using approximate values cannot be exact.

Emphasize the importance of always going back to the words of the problem as a final test.

Looking Ahead

This unit provides an overview of geometry, numerical trigonometry, probability, and statistics. The geometry sections explore the properties of angles, triangles, and similar triangles. The trigonometry sections develop the skills needed to solve problems using the sine, cosine, and tangent ratios and a trigonometric table. The probability sections present the concepts of sample space and events of a random experiment; the text also shows how to evaluate the probabilities of events. The final section deals with the mean, median, mode, and range of a frequency distribution. The topics of this unit are introductory, but sufficiently varied for students to see what future mathematics courses have to offer.

Points, Lines, and Angles (pages 576–578)

Key Mathematical Ideas

- representing points, lines, and angles
- measuring and classifying angles

Teaching Suggestions

This section presents some of the basic geometric ideas. Most of your students will probably be familiar with some, if not all, of the vocabulary. Students often tend to think of points, lines, angles, and planes as concrete objects. Discuss the abstract nature of geometry and geometric figures. For example, lines and planes extend indefinitely, although their representations do not.

Stress the importance of notation in precisely naming figures and their measures. Be sure that students differentiate between $\overleftrightarrow{AB}$, $\overline{AB}$, $\overrightarrow{AB}$, and AB. When introducing the notation for angles, emphasize that the middle letter names the vertex.

Point out that the numbers on a protractor are reference numbers just as they are on a number line. Note that for every ray there is exactly one number between 0 and 180, and for every number between 0 and 180 there is exactly one ray.

Pairs of Angles (pages 579–580)

Key Mathematical Idea

- using vertical angles, complementary angles, and supplementary angles

Teaching Suggestions

Draw the following diagrams on the chalkboard:

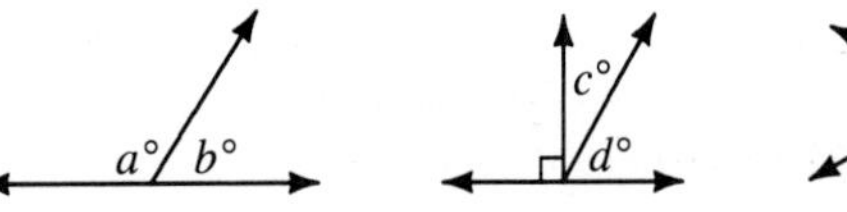

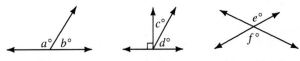

Challenge students to write an equation to represent each diagram.

$a + b = 180$, $c + d = 90$, and $e = f$

Use these diagrams and equations to introduce the concepts of supplementary angles, complementary angles, and vertical angles.

You can justify the idea that vertical angles have equal measures by pointing out that in the figure below $x + z = 180$. (Together they form a straight angle.) Also, $y + z = 180$. $x = 180 - z$ and $y = 180 - z$, so by substitution $x = y$.

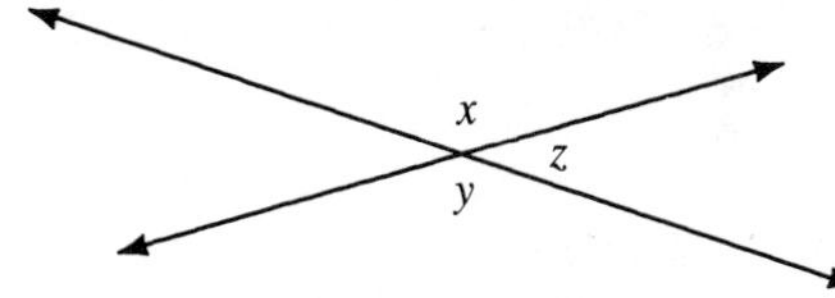

Point out that this section uses both geometric and algebraic concepts.

Suggested Extensions

1. Challenge students to find the measure of an angle such that the measure of its supplement is 10 more than two times the measure of its complement. 10
2. Have students solve Problem 1 if "20" is substituted for "10." 20

3. Ask students to use their results from Problems 1 and 2 to write an equation.
$180 - x = x + 2(90 - x)$

4. Have students show that the equation is an identity. $180 - x \stackrel{?}{=} x + 2(90) - 2x$; $180 - x = 180 - x$ √

Triangles (pages 581–583)

Key Mathematical Idea

- using properties of general and special triangles

Teaching Suggestions

Begin the class by performing the experiment suggested on page 581. Tear off the corners of a paper triangle and show students that the corners fit together to form a straight angle. Tell the class that the experiment suggests that the sum of the measures of the angles of a triangle is 180°. Then tell students that this theorem is proved in geometry courses.

Be sure students understand the characteristics of a right triangle, an isosceles triangle, and an equilateral triangle.

Suggested Extension

Two angles are given which may be the measures of two angles of a triangle. Have students state whether the triangle would be acute, right, or obtuse, or if no triangle is possible.

1. 22°, 88°	2. 47°, 33°
3. 52°, 136°	4. 17°, 73°
5. 82°, 7°	6. 48°, 43°
7. 124°, 56°	8. 46°, 44°

acute: Exs. 1, 6; right: Exs. 4, 8; obtuse: Exs. 2, 5; impossible: Exs. 3, 7

Similar Triangles (pages 584–586)

Key Mathematical Idea

- solving problems involving similar triangles

Teaching Suggestions

Discuss the idea of similarity as indicating objects with the same shape but not necessarily the same size. Photographs, maps, and scale drawings can provide good intuitive examples of similar figures.

Stress the idea that a statement like $\triangle GHK \sim \triangle STR$ establishes a correspondence and implies that $\frac{GH}{ST} = \frac{HK}{TR} = \frac{GK}{SR}$. Point out the need to write a similarity statement carefully; the statement $\triangle GHK \sim \triangle RST$ establishes a different correspondence than the one above.

Suggested Extension

Tell students to write a similarity statement if possible. If not, students should write "not similar."

1. 

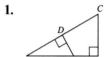

2. 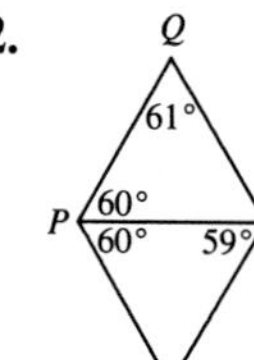

3. 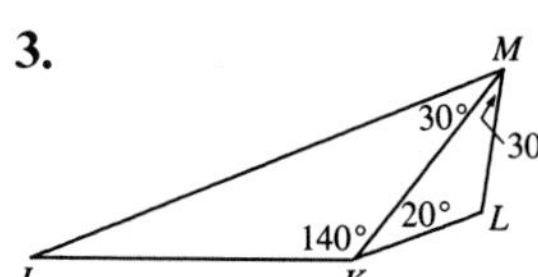

4. 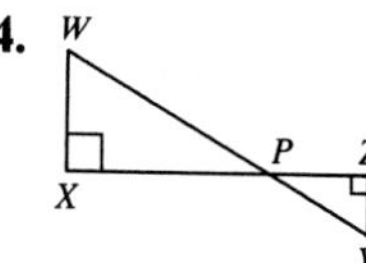

Answers may vary. Examples are given.
1. $\triangle ABC \sim \triangle ADE$ 2. $\triangle PQR \sim \triangle PSR$
3. not similar 4. $\triangle WXP \sim \triangle YZP$

Trigonometric Ratios (pages 587–589)

Key Mathematical Idea

- finding the sine, cosine, and tangent of an acute angle

Teaching Suggestions

Emphasize the importance of memorizing the definitions of the trigonometric ratios presented on page 587. Warn students against confusing the sine ratio and the tangent ratio.

Remind students that the hypotenuse of a right triangle is always the longest side. Show that this implies that the sine and the cosine of an acute angle must be less than 1. However, as illustrated in Examples 1 and 2, the tangent of an acute angle can be any positive number.

Point out the use of the Pythagorean theorem in Example 2. You can mention that students will need to use the Pythagorean theorem to do the Written Exercises.

Finally, draw students' attention to the discussion on page 588 that shows that the values of the trigonometric ratios of an angle depend only on the measure of the angle and not on the size of the triangle that contains the angle.

Using Trigonometric Tables (pages 590–591)

Key Mathematical Idea

- using a trigonometric table to find decimal values for measures of angles

Teaching Suggestions

When you introduce the trigonometric table on page 651, mention the following characteristics:

1. The sine and cosine of an acute angle are always less than 1.
2. As the angle increases from 0° to 90°, the sine increases between 0 and 1 and the cosine decreases between 1 and 0.
3. $\tan 45° = 1$.
4. If $m\angle A < 45°$, $\tan A < 1$ and if $m\angle A > 45$, $\tan A > 1$.

Point out that there are three exact values in the table, sin 30°, tan 45°, and cos 60°. All other values are approximations to four decimal places.

Numerical Trigonometry (pages 592–595)

Key Mathematical Idea

- using trigonometric ratios to solve problems

Teaching Suggestions

Encourage students to draw a diagram to solve a trigonometric problem if one is not given. Suggest that it is helpful to draw diagrams that are reasonably accurate. With a little practice, students should be able to draw acute angles of specified measure by using a 45° angle as a guide.

Some students may use a vertical ray as a side of an angle of depression. Stress that both an angle of depression and an angle of elevation must have a horizontal ray as one side.

Point out that sometimes one trigonometric ratio is more helpful than another. For instance, to find the value of x in Example 2, one might write

$$\tan 27° = \frac{86}{x} \quad \text{and so} \quad x = \frac{86}{\tan 27°}.$$

Note that the computation needed here is the quotient $86 \div 0.5095$. Most students without calculators will agree that the product $86(1.9626)$ is easier to compute.

Suggested Extension

Draw the diagram shown below on the chalkboard and ask students to prove that $\frac{\sin A}{a} = \frac{\sin C}{c}$.

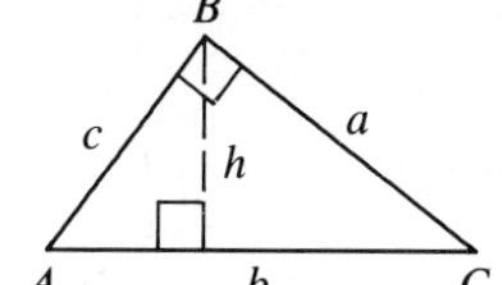

$\sin A = \frac{h}{c}$ and $\sin C = \frac{h}{a}$;
$h = c \sin A$ and $h = a \sin C$;
$c \sin A = a \sin C$;
$\frac{\sin A}{a} = \frac{\sin C}{c}$

Sample Spaces and Events (pages 596–598)

Key Mathematical Idea

- listing the sample space and events for a random experiment

Teaching Suggestions

Discuss the importance of organizing results of an experiment and the need for a precise notation to clarify these results. Stress the intuitive approach in the problems, but require students to use the correct language. In particular, stress the importance of identifying the set of *all possible outcomes* and that it is called the sample space.

You can conduct some random experiments in your classroom to motivate the students. For example, place known numbers of differently colored marbles in an opaque container. Ask the class to identify the sample space and the simple events when one marble is drawn at random. Discuss the sample space when two marbles are chosen at a time and ask students to specify events such as "the two marbles are of different colors."

Probability (pages 599–601)

Key Mathematical Idea

- finding the probability that an event will occur

Teaching Suggestions

Discuss the nature of probability in general and the fact that some probabilities are not of the type considered in this section: the probability of rain tomorrow, the probability that Jason will get a hit in his next time at bat. Stress the intuitive idea of probability of an event as a number between 0 and 1. The less likely an event is to occur, the closer the probability is to 0, and the more likely, the closer to 1.

It is not always feasible to write out the sample space (drawing cards from a 52-card deck), but Written Exercise 4, page 600, shows how helpful it is to have it clearly identified.

Suggested Extension

You may wish to discuss the "birthday problem" with the class. Ask them to guess the probability that two of them have the same birthdate.

For a group of 24 people, the probability is surprisingly $\frac{27}{50}$, or just over $\frac{1}{2}$. For 30 people, it is about $\frac{2}{3}$ and for 60 people, about 0.994.

Frequency Distributions (pages 602–604)

Key Mathematical Ideas

- working with frequency distributions and histograms
- finding the mean, median, mode, and range of a frequency distribution

Teaching Suggestions

Some of your students may have home computers, or your school may have computers available. If so, students should be able to work with sets of data and their statistics. Encourage students to write programs to find the mean, median, mode, and range. Discuss some of the types of data students find interesting and worthwhile to analyze: personal test scores, individual or team scores in any type of school competition, daily temperature variations, mileage on vacation trips, and so on.

Ask students to try to think of a situation in which the mean might be a significant statistic. (Grade-point averages are one example.) Point out that the owner of a shoe store would be interested in the mode of shoe sizes sold, since the modal size would require additional inventory. Finally, note that very high or low values can greatly affect the mean score; for this reason, a median income or a median test score might tell more about the central position of a large group of people than a mean would.

Suggested Extension

Ask the students to acquire the scores of this year's basketball team. Have them divide "our team" scores into two sets, home games and away games, and compute the mean, median, mode (if any), and range for each set.

For the more ambitious, have them list the set of differences between "our" scores and opponents' scores with a win being positive and a loss negative. Then ask them to compute the statistics on this set.

ALGEBRA

Structure and Method

Book 1

Teacher's Edition

Mary P. Dolciani
Richard G. Brown
William L. Cole

EDITORIAL ADVISER
Robert H. Sorgenfrey

TEACHER CONSULTANTS
Gail H. Clark
Allen C. Demmin
James F. Dudley
Donald Field
Lois A. Martin
Sister Patricia Supple, CSJ

HOUGHTON MIFFLIN COMPANY · BOSTON

Atlanta Dallas Geneva, Ill. Lawrenceville, N.J. Palo Alto Toronto

THE AUTHORS

Mary P. Dolciani, formerly Professor of Mathematical Sciences, Hunter College of the City University of New York.

Richard G. Brown, Mathematics Teacher, The Phillips Exeter Academy, Exeter, New Hampshire.

William L. Cole, Associate Professor of Mathematics Education, Michigan State University.

EDITORIAL ADVISER

Robert H. Sorgenfrey, Professor of Mathematics, University of California, Los Angeles.

TEACHER CONSULTANTS

Gail H. Clark, Mathematics Teacher, Johnson High School, Gainesville, Georgia.

Allen C. Demmin, Mathematics Coordinator, Middleton High School, Middleton, Wisconsin.

James F. Dudley, Mathematics Teacher, Rio Grande High School, Albuquerque, New Mexico.

Donald Field, Mathematics Teacher, Niles West High School, Skokie, Illinois.

Lois A. Martin, Mathematics Teacher, Downingtown High School, Downingtown, Pennsylvania.

Sister Patricia Supple, CSJ, Mathematics Teacher, Daniel Murphy Catholic High School, Los Angeles, California.

Printed in U.S.A.

ISBN: 0-395-43052-6

ABCDEFGHIJ-D-943210/8987

Contents

1 Introduction to Algebra

2 Working with Real Numbers

3 Solving Equations and Problems

4 Polynomials

5 Factoring Polynomials

6 Fractions

7 Applying Fractions

8 Linear Equations and Systems

9 Introduction to Functions

10 Inequalities

11 Rational and Irrational Numbers

12 Quadratic Functions

Looking Ahead

Using a Computer with This Course

There are two types of optional computer material in this text: Computer Key-In features and Computer Exercises. The Computer Key-In features can be used by students without previous programming experience. These features teach some programming in BASIC and usually include a program that students can run to explore an algebra topic covered in the chapter. Some writing of programs may be required in some of these features.

The optional Computer Exercises are designed for students who have some familiarity with programming in BASIC. Students are usually asked to write one or more programs related to the lesson just presented.

An appendix that summarizes BASIC programming may be found beginning on page 653. This appendix can be used as a summary by students who are learning BASIC or as a review by students who are familiar with BASIC.

Reading Your Algebra Textbook

An algebra textbook requires a different type of reading than a novel or a short story. Every paragraph of a mathematical text must be read with great care and concentration. You should not only read the words, but you should think about their meaning. You should read slowly through the explanations in this book. Algebra builds upon itself; the method of multiplying binomials you will study on page 196 will be useful to you on page 531. Read with a pencil in your hand; do calculations, draw sketches, take notes.

Vocabulary

You will be exposed to many new words in algebra. Some, such as *axiom* and *polynomial,* are mathematical in nature, while others, such as *line* and *side,* are used in everyday speech but have different meanings when used in algebra. Important words whose meanings you will learn are printed in heavy type. (See page 10.) Also, they are listed at the beginning of each Self-Test. If you cannot recall the meaning of a word, you can look it up in the Glossary or the Index at the back of the book. The Glossary will give you a definition, and the Index will give you page references for more information.

Symbols

Algebra, and mathematics in general, has its own symbolic language. You must be able to read these symbols in order to understand algebra. For example, $x \in \{-1, 0, 1, 2\}$ means "x is a member of the set whose members are -1, 0, 1, and 2." A list of symbols appears on page xii. If you cannot recall what a symbol means, check this list.

Diagrams

Throughout this book you will find many diagrams. These contain information that will help you to understand the concepts under discussion. Study these diagrams carefully when you read the text that accompanies them.

Displayed Material

Throughout the book important information is displayed in red boxes. This information includes axioms, properties, definitions, methods, and summaries. Be certain to read and understand the material in these boxes. You will also find these boxes useful when reviewing for tests and exams. Be sure to study the worked-out examples, such as the ones on page 218, as they will help you in doing many of the exercises and problems.

Reading Aids

Throughout this book you will find sections called Reading Algebra. These sections deal with such topics as problem-solving strategies and inequalities. Be sure to read these sections, as they will help you to better understand the subjects with which they deal.

SYMBOLS

Symbol	Meaning	Page
$\cdot$	$\times$ (times)	1
$=$	equals, is equal to	2
$\neq$	is not equal to	2
$(\ )$	parentheses—a grouping symbol	2
$[\ ]$	brackets—a grouping symbol	5
π	pi, a number approximately equal to $\frac{22}{7}$	8
$\therefore$	therefore	10
$\in$	is a member of, belongs to	10
$\stackrel{?}{=}$	is this statement true?	25
$-$	negative	30
$+$	positive	30
$-a$	opposite or additive inverse of a	34
$\|a\|$	absolute value of a	35
$<$	is less than	37
$>$	is greater than	37
$\frac{1}{b}$	reciprocal or multiplicative inverse of b	76
$\emptyset$	empty set, null set	112
$a:b$	ratio of a to b	277
(a, b)	ordered pair whose first component is a and second component is b	335
$f(x)$	f of x, the value of f at x	405
$\geq$	is greater than or equal to	449
$\leq$	is less than or equal to	449
$\cap$	the intersection of	465
$\cup$	the union of	465
$\approx$	is approximately equal to	506
$\sqrt{\ }$	principal square root	510
$\overleftrightarrow{AB}$	line AB	576
$\overline{AB}$	segment AB	576
AB	the length of $\overline{AB}$	576
$\overrightarrow{AB}$	ray AB	576
$\angle$	angle	576
$^\circ$	degree(s)	577
$\triangle$	triangle	581
$\sim$	is similar to	584
$\cos A$	cosine of A	587
$\sin A$	sine of A	587
$\tan A$	tangent of A	587
$P(A)$	probability of event A	599

Metric Units of Measure

Length:
- mm — millimeter
- cm — centimeter
- m — meter
- km — kilometer

Area:
- mm^2 — square millimeter
- cm^2 — square centimeter
- m^2 — square meter
- km^2 — square kilometer
- ha — hectare

Volume:
- cm^3 — cubic centimeter
- mL — milliliter
- L — liter

Time:
- s — second
- min — minute
- h — hour

Speed:
- m/s — meters per second
- km/h — kilometers per hour

Mass:
- mg — milligram
- g — gram
- kg — kilogram

Temperature: °C — degrees Celsius

Reading Algebra / Symbols

Close attention is needed to read mathematics because mathematical materials usually involve special symbols as well as words. And, often, those symbols can be read in several ways. Here are some examples.

$7 + 3$

"seven plus three"
"the sum of seven and three"
"add seven and three"
"seven increased by three"
"three more than seven"

$8 - 1$

"eight minus one"
"the difference of eight and one"
"subtract one from eight"
"eight decreased by one"
"one less than eight"

11×4

"eleven times four"
"the product of eleven and four"
"multiply eleven by four"

$10 \div 2$

"ten divided by two"
"the quotient of ten and two"
"divide ten by two"

$\frac{1}{2} \times 5$

"one half times five"
"one half of five"
"the product of one half and five"

$\frac{5}{2}$

"five halves"
"five divided by two"
"the quotient of five and two"

Exercises

Read each of the following expressions in at least three ways.

1. 4×8 **2.** $15 - 0$ **3.** $2 + 9$ **4.** $\frac{7}{4}$

Translate the given words into mathematical symbols and then write the common numeral for the number described.

Example Four increased by six ***Solution*** $4 + 6$; 10

5. Twelve decreased by five
6. Eleven more than six
7. The product of fifteen and three
8. Five less than thirty
9. Two thirds of six
10. Twice seven
11. The difference of fifty and thirty
12. The product of zero and nine

The symbols on the facing page are commonly used in mathematics. In studying this book, you will learn how to read and use them.

About the Photo

Deep-sea divers must exercise caution when diving because of the tremendous hydrostatic pressure at great depths. The increasing weight of the water as the diver descends causes hydrostatic pressure to increase, as is indicated in the table on page 1.

The air we breathe is a mixture of gases, approximately 78% nitrogen and 21% oxygen. However, at great depths these usually harmless gases can pose a hazard to divers. Under a pressure greater than two atmospheres oxygen becomes toxic. Breathing nitrogen at great depths can seriously impair a diver's judgment and reasoning ability. That is why breathing mixtures for divers generally consist of a large proportion of helium with a smaller proportion of oxygen.

Divers can descend as quickly as they like, but if they have been exposed to high pressure for a long period of time, they must ascend at a rate determined by the depth and duration of the dive and the breathing mixture used. A too rapid ascension can cause nitrogen, which is normally dissolved in body fluids, to form bubbles in blood vessels and tissues, resulting in the painful symptoms of decompression illness, or "the bends."

1 Introduction to Algebra

The diver in the photograph is swimming by a coral reef in the Red Sea. Depths below water level can be thought of as values of a variable, as discussed on the facing page.

Variables and Equations

1-1 Variables

Objective To simplify and to evaluate numerical expressions and variable expressions.

A scientist needed to gather data for an underwater experiment. Diving in sea water, the scientist measured the pressure of the water at different depths, as illustrated in the photograph at the left. These water pressures were then arranged in a table similar to the one below, which shows pressures at depths of 10, 20, 30, and 40 meters.

Depth in meters	Water pressure in atmospheres
10	0.104×10
20	0.104×20
30	0.104×30
40	0.104×40

Each of the expressions for water pressure fits the pattern

$$0.104 \times n$$

where the letter n stands for 10, 20, 30, or 40. We call n a *variable.*

A **variable** is a symbol used to represent one or more numbers. The numbers are called the **values of the variable.**

An expression, such as $0.104 \times n$, that contains a variable is called a **variable expression.** Expressions, such as 0.104×2, that name a particular number are called **numerical expressions** or **numerals.**

When you write a product that contains a variable, you usually omit the multiplication symbol.

$0.104 \times n$ is usually written $0.104n$.

$y \times z$ is usually written yz.

In numerical expressions for products like 0.104×20, you must use a multiplication symbol to avoid confusion. The raised dot $\cdot$ is also used as a multiplication sign.

0.104×20 can be written $0.104 \cdot 20$.

Teaching References

Lesson Commentary, pp. T72–T77

Assignment Guide, pp. T56–T57

Supplementary Materials

- Practice Masters 1-4
- Tests 1-3
- Resource Book
  - Diagnostic Tests in Arithmetic, pp. iv–4
  - Practice Exercises, pp. 67–69
  - Tests, pp. 5–8
  - Enrichment Activity, p. 146
- Algebra Action

Extra Practice

- Skills, pp. 607–608
- Problems, p. 633

Alternate Test, p. T10

Problem Solving Strategies

See p. T53 for a general discussion of problem solving strategies.

Looking for a Pattern
On p. 1 students are introduced to the concept of variable by observing the pattern formed by expressions for water pressure. In the Challenge on p. 39, students are asked to find the pattern that defines triangular numbers.

Drawing a Diagram
Students are encouraged to use sketches as problem solving aids in Sections 1-5 and 1-6. In Sections 1-7 and 1-8, number lines are used as diagrams that suggest important facts about real numbers.

Word Problem Plan
The useful five-step plan is presented on page 26 and used throughout the course.

Teaching Suggestions p. T72

Suggested Extensions p. T72

Chalkboard Examples

Simplify.

1. $(49 \div 7) + 5$
   $7 + 5 = 12$
2. $48 \div (8 - 2)$
   $48 \div 6 = 8$
3. $(15 + 12) \div (9 \div 3)$
   $27 \div 3 = 9$
4. The expression $(2 \times 6) + (2 \times 4)$ represents the perimeter of a rectangle with length 6 and width 4. Simplify the expression.
   $12 + 8 = 20$

Evaluate each expression if $n = 25$.

5. $(45 - n) + 10$
   $(45 - 25) + 10 =$
   $20 + 10 = 30$
6. $45 - (n + 10)$
   $45 - (25 + 10) =$
   $45 - 35 = 10$
7. Evaluate $(6x) - (2 + y)$ if $x = 9$ and $y = 6$.
   $(6 \times 9) - (2 + 6) =$
   $54 - 8 = 46$
8. Evaluate $\frac{x + 2}{3y}$ if $x = 4$ and $y = 2$.
   $\frac{4 + 2}{3 \times 2} = \frac{6}{6} = 1$

Common Error

Some students may need to be reminded that any number divided by itself is one. Students may think that the answer to Written Exercise 12, for example, is 0 because $\frac{4}{4}$ "cancels."

The number named by a numerical expression is called the **value of the expression.** Since the expressions $3 + 5$ and 8 name the same number, they have the same value. To show that these expressions have the same value, you use the *equals sign*, $=$. You write

$$3 + 5 = 8$$

and say "three plus five equals (or is equal to or is) eight." Of course, 8 is the *simplest*, or most common, name for the number eight.

The symbol $\neq$ means is not equal to. You write

$$3 + 5 \neq 7$$

to show that the expressions $3 + 5$ and 7 do not have the same value.

Replacing a numerical expression by the simplest name of its value is called **simplifying the expression.** In simplifying a numerical expression, you use the following principle.

Substitution Principle

Changing the numeral by which a number is named in an expression does not change the value of the expression.

Example 1 Simplify. **a.** $(56 \div 7) + 9$ **b.** $36 \div (9 - 3)$

Solution The parentheses ( ) show how the numerals in the expression are to be grouped. The numerals within parentheses are simplified first.

a. $(56 \div 7) + 9 = 8 + 9 = 17$
b. $36 \div (9 - 3) = 36 \div 6 = 6$

Note that to read the symbols "$(56 \div 7) + 9$," you may say "the sum of the *quantity* fifty-six divided by seven, plus nine."

Replacing each variable in a variable expression by a given value and simplifying the result is called **evaluating the expression** or **finding the value of the expression.**

Example 2 Evaluate $(5x) - (3 + y)$ if $x = 12$ and $y = 9$.

Solution Replace x with 12 and y with 9, and insert the necessary multiplication symbol. Then simplify the result.

$$\begin{aligned}(5x) - (3 + y) &= (5 \times 12) - (3 + 9)\\ &= 60 - 12\\ &= 48\end{aligned}$$

Oral Exercises

State whether or not each statement is true. Give a reason for your answer.

Example 1 $5 \times 4 = 10 + 10$ ***Solution*** True, because the value of both 5×4 and $10 + 10$ is 20.

Example 2 $2 \times 7 = 2 + 7$ ***Solution*** False, because $2 \times 7 = 14$, whereas $2 + 7 = 9$.

1. $9 \times 7 = 7 \times 9$

2. $4 \times 0 = 0 \times 6$

3. $8 \div 1 \neq 1 \div 8$

4. $48 \times \frac{1}{2} \neq 48 \times 0.5$

5. $3 \times (4 \times 9) = (3 \times 4) \times 9$

6. $(14 - 3) - 1 = 14 - (3 - 1)$

7. $\frac{(8 - 2)}{2} = 8 - 1$

8. $0.12 \times 5 = 1.2 \times 0.5$

Simplify each expression.

9. $9 + (5 \times 4)$ 29

10. $(9 + 5) \times 4$ 56

11. $17 - (3 \times 3)$ 8

12. $(17 - 3) \times 3$ 42

13. $\frac{(32 - 7)}{5}$ 5

14. $\frac{(13 + 11)}{(6 - 2)}$ 6

Evaluate each expression if $a = 1$, $b = 2$, and $c = 3$.

15. $4b$ 8

16. $6a$ 6

17. $c - 3$ 0

18. $9 - c$ 6

19. $\frac{2}{b}$ 1

20. $(5c) - 4$ 11

21. $b + (ac)$ 5

22. $(bc) + a$ 7

23. $3(a + 1)$ 6

24. $2(b - 2)$ 0

25. $\frac{a + b}{c}$ 1

26. $\frac{a}{c - b}$ 1

Written Exercises

Simplify each expression.

A

1. $(8 - 3) + 3$ 8

2. $9 + (18 - 2)$ 25

3. $5 \times (11 + 1)$ 60

4. $(13 - 6) \times 7$ 49

5. $(6 + 12) \div 3$ 6

6. $6 + (12 \div 3)$ 10

7. $29 - (0 \times 9)$ 29

8. $5 - (16 \div 4)$ 1

9. $(8 \times 17) + (2 \times 17)$ 170

10. $(12 \times 11) - (2 \times 11)$ 110

11. $(26 + 4) \div (30 \div 2)$ 2

12. $(40 \div 10) \div (1 \times 4)$ 1

Evaluate each expression if $x = 2$, $y = 1$, $z = 9$, $a = 7$, $b = 0$, and $c = 3$.

13. xy 2

14. ab 0

15. $z - (xc)$ 3

16. $y + (xa)$ 15

17. $(2c) + (2x)$ 10

18. $(3a) - (5y)$ 16

Additional Answers
Oral Exercises

1. true; both sides have value 63
2. true; both sides have value 0
3. true; $8 \neq \frac{1}{8}$
4. false; both sides have value 24
5. true; both sides have value 108
6. false; $(14 - 3) - 1 = 10$, $14 - (3 - 1) = 12$; $10 \neq 12$
7. false; $\frac{(8 - 2)}{2} = 3$, $8 - 1 = 7$; $3 \neq 7$
8. true; both sides have value 0.6

Additional A Exercises

Simplify each expression.

1. $(7 + 14) \times (6 \div 3)$ 42
2. $(2 \times 18) \div (9 \times 3)$ $\frac{4}{3}$
3. $(24 \div 12) \div 6$ $\frac{1}{3}$

Evaluate each expression if $x = 2$, $y = 1$, $z = 9$, $a = 7$, $b = 0$, and $c = 3$.

4. $3a - 2b$ 21
5. $4xyz - c$ 69
6. $\frac{2(a - x)}{ab + (x + c)}$ 2

Mixed Review Exercises

Perform the indicated operations.

1. $8 - 13 + 6 - 2$ $^{-}1$
2. a. $9 - (^{-}7)$ 16
   b. $16 - 17$ $^{-}1$
3. $^{-}315 \div 15$ $^{-}21$
4. $(^{-}6)(^{-}7)(^{-}8)$ $^{-}336$

Suggested Assignments

Minimum
3/1–20, 25–31 odd

Average
3/1–26, 29–38

Maximum
3/1–41 odd
7/1–14 odd, 15–17, 23–33

This assignment covers Sec. 1–1 and Sec. 1–2.

Evaluate each expression if $x = 2$, $y = 1$, $z = 9$, $a = 7$, $b = 0$, and $c = 3$.

19. $(bc) + 6y$ 6
20. $(xz) + (ca)$ 39
21. $(5y) \cdot (x + z)$ 55
22. $(4c) \cdot (z + b)$ 108
23. $\dfrac{(z - x)}{(a + b)}$ 1
24. $\dfrac{(c + z)}{(a - y)}$ 2

Simplify the expression on each side of the ___?___. Then make a true statement by replacing the ___?___ with the symbol $=$ or $\neq$.

B

25. $(8 + 3) \times (8 - 3)$ ___?___ $(8 \times 8) - (3 \times 3)$ 55; 55; $=$
26. $(5 + 2) \times (5 + 2)$ ___?___ $(5 \times 5) + (2 \times 2)$ 49; 29; $\neq$
27. $(7 - 1) \times (7 - 1)$ ___?___ $(7 \times 7) - (1 \times 1)$ 36; 48; $\neq$
28. $(6 + 4) \times (6 - 4)$ ___?___ $(6 \times 6) - (4 \times 4)$ 20; 20; $=$

Evaluate each expression shown in color for the given values of the variables.

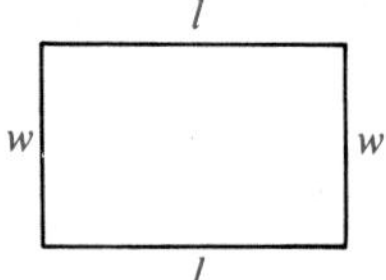

29. lw (Area of a rectangle)
    if $l = 25$ and $w = 12$ 300
30. $(2l) + (2w)$ (Perimeter of a rectangle)
    if $l = 50$ and $w = 40$ 180

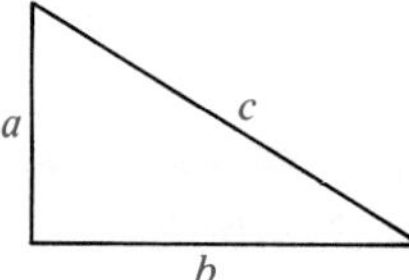

31. $(a + b) + c$ (Perimeter of a triangle)
    if $a = 29$, $b = 21$, and $c = 15$ 65
32. $\frac{1}{2} \cdot (ab)$ (Area of a right triangle)
    if $a = 17$ and $b = 36$ 306
33. $(1.8 \times C) + 32$ (Temperature in degrees Fahrenheit given degrees Celsius)
    if $C = 15$ 59
34. $\left(\frac{1}{2} \times g\right) \times (t \times t)$ (Distance in meters traveled by an object falling for t seconds)
    if $g = 9.8$ and $t = 16$ 1254.4
35. $P \times (rt)$ (Simple interest on a loan of P dollars)
    if $P = 5000$ (dollars), $r = 0.125$ (12.5% per year), and $t = 2$ (years) 1250
36. $\dfrac{W \times c}{1000}$ (Cost of electricity to operate an electric light for one hour)
    if $W = 75$ (watts) and $c = 9.5$ (cents) per kilowatt hour 0.7125

Make a true statement by replacing each variable with a numeral. If possible, find more than one replacement.

37. $n \times 1 = 1$ $n = 1$
38. $x + 5 = 5$ $x = 0$
39. $2\frac{1}{2} - y = 1 \times 2$ $y = \frac{1}{2}$
40. $\frac{3}{4} + m = 0.75 - m$ $m = 0$

C

41. $a \times a = 2a$ $a = 2, 0$
42. $(b \times b) + 3 = 4b$ $b = 1, 3$

1-2 Grouping Symbols

Objective To simplify expressions with and without grouping symbols.

Parentheses have been used to show you how to group the numerals in an expression. Different groupings may produce expressions for different numbers.

$$(600 \div 10) + 2 \text{ means } 60 + 2, \text{ or } 62.$$

$$600 \div (10 + 2) \text{ means } 600 \div 12, \text{ or } 50.$$

A **grouping symbol** is a device, such as a pair of parentheses, used to enclose an expression. Brackets [ ] are also used.

Multiplication symbols are often omitted from expressions with grouping symbols. For example,

$$9 \times (5 - 3) = 9(5 - 3) = 9(2).$$

Note that 9(2) stands for 9×2. Other ways to write this product using parentheses are (9)2 and (9)(2).

In a fraction such as $\frac{11 + 3}{12 - 5}$ the bar is a grouping symbol as well as a division sign.

$$\frac{11 + 3}{12 - 5} = \frac{14}{7} = 14 \div 7 = 2$$

Throughout your work in algebra you will use these symbols:

Grouping Symbols

Parentheses	Brackets	Fraction Bar
$9(5 - 3)$	$9[5 - 3]$	$\frac{11 + 3}{12 - 5}$

Example 1 Read each expression and then give its value.

a. $9(5 - 3)$ **b.** $9(5) - 3$

Solution

a. Solution 1 "Nine times the quantity five minus three."

Solution 2 "The product of nine and the difference of five and three."

Solution 3 "Multiply nine by the difference of five and three."

$$9(5 - 3) = 9(2) = 18$$

b. Solution 1 "Nine times five minus three."

Solution 2 "Multiply nine by five. Subtract three from the product."

$$9(5) - 3 = 45 - 3 = 42$$

Teaching Suggestions p. T73

Suggested Extensions p. T73

Chalkboard Examples

Read each expression and then give its value.

1. $4(6 - 3)$ "Four times the quantity six minus three;" $4(3) = 12$.
2. $4(6) - 3$ "Four times six minus three;" $24 - 3 = 21$.

Simplify.

3. $15 - [21 \div (3 + 4)]$
   $15 - [21 \div 7] =$
   $15 - 3 = 12$
4. $6 + 11 - 9 \div 3$
   $6 + 11 - 3 =$
   $17 - 3 = 14$
5. $\frac{5 + 30 \div 2}{12 - 8}$
   $\frac{5 + 15}{4} = \frac{20}{4} = 5$

Evaluate each expression if $a = 4$, $b = 7$, and $c = 10$.

6. $3a + 5b - 2c$
   $3(4) + 5(7) - 2(10) =$
   $12 + 35 - 20 =$
   $47 - 20 = 27$
7. $\frac{4a + 2b}{c - a}$
   $\frac{4(4) + 2(7)}{10 - 4} = \frac{16 + 14}{6} =$
   $\frac{30}{6} = 5$

Common Error

Many students mistakenly think that they should always multiply before dividing. Thus, when they attempt to simplify an expression such as $6 \div 3 \times 2$, they get 1 for an answer instead of the correct answer, 4.

Supplementary Material

Resource Book, p. 67

Suggested Assignments

Minimum
7/1–23, 25, 26
S 4/21–24
Average
7/1–20, 23–28, 31, 32
S 4/27, 28, 39–42
Maximum
Sec. 1–2 is covered in the assignment for Sec. 1–1.

Caution! When you read expressions that contain parentheses, be sure that your words show that the symbols inside any pair of parentheses name one quantity.

If an expression contains more than one grouping symbol, first simplify the numeral in the innermost grouping symbol. Then work toward the outermost grouping symbol until the simplest expression is found.

Example 2 Simplify $18 - [52 \div (7 + 6)]$.

Solution

$$\begin{aligned} 18 - [52 \div (7 + 6)] &= 18 - [52 \div 13] \\ &= 18 - 4 \\ &= 14 \end{aligned}$$

When there are no grouping symbols, you take the following steps to simplify an expression.

Step 1 Do all multiplications and divisions in order from left to right.

Step 2 Do all additions and subtractions in order from left to right.

$$\begin{array}{c} 29 + \underbrace{15 \times 4} \\ \underbrace{29 + 60} \\ 89 \end{array} \qquad \begin{array}{c} 19 - 7 + \underbrace{12 \times 2} \div 8 \\ 19 - 7 + \underbrace{24 \div 8} \\ \underbrace{19 - 7} + 3 \\ \underbrace{12 + 3} \\ 15 \end{array}$$

Example 3 Evaluate $\frac{4a + 5b}{3a - b}$ if $a = 3$ and $b = 8$.

Solution Replace a with 3 and b with 8, and insert the necessary multiplication symbols. Then simplify the result.

$$\begin{aligned} \frac{4a + 5b}{3a - b} &= \frac{4(3) + 5(8)}{3(3) - 8} \\ &= \frac{12 + 40}{9 - 8} \\ &= \frac{52}{1} = 52 \end{aligned}$$

Note that in Example 3 each of the variable expressions $4a$, $5b$, and $3a$ is considered to be grouped even though no grouping symbol is used; that is, $4a = (4 \times a)$, $5b = (5 \times b)$, and $3a = (3 \times a)$. Note also that

$$yz \div 10n \quad \text{means} \quad (y \times z) \div (10 \times n)$$

Oral Exercises

In Exercises 1-10, the given expression involves one or more operations to be performed. Describe the operation(s) for each expression.

Example $3(x + 1) + 5$

Solution 1 "Multiply three by the sum of x and one, and then add five to the product."

Solution 2 "Add x and one, multiply the sum by three, and then add five to the product."

1. $7y$ **2.** $z - 2$ **3.** $4 + 9x$ **4.** $8z - 5$ **5.** $6(z + 4)$

6. $4(2x - 1)$ **7.** $\frac{z - y}{x}$ **8.** $\frac{z}{x + y}$ **9.** $\frac{13 - x}{y} - 2$ **10.** $\frac{9 + 6x}{z + 8}$

11-20. In Exercises 1-10, evaluate each expression if $x = 1$, $y = 3$, and $z = 7$.

11. 21 12. 5 13. 13 14. 51 15. 66

16. 4 17. 4 18. $\frac{7}{4}$ 19. 2 20. 1

Written Exercises

Evaluate each expression if $x = 1$, $y = 0$, $z = 8$, $a = 2$, $b = 3$, and $c = 5$.

A **1.** $ay + z$ 8 **2.** $cx + y$ 5 **3.** $b - 2x$ 1 **4.** $xb - a$ 1

5. $8z + 5x$ 69 **6.** $7c - ab$ 29 **7.** $z(c - x) + a$ 34 **8.** $(z - a)x + y$ 6

9. $(3b - 2a)(c + y)$ 25 **10.** $(c - 4x)(2a + z)$ 12 **11.** $\frac{ac - z}{x + b}$ $\frac{1}{2}$

12. $\frac{bz - 2x}{31 - 4c}$ 2 **13.** $a(c + x) - \frac{zb}{a}$ 0 **14.** $y(ac - x) + \frac{z}{b}$ $\frac{8}{3}$

Simplify each expression.

15. $\frac{7 \times 2 + 2 \times 5 \times 5}{12 - 3 - 1}$ 8 **16.** $\frac{48 \div 6 + 2}{9 - 7}$ 5

17. $(26 - 5 + 9 \div 3) \div (18 \div 9)$ 12 **18.** $16(13 - 8) - 40 \div (10 - 5)$ 72

Evaluate each expression in color for the given values of the variables.

19. $2(a + b)$ (Perimeter of a parallelogram) if $a = 6.5$ and $b = 24.3$ 61.6

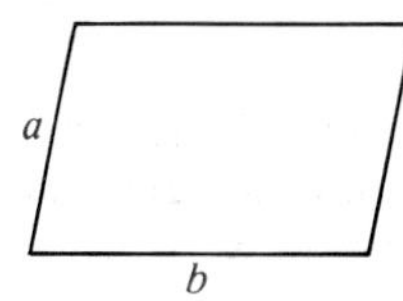

Ex. 19

Additional Answers
Oral Exercises

1. Multiply 7 by y.
2. Subtract 2 from z.
3. Multiply 9 by x, and then add 4.
4. Multiply 8 by z, and then subtract 5.
5. Add z and 4, and then multiply the sum by 6.
6. Multiply 2 by x, subtract 1, and then multiply the difference by 4.
7. Subtract y from z, and then divide the difference by x.
8. Add x and y, and then divide z by the sum.
9. Subtract x from 13, divide the difference by y, and then subtract 2 from the quotient.
10. Multiply 6 by x and add 9; add z and 8. Then divide the sum of 9 and $6x$ by the sum of z and 8.

Additional A Exercises

Evaluate each expression if $x = 1$, $y = 0$, $z = 8$, $a = 2$, $b = 3$, and $c = 5$.

1. $a(b + c) + 3a$ 22
2. $(x + y)(z - a)$ 6
3. $\frac{bc - 5}{z + a}$ 1
4. $(3z - 2a) - 6b$ 2

Simplify.

5. $84 \div 6 \div (2 + 5)$ 2

Evaluate for the given values of the variables.

6. $\frac{1}{2}bh$ (A of a triangle) $b = 12$, $h = 9$ 54

Mixed Review Exercises

Perform the indicated operations.

1. $7.35 - 2.473$ 4.877
2. $(9.6)(4.3)$ 41.28
3. $185.73 \div 12.3$ 15.1
4. $6.43 + 247.51 + 61 + 91.035$ 405.975

Evaluate each expression in color for the given values of the variables.

20. $2a + b + c$ (Perimeter of an isosceles trapezoid)
if $a = 34$, $b = 58$, and $c = 25$ 151

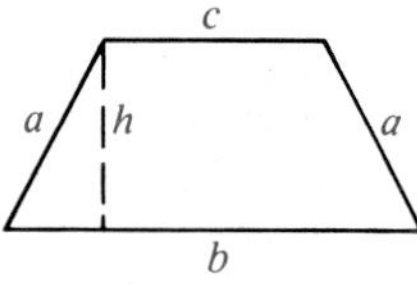

Exs. 20 and 21

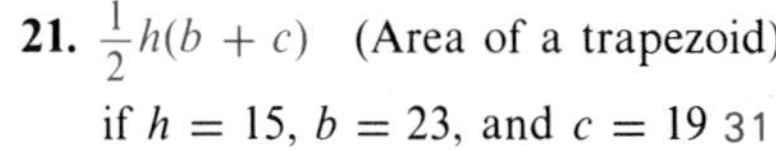

21. $\frac{1}{2}h(b + c)$ (Area of a trapezoid)
if $h = 15$, $b = 23$, and $c = 19$ 315

22. $(\pi r)r$ (Area of a circle)
if $r = 28$. Use $\frac{22}{7}$ as an approximate value for π. 2464

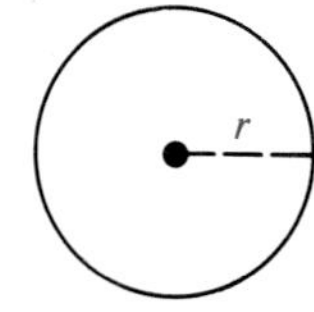

Ex. 22

B **23.** $2(r + h) + \pi r$ (Perimeter of a Norman window) 16.28
if $r = 2.00$ and $h = 3.00$. Use 3.14 as an approximate value for π.

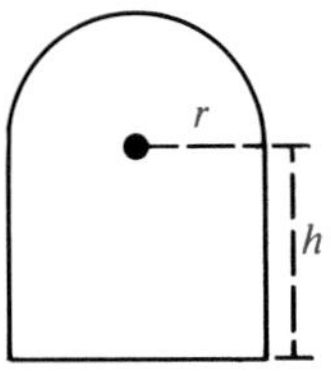

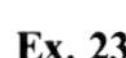

Ex. 23

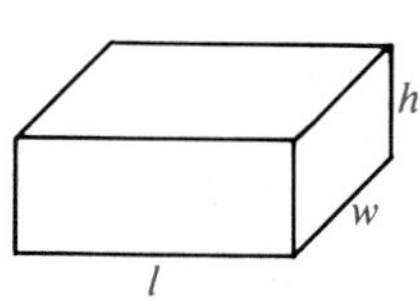

Ex. 24

24. $2(lw + wh + lh)$ (Surface area of a rectangular solid)
if $l = 14$, $w = 12$ and $h = 10$ 856

Simplify the expression on each side of the __?__. Then make a true statement by replacing the __?__ with the symbol = or ≠.

25. $\frac{24 \times 8}{12 + 4}$ __?__ $\frac{12 \times 4}{6 + 2}$ 12; 6; ≠

26. $\frac{23 + 19}{7 \times 2}$ __?__ $(54 \div 9) - 3$ 3; 3; =

27. $2[3(12 - 7)]$ __?__ $(5 \times 5) + 5$ 30; 30; =

28. $3[36 \div (3 + 6)]$ __?__ $30 - [(36 \div 3) + 6]$ 12; 12; =

29. $\frac{(16 \times 6) \div 24}{4 - (12 \div 4)} + 1$ __?__ $23 - \frac{34 + 4}{8 - 6}$ 5; 4; ≠

30. $1 + \frac{31 - 4}{7 + 2}$ __?__ $\frac{8 \times 12 - 16}{108 \div 3 + 4} + 2$ 4; 4; =

C **31.** $[(3 \times 2 + 5)2]2 - 4$ __?__ $3 \times 2 \times 2 \times 2 + 5 \times 2 \times 2 - 4$ 40; 40; =

32. $[(7 \times 3 - 4)3]3 + 6$ __?__ $7 \times 3 \times 3 - 4 \times 3 \times 3 + 6$ 159; 33; ≠

33. $1 \times 1 + 2 \times 2 + 3 \times 3 + 4 \times 4$ __?__ $\frac{4(4 + 1)(2 \times 4 + 1)}{6}$ 30; 30; =

34. $(4 \times 1 + 1) + (4 \times 2 + 1) + (4 \times 3 + 1) + (4 \times 4 + 1)$ __?__ $2[4(4 + 1)] + 4$ 44; 44; =

35. $\frac{[9 - (4 \times 2)] + (3 \times 8)}{[(28 \div 4) + 3] - 5}$ __?__ $[3 + (3 \times 3) - (33 \div 3)] \times \frac{14 - 4}{7 - 2}$ 5; 2; ≠

36. $(2)(2)(2) + (3)(3)(3) + (4)(4)(4) + (5)(5)(5)$ __?__ $(2 + 1)(2 + 1)(2 + 3)(2 + 3) - 1$ 224; 224; =

Computer Key-In

People communicate with computers by using *programs*. Programs tell the computer what to do. However, it is not always necessary for a person to be able to write a program in order to use a computer. Programs can be written in such a way that an operator can use them by answering a series of questions that are written into the program. Nevertheless, the best way to learn what a computer can and cannot do is to learn a little about programming. We shall use the programming language BASIC.

To program arithmetic calculations in BASIC, you use the following symbols:

+ for addition	* for multiplication
− for subtraction	/ for division

Parentheses are used when grouping symbols are needed.

BASIC follows the order of operations described on page 6.

A BASIC program is made up of numbered *statements*. These statements are usually numbered 10, 20, 30, . . . , instead of 1, 2, 3, . . . , so that additional statements may be inserted later, if they are found to be necessary.

Here is a two-line program:

```
10  PRINT 21 * 34 + 35/7
20  END
```

The last statement tells the computer that the program is finished. Line 10 tells the computer to compute $21 \times 34 + 35 \div 7$ and print the answer. Type in the program, and then type the *command* RUN. The computer will respond by typing 719.

Exercises

Change the expression in line 10 above to each of the following and RUN the changed program.

1. 20 * (48 + 72)/8 300

2. 20 * 48 + 72/8 969

3. 30 * 42 − 16 * 5 1180

4. 30 * (42 − 16) * 5 3900

Translate each expression into BASIC. Substitute the BASIC statement in line 10 above and RUN the program.

5. $\frac{21 + 33}{6}$ (21 + 33)/6; 9

6. 36(42 − 17) 36 * (42 − 17); 900

7. (24 + 10)(24 − 10)
(24 + 10) * (24 − 10); 476

8. $\frac{144 - 24}{100 - 40}$
(144 − 24)/(100 − 40); 2

Note: The program given above can be used to do Exercises 15–18 on page 7.

Teaching Suggestions p. T73

Suggested Extensions p. T74

Chalkboard Examples

1. Solve the equation $x + 3 = 7$ if the domain of x is $\{1, 2, 3, 4, 5\}$. $\{4\}$
2. Solve the equation $3 + n = n + 3$ if $n \in \{1, 2, 3\}$. $\{1, 2, 3\}$
3. Solve the equation $13 - y = 10$ if the domain of y is $\{0, 1, 2, 3\}$. $\{3\}$
4. Solve the equation $\frac{1}{4}n = 1$ if $n \in \{1, 2, 3, 4\}$. $\{4\}$
5. Solve the equation $2x + 3 = 7$ if $x \in \{0, 1, 2, 3\}$. $\{2\}$
6. Solve the equation $z(3 - z) = 2$ if $z \in \{0, 1, 2, 3\}$. $\{1, 2\}$

Common Error

Be sure that students do not write $x + 5 = 9 = 4$ instead of

$$x + 5 = 9$$
$$x = 4$$

in the process of solving an equation. Students should be reminded that an equation has exactly two sides separated by one = sign.

Supplementary Material

Practice Master 1

1-3 Equations

Objective To find solution sets of equations.

Here are three equations:

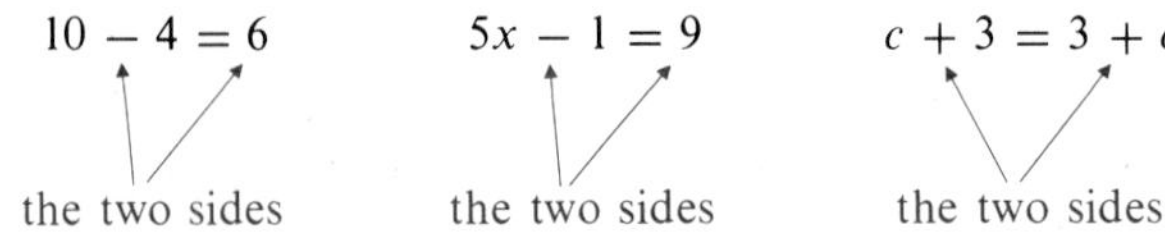

An **equation** is formed by placing an equals sign between two numerical or variable expressions, called the **sides** of the equation.

Sentences containing variables (like the equations $5x - 1 = 9$ and $c + 3 = 3 + c$) are called **open sentences.** The given set of numbers that a variable may represent is called the **domain** of the variable. When you replace each variable in an open sentence by one of the numbers in its domain, you obtain either a true statement or a false statement.

You may use *braces* { } to show a set of numbers. A short way to write "the set whose members are 1, 2, and 3" is $\{1, 2, 3\}$.

Example 1 The domain of x is $\{1, 2, 3\}$. Find any values in the domain of x for which $5x - 1 = 9$ becomes a true statement.

Solution Replace x in turn by 1, 2, and 3.

$$5x - 1 = 9$$
$$5(1) - 1 = 9 \quad \text{False}$$
$$5(2) - 1 = 9 \quad \text{True}$$
$$5(3) - 1 = 9 \quad \text{False}$$

$\therefore$ (read "therefore") the required value of x is 2. ***Answer***

Any value of a variable that converts an open sentence into a true statement is called a **solution** or **root** of the sentence, and is said to **satisfy** the sentence.

The set of *all* solutions of an open sentence is called the **solution set** of the sentence. Finding the solution set is called **solving** the sentence.

You may use braces to show a solution set. Thus, for Example 1, you may say either

"The solution is 2" or "The solution set is $\{2\}$."

Example 2 Solve the equation $y(4 - y) = 3$ if $y \in \{0, 1, 2, 3, 4\}$ (read "y is a member of (or belongs to) the set whose members are 0, 1, 2, 3, and 4").

Solution Replace y in turn by 0, 1, 2, 3, and 4.

$y(4 - y) = 3$
$0(4 - 0) = 3$ False
$1(4 - 1) = 3$ True
$2(4 - 2) = 3$ False
$3(4 - 3) = 3$ True
$4(4 - 4) = 3$ False

$\therefore$ the solution set is $\{1, 3\}$. ***Answer***

You can see that the solution set of the equation $c + 3 = 3 + c$ is the set of *all* numbers, because the sentence is true no matter what number is substituted for c. If you are asked to solve this equation *over the domain* $\{0, 1, 2, 3\}$, you state that the solution set is the domain itself, $\{0, 1, 2, 3\}$.

Oral Exercises

Solve each equation if $x \in \{0, 1, 2, 3, 4, 5, 6\}$. If there is no solution over the given domain, state, "No solution."

1. $x + 2 = 6$ {4} **2.** $x - 1 = 4$ {5} **3.** $2x = 6$ {3} **4.** $x \div 3 = 1$ {3}
5. $x - 3 = 3$ {6} **6.** $x + 1 = 5$ {4} **7.** $x + 2 = 2 + x$ **8.** $x + 4 = x$ No sol.
9. $3x = x + 2x$ {0, 1, 2, 3, 4, 5, 6} **10.** $3x = x + 2$ {1} **11.** $x + x = 0$ {0} **12.** $(5 - x)x = 0$ {0, 5}

7. {0, 1, 2, 3, 4, 5, 6}

Written Exercises

Solve each equation if $x \in \{0, 1, 2, 3, 4, 5, 6, 7\}$.

A

1. $x + 5 = 9$ {4} **2.** $6 + x = 11$ {5} **3.** $x - 2 = 3$ {5} **4.** $x - 5 = 1$ {6}
5. $7 - x = 2$ {5} **6.** $6 - x = 3$ {3} **7.** $2x = 12$ {6} **8.** $5x = 10$ {2}
9. $8x = 16$ {2} **10.** $2x = 14$ {7} **11.** $3x = 0$ {0} **12.** $0 = 4x$ {0}
13. $x \div 3 = 1$ {3} **14.** $x \div 3 = 2$ {6} **15.** $\frac{1}{2}x = 2$ {4} **16.** $\frac{1}{3}x = 1$ {3}
17. $x \cdot x = 1$ {1} **18.** $9x = 9$ {1} **19.** $x - x = 0$ {0, 1, 2, 3, 4, 5, 6, 7} **20.** $x \cdot x = 25$ {5}

Solve each equation over the domain $\{0, 1, 2, 3, 4, 5, 6, 7, 8, 9\}$.

B

21. $2a + 9 = 17$ {4} **22.** $3b - 4 = 11$ {5} **23.** $10 = 8c - 6$ {2}
24. $13 = 6d - 5$ {3} **25.** $9 + 9r = 81$ {8} **26.** $5 + 5s = 50$ {9}
27. $2t = t + 7$ {7} **28.** $3w = w \cdot 3$ {0, 1, 2, 3, 4, 5, 6, 7, 8, 9} **29.** $2z = z \cdot z$ {0, 2}
30. $y(8 - y) = 0$ {0, 8} **31.** $(6 - v)(1 + v)v = 0$ {0, 6} **32.** $27k = (3k)(3k)(3k)$ {0, 1}

Write two different equations for which the solution set over the domain $\{0, 1, 2, 3, 4\}$ is the given set.

C

33. $\{3\}$ **34.** $\{0\}$ **35.** $\{0, 1, 2, 3, 4\}$ **36.** $\{0, 3\}$

Suggested Assignments

Minimum
11/1–25
Average
11/2–20 even, 21–34
R 12/Self-Test 1
Maximum
11/2–20 even, 21–33, 35
S 8/34–36

Additional A Exercises

Solve each equation if $x \in \{0, 1, 2, 3, 4, 5, 6\}$.

1. $x + 5 = 10$ {5}
2. $16 - x = 13$ {3}
3. $9x = 36$ {4}
4. $x \div 4 = 1$ {4}
5. $\frac{1}{6}x = 1$ {6}
6. $x \cdot x = 16$ {4}

Mixed Review Exercises

Perform the indicated operations.

1. $11\frac{1}{3} + 2\frac{2}{5} + \frac{4}{15}$ 14
2. $6\frac{2}{3} \div \frac{5}{6}$ 8
3. $14\frac{1}{6} - 12\frac{1}{2}$ $1\frac{2}{3}$
4. $2\frac{1}{4} \times 5\frac{1}{3}$ 12

Additional Answers Written Exercises

33–36. Answers may vary. An example is given.

33. $x + 5 = 8$; $3z = 9$

34. $x(x + 7) = 0$; $m = 2m$

35. $4k - 2 = 2(2k - 1)$; $2x + 1 = 2x + 1$

36. $m(m - 3) = 0$; $p \cdot p = 3p$

Quick Quiz

Evaluate each expression if $a = 2$, $b = 5$, and $c = 4$.

1. $(4a - 3) + (3b - c)$ 16
2. $b + \frac{c}{a}$ 7
3. $ab - 3(c - a)$ 4
4. $\frac{3(a + 4)}{2b - c}$ 3

Solve each equation if $x \in \{0, 1, 2, 3, 4\}$.

5. $x + 3 = 6$ $\{3\}$
6. $14 - 3x = 8$ $\{2\}$

Additional Answers Calculator Key-In

Please note that answers to calculator exercises throughout the book may vary due to differences in calculators.

Self-Test 1

Vocabulary

variable (p. 1)
value of a variable (p. 1)
variable expression (p. 1)
numerical expression (p. 1)
value of a numerical expression (p. 2)
simplify an expression (p. 2)
substitution principle (p. 2)
evaluate an expression (p. 2)
grouping symbol (p. 5)
equation (p. 10)
side of an equation (p. 10)
open sentence (p. 10)
domain of a variable (p. 10)
solution (p. 10)
root (p. 10)
satisfy an open sentence (p. 10)
solution set (p. 10)
solve an open sentence (p. 10)

Evaluate each expression if $x = 5$, $y = 4$, and $z = 12$.

1. $(3x - 1) + (2y + z)$ 34 **2.** $x + \left(\frac{z}{y}\right)$ 8 **Obj. 1-1, p. 1**

3. $xy - 2(z - x)$ 6 **4.** $\frac{2(x + 3)}{7y - z}$ 1 **Obj. 1-2, p. 5**

Solve each equation if $x \in \{0, 1, 2, 3, 4\}$.

5. $x + 1 = 4$ $\{3\}$ **6.** $10 - 2x = 4$ $\{3\}$ **Obj. 1-3, p. 10**

Check your answers with those at the back of the book.

Calculator Key-In

Does your calculator follow the steps for simplifying an expression stated on page 6? Experiment with your calculator by entering the following example exactly as it appears here:

$$8 + 3 \times 4 =$$

If your calculator displays the answer 20, it followed the order of operations you learned for simplifying expressions: multiplication before addition. Your calculator has an algebraic operating system. The answer 20 is correct.

If your calculator displays the answer 44, it performed the addition and the multiplication in the order in which you pressed the keys. One way to get the correct answer on your calculator is to multiply 3 and 4 first and then add 8, just as you would if you were using pencil and paper.

Use a calculator to simplify each expression.

1. $21 - 2.8 \times 7.5$ 0 **2.** $0.8 + 1.2 \div 0.4$ 3.8

3. $0.75 \div 0.25 \times 0.5 - 1.4$ 0.1 **4.** $0.45 \times 369 + 0.55 \times 369$ 369

5. $364 \div 13 \times 15{,}873 - 5291 \times 7 \times 3$ 333,333

Applications and Problem Solving

1-4 Words into Symbols: Expressions

Objective To represent numerical relationships stated in words by mathematical expressions.

To solve problems using algebra, you must often translate word phrases about numbers into numerical or variable expressions.

Suppose you think of two numbers, one nine more than the other. If x stands for the smaller number, then the greater number is represented by

$$x + 9.$$

Example 1 Represent each word phrase by a variable expression.

a. Nine less than a number x

b. Nine times a number x

c. One ninth of a number x

d. Nine divided by a number x

Solution **a.** $x - 9$ **b.** $9x$ **c.** $\frac{1}{9}x$ **d.** $\frac{9}{x}$

Example 2 Jan is y years old. Use y to write an expression for each of the following numbers.

a. Jan's age two years ago

b. Jan's age five years from now

c. Jan's father's age, if he is three times as old as Jan

d. Jan's cousin's age, if he is half as old as Jan

e. Kit's age, if the sum of Jan's and Kit's ages is 28

Solution **a.** $y - 2$ **b.** $y + 5$ **c.** $3y$ **d.** $\frac{1}{2}y$ **e.** $28 - y$

Formulas are often used in algebra. **Formulas** are equations that state rules about measurements. Here are four formulas:

$A = lw$	Area of rectangle = length of rectangle × width of rectangle
$P = 2l + 2w$	Perimeter of rectangle = (2 × length) + (2 × width)
$D = rt$	Distance traveled = rate × time traveled
$C = np$	Cost = number of items × price per item

Teaching Suggestions p. T74

Suggested Extensions p. T74

Chalkboard Examples

Represent each word phrase by a variable expression.

1. Six less than a number x $x - 6$
2. Four times a number x $4x$
3. One fifth of a number x $\frac{1}{5}x$
4. Two more than twice a number x $2x + 2$

Lee weighs n lb (pounds). Use n to write an expression for each of the following numbers.

5. Lee's weight after losing two lb $n - 2$
6. Lee's weight after gaining three lb $n + 3$
7. Lee's uncle's weight, if he weighs twice as much as Lee $2n$
8. Lee's sister's weight, if the sum of their weights is 136 lb $136 - n$

Using the given variable, write an expression for the measure required to complete each statement.

9. A rectangle has length 8 cm and width $(w + 2)$ cm. The perimeter is _?_ cm. $2 \times 8 + 2(w + 2) = 16 + 2w + 4 = 20 + 2w$
10. You travel for $(x + 2)$ hours at 70 km/h. The distance you travel is _?_ km. $70(x + 2)$

(continued)

11. In 5 years Jan will be d years old. Jan is now ? years old. $d - 5$

12. You buy 6 apples at m cents each and 2 cans of juice at n cents each. The total cost is ? cents. $6m + 2n$

Common Error

A particularly troublesome type of phrase for many students is one such as "five less than a number." Many students will write $5 - x$ instead of $x - 5$. To get students to write the correct expression, point out that to have five less than a number we must have a number to subtract five from.

Suggested Assignments

Minimum
Day 1: 15/1–17
R 12/*Self-Test 1*
Day 2: 16/18–26
20/1–15
This assignment finishes Sec. 1-4 and starts Sec. 1-5.
Average
Day 1: 15/1–6, 7–31 odd
Day 2: 16/22–30 even
20/1–12
This assignment finishes Sec. 1-4 and starts Sec. 1-5.
Maximum
15/2–34 even
R 12/*Self-Test 1*

Example 3 Using the given variable, write an expression for the measure required to complete each statement.

a. A rectangle has length 10 units and width d units. The area is ? square units.

b. A rectangle has length 16 cm (centimeters) and width w cm. The perimeter is ? cm.

c. You travel $(t + \frac{1}{2})$ hours at 80 km/h (kilometers per hour). The distance you travel is ? km.

d. You buy 5 pencils at x cents each and 3 pads at y cents each. The total cost is ? cents.

Solution

a. Area = length × width = $10d$

b. Perimeter = (2 × length) + (2 × width) = $2 \times 16 + 2w = 32 + 2w$

c. Distance = rate × time = $80(t + \frac{1}{2})$

d. Cost of pencils = $5x$; cost of pads = $3y$; total cost = $5x + 3y$

Oral Exercises

Represent each word phrase by a variable expression. Use *n* for the variable.

Example Seven less than double the number ***Solution*** $2n - 7$

1. Eight times the number $8n$
2. The product of three and the number $3n$
3. Five greater than the number $n + 5$
4. One fourth of the number $\frac{1}{4}n$
5. The number decreased by four $n - 4$
6. The number divided by five $\frac{n}{5}$
7. Nine less than half the number $\frac{1}{2}n - 9$
8. Nine more than twice the number $2n + 9$

Complete each statement with a variable expression.

9. A rectangle has width 6 units and length $(x + 2)$ units. Its area is ? square units. $6(x + 2)$
10. You travel for $(t - 2)$ hours at 75 km/h. You travel ? km. $75(t - 2)$
11. You buy $(m + 5)$ rolls at 40 cents each. The cost is ? cents. $40(m + 5)$
12. Cheryl earns $(p + 3)$ dollars per hour. In 8 hours, she earns ? dollars. $8(p + 3)$
13. Hal is y years old. Four years ago he was ? years old. $y - 4$
14. The Eiffel Tower was erected n years ago. Three years from now it will have been standing ? years. $n + 3$
15. The Science Museum was d years old 15 years ago. It is now ? years old. $d + 15$
16. Nine years from now Jo will be g years old. She is now ? years old. $g - 9$

Written Exercises

Match the word phrase in Column I with the corresponding variable expression in Column II. (You will not use all the variable expressions.)

	COLUMN I	COLUMN II
A	1. Four less than half a number d	a. $2(x + 3)$
	2. Seven decreased by three times a number k	b. $3x + 1$
	3. Twice the sum of a number and three a	c. $3x - 7$
	4. The product of five and two more than a number i	d. $\frac{1}{2}x - 4$
	5. The difference of three times a number and one e	e. $3x - 1$
	6. Six times the difference of a number and five j	f. $5x + 2$
		g. $\frac{1}{2}(x - 4)$
		h. $2x + 3$
		i. $5(x + 2)$
		j. $6(x - 5)$
		k. $7 - 3x$
		l. $6x - 5$

Represent the required numbers in terms of the given variables.

7. What number is two more than twice the number a? $2a + 2$
8. What number is one less than half the number b? $\frac{1}{2}b - 1$
9. What number is six less than one third of the number y? $\frac{1}{3}y - 6$
10. What number is three more than eight times the number z? $8z + 3$
11. The sum of two numbers is thirty. One number is x. What is the other number? $30 - x$
12. The sum of two numbers is eighteen. One number is w. What is the other number? $18 - w$

Using the given variable, write an expression for the measure required to complete each statement.

13. Fred is t cm tall. Joe is 6 cm shorter than Fred. Joe is __?__ cm tall. $t - 6$
14. Wilma weighs m kg (kilograms). Fran is 3 kg heavier than Wilma. Fran weighs __?__ kg. $m + 3$
15. In x years there are __?__ months. $12x$
16. In y weeks there are __?__ days. $7y$
17. The length of a rectangular lot is 15 m (meters) less than twice its width, w m. The length is __?__ m. The perimeter is __?__ m. $2w - 15$; $2(2w - 15) + 2w$, or $6w - 30$

Additional A Exercises

Represent the required numbers in terms of the given variables.

1. What number is 5 times the sum of 6 and twice the number x? $5(2x + 6)$
2. What number is 3 times the number b, increased by 7? $3b + 7$
3. What number is the difference of 4 times the number z and 5? $4z - 5$
4. What number is 19 decreased by the product of 4 and the number a? $19 - 4a$
5. The sum of two numbers is 5. The smaller is x, what is the larger? $5 - x$
6. Dan is n years old. What will be his age in 5 years? $n + 5$

Mixed Review Exercises

Give the arithmetic operation indicated by the following phrases.

1. "diminished by" subtraction
2. "of" multiplication
3. "twice" mult. (by 2)
4. "increased by" addition
5. "quotient" division
6. "decreased by" subtraction
7. "difference" subtraction
8. "sum" addition
9. "product" multiplication

Using the given variable, write an expression for the measure required to complete each statement.

$\frac{1}{2}l + 3$; $2\left(\frac{1}{2}l + 3\right) + 2l$, or $3l + 6$

18. The width of a rectangular field is 3 km more than half the length, l km. The width is ? km. The perimeter is ? km.

19. Dick, who is a years old, is 4 years younger than Tom. Tom is ? years old. $a + 4$

20. Mae is 3 years older than Ray. If Mae is b years old, then Ray is ? years old. $b - 3$

B **21.** Oranges sell for s cents per pound at Lou's Convenience Store. They cost 5 cents per pound less at the Big L supermarket. Ten pounds of oranges cost ? cents at Lou's and ? cents at the Big L. $10s$; $10(s - 5)$

22. Vera drove at the rate of r km/h. Her friend's average speed was 3 km/h faster. In two hours, Vera traveled ? km and her friend traveled ? km. $2r$; $2(r + 3)$

23. For lunch, a student bought a glass of milk costing y cents and a sandwich costing eight times as much. The student spent ? for lunch. $y + 8y$, or $9y$ cents

24. One day a service station sold x L (liters) of gasoline for cash. Six times as much gasoline was bought that day with credit cards. The service station sold a total of ? L of gasoline on that day. $x + 6x$, or $7x$

25. The difference between two numbers is five. The greater number is n. The smaller number is ?. $n - 5$

26. The difference between two numbers is eight. The smaller number is m. The larger number is ?. $m + 8$

27. A store sold r cameras during the first week of December. Weekly sales increased by 120 cameras during each of the next two weeks of the month. During the third week of December the store sold ? cameras. $r + 240$

28. On the third weekly examination, the class average was 78. If the average had increased at the rate of p points per week, the class average on the first examination was ?. $78 - 2p$

29. Mel is t years old. Joe, who is twice as old as Mel was 6 years ago, is ? years old. $2(t - 6)$

30. Rhonda is k years old. Mary, who is half as old as Rhonda will be 5 years from now, is ? years old. $\frac{1}{2}(k + 5)$

31. Each of the congruent sides of an isosceles triangle is s cm long. The third side is 6 cm shorter. The perimeter of the triangle is ? cm. $2s + (s - 6)$, or $3s - 6$

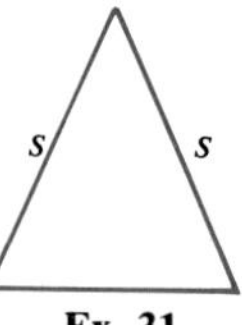

Ex. 31

32. One number is two more than a certain number n. Another number is five less than n. The sum of the three numbers is ?. $(n + 2) + n + (n - 5)$, or $3n - 3$

C **33.** An apple has 29 more calories than a peach and 13 fewer calories than a banana. If an apple has c calories, then there are __?__ calories in a fruit cup made with one apple, two peaches, and one banana.

34. A pound of peanuts contains about 10 fewer grams of carbohydrates than a pound of walnuts and 26 fewer grams of carbohydrates than a pound of almonds. If a pound of peanuts contains w grams of carbohydrates, then a mix of one pound of peanuts, one pound of walnuts, and one pound of almonds contains __?__ grams of carbohydrates.

33. $c + 2(c - 29) + (c + 13)$, or $4c - 45$

34. $w + (w + 10) + (w + 26)$, or $3w + 36$

Computer Key-In

BASIC uses variables to hold numerical values. One way to give a value to a variable is to use an INPUT statement. The INPUT statement causes the computer to print a question mark and wait for you to type in a value.

Given below is a program that will find the area and the perimeter of a rectangle. The expressions in quotation marks will be printed exactly as they appear in the program. The semicolon at the end of line 40 will cause the question mark from line 50 to be printed right after the quoted expression. The semicolon at the end of line 60 has the same effect on the question mark from line 70.

```
10  PRINT "TO FIND THE AREA AND THE PERIMETER OF A"
20  PRINT "                 RECTANGLE:"
30  PRINT                                    ← Leaves a blank line
40  PRINT "WHAT IS THE LENGTH";
50  INPUT L
60  PRINT "WHAT IS THE WIDTH";
70  INPUT W
80  PRINT "THE AREA IS: ";L*W
90  PRINT "THE PERIMETER IS: ";2*L+2*W
100  END
```

Notice that the computer has been given the area and perimeter formulas in the program. That is, we have solved the problems. The computer simply does the computation.

RUN this program with several sets of values for L and W.

Exercises

1. Write a program to find the area and perimeter of a square. RUN the program for several sets of values.
2. Write a program to find the area and perimeter of an isosceles trapezoid. RUN the program for several sets of values.

Teaching Suggestions p. T75

Suggested Extensions p. T75

Chalkboard Examples

Write an equation for each word sentence.

1. The sum of twice the number t and four is twenty. $2t + 4 = 20$
2. Three is six less than one third the number p. $3 = \frac{1}{3}p - 6$
3. Five times the number a is thirty more than twice a. $5a = 2a + 30$

Let x represent the number described by the words in parentheses. Write an equation that represents the given information.

4. A rectangle has an area of 45 cm^2 and a length of 9 cm. (width of the rectangle) $9x = 45$
5. Dana babysits for 3 hours and earns \$6. (Dana's hourly wage) $3x = 6$
6. Kerry walked to the library and back in 34 minutes. The trip to the library took four minutes more than the trip back.
   a. Choose a variable to represent the number of minutes Kerry took to walk back and use it to represent the minutes spent walking to the library. w; $w + 4$
   b. Write an equation that represents the given facts. $(w + 4) + w = 34$

1-5 Words into Symbols: Equations

Objective To translate word sentences describing the equality of numbers into equations.

Applications of algebra frequently require you to translate word sentences about numbers into equations.

Example 1 Write an equation for each word sentence.

a. The difference of the number t and nine is fifty-four.
b. Five is eight more than twice the number w.
c. One half of the number a is ten less than three times a.

Solution

a. $t - 9 = 54$
b. $5 = 2w + 8$
c. $\frac{1}{2}a = 3a - 10$

The next examples show how you can choose a variable to represent a number and then write an equation to relate the facts in a given situation.

Example 2 A gardener needs 78 m of fence to enclose a rectangular garden. The length of the garden is 9 m more than the width.

a. Choose a variable to represent the width in meters and use it to write an expression for the length.

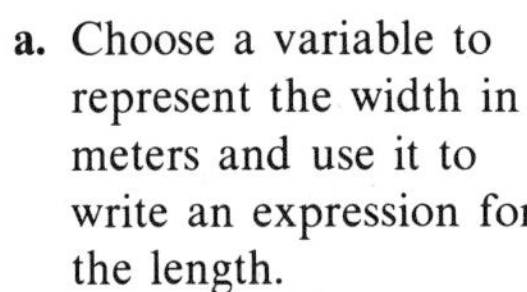

b. Write an equation that represents the given facts.

Solution

a. Let w = width in meters. Then $w + 9$ = length in meters.

b. Draw a sketch to help you see the relationship given. Since the perimeter is 78 m, you have:

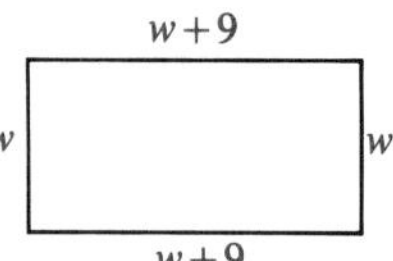

$$2(w + 9) + 2w = 78$$

Example 3 Fran rode her bicycle from her home to school and back in 23 min (minutes). The return trip took two minutes less than the trip to school.

a. Choose a variable to represent the number of minutes Fran rode from her home to school and use it to write an expression for the number of minutes for the return trip.

b. Write an equation that represents the given facts.

Solution 1 a. Let $x =$ the number of minutes Fran rode to school; then $x - 2 =$ the number of minutes to return.

b. Since the round-trip took 23 min you have:

$$x + (x - 2) = 23$$

Solution 2 a. Let $x =$ the number of minutes Fran rode to school; then $23 - x =$ the number of minutes to return.

b. Since the return trip took 2 min less than the trip to school,

$$23 - x = x - 2.$$

Notice that the equations obtained in Solutions 1 and 2 of Example 3 are not the same. However, as soon as your familiarity with algebra increases, you will see that these equations have the same solution set.

Oral Exercises

State an equation for each sentence.

1. Twelve more than the number p is 37. $p + 12 = 37$
2. Eight is 5 less than twice the number r. $8 = 2r - 5$
3. Forty decreased by the number m is 24.5. $40 - m = 24.5$
4. The number a increased by $\frac{2}{3}$ is $8\frac{1}{3}$. $a + \frac{2}{3} = 8\frac{1}{3}$
5. The sum of one third of the number s and 12 is 23. $\frac{1}{3}s + 12 = 23$
6. The product of 58 and the number n is 1. $58n = 1$
7. The quotient of the number b and 4 is 8. $\frac{b}{4} = 8$
8. Three fourths of the number h is 192. $\frac{3}{4}h = 192$
9. The product of 12 and the quantity 1 less than the number d is 84. $12(d - 1) = 84$
10. Multiply the sum of twice the number x and 3 by 7, and the product is 126. $7(2x + 3) = 126$

7. Gregg's room has an area of 15 m^2. The width is 2 m less than the length.

a. Choose a variable to represent the length and use it to write an expression for the width. x; $x - 2$

b. Draw a sketch to help you see the given relationship.

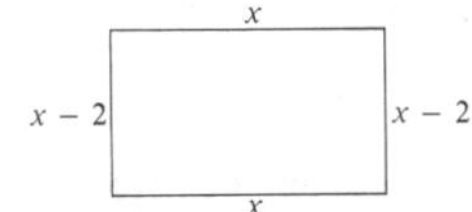

c. Write an equation that represents the given facts. $x(x - 2) = 15$

Supplementary Material

Test 1

Suggested Assignments

Minimum
21/16–27
S 11/26–29
Day 2 of Sec. 1-4 finishes Sec. 1-4 and starts Sec. 1-5.

Average
21/13–23 odd, 25–28
S 16/32, 33
Day 2 of Sec. 1-4 finishes Sec. 1-4 and starts Sec. 1-5.

Maximum
22/1–31 odd
S 4/40, 42

State an equation for each sentence.

11. Divide the difference of 15 and the number y by 4, and the quotient is 32. $\frac{15 - y}{4} = 32$
12. The product of the number that is one more than c and the number that is one less than c is 35. $(c + 1)(c - 1) = 35$

State an equation that represents the given sentence.

Example Rick has n dimes worth a total of \$9.80.

Solution Express n and \$9.80 in the same unit, cents. $10n = 980$

13. In m slices of cheese, each containing 115 calories, there are 920 calories. $115m = 920$
14. After a deposit of a dollars in an account containing \$74, the new balance is \$132. $74 + a = 132$
15. The customer received \$34.80 in change from a fifty-dollar bill given in payment for an item costing x dollars. $50 - x = 34.80$
16. A total of b twenty-four cent stamps costs \$4.32. $0.24b = 4.32$
17. A baseball priced at \$2.50 costs $\frac{2}{15}$ as much as a bat costing k dollars. $2.50 = \frac{2}{15}k$
18. The winner received 486 votes, or $\frac{2}{3}$ of the total number, v, of votes cast. $486 = \frac{2}{3}v$
19. The area of a rectangular field that is 8 m wide and y m long is 108 m^2 (square meters). $8y = 108$
20. After selling z cans of tomatoes from a 180-can shipment, the store had 38 cans left. $180 - z = 38$

Written Exercises

Use the given facts to state an equation that represents the sentence shown in color.

Example Yolanda is b years old. Sara is 2 years younger. The sum of their ages is 34.

Solution $b + (b - 2) = 34$

A 1. In April, the O'Briens spent \$150 more for food than for housing. Their food bill was p dollars. For both food and housing they spent \$675 in April. $p + (p - 150) = 675$

2. On a trip, the Romeros traveled 640 km farther by airplane than by automobile. They traveled q km by automobile. On the trip, they traveled 900 km. $q + (q + 640) = 900$

3. A house cost 5.5 times as much as the lot it stands on. The lot cost c dollars. The house and lot cost $105,000. $c + 5.5c = 105{,}000$

4. Jill is half as old as her brother, who is k years old. The sum of their ages is 32. $\frac{1}{2}k + k = 32$

5. Team A scored one point less than twice team B's score. Team B scored x points. Team A scored 47 points. $2x - 1 = 47$

6. Team X scored five points less than three times team Y's score. Team Y scored a points. Team X scored 67 points. $3a - 5 = 67$

7. Fred is 3 years older than Max, who is t years old. The sum of their ages is 29. $t + (t + 3) = 29$

8. The length of a rectangle is 9 cm more than its width. Its width is s cm. The area of the rectangle is 630 cm^2 (square centimeters). $s(s + 9) = 630$

9. A bag of potatoes weighing 74 kg weighs half a kilogram more than twice as much as a bag of onions weighing z kg. $74 = 2z + \frac{1}{2}$

10. The length of a corridor that is w meters wide is 2 m more than 5 times its width. $l = 5w + 2$

In Exercises 11–17,
a. Choose a variable to represent the number described by the words in parentheses.
b. Write an equation that represents the given information.

Example The perimeter of an equilateral triangle is 54 cm. (Length of a side)

Solution a. Recall that an equilateral triangle has three sides of equal length. Let s = the length of each side in centimeters.

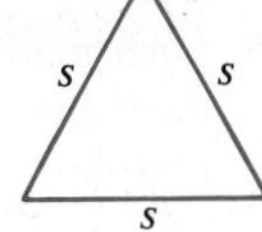

b. $3s = 54$

11. The perimeter of a square is 68 m. (Length of a side) s; $4s = 68$

12. A dozen eggs cost $1.49. (Cost of one egg) e; $12e = 1.49$

13. Ten years ago Roger was 7 years old. (Roger's age now) a; $a - 10 = 7$

14. Eight years from now Sue will be 23 years old. (Sue's age now) a; $a + 8 = 23$

15. A car dealer has sold all but 14 of the cars in a consignment of 285 subcompacts. (Number of cars sold) c; $285 - c = 14$

16. A student solved all but the last 3 problems in an assignment of 20. (Number of problems solved) p; $20 - p = 3$

17. One eighth of a pizza sold for 95¢. (Cost of the whole pizza) p; $\frac{1}{8}p = 0.95$

Additional A Exercises

Use the given facts to state an equation that represents the underlined sentence.

1. Jay's score on a test, t, was 7 points less than Janet's. Janet's score was 86. $t + 7 = 86$

2. Melinda's salary is $2000 more than half of her husband's salary, s. Their combined income is $45,000. $\left(\frac{1}{2}s + 2000\right) + s = 45{,}000$

3. A pool's width, w, is 5 m less than its length. The perimeter is 46 m. $2w + 2(w + 5) = 46$

4. Mary Wong spent only $\frac{4}{5}$ of her budgeted grocery money, g. She spent $72. $\frac{4}{5}g = 72$

In Exercises 5-7:
a. Choose a variable to represent the number described by the words in parentheses.
b. Write an equation that represents the given information.

5. Tomato sauce is on special at 5 cans for $1. (cost of one can) $5c = 1.00$

6. A bus traveled 640 km in 8 h. (rate of travel) $8r = 640$

7. $\frac{1}{2}$ acre of land sold for $12,000. (cost of one acre) $\frac{1}{2}a = 12{,}000$

Mixed Review Exercises

1. 25% of what number is 43? 172
2. What percent of 120 is 6? 5%
3. What number is 15% of 3300? 495
4. Sarah is being promoted to a new job with a salary increase of 10%. If her current salary is \$22,000, how much will she earn in her new job? \$24,200

In Exercises 18–34,
a. Choose a variable to represent the number described by the words in parentheses.
b. Write an equation that represents the given information.

18. A seventeen-year-old building is one fourth as old as a nearby bridge. (Age of the bridge) $b; \frac{1}{4}b = 17$

19. A train traveled 462 km at the rate of 132 km/h. (Number of hours traveled) $h; 132h = 462$

20. A rectangular floor is tiled with 928 square tiles. The floor is 32 tiles long. (Number of tiles in the width) $t; 32t = 928$

21. In the floor plan of a house, dimensions are shown $\frac{1}{100}$ of actual size. The length of the family room in the plan is 8.5 cm. (Actual length of the room) $l; \frac{1}{100}l = 8.5$

22. A season ticket good for fifteen admissions to a theme park sells for \$33.75. (Cost of one admission with this ticket) $a; 15a = 33.75$

23. An astronaut spent 42.8 days in space. This was 3.2 days longer than her previous record. (Number of days in her previous record) $d; d + 3.2 = 42.8$

24. The last check written on an account was for \$79.43. The next bank statement showed an overdraft of \$5.32 on the account. (Amount in the account before the last check was written) $a; a + 5.32 = 79.43$

B 25. Each marble in a bag of 24 marbles is either red or blue. There are 3 more blue marbles than twice the number of red ones. (Number of red marbles) $r; r + (2r + 3) = 24$

26. The sum of three numbers is 120. The second of the numbers is eight less than the first, and the third is four more than the first. (First number) $n; n + (n - 8) + (n + 4) = 120$

27. In an isosceles triangle whose perimeter is 54 cm, the base is 9 cm longer than each of the two congruent sides. (Length of each of the congruent sides) $s; s + s + (s + 9) = 54$

28. A purse contains \$3.50 in nickels and dimes. There are 16 more nickels than dimes in the purse. (Number of dimes) $d; 10d + 5(d + 16) = 350$

29. Ten years from now, Sofia will be three times as old as she was eight years ago. (Sofia's age now) $a; a + 10 = 3(a - 8)$

30. The hourly rate for a typist is seventy-five cents more than the hourly rate for a file clerk. In five hours, the typist earns as much as the file clerk does in six hours. (Hourly rate for the file clerk) $c; 5(0.75 + c) = 6c$

31. If a stone were 5 kg heavier, its mass would be 1 kg more than twice what it is. (Mass of the stone) $m;\ m + 5 = 1 + 2m$

32. Jill is three times as old as her brother, Jack. Two years ago, the sum of their ages was 12. (Jack's age now) $j;\ (j - 2) + (3j - 2) = 12$

C 33. The length of one side of a triangular lot is 6 m less than three times the length of the second side. The third side is 8 m longer than the first side. The perimeter of the lot is 80 m. (Length of the second side) $s;\ (3s - 6) + s + (3s + 2) = 80$

34. Phyl is 2 years older than Maria and Maria is 4 years older than Les. The sum of their ages is 37. (Maria's age) $m;\ (m + 2) + (m - 4) + m = 37$

Biographical Note / *Albert Einstein*

Albert Einstein was born in Ulm, Germany, in 1879. He attended school in Munich and did his college work in Switzerland where his family had moved. As he was not a very distinguished student (excelling only in mathematics and science), Einstein was unable to secure a teaching position upon graduation in 1901 and ended up working as a minor official in the Swiss patent office. The job, however, did leave him time to pursue his scientific studies.

In 1905 Einstein published five papers, three of which were to have a profound effect on science. One paper helped to establish the quantum, or particle, theory of light and for this Einstein was awarded the 1921 Nobel Prize in physics. A second paper contained equations that described molecular motion and that could be used to work out the size of molecules.

It was Einstein's paper on the special theory of relativity that made him famous. This theory, later generalized in 1915, supplanted Isaac Newton's theories of the universe when dealing with objects whose speeds approach that of light. The theory was essentially proved in 1919 by two teams of British astronomers who observed the bending of light during the solar eclipse of that year, an occurrence predicted by Einstein's theory.

After the publication of his papers, Einstein became a professor at the University of Zurich. In 1913 he went to the University of Berlin where he remained until 1933, when he took a position with the Institute for Advanced Study in Princeton, New Jersey. At the time of his death in 1955, Einstein, like Newton, left science vastly different from the way it was before he began his work.

Teaching Suggestions p. T75

Suggested Extensions p. T76

Chalkboard Examples

Use the five-step plan to solve each problem.

1. This year the football team won 3 more games than last year. If the total games won in both years is 15, how many games were won last year?

Step 1 The problem asks for the number of games won last year.

Step 2 Let g = the number of games won last year. Then $g + 3$ = the number won this year.

Step 3 $g + (g + 3) = 15$

Step 4 $g = 6$

Step 5 If the team won 6 games last year, they won $6 + 3 = 9$ games this year. Is the total equal to 15?

$6 + 9 \stackrel{?}{=} 15$

$15 = 15 \checkmark$

$\therefore$ the team won 6 games last year.

2. If twice a number is decreased by 3, the result is 15. Find the number.

Step 2 Let n = the number.

Step 3 $2n - 3 = 15$

Step 4 $n = 9$

$\therefore$ the number is 9.

1-6 Solving Problems

Objective To identify five steps in solving word problems.

An important type of problem in algebra is the *word problem.* A word problem describes a situation in which certain numbers are related to each other. If you can state the relationship in an equation, then you can solve the problem by solving the equation.

Here are two simple examples to show you a general plan for solving word problems. This five-step problem solving plan is summarized in the chart on page 26.

Example 1 On a street 75 m long, a fire hydrant is placed so that it is 1 m farther from one end of the street than from the other end. How far is the hydrant from each end of the street?

Solution

Step 1 Read the problem carefully a few times. What numbers are asked for? What information is given? Drawing a sketch may help.

The problem asks for the number of meters from the hydrant to each end of the street.

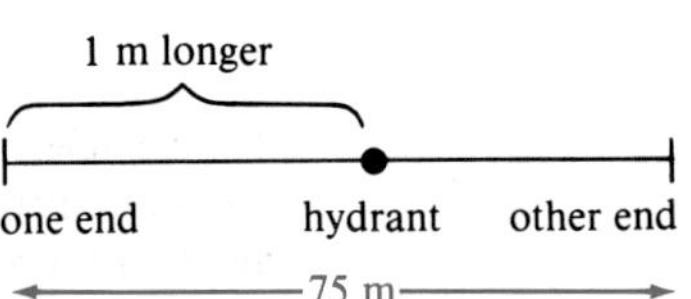

Step 2 Choose a variable. Use it with the given facts to represent the numbers in the problem.

Let d = distance in meters from the hydrant to the closer end of the street.

Then, $1 + d$ = distance in meters from the hydrant to the farther end.

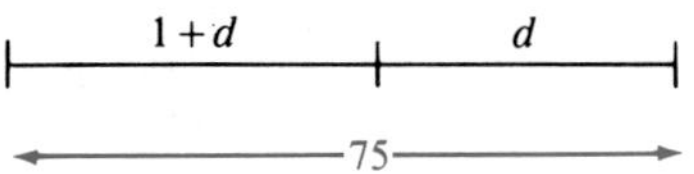

Step 3 Write an equation based on the given facts.

The sketch helps you to see that

$$(1 + d) + d = 75.$$

Step 4 Solve the equation.

The diagram below shows why

$$d + d = 74.$$

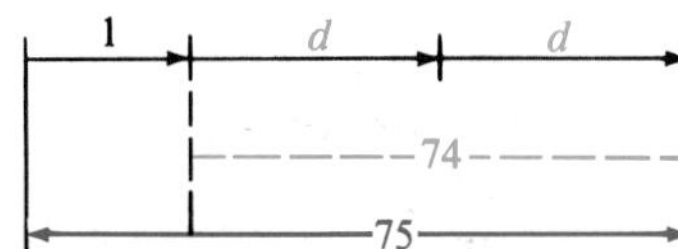

From arithmetic, you know that $37 + 37 = 74$.

$$\therefore d = 37$$
$$1 + d = 38$$

Step 5 Check your results with the statement of the problem. Give the answer.

Does the sum of the distances from the hydrant to the ends of the street equal the total length of the street?

$$37 + 38 \stackrel{?}{=} 75$$
$$75 = 75 \quad \checkmark$$

∴ the hydrant is 38 m from one end and 37 m from the other end of the street. ***Answer***

Example 2 A food scientist measured the vitamin C in an orange and a banana. She found that the orange contained 66 mg (milligrams) of the vitamin. That was 18 mg less than seven times the number of milligrams of vitamin C in the banana. How much vitamin C was in the banana?

Solution

Step 1 The problem asks for the number of milligrams of vitamin C in the banana. There are 66 mg in the orange. This is 18 less than 7 times the number in the banana.

Step 2 Let n = number of milligrams of vitamin C in the banana. Then $7n - 18$ = the number of milligrams of vitamin C in the orange.

(*Solution continued on next page.*)

3. A square tile has a perimeter of 60 cm. What is the length of one side of the tile?

Step 2 Let s = length of one side. Then $4s$ = the perimeter.
Step 3 $4s = 60$
Step 4 $s = 15$
∴ the length of one side is 15 cm.

4. A survey found that twice as many people preferred product B to product A. If 150 people were surveyed, how many preferred product A?

Step 2 Let p = people who preferred product A. Then $2p$ = people who preferred product B.
Step 3 $p + 2p = 150$
Step 4 $p = 50$
∴ 50 people preferred product A.

Common Error

Be sure that students represent each quantity described in the problem very specifically (Step 2). Students who do not, often write equations (Step 3) that do not represent the facts given in problems such as Problems 7-9 on page 27. For example, such a student might write the equation $x + 4 = 22$ instead of the correct equation, $x + (x + 4) = 22$, to represent the information given in Problem 7.

Supplementary Materials

Practice Master 2
Resource Book, p. 68

Suggested Assignments

Minimum
Day 1: 26/*P*: 1–7
Day 2: 27/*P*: 7–12
28/*Self-Test 2*

Average
Day 1: 27/*P*: 1–8
S 22/29–32
Day 2: 27/*P*: 9–14
R 28/*Self-Test 2*

Maximum
Day 1: 26/*P*: 1–8
S 23/32–34
Day 2: 27/*P*: 9–15
R 28/*Self-Test 2*

Step 3 The number of milligrams of vitamin C in the orange is 66.

$$7n - 18 = 66$$

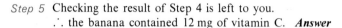

Step 4 The diagram suggests why

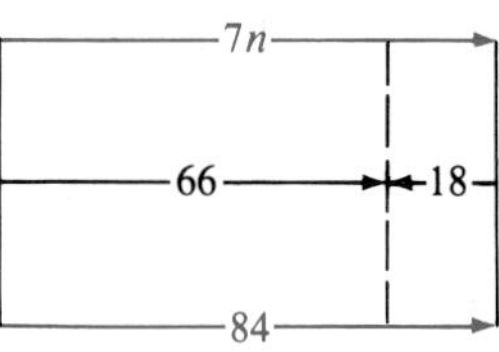

$$7n = 84.$$

From arithmetic, you know that

$$7 \cdot 12 = 84.$$
$$\therefore n = 12$$

Step 5 Checking the result of Step 4 is left to you.
$\therefore$ the banana contained 12 mg of vitamin C. ***Answer***

The five steps used to solve the problems in Examples 1 and 2 form a plan that often helps in solving word problems.

Plan For Solving a Word Problem

Step 1 Read the problem carefully a few times. Decide what numbers are asked for and what information is given. Making a sketch may be helpful.

Step 2 Choose a variable and use it with the given facts to represent the number(s) described in the problem.

Step 3 Reread the problem. Then write an open sentence that represents relationships among the numbers in the problem.

Step 4 Solve the open sentence and find the required numbers.

Step 5 Check your results with the words of the problem. Give the answer.

In Examples 1 and 2, we solved the equation obtained in Step 3 of this plan by inspection. Often, you cannot solve the equation that easily. Therefore, developing other methods to solve equations is an important goal of the study of algebra.

Problems

Use the five-step plan to solve each problem. Write out each step.

A
1. The area of a rectangle 12 units long is 103.2 square units. What is the width of the rectangle? 8.6 units

2. Ann is skimming across the water on a sailboard at an average rate of 20 km/h. How long will it take her to travel 8 km? 0.4 h

3. An airplane's altimeter reads 982.5 m. What is the plane's altitude if this reading is 2.8 m less than the true reading? 985.3 m

4. The first one-mile speed record was made by Henry Ford in 1904 when he drove the mile in 39.40 s (seconds). This time was 33.62 s slower than the record achieved in 1970. What was the record time in 1970? 5.78 s

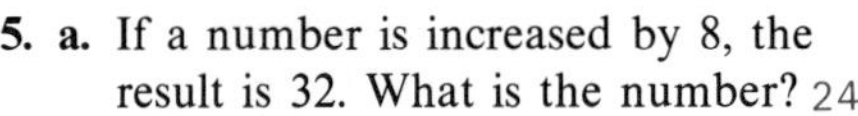

5. a. If a number is increased by 8, the result is 32. What is the number? 24
   b. If four times another number is increased by 8, the result is 32. Find the number. 6

6. a. If a number is decreased by 14, the result is 39. What is the number? 53
   b. If half of another number is decreased by 14, the result is 39. Find the number. 106

7. On a grand jury of 22 people, there were 4 more women than men. How many men were on the jury? 9

8. In a county election 7836 people cast valid votes for one or the other of two candidates for sheriff. The loser lost the election by 178 votes. How many votes did the winner receive? 4007

9. There were twice as many brown eggs as white eggs in a shipment of nine dozen eggs. How many white eggs were in the shipment? 36

10. Water is a compound made up of 8 parts "by mass" of oxygen and 1 part "by mass" of hydrogen. How many grams of hydrogen are there in 765 g (grams) of water? 85 g

B 11. A hockey team played 86 games and finished only 2 games in a tie. It lost one sixth as many games as it won. How many games did it win? 72

12. Algonquin City levies a tax of 5 cents per dollar on all restaurant meals. Including tax and tip, the cost of a meal was \$8.77. The tip was \$1.00. What was the cost of the meal before the tax and tip? \$7.40

13. A soccer field has a perimeter of 348 m. The width is 37 m less than the length. What are the dimensions of the field? 105.5 m long and 68.5 m wide

14. One of the longer sides of An Wong's rectangular lot borders on a straight river. He needs 500 m of fence to fence the three sides not on the river. If the length of the lot is 65 m more than the width, what are the dimensions of the lot? 145 m wide and 210 m long

C 15. At the beginning of a seven-week speed reading course, Ted read at the rate of 250 words per minute (wpm). At the end of the course, his reading speed was 1020 wpm. What was the average weekly increase in his reading speed over the course? 110 wpm

Additional A Exercises

Use the five-step plan to solve each problem. Write out each step.

1. The area of a triangle with altitude 7 cm is 63 cm^2. What is the base of the triangle? (Area of a triangle = $\frac{1}{2}bh$) 18 cm
2. Jane can bicycle 18 km/h. How long will it take her to travel 24 km? $1\frac{1}{3}$ h
3. In a class election, the winner had only 6 more votes than the loser. If 122 class members voted, how many votes did the loser get? 58
4. Sam weighs three times as much as his younger brother. If together they weigh 132 lb, how much does Sam weigh? 99 lb
5. In Laura's ski club, there are 17 more boys than girls. If there are 63 members, how many are boys? 40

Mixed Review Exercises

1. Find the solution set of $2 - x = 4$ if $x \in \{^{-}3, {}^{-}2, {}^{-}1, 0, 1, 2, 3\}$. $\{^{-}2\}$
2. Simplify: $42 - 7 \times 6 + 3$ 3
3. Write a variable expression for "the product of 9 and 7, decreased by the sum of 3 and 4." $9 \times 7 - (3 + 4)$
4. Write an equation for the word sentence "The sum of 94, 63 and the number m is 426." $94 + 63 + m = 426$

Quick Quiz

1. A variable expression for the sum of six and five times the number n is __?__. $6 + 5n$
2. In the morning, a cyclist rode for h hours at 20 km/h. In the afternoon, the cyclist, riding at the same speed, rode for 2 hours longer than in the morning. The distance traveled in the afternoon was __?__ km. $20(h + 2)$

Write an equation that represents the given information.

3. One fourth of the number x is nine less than x. $\frac{1}{4}x = x - 9$
4. A piece of wire 17 m long is cut so that one piece is y m long and the other is 2 m more than twice as long as the first piece. $y + (2y + 2) = 17$
5. Use the five-step plan to solve this problem. Together Sean and Kim spent 8 hours painting a room. Kim painted for 2 hours longer than Sean. How many hours did Sean spend painting? *S.1*: The problem asks for the number of hours Sean painted; *S.2*: Let p = no. of hours Sean painted. Then $p + 2$ = no. of hours Kim painted; *S.3*: $p + (p + 2) = 8$; *S.4*: $p = 3$; *S.5*: $3 + (3 + 2) = 8$; $\therefore$ Sean painted for 3 h.

Self Test 2

Vocabulary formula (p. 13)

1. A variable expression for nine times the difference of the number n and one is __?__. $9(n - 1)$ **Obj. 1-4, p. 13**
2. One person traveled for t hours at 60 km/h. Another person traveled three hours longer at the same speed. The second person traveled __?__ km. $60(t + 3)$

Write an equation that represents the given information.

3. Half of the number a is 7 less than a. $\frac{1}{2}a = a - 7$ **Obj. 1-5, p. 18**
4. A 100-meter length of coaxial cable is cut so that one piece is c m long and the other is 10 m more than twice as long as the first piece. $c + (2c + 10) = 100$
5. Use the five-step plan to solve this problem. **Obj. 1-6, p. 24**
Carmen worked 7 hours on a computer program. She spent 2 hours longer testing the program than writing it. How long did she spend writing the program? 2.5 hours

Check your answers with those at the back of the book.

Historical Note / *Why We Call It "Algebra"*

The word "algebra" comes from the title of a ninth-century mathematical treatise by the mathematician and astronomer Muhammed ibn-Musa al-Khwarizmi. The book, entitled *hisab al-jabr w'al muqabalah,* which means "the science of reduction and comparison," deals with the solving of equations. While the entire work may not have been original, it was the first time that algebra was systematically discussed as a distinct branch of mathematics. Al-Khwarizmi's book made its way into Europe and was translated into Latin in the twelfth century as *Ludus algebrae et almucgrabalaeque*. The title was eventually shortened to "algebra," which is what this branch of mathematics is called today.

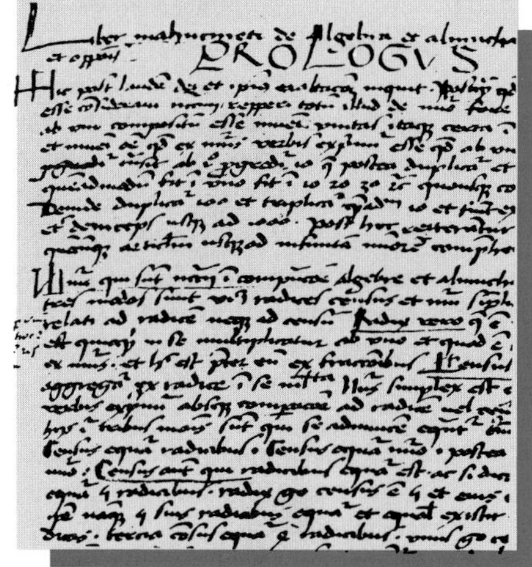

Reading Algebra / *Problem-Solving*

Accurate reading is a vital part of problem solving. When you read a problem, go very slowly and carefully to be sure that you fully understand every word, fact, and idea. Look up any words that you do not know in a dictionary (or in the glossary at the back of this book if they are mathematical terms). Reread the problem several times and give special attention to any parts that give you difficulty.

When you have read the information carefully, try to answer any questions asked. You can then check your answers with those printed at the back of the book or with your teacher. If your answer is wrong, try rereading the problem. Try to discover your error, because good problem solvers learn from their mistakes as well as their successes.

A good way to find your error is to explain to a classmate or other friend how you reached your answer. Explaining to someone else—or even explaining aloud to yourself—often helps you to clarify your own thinking.

Now try these exercises and remember: *good problem solvers are careful readers*.

Exercises

One day a cafeteria served twice as much milk as apple juice, and three times as much milk as fruit juice. A total of 660 cartons of the three drinks, at an average cost of 45 cents each, was served. This is 100 more than 80% of the usual number of cartons served.

1. If x represents the number of cartons of fruit juice sold, write an expression to represent the number of cartons of apple juice. $a = \frac{3}{2}x$
2. Which of the given information is necessary to determine the number of cartons of milk sold? served twice as much milk as apple juice, served three times as much milk as fruit juice; total $= 660$
3. Write an equation to determine the number of cartons usually sold. $0.8n + 100 = 660$
4. Rob found the number of cartons of milk served by using the equation $x + 2x + 3x = 660$, where x represents the number of cartons of milk served. Was this method correct? Explain. No, correct equation is $x + \frac{1}{2}x + \frac{1}{3}x = 660$
5. If x represents the number of cartons of apple juice served, what does $\frac{2}{3}(660 - x)$ represent? $\frac{2}{3}$ the total of milk and fruit juice served
6. Which is greater, the number of cartons of apple juice served, or the number of cartons of fruit juice served? Apple juice
7. Based on the given information, is it possible to determine the total cost of the cartons served? Yes; $c = 0.45(660)$
8. If 180 cartons of apple juice were served, how many cartons of fruit juice were served? 120
9. Write an equation to determine the number of cartons of milk served. $x + \frac{1}{2}x + \frac{1}{3}x = 660$
10. Given the equation $x = 0.45\left(\frac{660 - 100}{0.8}\right)$, what does x represent? cost of usual number of cartons served

Teaching Suggestions p. T76

Chalkboard Examples

1. Using a number line, pair the letter A with the point whose coordinate is $^-10$, B with the point whose coordinate is $^-9$, and so on, so that K has coordinate 0 (zero), L has coordinate $^+1$, and Z has coordinate $^+15$.
   a. Name the coordinates of the points G, R, A, P, and H. $^-4$, 7, $^-10$, 5, $^-3$
   b. Name the points with the coordinates $^-8$, 4, 2, 5, 10, 9, $^-6$, and 7. *C, O, M, P, U, T, E, R*
2. Name the coordinates of the points shown.

$^-3$ $^-2$ $^-1$ 0 1 2

$^-2.5$, $^-1$, 0.5, 2

Graph the given numbers on a number line. Draw a separate line for each exercise.

3. $^-3$, $^-1$, 4

$^-4$ $^-3$ $^-2$ $^-1$ 0 1 2 3 4

4. $^-3.5$, $^-2$, 0, 2.5

$^-4$ $^-3$ $^-2$ $^-1$ 0 1 2 3 4

Name a positive or negative number for each measurement.

5. 4 under par $^-4$
6. Profit of \$16.50 $^+16.50$

Numbers on a Line

1-7 Number Lines

Objective To graph real numbers on a number line.

When you count or measure, you use real numbers. These numbers can be pictured as points on a line, called a *number line.* To construct a number line:

1. Choose a starting point on a line and label it "0" (zero). This point is called the **origin.** The origin separates the line into two sides, the **positive side** and the **negative side.** If the line is horizontal, the side to the right of the origin is taken to be the positive side.
2. Mark off equal units of distance on both sides of the origin. On the positive side, pair the endpoint of successive units with the **positive integers**

   1, 2, 3, 4, 5, . . .

   The three dots are read "and so on" and indicate that the list continues without end. On the negative side, pair the endpoints with the **negative integers**

   $^-1$, $^-2$, $^-3$, $^-4$, $^-5$, . . .

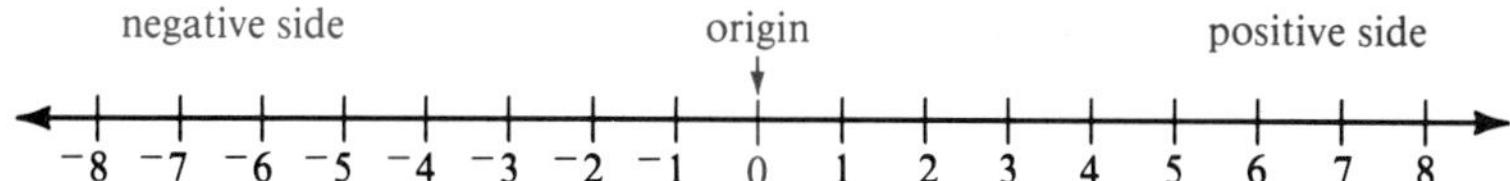

You read $^-1$ as "negative one." You usually read 1 as "one." You may also read 1 as "positive one," and you may write it as $^+1$.

The positive integers, the negative integers, and zero make up the set of **integers.** The positive integers and zero are often called **whole numbers.**

$$\{\text{the integers}\} = \{\ldots\ ^-3, ^-2, ^-1, 0, 1, 2, 3, \ldots\}$$
$$\{\text{the whole numbers}\} = \{0, 1, 2, 3, \ldots\}$$

In general, a **positive number** is a number paired with a point on the positive side of a number line. A **negative number** is a number paired with a point on the negative side of a number line. For example:

A is 1.5 units from 0 on the *positive* side. The *positive* number 1.5 is paired with A.

B is 1.5 units from 0 on the *negative* side. The *negative* number $^-1.5$ is paired with B.

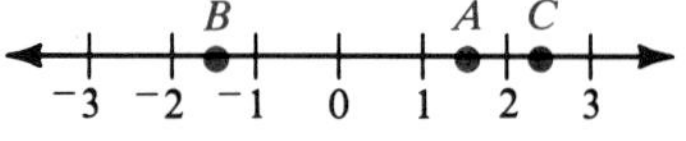

On a number line, the point paired with a number is called the **graph** of the number. The number paired with a point is called the **coordinate** of the point. On the number line on the previous page, point C is the graph of $2\frac{1}{3}$, and $2\frac{1}{3}$ is the coordinate of C. Any number that is either a positive number, a negative number, or zero is called a **real number.** When you graph real numbers, you take the following for granted:

1. Each real number is paired with exactly one point on a number line.
2. Each point on a number line is paired with exactly one real number.

Thus, the graphs of *all* the real numbers make up the entire number line:

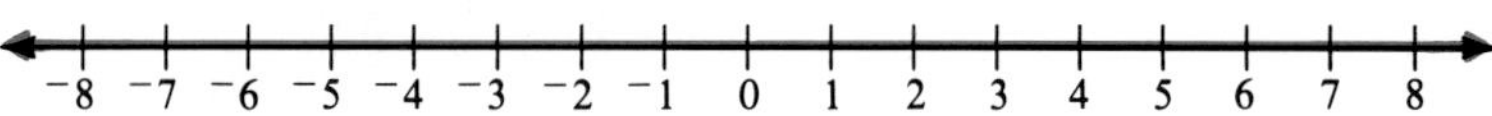

The arrowheads indicate that the number line and the graphs go on indefinitely in both directions.

Because positive and negative numbers suggest opposite directions, they are sometimes called *directed numbers.* You use them for measurements that have *direction* as well as size. For example:

A wage *increase* of \$15: 15

A wage *decrease* of \$15: ⁻15

A *gain* of 10 yards: 10

A *loss* of 10 yards: ⁻10

71 km *north:* 71

71 km *south:* ⁻71

A temperature *rise* of 8.25°C (degrees Celsius): 8.25

A temperature *drop* of 8.25°C: ⁻8.25

Suggested Assignments

Minimum
32/2–42 even
S 27/*P*: 13

Average
32/1–16, 21–24, 31, 34–37, 39–45

Maximum
32/2–22 even, 27–46
36/1–33 odd, 45

This assignment covers Sec. 1–7 and starts Sec. 1–8.

Oral Exercises

Exercises 1–16 refer to the number line below.

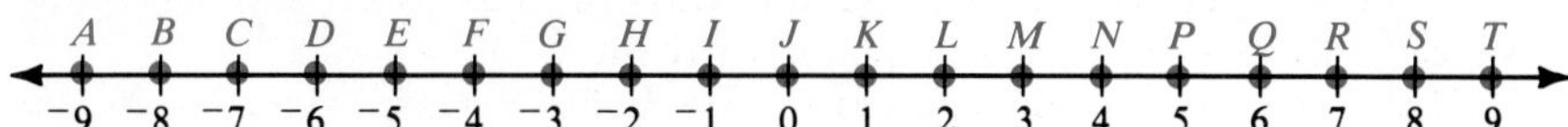

Name the point that is the graph of the given number.

Example 1 ⁻7 ***Solution*** Point C

1. 8 *S* **2.** 0 *J* **3.** ⁻1 *I* **4.** ⁻6 *D* **5.** 4 *N* **6.** ⁻4 *F*

State the coordinate of the given point.

7. G ⁻3 **8.** R 7 **9.** T 9 **10.** H ⁻2 **11.** B ⁻8 **12.** J 0

Example 2 The point halfway between P and Q ***Solution*** 5.5

13. The point halfway between L and M 2.5 **14.** The point halfway between D and E ⁻5.5

15. The point one third of the way from E to K ⁻3

16. The point one fourth of the way from I to A ⁻3

Additional A Exercises

Write a positive or negative number for each measurement.

1. 6 dollar loss $^-6$
2. a bank withdrawal of \$90 $^-90$
3. 7 losses $^-7$
4. debts of \$423.98 $^-423.98$
5. weight gain of 15 pounds $^+15$
6. 8 passengers boarding a bus $^+8$

Additional Answers Written Exercises

1. 5; $^-5$; five floors down
2. 2; $^-2$; two steps to the left
3. 190; $^-190$; 190 m below sea level
4. 9; $^-9$; nine degrees below freezing
5. 18; $^-18$; a loss of \$18
6. 4; $^-4$; four losses
7. 15; $^-15$; 15 km west
8. 41; $^-41$; latitude 41° south
9. 85; $^-85$; payments of \$85
10. 25; $^-25$; a withdrawal of \$25
11. 1; $^-1$; one second before liftoff
12. 3; $^-3$; 3 below par
13. 50; $^-50$; a debit of \$50
14. 20; $^-20$; a clockwise angle of 20°

31. $^-2$ $^-1$ 0 1 2

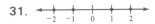

32. $^-6$ $^-2$ 0 2 6

33. $^-4$ $^-3$ $^-2$ $^-1$ 0 1

Written Exercises

Write a positive number for each measurement. Then write the opposite of that number and describe the measurement indicated by that opposite.

A

1. Five floors up
2. Two steps to the right
3. 190 m above sea level
4. Nine degrees above freezing (0°C)
5. A profit of \$18
6. Four wins
7. 15 km east
8. Latitude 41° north
9. Receipts of \$85
10. A bank deposit of \$25
11. One second after liftoff
12. 3 points above par
13. A credit of \$50
14. A counterclockwise angle of 20°

Name the coordinates of the points shown in color.

15. 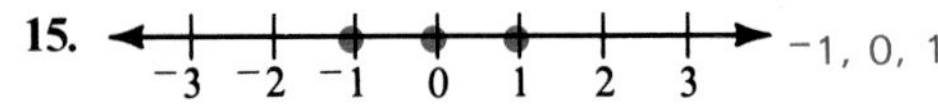 $-1, 0, 1$

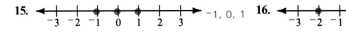

16. $^-3$ $^-2$ $^-1$ 0 1 2 3 — $-2, 0, 2$

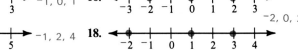

17. $^-1$ 0 1 2 3 4 5 — $-1, 2, 4$

18. 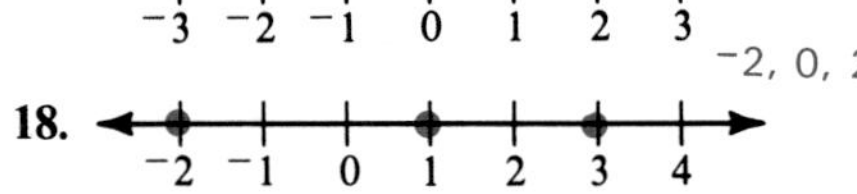 $-2, 1, 3$

19. 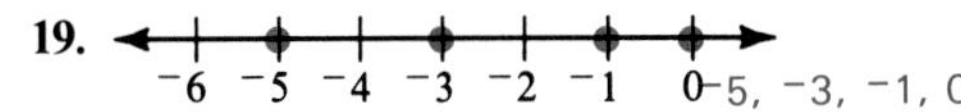 $-5, -3, -1, 0$

20. 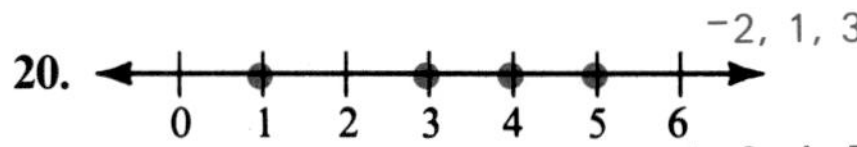 $1, 3, 4, 5$

21. 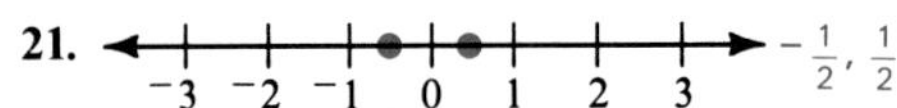 $-\frac{1}{2}, \frac{1}{2}$

22. 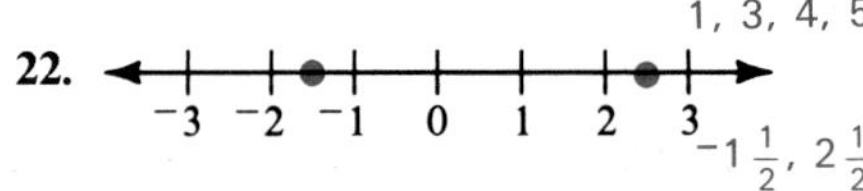 $-1\frac{1}{2}, 2\frac{1}{2}$

List the letters for the points whose coordinates are given.

23. $^-8$, 2 *S, F*
24. $^-5$, 4 *M, V*
25. 0, $^-9$ *N, R*
26. $^-6$, 8 *A, G*
27. 6, $^-6$, $^-6\frac{1}{2}$ *Q, A, U*
28. 1, $^-1$, $^-1\frac{1}{2}$ *H, D, B*
29. $^-5$, $^-4$, $^-4\frac{1}{2}$ *M, P, T*
30. $^-8$, $^-7$, $7\frac{1}{2}$ *S, Z, Y*

Graph the given numbers on a number line. Draw a separate line for each exercise.

31. $^-2$, $^-1$, 1, 2
32. 3, 6, $^-3$, $^-6$
33. $^-4$, 0, $\frac{1}{2}$, 1
34. $^-2$, $^-1.5$, $^-1$, 0

B

35. $^-3$, $^-1\frac{2}{3}$, $\frac{-1}{3}$, 0
36. $^-1$, $^-0.5$, 0, 1.5
37. $^-1\frac{1}{4}$, $\frac{-1}{4}$, $\frac{3}{4}$, $2\frac{1}{4}$
38. $\frac{-2}{3}$, $\frac{2}{3}$, $\frac{5}{3}$, $\frac{10}{3}$

On a horizontal number line, point P has coordinate $^-5$ and point Q has coordinate 3. Write the coordinate of each point described.

39. 4 units to the right of Q 7

40. 4 units to the left of P $^-9$

41. 7 units to the left of Q $^-4$

42. 7 units to the right of P 2

43. Halfway between P and Q $^-1$

44. One fourth of the way from P to Q $^-3$

C **45.** On a number line, point M has coordinate 2 and point T has coordinate 5. What is the coordinate of the point between M and T that is half as far from M as it is from T? 3

46. On a number line, point C has coordinate $^-2$ and point D has coordinate 4. What is the coordinate of the point between C and D that is twice as far from C as it is from D? 2

Career Note / Astronomer

Present-day astronomers do very little observation with telescopes. Instead, they use mathematics and physics to explore the nature of the universe. Theories are represented as mathematical equations, and astronomers spend time analyzing these theories with computers, using data collected by observatories.

Observatories gather much of this data with spectroscopes and radio telescopes. Spectroscopes analyze light from stars and assist scientists in determining a star's composition. Radio telescopes gather x rays and radio waves that tell astronomers even more about these stellar bodies.

Astronomers work primarily as researchers and teachers. Most have a Ph.D. in astronomy and are highly trained in mathematics and physics. They are most often employed by universities or by government space programs.

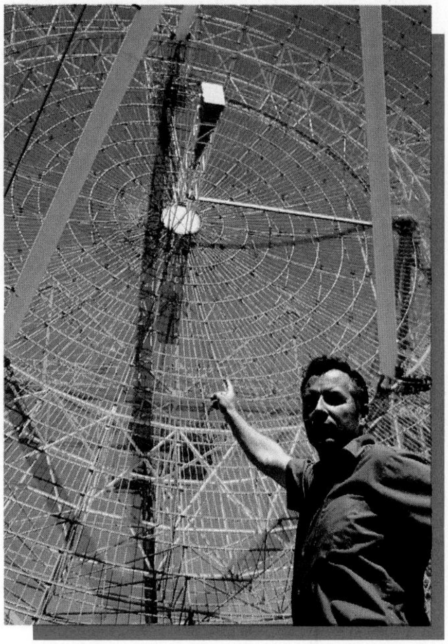

34. 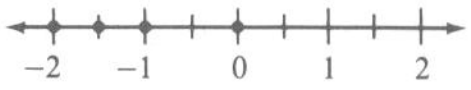

35. 

36. 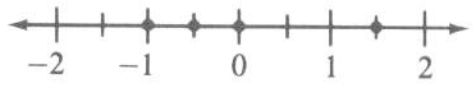

37. 

38. 

Mixed Review Exercises

1. Add: $(^-7) + (^-3) + (^-2)$ $^-12$

2. Simplify: $14(8 + 2) - 5$ 135

3. Evaluate $m - 3n + 2p$ if $m = {}^-1$, $n = 0$ and $p = 2$. 3

4. Sally and Paul earned \$180 last week. Paul earned \$30 more than Sally. How much did Sally earn? \$75

Teaching Suggestions p. T77

Suggested Extensions p. T77

Chalkboard Examples

Simplify.

1. $-(4 + 9)$ -13
2. $-(-2.5)$ 2.5
3. $-(-m)$ m
4. $7 + |-8|$ 15
5. $3|-6|-|0|$ 18
6. $-4 - (-5)$ 1
7. $|-4|-|-5|$ -1

Evaluate each expression if $n = {}^{-}6$.

8. $-n + 20$ 26
9. $15 + |n|$ 21

Give the solution of each equation over the set of real numbers.

10. $|n| = \frac{1}{3}$ $n = \frac{1}{3}$ or $n = -\frac{1}{3}$
11. $|t| = 2.4$ $t = 2.4$ or $t = -2.4$

Common Error

Students become so accustomed to working exercises like Oral Exercise 22 and Written Exercises 3, 19, and 20, which eventually involve adding a number and its opposite, that they often mistakenly guess that examples such as $|-2| - (-2)$ and $-2 - 2$ are equal to 0. Caution them against guessing in such instances. Show them, for example, that $|-2| - (-2) = 2 + 2 = 4$ and $-2 - 2 = -2 + (-2) = -4$.

1-8 Opposites and Absolute Values

Objective To use opposites and absolute values.

The diagram below shows pairings of points on a number line. The paired points are at the same distance from the origin but on opposite sides of the origin. The origin is paired with itself.

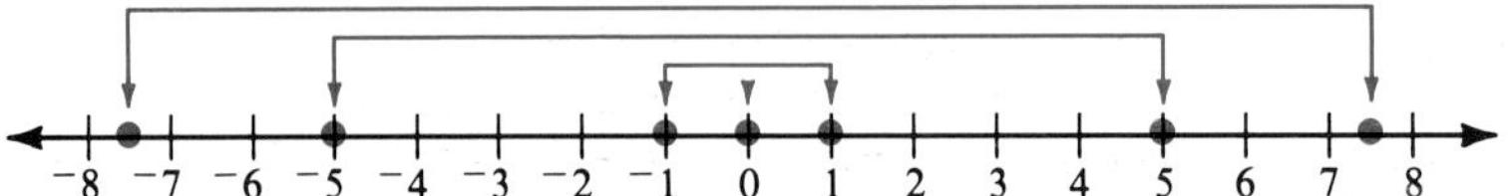

The coordinates of the paired points can also be paired:

0 with 0 $\quad$ ⁻1 with 1 $\quad$ ⁻5 with 5 $\quad$ ⁻7.5 with 7.5

Each number in a pair such as 5 and ⁻5 is called the **opposite** of the other number. The symbol for the opposite of a number a is

$-a$ (note the lowered position of the minus sign)

For example:

$-5 = {}^{-}5$, read "The opposite of five equals negative five."

$-({}^{-}1) = 1$, read "The opposite of negative one equals one."

$-0 = 0$, read "The opposite of zero equals zero."

Notice that the numerals -5 (lowered minus sign) and ⁻5 (raised minus sign) name the same number. Thus, -5 can mean "negative five" as well as "the opposite of five." Therefore:

To simplify notation, lowered minus signs will be used in the numerals for negative numbers throughout the rest of this book.

Be sure you understand the meaning of the expression $-a$, the opposite of a. If the value of a is -3, then $-a$ is the positive number 3. In general:

1. If a is a positive number, then $-a$ is a negative number; if a is a negative number, then $-a$ is a positive number; if a is 0, then $-a$ is 0.
2. The opposite of $-a$ is a; that is $-(-a) = a$.

Example 1 Simplify.

a. $-(8 + 3)$ **b.** $-(-1.6)$ **c.** -0 **d.** $-(-t)$

Solution **a.** -11 **b.** 1.6 **c.** 0 **d.** t

Example 2 Evaluate $-n + 14$, if $n = -8$.

Solution $-(-8) + 14 = 8 + 14 = 22$

In any pair of nonzero opposites, such as -5 and 5, one number is negative and the other is positive. The positive number of any pair of opposite nonzero real numbers is called the **absolute value** of each number in the pair.

The absolute value of a number a is denoted by $|a|$. For example,

$$|-5| = 5 \quad \text{and} \quad |5| = 5.$$

Notice that the absolute value of a real number a is a if a is nonnegative and $-a$ (the opposite of a) if a is negative. (See Exercise 45, page 36.)

The absolute value of a number may also be thought of as the distance of the graph of the number from the origin on a number line. The graphs of both -5 and 5 are 5 units from the origin.

The absolute value of 0 is defined to be 0 itself:

$$|0| = 0.$$

Example 3 $8|-3| + |-15| = (8 \times 3) + 15 = 24 + 15 = 39$

Example 4 Give the solution of $|x| = 3$ over the set of real numbers.

Solution $|x| = 3$; $x = 3$ or $x = -3$

Oral Exercises

Name the opposite and the absolute value of each number.

1. 6 −6, 6 **2.** 5 −5, 5 **3.** −1 1, 1 **4.** −9 9, 9 **5.** 194 −194, 194

6. −78 78, 78 **7.** 0 0,0 **8.** 0.3 −0.3, 0.3 **9.** 2.8 −2.8, 2.8 **10.** $-1\frac{1}{4}$ $1\frac{1}{4}$, $1\frac{1}{4}$

Simplify.

11. $-(-7)$ 7 **12.** $-\left(-\frac{1}{2}\right)$ $\frac{1}{2}$ **13.** $|12|$ 12

14. $-(7 + 3)$ −10 **15.** $-(7 - 3)$ −4 **16.** $-[-(-3)]$ −3

17. $-[-(-0)]$ 0 **18.** $|-14|$ 14 **19.** $|-2.7|$ 2.7

20. $-|-4|$ −4 **21.** $-|0|$ 0 **22.** $9 - |-9|$ 0

Complete.

23. If n is a negative number, then $-n$ is a __?__ number. positive

24. If n is a positive number, then $-n$ is a __?__ number. negative

25. The one and only number whose absolute value is zero is __?__. 0

26. A real number that is its own opposite is __?__. 0

Suggested Assignments

Minimum
36/1–28 odd, 35–38
S 32/1–13 odd

Average
36/1–41 odd
38/1–43 odd
R 40/*Self-Test 3*
This assignment covers Sec. 1-8 and Sec. 1-9.

Maximum
36/39–44, 46
38/1–55 odd
This assignment finishes Sec. 1-8 and covers Sec. 1-9.

Additional A Exercises

Simplify.

1. $-(-10 + 2)$ 8
2. $6 - (-3)$ 9
3. $-5 - [-(-1) - 5]$ −1
4. $|-6| + |4|$ 10
5. $|16| - |-7|$ 9

Give the solution set over the set of real numbers.

6. $|x| = 0.77$ $x = \pm 0.77$

Mixed Review Exercises

1. Evaluate $x - 2y - z$ if $x = 3$, $y = -\frac{1}{2}$ and $z = -2$. 6
2. Find the solution set of $\frac{1}{5}m = 2$ if $m \in \{0, 2, 4, 6, 8, 10\}$. $\{10\}$
3. If P has coordinate -2 on a number line and Q has coordinate 4, give the coordinate of the point midway between them. 1
4. If a drop of 33° is represented by -33, write the opposite of this number and describe the measurement indicated by that opposite. $+33$, a rise of 33°

Additional Answers Written Exercises

25. no solution; the absolute value of a number must be 0 or positive.

26. no solution; the absolute value of a number must be 0 or positive.

45. If a is positive $|a| = a$ because a is the positive number in the pair of a and its opposite. If $a = 0$, then $|0| = 0$ by definition. If a is negative, then the opposite of a, $-a$, would be positive, and so, by definition $|a| = -a$.

Written Exercises

Simplify.

A

1. $-(8 + 5)$ -13 **2.** $-(9 - 3)$ -6 **3.** $-(12 - 12)$ 0 **4.** $-(0 + 0)$ 0

5. $[-(-9)] + 10$ 19 **6.** $[-(-7)] + 1$ 8 **7.** $6 + [-(-2)]$ 8 **8.** $5 - [-(-1)]$ 4

9. $8 + |-3|$ 11 **10.** $|-11| + 4$ 15 **11.** $|-8| + |6|$ 14

12. $|2| + |-9|$ 11 **13.** $\left|-\frac{3}{2}\right| + |0|$ $\frac{3}{2}$ **14.** $|-1| - |0|$ 1

15. $|-0.4| + |-3.6|$ 4 **16.** $|-2.8| + |2.8|$ 5.6 **17.** $\left|\frac{1}{2}\right| + \left|-\frac{1}{2}\right|$ 1

18. $\left|-\frac{3}{4}\right| - \left|\frac{1}{4}\right|$ $\frac{1}{2}$ **19.** $|6| - |6|$ 0 **20.** $|6| - |-6|$ 0

Give the solution set of each equation over the set of real numbers. If there is no solution, explain why there is none.

21. $|n| = 0$ $\{0\}$ **22.** $|p| = 2$ $\{2, -2\}$ **23.** $|t| = \frac{1}{2}$ $\left\{\frac{1}{2}, -\frac{1}{2}\right\}$ **24.** $|z| = 0.3$ $\{0.3, -0.3\}$

B

25. $|a| = -2$ **26.** $|b| = -9$ **27.** $|-q| = 1$ $\{1, -1\}$ **28.** $|-x| = 5$ $\{5, -5\}$

29. $|q| + 1 = 6$ $\{5, -5\}$ **30.** $12 + |w| = 20$ $\{8, -8\}$ **31.** $|m| - 3 = 2$ $\{5, -5\}$

32. $|p| - 20 = |-2|$ $\{22, -22\}$ **33.** $10 - |s| = |-8|$ $\{2, -2\}$ **34.** $7 - |t| = 4$ $\{3, -3\}$

Evaluate each expression if $a = 1.5$, $b = -2$, and $c = -1.7$.

35. $|a| + |b| - (-c)$ 1.8 **36.** $a + |-b| + (-c)$ 5.2

37. $4a - |b| - |c|$ 2.3 **38.** $2|b| - |a| + |c|$ 4.2

39. $(a + 8.5) - [(-b) + |c|]$ 6.3 **40.** $(10 \cdot 5 - a) - [|c| + (-b)]$ 44.8

41. $|c| + [-(-|a + |b||)]$ 5.2 **42.** $|a - 1.5| + [-(-|(-b) + (-c)|)]$ 3.7

43. $|a - |b| + |-c| - (b + a)|$ 1.7 **44.** $\left|\frac{3b}{-a} - c\right| - \left|-c + \left|\frac{6}{ab}\right| - bc\right|$ 5.4

C

45. Explain why the following statement is true.

If a is a real number, then

$$|a| = a \quad \text{if } a \text{ is zero or a positive number;}$$
$$|a| = -a \quad \text{if } a \text{ is a negative number.}$$

46. Two of the following statements are true and one is false. Which one is false? Why is it false?

a. The absolute value of every real number is a positive number.
b. There is at least one real number whose absolute value is zero.
c. The absolute value of a real number is never a negative number.

a. False. 0 is a real number and its absolute value, 0, is not positive

1-9 Comparing Real Numbers

Objective To show the order of real numbers.

You know that 3 is less than 7 and that 7 is greater than 3. **Inequality symbols** are used to show the *order* of pairs of real numbers.

$<$ means is less than: $3 < 7$

$>$ means is greater than: $7 > 3$

To avoid confusing the symbols $>$ and $<$, notice that the name of the greater number is placed at the greater (or open) end of the inequality symbol. The statements $3 < 7$ and $7 > 3$ give the same information.

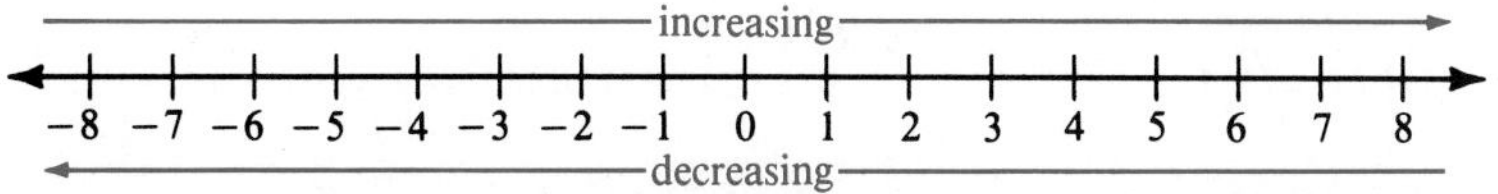

On a horizontal number line, such as the one above, the numbers increase from left to right and decrease from right to left. By studying the number line, you can see that the following statements are true.

$-5 < -2$ $\quad -5 < 0$ $\quad -5 < 3$

$-2 > -5$ $\quad 0 > -5$ $\quad 3 > -5$

Example Graph the numbers 4, -1, 2.5, 0, $|-6|$, -3 on a number line, and then name them in order from least to greatest.

Solution

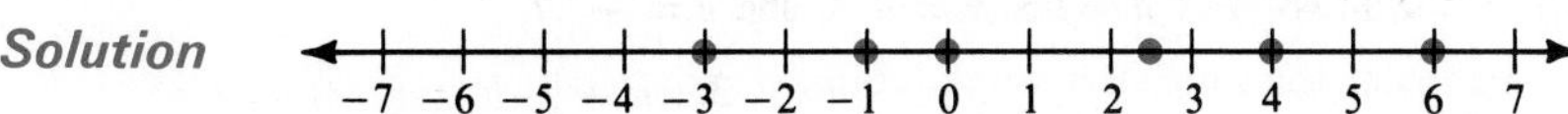

From least to greatest, the numbers are

$-3, -1, 0, 2.5, 4, |-6|$.

Oral Exercises

Translate the following statements into words. (Answers appear on page 43.)

1. $3 < 8$
2. $0 < 1$
3. $0 > -1$
4. $-2 > -3$
5. $-5 > -9$
6. $\frac{1}{2} < \frac{3}{4}$
7. $-\frac{1}{2} > -\frac{3}{4}$
8. $1.25 < 1.40$
9. $-0.5 > -2.5$
10. $0 > -100$
11. $3 > -30$
12. $|3| < |-30|$
13. $|-8| > |3|$
14. $-\frac{2}{3} < -\frac{1}{2}$
15. $-2.4 > -7.1$
16. $|2| < |-12|$

Teaching Suggestions p. T77

Suggested Extensions p. T77

Chalkboard Examples

1. Graph the numbers 3, -1.5, -2, 0, 0.5, $|-2|$ on a number line,

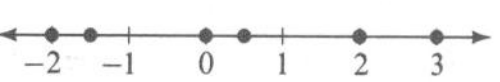

and then name them in order from least to greatest. $-2, -1.5, 0, 0.5, |-2|, 3$

2. Write another inequality that gives the same information as $7 > -1$. $-1 < 7$
3. Translate into symbols: Five is greater than negative six. $5 > -6$

Replace each _?_ with one of the symbols $<$ or $>$ to make a true statement.

4. 0 _?_ -7 $>$
5. -4 _?_ -3.5 $<$
6. 9 _?_ $5 + 6$ $<$
7. $-\frac{3}{8}$ _?_ $-\frac{1}{8}$ $<$
8. $|-11|$ _?_ $|-3|$ $>$
9. $-5 - (-1)$ _?_ $|-4|$ $<$

Common Error

Students sometimes confuse the symbolic translations of statements such as "3 is less than 7" and "3 is 4 less than 7." Explain that the first statement compares two numbers and would be represented mathematically by the symbols $3 < 7$, whereas the second is a statement of equality, which would be represented symbolically by $3 = 7 - 4$.

Supplementary Materials

Practice Master 3
Test 2
Resource Book, p. 69

Suggested Assignments

Minimum
38/1–32
R 40/*Self-Test 3*
Average
Sec. 1-9 is covered in the assignment for Sec. 1-8.
Maximum
Sec. 1-9 is covered in the assignment for Sec. 1-8.

Additional A Exercises

Translate each statement into symbols.

1. Negative 5 is less than negative 3. $-5 < -3$
2. Twenty-three is greater than negative fifty-four. $23 > -54$

Replace each _?_ with one of the symbols $<$ or $>$ to make a true statement.

3. 8 _?_ $9 - 4$ $>$
4. $|-6|$ _?_ $|4| - 2$ $>$
5. $-(8 - 3)$ _?_ $|-7|$ $<$
6. $18.5 - 3.6$ _?_ $|2.8 + 13.9|$ $<$

Mixed Review Exercises

1. $31.2 - (-18.9)$ 50.1
2. Find the solution set of $|x| = \frac{1}{3}$. $\left\{\pm\frac{1}{3}\right\}$
3. Simplify: $|-3| - |4|$ -1
4. Write the algebraic expression for the word phrase "the sum of 18 and the opposite of 52." $18 + (-52)$

In Exercises 17–24, tell whether or not the given statement is true. Give a reason for your answer.

Example $7 \times |-3| > 7 + |-3|$

Solution True, because
$7 \times |-3| = 7 \times 3 = 21$,
$7 + |-3| = 7 + 3 = 10$, and
$21 > 10$.

17. $-2 < 0 + \frac{1}{2}$ True; $-2 < \frac{1}{2}$
18. $\frac{2}{3} \times \frac{1}{3} > \frac{2}{3} + \frac{1}{3}$ False; $\frac{2}{9} < 1$
19. $5 \times 6 < 6 \times 5$ False; $30 = 30$
20. $7 + (1 + 29) < (7 + 1) + 29$ False; $37 = 37$
21. $\frac{7+1}{2} > -\left(\frac{17-1}{4}\right)$ True; $4 > -4$
22. $-1 < \frac{4+10}{8+6}$ True; $-1 < 1$
23. $-[4(3 - 1)] < -[3(4 - 1)]$ False; $-8 > -9$
24. $5(0 + 8) > (5 \times 0) + (5 \times 8)$ False; $40 = 40$

Written Exercises

Translate each statement into symbols.

A

1. Six is greater than negative nine. $6 > -9$
2. Negative eleven is less than negative one. $-11 < -1$
3. Negative eight is greater than negative twenty. $-8 > -20$
4. Ten is greater than seven. $10 > 7$
5. Six is less than six and five tenths. $6 < 6.5$
6. Zero is greater than negative three tenths. $0 > -0.3$
7. Negative thirteen is less than zero. $-13 < 0$
8. One eighth is less than one seventh. $\frac{1}{8} < \frac{1}{7}$
9. The absolute value of negative five is greater than two. $|-5| > 2$
10. Four is less than the absolute value of negative ten. $4 < |-10|$
11. The opposite of negative two is greater than the opposite of negative one. $-(-2) > -(-1)$ or $2 > 1$
12. The opposite of eight is less than the opposite of four. $-8 < -4$

Replace each _?_ with one of the symbols $<$ or $>$ to make a true statement.

13. -4 _?_ 0 $<$
14. 0 _?_ -5 $>$
15. 6 _?_ $5 + 4$ $<$
16. $8 - 7$ _?_ -1 $>$
17. $|0|$ _?_ -1 $>$
18. 0×0 _?_ 1 $<$
19. -3.1 _?_ -3.2 $>$
20. $-\frac{2}{5}$ _?_ $-\frac{1}{5}$ $<$
21. $|-7|$ _?_ $-(-9)$ $<$
22. $-(-2)$ _?_ $|-3|$ $<$
23. $|-8|$ _?_ $|-10|$ $<$
24. $|-15|$ _?_ $|-6|$ $>$
25. $-(8 + 2)$ _?_ $|-20|$ $<$
26. $|-40|$ _?_ $-(9 + 11)$ $>$
27. $21.5 - 15.9$ _?_ $\frac{18.1 + 16.1}{6}$ $<$
28. $3(36 \div (5 + 4))$ _?_ $64 - 8 \times 8$ $>$

Write the given numbers in order from least to greatest.

B **29.** $0, -5, 8, -7$ **30.** $-5, -8, 0, -9$ **31.** $-1, 5, -3, 2$

32. $-8, 7, -7, -1$ **33.** $-\frac{1}{2}, -\frac{1}{4}, -\frac{1}{3}, -\frac{1}{6}$ **34.** $-\frac{2}{3}, -\frac{3}{4}, -\frac{1}{7}, -\frac{1}{10}$

35. $-1.5, 1.4, -0.7, 0.3$ **36.** $2.7, -3.6, -2, 3.5$ **37.** $3.14, -3.141, 3.1416$

38. $-1.7, -1.732, 1.7$ **39.** $-4\frac{1}{3}, -4\frac{1}{6}, -4\frac{1}{2}$ **40.** $-5\frac{1}{3}, -5\frac{1}{7}, -5\frac{1}{2}$

41. $|-3|, -(-2), |-6|, -(-1)$ **42.** $-(-4), |-7|, |-1|, -(-3)$

43. Flo is taller than Cal but shorter than Sal. Sal is taller than Flo but shorter than Nell. List the names of these four people in order from shortest to tallest. Cal, Flo, Sal, Nell

44. Jack and Nick are both older than Mel, while Pete is older than Jack but younger than Nick. List the names of these four people in order from oldest to youngest. Nick, Pete, Jack, Mel

45. False; any positive number > any negative number.

In Exercises 45-54, let x be any positive number and y any negative number. Classify each sentence as true or false. If the sentence is false, give a reason.

48. False; every positive num. > 0. 49. False; $-y$ is pos., so it is > 0.

C **45.** $x < y$ **46.** $y < 0$ True **47.** $x > y$ True **48.** $0 > x$

49. $-y < 0$ **50.** $-x < -y$ True **51.** $-x < 0$ True **52.** $-y > 0$ True

53. On a number line, the graphs of x and y are on opposite sides of the origin. True

54. On a number line, the graph of y is on the opposite side of the origin from the graph of 1. True

55. Why is the following statement false?
Every real number is greater than its opposite. 0 is not greater than its opposite, 0; any negative number is not greater than its opposite.

Challenge

1, 3, 6, 10, 15, . . . are called triangular numbers because they can be represented by dots arranged to form triangles.

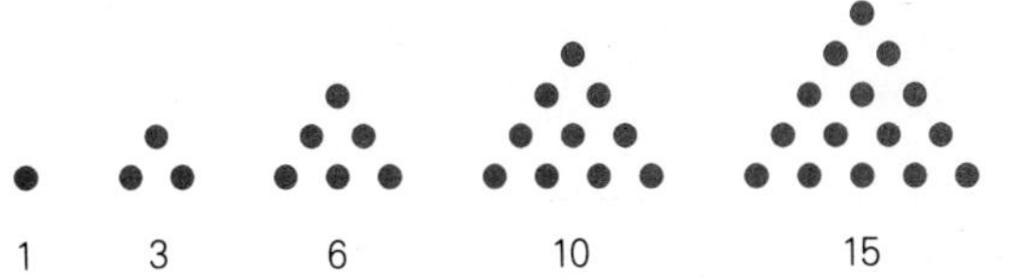

1. Find the next five triangular numbers. 21, 28, 36, 45, 55
2. If n represents the number of the triangular number in the list ($n = 1$ for 1, $n = 2$ for 3, and so on), verify for the first ten triangular numbers that the nth triangular number $= \frac{n(n+1)}{2}$.

Additional Answers
Written Exercises

29. $-7, -5, 0, 8$
30. $-9, -8, -5, 0$
31. $-3, -1, 2, 5$
32. $-8, -7, -1, 7$
33. $-\frac{1}{2}, -\frac{1}{3}, -\frac{1}{4}, -\frac{1}{6}$
34. $-\frac{3}{4}, -\frac{2}{3}, -\frac{1}{7}, -\frac{1}{10}$
35. $-1.5, -0.7, 0.3, 1.4$
36. $-3.6, -2, 2.7, 3.5$
37. $-3.141, 3.14, 3.1416$
38. $-1.732, -1.7, 1.7$
39. $-4\frac{1}{2}, -4\frac{1}{3}, -4\frac{1}{6}$
40. $-5\frac{1}{2}, -5\frac{1}{3}, -5\frac{1}{7}$
41. $-(-1), -(-2), |-3|, |-6|$
42. $|-1|, -(-3), -(-4), |-7|$

Additional Answer
Self-Test 3

1. 

Quick Quiz

1. Graph the given numbers on the same number line: −4, −3, 0, 2, 3.

Simplify.

2. $-(-15) + 3$ 18
3. $|-7| + 7$ 14
4. Translate the given statement into words: $-5 < -1$. Negative five is less than negative one.
5. Write the given numbers in order from least to greatest: −2, 0, −4, 4. −4, −2, 0, 4

Self-Test 3

Vocabulary

origin (p. 30)
positive side (p. 30)
negative side (p. 30)
positive integer (p. 30)
negative integer (p. 30)
integers (p. 30)
whole numbers (p. 30)
positive number (p. 30)
negative number (p. 30)
graph (p. 30)
coordinate (p. 30)
real numbers (p. 31)
opposite (p. 34)
absolute value (p. 35)
inequality symbols (p. 37)

1. Graph the given numbers on the same number line: $^-3$, $^-1$, 0, 4 **Obj. 1-7, p. 30**

Simplify.

2. $-(-12) + 4$ 16 **3.** $|-3| + 2$ 5 **Obj. 1-8, p. 34**

4. Translate the given statement into words: $-2 < 1$ **Obj. 1-9, p. 37**

5. Write the given numbers in order from least to greatest: 6, 0, −5, −1 −5, −1, 0, 6

4. Negative 2 is less than 1.

Check your answers with those at the back of the book.

Chapter Summary

1. A numerical expression represents a particular number. To simplify a numerical expression, replace the expression by the simplest name of the number that the expression represents.
2. A variable expression is evaluated by replacing each variable with its given value and simplifying the resulting numerical expression.
3. Grouping symbols are used to show the order in which operations are to be performed to simplify an expression. If no grouping symbols appear, the steps listed on page 6 are followed.
4. Replacing each variable in an open sentence by each of its values in the domain, in turn, is a way to find solutions of the open sentence.
5. A word problem can often be solved by using the plan outlined on page 26 to write an open sentence based on the given facts and then solving the open sentence.
6. The positive numbers, the negative numbers, and zero make up the real numbers and can be paired with the points on a number line, thereby showing their order.
7. The opposite of a number a is denoted by $-a$. The positive number of any pair of opposite nonzero real numbers is called the absolute value of each number in the pair. The absolute value of a number a is denoted by $|a|$.

Chapter Review

Give the letter of the correct answer.

1. Simplify $36 \div (9 \times 4)$. 1-1
a. 16 **b.** 0 **c.** 81 **d.** 1

2. Evaluate $(x + y) - 3z$ if $x = 7$, $y = 8$, and $z = 0$.
a. 12 **b.** 0 **c.** 15 **d.** 5

3. Simplify $\frac{24 - 6 \times 2}{8 + 16 \div 4}$. 1-2
a. 1 **b.** 3 **c.** 2 **d.** 6

4. Find the solution set of the equation $\frac{1}{3}w = 0$ if $w \in \{0, 1, 2, 3, 4, 5, 6\}$. 1-3
a. $\{0, 1, 2, 3, 4, 5, 6\}$ **b.** $\{0\}$
c. $\{3\}$ **d.** $\{0, 3, 6\}$

5. Write a variable expression for the word phrase "the difference of seven times the number n and three." 1-4
a. $7(n - 3)$ **b.** $3 + 7n$ **c.** $7n - 3$ **d.** $7(3 - n)$

6. Write an equation for the word sentence "The product of nine and four less than the number n is twenty-seven."
a. $9n - 4 = 27$ **b.** $9(n - 4) = 27$
c. $9(4 - n) = 27$ **d.** $9 + 4 - n = 27$

7. Use the given facts to choose the equation that represents the sentence shown in color. The length of a rectangle is 3 cm longer than its width. Its width is x cm. Its perimeter is 54 cm. 1-5
a. $3x = 54$ **b.** $2x + 2(x + 3) = 54$
c. $2x + 3 = 54$ **d.** $x + 3 = 54$

8. Choose the equation you would write in Step 3 of the five-step plan to solve the following problem. Lesley and Michael jogged a total of thirteen miles. If Michael jogged three less miles than Lesley, now many miles did Lesley jog? 1-6
a. $x - 3 = 13$ **b.** $2x - 3 = 13$ **c.** $3 - x = 13$ **d.** $3 - 2x = 13$

9. If a surplus of 45 items is represented by $^{+}45$, choose the opposite of that number and describe the measurement indicated by that opposite. 1-7
a. 45; a gain of 45 items. **b.** $\frac{1}{45}$; each item is $\frac{1}{45}$ of the total.
c. $|45|$; there are 45 items. **d.** -45; a shortage of 45 items.

10. Simplify $|^{+}7| - |-7|$. 1-8
a. 14 **b.** 49 **c.** 0 **d.** 1

11. Give the solution set of $|m| + 3 = 2$ over the set of real numbers.
a. no solution **b.** $\{-5\}$ **c.** $\{-1, 1\}$ **d.** $\{-2, 2\}$

12. Which of the following is a true statement? 1-9
a. $-5(0) > |-5| + 0$ **b.** $6 < -(-6)$ **c.** $-\frac{3}{4} > -\frac{5}{4}$ **d.** $6 - |-4| > 9$

Supplementary Materials

Practice Master 4
Test 3
Resource Book, pp. 5–8, 146

Extra Practice

Skills, pp. 607–608
Problem-Solving, p. 633

Alternate Test p. T10

Chapter Test

Simplify.

1. $(42 + 9) \times 3$ 153   2. $4 + 5(6 - 2)$ 24   1-1
3. Evaluate $a \div bc$ if $a = 315$, $b = 35$, and $c = 3$. 3   1-2

Simplify.

4. $38 + 38 \div (15 + 4)$ 40   5. $25 + 15 \cdot 5 \div 25$ 28
6. Evaluate $2\pi r$ (circumference of a circle) if $r = 49$. Use $\frac{22}{7}$ as an approximate value for π. 308

Solve. $x \in \{0, 1, 2, 3, 4, 5, 6\}$

7. $56 = 14 + 7x$ $\{6\}$ 8. $x \cdot x = 0$ $\{0\}$ 9. $\frac{1}{2}x = \frac{x}{2}$ $\{0, 1, 2, 3, 4, 5, 6\}$ 1-3
10. Inga is 3 times as old as Adriano. If Adriano is n years old, represent Inga's age 5 years ago. $3n - 5$ 1-4
11. Use the given facts to state an equation that represents the sentence shown in color. Marta spent one hour less than twice as long researching a paper than she spent writing it. It took her x hours to write the paper. She spent five hours total working on the paper. $x + 2x - 1 = 5$ 1-5
12. Use the five-step plan to solve the following problem.   1-6
Diane plans to plant a rectangular garden next to a barn so that she only has to fence the other three sides. She has 63 m of fencing and wants to use it all. She also wants the length of the garden to be 6 m more than the width. Find the dimensions of the garden.
19 m by 25 m or 17 m by 23 m

On a horizontal number line, point P has coordinate -1 and point Q has coordinate -4. Write the coordinate of each point described.

13. $\frac{1}{2}$ unit to the left of P $-1\frac{1}{2}$ 14. 8 units to the right of Q 4   1-7

Simplify.

15. $5 - |-1.6|$ 3.4   16. $6 - \left(-2\frac{3}{4}\right)$ $8\frac{3}{4}$ 17. $-|(4 + 1.5)|$ -5.5 1-8

Give the solution set of each equation over the set of real numbers. If there is no solution, explain why.

18. $|t| = 6.75$ $\{6.75, -6.75\}$ 19. $|x| = -\frac{1}{2}$ No solution; $|x|$ is not negative for any real number.
20. Translate $-8 < -(-7)$ into words.   1-9
Negative 8 is less than the opposite of negative 7.

Replace each __?__ with $<$ or $>$ to make a true statement.

21. $-(-5)$ __?__ -4 $>$ 22. $-|-10|$ __?__ $|8|$ $<$

Maintaining Skills

Perform the indicated operations.

Example 1

$$\begin{array}{r} {\scriptstyle 12\ \ 1} \\ 729.35 \\ 84. \\ +\ 68.29 \\ \hline 881.64 \end{array}$$

Example 2

$$\begin{array}{r} 625.3 \\ \times\ 32.1 \\ \hline 6253 \\ 12506 \\ 18759 \\ \hline 20072.13 \end{array}$$

1. $0.0056 + 2.3 + 18.232 + 9.41$ — Answer: 29.9476
2. $42.31 + 8.79 + 13.26$ — Answer: 64.36
3. $22.6 + 153.3 + 201.8$ — Answer: 377.7
4. $27 + 6.25 + 108.1 + 35.72$ — Answer: 177.07
5. 318×5.2 — Answer: 1653.6
6. 208.2×10.3 — Answer: 2144.46
7. 7.51×2.2 — Answer: 16.522
8. 0.876×0.09 — Answer: 0.07884
9. 824.2×1.2 — Answer: 989.04
10. 0.222×11.1 — Answer: 2.4642
11. $35.83 + 9.96$ — Answer: 45.79
12. $20.05 + 8.87$ — Answer: 28.92

Rewrite the fractions with their least common denominator.

Example 3 $\frac{7}{8}$ and $\frac{2}{3}$

Solution The least common denominator is 24.

$$\frac{7}{8} = \frac{7}{8} \times \frac{3}{3} = \frac{21}{24} \qquad \frac{2}{3} = \frac{2}{3} \times \frac{8}{8} = \frac{16}{24}$$

13. $\frac{5}{8}$ and $\frac{3}{4}$ $\quad \frac{5}{8}, \frac{6}{8}$
14. $\frac{2}{3}$ and $\frac{3}{5}$ $\quad \frac{10}{15}, \frac{9}{15}$
15. $\frac{2}{7}$ and $\frac{2}{3}$ $\quad \frac{6}{21}, \frac{14}{21}$
16. $\frac{5}{12}$ and $\frac{3}{2}$ $\quad \frac{5}{12}, \frac{18}{12}$

Perform the indicated operations.

Example 4 $\frac{3}{7} + \frac{2}{3}$

Solution $\frac{3}{7} + \frac{2}{3} = \frac{3}{7} \times \frac{3}{3} + \frac{2}{3} \times \frac{7}{7} = \frac{9}{21} + \frac{14}{21} = \frac{23}{21}$

Example 5 $\frac{2}{5} \times \frac{7}{8}$

Solution $\frac{2}{5} \times \frac{7}{8} = \frac{\overset{1}{\cancel{2}} \times 7}{5 \times \underset{4}{\cancel{8}}} = \frac{7}{20}$ (cancel 8 to 4)

17. $\frac{3}{5} + \frac{4}{9}$ $\quad \frac{47}{45}$
18. $\frac{2}{7} + \frac{1}{4}$ $\quad \frac{15}{28}$
19. $\frac{3}{8} + \frac{5}{9}$ $\quad \frac{67}{72}$
20. $\frac{7}{10} + \frac{2}{5}$ $\quad \frac{11}{10}$
21. $\frac{5}{13} \times \frac{3}{4}$ $\quad \frac{15}{52}$
22. $\frac{5}{9} \times \frac{3}{5}$ $\quad \frac{1}{3}$
23. $\frac{10}{11} \times \frac{11}{12}$ $\quad \frac{5}{6}$
24. $\frac{5}{6} \times \frac{15}{16}$ $\quad \frac{25}{32}$
25. $\frac{2}{3} + \frac{3}{7}$ $\quad \frac{23}{21}$
26. $\frac{9}{10} \times \frac{5}{3}$ $\quad \frac{3}{2}$
27. $\frac{7}{8} \times \frac{14}{16}$ $\quad \frac{49}{64}$
28. $\frac{9}{13} + \frac{2}{5}$ $\quad \frac{71}{65}$

Additional Answers
Oral Exercises (*p. 37*)

1. 3 is less than 8.
2. 0 is less than 1.
3. 0 is greater than negative 1.
4. Negative 2 is greater than negative 3.
5. Negative 5 is greater than negative 9.
6. $\frac{1}{2}$ is less than $\frac{3}{4}$.
7. Negative $\frac{1}{2}$ is greater than negative $\frac{3}{4}$.
8. 1.25 is less than 1.4.
9. Negative 0.5 is greater than negative 2.5.
10. 0 is greater than negative 100.
11. 3 is greater than negative 30.
12. The absolute value of 3 is less than the absolute value of negative 30.
13. The absolute value of negative 8 is greater than the absolute value of 3.
14. Negative $\frac{2}{3}$ is less than negative $\frac{1}{2}$.
15. Negative 2.4 is greater than negative 7.1.
16. The absolute value of 2 is less than the absolute value of negative 12.

About the Photo

Death Valley, located in southeastern California, is the lowest, hottest, and driest geographical area in the United States and is located about 120 km from Mt. Whitney, which, outside Alaska, is the highest point in the United States. Over 1425 km² of Death Valley lies below sea level. During the summer months temperatures in Death Valley exceed 49°C (about 120°F), and on July 10, 1913 a record temperature of 57°C (134°F) was set. Annual rainfall averages about 50 mm, or about 2 inches.

Your students may be interested in studying how Death Valley was formed. Geologists consider Death Valley to be land formed millions of years ago by the gradual sinking of a huge land area between two parallel faults in Earth's crust. The bedrock of the valley floor is now buried under tons of sediment. Your students might want to investigate erosion, the process by which mountains are leveled, and sedimentation, the process by which valleys are filled.

2 Working with Real Numbers

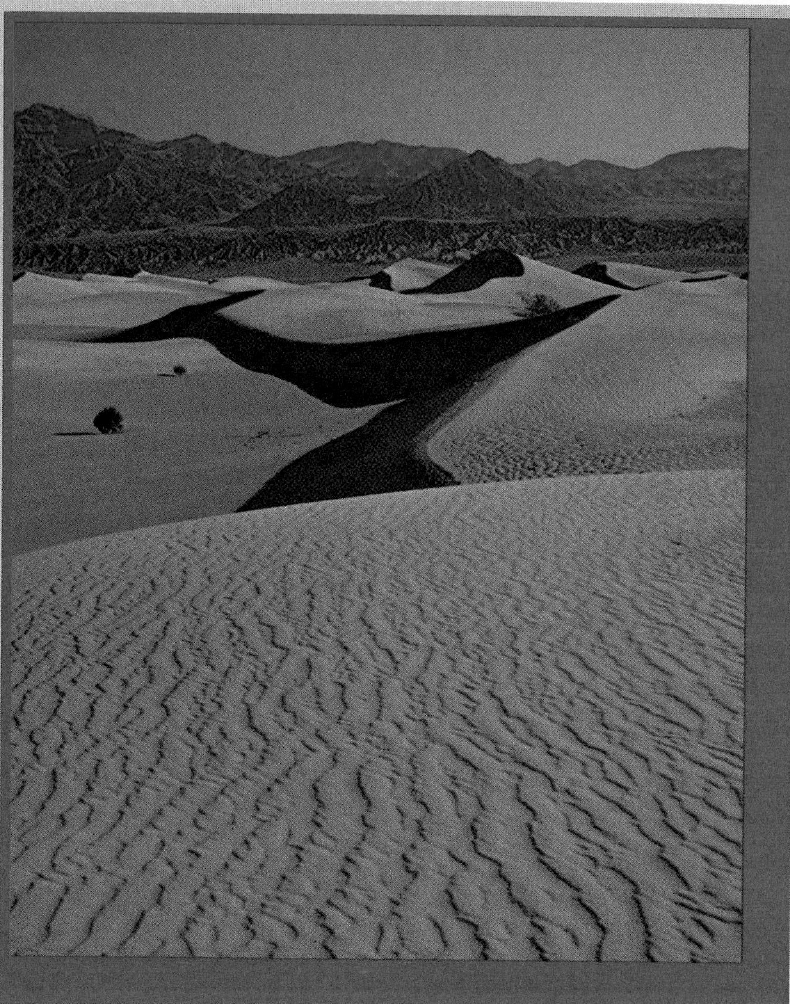

The lowest point in Death Valley, California, is 86 m below sea level. Altitudes below sea level can be thought of as negative numbers, while those above sea level can be thought of as positive numbers.

Addition and Subtraction

2-1 Basic Assumptions

Objective To use number properties to simplify expressions.

The rules used in adding and multiplying real numbers are based on several properties that you can take for granted. For example, the following statements are accepted as facts.

1. Every pair of real numbers has a unique (one and only one) sum that is also a real number.
2. Every pair of real numbers has a unique product that is also a real number.
3. When you add two real numbers, you get the same sum no matter what order you use in adding them.

$$8 + 5 = 5 + 8 \qquad 3.2 + 0.4 = 0.4 + 3.2$$

4. When you multiply two real numbers, you get the same product no matter what order you use in multiplying them.

$$2 \times 9 = 9 \times 2 \qquad \frac{1}{7} \times \frac{2}{5} = \frac{2}{5} \times \frac{1}{7}$$

Statements that are assumed to be true are called **axioms,** or **postulates.** Statements (1) and (2) above may be stated more formally as follows.

Axioms of Closure

For all real numbers a and b:

$\boldsymbol{a + b}$ is a unique real number.

$\boldsymbol{ab}$ is a unique real number.

Statements (3) and (4) above may be stated as follows.

Commutative Axioms

For all real numbers a and b:

$$\boldsymbol{a + b = b + a}$$

$$\boldsymbol{ab = ba}$$

Teaching References

Lesson Commentary, pp. T78–T83

Assignment Guide, pp. T57–T58

Supplementary Materials

- Practice Masters 5–10
- Tests 4–7
- Resource Book
  - Practice Exercises, pp. 70–73
  - Tests, pp. 9–12
  - Enrichment Activity, pp. 147–148
- Algebra Action

Extra Practice

- Skills, pp. 609–611
- Problems, pp. 633–634

Alternate Test, p. T11

Problem Solving Strategies

Generalizing from Specific
Throughout the chapter, the properties of real numbers are first discussed in terms of specific examples and then presented in general form. See, e.g., pp. 45–46, 53–54, 59–60, 64, 80.

Looking for a Pattern
The Challenge on p. 63 extends the discussion of triangular numbers on p. 39 and asks students to analyze the pattern of square numbers.

Drawing a Diagram
In Section 2-2 number line diagrams are used to illustrate the properties of addition of real numbers. On p. 65, the distributive property is illustrated by area diagrams.

Reasoning Backward
The Challenge on p. 52 can be solved using this technique.

Teaching Suggestions p. T78

Suggested Extensions p. T78

Chalkboard Examples

Simplify.

1. $21 + 3 + 10$ 34
2. $50 \times 9 \times 2 \times 9$ 8100
3. $4 + 6y + 3$ $6y + 7$
4. $3\frac{1}{4} + \frac{3}{5} + 1\frac{3}{4} + 2\frac{2}{5}$ 8

Name the axiom or property illustrated.

5. $(5 + 19) + 1 = 5 + (19 + 1)$ Associative axiom for addition
6. $(-5) \times 7 = 7 \times (-5)$ Commutative axiom for multiplication
7. Since 5 and $\frac{2}{5}$ are real numbers, $\left(5 \times \frac{2}{5}\right)$ must be a real number. Closure axiom for multiplication
8. If $m - 2 = 5$ and $5 = 7 - 2$, then $m - 2 = 7 - 2$. Transitive property of equality

In the sum $a + b$, a and b are called **terms.** In the product ab, a and b are called **factors.**

You find a sum or a product by working with two numbers at a time. To find the sum of several numbers, such as

$$79 + 65 + 35,$$

you usually do the additions in order from left to right:

$$(79 + 65) + 35 = 144 + 35 = 179$$

This example would be easier to compute if the terms were grouped as follows:

$$79 + (65 + 35) = 79 + 100 = 179$$

Note that the sum is 179 no matter which way the terms are grouped. When you add three or more real numbers, you get the same sum no matter how you group, or *associate,* the numbers.

Similarly, products of three or more real numbers do not depend on the way you group the factors. For example, you can verify that

$$\left(7 \times \frac{1}{2}\right) \times 20 = 7 \times \left(\frac{1}{2} \times 20\right).$$

Associative Axioms

For all real numbers a, b, and c:

$$(a + b) + c = a + (b + c)$$

$$(ab)c = a(bc)$$

The commutative and associative axioms permit you to add or multiply numbers *in any order* and *in any groups of two.* Thoughtful use of these axioms can sometimes help you simplify expressions.

Example 1 Simplify $7 \times 25 \times 31 \times 4$.

Solution

$$\begin{aligned} 7 \times 25 \times 31 \times 4 &= (7 \times 31)(25 \times 4) \\ &= 217 \times 100 \\ &= 21{,}700 \end{aligned}$$

Example 2 Simplify $5 + 8a + 4$.

Solution

$$\begin{aligned} 5 + 8a + 4 &= 8a + 5 + 4 \\ &= 8a + 9 \end{aligned}$$

You use the sign = to show that two expressions name the same number (page 2). In your work, you will usually use the following **properties of equality** without mention.

For all real numbers a, b, and c:

Reflexive Property	$a = a$
Symmetric Property	If $a = b$, then $b = a$.
Transitive Property	If $a = b$ and $b = c$, then $a = c$.

Throughout the rest of this book, the domain of all variables is the set of real numbers unless otherwise specified.

Oral Exercises

Name the axiom or property illustrated.

Example $7 + x = x + 7$ ***Solution*** Commutative axiom for addition

1. $9 \times (-6) = (-6) \times 9$ Comm. ax. for mult.
2. $(83 + 99) + 1 = 83 + (99 + 1)$ Assoc. ax. for add.
3. $\frac{1}{3} + 4 = 4 + \frac{1}{3}$ Comm. ax. for add.
4. $7(6 \times 0) = (7 \times 6)0$ Assoc. ax. for mult.
5. $n + 3.5 = 3.5 + n$ Comm. ax. for add.
6. If $28 = 2y$, then $2y = 28$. Sym. prop. of eq.
7. $\frac{1}{3}(12p) = \left(\frac{1}{3} \cdot 12\right)p$ Assoc. ax. for mult.
8. If $4 + s = 15$, then $15 = 4 + s$. Sym. prop. of eq.
9. $(5 + b) + (-3) = (b + 5) + (-3)$ Comm. ax. for add.
10. There is only one real number that is the sum of 0.8 and 7.2. Ax. of closure for add.
11. Every real number is equal to itself. Reflexive prop. of equality
12. If $z + 2 = 7$ and $7 = 5 + 2$, then $z + 2 = 5 + 2$. Transitive prop. of equality
13. $r + 33 + 27 + s = r + (33 + 27) + s$ Assoc. ax. for add.
14. $3 \times (5x)y = (3 \times 5)xy$ Assoc. ax. for mult.

Name the axiom that justifies each step. A check (√) shows that the step is justified by the substitution principle (page 2).

15. $57 + (32 + 13) = 57 + (13 + 32)$ (1) ___?___ Comm. ax. for add.
$= (57 + 13) + 32$ (2) ___?___ Assoc. ax. for add.
$= 70 + 32$ (3) √
$= 102$ (4) √

Common Error

Students sometimes think that equations such as $(2 + x) + 5 = (x + 2) + 5$ illustrate the associative axiom for addition because of the parentheses. Point out that x and 2 have been grouped together on each side of the equation but the *order* in which they have been added is different.

Suggested Assignments

Minimum
48/1–22
Average
48/1–25
Maximum
48/1–28

Name the axiom that justifies each step. A check (√) shows that the step is justified by the substitution principle (page 2).

16. $25 \times (83 \times 8) = 25 \times (8 \times 83)$ (1) ? Comm. ax. for mult.
$= (25 \times 8) \times 83$ (2) ? Assoc. ax. for mult.
$= 200 \times 83$ (3) √
$= (100 \times 2) \times 83$ (4) √
$= 100 \times (2 \times 83)$ (5) ? Assoc. ax. for mult.
$= 100 \times 166$ (6) √
$= 16{,}600$ (7) √

Written Exercises

In each of Exercises 1–22, simplify the expression.

A

1. $439 + 42 + 61 + 8$ 550
2. $833 + 26 + 67 + 24$ 950
3. $2 \times 27 \times 5 \times 3$ 810
4. $50 \times 7 \times 7 \times 20$ 49,000
5. $25 \times 53 \times 2 \times 2$ 5300
6. $8 \times 17 \times 9 \times 25$ 30,600
7. $6\frac{1}{2} + 4\frac{1}{3} + 1\frac{1}{2} + \frac{2}{3}$ 13
8. $89\frac{7}{8} + \frac{3}{5} + \frac{1}{8} + 2\frac{2}{5}$ 93
9. $0.1 + 1.8 + 5.9 + 0.2$ 8
10. $4.75 + 2.95 + 1.05 + 10.25$ 19

Example $a + 3 + b + 9 = a + b + 3 + 9 = a + b + 12$

11. $7 + 2p + 3$ $10 + 2p$
12. $18 + 4s + 7$ $25 + 4s$
13. $6(5x)$ $30x$
14. $4(9y)$ $36y$
15. $(8t)(12)$ $96t$
16. $(3c)7$ $21c$

B

17. $m + 8 + f + 3 + g$ $m + f + g + 11$
18. $5 + k + t + 7 + n$ $12 + k + t + n$
19. $(2m)(11k)(5h)$ $110mkh$
20. $(3p)(10q)(9r)$ $270pqr$
21. $(75c)(7d)(10e)(2)$ $10{,}500cde$
22. $(250)(25b)(25c)(4)(8)$ $5{,}000{,}000bc$
23. Find the values of $(7 - 4) - 2$ and $7 - (4 - 2)$. Is subtraction of real numbers associative? 1; 5; no
24. Find the values of $(48 \div 8) \div 2$ and $48 \div (8 \div 2)$. Is division of real numbers associative? 3; 12; no

C

25. Is division of real numbers commutative? Why or why not?
No. Counterexample: $2 \div 4 \neq 4 \div 2$

In each of Exercises 26–28, an operation * is defined over the set of positive integers.
a. Find 3 * 4.
b. State whether or not * is a commutative operation.
c. State whether or not * is an associative operation.

26. $a * b = a + b + 2$
9; yes; yes
27. $a * b = ab + 1$
13; yes; no
28. $a * b = a + 2b$
11; no; no

Additional A Exercises

Simplify each expression.

1. $277 + 93 + 23 + 7$
400
2. $5 \times 8 \times 7 \times 20$ 5600
3. $0.89 + 9.21 + 0.11 + 0.79$ 11
4. $44\frac{2}{3} + 1\frac{1}{4} + 6\frac{1}{3} + 4\frac{3}{4}$
57
5. $25 \times 18 \times 4 \times 2$ 3600
6. $12 + 3p + 48$
$3p + 60$

Mixed Review Exercises

1. Solve: $|x| = 3.64$
± 3.64
2. Represent "Pat is 8 years older than Mike and the sum of their ages is 23" by an equation.
$m + (m + 8) = 23$
3. Translate $-5 < |-4|$ into words. The opposite of 5 is less than the absolute value of the opposite of 4.
4. Use the five-step plan to solve: The area of a rectangle whose width is 6.5 is 85.8. Find the length of the rectangle.
13.2

2-2 Addition on a Number Line

Objective To use a number line to add real numbers.

You already know how to add two positive numbers. You can use a horizontal number line to help you find the sum of *any* two real numbers.

To find the sum of -2 and -5, draw a number line and follow these directions. Starting at the origin, move your pencil along your number line 2 units to the left. Then, from that position, move your pencil 5 units to the left. Moves to the left represent negative numbers. Together, the two moves amount to a move of 7 units to the left from the origin. The arrows in the diagram below show the moves.

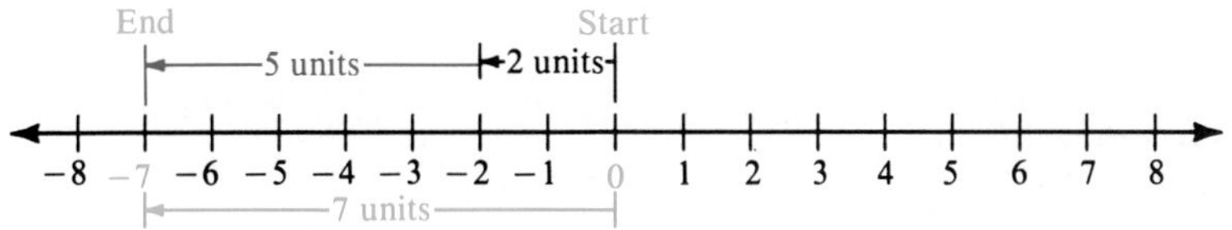

Thus, $-2 + (-5) = -7$

Note the use of parentheses in "$-2 + (-5)$" to separate the plus sign that means "add" from the minus sign that is part of the numeral for negative five.

To find the sum $-2 + 5$, first move 2 units to the left from the origin. Then, from that position, move 5 units to the right. Moves to the right represent positive numbers. The two moves amount to a move of 3 units to the right, as shown below.

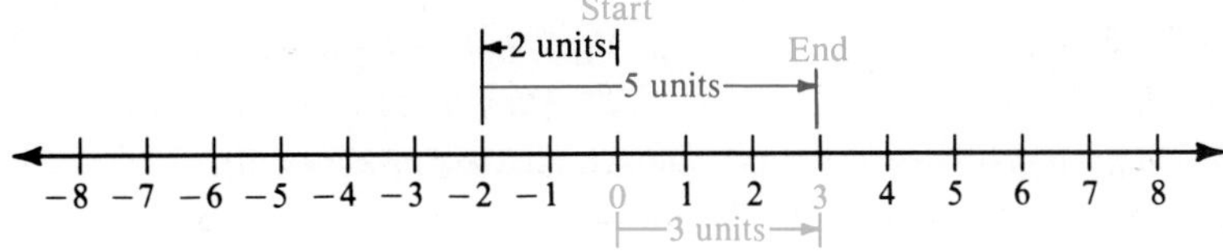

Thus, $-2 + 5 = 3$.

The next diagram shows how to find the sum $2 + (-5)$.

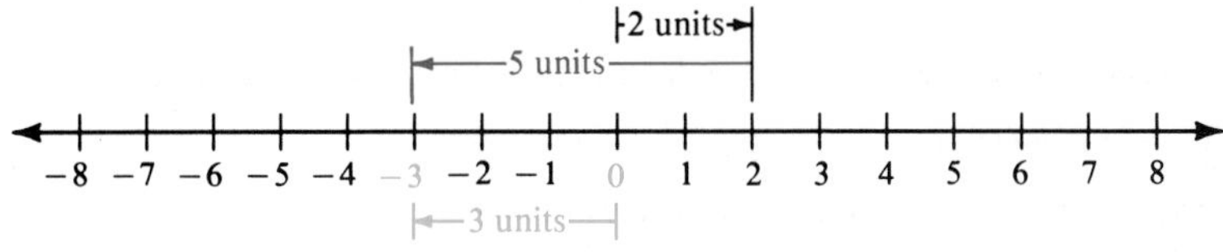

Thus, $2 + (-5) = -3$.

Teaching Suggestions p. T78

Suggested Extensions p. T79

Chalkboard Examples

1. Use arrows along a number line to represent the sum $-5 + 3$.

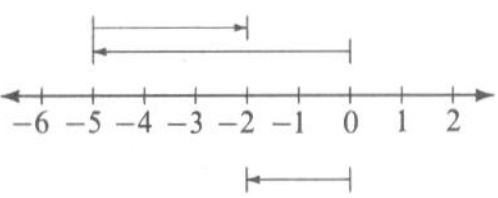

2. Give an addition statement illustrated by the diagram.

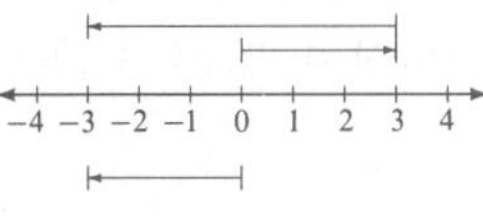

$3 + (-6) = -3$

Find each sum. If necessary, use a number line to help you.

3. $-6 + (-3)$ -9
4. $-4 + 4$ 0
5. $(-2 + 6) + (-5)$ -1
6. $-1.5 + (-3.5) + 8.6$ 3.6
7. Solve the equation $-4 + w = 2$ by using a number line.

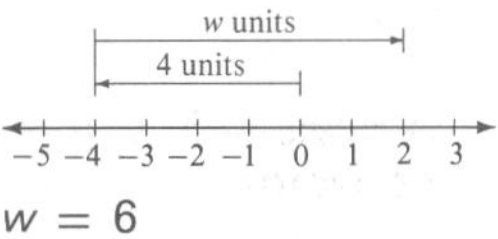

$w = 6$

Supplementary Material

Practice Master 5

Suggested Assignments

Minimum
51/1–35 odd
S 48/23, 24

Average
51/1–23 odd, 25–38
S 48/26–28

Maximum
51/1–23 odd, 25–40

Can you visualize $-3 + 0$ on a number line? Interpret "add 0" to mean "move no units." Then you can see that

$$-3 + 0 = -3 \quad \text{and} \quad 0 + (-3) = -3.$$

These equations illustrate the special property of zero for addition of real numbers: When 0 is added to any given number, the sum is *identical* to the given number. We call 0 the **identity element for addition.**

Identity Axiom for Addition

There is a unique real number 0 such that for every real number a,

$$\boldsymbol{a + 0 = a} \quad \text{and} \quad \boldsymbol{0 + a = a.}$$

Think of adding a pair of opposites, such as 4 and -4, on a number line. As shown below,

$$4 + (-4) = 0 \quad \text{and} \quad -4 + 4 = 0.$$

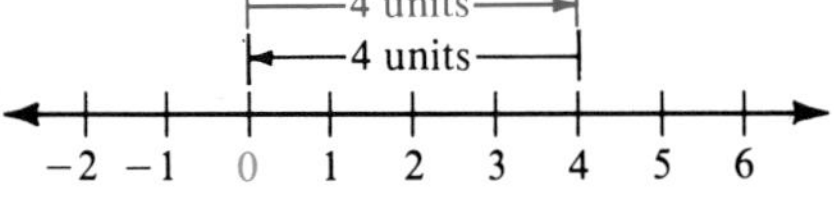

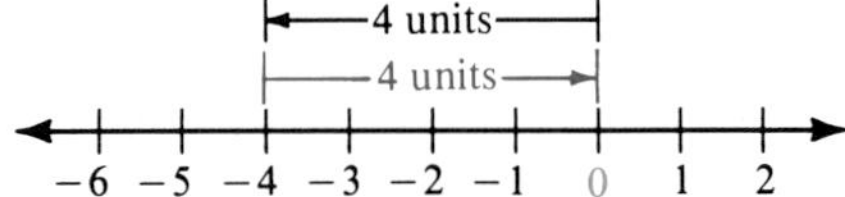

The following axiom is a formal way of saying that the sum of a number and its opposite is always zero.

Axiom of Opposites

For every real number a, there is a unique real number $-a$ such that

$$\boldsymbol{a + (-a) = 0} \quad \text{and} \quad \boldsymbol{-a + a = 0.}$$

A number and its opposite are called **additive inverses** of each other because their sum is zero, the identity element for addition. Thus, the numeral -4 can be read "negative four," "the opposite of four," or "the additive inverse of four."

Oral Exercises

Give an addition statement illustrated by each diagram.

1. $5 + (-7) = -2$

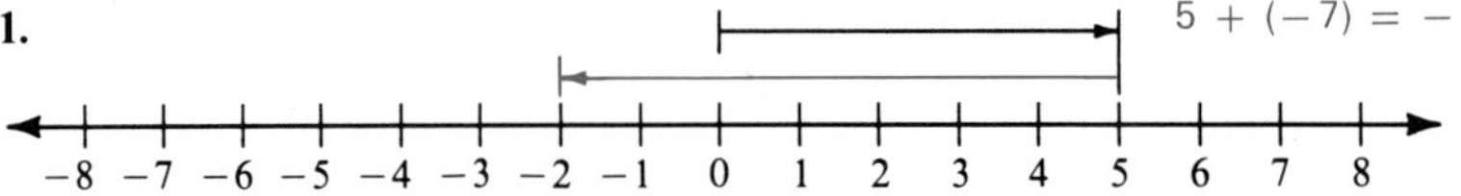

2. −4 + 10 = 6

−8 −7 −6 −5 −4 −3 −2 −1 0 1 2 3 4 5 6 7 8

3.

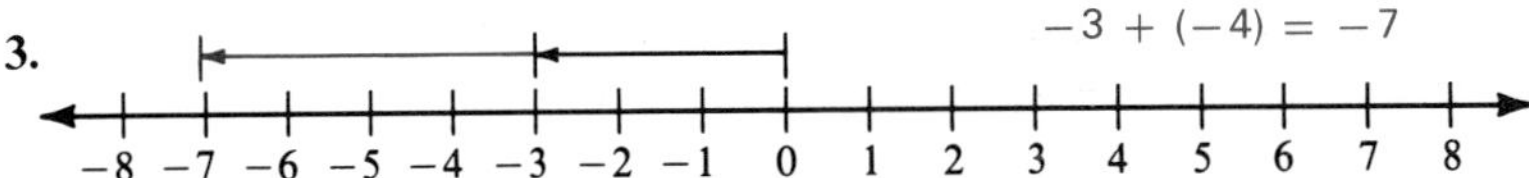

4.

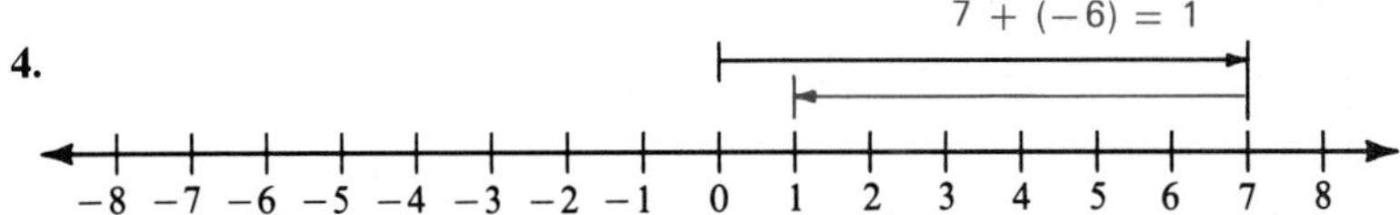

Simplify each expression. If necessary, think of moves along a number line.

5. $-8 + 0$ −8 **6.** $0 + (-5)$ −5 **7.** $-6 + 6$ 0 **8.** $1 + (-1)$ 0

9. $-4 + (-8)$ −12 **10.** $-9 + (-1)$ −10 **11.** $5 + (-1)$ 4 **12.** $-4 + 9$ 5

13. $-8 + 7$ −1 **14.** $6 + (-4)$ 2 **15.** $16 + (-19)$ −3 **16.** $-1 + (-99)$ −100

17. $102 + (-2)$ 100 **18.** $-100 + 1$ −99 **19.** $-10 + 0$ −10 **20.** $-67 + 67$ 0

Written Exercises

Simplify each expression. If necessary, draw a number line such as the one below to help you.

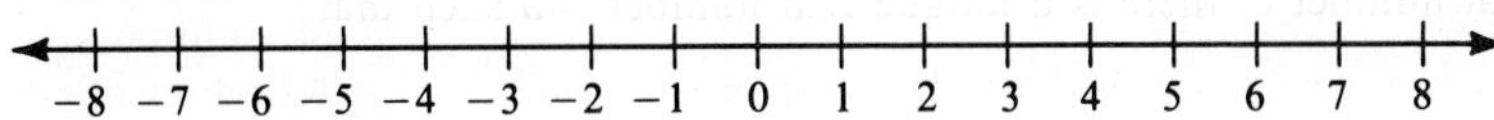

A

1. $(-3 + 7) + 6$ 10 **2.** $(-5 + 8) + 2$ 5

3. $(-9 + 11) + (-2)$ 0 **4.** $(-6 + 9) + (-3)$ 0

5. $[14 + (-20)] + 5$ −1 **6.** $[5 + (-15)] + 7$ −3

7. $[-9 + (-8)] + 9$ −8 **8.** $[-4 + (-12)] + 4$ −12

9. $35 + [7 + (-14)]$ 28 **10.** $32 + [8 + (-16)]$ 24

11. $-26 + [-2 + (-8)]$ −36 **12.** $-7 + [-11 + (-19)]$ −37

13. $[28 + (-8)] + [1 + (-1)]$ 20 **14.** $(-3 + 3) + [16 + (-6)]$ 10

15. $[0 + (-8)] + [-7 + (-23)]$ −38 **16.** $(-9 + 9) + [8 + (-12)]$ −4

17. $-2 + (-3) + (-8)$ −13 **18.** $(-5) + (-7) + (-9)$ −21

19. $-4 + (-10) + 9 + (-6)$ −11 **20.** $-12 + 16 + (-2) + (-17)$ −15

21. $-6.4 + (-2.3) + 8.7$ 0 **22.** $5.9 + (-3.2) + (-7.8)$ −5.1

23. $-\frac{3}{2} + 5 + \left(-\frac{7}{2}\right)$ 0 **24.** $-\frac{13}{3} + (-2) + \left(-\frac{2}{3}\right)$ −7

Additional A Exercises

Simplify each expression. If necessary, draw a number line to help you.

1. $(-4 + 6) + 2$ 4
2. $[3 + (-14)] + 15$ 4
3. $-8 + (-11 + 3)$ −16
4. $(-9 + 6) + (-4 + 5)$ −2
5. $[6 + (-3)] + (5 + 2)$ 10
6. $-1 + 6 + 4$ 9

Mixed Review Exercises

Simplify.

1. $341 + 24 + 59 + 276$ 700
2. $\frac{(7 - 6) \times 21}{7}$ 3
3. Find the solution set of $|k| - 3 = 8$ over the set of real numbers. $\{-11, 11\}$
4. True or false: $|-8| \leq -|-9|$. false

Additional Answers
Written Exercises

37. $b + [a + (-b)]$
$= b + [(-b) + a]$
(Comm. ax. of add.)
$= [b + (-b)] + a$
(Assoc. ax. of add.)
$= 0 + a$
(Ax. of opp.)
$= a$
(Iden. ax. for add.)

38. $-m + (k + m)$
$= -m + (m + k)$
(Comm. ax. of add.)
$= (-m + m) + k$
(Assoc. ax. of add.)
$= 0 + k$
(Ax. of opp.)
$= k$
(Iden. ax. for add.)

39. $-m + [-h + (m + h)]$
$= -m + [-h + (h + m)]$
(Comm. ax. of add.)
$= -m + [(-h + h) + m]$
(Assoc. ax. of add.)
$= -m + [0 + m]$
(Ax. of opp.)
$= -m + m$
(Iden. ax. for add.)
$= 0$
(Ax. of opp.)

40.
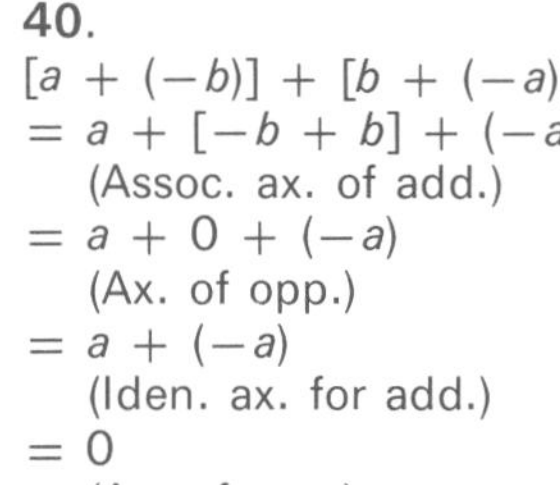
$[a + (-b)] + [b + (-a)]$
$= a + [-b + b] + (-a)$
(Assoc. ax. of add.)
$= a + 0 + (-a)$
(Ax. of opp.)
$= a + (-a)$
(Iden. ax. for add.)
$= 0$
(Ax. of opp.)

Additional Answer
Challenge

Fill two 5-liter containers. Empty them into the 8-liter container until it is full. The liquid left in the second 5-liter container will be 2 L.

In Exercises 25–36, solve each equation. Use a number line as needed.

Example $-2 + n = 8$

Solution The equation states that -2 plus a number is 8. To go from -2 to 8 on the number line below, you move 10 units to the right.

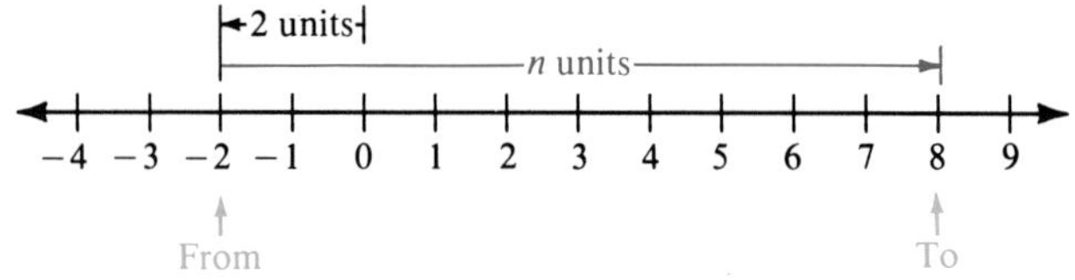

$\therefore$ the solution is 10. ***Answer***

B

25. $-5 + x = 1$ 6	**26.** $-3 + y = 14$ 17	**27.** $0 = 15 + a$ −15
28. $w + 0 = -7$ −7	**29.** $-18 + p = -9$ 9	**30.** $-1 + s = -8$ −7
31. $-30 = 8 + t$ −38	**32.** $13 = -5 + b$ 18	**33.** $c + (-2.5) = -3$ −0.5
34. $m + (-1.75) = -2$ −0.25	**35.** $-83 + d = -83$ 0	**36.** $0 = -25 + k$ 25

In Exercises 37–40, write equations leading to the given equation. Justify each step.

Example $(a + b) + [-a + (-b)] = 0$

Solution

$(a + b) + [-a + (-b)] = [a + (-a)] + [b + (-b)]$	Commutative and associative axioms of addition
$= 0 + 0$	Axiom of opposites
$= 0$	Identity axiom for addition

C

37. $b + [a + (-b)] = a$

38. $-m + (k + m) = k$

39. $-m + [-h + (m + h)] = 0$

40. $[a + (-b)] + [b + (-a)] = 0$

Challenge

In order to conduct an experiment, a scientist needed exactly two liters of a solution. After searching the storeroom, the scientist could find only five-liter containers and eight-liter containers. How could the scientist measure exactly two liters of the solution?

2-3 Rules for Addition

Objective To add real numbers.

The expression $-(2 + 5)$ represents the opposite of the sum of 2 and 5. Since $2 + 5 = 7$,

$$-(2 + 5) = -7.$$

The expression $-2 + (-5)$ represents the sum of the opposite of 2 and the opposite of 5. Using a number line, you know (page 49) that

$$-2 + (-5) = -7.$$

Since $-(2 + 5) = -7$ and $-2 + (-5) = -7$, it follows that

$$-(2 + 5) = -2 + (-5).$$

With a number line you can also show:

$$-[-4 + (-1)] = 4 + 1$$

$$-[8 + (-6)] = -8 + 6$$

$$-(-9 + 7) = 9 + (-7)$$

These equations suggest the following property.

Property of the Opposite of a Sum

The opposite of a sum of real numbers is equal to the sum of the opposites of the numbers. That is, for all real numbers a and b,

$$\mathbf{-(a + b) = -a + (-b).}$$

Using the property of the opposite of a sum along with axioms you have learned and the familiar addition facts for positive numbers, you can compute sums of any real numbers without thinking of a number line.

Example 1 Simplify $-8 + (-3)$.

Solution

$$\begin{aligned} -8 + (-3) &= -(8 + 3) \\ &= -11 \end{aligned}$$

Example 2 Simplify $14 + (-5)$.

Solution

$$\begin{aligned} 14 + (-5) &= (9 + 5) + (-5) \\ &= 9 + [5 + (-5)] \\ &= 9 + 0 \\ &= 9 \end{aligned}$$

Teaching Suggestions p. T79

Suggested Extensions p. T79

Chalkboard Examples

Simplify.

1. $-9 + (-8)$ -17
2. $-8 + 9$ 1
3. $8 + (-9)$ -1
4. $8 + (-11) + 7 + (-20)$ -16
5. $15 + (-2) + 6 + 8 + (-5)$ 22

Add.

6. -312, 476, 297, -165; sum 296
7. 502, -423, -256, 129; sum -48

Supplementary Material

Resource Book, p. 70

Suggested Assignments

Minimum

Day 1: 55/1–13, 23–26
56/*P*: 1–5

Day 2: 55/14–20, 27–30
57/*P*: 6–10
60/1–12

Day 2 finishes Sec. 2-3 and starts Sec. 2-4.

Average

55/1–19 odd, 24–34 even
56/*P*: 1, 4–6, 11, 13

Maximum

55/3–21 odd, 24–38 even
56/*P*: 9–15

After computing many sums by using either a number line or the methods of Examples 1 and 2, you would probably discover the following rules.

Rules for Addition of Positive and Negative Numbers

1. If a and b are both positive, then $a + b = |a| + |b|$.
   Example. $3 + 7 = 10$
2. If a and b are both negative, then $a + b = -(|a| + |b|)$.
   Example. $-6 + (-2) = -(6 + 2) = -8$
3. If a is positive and b is negative and a has the greater absolute value, then $a + b = |a| - |b|$.
   Example. $8 + (-5) = 8 - 5 = 3$
4. If a is positive and b is negative and b has the greater absolute value, then $a + b = -(|b| - |a|)$.
   Example. $4 + (-9) = -(9 - 4) = -5$
5. If a and b are opposites, then $a + b = 0$.
   Example. $2 + (-2) = 0$

The following examples show how to add more than two real numbers.

Example 3 Simplify $7 + (-9) + 15 + (-12)$.

Solution 1 Add the numbers in order from left to right.

$7 + (-9) = -2;\ -2 + 15 = 13;\ 13 + (-12) = 1$ ***Answer***

Solution 2

Add positive numbers.	Add negative numbers.	Add the sums.
7	−9	22
15	−12	−21
22	−21	1 ***Answer***

Example 4 Add.

$$\begin{array}{r} -291 \\ 379 \\ 185 \\ -462 \\ \hline \end{array}$$

Solution

Step 1	Step 2	Step 3
379	−291	−753
185	−462	564
564	−753	−189 ***Answer***

Oral Exercises

Add.

1. $\begin{array}{r} 8\\ 8\\ \hline 16\end{array}$ **2.** $\begin{array}{r} -4\\ -3\\ \hline -7\end{array}$ **3.** $\begin{array}{r} -9\\ 6\\ \hline -3\end{array}$ **4.** $\begin{array}{r} 11\\ -7\\ \hline 4\end{array}$ **5.** $\begin{array}{r} -14\\ -29\\ \hline -43\end{array}$ **6.** $\begin{array}{r} -1\\ 10\\ \hline 9\end{array}$

7. $\begin{array}{r} -16\\ 7\\ \hline -9\end{array}$ **8.** $\begin{array}{r} -5\\ -12\\ \hline -17\end{array}$ **9.** $\begin{array}{r} -17\\ 47\\ \hline 30\end{array}$ **10.** $\begin{array}{r} 35\\ -75\\ \hline -40\end{array}$ **11.** $\begin{array}{r} -98\\ 36\\ \hline -62\end{array}$ **12.** $\begin{array}{r} 75\\ -28\\ \hline 47\end{array}$

Simplify.

13. $-9 + (-12)$ -21
14. $-18 + 8$ -10
15. $14 + (-15)$ -1
16. $14 + (-6)$ 8
17. $2 + (-17)$ -15
18. $-5 + 22$ 17
19. $4 + (-1) + (-3)$ 0
20. $-2 + (-8) + 8$ -2
21. $-3 + (-6) + 9$ 0

Written Exercises

Add.

A **1.** $\begin{array}{r} 8\\ 7\\ -1\\ 5\\ \hline 19\end{array}$ **2.** $\begin{array}{r} -5\\ -6\\ 9\\ 1\\ \hline -1\end{array}$ **3.** $\begin{array}{r} 53\\ -43\\ 57\\ -18\\ \hline 49\end{array}$ **4.** $\begin{array}{r} -45\\ 21\\ 58\\ -72\\ \hline -38\end{array}$ **5.** $\begin{array}{r} 184\\ -27\\ -37\\ -13\\ \hline 107\end{array}$ **6.** $\begin{array}{r} -173\\ 412\\ -58\\ -93\\ \hline 88\end{array}$

Simplify.

7. $-17 + 4 + (-12) + 39$ 14
8. $-16 + (-9) + 8 + 25$ 8
9. $109 + (-56) + (-91) + 26$ -12
10. $-308 + (-87) + 272 + 64$ -59
11. $-[31 + (-9)] + [-(-3 + 7)]$ -26
12. $[-7 + (-1)] + [-(-7 + 1)]$ -2
13. $3.7 + 4.2 + (-2.3) + 0 + 6.4 + 12.8$ 24.8
14. $-7.2 + 11.4 + (-8.1) + (-9.7) + 0.6$ -13
15. $27 + 43 + (-14) + 11 + (-57) + 5 + (-36) + (-14)$ -35
16. $46 + (-33) + 18 + 0 + (-93) + (-2) + (-34)$ -98
17. $-\frac{1}{3} + \left(-1\frac{2}{3}\right) + 2$ 0
18. $3 + \left(-\frac{5}{2}\right) + \left(-\frac{7}{2}\right)$ -3
19. $-1\frac{3}{4} + 2\frac{1}{4}$ $\frac{1}{2}$
20. $-3\frac{2}{5} + \left(-1\frac{4}{5}\right)$ $-5\frac{1}{5}$
21. $-\frac{7}{8} + \left(-\frac{11}{8}\right)$ $-\frac{9}{4}$
22. $\frac{16}{3} + \left(-\frac{10}{3}\right)$ 2

Evaluate each expression if $x = -4$, $y = |-7|$, and $z = -5$.

B **23.** $x + y + (-1)$ 2
24. $-21 + x + z$ -30
25. $-15 + (-x) + y$ -4
26. $-z + (-8) + y$ 4
27. $1 + (-y) + z$ -11
28. $-y + (-11) + x$ -22

Additional A Exercises

Add.

1. $\begin{array}{r} 15\\ -12\\ 9\\ 6\\ -22\\ \hline -4\end{array}$ **2.** $\begin{array}{r} 193\\ -24\\ -33\\ -61\\ \hline 75\end{array}$

Simplify.

3. $(-9) + (-8) + 10 + 7$ 0
4. $[-3 + (-2)] + [-4 + (-7)]$ -16
5. $14 + 29 + (-3) + (-16) + 22$ 46
6. $-\frac{5}{6} + \left(-\frac{7}{6}\right)$ -2

Mixed Review Exercises

Simplify.

1. $(13n)(12m)$ $156mn$
2. $15 + 75 \div (12 + 3)$ 20
3. $82\frac{2}{3} + 5\frac{4}{7} + 2\frac{1}{3} + \frac{3}{7}$ 91
4. Give the opposite of 7 and graph it on a number line. -7

−8 −7 −6 −5 −4 −3 −2 −1 0

Additional Answers
Written Exercises

37. $r + s + [-(r + s + t)]$
$= r + s + [-r + (-s) + (-t)]$
$= [r + (-r)] + [s + (-s)] + (-t)$
$= 0 + 0 + (-t)$
$= -t$

38. $a + [-(a + b)]$
$= a + [-a + (-b)]$
$= [a + (-a)] + (-b)$
$= 0 + (-b)$
$= -b$

Replace each ? with a number to make a true statement.

29. $\underline{?} + (-7) = 3$ 10
30. $-13 + \underline{?} = 6$ 19
31. $4 + \underline{?} = -11$ −15
32. $\underline{?} + (-6) = 3$ 9
33. $0.6 + \underline{?} = -1$ −1.6
34. $\underline{?} + 0.25 = -0.75$ −1

In Exercises 35–38, write equations leading to the given equation. Justify each step.

C 35. $-6 + [-a + (a + 6)] = 0$
36. $-(-x + y) + y = x$
37. $r + s + [-(r + s + t)] = -t$
38. $a + [-(a + b)] = -b$

35. $-6 + [-a + (a + 6)] = -6 + [-a + a + 6]$
$= -6 + (-a + a) + 6$
$= -6 + 6 + (-a + a)$
$= 0 + 0 = 0$

36. $-(-x + y) + y = [-(-x) + (-y)] + y$
$= [x + (-y)] + y$
$= x + [-y + y]$
$= x + 0 = x$

Problems

a. Name a positive or a negative number to represent each measurement given in the problem.
b. Compute the sum of the numbers.
c. Answer each question.

Example A football team made the following yardage on five plays: lost 3, gained 15, gained 8, lost 9, and lost 4. What was the net yardage on the five plays?

Solution
a. −3, 15, 8, −9, −4
b. $-3 + 15 + 8 + (-9) + (-4) = 7$
c. The team had a net gain of 7 yards.

A 1. Marie Corot has \$784 in her checking account. She deposits \$96 and then writes two checks, one for \$18, the other for \$44. What is the new balance in the account? \$818

2. A jet plane flying at an altitude of 28,600 ft descended 1200 ft and then rose 3500 ft. What was its new altitude? 30,900 ft

3. An elevator started at the eighteenth floor. It then went down seven floors and up nine floors. At what floor was the elevator then located? 20th floor

4. A diving bell descended to a level 230 m below the surface of the ocean. Later it ascended 95 m and then dove 120 m. What was the new depth of the bell? 255 m below sea level

5. The Drama Society had $498 in its treasury. The society presented a play, for which they paid a royalty of $125. Scenery and costumes cost $184, and programs and other expenses, $179. The sale of tickets amounted to $590. What was in the treasury after the play? $600

6. The stock of Ballard Foods Corporation opened on Monday at $32 per share. It lost $5 that day, dropped another $3 on Tuesday, but rallied to gain $4 on Wednesday and $2 on Thursday. On Friday it was unchanged. What was its closing price for the week? $30 per share

7. During a four-day period at the Center Hotel, the numbers of guests checking in and out were as follows: 32 in and 27 out, 28 in and 31 out, 12 in and 18 out, and 15 in and 23 out. How did the number of guests in the hotel at the end of the fourth day compare with the number at the start of the four-day period? 12 fewer on the 4th day

8. During their first year after opening a restaurant, the Cataldos had a loss of $14,250. In their second year of operation, they broke even. During their third and fourth years, they had gains of $18,180 and $29,470, respectively. What was the restaurant's net gain or loss over the four-year period? net gain of $33,400

9. A boy walked 5 blocks west and 3 blocks north. Then he walked 8 blocks east and 12 blocks south. After his walk, where was he relative to his starting point? 3 blocks east and 9 blocks south

10. During a freak storm, the temperature fell 8°C, rose 5°C, fell 4°C, and then rose 6°C. If the temperature was 32°C at the outset of the storm, what was it after the storm was over? 31°C

B 11. The Qattâra Depression in Egypt is 133 m below sea level. A helicopter flying at an altitude of 41 m above the Qattâra Depression climbed 28 m and then dropped 37 m. At what altitude relative to sea level was it then flying? 101 m below sea level

12. The rim of a canyon is 156 ft below sea level. If a stranded hiker 71 ft below the rim fired a warning flare that rose 29 ft, to what altitude relative to sea level would the flare rise? 198 ft below sea level

13. Departing from Eastville at 1:00 P.M., Jennifer flew to Center City. The flight took 1.5 hours, but the time in Center City is 2 hours earlier than it is in Eastville. What time was it in Center City when Jennifer landed? 12:30 P.M.

14. A passenger on a train traveling east at 135 km/h walks toward the back of the train at a rate of 7 km/h. What is the passenger's rate of travel with respect to the ground? 128 km/h

C **15.** Jim Martin charged \$175 worth of clothing and \$287 worth of camera equipment to his charge account. He then made two payments of \$50 each to the account. The next bill showed that he owed a balance of \$495.25, including \$11.50 in interest charges. How much had Jim owed on the account before making his purchases? \$121.75

16. The volume of water in a tank during a five-day period changed as follows: up 375 L, down 240 L, down 164 L, up 93 L, and down 157 L. What was the volume of water in the tank at the beginning of the five-day period if the final volume was 54 L? 147 L

Computer Key-In

Suppose that you want to write a program to find the sum of a list of nonnegative numbers and that the list may vary in length from application to application. One way of doing this is shown by the program below.

You have used INPUT statements to give values to variables. Another way to give a value to a variable is to use a LET statement. For example,

```
LET A = 6
```

assigns the value 6 on the right side of the equals sign to the variable *A* on the left.

The following program allows you to INPUT as many nonnegative numbers as you wish. When you want to end the INPUT, you type -1.

```
10  PRINT "TO FIND THE SUM OF SEVERAL"
20  PRINT "     NUMBERS (> = 0)"
30  PRINT "(TO END, TYPE -1):"
40  LET S=0
50  PRINT "NUMBER";
60  INPUT N
70  IF N<0 THEN 100
80  LET S=S+N
90  GOTO 50
100  PRINT "SUM = ";S
110  END
```

Line 80 is not an equation. It adds each new value of *N* to *S*. It means, "Take the value of *S*, add the value of *N* to it, and then put the new value into *S*."

Lines 50–90 form one kind of loop; that is, lines 50–90 will be repeated until line 70 ends the INPUT when -1 is entered. Line 90 sends the program back to line 50 to get a new value of *N*. Line 100 prints the final value of *S*. (If possible, save this program for later use.)

Exercises

Find the sum of each list.

1. 2, 4, 6, 8, 10, 12, 14, 16, 18, 20 110

2. 1, 4, 9, 16, 25, 36, 49, 64, 81, 100 385

3. 2.25, 3.42, 5.15, 1.98, 4.82 17.62

4. 12.95, 27.59, 21.76, 38.25, 47.34 147.89

2-4 Subtracting Real Numbers

Objective To subtract real numbers and to simplify expressions involving differences.

The first column below lists a few examples of subtraction of 2. The second column lists related examples of addition of -2.

Subtracting 2	Adding -2
$3 - 2 = 1$	$3 + (-2) = 1$
$4 - 2 = 2$	$4 + (-2) = 2$
$5 - 2 = 3$	$5 + (-2) = 3$
$6 - 2 = 4$	$6 + (-2) = 4$

Comparing the entries in the two columns shows that subtracting 2 gives the same result as adding the opposite of 2. This suggests the following **definition of subtraction.**

For all real numbers a and b, the **difference** $a - b$ is defined by:

$$\mathbf{a - b = a + (-b)}$$

To subtract b, add the opposite of b.

Example Simplify.

a. $12 - (-3)$
b. $-7 - 1$
c. $-4 - (-10)$
d. $y - (y + 6)$

Solution

a. $12 - (-3) = 12 + 3 = 15$
b. $-7 - 1 = -7 + (-1) = -8$
c. $-4 - (-10) = -4 + 10 = 6$
d. $y - (y + 6) = y + [-(y + 6)] = y + (-y) + (-6) = -6$

Note that in part (d) the property of the opposite of a sum is used. The opposite of $(y + 6)$ is $-y + (-6)$.

Using the definition of subtraction, you may replace any difference with a sum. For example,

$$12 - 8 - 7 + 4 \quad \text{means} \quad 12 + (-8) + (-7) + 4.$$

As shown at the right, you may simplify this expression by grouping from left to right.

$12 - 8 - 7 + 4$
4
-3
1

Teaching Suggestions p. T80

Suggested Extensions p. T80

Chalkboard Examples

Simplify.

1. $9 - (-5)$ 14
2. $-8 - 8$ -16
3. $-6 - (-10)$ 4
4. $x - (x + 7)$ -7
5. $-y - (-4 - y)$ 4
6. 15 less than -3 -18
7. -11 decreased by -5 -6
8. $29 - (18 - 24)$ 35
9. $(2 - 11) - (-7 + 4)$ -6

Supplementary Materials

Practice Master 6
Test 4

Suggested Assignments

Minimum
61/14–40 even
62/*P*: 1–3, 5, 8

Day 2 of Sec. 2-3 finishes Sec. 2-3 and starts Sec. 2-4.

Average
60/2–40 even, 45–50
62/*P*: 2, 3, 5, 8–10
R 63/*Self-Test 1*

Maximum
60/2–52 even, 53
62/*P*: 2, 3, 5, 8–10
R 63/*Self-Test 1*

The preceding method is convenient if you are doing the work mentally or with a hand calculator. For written work, you may want to group positive terms and negative terms:

$$12 - 8 - 7 + 4 = (12 + 4) - (8 + 7) = 16 - 15 = 1$$

Certain sums are usually replaced by differences. For example,

$9 + (-2x)$ is usually written $9 - 2x$.

Here are some important questions and answers about subtraction of real numbers:

1. Is subtraction commutative? No; for example,
$$8 - 3 = 5 \quad \text{but} \quad 3 - 8 = -5.$$
2. Is subtraction associative? No; for example,
$$(6 - 4) - 2 = 0 \quad \text{but} \quad 6 - (4 - 2) = 4.$$
3. What is the opposite of the difference $a - b$?
$$-(a - b) = -a + b.$$
To see why, write $a - b$ as a sum and use the property of the opposite of a sum.
$$-(a - b) = -[a + (-b)]$$
$$= -a + [-(-b)] = -a + b.$$
Thus, $-(a - 1) = -a + 1$ and
$-(-2 - b) = 2 + b$.

Oral Exercises

Simplify.

1. $46 - 5$ 41 **2.** $19 - 12$ 7 **3.** $8 - 13$ -5 **4.** $7 - 27$ -20
5. $0 - 8$ -8 **6.** $0 - (-4)$ 4 **7.** $-16 - 0$ -16 **8.** $-9 - 3$ -12
9. $2 - (-1)$ 3 **10.** $7 - (-3)$ 10 **11.** $-7 - (-14)$ 7 **12.** $-6 - (-4)$ -2
13. $x - (x + 1)$ -1 **14.** $y - (y + 5)$ -5 **15.** $-(a - 3)$ $-a + 3$ **16.** $-(c - 6)$ $-c + 6$
17. $-(4 - t)$ $-4 + t$ **18.** $-(-1 - m)$ $1 + m$ **19.** $5 - (r + 5)$ $-r$ **20.** $2 - (k - 2)$ $4 - k$

Written Exercises

Simplify.

A **1.** $52 - 312$ -260 **2.** $154 - 281$ -127 **3.** $39 - (-32)$ 71 **4.** $47 - (-49)$ 96
5. $-19 - (-3)$ -16 **6.** $-25 - (-9)$ -16 **7.** $-2.8 - 4.4$ -7.2 **8.** $-5.1 - 6.7$ -11.8
9. $157 - (-27)$ 184 **10.** $-206 - (-59)$ -147 **11.** $1.91 - (-1.03)$ 2.94 **12.** $2.95 - (-2.55)$ 5.5

13. −18 decreased by 7 −25

14. −6 decreased by −32 26

15. 24 less than −1 −25

16. 16 less than −2 −18

17. $132 - (72 - 61)$ 121

18. $275 - (80 - 65)$ 260

19. $324 - (65 - 78)$ 337

20. $193 - (30 - 75)$ 238

21. $(22 - 33) - (55 - 66)$ 0

22. $(63 - 70) - (92 - 80)$ −19

23. $(3 - 8) - (-15 + 19)$ −9

24. $(42 - 33) - (-7 + 12)$ 4

25. $1066 - 1492 + 1776$ 1350

26. $1910 - 1939 - 2010$ −2039

27. $12 - (-9) - [5 - (-4)]$ 12

28. $-15 - 6 - [-7 - (-10)]$ −24

29. $4 - 5 + 8 - 17 + 31$ 21

30. $18 - 14 + 15 + 7 - 26$ 0

31. $-6 - 19 + 4 - 8 + 20$ −9

32. $-11 - 43 + 1 - 9 + 30$ −32

33. $-x - (-3 - x)$ 3

34. $-t - (-t - 5)$ 5

35. The difference of 81 and −6, decreased by −29. 116

36. −54 decreased by the difference of −37 and 15. −2

37. −46 decreased by the difference of −23 and −61. −84

38. The difference of −59 and 12, decreased by 72. −143

B

39. $7 + y - (7 - y) - y$ y

40. $s - (-3) - [s + (-3)] - 3$ 3

41. $h + 8 - (-9 + h)$ 17

42. $-(10 - k) - (k - 12)$ 2

43. $(\pi + 2)$ subtracted from $\pi - 17$ −19

44. $(7 - 2\pi)$ subtracted from $11 - 2\pi$ 4

Evaluate each expression if $a = -3$, $b = 7$, and $c = -1$.

45. $c - |a - b|$ −11

46. $b - |c - a|$ 5

47. $|c - a| - b$ −5

48. $|b - c| - a$ 11

49. $a - |c| - (|a| - b)$ 0

50. $|c| - b - (|a| - c)$ −10

51. $(a - |c|) - |a| - b$ −14

52. $(|c| - b) - |a| - c$ −8

In Exercises 53 and 54, name the definition, axiom, or property that justifies each step marked with __?__.

C

53. a. $b + (a - b) = b + [a + (-b)]$ (1) __?__ Def. of subtraction
$= b + [(-b) + a]$ (2) __?__ Comm. ax. of add.
$= [b + (-b)] + a$ (3) __?__ Assoc. ax. of add.
$= 0 + a$ (4) __?__ Ax. of opp.
$= a$ (5) __?__ Ident. ax. for add.

b. Use the result of part (a) to complete the following sentence:

$a - b$ is the number to add to b to obtain __?__. a

54. a. $-(a - b) = -a + b$ (1) See page 60.
$= b + (-a)$ (2) __?__ Comm. ax. of add.
$= b - a$ (3) __?__ Def. of subtraction

b. Use the result of part (a) to complete the following sentence:

The opposite of $a - b$ is __?__. $b - a$

Additional A Exercises

Simplify.

1. $32 - (-14)$ 46
2. $-56 - 22$ −78
3. $-95 - (-3)$ −92
4. $74 - 35$ 39
5. $16 - 22 + 59 - (-32) - 64$ 21
6. $n - (n - 7)$ 7

Mixed Review Exercises

1. Simplify: $-6 + (-3.2) + 5.7$ −3.5
2. Replace __?__ with < or > to make a true statement. $-(-6)$ __?__ -3 >
3. Solve $3 + 9x = 30$ if $x \in \{0, 1, 2, 3, 4, 5\}$. {3}
4. Add: −182, −36, 517, −22 277

Problems

Express the answer to each question as the difference between two real numbers. Compute the difference. Answer the question and interpret the sign of the answer.

Example The floor of the Puerto Rico Trench in the Atlantic Ocean is about 9460 m below sea level. If a minisub is 1338 m below sea level, how far is the sea floor from the minisub?

Solution $-9460 - (-1338) =$
$-9460 + 1338 = -8122$
The sea floor is 8122 m *below* the minisub.

A **1.** An astronaut entered her space capsule $1\frac{1}{2}$ hours before liftoff. How long had she been in the capsule $2\frac{1}{2}$ hours after liftoff? 4 h

2. Find the difference in altitude between Death Valley, California, 86 m below sea level, and Mount Rainier, Washington, 4392 m above sea level. 4478 m

3. If Pythagoras, the Greek mathematician, was born in 582 B.C. and died on his birthday in 497 B.C., how old would he have been when he died? 85 years old

4. The Roman poet Virgil was born in 70 B.C. How old was he on his birthday in 42 B.C.? 28 years old

5. What is the difference of the melting and boiling points of krypton if it boils at 153.4° below 0°C and melts at 157.2° below 0°C? 3.8°C

6. Including the wind-chill factor, the temperature in Iroquois Heights was 8°C below zero at midnight and seventeen below at dawn. What was the change in temperature? −9°C

7. Sally Ryder took the bus from a stop 52 blocks east of Central Square to a stop 39 blocks west of Central Square. How many blocks did she ride? 91 blocks

8. Bill Duff drove a golf ball from a point 176 yd (yards) north of the ninth hole to a point 53 yd south of the hole. How far did the ball travel? 229 yd

B 9. The highest recorded weather temperature on Earth is 58.0°C. The difference of that record and the lowest recorded weather temperature is 146.3°C. What is the record low? −88.3°C

10. The difference in altitude between the highest and lowest points in Louisiana is 164.592 m. If Driskill Mountain, the highest point, is 163.068 m above sea level, what is the altitude of New Orleans, the lowest point? 1.524 m below sea level

Self-Test 1

Vocabulary

axiom (p. 45)
postulate (p. 45)
axioms of closure (p. 45)
terms (p. 46)
factors (p. 46)
associative axioms (p. 46)
reflexive property (p. 47)
symmetric property (p. 47)
transitive property (p. 47)
identity element for addition (p. 50)
additive inverses (p. 50)
opposite of a sum (p. 53)
subtraction (p. 59)
difference (p. 59)

Simplify.

1. $25 \times 97 \times 4$ 9700	**2.** $4 + 3x + 16$ $20 + 3x$	**Obj. 2-1, p. 45**

Simplify. If necessary, think of moves along a number line.

3. $8 + (-8)$ 0	**4.** $-5 + 0$ −5	**5.** $-4 + (-2)$ −6	**Obj. 2-2, p. 49**
6. $-15 + (-12)$ −27		**7.** $-17 + 9 + (-6) + 5$ −9	**Obj. 2-3, p. 53**
8. $24 - 35$ −11		**9.** $-8 - (-10)$ 2	**Obj. 2-4, p. 59**

Check your answers with those at the back of the book.

Challenge

Recall (page 39) that the triangular numbers are

1, 3, 6, 10, 15, and so on.

The square numbers are

1, 4, 9, 16, 25, and so on.

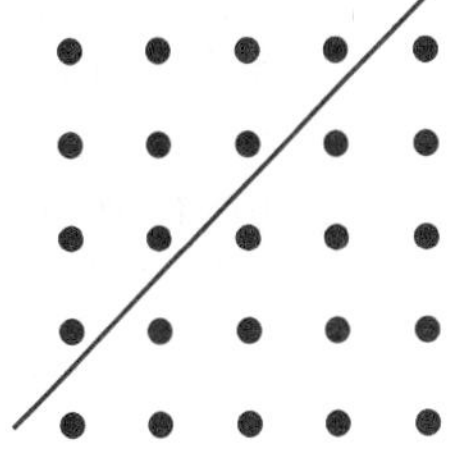

1. Verify that each square number from 4 to 100 is the sum of two consecutive triangular numbers.
2. Illustrate Exercise 1 by dividing the square array of dots shown at the right into two triangular arrays.

Working with Real Numbers **63**

Quick Quiz

Simplify.

1. $4 \times 18 \times 25$ 1800
2. $3 + 5x + 17$ $5x + 20$

Simplify.

3. $2 + (-2)$ 0
4. $-7 + 0$ −7
5. $-6 + (-3)$ −9
6. $-14 + (-16)$ −30
7. $-12 + 6 + (-7) + 2$ −11
8. $19 - 40$ −21
9. $-3 - (-11)$ 8

Additional Answer Challenge

1.
$4 = 1 + 3$
$9 = 3 + 6$
$16 = 6 + 10$
$25 = 10 + 15$
$36 = 15 + 21$
$49 = 21 + 28$
$64 = 28 + 36$
$81 = 36 + 45$
$100 = 45 + 55$

Teaching Suggestions p. T80

Suggested Extensions p. T81

Chalkboard Examples

Use the distributive axiom to simplify.

1. $36\left(\frac{1}{4} + \frac{1}{12}\right)$ 12
2. 12(4.25) 51
3. 76×8 608
4. $45 \times 19 + 55 \times 19$ 1900
5. $8x + 14x$ $22x$
6. $-4d + 5 + 6d + 3$ $2d + 8$

Multiplication

2-5 The Distributive Axiom

Objective To use the distributive axiom to simplify expressions.

The board of a sailboard weighed 40 lb (pounds). The mast with sail and boom weighed 25 lb. Therefore, the total weight in pounds of a shipment of 4 sailboards was:

$$4(40 + 25) = 4 \times 65$$
$$= 260$$

The total weight was also the sum of the weights of the boards and the masts:

$$(4 \times 40) + (4 \times 25) = 160 + 100$$
$$= 260$$

Either way you compute it, the total weight is the same.

$$4(40 + 25) = (4 \times 40) + (4 \times 25)$$

Note that 4 is *distributed* as a multiplier of each term of 40 + 25. This example illustrates another axiom that we use in working with real numbers: multiplication is *distributive with respect to addition.*

Distributive Axiom of Multiplication with Respect to Addition

For all real numbers a, b, and c,

$$a(b + c) = ab + ac \quad \text{and} \quad (b + c)a = ba + ca.$$

By applying the symmetric property of equality, you can also state the distributive axiom in the following form.

For all real numbers a, b, and c,

$$ab + ac = a(b + c) \quad \text{and} \quad ba + ca = (b + c)a.$$

For example, the diagram below illustrates that

$$(3 \times 4) + (3 \times 2) = 3(4 + 2).$$

Area: 3×4 + Area: 3×2 = Area: $3(4+2)$

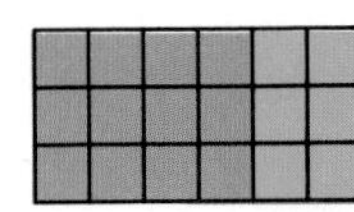

The following examples show some uses of the distributive axiom.

Example 1 **a.** $72\left(\frac{1}{6} + \frac{1}{4}\right) = 72 \times \frac{1}{6} + 72 \times \frac{1}{4} = 12 + 18 = 30$

b. $8(9.5) = 8(9 + 0.5) = (8 \times 9) + (8 \times 0.5) = 72 + 4 = 76$

c. $83 \times 7 = (80 \times 7) + (3 \times 7) = 560 + 21 = 581$

d. $75 \times 13 + 25 \times 13 = (75 + 25)13 = (100)13 = 1300$

Example 2 Show that $9x + 5x = 14x$ for every real number x.

Solution

$9x + 5x = (9 + 5)x$	Distributive axiom
$= 14x$	Substitution principle

Because properties of real numbers and equality guarantee that for all values of the variable

$$9x + 5x \quad \text{and} \quad 14x$$

represent the same number, the two expressions are said to be **equivalent.** The expression $9x + 5x$ has two terms. The expression $14x$ has one term. Replacing an expression containing a variable by an equivalent expression with as few terms as possible is called **simplifying the expression.**

Example 3 Simplify $7r + 1 + (-2)r + 31$.

Solution

$$\begin{aligned} 7r + 1 + (-2)r + 31 &= [7r + (-2)r] + (1 + 31) \\ &= [7 + (-2)]r + 32 \\ &= 5r + 32 \end{aligned}$$

Is multiplication distributive with respect to subtraction? Yes, it is! (See Exercise 44, page 71.)

For all real numbers a, b, and c,

$$\boldsymbol{a(b - c) = ab - ac} \quad \text{and} \quad \boldsymbol{(b - c)a = ba - ca}.$$

Common Errors

Students frequently write, for example, $3(x - 8) = 3x - 8$. Remind them to multiply the factor outside the parentheses by *each* term inside the parentheses.

Many students also combine unlike terms, writing, for example, $3x + 2 = 5x$ or $2x + 3y = 5xy$. Point out that unlike terms cannot be added together just as 2 apples and 3 oranges do not give you a total of 5 orange apples.

Supplementary Material

Resource Book, p. 71

Suggested Assignments

Minimum
66/1–36
R 63/*Self-Test 1*

Average
66/1–29 odd, 31–38, 41–44, 47
S 57/*P*: 14

Maximum
66/1–29 odd, 31–44, 47–49
S 56/35, 37

Example 4 Simplify $8(n - 1) - 3n$.

Solution

$$\begin{aligned} 8(n-1) - 3n &= 8n - 8 \cdot 1 - 3n \\ &= 8n - 8 - 3n \\ &= 8n - 3n - 8 \\ &= (8-3)n - 8 \\ &= 5n - 8 \end{aligned}$$

Oral Exercises

Use the distributive axiom to simplify each expression.

1. $2(50 + 3)$ 106 **2.** $3(40 + 1)$ 123 **3.** $4(20 - 1)$ 76

4. $5(60 - 2)$ 290 **5.** $4(15)$ 60 **6.** $6 \times 2\frac{1}{3}$ 14

7. $10\left(5\frac{1}{2}\right)$ 55 **8.** $8(2.25)$ 18 **9.** $(35 + 56)\frac{1}{7}$ 13

10. $\frac{1}{4}(24 + 52)$ 19 **11.** $\left(\frac{1}{3} \times 20\right) - \left(\frac{1}{3} \times 2\right)$ 6 **12.** $\left(37 \times \frac{1}{8}\right) + \left(3 \times \frac{1}{8}\right)$ 5

Simplify.

13. $2x + 15x$ $17x$ **14.** $12y + 8y$ $20y$ **15.** $a + 5a$ $6a$

16. $3b + b$ $4b$ **17.** $(-2)x + (-6)x$ $-8x$ **18.** $(-3)y + (-8)y$ $-11y$

19. $6s + (-2)s$ $4s$ **20.** $7t + (-9)t$ $-2t$ **21.** $5m - 3m$ $2m$

22. $11k - 15k$ $-4k$ **23.** $2c - 4c$ $-2c$ **24.** $3(1 + z) + 7$ $10 + 3z$

Written Exercises

Simplify.

A

1. $60\left(\frac{1}{5} + \frac{1}{4}\right)$ 27 **2.** $14\left(1\frac{1}{7}\right)$ 16 **3.** $\frac{1}{6}(17) + \frac{1}{6}(13)$ 5

4. $(0.75)(21) + (0.25)(21)$ 21 **5.** $(14 \times 83) - (4 \times 83)$ 830 **6.** $(62 \times 27) + (38 \times 27)$ 2700

7. $13a + 4a$ $17a$ **8.** $21c + 19c$ $40c$ **9.** $7n + 18n$ $25n$

10. $99p + 5p$ $104p$ **11.** $16t + (-7)t$ $9t$ **12.** $28m + (-14)m$ $14m$

13. $83q - 150q$ $-67q$ **14.** $68v - 59v$ $9v$ **15.** $4x + 5x + 12$ $9x + 12$

16. $8 + 12y + 9y$ $8 + 21y$ **17.** $9(r + 3) + 7$ $9r + 34$ **18.** $8(g + 9) + 18$ $8g + 90$

19. $25 + 3(2w - 6)$ $7 + 6w$ **20.** $38 + 4(5d - 3)$ $26 + 20d$

21. $8a + 7 + 5a + 6$ $13a + 13$ **22.** $21 + 11c + 19c + 4$ $25 + 30c$

23. $(-3)x + 2 + 14x + 29$ $11x + 31$

24. $(-9)y + 6 + 17y - 12$ $8y - 6$

25. $-9 + 9p + 9 + (-1)p$ $8p$

26. $14k + 7 + (-7)k - 7$ $7k$

27. $10n + (-4)n + (-2)n$ $4n$

28. $(-5)s + (-2)s + 21s$ $14s$

29. $4h - 2 - 3h - 8$ $h - 10$

30. $17b - 9 - 11b + 16$ $6b + 7$

B 31. $5e + 7f + (-1)e + 13f$ $4e + 20f$

32. $7k + (-3)m + 6k + 9m$ $13k + 6m$

33. $10x + 15y + 8 - 2x - 4y + 1$ $8x + 11y + 9$

34. $9r + 4s - 6r - 1 - 3s + 5$ $3r + s + 4$

Example $2(x + y - z) + 5(4x + 3y)$

Solution
$$2(x + y - z) + 5(4x + 3y) = 2x + 2y - 2z + 20x + 15y$$
$$= (2x + 20x) + (2y + 15y) - 2z$$
$$= 22x + 17y - 2z$$

35. $9(a + b) + 4(3a + 2b)$ $21a + 17b$

36. $8(k + m) + 15(2k + 5m)$ $38k + 83m$

37. $6(r + 5) + 9(r - 2) - 4r$ $11r + 12$

38. $4(s + 7) + 5(s - 3) - 2s$ $7s + 13$

39. $7(c + 2d + 8) + 3(9c - 2)$ $34c + 14d + 50$

40. $4(5x + 3y + 6) + 14(2y - 1)$ $20x + 40y + 10$

In Exercises 41–44, represent each word phrase by a variable expression. Then simplify it.

41. Seven times the sum of c and d, increased by twice the sum of $3c$ and $2d$ $13c + 11d$

42. Twice the sum of eleven and x, increased by three times the difference of x and 7 $5x + 1$

43. Eight more than the sum of negative five and $15y$, increased by one half of the difference of $12y$ and eight $21y - 1$

44. Six more than three times the sum of a and b, increased by five less than the product of negative three and b $3a + 1$

45. On Friday a store sold x cameras at $69.95 each. The next day the store sold 3 more than were sold on Friday at the same price. What were the store's receipts from this two-day sale? $139.90x + 209.85$

46. On Monday, Yolanda worked for H hours at $4.85 per hour. The next day she worked 2 hours less at the same rate of pay. How much did she earn for those days? $9.70H - 9.70$

Simplify.

C 47. $8[5x + 7(3 + 4x)] - 16x - 8$ $248x + 160$

48. $-24 + 3[4y + 2(5y - 8)] - 9y$ $33y - 72$

49. $12(3n + 2p) + 11[n + 3(2n - p - 3)]$ $113n - 9p - 99$

50. $9[7(3a + 2b - 4) + 12(a - 2)] + 3(5a - 8b)$ $312a + 102b - 468$

Additional A Exercises

Simplify.

1. $36\left(\frac{1}{9} + \frac{1}{6}\right)$ 10
2. $(65 \times 23) + (23 \times 35)$ 2300
3. $7(m - 4) + 18$ $7m - 10$
4. $12n - 6 + (-13)n + 4$ $-n - 2$
5. $13 + 3n + 2n + 5$ $5n + 18$
6. $(-3)s + (-2)s - 14 + 22s$ $17s - 14$

Mixed Review Exercises

Simplify.

1. $(5 - 9) - (-16 + 12)$ 0
2. $-6 + (-2.3) + 1.7$ -6.6
3. $(12ab)(-3c^2)$ $-36abc^2$
4. John's father's age is three times the sum of John's age, j, and Pete's age, p. Represent John's father's age. $3(j + p)$

Teaching Suggestions p. T81

Suggested Extensions p. T81

2-6 Rules for Multiplication

Objective To multiply real numbers.

When you multiply any given real number by 1, the product is identical to the given number. For example,

$$3 \times 1 = 3 \quad \text{and} \quad 1 \times 3 = 3.$$

The **identity element for multiplication** is 1.

Identity Axiom for Multiplication

There is a unique real number 1 such that for every real number a,

$$\boldsymbol{a \cdot 1 = a} \quad \text{and} \quad \boldsymbol{1 \cdot a = a.}$$

The equations

$$3 \times 0 = 0 \quad \text{and} \quad 0 \times 3 = 0$$

illustrate the *multiplicative property of zero:* When one of the factors of a product is zero, the product itself is zero.

Multiplicative Property of Zero

For every real number a,

$$\boldsymbol{a \cdot 0 = 0} \quad \text{and} \quad \boldsymbol{0 \cdot a = 0.}$$

Would you guess that $3 \times (-1) = -3$? You can verify this product by noticing that

$$3 \times (-1) = (-1) + (-1) + (-1) = -3.$$

Multiplying *any* real number by -1 produces the opposite of the number (Exercise 43, page 71).

Multiplicative Property of −1

For every real number a,

$$\boldsymbol{a(-1) = -a} \quad \text{and} \quad \boldsymbol{(-1)a = -a.}$$

A special case of the multiplicative property of -1 occurs when the value of a is -1:

$$(-1)(-1) = 1.$$

Using the multiplicative property of -1 with the familiar multiplication facts for positive numbers and axioms that you have learned, you can compute the product of *any* two real numbers. Here are some examples:

1. $3(5) = 15$
2. $(-3)(5) = (-1)3(5) = (-1)15 = -15$
3. $3(-5) = 3(-1)(5) = 3(5)(-1) = 15(-1) = -15$
4. $(-3)(-5) = (-1)3(-1)5 = (-1)(-1)3(5) = 1(15) = 15$

Similarly, the following property can be shown.

Property of Opposites in Products

For all real numbers a and b:

$$(-a)(b) = -ab \qquad a(-b) = -ab \qquad (-a)(-b) = ab$$

Practice in computing products will lead you to discover the following rules for multiplication of positive and negative numbers.

Rules for Multiplication of Positive and Negative Numbers

1. The product of a positive number and a negative number is a negative number.
2. The product of two positive numbers or of two negative numbers is a positive number.
3. The absolute value of the product of two real numbers is the product of the absolute values of the numbers:

$$|ab| = |a| \times |b|.$$

By pairing the negative numbers in a product of more than two factors, you will find that

the product of an *even* number of negative numbers is *positive;*
the product of an *odd* number of negative numbers is *negative.*

Chalkboard Examples

State whether each expression names a positive number, a negative number, or zero. Then simplify the expression.

1. $(-2)(5)(-4)$ Positive; 40
2. $(-23)(0)(15)$ Zero; 0
3. $(-8)(-2)(-3)$ Negative; -48
4. $(-1)(3)(-2)(-5)$ Negative; -30

Simplify.

5. $(6x)(-9y)$ $-54xy$
6. $6p + (-11p)$ $-5p$
7. $-3(4 - 7)$ 9
8. $-5(-x + 2y)$ $5x - 10y$
9. $-1(2m - n) + 3m$ $m + n$

Supplementary Material

Practice Master 7

Suggested Assignments

Minimum
70/1-33
S 67/37, 38

Average
70/1-15 odd, 19-36, 41, 42
S 67/39, 40, 45, 46, 48

Maximum
70/1-25 odd, 27-44
S 61/54
67/50

Example 1 State whether the expression names a positive number, a negative number, or zero. Then simplify the expression.
a. $-9(-2)(-5)$ **b.** $16(74)(0)$ **c.** $8(-7)(-2)$

Solution **a.** Negative; -90 **b.** Zero; 0 **c.** Positive; 112

Example 2 Simplify. **a.** $(-3x)(-12y)$ **b.** $4p + (-5p)$ **c.** $-2(a - 3b) + 5a$

Solution
a. $(-3x)(-12y) = (-3)x(-12)y = (-3)(-12)xy = 36xy$
b. $4p + (-5p) = 4p + (-5)p = [4 + (-5)]p = (-1)p = -p$
c. $-2(a - 3b) + 5a = (-2)a - (-2)(3b) + 5a$
$= (-2 + 5)a - (-6)b$
$= 3a - (-6b)$
$= 3a + 6b$

Oral Exercises

Simplify.

1. $(-7)(-1)$ 7
2. $10(-8)$ -80
3. $(-3)(-9)$ 27
4. $(-8)(-5)$ 40
5. $(-1)(4)(-4)$ 16
6. $2(-6)(-1)$ 12
7. $(-1)(-3)(-5)$ -15
8. $(-2)(-4)(-6)$ -48
9. $17(0)(-21)$ 0
10. $-10(-8)(0)$ 0
11. $(-6)(-10g)$ $60g$
12. $(-7)(12p)$ $-84p$
13. $(-3p)(-4q)$ $12pq$
14. $(5x)(-7y)$ $-35xy$
15. $(-9v)(12w)$ $-108vw$
16. $6m + (-3m)$ $3m$
17. $8t + (-14t)$ $-6t$
18. $-7b + 2b$ $-5b$
19. $-2h + 15h$ $13h$
20. $7c + (-7c)$ 0
21. $-5xy + 4xy$ $-xy$
22. $-2ab - 3ab$ $-5ab$
23. $-w + 6w$ $5w$
24. $-14n - n$ $-15n$
25. $5t + (-4t)$ t
26. $8u + (-8u)$ 0
27. $-9xy + 8xy$ $-xy$
28. $-4mn + (-6mn)$ $-10mn$
29. $-a + 12a$ $11a$
30. $(-39k) + (-k)$ $-40k$

Written Exercises

Simplify.

A

1. $(-28)(-3)$ 84
2. $23(-5)$ -115
3. $(-4)(10)(-12)$ 480
4. $(-6)(-9)(20)$ 1080
5. $(-3)(-7)(-4)$ -84
6. $(-2)(-8)(-4)$ -64
7. $(-17)(-18)(0)$ 0
8. $54(-47)(0)$ 0
9. $5(-3)(-10)(-2)$ -300
10. $(-4)(25)(-2)(-3)$ -600
11. $(-6)(-1)(-7)(-10)$ 420
12. $(-9)(-5)(-1)(-3)$ 135

13. $-2(-1-8)$ 18
14. $(-16+8)(-1)$ 8
15. $(8 \times 1)+8(-11)$ -80
16. $(-7 \times 18)+(-7 \times 12)$ -210
17. $(-9 \times 12)-(-9 \times 2)$ -90
18. $-34 \times(-1)-[-34 \times(-11)]$ -340
19. $8(-a+5d)$ $-8a+40d$
20. $-9(2m-k)$ $-18m+9k$
21. $-2(-r-5s)$ $2r+10s$
22. $-4(3v-9w)$ $-12v+36w$
23. $-x+8+5x-4$ $4x+4$
24. $5-b-7-8b$ $-2-9b$
25. $14u-3p-8u-8p$ $6u-11p$
26. $-y-6z+3y+4z-y$ $y-2z$

B

27. $3.4t+1.6s-(-1.9t)-3.6s$ $5.3t-2s$
28. $-0.8c+4.1h-(-3.2c)-0.1h$ $2.4c+4h$
29. $-m+\frac{2}{3}m-\frac{1}{2}n+\frac{5}{2}n$ $-\frac{1}{3}m+2n$
30. $-5a-\left(-\frac{1}{2}b\right)+3\frac{1}{2}a-\frac{1}{2}b$ $-1\frac{1}{2}a$
31. $2(x+5y)+(-3)(7x-y)$ $-19x+13y$
32. $8(t-u)+5(2u-3t)$ $-7t+2u$
33. $-2(2q+w)-7(w-q)$ $3q-9w$
34. $-3(7c+d)-2(10d-c)$ $-19c-23d$
35. $-4(-e+3f)-3[e+(-5f)]$ $e+3f$
36. $-6[v+(-9w)]+(-5)(3v-w)$
37. $2[-7(r+2s)-r]-3(s+2r)$ $-22r-31s$
38. $4[2(-5x+y)-y]-10(y-4x)$ $-6y$
39. $-15+(-3)[2(g-7)-2(1-g)]$ $33-12g$
40. $-50+(-2)[3(1-f)-3(-2+f)]$

36. $-21v+59w$ 40. $-68+12f$

41. Sally owned 500 shares of Acme Tube. On Monday each share of the stock gained p points. On Tuesday each share lost one more than twice as many points as it had gained the day before. By how much had the total value of Sally's shares of Acme Tube changed between the opening of trading on Monday morning and the closing on Tuesday afternoon? The stock had gone down $500+500p$ points.

42. A discount store bought a gross (12 dozen) of pocket radios, each to sell at \$15 above cost. Suppose that x of the radios were sold at that price. Each of the rest was sold at \$4 below cost. If the discount store paid \$11 for each radio, what was the store's gross income from the sale? $19x+1008$ dollars

C

43. To show that $a(-1)$ is the opposite of a for every real number a, you can show that the sum of $a(-1)$ and a is zero as follows. Name the axiom or property that justifies each step.

$$\begin{aligned} a(-1)+a &= a(-1)+a(1) && (1)\ \underline{\ ?\ }\ \text{Ident. ax. for mult.} \\ &= a[(-1)+1] && (2)\ \underline{\ ?\ }\ \text{Dist. ax.} \\ &= a(0) && (3)\ \underline{\ ?\ }\ \text{Ax. of opp.} \\ &= 0 && (4)\ \underline{\ ?\ }\ \text{Mult. prop. of 0} \end{aligned}$$

44. Name the axiom, property, or definition that justifies each step.

$$\begin{aligned} a(b-c) &= a[b+(-c)] && (1)\ \underline{\ ?\ }\ \text{Def. of subtraction} \\ &= a(b)+a(-c) && (2)\ \underline{\ ?\ }\ \text{Dist. prop.} \\ &= ab+(-ac) && (3)\ \underline{\ ?\ }\ \text{Prop. of opp. in prod.} \\ &= ab-ac && (4)\ \underline{\ ?\ }\ \text{Def. of subtraction} \end{aligned}$$

Additional A Exercises

Simplify.

1. $(-25)(-4)$ 100
2. $(16)(-7)$ -112
3. $(-9)(-4)(-3)(-25)$ 2700
4. $(-5+13)(-12)$ -96
5. $-6(7n-3k)$ $18k-42n$
6. $12a+12p-42a+18p-p$ $-30a+29p$

Mixed Review Exercises

Simplify.

1. $12x-3y+15x+72y$ $27x+69y$
2. $x-(-3)-[x+(-5)]$ 8
3. $240\left(\frac{3}{8}+\frac{1}{20}\right)$ $90+12=102$
4. Write an equation to represent the sentence, "Mary is 20 pounds heavier than her brother and their combined weight is 110 pounds." $b+(b+20)=110$

Teaching Suggestions p. T81

Suggested Extensions p. T82

Chalkboard Examples

An integer is represented by d.

1. Write the next four integers in natural order after d. $d + 1$, $d + 2$, $d + 3$, $d + 4$
2. Write in decreasing order the four integers that immediately precede d. $d - 1$, $d - 2$, $d - 3$, $d - 4$
3. If $d = 6$, what are $d + 1$ and $d - 1$? 7; 5

Write an equation to represent the given sentence.

4. The sum of three consecutive integers is 15. $x + (x + 1) + (x + 2) = 15$
5. The product of two consecutive odd integers is 99. $m(m + 2) = 99$
6. The sum of two consecutive integers is four less than half their product. $t + (t + 1) = \frac{1}{2}[t(t + 1)] - 4$

Common Error

Students often represent three consecutive odd integers in natural order as n, $n + 1$, and $n + 3$ because 1 and 3 are odd integers. Remind them that the difference between any two consecutive odd integers, like the difference between any two consecutive even integers, is 2.

2-7 Solving Problems; Consecutive Integers

Objective To write equations to represent relationships among integers.

When you count by ones from any number in the set of integers

$$\ldots, -4, -3, -2, -1, 0, 1, 2, 3, 4, \ldots$$

you obtain **consecutive integers.** For example, -3, -2, -1, 0, 1, and 2 are six consecutive integers. Those integers are listed in **natural order,** that is, in order from least to greatest.

Example 1 An integer is represented by m.

a. Write the next three integers in natural order after m.
b. Write in decreasing order the three integers that immediately precede m.
c. Write an equation that states that the sum of seven consecutive integers is 63.

Solution

a. $m + 1, m + 2, m + 3$
b. $m - 1, m - 2, m - 3$
c. $(m - 3) + (m - 2) + (m - 1) + m + (m + 1) + (m + 2) + (m + 3) = 63$

Ten is called an *even* integer because $10 = 2 \times 5$. The integers that are the products of 2 and any integer are the **even integers.** In natural order, they are:

$$\ldots, -4, -2, 0, 2, 4, 6, 8, \ldots$$

An **odd integer** is an integer that is not even. In natural order, the odd integers are:

$$\ldots, -5, -3, -1, 1, 3, 5, \ldots$$

If you count by *twos* from any even integer, you obtain **consecutive even integers.** For example:

Three consecutive even integers: 8; $8 + 2$, or 10; $10 + 2$, or 12

If you count by *twos* from any odd integer, you obtain **consecutive odd integers.** For example:

Three consecutive odd integers: 9; $9 + 2$, or 11; $11 + 2$, or 13

Thus, in natural order,

$$m, m + 2, m + 4$$

are consecutive even integers if m is even, and consecutive odd integers if m is odd.

Example 2 Write an equation to represent the data.

There are four consecutive odd integers. The third in natural order is the sum of the fourth and twice the second.

Solution Let m = the first of the four consecutive odd integers; then the four integers are:

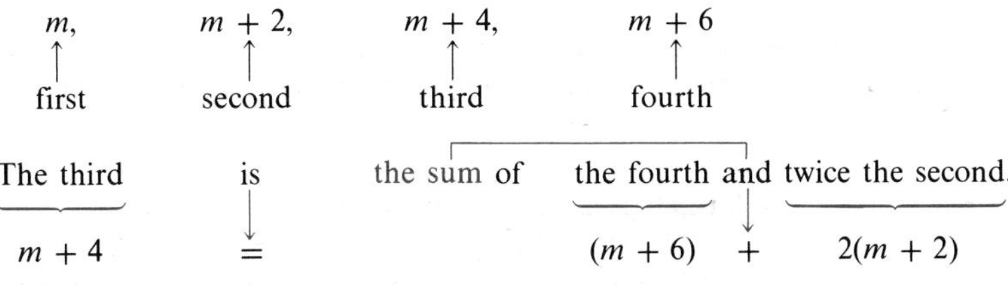

$\therefore$ the equation is $m + 4 = (m + 6) + 2(m + 2)$. ***Answer***

Oral Exercises

1. If $k = 3$, what are $k + 1$, $k + 2$, and $k + 3$? 4, 5, 6
2. If $r = 1$, what are $r - 1$, $r - 2$, and $r - 3$? 0, -1, -2
3. The least of four consecutive integers is -1. What are the other three integers? 0, 1, 2
4. The greatest of four consecutive integers is 20. What are the other three integers? 19, 18, 17
5. If $x = 15$, represent 14 and 16 in terms of x. $14 = x - 1$, $16 = x + 1$
6. If $p = 20$, represent 18 and 22 in terms of p. $18 = p - 2$, $22 = p + 2$
7. If $d = 7$, represent 3, 5, and 9 in terms of d. $3 = d - 4$, $5 = d - 2$, $9 = d + 2$
8. If $e = 12$, represent 8, 10, 14, and 16 in terms of e. $8 = e - 4$, $10 = e - 2$, $14 = e + 2$, $16 = e + 4$
9. Let t represent an odd integer. Is $t + 1$ odd or even? $t + 2$? $t - 1$? even; odd; even
10. If n is an integer, is $2n$ odd or even? What are the next two even integers greater than $2n$? the next smaller even integer? even; $2n + 2$; $2n + 4$; $2n - 2$
11. If n is an integer, is $2n + 1$ odd or even? What are the next two odd integers greater than $2n + 1$? the next smaller odd integer? odd; $2n + 3$; $2n + 5$; $2n - 1$
12. If m and n are even, is $m + n$ odd, or is it even? What about $m - n$ and mn? even; even; even
13. If m and n are odd, is $m + n$ odd, or is it even? What about $m - n$ and mn? even; even; odd
14. If m is odd, but n is even, is $m + n$ odd, or is it even? What about $m - n$ and mn? odd; odd; even

Supplementary Materials

Test 5

Resource Book, p. 72

Suggested Assignments

Minimum
74/1–12
R 75/*Self-Test 2*

Average
74/1–11 odd, 13–16, 18
R 75/*Self-Test 2*

Maximum
74/1–11 odd, 13–17, 20, 21
R 75/*Self-Test 2*

Additional A Exercises

Write an equation to represent the stated relationship among integers.

1. The sum of two consecutive integers is 93. $x + (x + 1) = 93$
2. The sum of three consecutive integers is 192. $x + (x + 1) + (x + 2) = 192$
3. The product of two consecutive even integers is 120. $x(x + 2) = 120$
4. The largest of three consecutive integers is three times the smallest. $x + 2 = 3x$
5. Twice the smaller of two consecutive odd integers is seven more than the larger. $2x = (x + 2) + 7$
6. The sum of four consecutive odd integers is 56. $x + (x + 2) + (x + 4) + (x + 6) = 56$

Mixed Review Exercises

Simplify.

1. $-6 + 13 + (-8)$ -1
2. $m - 18 - (m - 9)$ -9
3. $(-3)(-12) - (9)(-5)$ 81
4. Find the solution over the set of real numbers: $|m| = -2$ no sol.

Written Exercises

Write an equation to represent the stated relationship among integers.

Example The product of two consecutive integers is 8 more than twice their sum.

Solution Let x = the first of the integers. Then $x + 1$ = the second integer.

Their product is 8 more than twice their sum.

$$x(x + 1) = 2[x + (x + 1)] + 8$$

$\therefore$ the equation is $x(x + 1) = 2[x + (x + 1)] + 8$. ***Answer***

A

1. The sum of two consecutive integers is 87. $x + (x + 1) = 87$
2. The sum of three consecutive integers is 69. $x + (x + 1) + (x + 2) = 69$
3. The sum of four consecutive integers is -106. $x + (x + 1) + (x + 2) + (x + 3) = -106$
4. The sum of four consecutive integers is -42. $x + (x + 1) + (x + 2) + (x + 3) = -42$
5. The sum of three consecutive odd integers is 81. $x + (x + 2) + (x + 4) = 81$
6. The sum of three consecutive odd integers is 147. $x + (x + 2) + (x + 4) = 147$
7. The product of two consecutive even integers is 168. $x(x + 2) = 168$
8. The sum of four consecutive even integers is -100. $x + (x + 2) + (x + 4) + (x + 6) = -100$
9. The greater of two consecutive even integers is six less than twice the smaller. $x + 2 = 2(x) - 6$
10. The smaller of two consecutive even integers is five more than one half of the greater. $x = \frac{1}{2}(x + 2) + 5$
11. The four Smith children were born at two-year intervals. The sum of their ages is 36. $x + (x + 2) + (x + 4) + (x + 6) = 36$
12. A rectangle has a perimeter of 62 cm. The lengths in centimeters of its adjacent sides are consecutive integers. $2x + 2(x + 1) = 62$

B

13. There are four consecutive integers. Their sum is 100 decreased by twice the difference between the greatest and twice the least. $x + (x + 1) + (x + 2) + (x + 3) = 100 - 2[(x + 3) - 2(x)]$
14. There are four consecutive integers. Three times the greatest is 6 more than the sum of the other three. $3(x + 3) = 6 + [x + (x + 1) + (x + 2)]$
15. There are three consecutive integers listed in natural order. The sum of the second and the third is half the first decreased by 6. $(x + 1) + (x + 2) = \frac{1}{2}x - 6$
16. There are three consecutive integers listed in natural order. The sum of the first and half the third is 13 less than the second. $x + \frac{1}{2}(x + 2) = (x + 1) - 13$

$2[x + (x + 1)] - [(x + 2) + (x + 3)] = 15$

17. Find four consecutive integers such that the sum of the two largest subtracted from twice the sum of the two smallest is 15. 9, 10, 11, 12

18. Dick is younger than Tom, but older than Harry. Their ages in years are consecutive odd integers. Dick's mother is three times as old as Dick, and 13 years older than twice as old as Tom. $3(x + 2) = 13 + 2(x + 4)$

19. Kate is taller than Ginger, but shorter than Rose. Their heights in centimeters are consecutive integers. If Kate were half as tall as she is, she would be just as tall as her sister who is 80 cm shorter than Rose. 157, 158, 159 G K R

$\frac{1}{2}(x + 1) = (x + 2) - 80$

For Exercises 20 and 21, use this definition:

The product of any real number and an integer is called a ***multiple*** *of the real number.*

C **20.** The ages in years of three children are consecutive multiples of 3. Four years ago the sum of their ages was 42. $(x - 4) + (x - 1) + (x + 2) = 42$

21. Jim weighs more than Joe but less than Jack. Their weights in kilograms are consecutive multiples of 7. If they each weighed 5 kg less, the sum of their weights would be 195 kg. $(x - 5) + (x + 2) + (x + 9) = 195$

Self-Test 2

Vocabulary

distributive axiom (p. 64)
equivalent expressions (p. 65)
simplify a variable expression (p. 65)
identity element for multiplication (p. 68)
consecutive integers (p. 72)
natural order (p. 72)
even integer (p. 72)
odd integer (p. 72)
consecutive even integers (p. 72)
consecutive odd integers (p. 72)

Simplify.

Obj. 2-5, p. 64

1. $-5y + 11y + 7$ $6y + 7$
2. $4(x - 3) + 1$ $4x - 11$
3. $7(4 + z) - 6$ $22 + 7z$
4. $18 + 8t - 3t$ $18 + 5t$

Obj. 2-6, p. 68

5. $9(-5)(-2)(-3)$ -270
6. $(-a)(-1) + (-3)7$ $a - 21$
7. $-6(3a - 5b)$ $-18a + 30b$
8. $(7 \times -13) + (7 \times 3)$ -70

Obj. 2-7, p. 72

9. If $n = 54$, then in terms of n, $53 = \underline{\ ?\ }$ and $55 = \underline{\ ?\ }$. $n - 1$; $n + 1$

10. Write an equation to represent the relationship among the integers described as follows:

The sum of the least and the greatest of three consecutive integers is -44. $x + (x + 2) = -44$

Check your answers with those at the back of the book.

Quick Quiz

Simplify.

1. $-4t + 9t - 3$ $5t - 3$
2. $5(y + 5) - 10$ $5y + 15$
3. $8(1 - m) - 2$ $6 - 8m$
4. $20 - 2x + 9x$ $20 + 7x$
5. $(-2)(15)(-1)(-3)$ -90
6. $(-2)(-y) + 4(-5)$ $2y - 20$
7. $-3(4x - 8y)$ $-12x + 24y$
8. $(-18 \times 4) + (8 \times 4)$ -40
9. If $x = 27$, then in terms of x, $26 = \underline{\ ?\ }$ and $28 = \underline{\ ?\ }$. $x - 1$; $x + 1$
10. Write an equation to represent the following relationship among integers: The product of the least and the greatest of three consecutive integers is 80. $n(n + 2) = 80$

Teaching Suggestions p. T82

Suggested Extensions p. T82

Division

2-8 The Reciprocal of a Real Number

Objective To use reciprocals.

Two numbers whose product is 1 are called **reciprocals,** or **multiplicative inverses,** of each other. For example:

1. 3 and $\frac{1}{3}$ are reciprocals because $3 \times \frac{1}{3} = 1$.
2. -1.25 and -0.8 are reciprocals because $(-1.25)(-0.8) = 1$.
3. $\frac{2}{3}$ and $\frac{3}{2}$ are reciprocals because $\frac{2}{3} \cdot \frac{3}{2} = 1$.
4. 1 is its own reciprocal because $1 \times 1 = 1$.
5. -1 is its own reciprocal because $(-1)(-1) = 1$.
6. 0 has no reciprocal because the product of 0 and *any* real number is 0, *not* 1.

The symbol for the reciprocal or multiplicative inverse of a nonzero real number a is $\frac{1}{a}$.

Every real number except 0 has a reciprocal. This fact is stated as an axiom.

Axiom of Reciprocals

For every nonzero real number a, there is a unique real number $\frac{1}{a}$ such that

$$\boldsymbol{a \cdot \frac{1}{a} = 1 \quad \text{and} \quad \frac{1}{a} \cdot a = 1.}$$

You know that -3 and $-\frac{1}{3}$ are reciprocals because $(-3)\left(-\frac{1}{3}\right) = 1$. You can show in general that $(-a)\left(-\frac{1}{a}\right) = 1$ for $a \neq 0$ as follows:

$$(-a)\left(-\frac{1}{a}\right) = (-1 \cdot a)\left(-1 \cdot \frac{1}{a}\right) = [(-1)(-1)]\left(a \cdot \frac{1}{a}\right) = 1 \times 1 = 1.$$

Therefore, for every nonzero real number a,

$$\frac{1}{-a} = -\frac{1}{a}, \text{ read "The reciprocal of } -a \text{ is } -\frac{1}{a}\text{."}$$

Example 1 Simplify each expression.

a. $(7 \times 6)\left(\frac{1}{7} \times \frac{1}{6}\right)$

b. $(ab)\left(\frac{1}{a} \cdot \frac{1}{b}\right)$, $a \neq 0$, $b \neq 0$

Solution **a.** $(7 \times 6)\left(\frac{1}{7} \times \frac{1}{6}\right) = \left(7 \times \frac{1}{7}\right)\left(6 \times \frac{1}{6}\right) = 1 \times 1 = 1$

b. $(ab)\left(\frac{1}{a} \cdot \frac{1}{b}\right) = \left(a \cdot \frac{1}{a}\right)\left(b \cdot \frac{1}{b}\right) = 1 \times 1 = 1$

Example 1(b) shows that the product of ab and $\frac{1}{a} \cdot \frac{1}{b}$ is 1. Therefore, $\frac{1}{a} \cdot \frac{1}{b}$ is the reciprocal of ab. This fact can be stated as follows:

Property of the Reciprocal of a Product

The reciprocal of a product of nonzero real numbers is the product of the reciprocals of the numbers. That is, for all nonzero real numbers a and b,

$$\frac{1}{ab} = \frac{1}{a} \cdot \frac{1}{b}.$$

Example 2 Simplify: **a.** $\frac{1}{4} \cdot \frac{1}{-7}$ **b.** $(xy)\frac{1}{x}$, $x \neq 0$

Solution **a.** $\frac{1}{4} \cdot \frac{1}{-7} = \frac{1}{4(-7)} = \frac{1}{-28} = -\frac{1}{28}$

b. $(xy)\frac{1}{x} = (yx)\frac{1}{x} = y\left(x \cdot \frac{1}{x}\right) = y \cdot 1 = y$

Oral Exercises

State the reciprocal of each number in simplest form.

1. 8 $\frac{1}{8}$ **2.** 1 1 **3.** -1 -1 **4.** $\frac{1}{11}$ 11

5. -2 $-\frac{1}{2}$ **6.** $\frac{3}{5}$ $\frac{5}{3}$ **7.** 0.25 4 **8.** $-\frac{1}{7}$ -7

9. $-\frac{11}{6}$ $-\frac{6}{11}$ **10.** d, $d \neq 0$ $\frac{1}{d}$ **11.** $\frac{a}{4}$, $a \neq 0$ $\frac{4}{a}$ **12.** $-\frac{1}{s}$, $s \neq 0$ $-s$

Simplify.

13. $\frac{1}{10} \cdot \frac{1}{5}$ $\frac{1}{50}$ **14.** $\frac{1}{-2} \cdot \frac{1}{-12}$ $\frac{1}{24}$ **15.** $\frac{1}{6} \cdot \frac{1}{-4}$ $-\frac{1}{24}$ **16.** $\frac{1}{-x} \cdot \frac{1}{y}$, $x \neq 0$, $y \neq 0$ $-\frac{1}{xy}$

Chalkboard Examples

Simplify.

1. $(3 \times 5)\left(\frac{1}{3} \times \frac{1}{5}\right)$ 1
2. $\frac{1}{a} \cdot \frac{1}{-b}$ $-\frac{1}{ab}$
3. $\frac{1}{m}(4mn)$ $4n$
4. $-56\left(\frac{1}{7}\right)$ -8
5. $4 \cdot \frac{1}{9} \cdot \frac{1}{-4}$ $-\frac{1}{9}$
6. $-64mn\left(-\frac{1}{8}\right)$ $8mn$
7. $\frac{1}{4}(20a - 8)$ $5a - 2$
8. $-\frac{1}{6}(-24x + 6y)$ $4x - y$

Common Error

Students sometimes say that the reciprocal of 0 is 0, that the reciprocal of 1 is -1, and that the reciprocal of -1 is 1. Point out that $\frac{1}{0}$ is undefined, $\frac{1}{1} = 1$, and $\frac{1}{-1} = -1$.

Suggested Assignments

Minimum
78/1–24
S 74/13, 14

Average
78/2–18 even, 19–31
S 75/17, 19

Maximum
78/1–27 odd, 29–34

Additional A Exercises

Simplify each expression.

1. $-\frac{1}{3}(18)$ -6
2. $112\left(-\frac{1}{4}\right)\left(-\frac{1}{7}\right)$ 4
3. $12mn\left(-\frac{1}{3}\right)$ $-4mn$
4. $\frac{1}{n}(15mn)$ $15m$
5. $\frac{1}{5}(25k - 30)$ $5k - 6$
6. $(16n - 12m)\left(-\frac{1}{4}\right)$ $3m - 4n$

Mixed Review Exercises

Simplify.

1. $19 - 4(m - 3)$ $31 - 4m$
2. $-9.6 + 2.3 - 8.8$ -16.1
3. Use the five-step plan to solve: A rectangle's width is 5 cm shorter than its length; its perimeter is 90 cm. What is its width? 20 cm
4. Write an equation to represent the relationship: The sum of 4 consecutive odd integers is 136. $n + (n + 2) + (n + 4) + (n + 6) = 136$

Written Exercises

Simplify each expression.

Example 1 $-72ab\left(-\frac{1}{9}\right) = (-1 \cdot 72)ab\left(-1 \cdot \frac{1}{9}\right)$

$= [(-1)(-1)]\left(72 \cdot \frac{1}{9}\right)ab$

$= 1 \cdot \left(8 \cdot 9 \cdot \frac{1}{9}\right)ab = 1 \cdot (8 \cdot 1)ab = 8ab$

A

1. $\frac{1}{4}(-20)$ -5
2. $-\frac{1}{12}(48)$ -4
3. $-1000\left(\frac{1}{100}\right)$ -10
4. $-70\left(-\frac{1}{7}\right)$ 10
5. $108\left(-\frac{1}{9}\right)\left(-\frac{1}{12}\right)$ 1
6. $-63\left(-\frac{1}{3}\right)\left(-\frac{1}{21}\right)$ -1
7. $\frac{1}{-3}(36)\left(\frac{1}{4}\right)$ -3
8. $-150\left(\frac{1}{2}\right)\left(\frac{1}{-3}\right)$ 25
9. $4rs\left(-\frac{1}{4}\right)$ $-rs$
10. $33sp\left(-\frac{1}{11}\right)$ $-3sp$
11. $\frac{1}{x}(5xy),\ x \neq 0$ $5y$
12. $(7tk)\left(\frac{1}{t}\right),\ t \neq 0$ $7k$

Example 2 $\frac{1}{3}(42m - 3v) = \frac{1}{3}(42m) - \frac{1}{3}(3v)$

$= \left(\frac{1}{3} \times 42\right)m - \left(\frac{1}{3} \times 3\right)v = 14m - v$

22. $8p - 9q$
24. $-\frac{39}{2} + \frac{1}{2}n$
26. $\frac{2}{5}w$

13. $\frac{1}{2}(-16a + 20)$ $-8a + 10$
14. $\frac{1}{3}(18b - 39)$ $6b - 13$
15. $-\frac{1}{5}(-45c + 10d)$ $9c - 2d$
16. $-\frac{1}{8}(56g - 72h)$ $-7g + 9h$
17. $(-42m - 91k)\left(-\frac{1}{7}\right)$ $6m + 13k$
18. $(-39n - 52p)\left(-\frac{1}{13}\right)$ $3n + 4p$

B

19. $\frac{1}{2}(8u + 10v) - \frac{1}{3}(15u - 3v)$ $-u + 6v$
20. $\frac{1}{5}(-5a + 20b) - \frac{1}{2}(2b - 6a)$ $2a + 3b$
21. $6\left(\frac{1}{3}x - \frac{1}{2}y\right) + 42\left(-\frac{1}{3}y - \frac{1}{7}x\right)$ $-4x - 17y$
22. $-8\left(-\frac{1}{8}p + q\right) + \frac{1}{9}(63p - 9q)$
23. $-\frac{1}{8}(48m - 16) - \frac{1}{4}(84m + 8)$ $-27m$
24. $-5\left(4 - \frac{1}{2}n\right) + \frac{1}{16}(-32n + 8)$
25. $\left(-\frac{1}{12}\right)(6r + 4s) + 7\left(\frac{1}{21}s - \frac{1}{14}r\right)$ $-r$
26. $\left(-\frac{1}{20}\right)(5z - 4w) - 6\left(-\frac{1}{30}w - \frac{1}{24}z\right)$
27. $-3\left[\frac{1}{4}(12t + 1) - \frac{1}{4}\right] + 10t$ t
28. $3s + \left(-\frac{1}{2}\right)\left[6 + 24\left(-\frac{1}{3} + \frac{1}{4}s\right)\right]$ 1

Use the definition of reciprocals to find the value of x that satisfies the equation.

C

29. $-\frac{1}{4}x = 1$ -4
30. $-0.5x = 1$ -2
31. $x \cdot \frac{1}{\pi} = 1$ π
32. $\frac{1}{x} = 5$ $\frac{1}{5}$
33. $\frac{1}{\frac{1}{x}} = 2$ 2
34. $\frac{1}{\frac{1}{x}} = -3$ -3

Computer Key-In

The program given on page 58 can be modified to find the average of the numbers being added. This can be done by introducing a variable "counter" as follows:

```
45  LET C = 0
85  LET C = C + 1
105  PRINT "AVERAGE = ";S/C
```

If you were able to save the earlier program, you need only type the three lines above, and then type the command LIST to get a clean copy of the revised program. If you were not able to save the earlier program, retype it, adding the three new lines.

Exercises

Find the average for each list of numbers.

1. 2, 4, 6, 8, 10, 12, 14, 16, 18, 20 11
2. 1, 4, 9, 16, 25, 36, 49, 64, 81, 100 38.5
3. 2.25, 3.42, 5.15, 1.98, 4.82 3.524
4. 12.95, 27.59, 21.76, 38.25, 47.34 29.578

Calculator Key-In

Use the reciprocal key on a calculator to find the reciprocal of each number.

1. 0.0625 16 2. −32 −0.03125 3. 3125 0.00032 4. 0.000064 15625

5. For each number in Exercises 1–4, press the reciprocal key twice. Your results illustrate the property: The reciprocal of the reciprocal of a number is __?__. the number

6. a. Copy and complete the table.

a	b	$\frac{1}{ab}$	$\frac{1}{a}\cdot\frac{1}{b}$
4	16	? 0.015625	? 0.015625
−32	−0.5	? 0.0625	? 0.0625
0.234	0.654	? 6.5344102	? 6.5344102
555	222	? 0.0000081	? 0.0000081

b. What property does your completed table illustrate? $\frac{1}{ab} = \frac{1}{a}\cdot\frac{1}{b}$

Teaching Suggestions p. T83

Suggested Extensions p. T83

Chalkboard Examples

Rewrite each quotient as a product. Then simplify.

1. $-35 \div 5$
   $-35\left(\frac{1}{5}\right) = -7$
2. $-24 \div \left(-\frac{1}{3}\right)$
   $-24 \times (-3) = 72$
3. $45n \div (-9n),\ n \neq 0$
   $45n \times \left(-\frac{1}{9n}\right) = -5$

Simplify.

4. $-213 \div 3$ -71
5. $24 \div \left(-\frac{1}{3}\right)$ -72
6. $\dfrac{-16}{-\frac{1}{2}}$ 32
7. $\dfrac{48a}{-8a},\ a \neq 0$ -6
8. $-6 \cdot \frac{x}{6}$ $-x$
9. Find the average of the following numbers: $-18, 5, -6, 3.$ -4

2-9 Dividing Real Numbers

Objective To divide real numbers and to simplify expressions involving quotients.

The first column below lists a few examples of division by 2. The second column lists related examples of multiplication by $\frac{1}{2}$.

Dividing by 2	Multiplying by $\frac{1}{2}$
$2 \div 2 = 1$	$2 \times \frac{1}{2} = 1$
$4 \div 2 = 2$	$4 \times \frac{1}{2} = 2$
$6 \div 2 = 3$	$6 \times \frac{1}{2} = 3$
$8 \div 2 = 4$	$8 \times \frac{1}{2} = 4$

Comparing the entries in the two columns shows that dividing by 2 gives the same result as multiplying by the reciprocal of 2. This suggests the following **definition of division.**

For every real number a and every *nonzero* real number b, the **quotient** $a \div b$ is defined by:

$$\boldsymbol{a \div b = a \cdot \frac{1}{b}}$$

To divide by b, *multiply by the reciprocal of* b.

A quotient is often represented as a fraction:

$$a \div b = \frac{a}{b}$$

You can use the definition of division to replace any quotient by a product.

$$\frac{21}{7} = 21 \times \frac{1}{7} = 3 \qquad \frac{21}{-7} = 21\left(-\frac{1}{7}\right) = -3$$

$$\frac{-21}{7} = -21 \times \frac{1}{7} = -3 \qquad \frac{-21}{-7} = (-21)\left(-\frac{1}{7}\right) = 3$$

The quotient of two positive numbers or two negative numbers is positive.

The quotient of a positive number and a negative number is negative.

Here are some important questions and answers about division of real numbers:

1. Why can you never divide by zero? Dividing by 0 would mean multiplying by the reciprocal of 0. But 0 has no reciprocal (page 76). Therefore, *division by zero has no meaning in the set of real numbers.*
2. You cannot divide zero by zero, but can you divide zero by any other number? Look at these examples:

$$\frac{0}{5} = 0 \times \frac{1}{5} = 0 \qquad 0 \div (-2) = 0 \times \left(-\frac{1}{2}\right) = 0$$

When zero is divided by any nonzero number, the quotient is zero.

3. Is division commutative? No; for example,

$$8 \div 2 = 4 \quad \text{but} \quad 2 \div 8 = 0.25.$$

4. Is division associative? No; for example,

$$(12 \div 3) \div 2 = 4 \div 2 = 2 \quad \text{but} \quad 12 \div (3 \div 2) = 12 \div 1.5 = 8.$$

5. Is division distributive with respect to addition and with respect to subtraction? Yes, it is! (See Exercises 30 and 31, page 83.)

For all real numbers a, b, and c such that $c \neq 0$,

$$\frac{a+b}{c} = \frac{a}{c} + \frac{b}{c} \quad \text{and} \quad \frac{a-b}{c} = \frac{a}{c} - \frac{b}{c}.$$

Oral Exercises

Read each quotient as a product. Then simplify.

Example 1 $8 \div \left(-\frac{1}{6}\right)$ ***Solution*** $8 \times (-6)$; -48

Example 2 $\frac{54r}{-9}$ ***Solution*** $54r\left(-\frac{1}{9}\right)$; $-6r$

1. $\frac{-12}{3}$ -4 **2.** $\frac{0}{8}$ 0 **3.** $-25 \div 5$ -5 **4.** $18 \div (-18)$ -1

5. $\frac{0}{-9}$ 0 **6.** $\frac{-6}{-6}$ 1 **7.** $\frac{-2}{2}$ -1 **8.** $\frac{49}{-7}$ -7

9. $\frac{38}{-2}$ -19 **10.** $\frac{-56}{-8}$ 7 **11.** $\frac{4}{-64}$ $\frac{1}{-16}$ **12.** $\frac{-8}{72}$ $-\frac{1}{9}$

13. $x \div 1$ x **14.** $x \div (-1)$ $-x$ **15.** $8a \div (-2)$ $-4a$ **16.** $(-18b) \div 3$ $-6b$

17. $(-60a) \div (-10)$ $6a$ **18.** $(-84b) \div (-7)$ $12b$ **19.** $\frac{a}{a}$, $a \neq 0$ 1 **20.** $\frac{-a}{a}$, $a \neq 0$ -1

Supplementary Materials

Practice Master 8
Test 6
Resource Book, p. 73

Suggested Assignments

Minimum
82/1–26
R 84/*Self-Test 3*

Average
82/1–18, 21–27
S 78/32–34
R 84/*Self-Test 3*

Maximum
82/1–31
R 84/*Self-Test 3*

Simplify.

Example 3 $\frac{t}{15} \cdot 15$ *Solution* $\frac{t}{15} \cdot 15 = t \cdot \frac{1}{15} \cdot 15 = t \cdot 1 = t$

21. $6 \cdot \frac{x}{6}$ x **22.** $\left(-\frac{s}{5}\right)(-5)$ s **23.** $2\left(\frac{y}{-2}\right)$ $-y$ **24.** $-3 \cdot \frac{n}{3}$ $-n$

Written Exercises

Simplify.

A

1. $-512 \div 64$ -8 **2.** $408 \div (-34)$ -12 **3.** $33 \div \left(-\frac{1}{3}\right)$ -99 **4.** $0 \div (-47)$ 0

5. $\frac{-49}{-\frac{1}{7}}$ 343 **6.** $\frac{9}{-\frac{1}{4}}$ -36 **7.** $\frac{-10}{\frac{1}{8}}$ -80 **8.** $\frac{0}{-\frac{1}{5}}$ 0

9. $\frac{156a}{-13}$ $-12a$ **10.** $\frac{384b}{-8}$ $-48b$ **11.** $\frac{-852x}{6x}, x \neq 0$ -142 **12.** $\frac{-216y}{-24y}, y \neq 0$ 9

13. $\frac{-w}{18}(-18)$ w **14.** $-8 \cdot \frac{v}{8}$ $-v$ **15.** $\frac{5c}{4} \cdot 4$ $5c$ **16.** $\frac{-7d}{3}(-3)$ $7d$

Find the average of the numbers given in Exercises 17–20. (The *average* is the sum of the numbers divided by the number of numbers.)

Example 1 19, −3, −18, −2

Solution $\frac{19 + (-3) + (-18) + (-2)}{4} = \frac{19 - 23}{4} = \frac{-4}{4} = -1$

17. −17, 4, −11, 2 $-5\frac{1}{2}$ **18.** 8, −21, −7, 12 -2

19. 21, −17, −22, 13, 0 -1 **20.** 21, −17, −22, 13 $-1\frac{1}{4}$

Evaluate each expression if $a = -3$, $b = -1$, $c = 2$, and $d = 6$.

Example 2 $\frac{abd}{a + c} = \frac{(-3)(-1)(6)}{-3 + 2}$
$= \frac{3(6)}{-1} = \frac{18}{-1} = -18$

B

21. $\frac{5c + b}{3 - d}$ -3 **22.** $\frac{cbd}{(1 - b)a}$ 2 **23.** $\frac{bca}{(1 - c)d}$ -1

24. $\frac{d + 7a}{a + c}$ 15 **25.** $\frac{a - 2d}{3c + b}$ -3 **26.** $\frac{4a - d}{abc}$ -3

27. $\frac{a - 3b}{bcd}$ 0 **28.** $\frac{(c + a)(c - a)}{b + d}$ -1 **29.** $\frac{(d + 5c)(d - 5c)}{a + b}$ 16

Additional A Exercises

Simplify.

1. $-374 \div 11$ -34
2. $-96 \div (-24)$ 4
3. $\frac{16}{-\frac{1}{6}}$ -96
4. $\frac{-396ab}{-4}$ $99ab$
5. $\frac{18m}{-6}(-2)$ $6m$

Find the average of the numbers given.

6. 9, −3, −16, 15 $1\frac{1}{4}$

Mixed Review Exercises

1. Translate $-15 < -(-22)$ into words. The opposite of 15 is less than the opposite of negative 22.

Simplify.

2. $-18(-2 + 7p)$ $36 - 126p$
3. "92 decreased by negative 19." $92 - (-19) = 111$
4. $96\left(-\frac{1}{4}\right)\left(\frac{2}{3}\right)$ -16

In Exercises 30 and 31 assume that *a*, *b*, and *c* are any real numbers and $c \neq 0$.

C **30.** Name the axiom, property, or definition that justifies each numbered step.

$$\frac{a+b}{c} = (a+b)\cdot\frac{1}{c} \qquad (1)\ \underline{\ ?\ }\text{Def. of division}$$

$$= \left(a\cdot\frac{1}{c}\right) + \left(b\cdot\frac{1}{c}\right) \qquad (2)\ \underline{\ ?\ }\text{Dist. prop.}$$

$$= \frac{a}{c} + \frac{b}{c} \qquad (3)\ \underline{\ ?\ }\text{Def. of division}$$

31. Using the fact that multiplication is distributive with respect to subtraction, show that $\frac{a-b}{c} = \frac{a}{c} - \frac{b}{c}$. (*Hint:* See Exercise 30.)

$$\frac{a-b}{c} = (a-b)\cdot\frac{1}{c} = \left(a\cdot\frac{1}{c}\right) - \left(b\cdot\frac{1}{c}\right) = \frac{a}{c} - \frac{b}{c}$$

Application / *Understanding Product Prices*

You may have noticed the Universal Product Code (UPC) on items in your supermarket. This code is a series of bands of alternating light and dark spaces of varying widths that represent the numbers printed underneath. Many supermarkets have installed electronic check-out counters that contain an optical reader that scans the UPC on items and transmits the information to a central computer. The computer "looks up" the price of the item and subtracts the item from the store's inventory listing of products. The name of the product and its price are then printed on the sales slip for the customer. Thus, the customer benefits by having a record of the transaction and the store benefits by having up-to-date inventory records.

Consumers must make many choices while shopping. Quality, price, and convenience are all important considerations. Sometimes it is difficult to compare prices of products in different-sized packages. Unit pricing can help you make the comparison. The unit price of an item is its price per unit of measure. In many supermarkets, unit prices are posted on the shelves with the products. The product with the lowest unit price is the best buy provided the quality is comparable and the quantity is convenient.

Example Find the unit price of this beverage: \$.35 for 250 mL

Solution 1 L = 1000 mL or 250 mL = $\frac{1}{4}$ L

\$.35 × 4 = \$1.40 per liter

Quick Quiz

State the reciprocal of each number.

1. $-\frac{1}{3}$ -3
2. $4a,\ a \neq 0$ $\frac{1}{4a}$

Simplify.

3. $\frac{1}{9} \cdot 9b$ b
4. $-\frac{1}{5}(15 - 20x)$ $-3 + 4x$
5. $\frac{84}{-4}$ -21
6. $-36 \div 12$ -3
7. $-72 \div (-9)$ 8
8. $6m \div \left(-\frac{1}{6}\right)$ $-36m$

Self-Test 3

Vocabulary reciprocals (p. 76) multiplicative inverse (p. 76) reciprocal of a product (p. 77) division (p. 80) quotient (p. 80)

State the reciprocal of each number.

1. $-\frac{1}{6}$ -6 **2.** $2x,\ x \neq 0$ $\frac{1}{2x}$ **Obj. 2-8, p. 76**

Simplify.

3. $\frac{1}{7} \cdot 7n$ n **4.** $-\frac{1}{4}(24c - 32)$ $-6c + 8$

5. $\frac{48}{-3}$ -16 **6.** $-54 \div 9$ -6 **Obj. 2-9, p. 80**

7. $-28 \div (-14)$ 2 **8.** $-3y \div \frac{1}{3}$ $-9y$

Check your answers with those at the back of the book.

Chapter Summary

1. A number line can be used to find the sum of two real numbers.
2. Opposites and absolute values are used in the rules for adding real numbers (page 54) and multiplying real numbers (page 69).
3. Real-number axioms are statements about numbers that are accepted as true and are the basis for computation in arithmetic and in algebra. The statements in the chart on the next page are true for all real values of each variable except as noted.
4. Useful properties about addition or multiplication:

Property of the opposite of a sum:	$-(a + b) = -a + (-b)$
Multiplicative property of zero:	$a \cdot 0 = 0 \cdot a = 0$
Multiplicative property of -1:	$a(-1) = (-1)a = -a$
Property of opposites in products:	$(-a)(b) = -ab;\ a(-b) = -ab;\ (-a)(-b) = ab$
Property of the reciprocal of a product:	$\frac{1}{ab} = \frac{1}{a} \cdot \frac{1}{b};\ a \neq 0,\ b \neq 0$

5. Subtraction and division are defined as follows:

$$a - b = a + (-b) \qquad a \div b = \frac{a}{b} = a \cdot \frac{1}{b} \quad (b \neq 0)$$

Axioms of Real Numbers

Equality:	Reflexive property	$a = a$
	Symmetric property	If $a = b$, then $b = a$.
	Transitive property	If $a = b$ and $b = c$, then $a = c$.

	Addition	Multiplication
Axioms of closure	$a + b$ is a unique real number.	ab is a unique real number.
Commutative axioms	$a + b = b + a$	$ab = ba$
Associative axioms	$(a + b) + c = a + (b + c)$	$(ab)c = a(bc)$
Identity axioms	$a + 0 = 0 + a = a$	$a \cdot 1 = 1 \cdot a = a$
Axiom of opposites	$a + (-a) = (-a) + a = 0$	
Axiom of reciprocals		$a \cdot \frac{1}{a} = \frac{1}{a} \cdot a = 1;\ a \neq 0$
Distributive axiom	$a(b + c) = ab + ac$ and $(b + c)a = ba + ca$	

Supplementary Materials

Practice Masters 9–10
Test 7
Resource Book,
pp. 9–12, 147–148

Extra Practice

Skills, pp. 609–611
Problems, pp. 633–634

Chapter Review

Give the letter of the correct answer.

1. Simplify $74\frac{3}{8} + 1\frac{3}{5} + 7\frac{5}{8} + \frac{2}{5}$. **2-1**

a. 83 **b.** 82 **c.** $82\frac{13}{40}$ **(d.)** 84

2. Simplify $(16p)(5q)$.

a. $21pq$ **(b.)** $80pq$ **c.** $21p + q$ **d.** $80(p + q)$

3. Simplify $-5 + (-1.7) + 1.3$. **2-2**

a. -0.9 **b.** -8 **(c.)** -5.4 **d.** 8

4. Solve the equation $-16 + x = -1$.

(a.) 15 **b.** -15 **c.** 17 **d.** -17

5. Simplify $-4 + (-4) + [-(-6 + 2)]$. **2-3**

a. 4 **(b.)** -4 **c.** 0 **d.** -12

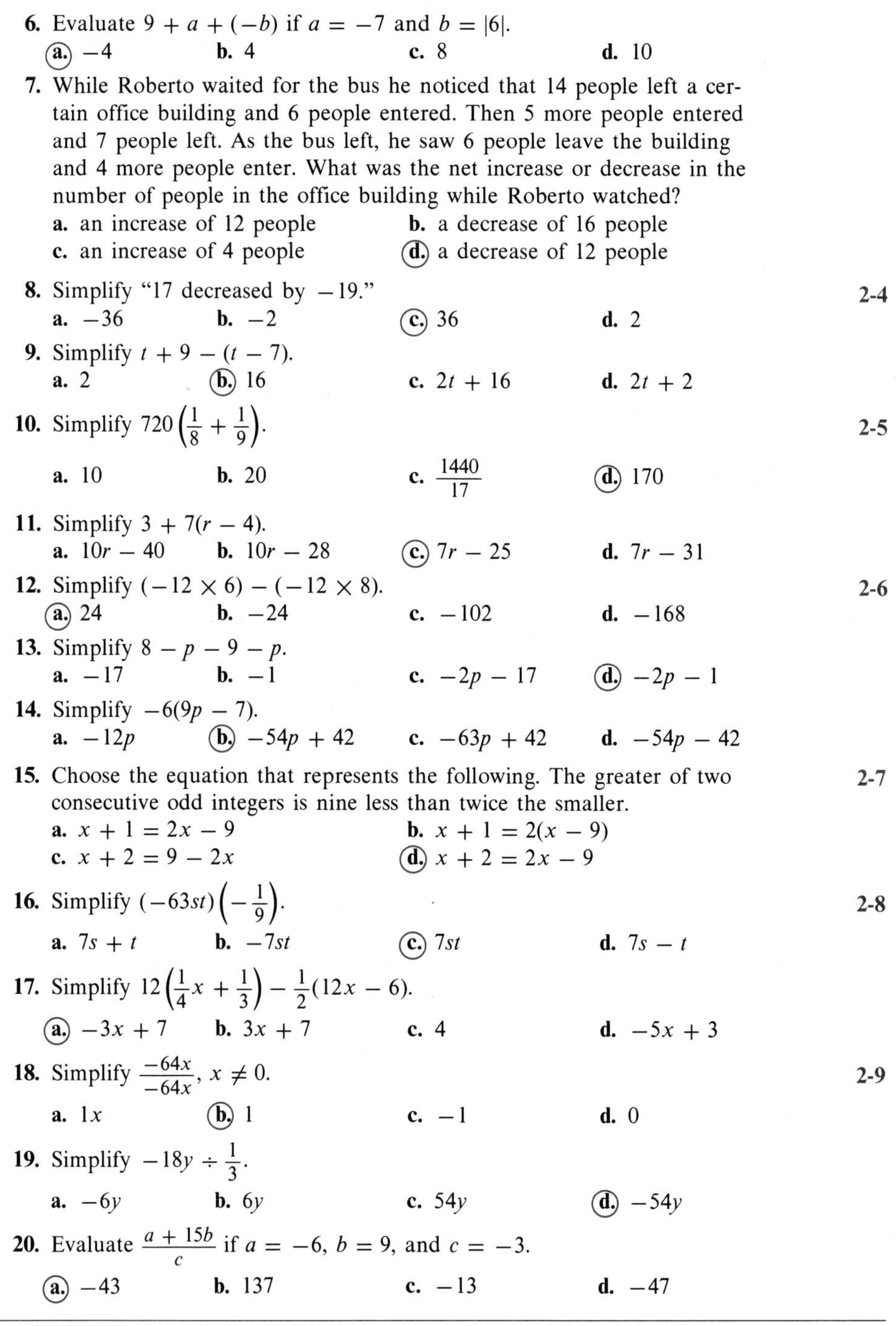

6. Evaluate $9 + a + (-b)$ if $a = -7$ and $b = |6|$.
a. -4 b. 4 c. 8 d. 10

7. While Roberto waited for the bus he noticed that 14 people left a certain office building and 6 people entered. Then 5 more people entered and 7 people left. As the bus left, he saw 6 people leave the building and 4 more people enter. What was the net increase or decrease in the number of people in the office building while Roberto watched?
a. an increase of 12 people b. a decrease of 16 people
c. an increase of 4 people d. a decrease of 12 people

8. Simplify "17 decreased by -19." 2-4
a. -36 b. -2 c. 36 d. 2

9. Simplify $t + 9 - (t - 7)$.
a. 2 b. 16 c. $2t + 16$ d. $2t + 2$

10. Simplify $720\left(\frac{1}{8} + \frac{1}{9}\right)$. 2-5
a. 10 b. 20 c. $\frac{1440}{17}$ d. 170

11. Simplify $3 + 7(r - 4)$.
a. $10r - 40$ b. $10r - 28$ c. $7r - 25$ d. $7r - 31$

12. Simplify $(-12 \times 6) - (-12 \times 8)$. 2-6
a. 24 b. -24 c. -102 d. -168

13. Simplify $8 - p - 9 - p$.
a. -17 b. -1 c. $-2p - 17$ d. $-2p - 1$

14. Simplify $-6(9p - 7)$.
a. $-12p$ b. $-54p + 42$ c. $-63p + 42$ d. $-54p - 42$

15. Choose the equation that represents the following. The greater of two consecutive odd integers is nine less than twice the smaller. 2-7
a. $x + 1 = 2x - 9$ b. $x + 1 = 2(x - 9)$
c. $x + 2 = 9 - 2x$ d. $x + 2 = 2x - 9$

16. Simplify $(-63st)\left(-\frac{1}{9}\right)$. 2-8
a. $7s + t$ b. $-7st$ c. $7st$ d. $7s - t$

17. Simplify $12\left(\frac{1}{4}x + \frac{1}{3}\right) - \frac{1}{2}(12x - 6)$.
a. $-3x + 7$ b. $3x + 7$ c. 4 d. $-5x + 3$

18. Simplify $\frac{-64x}{-64x}$, $x \neq 0$. 2-9
a. $1x$ b. 1 c. -1 d. 0

19. Simplify $-18y \div \frac{1}{3}$.
a. $-6y$ b. $6y$ c. $54y$ d. $-54y$

20. Evaluate $\frac{a + 15b}{c}$ if $a = -6$, $b = 9$, and $c = -3$.
a. -43 b. 137 c. -13 d. -47

Chapter Test

Alternate Test p. T11

Simplify.

1. $16 + p + q + 5$ $21 + p + q$ **2.** $2 \times 187 \times 5$ 1870 2-1

3. $-5 + [-9 + (-9)]$ -23 **4.** $(-7 + 13) + (-9)$ -3 2-2

5. Solve the equation $-16 = 9 + b$. -25

Simplify.

6. $-\frac{8}{3} + \frac{7}{3} + 1$ $\frac{2}{3}$ **7.** $-7.6 + 5.9 - 4$ -5.7 2-3

8. Meredith left home in the morning with \$32.66 in her purse. The subway fare to the city was \$1.45. She bought a magazine for \$1.75 and a skirt on sale for \$23. Lunch cost \$3.84. Her subway fare home was also \$1.45. As she left the station a friend caught up to her and repaid a \$2 loan. How much money did Meredith have at the end of the day? \$3.17

Simplify.

9. $(63 - 72) - (13 + 19)$ -41 **10.** $x - (-8) - [x + (-8)]$ 16 2-4

11. Camilla got up $1\frac{3}{4}$ hours before her first class. How long had she been up $1\frac{1}{2}$ hours after her first class started? $3\frac{1}{4}$ hours

Simplify.

12. $23(0.25) - 7(0.25)$ 4 **13.** $5(b - 1) + (-23)b + 5$ $-18b$ 2-5

14. $2a(3.69) + 2a(1.31)$ $10a$ **15.** $12x + 7 - (8x + 17)$ $4x - 10$

16. $-16(-3)$ 48 **17.** $(-11 + 11)19$ 0 2-6

18. $(-16 + 27)(-1)$ -11 **19.** $(-5)(13)(-7)(-10)$ -4550

20. Write an equation to represent the following. 2-7
There are three consecutive integers listed in natural order. The sum of the first and third is seven more than the first. $x + (x + 2) = x + 7$

21. State the reciprocal of -1. -1 2-8

Simplify.

22. $-51\left(\frac{1}{7}\right)\left(-\frac{1}{13}\right)$ $\frac{51}{91}$ **23.** $-\frac{1}{7}(-56m + 49n)$ $8m - 7n$

24. $\frac{-96}{\frac{1}{6}}$ -576 **25.** $-\frac{w}{7}(-343)$ $49w$ 2-9

26. Find the average of the numbers $-9, 8, 23, -26$. -1

Cumulative Review (Chapters 1 and 2)

Simplify.

1. $(52 \div 4) - (33 \div 3)$ 2
2. $\frac{12 + 72}{6 + 8}$ 6
3. $|-12| - |-6|$ 6
4. $-|20| \div |-4|$ -5
5. $47 + [12 + (-2)]$ 57
6. $3[27 \div (12 \div 4)]$ 27
7. $2 + 10 \times 15 \div 5$ 32
8. $2\frac{5}{9} + 7\frac{1}{8} + 8\frac{4}{9}$ $18\frac{1}{8}$
9. $-89 - (-74)$ -15
10. $-54 + 28 + (-41) + 66$ -1
11. $3(x + 2y) + 5(2x + y)$ $13x + 11y$
12. $(-9)(-5)(4) - 9(5)$ 135
13. $-4(a + 2b) - 3(-a + b)$
14. $\frac{1}{12}(-552xy) \div (-23)$ $2xy$
15. $35 \div 7(4a - 3b) - \frac{5}{2}(8a - 6b)$ 0

13. $-a - 11b$

Evaluate each expression if $a = -2$, $b = 2$, and $c = 3$.

16. $a - |b| + |-c|$ -1
17. $-a + (-4) - b$ -4
18. $\frac{(a - b)(-c + b)}{b - c}$ -4

Write the numbers in order from least to greatest.

19. $5, -3, 0, -\frac{1}{2}, 7, -2$ $-3, -2, -\frac{1}{2}, 0, 5, 7$
20. $-5, |5|, -\frac{1}{3}, -\frac{2}{3}, |-3|$ $-5, -\frac{2}{3}, -\frac{1}{3}, |-3|, |5|$
21. Graph the numbers $-4, 4, 3, 2, -\frac{1}{2}$, and 0 on a number line.

Additional Answer
Cumulative Review

21. 

Solve. If the equation has no solution, state that fact.

22. $|x| + 1 = 4$ $x = 3$ or $x = -3$
23. $|-x| = 10$ $x = 10$ or $x = -10$
24. $|y| = -3$ no solution
25. $c + 12 = 0$ $c = -12$
26. $b + 9 = 1$ $b = -8$
27. $a + 25 = 25$ $a = 0$

Represent each word phrase or sentence by a variable expression.

28. twelve less than the product of fourteen and z $14z - 12$
29. five less than the sum of negative two and b, increased by twice the product of twelve and b $[(-2 + b) - 5] + 2(12b)$
30. The opposite of negative seven is five more than the opposite of x. $-(-7) = -x + 5$
31. The sum of two consecutive odd integers is two less than twice the greater integer. $x + (x + 2) = 2(x + 2) - 2$

Solve.

32. One morning in January the temperature in Winnipeg, Manitoba, was $-13.3°C$. By noon the temperature had risen $1.7°C$. That night the temperature dropped $4.4°C$. What was the temperature then? $-16°C$

Maintaining Skills

Perform the indicated operations.

Example 1

$$\begin{array}{r} \scriptstyle 8\ 11\ \ 2\ 18 \\ \not{9}\not{1}7.\not{3}\not{8} \\ -\ 55.19 \\ \hline 862.19 \end{array}$$

Example 2

$$\begin{array}{r} 2.75 \\ 2.6\overline{)7.150} \\ \underline{5\,2} \\ 1\,95 \\ \underline{1\,82} \\ 130 \\ \underline{130} \\ 0 \end{array}$$

1. $49.92 - 38.6$ 11.32

2. $575.25 - 9.009$ 566.241

3. $337.14 - 45.32$ 291.82

4. $700.07 - 38$ 662.07

5. $3.4276 - 0.828$ 2.5996

6. $16.8 - 9.25$ 7.55

7. $5.52 - 4.763$ 0.757

8. $877.3 - 94.3$

9. $0.02\overline{)1.10}$ 55

10. $0.8\overline{)0.036}$ 0.045

11. $5.1\overline{)3376.2}$ 662

12. $1.9\overline{)860.7}$

13. $3.4\overline{)0.0085}$ 0.0025

14. $0.05\overline{)2.367}$ 47.34

15. $0.25\overline{)48}$ 192

16. $0.34\overline{)1156}$

8. 783 12. 453 16. 3400

Express each fraction in simplest form.

Example 3 $\frac{16}{24}$ ***Solution*** $\frac{16}{24} = \frac{2 \times 8}{3 \times 8} = \frac{2}{3}$

17. $\frac{14}{49}$ $\frac{2}{7}$ **18.** $\frac{21}{24}$ $\frac{7}{8}$ **19.** $\frac{39}{52}$ $\frac{3}{4}$ **20.** $\frac{27}{54}$ $\frac{1}{2}$ **21.** $\frac{27}{33}$ $\frac{9}{11}$

Perform the indicated operations. Express the answers in simplest form.

Example 4 $\frac{5}{6} - \frac{2}{13}$ ***Solution*** The least common denominator is 78.

$$\frac{5}{6} - \frac{2}{13} = \frac{5}{6} \times \frac{13}{13} - \frac{2}{13} \times \frac{6}{6}$$

$$= \frac{65}{78} - \frac{12}{78} = \frac{65 - 12}{78} = \frac{53}{78}$$

Example 5 $\frac{7}{18} \div \frac{14}{15}$ ***Solution*** $\frac{7}{18} \div \frac{14}{15} = \frac{7}{18} \times \frac{15}{14} = \frac{\overset{1}{\not{7}} \times \overset{5}{\not{15}}}{\underset{6}{\not{18}} \times \underset{2}{\not{14}}} = \frac{5}{12}$

22. $\frac{2}{3} - \frac{1}{6}$ $\frac{1}{2}$ **23.** $\frac{5}{7} - \frac{2}{3}$ $\frac{1}{21}$ **24.** $\frac{3}{4} - \frac{15}{21}$ $\frac{1}{28}$ **25.** $\frac{3}{4} - \frac{5}{12}$ $\frac{1}{3}$

26. $\frac{5}{6} - \frac{2}{13}$ $\frac{53}{78}$ **27.** $\frac{3}{7} - \frac{11}{28}$ $\frac{1}{28}$ **28.** $\frac{15}{16} - \frac{7}{8}$ $\frac{1}{16}$ **29.** $\frac{7}{12} - \frac{1}{3}$ $\frac{1}{4}$

30. $\frac{5}{6} \div \frac{5}{2}$ $\frac{1}{3}$ **31.** $\frac{12}{21} \div \frac{8}{14}$ 1 **32.** $\frac{21}{25} \div \frac{9}{20}$ $\frac{28}{15}$ **33.** $\frac{10}{7} \div \frac{7}{10}$ $\frac{100}{49}$

34. $\frac{24}{25} \div \frac{5}{6}$ $\frac{144}{125}$ **35.** $\frac{24}{25} \div \frac{6}{5}$ $\frac{4}{5}$ **36.** $\frac{7}{8} \div \frac{14}{12}$ $\frac{3}{4}$ **37.** $\frac{24}{35} \div \frac{36}{25}$ $\frac{10}{21}$

Mixed Review

Skills and Problem Solving

Simplify.

1. $\frac{105xy}{-7x}$, $x \neq 0$ $-15y$ **2.** $-2(3 + 5c) + 4(-2 + 3c)$ $-14 + 2c$

3. $\left|\frac{3}{4}\right| + \left|-\frac{3}{4}\right|$ $\frac{3}{2}$ **4.** $-412 - (-38)$ -374

5. $125 + 17 + (-25)$ 117 **6.** $-7.2 - (-5.4) + (-0.3)$ -2.1

7. Graph the numbers -4, 5, 3, -2, 0, 2 on a number line.

8. The average summer high temperature in Mason City is 31.4°C. The average winter low temperature is -3.2°C. What is the difference between the two extremes? 34.6°C

9. Evaluate the expression $\frac{-|b - a|}{-c}$ if $a = 4$, $b = 3$, and $c = -2$. $-\frac{1}{2}$

10. Solve the equation $2x - 7 = 9$ if $x \in \{0, 1, 2, 3, 4, 5, 6, 7, 8, 9, 10\}$. 8

11. Eight more than a number is 3. Find the number. -5

12. Replace _?_ with <, =, or > to make a true statement.

$$[76 \div (-4)] + 15 \ \underline{\ ?\ }\ 76 \div (-4 + 15)$$ <

13. Write an equation for the following word sentence.

The sum of twice x and seven is five greater than the difference between x and three. $2x + 7 = (x - 3) + 5$

14. Evaluate the expression $\frac{a(-b + 3c) + b(-b + 3c)}{2c - 1}$ if $a = -3$, $b = 3$, and $c = 7$. 0

15. Eight less than the absolute value of a negative number is four. Find the number. -12

16. On a number line, point X has coordinate -4 and point Y has coordinate 6. Write the coordinate of the point halfway between X and Y. 1

17. A submarine was at a depth of 195 m. It rose 65 m and then dove 25 m. If its original position is given as -195, write a positive or negative number to represent its final position relative to the surface of the water. -155

18. Write an equation to represent the relationship between two consecutive odd integers if their product is one less than 6 times their sum. $x(x + 2) = 6[x + (x + 2)] - 1$

19. Write the numbers in order from least to greatest:

$-7, -6, -\frac{1}{2}, 0, \frac{1}{5}, 0.3, \frac{1}{2}$ $-7, 0, -\frac{1}{2}, \frac{1}{5}, \frac{1}{2}, -6, 0.3$

20. The Forbes' checking account was overdrawn by \$72.50. They deposited \$323.00 in the account. What was their balance then? \$250.50

Additional Answer
Mixed Review

7. 

Preparing for College Entrance Exams

Strategy for Success

If a problem that requires determining whether an algebraic expression has certain properties becomes too time-consuming, try appropriate substitution for the variables. For example, when appropriate, first try positive replacements for the variables and then negative replacements. You may be able to determine the answer without manipulating the variables.

Decide which is the best of the choices given and write the corresponding letter on your answer sheet.

1. Write an expression that corresponds to the following word sentence. Twice the sum of two consecutive even integers is twelve less than one third of their product. D

(A) $2[n + (n + 1)] = \frac{1}{3}[n(n + 1) - 12]$ **(B)** $2[n + (n + 1) = \frac{1}{3}[n(n + 1)] - 12$

(C) $2[n + (n + 2)] = \frac{1}{3}[n(n + 2) - 12]$ **(D)** $2[n + (n + 2)] = \frac{1}{3}[n(n + 2)] - 12$

2. Brad is four years older than twice his sister Miriam's age. Which equation represents the relationship between Brad's age, b, and Miriam's age, m? B

(A) $m = 2b - 4$ **(B)** $b = 2m + 4$ **(C)** $b = 2m - 4$ **(D)** $m = 2b + 4$

3. Simplify the expression $73(19 + 31) - 48(24 + 26)$. A

(A) 1250 **(B)** 6050 **(C)** 1200 **(D)** 1750

4. On a number line, point A has coordinate -4 and point B has coordinate 8. What is the coordinate of the point one fourth of the way from A to B? C

(A) 2 **(B)** -2 **(C)** -1 **(D)** 5 **(E)** 6

5. $*$ is an operation defined for all real numbers a and b by $a * b = ab + a + b$. Which of the following properties does $*$ have? E

I. Closure II. Commutativity III. Associativity

(A) I only **(B)** II only **(C)** III only **(D)** I and II only **(E)** I, II, and III

6. Suppose x is a nonzero real number. Which of the following is (are) always true? A

I. $\frac{1}{|x|} > 0$ II. $|x| > x$ III. $|x| > -x$

(A) I only **(B)** II only **(C)** III only **(D)** II and III only **(E)** I and III only

7. a, b, c, and d are positive real numbers. Which of the following guarantees that $\frac{a - b}{c - d} < 0$? C

(A) $a > b$ and $c > d$ **(B)** $a < b$ and $c < d$ **(C)** $a > b$ and $c < d$
(D) $|a - b| > 0$ and $|c - d| > 0$ **(E)** $|a - b| > 0$ and $|c - d| < 0$

About the Photo

Skillful athletes must have coordination, agility, and strength. They must also be mentally alert and have the ability to estimate and make decisions quickly. The soccer player shown must decide whether she should attempt to score or pass the ball to another player. She must also inductively calculate the right amount of force to apply at just the right moment. A physicist studying this moment analytically might simulate the situation, apply the laws of dynamics and the laws of motion, and then agree or disagree with her decision.

Because of advances made in computer technology and high-speed photography, athletes can study instant replays and use computer simulations to improve their performances. As a result, many long-standing records once thought to represent the peak of human performance are likely to be broken in the future.

3 Solving Equations and Problems

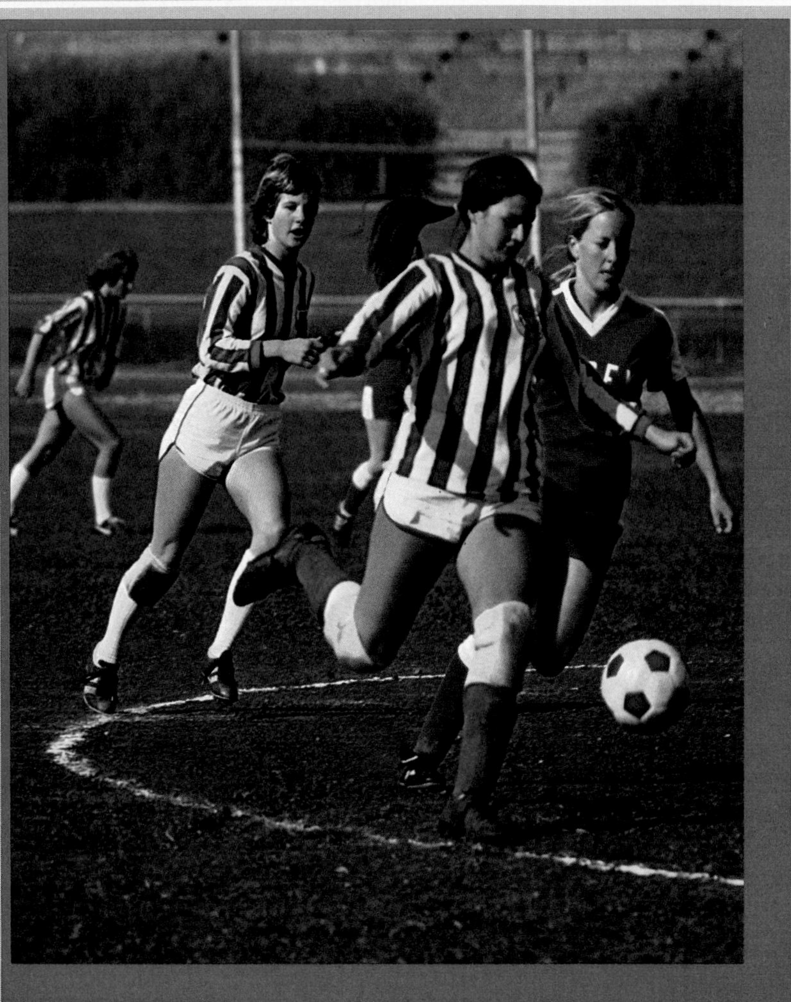

When two soccer teams that are tied score the same number of goals, the score remains tied. This illustrates the Addition Property of Equality given on the facing page.

Transforming Equations

3-1 Transforming Equations: Addition and Subtraction

Objective To solve equations using addition or subtraction.

Two soccer teams are tied: 4 to 4. If each team scores 2 goals in the next period, then the score is still tied:

$$4 + 2 = 4 + 2$$

Two service stations both charge 29.9¢ for a liter of gasoline. If each reduces the price by 3 cents a liter, they are still both charging the same price:

$$29.9 - 3 = 29.9 - 3$$

These examples illustrate the **addition and subtraction properties of equality:** *If the same number is added to equal numbers, the sums are equal. If the same number is subtracted from equal numbers, the differences are equal.*

Addition Property of Equality

If a, b, and c are any real numbers, and $a = b$, then

$$\mathbf{a + c = b + c} \quad \text{and} \quad \mathbf{c + a = c + b}.$$

Of course, because $a - c = a + (-c)$ and $b - c = b + (-c)$, the subtraction property of equality is just a special case of the addition property. For, if $a = b$, then the addition property of equality guarantees that

$$a + (-c) = b + (-c), \quad \text{or}$$
$$a - c = b - c.$$

Subtraction Property of Equality

If a, b, and c are any real numbers and $a = b$, then

$$\mathbf{a - c = b - c}.$$

Teaching References

Lesson Commentary, pp. T83–T87

Assignment Guide, pp. T58–T59

Supplementary Materials

- Practice Masters 11–17
- Tests 8–11
- Resource Book
  - Practice Exercises, pp. 74–78
  - Tests, pp. 13–18
  - Enrichment Activity, pp. 149–150
  - Mixed Review, pp. 133–134
  - Practice in Problem Solving/Word Problems, pp. 161–164
- Algebra Action, Disk 1

Extra Practice

- Skills, pp. 611–613
- Problems, pp. 634–636

Alternate Test, p. T12

Cumulative Review, p. T22

Problem Solving Strategies

Generalizing from Specific
As in Chapter 2, properties of real numbers are first discussed in terms of specific examples and then presented in general form. See pp. 93, 99, 103.

Word Problem Plan
The five-step plan is reintroduced in the exercises on p. 97 and is illustrated in detail in Section 3-4, p. 108.

Using a Chart
The technique of using a chart to organize the information in a word problem is discussed in Sections 3-6 and 3-7. This helpful strategy is then used throughout the book.

Teaching Suggestions p. T83

Suggested Extensions p. T83

Chalkboard Examples

State whether the given number is a root of the equation.

1. $y + 6 = 2; -4$ yes
2. $3 + t = -7; 10$ no

Solve.

3. $x + 9 = 4$ -5
4. $m - 9 = 11$ 20
5. $-3 = -8 + y$ 5
6. $-15 + z = 18$ 33
7. $p + 7 = -10$ -17
8. $0 = b + 6$ -6

Common Errors

There are several common errors that students make when solving equations using addition or subtraction. Encourage students who are having difficulty to show *all* their work and check their answers. Stress that to preserve the equality of the sides, the number added to or subtracted from one side of an equation must be added to or subtracted from the other side as well.

Some students trying to solve an equation such as $x + 6 = 7$, notice "$+6$" on the left side of the equation, add 6 to the right side only, and get 13 for the solution. Other students subtract 7 from both sides of the equation, and mistakenly conclude that $x = -1$.

Remind students that to solve an equation such as $-x + 9 = 1$, they must solve for x, not $-x$, and cannot overlook the $-$ sign.

You can use these properties of equality to solve some equations. For example, study what occurs in the following steps when working with the equation $x - 5 = 7$.

$$\begin{aligned} &(1) & x - 5 &= 7 \\ &(2) & x - 5 + 5 &= 7 + 5 \\ &(3) & x &= 12 \end{aligned}$$

When you add 5 to each side of equation (1), as shown in equation (2), and simplify the result you obtain equation (3).

On the other hand, when you subtract 5 from (or add -5 to) each side of equation (3), as shown in equation (2′), you obtain equation (1), as shown below.

$$\begin{aligned} &(3) & x &= 12 \\ &(2') & x - 5 &= 12 - 5 \\ &(1) & x - 5 &= 7 \end{aligned}$$

The addition and subtraction properties of equality guarantee that any root, or solution, of equation (1) is also a root of equation (3), and any root of (3) is also a root of (1). Therefore the two equations have the same solution, namely 12.

Equations having the same solution set over a given domain are called **equivalent equations** over that domain. To solve an equation, you usually try to change, or *transform,* it into a simple equivalent equation whose solution or solutions can be seen at a glance. This transformation into a simple equivalent equation can be done by substitution, addition, or subtraction.

Ways to Transform an Equation into an Equivalent Equation

Transformation by Substitution: Substitute for any expression in a given equation an equivalent expression.

Transformation by Addition: Add the same real number to each side of a given equation.

Transformation by Subtraction: Subtract the same real number from each side of a given equation.

Example 1 Solve $v + 8 = 3$.

Solution

$$\begin{aligned} v + 8 &= 3 \\ v + 8 - 8 &= 3 - 8 \\ v &= -5 \end{aligned}$$

To obtain v alone as the left side, subtract 8 from each side (or add -8 to each side).

Because errors may occur in transforming equations, you should check your work by showing that each root of the transformed equation satisfies the *original equation.*

Check: $v + 8 = 3$ ⟵ original equation
$$-5 + 8 \stackrel{?}{=} 3$$
$$3 = 3 \quad \surd$$

∴ the solution is -5. ***Answer***

Example 2 Solve $-2 = -15 + p$.

Solution

$$-2 = -15 + p$$
$$-2 + 15 = -15 + p + 15$$
$$13 = p$$

To obtain p alone as the right side, add 15 to each side.

Check:
$$-2 = -15 + p$$
$$-2 \stackrel{?}{=} -15 + 13$$
$$-2 = -2 \quad \surd$$

∴ the solution is 13. ***Answer***

Oral Exercises

State the number to add to or to subtract from each side of the given equation to produce an equivalent equation with the variable alone as one side. Then state this equivalent equation.

Example 1 $t - 3 = -1$ ***Solution*** Add 3; $t = 2$

Example 2 $z + 5 = 4$ ***Solution*** Subtract 5; $z = -1$

1. $x + 6 = 7$ Subt. 6; $x = 1$
2. $y + 2 = 5$ Subt. 2; $y = 3$
3. $v - 1 = 8$ Add 1; $v = 9$
4. $w - 11 = 4$ Add 11; $w = 15$
5. $a + 9 = 1$ Subt. 9; $a = -8$
6. $b + 7 = 6$
7. $5 + m = 0$ Subt. 5; $m = -5$
8. $-1 + n = 0$ Add 1; $n = 1$
9. $-2 + p = 2$
10. $-1 + r = -1$ Add 1; $r = 0$
11. $-8 + t = -8$ Add 8; $t = 0$
12. $-5 = u + 9$
13. $-6 = k - 10$ Add 10; $k = 4$
14. $-8 = -2 + t$ Add 2; $t = -6$
15. $1 = 3 + s$
16. $z - \frac{1}{4} = \frac{1}{4}$ Add $\frac{1}{4}$; $z = \frac{1}{2}$
17. $\frac{4}{5} = \frac{1}{5} + d$ Subt. $\frac{1}{5}$; $d = \frac{3}{5}$
18. $h + 1.7 = -2.1$ Subt. 1.7; $h = -3.8$

State the addition property of equality when:

19. a and b are replaced with $-x$ and $-y$, respectively
20. c is replaced with $5d$

Suggested Assignments

Minimum
Day 1: 96/1–23 odd
97/*P*: 1, 2, 5
Day 2: 96/10–34 even
97/*P*: 6, 8–11

Average
Day 1: 96/1–23 odd, 25–36
97/*P*: 1, 2, 5, 8
Day 2: 96/37–48
97/*P*: 10, 11, 13, 14
101/1–31 odd
Day 2 finishes Sec. 3-1 and starts Sec. 3-2.

Maximum
96/1–53 odd
97/*P*: 1–15 odd

Additional Answers
Oral Exercises

6. Subt. 7; $b = -1$
9. Add 2; $p = 4$
12. Subt. 9; $u = -14$
15. Subt. 3; $s = -2$
19. If $-x$, $-y$ and c are real numbers and $-x = -y$, then $-x + c = -y + c$ and $c - x = c - y$.
20. If a, b and $5d$ are real numbers and $a = b$, then $a + 5d = b + 5d$ and $5d + a = 5d + b$.

Additional A Exercises

Solve.

1. $z - 8 = 53$ 61
2. $a + 6 = 92$ 86
3. $36 = b + 6$ 30
4. $-22 = a - 24$ 2
5. $f - 2 = -4$ -2
6. $-32 = x + |22|$ -54

Mixed Review Exercises

Simplify.

1. $72(0.33) + 28(0.33)$ 33
2. $-28m \div \frac{4}{7}$ $-49m$
3. Write an open sentence that represents "Given 3 consecutive integers, the sum of the first and third is greater than the second."
   $n + (n + 2) > n + 1$
4. Find the average of the numbers 18, -6, -4, 22, -1. 5.8

Written Exercises

6. 112
9. -50
15. -10

Solve.

A

1. $a - 11 = 15$ 26 **2.** $b - 8 = 17$ 25 **3.** $y + 7 = 29$ 22

4. $x + 18 = 31$ 13 **5.** $-76 + m = 92$ 168 **6.** $-49 + n = 63$

7. $c - 30 = -19$ 11 **8.** $d - 24 = -15$ 9 **9.** $p + 18 = -32$

10. $s + 90 = -55$ -145 **11.** $24 + t = 0$ -24 **12.** $0 = z - 14$ 14

13. $v - 37 = -54$ -17 **14.** $w - 94 = -110$ -16 **15.** $-7 + k = -17$

16. $-18 + h = -38$ -20 **17.** $45 = x + 16$ 29 **18.** $39 = y + 12$ 27

19. $-19 + a = -23$ -4 **20.** $-32 + b = -82$ -50 **21.** $c + 9 = |-5|$ -4

22. $l - 8 = |25|$ 33 **23.** $f + 7 = |2 - 9|$ 0 **24.** $g - 6 = |8 - 14|$ 12

Example 1 $-x + 9 = 1$

Solution

$$-x + 9 - 9 = 1 - 9$$
$$-x = -8$$
$$x = 8 \quad \text{(Definition of opposite of a number)}$$

$\therefore$ the solution is 8. ***Answer***

33. -11
36. 11

B

25. $-x + 9 = 7$ 2 **26.** $-y + 3 = 21$ -18 **27.** $31 - k = 37$ -6

28. $-7 - h = 8$ -15 **29.** $5 = -11 - s$ -16 **30.** $12 = -t + 4$ -8

31. $(m + 3) + 6 = 5$ -4 **32.** $(r + 4) + 2 = 1$ -5 **33.** $2 = 11 + (x + 2)$

34. $3 = 16 + (y + 1)$ -14 **35.** $-2 + (1 + p) = 5$ 6 **36.** $-3 + (1 + n) = 9$

37. $(a - 3) + 19 = 125$ 109 **38.** $(b - 6) + 14 = 100$ 92 **39.** $4 - (1 + x) = 5$ -2

40. $2 - (3 + y) = 6$ -7 **41.** $-2 - (4 - w) = 1$ 7 **42.** $7 - (1 - q) = 11$ 5

Example 2 $|x| + 4 = 13$

Solution

$$|x| + 4 - 4 = 13 - 4$$
$$|x| = 9$$
$$x = 9 \text{ or } x = -9 \quad \text{(Definition of absolute value)}$$

$\therefore$ the solutions are 9 and -9. ***Answer***

C

43. $|y| - 2 = 8$ $\{-10, 10\}$ **44.** $|z| + 10 = 28$ $\{-18, 18\}$

45. $-7 + |s| = 0$ $\{-7, 7\}$ **46.** $6 + |t| = 14$ $\{-8, 8\}$

47. $|x| + (-2) = 4$ $\{-6, 6\}$ **48.** $|y| + (-1) = 1$ $\{-2, 2\}$

49. $-5 + |r| = 0$ $\{-5, 5\}$ **50.** $6 + |w| = 2$ no solution

51. $-(|a| - 9) = 1$ $\{-8, 8\}$ **52.** $-(|x| + 2) = -6$ $\{-4, 4\}$

53. $4 - (2 - |n|) = 2$ $\{0\}$ **54.** $7 - (3 - |m|) = 8$ $\{-4, 4\}$

55. $9 - (|s| + 7) = 4$ no solution **56.** $-3 + (15 - |a|) = 12$ $\{0\}$

Problems

Write an equation based on the facts of each problem. Then, solve the equation and answer the question posed in the problem.

Example Nat has a temperature of 35.5°C. This is 1.5°C below normal body temperature. What is normal body temperature?

Solution

Step 1 The problem asks for the number of degrees in normal body temperature.

Step 2 Let n = normal temperature in degrees Celsius.
Then $n - 1.5$ = Nat's temperature

Step 3 $n - 1.5 = 35.5$

Step 4 $n - 1.5 + 1.5 = 35.5 + 1.5$
$n = 37$

Step 5 The check is left to you.

∴ normal body temperature is 37°C. ***Answer***

A

1. Nine more than a number is 58. What is the number? 49
2. Eighteen less than a number is 46. What is the number? 64
3. A number decreased by 8 is −31. What is the number? −23
4. A number increased by 13 is −11. What is the number? −24
5. A basketball player scored 56 points in a game. This was 12 points more than he had scored in an earlier game. What was his score in the earlier game? 44
6. A gymnast outscored her competitor by 9 points. If her score was 56.5 points, what was her competitor's score? 47.5
7. Three members of the School Committee missed the last meeting. Twelve members were present at the meeting. How many members does the committee have? 15
8. Marita ran the 400-meter dash in 56.8 s. This was 1.3 s faster than her previous time. What was her previous time? 58.1 s
9. If the temperature of the water in a beaker rises six degrees Celsius above what it is now, the water will be at the boiling point (100°C). What is the temperature of the water now? 94°C

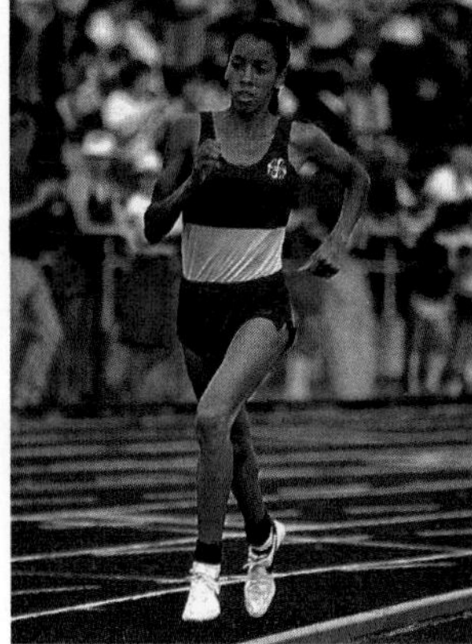

10. The temperature at dawn was $-2.5°C$. How many degrees did it rise to reach a temperature of 8°C at noon? 10.5°C

11. If the latitude of New York is about 41°N and the latitude of Rio de Janeiro is about 23°S, what is the difference in latitude between the two cities? 64°

12. The Busy Bee Diner charges 65 cents for a glass of juice. A customer paid $2.25 for a sandwich and a glass of juice. How much was the sandwich? $1.60

B 13. A discount store chain hired 130 new employees during a year in which 27 employees retired and 59 left for other reasons. If there were 498 employees in the chain at the end of the year, how many were there at the beginning? 454

14. During one day on the stock market, an investor lost $2500 on one stock, but gained $1700 on another. At the end of trading that day, the investor's holdings were worth $52,400. What were they worth when the market opened that day? $53,200

15. Rona paid $3.23 for 2 tubes of toothpaste. She paid the regular price of $1.79 for one tube, but bought the other one for less, because she used a "cents-off" coupon. What was the coupon worth? $.35

16. During a sale, Art bought a tire pump for $4.69. A week later, he returned to the store to buy another pump. However, because the sale was over, he had to pay the regular price for the second one. If the two pumps cost Art $10.64, by how much had the store reduced the price for the sale? $1.26

Calculator Key-In

Use the division key on a calculator to find a decimal equal to each expression.

Example 1 $\frac{-36}{8}$ ***Solution*** $\frac{-36}{8} = -36 \div 8 = -4.5$

1. $\frac{3}{4}$ 0.75 **2.** $\frac{-5}{8}$ −0.625 **3.** $\frac{7}{-16}$ −0.4375 **4.** $\frac{-3}{-20}$ 0.15 **5.** $\frac{1}{40}$ 0.025

6. $\frac{-11}{4}$ −2.75 **7.** $\frac{12}{-50}$ −0.24 **8.** $\frac{-7}{-8}$ 0.875 **9.** $\frac{31}{32}$ 0.96875 **10.** $\frac{43}{-64}$ −0.671875

11–20. Use the reciprocal key on a calculator to find a decimal equal to each expression in Exercises 1–10. Are your answers the same as before? Yes

Example 2 $\frac{-36}{8}$ ***Solution*** $\frac{-36}{8} = -36 \times \frac{1}{8} = -4.5$

3-2 Transforming Equations: Multiplication and Division

Objective To solve equations using multiplication or division.

Suppose that a pound of peas costs the same as a pound of string beans. Then, you would expect to pay the same price for *two* pounds of peas as for *two* pounds of string beans, and the same price for *one-half* pound of peas as for *one-half* pound of string beans.

The ideas involved in this example are the **multiplication and division properties of equality.** *If equal numbers are multiplied by the same number, the products are equal. If equal numbers are divided by the same nonzero number, the quotients are equal.*

Multiplication Property of Equality

If a, b, and c are any real numbers and $a = b$, then

$$ca = cb \quad \text{and} \quad ac = bc.$$

Division Property of Equality

If a and b are any real numbers, c is any nonzero real number, and $a = b$, then

$$\frac{a}{c} = \frac{b}{c}.$$

These properties provide two more ways to transform an equation into an equivalent equation.

Transformation by Multiplication: Multiply each side of a given equation by the same *nonzero* real number.

Transformation by Division: Divide each side of a given equation by the same *nonzero* real number.

Example 1 Solve $6x = 222$.

Solution

$$6x = 222$$
$$\frac{6x}{6} = \frac{222}{6}$$
$$x = 37$$

To obtain x alone as the left side, divide each side by 6 (or multiply by $\frac{1}{6}$, the reciprocal of 6).

Check: $6x = 222$
$6(37) \stackrel{?}{=} 222$
$222 = 222$ √

∴ the solution is 37 ***Answer***

Teaching Suggestions p. T84

Chalkboard Examples

Solve.

1. $12a = 48$ 4
2. $-\frac{1}{6}x = 6$ -36
3. $15 = \frac{m}{3}$ 45
4. $-4p = -40$ 10
5. $20 = -\frac{c}{4}$ -80
6. $-\frac{1}{7}d = 0$ 0
7. $5g = -35$ -7
8. $2h = -\frac{2}{9}$ $-\frac{1}{9}$

Common Error

In solving equations like Written Exercise 25, some students will write $3 \cdot \frac{1}{3}x = 2\frac{1}{3} \cdot 3$ and "cancel" the 3's on the right side of the equation. They will therefore get 2 instead of 7 for the answer. Remind students that when a factor of a product is a mixed number they should express the mixed number as an improper fraction.

Supplementary Material

Practice Master 11

Example 2 Solve $-\frac{1}{3}t = 8$.

Solution

$$-\frac{1}{3}t = 8$$
$$-3\left(-\frac{1}{3}t\right) = -3(8)$$
$$t = -24$$

To obtain t alone as the left side, multiply each side by -3, the reciprocal of $-\frac{1}{3}$.

Check: $-\frac{1}{3}t = 8$

$$-\frac{1}{3}(-24) \stackrel{?}{=} 8$$
$$8 = 8 \quad \checkmark$$

$\therefore$ the solution is -24. ***Answer***

You know that zero cannot be a divisor (page 81). Do you know why zero is not allowed as a multiplier in transforming an equation? Look at the following equations.

(1) $5z = 45$
(2) $0 \cdot 5z = 0 \cdot 45$
(3) $(0 \cdot 5)z = 0 \cdot 45$
(4) $0 \cdot z = 0$

Equation (1) has just one root, namely 9. Equation (4) is satisfied by *any* real number. Equations (1) and (4) are *not* equivalent (see page 94). *In transforming an equation, never multiply by zero.*

Oral Exercises

State the number by which to multiply or divide each side of the given equation to produce an equivalent equation with the variable alone as one side. Then, state this equivalent equation.

1. $36x = 72$ Div. by 36; $x = 2$
2. $10y = -10$ Div. by 10; $y = -1$
3. $3c = -21$
4. $-8a = 32$ Div. by -8; $a = -4$
5. $\frac{1}{2}b = 4$ Mult. by 2; $b = 8$
6. $\frac{1}{3}t = 7$
7. $-\frac{1}{10}r = 5$ Mult. by -10; $r = -50$
8. $-\frac{1}{9}s = 9$ Mult. by -9; $s = -81$
9. $0 = -4k$
10. $-7 = -7p$ Div. by -7; $p = 1$
11. $c \div 4 = -1$ Mult. by 4; $c = -4$
12. $\frac{d}{2} = -6$
13. $-11f = -88$ Div. by -11; $f = 8$
14. $-27p = -81$ Div. by -27; $p = 3$
15. $4 = -\frac{u}{3}$
16. $-1 = \frac{n}{13}$ Mult. by 13; $n = -13$
17. $-0.1x = -3$ Div. by -0.1; $x = 30$
18. $0.01y = -8$

Suggested Assignments

Minimum
101/11–31 odd,
P: 1–11 odd

Average
101/14–32 even,
P: 7, 9, 10, 13
105/1–9
Day 2 of Sec. 3-1 finishes Sec. 3-1 and starts Sec. 3-2. This assignment finishes Sec. 3-2 and starts Sec. 3-3.

Maximum
101/1–29 odd, 30–35,
P: 9, 10, 13, 14
S 96/54–56

Additional Answers
Oral Exercises

3. Div. by 3; $c = -7$
6. Mult. by 3; $t = 21$
9. Div. by -4; $k = 0$
12. Mult. by 2; $d = -12$
15. Mult. by -3; $-12 = u$
18. Div. by 0.01; $y = -800$

Written Exercises

Solve.

A
1. $17m = 527$ 31
2. $50n = 650$ 13
3. $-1024 = 32a$ −32
4. $-351 = 9b$
5. $\frac{1}{8}x = -32$ −256
6. $\frac{1}{9}y = -27$ −243
7. $-\frac{1}{13}p = -13$ 169
8. $-\frac{1}{12}q = -24$
9. $-48 = -\frac{1}{8}r$ 384
10. $-\frac{1}{6}s = 60$ −360
11. $14v = -252$ −18
12. $-32x = 768$
13. $600 = -25w$ −24
14. $-675 = 27e$ −25
15. $-35 = \frac{d}{7}$ −245
16. $-28 = \frac{c}{4}$
17. $99 = -\frac{h}{3}$ −297
18. $65 = -\frac{t}{5}$ −325
19. $-\frac{1}{91}m = 0$ 0
20. $-\frac{n}{10} = -64$
21. $-13f = -858$ 66
22. $-74g = -962$ 13
23. $2k = -\frac{4}{7}$ $-\frac{2}{7}$
24. $3p = -\frac{9}{16}$

B
25. $\frac{1}{3}x = 2\frac{1}{3}$ 7
26. $\frac{1}{2}q = 3\frac{1}{2}$ 7
27. $-1 = 2.5x$ −0.4
28. $0 = -1.5y$ 0
29. $\frac{1}{5}a = 6\frac{4}{5}$ 34
30. $\frac{1}{2}b = 14\frac{1}{2}$ 29
31. $-\frac{1}{3}y = 3\frac{2}{3}$ −11
32. $-\frac{1}{2}z = 11\frac{1}{2}$ −23

C
33. $-2|x| = -30$ {−15, 15}
34. $\frac{|v|}{7} = 42$ {−294, 294}
35. $9 - \frac{|a|}{2} = 1$ {−16, 16}
36. $10 - 3|b| = 1$ {−3, 3}

Problems

Write an equation based on the facts of each problem. Then solve the equation and answer the question posed in the problem.

A
1. Negative eight times a number is 376. What is the number? −47
2. Twelve times a number is −564. What is the number? −47
3. One third of a number is −912. What is the number? −2736
4. The opposite of one fourth of a number is 1132. What is the number? −4528
5. Daniel Erik paid $147 for six theater tickets. How much did each ticket cost? $24.50
6. Denise Thomas paid $184.80 for a railroad pass allowing her 42 trips between Greenville and Central City. How much is that for each trip? $4.40
7. The perimeter of a square lot is 156 m. How long is each side of the lot? 39 m
8. A park in the shape of an equilateral triangle (a triangle with all sides equal) has a perimeter of 495 m. How long is each side of the park? 165 m
9. Twelve-year-old Lola is one fourth as old as her Uncle Hector. How old is Hector? 48 years old

Additional A Exercises

Solve.

1. $22m = 132$ 6
2. $\frac{1}{4}j = 12$ 48
3. $13n = -286$ −22
4. $-4k = -396$ 99
5. $-\frac{x}{5} = -5$ 25
6. $-86z = -258$ 3

Additional Answers Written Exercises

4. −39
8. 288
12. −24
16. −112
20. 640
24. $-\frac{3}{16}$

Mixed Review Exercises

Simplify.

1. $42 \div (7 + 7)$ 3
2. $(-9)(-3)(-2)$ −54
3. Write a variable expression for "The sum of 6 times the number m and 18." $6m + 18$
4. Solve: $m - 9 = |32|$ 41

10. A restaurant charges \$1.75 for one eighth of a quiche. How much does the restaurant receive for the whole quiche? \$14

11. A 75-watt bulb consumes 0.075 kW · h (kilowatt hours) of energy when it burns for one hour. How long was the bulb left burning during a period when it consumed 3.3 kW · h of energy? 44 h

12. How many apples, averaging 0.2 kg each, are in a 50-kg shipment of apples? 250

B 13. A police helicopter clocked an automobile for 10 seconds over a stretch of highway one fifth of a mile long. At what rate was the automobile traveling in miles per **a.** second? **b.** hour? a. $\frac{1}{50}$ mi/s b. 72 mi/h

14. How many hard-cover copies of a book selling for \$16.50 each must a dealer sell to take in as much money as for 30 paperback copies of the book selling at \$4.95 each? 9

15. For selling a home, an agent receives \$6 for every one hundred dollars in the selling price. What was the selling price of a home for which the agent received \$4725? \$78,750

16. An employer claimed that each worker received \$24 in "fringe benefits" for every \$100 in wages. At this rate, what wages were earned by a worker whose fringe benefits were calculated to be \$4140? \$17,250

Career Note / *Medical Laboratory Technician*

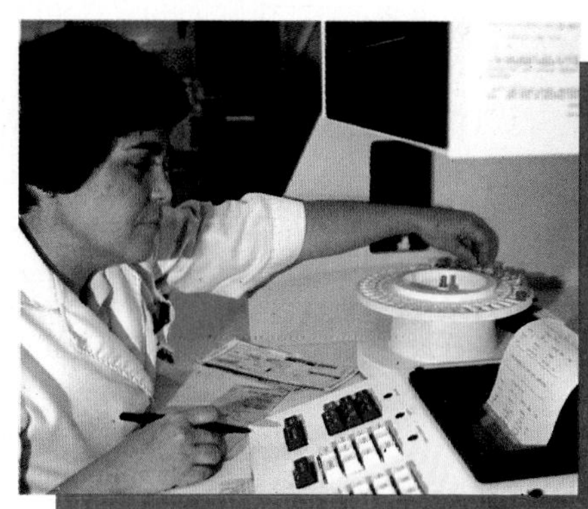

An eye for detail, the ability to work under pressure, and the ability to get accurate results are necessary qualities for a medical laboratory technician. Under the direction of physicians, medical laboratory technicians perform tests that are important in the diagnosis and treatment of many illnesses. They often use precision instruments in their work.

A medical technician needs two or more years of training after high school. Medical technicians take courses in biology, chemistry, and mathematics. Sometimes the training is specialized and involves some clinical experience. For those technicians who wish to teach or do research, many universities offer graduate programs in medical technology.

3-3 Using Several Transformations

Objective To use several transformations to solve an equation.

The equations

$$(16 + 4) - 4 = 16 \quad \text{and} \quad (16 - 4) + 4 = 16$$

are true statements. In fact:

For all real numbers a and b,

$$(a + b) - b = a \quad \text{and} \quad (a - b) + b = a.$$

To "undo" addition of a number, you subtract that number. To "undo" subtraction of a number, you add that number. We call addition and subtraction **inverse operations.**

Similarly, multiplication and division are inverse operations.

For all real numbers a and all nonzero real numbers b,

$$(ab) \div b = a \quad \text{and} \quad (a \div b)b = a.$$

To "undo" multiplication by a nonzero number, you divide by that number. To "undo" division by a nonzero number, you multiply by that number.

In transforming equations, you often use inverse operations.

Example 1 Solve $4y + 43 = 19$.

Solution

$$4y + 43 = 19$$
$$4y + 43 - 43 = 19 - 43$$
$$4y = -24$$

To undo the addition of 43 to $4y$, subtract 43 from each side.

$$\frac{4y}{4} = \frac{-24}{4}$$
$$y = -6$$

To undo the multiplication of y by 4, divide each side by 4.

Check: $4y + 43 = 19$
$$4(-6) + 43 \stackrel{?}{=} 19$$
$$-24 + 43 \stackrel{?}{=} 19$$
$$19 = 19 \quad \checkmark$$

$\therefore$ the solution is -6. ***Answer***

Teaching Suggestions p. T84

Suggested Extensions p. T84

Chalkboard Examples

Solve.

1. $4x + 21 = 5$ -4
2. $-9 + 3y = -6$ 1
3. $\frac{a}{4} + 7 = -3$ -40
4. $-10k + 6k = 36$ -9
5. $17b - 6b + 55 = 0$ -5
6. $8(n - 5) = -32$ 1
7. $4(c + 3) + 10 = -2$ -6
8. $2(z - 2) - z = 7$ 11

Common Errors

Students may need to be reminded not to combine unlike terms, and you may need to review the distributive axiom. You may find students making a more surprising error when they do Oral Exercise 12, for example. Some students will think that they should add 1 to both sides of the equation. Remind them that $1 = {}^{+}1$. The sign of a number is never written after it.

Supplementary Materials

Test 8
Resource Book, p. 74

Suggested Assignments

Minimum
Day 1: 105/2–30 even
S 101/*P*: 2, 6, 8
Day 2: 105/7–37 odd
S 98/*P*: 12–14

Average
105/10–40 even
S 102/*P*: 15, 16
R 106/*Self-Test 1*

Maximum
105/10–48 even
S 102/*P*: 15, 16
R 106/*Self-Test 1*

Additional Answers
Oral Exercises

1. Subtract 1; divide by 6
2. Add 4; divide by 3
3. Add 2; mult. by 4
4. Subtract 9; mult. by -2
5. Add 8; mult. by 3
6. Add 1; mult. by -3
7. Mult. by $\frac{4}{3}$
8. Mult. by $-\frac{9}{5}$
9. Add n and $7n$; divide by 8
10. Add $-11r$ and $13r$; divide by 2

The following steps are usually helpful when you solve an equation in which all the variables are on the same side.

1. Simplify each side of the equation.
2. If there are still indicated additions or subtractions, use the inverse operations to undo them.
3. If there are indicated multiplications or divisions involving the variable, use the inverse operations to undo them.

Example 2 Solve $7(y-1)-2y=13$.

Solution

$$7(y-1)-2y=13$$
$$7y-7-2y=13 \quad \text{Use the distributive property and simplify the left side.}$$
$$5y-7=13$$
$$5y-7+7=13+7 \quad \text{Add 7 to each side.}$$
$$5y=20$$
$$\frac{5y}{5}=\frac{20}{5} \quad \text{Divide each side by 5.}$$
$$y=4$$

Condensed Solution

$$7(y-1)-2y=13$$
$$7y-7-2y=13$$
$$5y-7=13$$
$$5y=20$$
$$y=4$$

Check:
$$7(y-1)-2y=13$$
$$7(4-1)-2(4)\stackrel{?}{=}13$$
$$7(3)-8\stackrel{?}{=}13$$
$$13=13 \ \checkmark$$

∴ the solution is 4. ***Answer***

Oral Exercises

Describe how you would solve each equation.

Example 1 $\frac{1}{5}z+2=-1$

Solution First subtract 2 from each side; then multiply each side by 5.

Example 2 $14=\frac{2}{3}m$

Solution 1 Multiply each side by $\frac{3}{2}$.

Solution 2 Multiply each side by 3; then divide each side by 2.

1. $6x+1=7$

2. $3y-4=14$

3. $\frac{1}{4}a-2=-3$

4. $-\frac{1}{2}b+9=5$

5. $-8+\frac{t}{3}=7$

6. $4=-1-\frac{x}{3}$

7. $\frac{3}{4}n = -12$

8. $-\frac{5}{9}z = 30$

9. $n + 7n = 16$

10. $-11r + 13r = -38$

11. $\frac{7}{8}s + 2 = 16$

12. $1 - \frac{4}{5}n = -19$

13. $5 = c + 8c - 4$

14. $10p - p + 2 = -7$

15. $-5(z + 9) = 40$

16. $\frac{y-2}{3} = 7$

17. $\frac{3}{7}w + 2 = 17$

18. $1 - \frac{2}{9}v = 4$

Written Exercises

Solve.

A

1. $3y + 7 = 16$ 3
2. $2x - 9 = 13$ 11
3. $-15 + 4g = -39$ −6
4. $16 + 5p = -74$ −18
5. $\frac{r}{2} - 6 = 6$ 24
6. $\frac{s}{3} + 9 = 12$ 9
7. $\frac{n}{5} + 25 = -10$ −175
8. $-\frac{d}{4} + 3 = -2$ 20
9. $11 = 7 - 2k$ −2
10. $14 = -1 - 5h$ −3
11. $-7v + 4v = 21$ −7
12. $4w - w = -48$ −16
13. $9t + 7t = -64$ −4
14. $4m - 7m = -54$ 18
15. $13a + 7a = 0$ 0
16. $8z - 11z = 0$ 0
17. $\frac{3}{7}c + 45 = 0$ −105
18. $\frac{4}{5}f + 60 = 0$ −75
19. $15g - 13g + 14 = 0$ −7
20. $3e - e + 2 = 0$ −1
21. $u - 4u + 4 = 7$ −1
22. $x - 9 - 4x = -6$ −1
23. $0 = y - 16 - 2y$ −16
24. $0 = a + 25 + 4a$ −5
25. $z + 2z + 3z = 36$ 6
26. $3w - 2w + w = 24$ 12
27. $7(m - 1) = -63$ −8
28. $8(q + 7) = -72$ −16
29. $-\frac{3}{2}(s - 2) = 21$ −12
30. $-\frac{6}{5}(r + 3) = 66$ −58

B

31. $3(a - 5) + 19 = -2$ −2
32. $2(b + 8) - 9 = 5$ −1
33. $4(k + 7) - 15 = -3$ −4
34. $7(h - 2) + 17 = 3$ 0
35. $4c + 3(c - 2) = -34$ −4
36. $d + 4(d + 6) = -1$ −5
37. $1 - \frac{3}{4}(v + 2) = -5$ 6
38. $9 - \frac{4}{5}(u - 3) = 1$ 13
39. $-9 - 3(2q - 1) = -18$ 2
40. $-10 + 4(3p + 10) = 18$ −1
41. $4(s + 8) - 3s = -2$ −34
42. $3(t - 5) - t = -7$ 4
43. $(x - 13) - (x - 5) + 2x = 0$ 4
44. $(5 - y) + (6 - y) - (5 - y) = 0$ 6
45. $b - (1 - 2b) + (b - 3) = -4$ 0
46. $(c + 3) - 2c - (1 - 3c) = 2$ 0

C

47. $5m - 3[7 - (1 - 2m)] = 0$ −18
48. $\frac{1}{5}[4(k + 2) - (3 - k)] = 4$ 3
49. $5(g - 7) + 2[g - 3(g - 5)] = 0$ 5
50. $7n + 2[3(1 - n) - 2(1 + n)] = 14$ −4
51. $3|z| - (2|z| - 2) = 9$ {−7, 7}
52. $9(|x| - 3) - 5|x| - 3 = 2$ {−8, 8}

11. Subtract 2; mult. by $\frac{8}{7}$
12. Subtract 1; mult. by $-\frac{5}{4}$
13. Add c and $8c$; add 4; divide by 9
14. Add $10p$ and $-p$; subtract 2; divide by 9
15. Divide by −5; subtract 9
16. Mult. by 3; add 2
17. Subtract 2; mult. by $\frac{7}{3}$
18. Subtract 1, mult. by $-\frac{9}{2}$

Additional A Exercises

Solve.

1. $4m + 7 = 39$ 8
2. $3x - 8 = -17$ −3
3. $\frac{j}{4} + 25 = 35$ 40
4. $-8u + 3u = -35$ 7
5. $12x - 4 - x = 40$ 4
6. $9(m - 3) = -45$ −2

Mixed Review Exercises

1. Simplify: $-\frac{9}{5} + \frac{11}{5} + 3$ $3\frac{2}{5}$
2. State the reciprocal of $-\frac{4}{5}$. $-\frac{5}{4}$

Solve.

3. $4 + x = 29$ $x = 25$
4. $-8m = 176$ $m = -22$

The optional Computer Exercises that appear throughout this book require familiarity with the fundamental concepts and terminology of programming in BASIC. The appendix on page 653 summarizes these fundamentals.

Computer Exercises

1. Write a BASIC program to solve an equation of the form $Ax + B = C$, where the values of A, B, and C are entered with INPUT statements. Use the program to solve the following equations.

   a. $7x + 8 = 64$ 8 **b.** $3y - 2 = 4$ 2 **c.** $\frac{2}{5}n + 11 = 7$ −10

   d. $\frac{2}{3}j - 8 = 14$ 33 **e.** $\frac{w}{6} - 5 = 0$ 30 **f.** $\frac{z}{2} + 4 = 13$ 18

2. Use the program from Exercise 1 to solve $0x + 9 = 12$. What happens? What is the correct solution? Modify the program in Exercise 1 so that an appropriate response will appear if the value of A is 0.

3. Modify the program from Exercise 1 to solve an equation of the form $A|x| + B = C$. Use this program to solve the following equations.

   a. $|x| + 8 = 10$ {2, −2} **b.** $|v| + 10 = 8$ No sol. **c.** $6|m| + 2 = 5$ {0.5, −0.5}

   d. $\frac{|s|}{2} - 4 = 11$ {30, −30} **e.** $\frac{4}{3}|c| = 24$ {18, −18} **f.** $\frac{2}{3}|y| + 4 = 16$ {18, −18}

Self-Test 1

Vocabulary equivalent equations (p. 94)
transformation by substitution (p. 94)
transformation by addition (p. 94)
transformation by subtraction (p. 94)
transformation by multiplication (p. 99)
transformation by division (p. 99)
inverse operations (p. 103)

Solve.

1. $x + 17 = 59$ 42
2. $-14 + y = -1$ 13 **Obj. 3-1, p. 93**
3. $7r = -119$ −17
4. $18 = -\frac{1}{5}t$ −90 **Obj. 3-2, p. 99**

Write an equation to represent the relationship in Exercise 5. Then solve the equation and answer the question.

5. In a school cafeteria one week, 1125 containers of milk were sold. Three times as many containers of milk as containers of juice were sold. How many containers of juice were sold? 375

Solve.

6. $5z - 2 = 33$ 7
7. $m - 4m + 10 = 1$ 3 **Obj. 3-3, p. 103**

Check your answers with those at the back of the book.

Quick Quiz

Solve.

1. $a + 12 = 30$ 18
2. $-9 + x = -3$ 6
3. $4k = -52$ −13
4. $12 = -\frac{1}{3}b$ −36

Write an equation to represent the relationship in Exercise 5. Then solve the equation and answer the question.

5. For an evening performance, a theater sold 420 adult tickets. Four times as many adult tickets as children's tickets were sold. How many children's tickets were sold? $420 = 4c$; $c = 105$; 105 children's tickets were sold.

Solve.

6. $6m - 4 = 44$ 8
7. $2y - 5y + 17 = 2$ 5

Computer Key-In

Everyday calculations are done either by hand or by calculator. Generally, computers are used only for more elaborate or tedious computations, or when a great deal of data must be processed.

However, it is informative sometimes to use a computer program to demonstrate the steps of a process. The program given below illustrates the use of inverse operations to solve simple equations. The program also introduces a *string variable,* which is used to represent a symbol. The first time S$ (note the dollar sign) is used, its value is to be one of +, −, *, or /. The second time S$ is used its value is to be Y or any other single letter. In line 190, Y stands for "yes" and N for "no."

```
10  PRINT "TO SOLVE AN EQUATION OF THE FORM"
20  PRINT "      X (SIGN) A = B:"
30  PRINT "INPUT SIGN,A,B";
40  INPUT S$,A,B
50  IF S$="+" THEN 110
60  IF S$="-" THEN 130
70  IF S$="*" THEN 150
80  IF S$="/" THEN 170
90  PRINT "WHAT DID YOU INTEND?"
100  GOTO 30
110  PRINT "X = ";B-A  <-[- is the inverse of +
120  GOTO 180
130  PRINT "X = ";B+A  <-[+ is the inverse of -
140  GOTO 180
150  PRINT "X = ";B/A  <-[/ is the inverse of *
160  GOTO 180
170  PRINT "X = ";B*A  <-[* is the inverse of /
180  PRINT
190  PRINT "ANOTHER (Y/N)";
200  INPUT S$
210  IF S$="Y" THEN 30
220  END
```

Exercises

RUN the program to solve these equations.

1. $x + 4 = 20$ 16 **2.** $x - 4 = 20$ 24 **3.** $x \times 4 = 20$ 5 **4.** $x \div 4 = 20$ 80

RUN the program twice to solve these two-step equations.

5. $3x - 8 = 22$ 10 **6.** $(x \div 5) + 6 = 30$ 120

7. Write a program to solve $Ax + Bx + C + D = 0$.

Note: The program given above can be used to do Exercises 1–18 on page 96 and Exercises 1–20 on page 101.

Computer Key-In Commentary

Line 40 has several variables in one INPUT statement. When data is typed in, the user must type in the values separated by commas. The first item typed should be the symbol. If an attempt is made to store symbols in a numeric variable, then a message may be printed asking the user to re-enter the data.

Each time an INPUT S$ is executed, old values of S$ are replaced.

Notice in line 210 that strings can be compared. When a comparison is made between what is typed and the string in quotes, the two strings must match exactly to be considered equal. For example, "YES" ≠ "Y ES". Although the user does not type a Y in quotes, the letter Y in the program must be in quotes or the computer will try to compare the value of S$ with the value of Y (zero) and an error message will result.

Teaching Suggestions p. T84

Suggested Extensions p. T85

Chalkboard Examples

Use the five-step plan to solve each problem.

1. The sum of three consecutive even integers is 36. Find the integers.
   Step 2 Let n = first even integer. Then $n + 2$ and $n + 4$ = second and third integers.
   Step 3 $n + (n + 2) + (n + 4) = 36$
   Step 4 $n = 10$
   $\therefore$ the integers are 10, 12, and 14.
2. A rectangle has length 15 and perimeter 42. Find its width.
   Step 2 Let w = width.
   Step 3 $2(15) + 2w = 42$
   Step 4 $w = 6$
   $\therefore$ the width is 6.
3. A gardener bought four times as many tomato plants as zucchini plants. If 30 plants were purchased in all, how many were tomato?
   Step 2 Let z = number of of zucchini plants. Then $4z$ = number of tomato plants.
   Step 3 $z + 4z = 30$
   Step 4 $z = 6$; $4z = 24$
   $\therefore$ 24 tomato plants were bought.
4. A sporting goods store sells a tennis racket for \$64. This price is \$40 less than twice the price of the same racket at a discount store. What is the price at the discount store?

(continued)

Solving Problems

3-4 Using Equations to Solve Problems

Objective To use the five-step plan to solve word problems.

The skill you have gained in solving equations can often help you to solve a word problem. Use the five-step plan on page 26 to guide yourself to the solution.

Example 1

Towne Florists, Inc. paid \$3250 down toward the purchase of a delivery van. The balance of the cash price together with interest was paid over the next 60 months. The interest amounted to one half of the balance. If the total deferred payment price was \$19,150, what was the cash price of the van?

Solution

Step 1 The problem asks for the cash price.

$$\text{Cash price} = \underbrace{\text{Down payment}}_{\$3250} + \text{Balance}$$

$$\underbrace{\text{Total deferred payment price}}_{\$19,150} = \text{Cash price} + \text{Interest}$$

Interest = One half of Balance

Step 2 Let b = the balance in dollars. Then:

Cash price $= 3250 + b$

Interest $= \frac{1}{2}b$

$$\underbrace{\text{Total deferred payment price}} = \underbrace{3250 + b + \frac{1}{2}b}$$

Step 3
$$19,150 = 3250 + b + \frac{1}{2}b$$

Step 4
$$19,150 = 3250 + \frac{3}{2}b$$
$$15,900 = \frac{3}{2}b$$
$$b = 10,600 \text{ (balance)}$$
$$3250 + b = 13,850 \text{ (cash price)}$$
$$\frac{1}{2}b = 5300 \text{ (interest)}$$

Step 5 Does the cash price plus interest equal the total deferred payment price?

$$13{,}850 + 5300 \stackrel{?}{=} 19{,}150$$
$$19{,}150 = 19{,}150 \quad \checkmark$$

$\therefore$ the cash price was \$13,850. ***Answer***

Notice that in Example 1 you did not use the fact that the balance was paid over 60 months. Sometimes word problems contain unnecessary information. When this occurs, you have to select the facts that are necessary in order to find the solution.

To solve the problem in the next example, you must recall your work with consecutive integers. You may wish to reread Section 2-7, pages 72–75, at this time.

Example 2 The width and the length, in meters, of a rectangle are consecutive even integers. The perimeter is 292 m. What are the dimensions of the rectangle?

Solution

Step 1 The problem asks for the numbers of meters in the width and the length of a rectangle whose perimeter (p) is 292 m. The width and length are consecutive even integers.

Step 2 Let w = the width in meters.
Then $w + 2$ = the length in meters.

w+2

w w

w+2

Step 3 $2l + 2w = p$
$\therefore 2(w + 2) + 2w = 292$

Step 4
$$2w + 4 + 2w = 292$$
$$4w + 4 = 292$$
$$4w = 288$$
$$w = 72$$
$$w + 2 = 74$$

Step 5 Does the sum of two times the width and two times the length equal the perimeter of 292 m?

$$2(72) + 2(74) \stackrel{?}{=} 292$$
$$144 + 148 \stackrel{?}{=} 292$$
$$292 = 292 \quad \checkmark$$

$\therefore$ the dimensions are 72 m and 74 m. ***Answer***

Step 2 Let c = cost at discount store.
Step 3 $2c - 40 = 64$
Step 4 $c = 52$
$\therefore$ the discount store charges \$52.

Common Error

Students who do not draw diagrams to illustrate perimeter problems or who indicate the length and the width of a rectangle next to two adjacent sides of their diagrams only, may use the incorrect formula, $l + w = p$ to represent the perimeter of a rectangle. Encourage such students to draw a diagram and to mark the length and width next to all four sides of the rectangle as shown in Example 2 on page 109.

Supplementary Material

Practice Master 12

Problems

Use the five-step plan on page 26 to solve each problem.

A **1.** The sum of 85 and twice a number is 237. Find the number. 76

2. The sum of three times a number and 28 is 484. Find the number. 152

3. Five times a number, decreased by 87, is -12. Find the number. 15

4. Six times a number, increased by 13, is -161. Find the number. -29

5. If you add 15 to the product of 4 and a number, you get 363. Find the number. 87

6. If you subtract 27 from the product of 8 and a number, you get 1789. Find the number. 227

7. The perimeter of a rectangle is 326 and its length is 94. Find its width. 69

8. The perimeter of a rectangle is 908 and its width is 220. Find its length. 234

9. Together, a boat and outboard motor cost $1500. The boat cost five times as much as the motor. What was the cost of each? motor: $250, boat: $1250

10. Bill's Burger Barn sold 584 hamburgers today. Three times as many hamburgers were sold with cheese as were sold without cheese. How many cheeseburgers were sold? 438

11. When Joe Darrico retired from his parcel delivery service, his daughter Rose took over the business. By now, Rose has been running the service three years longer than her father did. If the business has been in operation for 27 years, how long did Joe run it? 12 years

12. An oil tank contains 250 barrels of oil more than another tank. Together they contain 2750 barrels of oil. How much oil does each tank contain? 1250 barrels and 1500 barrels

13. Eighteen-year-old Manolo is 4 years older than twice as old as his sister, Julia. How old is Julia? 7 years old

14. A sports jacket costing $129 is priced $11 more than twice the cost of a coordinated pair of slacks. How much are the slacks? $59

15. Find three consecutive integers whose sum is 81. 26, 27, 28

16. Find four consecutive integers whose sum is 50. 11, 12, 13, 14

17. Find four consecutive odd integers whose sum is -112. $-31, -29, -27, -25$

18. Find three consecutive odd integers whose sum is -129. $-45, -43, -41$

19. The lengths in meters of the sides of a triangle are consecutive even integers. The perimeter is 210 m. How long are the sides? 68 m, 70 m, 72 m

20. The lengths in centimeters of the sides of a triangle are consecutive odd integers. The perimeter is 171 cm. How long are the sides? 55 cm, 57 cm, 59 cm

B **21.** Two numbers differ by 3. Four times the lesser diminished by three times the greater is 7. Find the numbers. 16, 19

Suggested Assignments

Minimum
Day 1: 110/*P*: 1–15 odd
S 105/32–38 even
R 106/*Self-Test 1*
Day 2: 110/*P*: 2–20 even

Average
Day 1: 110/*P*: 1–11 odd, 15, 16, 21, 22
S 105/43–46
Day 2: 111/*P*: 23, 24, 26, 27, 30, 31, 32
S 96/53, 54

Maximum
Day 1: 110/*P*: 1–11 odd, 15, 16, 21, 22
S 105/49–52
Day 2: 111/*P*: 25–33
S 101/36

Additional A Exercises

Use the five-step plan on p. 26 to solve each problem.

1. The sum of 92 and three times a number is 128. Find the number. 12

2. If you decrease the product of 16 and a number by 52, the result is 300. Find the number. 22

3. The perimeter of a rectangle is 130. If its width is 12, find its length. 53

4. Harry and George are twins. Their brother, who is 15 years younger than the sum of their ages, is 25. How old are the twins? 20

5. Find 4 consecutive odd integers whose sum is 96. 21, 23, 25, 27

22. A magazine reported that in a survey of 100 teenagers, the number preferring broiled steak for dinner was 8 more than the number preferring beef stew. But the number preferring macaroni and cheese was 2 more than 4 times the number preferring beef stew. How many teenagers in the survey preferred beef stew? 15

23. Of the 10 highest waterfalls of the world, one is in Africa and another is in New Zealand. There are just as many in Europe as in South America, but there are twice as many in North America as in South America. How many are in Europe? 2

24. In triangle ABC, side AB is 2 cm shorter than side AC, while side BC is 1 cm longer than AC. If the perimeter is 62 cm, find the lengths of the 3 sides. $AC = 21$ cm, $AB = 19$ cm, $BC = 22$ cm

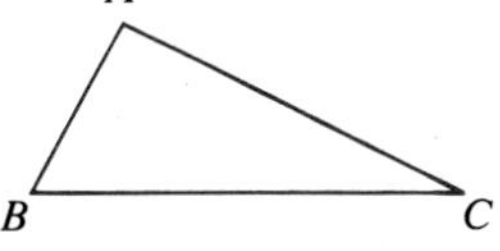

25. Five centimeters are cut off one side of a square piece of paper and 8 cm are added to an adjacent side. The resulting rectangular piece of paper has perimeter 98 cm. What was the area of the original square? 529 cm^2

26. Tom has \$5 more than Dick and Dick has \$11 more than Harry. Together they have \$45. How much does each have?

27. Carol has twice as much money as Nina, and Nina has \$6 less than Lynn. Together they have \$54. How much does each have?

28. Ray is 15 years older than Sam and Sam is 12 years younger than Bert. Their ages total 42 years. How old is each?

29. Sally is 17 years younger than Tilly and Tilly is 10 years older than Angie. Their ages total 60 years. How old is each?

30. The total cost of a sandwich, a glass of milk, and an apple is \$2.35. What was the price of each, if the sandwich cost twice as much as the milk and the apple cost 90 cents less than the sandwich?

31. In one day, Machine A caps twice as many bottles as Machine B. Machine C caps 500 more bottles than Machine A. If the total number of bottles capped in a day is 40,000, how many bottles does each machine cap? B caps 7900, A caps 15,800 and C caps 16,300.

C 32. With the major options package and destination charge, a sports car cost \$24,416. The base price of the car was ten times the price of the major options package and fifty times the destination charge. What was the base price of the car? \$21,800

33. On the first of three tests, Juan scored 72 points. On the next test, he got a higher score. On the third test, his score was 1 more than on the second. His average on the three tests was 83. What were his grades on the second and third tests? 88 and 89

34. The perimeter of a rectangular lot is 260 m. The length exceeds the width by 20 m. Find the dimensions of the lot. 55 m wide by 75 m long

Mixed Review Exercises

1. Evaluate $x - 2(y + z)$ if $x = -1$, $y = 2$ and $z = -3$. 1
2. Replace _?_ with $>$ or $<$ to make a true statement. $-(-5)$ _?_ $|-14|$ $<$
3. Evaluate $\frac{a \cdot 6b}{3c}$ if $a = 6$, $b = -2$ and $c = 3$. -8
4. Solve: $3(x + 2) - 4 = 23$ 7

Additional Answers Problems

26. Harry, \$6; Dick, \$17; Tom, \$22
27. Nina, \$12; Lynn, \$18; Carol, \$24
28. Sam is 5, Bert is 17 and Ray is 20.
29. Sally is 12, Tilly is 29, and Angie is 19.
30. Milk, \$.65; sandwich, \$1.30; apple, \$.40

Teaching Suggestions p. T85

Suggested Extensions p. T86

Chalkboard Examples

Solve. If the equation is an identity or if it has no root, state that fact.

1. $10n = 4n - 42$ -7
2. $2y - 49 = -5y$ 7
3. $4(k - 1) = 4(k + 1)$ no root
4. $5(x - 4) = 3x - 10$ 5
5. $2(s - 1) = 2(s - 2) + 2$ identity
6. $7h - 5 = 4h + 22$ 9
7. $6m - 4 = 8 - 6m$ 1
8. $\frac{1}{4}(12 - 4h) = 3h + 7$ -1

Common Errors

Often a student who is solving an equation that is an identity will assume, for example, that getting $4 = 4$ means that the solution is 4. Be sure to point out that this is not the case; show that numerous other values of the variable satisfy the equation.

Thinking of the axiom of opposites, students sometimes write "$0 = 4$; no solution" when solving the equation $n = -n + 4$, for example. Encourage students who make this mistake to show their work.

Supplementary Material

Resource Book, p. 75

3-5 Equations Having the Variable in Both Sides

Objective To solve equations having the variable in both sides.

The variable appears in both sides of the equation

$$7z = z - 54.$$

Are you allowed to transform the equation by subtracting z from both sides? The answer is yes. Because variables represent numbers, you may transform an equation by adding a variable expression to each side or by subtracting a variable expression from each side.

Example 1 Solve $7z = z - 54$.

Solution

$$\begin{aligned} 7z &= z - 54 \\ 7z - z &= z - 54 - z \\ 6z &= -54 \\ \frac{6z}{6} &= \frac{-54}{6} \\ z &= -9 \end{aligned}$$

Condensed Solution

$$\begin{aligned} 7z &= z - 54 \\ 6z &= -54 \\ z &= -9 \end{aligned}$$

Check:

$$\begin{aligned} 7z &= z - 54 \\ 7(-9) &\stackrel{?}{=} -9 - 54 \\ -63 &= -63 \ \checkmark \end{aligned}$$

$\therefore$ the solution is -9. ***Answer***

It is possible that an equation may have *no* roots, or that it may be satisfied by *every* real number. Example 2 illustrates a situation in which an equation has no roots. Example 3 illustrates a situation in which an equation is satisfied by every real number.

Example 2 Solve $3(1 - r) + 5r = 2(r + 1)$.

Solution

$$\begin{aligned} 3(1 - r) + 5r &= 2(r + 1) \\ 3 - 3r + 5r &= 2r + 2 \\ 3 + 2r &= 2r + 2 \\ 3 + 2r - 2r &= 2r + 2 - 2r \\ 3 &= 2 \end{aligned}$$

Since the given equation is equivalent to the false statement, "$3 = 2$," it has no root. ***Answer***

It is customary to call the set with no members the **empty set,** or the **null set.** It is denoted by the symbol $\emptyset$. Thus, you may say that the solution set of the equation in Example 2 is $\emptyset$.

Example 3 Solve $\frac{1}{3}(12x - 21) + 16 = 1 + 4(x + 2)$.

Solution

$$\frac{1}{3}(12x - 21) + 16 = 1 + 4(x + 2)$$
$$4x - 7 + 16 = 1 + 4x + 8$$
$$4x + 9 = 9 + 4x$$

The given equation is equivalent to $4x + 9 = 9 + 4x$, which is satisfied by every real number.

∴ the solution is the set of real numbers. ***Answer***

An equation that is true for every value of the variable(s) is called an **identity**. Thus, the equation in Example 3,

$$\frac{1}{3}(12x - 21) + 16 = 1 + 4(x + 2),$$

is an identity.

Oral Exercises

Solve. If the equation is an identity or if it has no root, state that fact.

1. $4x = 3x + 5$ 5
2. $2y + 9 = 3y$ 9
3. $8r + 1 = 9r$ 1
4. $2p - 1 = 3p$ -1
5. $a + 4 = 1 + a$ No solution
6. $2b = 6 + 2b$ No solution
7. $3k = 2k + k$ Identity
8. $4c = c$ 0
9. $3s = s - 2$ -1
10. $4t + 1 = 4t + 3$ No solution
11. $2(v - 1) = 2v - 2$ Identity
12. $3(w + 1) = 2w$ -3

Written Exercises

Solve each equation. If the equation is an identity or if it has no root, state that fact.

A

1. $9n = 7n + 16$ 8
2. $16m = 45 + 11m$ 9
3. $y = 57 - 2y$ 19
4. $2k = 90 - 8k$ 9
5. $12v - 84 = 5v$ 12
6. $4x + 49 = -3x$ -7
7. $39q + 78 = 33q$ -13
8. $61w - 56 = 54w$ 8
9. $98 - 4b = -11b$ -14
10. $126 - 13t = -19t$ -21
11. $-7a = -12a - 65$ -13
12. $-8y - 27 = -17y$ 3
13. $9h + 4 = 6h - 2$ -2
14. $5r - 9 = 2r + 12$ 7
15. $2p - 7 = 7 + 2p$ No solution
16. $3 - d = 7d + 27$ -3
17. $59 + x = 2 - 2x$ -19
18. $5c + 1 = -1 + 5c$ No solution
19. $2(y - 8) = 3y$ -16
20. $3(f + 7) = 2f$ -21
21. $4w - 1 = 7(w + 2)$ -5
22. $8v + 77 = 5(5 - v)$ -4
23. $\frac{1}{3}(12 - 9n) = 4 - 3n$ Identity
24. $m - 6 = \frac{1}{2}(8 - 18m)$ 1

Suggested Assignments

Minimum
Day 1: 113/1–25 odd
S 110/*P*: 21–25
Day 2: 113/10–22 even
114/*P*: 2–14 even

Average
113/2–32 even, 33
114/*P*: 2, 6, 9, 16, 17
R 116/*Self-Test 2*

Maximum
113/2–38 even
114/*P*: 6, 9, 14, 16–18
R 116/*Self-Test 2*

Additional A Exercises

Solve.

1. $10m = 6m - 16$ -4
2. $3x = 9x - 24$ 4
3. $8z - 4 = 6 - 2z$ 1
4. $16h + 22 = 8h - 2$ -3
5. $4(n + 3) = n$ -4
6. $\frac{1}{2}(4x - 4) = 16$ 9

Mixed Review Exercises

Solve.

1. $7 = 9 + x$ -2
2. $\frac{1}{5}x = 19$ 95
3. $4m - 5 = 15$ 5
4. Use the five-step plan to solve: The sum of three consecutive odd integers is 99. Find the integers. 31, 33 and 35

Solve each equation. If the equation is an identity or if it has no root, state that fact.

B

25. $5(2 + n) = 3(n + 6)$ 4

26. $3(30 + s) = 4(s + 19)$ 14

27. $5u + 5(1 - u) = u + 8$ -3

28. $2(g - 2) - 4 = 2(g - 3)$ No solution

29. $3(m + 5) - 6 = 3(m + 3)$ Identity

30. $3(2 + v) - 4v = v + 16$ -5

31. $3(5t + 2) - t = 2(t - 3)$ -1

32. $4(3y - 1) + 13 = 5y + 2$ -1

33. $6r - 2(2 - r) = 4(2r - 1)$ Identity

34. $5x + 2(1 - x) = 2(2x - 1)$ 4

35. $3 + 4(p + 2) = 2p + 3(p + 4)$ -1

36. $4(a + 2) = 14 - 2(3 - 2a)$ Identity

C

37. $3x + 2[1 - 3(x + 2)] = 2x$ -2

38. $2[5(w + 3) - (w + 1)] = 3(1 + w)$ -5

39. $5(2m + 3) - (1 - 2m) = 2[3(3 + 2m) - (3 - m)]$ 1

40. $3(r + 1) - [2(3 - 2r) - 3(3 - r)] = 2(r + 5) - 4$ 0

Problems

Solve.

A

1. Find a number that is 96 greater than its opposite. 48

2. Find a number that is 38 less than its opposite. -19

3. Find a number whose product with 9 is the same as its sum with 56. 7

4. Find a number that is 68 greater than three times its opposite. 17

5. Three times a number, decreased by 8, is the same as twice the number, increased by 15. Find the number. 23

6. Four times a number, increased by 25, is 13 less than six times the number. Find the number. 19

7. The sum of two numbers is 15. Three times one of the numbers is 11 less than five times the other. Find the numbers. 7 and 8

8. The difference of two integers is 9. Five times the smaller is 7 more than three times the larger. Find the integers. 17 and 26

9. The greater of two consecutive integers is 15 more than twice the lesser. Find the integers. -14 and -13

10. The greater of two consecutive even integers is 20 more than twice the lesser. Find the integers. -18 and -16

11. Dina has 6 steel balls of equal mass. If she puts 5 of them in one pan of a beam balance and one ball along with a mass of 100 g in the other pan, the pans balance each other. What is the mass of each steel ball? 25 g

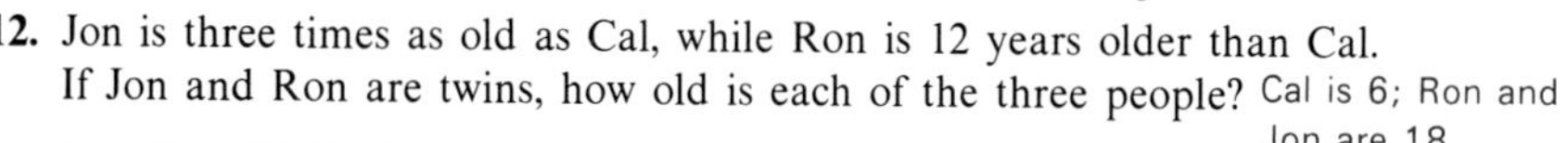

12. Jon is three times as old as Cal, while Ron is 12 years older than Cal. If Jon and Ron are twins, how old is each of the three people? Cal is 6; Ron and Jon are 18.

B 13. The lengths of the sides of a triangle are consecutive even integers. Find the length of the longest side if it is 14 units shorter than the perimeter. 10 units

14. The lengths of the sides of a triangle are consecutive odd integers. Find the length of the shortest side if the perimeter is 19 units shorter than four times the length of that side. 25 units

15. Jean Ackyroyd's starting salary is $18,000, with semi-annual raises of $750. Sue Bathgate's starting salary is $16,200, with semi-annual raises of $900. After how many years will the two women be earning the same salary? 6 years

16. An 800-liter tank is half full of water and is being filled with water pumped at the rate of 45 liters per minute from a full 940-liter tank. How long will it take before the two tanks contain the same amount of water? 6 min

17. Mary has $6 more than Frank. Together Mary and Frank have $90 more than Joe, who has half as much money as Frank. How much does Frank have? $56

18. A sofa costs $160 more to manufacture than a matching lounge chair. Three lounge chairs cost as much to manufacture as two sofas. How much does it cost to manufacture a lounge chair? $320

C 19. Find four consecutive multiples of 4 such that twice the sum of the least and greatest exceeds three times the least by 32. 8, 12, 16, 20

20. Find four consecutive multiples of 5 such that three times the sum of the two least exceeds twice the sum of the two greatest by 55. 45, 50, 55, 60

Computer Exercises

For students with some programming experience

Write a BASIC program to solve an equation of the form $AX + B = CX + D$, where the values of A, B, C, and D are entered with INPUT statements. Be sure that the program works correctly for identities and for equations that have no solution. Use the program to solve the following equations.

1. $3x + 4 = 5x + 10$ −3
2. $\frac{r}{2} + 1 = -2r + 11$ 4
3. $4m - 7 = 3 + 4m$ No solution
4. $\frac{k}{2} + 5 = 5 + \frac{1}{2}k$ Identity
5. $3y - 7 = \frac{2}{3}y$ 3
6. $a - 10 = -2a + 2$ 4

Quick Quiz

1. The opening of a new art exhibit had an attendance of 835 people. Four times as many people attended in the afternoon as in the morning. How many people attended in the afternoon?
   Step 2 Let m = morning attendance. Then $4m$ = afternoon attendance.
   Step 3 $m + 4m = 835$
   Step 4 $m = 167$; $4m = 668$
   $\therefore$ 668 people attended in the afternoon.

Solve.

2. $5b - 1 = 2b + 17$ 6
3. $3(2 - y) = 4(y + 5)$ -2
4. The sum of two numbers is 18. Five times one of the numbers is six less than three times the other. Find the numbers.
   Step 2 Let n = one number. Then $18 - n$ = the other.
   Step 3 $5n = 3(18 - n) - 6$
   Step 4 $n = 6$; $18 - n = 12$
   $\therefore$ the numbers are 6 and 12.

Self-Test 2

Vocabulary empty set (p. 112) identity (p. 113)
null set (p. 112)

1. In a 2-hour TV movie program, 9 times as many minutes were devoted to the movie as to commercials. How long did it take to show the movie? 108 min **Obj. 3-4, p. 108**

Solve.

2. $3t - 7 = t + 11$ 9
3. $2(1 - x) = 3(x + 9)$ -5 **Obj. 3-5, p. 112**
4. In a baseball game, the Hawks had 3 more hits than the Eagles. If 3 times the number of hits by the Eagles was 8 greater than twice the number of hits by the Hawks, how many hits did each team make? The Eagles had 14 hits and the Hawks had 17.

Check your answers with those at the back of the book.

Historical Note / *Variables*

Until the sixteenth century, there was no symbolic convention for representing unknowns in equations. Unknown quantities were represented by words such as "heap," "root," or "thing." Occasionally the unknown quantity acted as the narrator of the problem, as was the case in Problem 36 of the Rhind mathematical papyrus: "I go three times, and my third and my fifth are then added to me. . . ." The Chinese used the position of rods on a computing board to represent unknown quantities. In India the names of various colors were used. Eventually, abbreviations and drawings of squares and cubes were used to symbolize unknowns.

In the late sixteenth century, a lawyer and member of the Bretagne parliament, François Vieta (Viète), who enjoyed studying algebra during his leisure hours, wrote his most famous work, *In artem*. Vieta introduced vowels to represent unknowns and the use of consonants to represent constants. The later widespread adoption of algebraic symbols is largely due to the printing of Vieta's book. An English mathematician, Thomas Harriot, later adopted lower case letters to stand for variables. In 1637, René Descartes, a French mathematician, began using the final letters of the alphabet to represent the unknowns and the first letters of the alphabet to represent constant coefficients, thus giving his work a modern appearance. Compare, for example, the modern form of the equation

$$y^2 = cy - \frac{cx}{b}y + ay - ac$$

with the form that Descartes used:

$$yy \propto cy - \frac{cx}{b}y + ay - ac$$

Computer Key-In

The program given below will compute the wages of employees when their hourly rates and the numbers of hours they worked are given.

Lines 70–130 form a FOR-NEXT loop. This kind of loop can be used when we know how many times we want to have a sequence of steps repeated. The steps between line 70 and line 130 will be repeated T times.

Line 80 will print only one question mark, but 3 values (for N, R, H) separated by commas must be INPUT.

In line 100, the symbol <= means "less than or equal to." Line 110 will compute "overtime" pay—at time and a half for any time over 40 hours.

In line 120, the comma will cause the items to be spaced out across the line. In this case, the "first column" is blank.

```
10  PRINT "HOW MANY EMPLOYEES";
20  INPUT T
30  PRINT "FOR EACH EMPLOYEE:"
40  PRINT "INPUT EMPLOYEE ID NO.,";
50  PRINT " PAY/HOUR,"
60  PRINT "       NO. OF HOURS:"
70  FOR I=1 TO T
80  INPUT N,R,H
90  LET W=R*H
100  IF H <= 40 THEN 120
110  LET W=W+.5*R*(H-40)
120  PRINT " ","WAGES  = ";W
130  NEXT I
140  END
```

(If possible, save this program for use in the next computer section.)

Exercises

1. Write out in words what happens in line 110. The extra overtime pay is added to the regular wages.
2. RUN the program for three employees:

ID NO.	WAGES PER HOUR	HOURS	wages
1234	11.50	37	\$425.50
3412	10	40	\$400
4321	12	42	\$516

3. RUN the program for these employees.

ID NO.	WAGES PER HOUR	HOURS	wages
7890	9.75	38.5	\$375.38
9870	11.25	41.75	\$479.54
7809	10.85	40.25	\$438.07

Computer Key-In Commentary

The Appendix on page 653 gives more information about FOR...NEXT loops. Here, if T is given the value of 3, then I "counts" from 1 to 3, so that lines 80–120 are executed three times.

In line 120, the comma causes output to be printed in columns. The amount of space between the beginning of the columns varies slightly from machine to machine.

Teaching Suggestions p. T86

Chalkboard Examples

Use the given information to complete each chart.

1. Frank is 4 years older than Kim.

	Age now	Age in 2 years
Kim	k	$k + 2$
Frank	$k + 4$	$(k + 4) + 2$, or $k + 6$

2. A rectangle is 5 cm longer than it is wide. A second rectangle is half as wide and twice as long as the first.

	Length	Width
First rectangle	$w + 5$	w
Second rectangle	$2(w + 5)$	$\frac{1}{2}w$

3. Complete the chart and solve the following problem: Margo is three times as old as her nephew. In eleven years she will be only twice as old. Find the age of each now.

	Age now	Age in 11 years
Margo	$3x$	$3x + 11$
Nephew	x	$x + 11$

Step 3 $3x + 11 = 2(x + 11)$

Step 4 $x = 11$; $3x = 33$

$\therefore$ Margo is 33 and her nephew is 11.

Extending Your Problem Solving Skills

3-6 Using Charts in Solving Problems

Objective To arrange the facts of a problem in a chart.

Using a chart to organize the facts of a problem can be a helpful strategy in solving the problem. Charts are especially useful in solving problems about ages.

Example Lisa is one third as old as her father. Next year their ages in years will total 50. How old is each now?

Solution

Step 1 The problem asks for the ages of Lisa and her father.

Step 2 Let x = Lisa's age in years now.
Then $3x$ = father's age in years now.
Make a chart of the given facts.

	Age now	Age next year
Lisa	x	$x + 1$
Father	$3x$	$3x + 1$

Step 3 The only fact not recorded in the chart is that next year their ages will total 50. Use this fact to write an equation.

$$(x + 1) + (3x + 1) = 50$$

Step 4

$$(x + 1) + (3x + 1) = 50$$
$$4x + 2 = 50$$
$$4x = 48$$
$$x = 12$$
$$3x = 36$$

Step 5 Will the sum of Lisa's age next year and her father's age next year total 50?

$$(12 + 1) + (36 + 1) \stackrel{?}{=} 50$$
$$13 + 37 \stackrel{?}{=} 50$$
$$50 = 50 \quad \checkmark$$

$\therefore$ Lisa is 12 years old now and her father is 36 years old now. ***Answer***

Oral Exercises

Use the given information to complete each chart.

1. Dana is 2 years younger than Gary.

	Age now	Age next year
Gary	x	? $x + 1$
Dana	? $x - 2$	? $x - 1$

2. Mark is half as old as Sue.

	Age now	Age 3 years ago
Sue	x	? $x - 3$
Mark	? $\frac{1}{2}x$	? $\frac{1}{2}x - 3$

3. Tim was twice as old as Tom last year.

	Age last year	Age now
Tom	y	? $y + 1$
Tim	? $2y$	? $2y + 1$

4. A mat is 4 cm longer than it is wide. A second mat is 1 cm wider and 2 cm longer than the first.

	Length	Width
First mat	? $z + 4$	z
Second mat	? $z + 6$	? $z + 1$

5. In a game played with white, blue, and red chips, one player had twice as many blue chips as white ones and 3 more red ones than blue ones. Each chip has the point value shown in the chart.

	Number	Point value of each chip	Total value of all chips of this kind
White	w	1	w
Blue	? $2w$	2	? $4w$
Red	? $2w + 3$	5	? $10w + 15$

6. The ages in years of three sisters are consecutive odd integers.

	Age now	Age last year	Age 10 years from now
The youngest sister	? $m - 2$	? $m - 3$	? $m + 8$
The middle sister	m	? $m - 1$	? $m + 10$
The oldest sister	? $m + 2$	? $m + 1$	? $m + 12$

Supplementary Materials

Practice Master 13
Test 9
Resource Book, pp. 161-162

Suggested Assignments

Minimum
Day 1: 120/*P*: 1–7
R 116/*Self-Test 2*
Day 2: 120/*P*: 8–12
123/*P*: 1–5
Day 2 finishes Sec. 3-6 and starts Sec. 3-7.

Average
Day 1: 120/*P*: 1–3, 7, 9–11
S 114/34–37
Day 2: 120/*P*: 12, 14–17, 19
123/*P*: 2, 4, 5
Day 2 finishes Sec. 3-6 and starts Sec. 3-7.

Maximum
Day 1: 120/*P*: 3, 7, 9–13
S 115/*P*: 19, 20
Day 2: 120/*P*: 15–20
123/*P*: 2, 4–6
Day 2 finishes Sec. 3-6 and starts Sec. 3–7.

Additional A Exercises

1. Liza is 4 years older than John. Two years ago, their ages totaled 16. How old is each now? John is 8; Liza is 12.
2. Kathleen is 30 years younger than her mother. In four years she will be $\frac{1}{4}$ of her mother's age. How old is each now? Kathleen is 6; her mother is 36.
3. Jack is 5 times as old as his 7-year-old daughter. How long will it be before he is twice as old as she? 21 y
4. The length of a rectangle is 5 cm longer than the width. A second rectangle, 10 cm wider and 15 cm longer than the first, has perimeter 132 cm. What are the dimensions of the smaller rectangle? 18 cm by 23 cm
5. A school librarian spent twice as much money on books as she did on records. However, her total expenditures were only $\frac{1}{3}$ of the money in her budget for the month, which was $189. How much money did she spend on books? $42

Additional Answers Problems

7. First: 9 cm by 24 cm; second: 14 cm by 22 cm
8. First: base 36 cm, each leg 24 cm; second: base 21 cm, each leg 32 cm

Problems

A

1. Toby is 3 years older than Sarah. Last year their ages totaled 37. How old is each now? Sarah, 18; Toby, 21
2. Luisa is 5 years younger than José. Next year their ages will total 53. How old is each now? José, 28; Luisa, 23
3. Bob is 24 years younger than his father. In 2 years he will be half as old as his father. How old is each now? Bob, 22; Father, 46
4. Karl is seven times as old as Jane, but in six years he will be only three times as old. Find the age of each now. Jane, 3; Karl, 21
5. Tom is 8 and his mother is 31. How long will it be before she is twice as old as he? 15 years
6. Bill Phipps is six times as old as his five-year-old niece. How long will it be before he is twice as old as she? 20 years
7. The length of a rectangle is 15 cm more than the width. A second rectangle whose perimeter is 72 cm is 5 cm wider but 2 cm shorter than the first rectangle. What are the dimensions of each rectangle?
8. The base of an isosceles triangle is 12 cm longer than each of its equal legs. A second isosceles triangle whose perimeter is 85 cm has a base that is 15 cm shorter than the base of the first triangle. Each of the equal legs of the second triangle is 8 cm longer than each leg of the first. How long are the three sides of each triangle?
9. Zelda Carter weighs 55 lb less than her husband. Their combined weight is 215 lb more than that of their daughter, who weighs half as much as her father. How much does Zelda Carter weigh? 125 lb
10. Fran Massey earns three times as much as an actuary than she does as a writer. Her total income is $40,000 more than that of her brother, who earns only half as much as Fran does as an actuary. What is Fran's salary as an actuary? $48,000

B

11. Jack's age next year will be twice Jill's age last year. Their present ages total 45. How old is each now? Jack, 29; Jill, 16
12. Al is $\frac{3}{4}$ as old as Ann. Six years ago Al was $\frac{1}{2}$ as old as Ann. How old is each now? Ann, 12; Al, 9
13. Susan is six years older than Ralph and Ralph is twice as old as Neil. Next year Susan's age will total the ages of Ralph and Neil. How old is each now? Neil, 5; Ralph, 10; Susan, 16
14. Ruby is 6 years younger than Carlo, and the average of their ages is twice Ruby's age 5 years ago. How old are they? Carlo, 19; Ruby, 13
15. George Washington was born eleven years before Thomas Jefferson. In 1770 Washington's age was three years more than seven times the age of Jefferson in 1748. How old was each man in 1750? Washington, 18; Jefferson, 7

16. In one match Marcia scored three times as many points as Dina. In the next match, Marcia scored 7 fewer points than she did in the first match, while Dina earned 9 more than she did in the first match. If they tied in the second match, what were their scores in the first match? Dina, 8; Marcia, 24

17. Suppose that 9 servings of juice cost the same as 5 fruit cups. Suppose, also, that one fruit cup costs 50 cents more than one bowl of soup, while one bowl of soup costs 50 cents more than one serving of juice. What would be the cost of each item: serving of juice, fruit cup, bowl of soup?

18. The upper falls of Angel Falls, the highest waterfall on Earth, are 750 m higher than Niagara Falls. If each of the falls were 7 m lower, the upper Angel Falls would be sixteen times as high as Niagara Falls. How high is the upper Angel Falls? Niagara Falls?

19. One serving $\left(\frac{1}{2}\text{ cup}\right)$ of cooked green peas contains 45 more calories than 1 serving of cooked carrots and 50 more calories than 1 serving of cooked green beans. If 1 serving of cooked carrots and 3 servings of cooked green beans contain the same number of calories as 1 serving of cooked green peas, how many calories are there in 1 serving of cooked green peas? 65 calories

C **20.** Ann is 6 years older than Mary. She is also twice as old as Mary was when Ann was as old as Mary is now. How old is each now? Ann, 24; Mary, 18

21. Two years ago, Paul was 7 times as old as Matt was. Two years from now, Paul will be 5 times as old as Matt will be. Find the present age of each. Matt, 10; Paul, 58

22. For six consecutive years, a man's age was a multiple of his granddaughter's age. How old was each during the sixth year? Man, 66; granddaughter, 6
Note: Ex. 22 is particularly challenging. It can be solved by determining ranges within which the grandfather's age can fall and then using trial and error. See *Solution Key*, page 61.

Challenge

Ross Clevons received a license plate for his new car. He noted that all five digits were different and that if the plate was upside down his registration number would be increased by 7920. What was the number on the license plate? 90186 or 60189

Additional Answers
Problems

17. Juice, \$1.25; soup, \$1.75; fruit cup, \$2.25
18. Angel Falls, 807 m; Niagara Falls, 57 m

Mixed Review Exercises

1. John's income is m dollars. Phillip's is \$1000 less than twice John's. Represent Phillip's income in terms of m. $2m - 1000$
2. Write an equation to represent "The sum of the number n and 2 is multiplied by the reciprocal of $\frac{4}{3}$, giving an answer of 12." $\frac{3}{4}(n + 2) = 12$
3. Evaluate $\frac{2a + 3b}{4c}$ if $a = -5$, $b = -2$, and $c = 4$. -1
4. Solve: $15n + 96 = 3n$ -8

Teaching Suggestions p. T86

Chalkboard Examples

1. What is the total value in cents of 8 dimes and 11 quarters?
$8(10) + 11(25) = 80 + 275 = 355$; 355 cents
2. If 8 cans of juice cost \$7.60, what is the cost per can? $\frac{7.60}{8} = 0.95$; 95 cents
3. How much would you earn working for 15 h at \$7.50 per hour?
$15 \times 7.50 = 112.50$; \$112.50
4. Complete the chart and solve the following problem. Sarah and Bob went to a book sale, where each book cost 35 cents. If together they spent \$4.55, and Sarah bought 5 more books than Bob, how many books did each buy?

	No.	× Price =	Total price
Sarah	$x + 5$	35	$35(x + 5)$
Bob	x	35	$35x$

$$35(x + 5) + 35x = 455$$
$$x = 4$$
$$x + 5 = 9$$
∴ Bob bought 4 books and Sarah bought 9 books.

3-7 Cost and Value Problems

Objective To solve some problems involving cost and value.

The word problems in this section all involve cost, wages, and value, usually in terms of money. Organizing the given facts in a chart will help you to solve such word problems.

The following formulas will be useful in setting up your charts.

Number × price = cost
Hours worked × wage per hour = income
Number of items × value per item = total value

Example Roger paid 50 cents each for several programs for the football game. He sold all but 15 of them for \$1 each, making a profit of \$22.50. How many programs did he buy?

Solution

Step 1 The problem asks for the number of programs Roger bought.

Step 2 Let x = number of programs Roger bought.
Then $x - 15$ = number of programs Roger sold.
Make a chart.

	Number	Unit Price	Cost = Number × Unit Price
Bought	x	50	$50x$
Sold	$x - 15$	100	$100(x - 15)$

Step 3 The only fact not recorded in the chart is the \$22.50 profit. Use this fact to write an equation. (Since the prices are in cents, write the profit as 2250 cents.)

Profit = Selling Cost − Buying Cost
$2250 = 100(x - 15) - 50x$

Step 4
$2250 = 100x - 1500 - 50x$
$2250 = 50x - 1500$
$3750 = 50x$
$75 = x;\ x - 15 = 60$

Step 5 *Check:* 75 programs at 50 cents each cost Roger 3750 cents.
60 programs at 100 cents each brought in 6000 cents.
Profit $= 6000 - 3750 \stackrel{?}{=} 2250$
$2250 = 2250$ ✓

∴ Roger bought 75 programs. ***Answer***

Problems

Copy and complete each chart and then solve each problem.

A 1. Lex spent \$8.40 for several pencils costing 20 cents each and some notebooks costing \$1.20 each. He bought 7 more pencils than notebooks. How many notebooks did he buy? 5

	Number ×	Price =	Cost	
Pencils	? $x + 7$	? 20	?	$20(x + 7)$
Notebooks	x	? 120	?	$120x$

2. Fritz makes \$4 an hour working after school and \$5 an hour working on Saturdays. Last week he made \$52.50 working a total of 12 hours. How many hours did he work on Saturday? 4.5 h

	Hours worked ×	Wage per hour =	Income	
Saturdays	s	? 5	? $5s$	
Weekdays	? $12 - s$	? 4	?	$4(12 - s)$

3. Della has some nickels, dimes, and quarters worth \$6.10. She has twice as many dimes as quarters and 50 coins in all. How many of each kind of coin has she? 12 quarters, 24 dimes, and 14 nickels

	Number ×	Value of coin =	Total value	
Nickels	? $50 - 3q$	? 5	?	$5(50 - 3q)$
Dimes	? $2q$	? 10	? $10(2q)$	
Quarters	q	? 25	? $25q$	

4. Ruth purchases some one-cent stamps, some fifteen-cent stamps, and some twenty-cent stamps for \$5. There are three times as many one-cent stamps as twenty-cent stamps, and 8 fewer twenty-cent stamps than fifteen-cent stamps. How many stamps in all does she buy? 58

	Number ×	Value of stamp =	Total value	
One-cent	? $3t$	? 1	? $3t$	
Fifteen-cent	? $t + 8$	? 15	?	$15(t + 8)$
Twenty-cent	t	? 20	? $20t$	

Common Error

Often students do not represent quantities such as the hours worked weekdays in Problem 2 correctly. Instead of representing the hours worked weekdays by $12 - s$, they use $s - 12$. Point out that this is not reasonable since the total, 12 h, must be larger than the number of hours worked weekdays or Saturdays; the expression $s - 12$ would represent a negative number of hours.

Supplementary Material

Resource Book, pp. 163–164

Suggested Assignments

Minimum
124/*P*: 6–10
R 131/*Self-Test 3*, 1–3
Day 2 of Sec. 3-6 finishes Sec. 3-6 and starts Sec. 3-7.

Average
123/*P*: 3, 6, 7, 9, 11, 12, 15
S 105/49–50
Day 2 of Sec. 3-6 finishes Sec. 3-6 and starts Sec. 3-7.

Maximum
124/*P*: 9, 11, 12, 15, 16
S 121/*P*: 21, 22
Day 2 of Sec. 3-6 finishes Sec. 3-6 and starts Sec. 3-7.

Additional A Exercises

Copy and complete each chart and then solve each problem.

1. Homeroom 131 ordered some small and some medium pizzas for a party. The small ones cost \$3.75 each and the medium ones cost \$5 each, and they bought 3 more medium than small. Their bill came to \$32.50. How many pizzas of each size did they order?

	No.	× Price =	Cost
Small	x	? 3.75	? $3.75x$
Medium	? $x + 3$	? 5.00	? $5x + 15$

2 small, 5 medium

2. John works at a gas station 3 nights a week, making \$3.50/h and at a supermarket on Saturdays, making \$4/h. Last week he worked 14 h and earned \$51. How many hours did he work at the gas station? 10 h

	Wage ×	No. hrs =	Salary
Gas station	? 3.50	x	$3.5x$
Supermarket	? 4.00	? $14 - x$	$56 - 4x$

3. Michelle has \$6.82 in change. The number of pennies, dimes, nickels and quarters are, in that order, consecutive even integers. How many coins does she have? 60 coins

	No.	× Value =	Total value
Pennies	x	? .01	? $.01x$
Dimes	? $x + 2$	? .10	? $.1x + .2$
Nickels	? $x + 4$	? .05	? $.05x + .2$
Quarters	? $x + 6$	? .25	? $.25x + 1.5$

5. Each of the 24 members of the Boosters' Club bought either a pennant or a cap at the football game. The pennants were \$1.25 each and the caps were \$1.50 each. If the total bill was \$34, how many people bought pennants? 8 people

6. Adult tickets for the senior class play were \$4 each and student tickets were \$2. A total of 1250 tickets worth \$3400 were sold. How many student tickets were sold? 800

7. A plumber makes \$4.50 per hour more than an apprentice. During an 8 hour day, their earnings total \$284. How much does each make per hour? Apprentice, \$15.50; plumber, \$20

8. Sixty-five members of the Medical Society attended the annual dinner of the society. An equal number of nonmembers also attended. Tickets for nonmembers cost \$10 more than for members. If ticket sales totaled \$4095, how much did each ticket cost? Members, \$26.50; nonmembers, \$36.50

B 9. I have 40 coins, all dimes, nickels, and quarters, worth \$4.05. I have 7 more nickels than dimes. How many quarters do I have? 7 quarters

10. Lizzie bought several apples at 20 cents each, ate two of them, and sold the rest for 30 cents each. She made a profit of \$2.20. How many did she buy? 28 apples

11. Mercedes had a total of 37 nickels, dimes, and quarters. She had 3 fewer dimes than nickels and 4 more quarters than nickels. How much money did she have? \$5.50

12. Gunnar bought 47 stamps. He bought 5 more ten-cent stamps than fifteen-cent stamps and 6 fewer twenty-cent stamps than fifteen-cent stamps. How much did he pay for the stamps? \$6.50

13. Roger claims: "I have \$20 in quarters, half-dollars, and one-dollar bills. I have twice as many quarters as half-dollars, and half as many one-dollar bills as half-dollars." Explain why Roger must be wrong.

14. Can 46 pennies and nickels have a total value of a dollar? Justify your answer.

15. In a collection of coins worth \$9.13, there are twice as many dimes as quarters, four more nickels than dimes, and twice as many pennies as nickels. How many of each kind of coin are in the collection? 15 quarters, 30 dimes, 34 nickels, and 68 pennies

C 16. Nadia has seven more nickels than Dean has dimes. If Dean gives Nadia four of his dimes, then Dean will have the same value of money as Nadia. How much money do they have together? (Assume that Nadia has only nickels and Dean has only dimes.) \$3.80

17. Ned has some nickels, Dick has some dimes, and Quincy has some quarters. Dick has five more dimes than Quincy has quarters. If Ned gives Dick a nickel, Dick gives Quincy a dime, and Quincy gives Ned a quarter, they will all have the same value of money. How many coins did each have originally? Ned, 13 nickels; Dick, 9 dimes; Quincy, 4 quarters

Computer Exercises

For students with some programming experience

Jane has a total of 25 coins, some of which are nickels and the rest, dimes.

1. Using a FOR . . . NEXT loop, write a BASIC program to display in chart form every possible combination of nickels and dimes. Have the program give the value of the coins in each case.
2. Modify the program in Exercise 1 so that Jane has a total of k coins, where the value of k is entered with an INPUT statement.

Biographical Note / *Maria Mitchell*

Maria Mitchell (1818–1889) was the first woman in the United States to be recognized for her work in astronomy. She was born on Nantucket, an island located off the southern coast of Massachusetts. As a child, Mitchell helped her father with astronomical calculations that he needed to rate the chronometers of whaling ships.

In 1836 Mitchell became the librarian of the Nantucket Atheneum. While there, she continued her studies in mathematics and astronomy and taught herself German.

In 1831 the king of Denmark had offered a gold medal to anyone who could discover a previously unknown comet. On October 1, 1847, while conducting telescopic observations, Mitchell discovered a new comet that was later named for her. She was awarded the medal and so gained worldwide recognition. The following year she became the first woman elected to the American Academy of Arts and Sciences. She was later elected to the American Association for the Advancement of Science.

In 1865 she became the first professor of astronomy and the director of the observatory at Vassar College. While at Vassar, she continued to study sunspots and solar eclipses and observed changes on the surfaces of the planets and their moons. In 1869 she was elected to the American Philosophical Society for her scientific achievements, the first woman accorded this honor. Mitchell was also a founder of the American Association for the Advancement of Women, serving as its president. In this office she worked for the recognition of the scientific abilities of women.

Solve.

4. The local youth club offered an aerobics class to the public. The cost was \$10 for members and \$15 for non-members. If 22 people took the class and the revenue was \$265, how many members took the class? 13 members

Additional Answers Problems ***(page 124)***

13. $50x + 50x + 50x = 2000$; $150x = 2000$; $x = 13\frac{1}{3}$. This is impossible because there cannot be a fractional number of coins.
14. No; $x + 5(46 - x) = 100$; $x + 230 - 5x = 100$; $4x = 130$; $x = 32\frac{1}{2}$. This is impossible because there cannot be a fractional number of coins.

Mixed Review Exercises

1. Write an equation to represent "The smaller of 2 consecutive integers is $\frac{1}{2}$ the larger." $n = \frac{1}{2}(n + 1)$

Simplify.

2. $|19| - |-21|$ -2
3. $20 \times 295 \times 5$ 29,500
4. $6(m - 3) - 2(2m + 4)$ $2m - 26$

Teaching Suggestions p. T87

Suggested Extensions p. T87

Chalkboard Examples

Write the missing reasons.
Prove: If $a + b = 0$, then $b = -a$.
Proof:

1. $a + b = 0$ Given
2. $-a + (a + b) = -a + 0$ Add. prop. of equality
3. $(-a + a) + b = -a + 0$ Assoc. ax. for addition
4. $0 + b = -a + 0$ Axiom of opposites
5. $b = -a$ Identity ax. for addition

Supplementary Materials

Practice Master 14
Test 10
Resource Book, p. 76

Suggested Assignments

Average
128/1, 2, 4, 5, 7
R 131/*Self-Test 3*

Maximum
128/1–11
R 131/*Self-Test 3*

3-8 Proving Statements

Objective To prove statements in algebra.

Many number properties and rules have been stated earlier in this book. Some of these are axioms, that is, statements *assumed* to be true. Others are theorems. A **theorem** is a statement that is *shown* to be true by using axioms, definitions, and other proved theorems in a logical development.

Logical reasoning using definitions, given facts, and axioms to show a theorem is true is called a **proof.** The following example shows how a theorem is proved in algebra.

Example 1 Prove: For all real numbers a and b, $(a + b) - b = a$.

Proof

STATEMENTS	REASONS
1. $(a + b) - b = (a + b) + (-b)$	1. Definition of subtraction
2. $(a + b) + (-b) = a + [b + (-b)]$	2. Associative axiom for addition
3. $b + (-b) = 0$	3. Axiom of opposites
4. $a + [b + (-b)] = a + 0$	4. Substitution principle
5. $a + 0 = a$	5. Identity axiom for addition
6. $(a + b) - b = a$	6. Transitive property of equality

Generally, a shortened form of proof is given, in which only the *key reasons* are stated. (The substitution principle and axioms of equality are usually not stated.)

The proof shown in the example above may be shortened to the four steps shown below.

STATEMENTS	REASONS
1. $(a + b) - b = (a + b) + (-b)$	1. Definition of subtraction
2. $= a + [b + (-b)]$	2. Associative axiom for addition
3. $= a + 0$	3. Axiom of opposites
4. $= a$	4. Identity axiom for addition

Example 2 Prove the property of the reciprocal of a product, given on page 77: For all real numbers a and b such that $a \neq 0$ and $b \neq 0$, $\frac{1}{ab} = \frac{1}{a} \cdot \frac{1}{b}$.

Proof Since $\frac{1}{ab}$ is the reciprocal of ab, we can prove that $\frac{1}{ab} = \frac{1}{a} \cdot \frac{1}{b}$ by showing that the product of ab and $\frac{1}{a} \cdot \frac{1}{b}$ is 1:

STATEMENTS	REASONS
1. $(ab)\left(\frac{1}{a}\cdot\frac{1}{b}\right) = \left(a\cdot\frac{1}{a}\right)\left(b\cdot\frac{1}{b}\right)$	1. Commutative and associative axioms for multiplication
2. $= 1 \cdot 1$	2. Axiom of reciprocals for multiplication
3. $= 1$	3. Identity axiom for multiplication

Once a theorem has been proved, it can be used as a reason in other proofs.

You may refer to the Chapter Summary on pages 84–85 for listings of axioms and theorems that you can use as reasons in your proofs in the following exercises.

Oral Exercises

State the missing reasons.

1. Prove the *addition property of equality:*
If $a = b$, then $a + c = b + c$. Also, $c + a = c + b$.

Proof:

1. $a + c = a + c$	1. ? Reflex. prop. of =
2. $a = b$	2. Given
3. $a + c = b + c$	3. ? Substitution prin.
4. $a + c = c + a$; $b + c = c + b$	4. ? Comm. ax. for add.
5. $c + a = c + b$	5. ? Substitution prin.

2. Prove: If $a = b$, then $-a = -b$.

Proof:

1. $a = b$	1. Given
2. $-a$ and $-b$ are unique real numbers.	2. ? Closure prop.
3. $a + (-b) = b + (-b)$	3. Addition property of equality
4. $b + (-b) = 0$	4. ? Ax. of opposites
5. $a + (-b) = 0$	5. ? Substitution prin.
6. $-a + [a + (-b)] = -a + 0$	6. ? Add. prop. of =
7. $(-a + a) + (-b) = -a + 0$	7. ? Assoc. ax. for add.
8. $0 + (-b) = -a + 0$	8. ? Ax. of opposites
9. $-b = -a$	9. ? Identity ax. for add.
10. $-a = -b$	10. ? Sym. prop. of =

Additional A Exercises

Prove:
$-(a + b) = (-a) + (-b)$
Proof:
Since $-(a + b)$ is the opposite of $a + b$, you can prove that $-(a + b) = (-a) + (-b)$ by showing that $a + b + [(-a) + (-b)] = 0$.

1. $a + b + [(-a) + (-b)] = [a + (-a)] + [b + (-b)]$
Assoc. and comm. axs. for add.

2. $= 0 + 0$
Axiom of opposites

3. $= 0$
Identity axiom for add.

Mixed Review Exercises

Simplify.

1. $(-3)(-27)(5)$ 405

2. $-25mn \div \left(-\frac{1}{7}\right)$
$175mn$

3. A rectangle has sides which can be represented by consecutive even integers. If the perimeter is 76, what are the lengths of the sides? 18 and 20

4. Madeleine is 7 years older than Michelle. Eight years ago, she was twice as old as Michelle. How old is Madeleine now? 22

Additional Answers
Written Exercises

7. Proof:

   1. $a \neq 0$ (Given)
   2. $\frac{a}{a} = a \cdot \frac{1}{a}$ (Def. of division)
   3. $= 1$ (Ax. of reciprocals)

8. Proof: Since $\frac{1}{\frac{a}{b}}$ is the reciprocal of $\frac{a}{b}$, you can prove that $\frac{1}{\frac{a}{b}} = \frac{b}{a}$ by showing that $\frac{b}{a}$ is the reciprocal of $\frac{a}{b}$; that is, $\frac{a}{b} \cdot \frac{b}{a} = 1$.

   1. $a \neq 0, b \neq 0$ (Given)
   2. $\frac{a}{b} \cdot \frac{b}{a} = \left(a \cdot \frac{1}{b}\right)\left(b \cdot \frac{1}{a}\right)$ (Def. of division)
   3. $= \left(a \cdot \frac{1}{a}\right)\left(b \cdot \frac{1}{b}\right)$ (Assoc. and comm. axs. for mult.)
   4. $= (1)(1)$ (Ax. of reciprocals)
   5. $= 1$ (Ident. ax. for mult.)

9. Proof:

   1. $a = b, c \neq 0$ (Given)
   2. $a \cdot \frac{1}{c} = b \cdot \frac{1}{c}$ (Mult. prop. of equal.)
   3. $\frac{a}{c} = \frac{b}{c}$ (Def. of division)

Written Exercises

Write the missing reasons in Exercises 1-6. Assume that each variable represents any real number, except as noted.

A

1. a. Prove: If $b \neq 0$, then $\frac{1}{b}(ba) = a$.

Proof: 1. $\frac{1}{b}(ba) = \left(\frac{1}{b} \cdot b\right)a$ — 1. ? Associative axiom for mult.

2. $= 1 \cdot a$ — 2. ? Axiom of reciprocals

3. $= a$ — 3. ? Identity axiom for mult.

b. From step 3 prove that $(ab)\frac{1}{b} = a$.

Proof: 3. $\frac{1}{b}(ba) = a$ — (above)

4. $(ba)\frac{1}{b} = a$ — 4. ? Commutative axiom for mult.

5. $(ab)\frac{1}{b} = a$ — 5. ? Commutative axiom for mult.

$\therefore$ if $b \neq 0$, $\frac{1}{b}(ba) = a$ and $(ab)\frac{1}{b} = a$.

2. Prove the *multiplication property of equality:*

If $a = b$, then $ca = cb$ and $ac = bc$.

Proof: 1. $ca = ca$ — 1. ? Reflexive prop. of =

2. $a = b$ — 2. Given

3. $ca = cb$ — 3. ? Substitution prin.

4. $ca = ac$; $cb = bc$ — 4. ? Commutative axiom for mult.

5. $ac = bc$ — 5. ? Transitive prop. of =

3. Prove: If $a + c = b + c$, then $a = b$.

Proof: 1. $a + c = b + c$ — 1. Given

2. $(a + c) + (-c) = (b + c) + (-c)$ — 2. ? Addition property of =

3. $(a + c) - c = (b + c) - c$ — 3. ? Def. of subtraction

4. $a = b$ — 4. ? Assoc. axiom; axiom of opposites

4. Prove: If $ac = bc$ and $c \neq 0$, then $a = b$.

Proof: 1. $ac = bc$ — 1. Given

2. $(ac) \cdot \frac{1}{c} = (bc) \cdot \frac{1}{c}$ — 2. ? Mult. property of =

3. $a = b$ — 3. ? Assoc. axiom; axiom of reciprocals

B

5. Prove: $-(-a - b) = a + b$

Proof: 1. $-(-a - b) = -[-a + (-b)]$ — 1. ? Def. of subtraction

2. $= -(-a) + [-(-b)]$ — 2. ? Distributive axiom

3. $= a + b$ — 3. ? Mult. prop. of -1

6. Prove: $-(a - b) = b - a$.

Proof: 1. $-(a - b) = -[a + (-b)]$ 1. __?__ Def. of subtraction
2. $= -a + [-(-b)]$ 2. __?__ Distributive ax.
3. $= -a + b$ 3. __?__ Mult. prop. of -1
4. $= b + (-a)$ 4. __?__ Comm. ax
5. $= b - a$ 5. __?__ Def. of subtraction

Write proofs, including statements and reasons, for Exercises 7-12.

7. Prove: If a is any nonzero real number, then $\frac{a}{a} = 1$.

8. Prove: If $a \neq 0$ and $b \neq 0$, then $\frac{1}{\frac{a}{b}} = \frac{b}{a}$. $\left(\text{Hint: Show that } \frac{a}{b} \cdot \frac{b}{a} = 1.\right)$

9. Prove: If $a = b$ and $c \neq 0$, then $\frac{a}{c} = \frac{b}{c}$.

10. Prove: If $c \neq 0$ and $\frac{a}{c} = \frac{b}{c}$, then $a = b$.

C 11. Prove: If $a \neq 0$ and $b \neq 0$, then $\frac{a+b}{ab} = \frac{1}{a} + \frac{1}{b}$.

12. Prove: $a + b + [(-a) + (-b)] = 0$

Application / Consumer Credit

A car is one of the most important and expensive purchases a person may make. Many people do not have the money to pay for a car with cash. Instead, they pay a percentage of the cash price as a down payment and borrow the rest. The car buyer must pay the lender the amount of money borrowed (principal) plus interest. Often the buyer chooses to pay the lender over a period of two, three, or four years. The lender calculates the amount the buyer will owe in interest and then adds it to the principal. By dividing this total by the number of months, the amount of each monthly payment can be calculated.

Suppose you want to purchase a car. You see an advertisement in the newspaper such as the following:

ONLY $3600 USED CAR

⋮

just $630 down and small monthly payments of $95 each month for 36 months.

How do you determine the total amount you must pay for the car and the amount of interest you are being charged?

10. Proof:

1. $c \neq 0$, $\frac{a}{c} = \frac{b}{c}$ (Given)
2. $a \cdot \frac{1}{c} = b \cdot \frac{1}{c}$ (Def. of division)
3. $\left(a \cdot \frac{1}{c}\right) \cdot c = \left(b \cdot \frac{1}{c}\right) \cdot c$ (Mult. prop. of equal.)
4. $a \cdot \left(\frac{1}{c} \cdot c\right) = b \cdot \left(\frac{1}{c} \cdot c\right)$ (Assoc. ax. for mult.)
5. $a \cdot 1 = b \cdot 1$ (Ax. of reciprocals)
6. $a = b$ (Ident. ax. for mult.)

11. Proof:

1. $a \neq 0$, $b \neq 0$ (Given)
2. $\frac{a+b}{ab} = (a + b) \cdot \frac{1}{ab}$ (Def. of division)
3. $= a \cdot \frac{1}{ab} + b \cdot \frac{1}{ab}$ (Distributive axiom)
4. $= a \cdot \left(\frac{1}{a} \cdot \frac{1}{b}\right) + b \cdot \left(\frac{1}{a} \cdot \frac{1}{b}\right)$ (Prop. of the recip. of a product)
5. $= \left(a \cdot \frac{1}{a}\right) \cdot \frac{1}{b} + \left(b \cdot \frac{1}{b}\right) \cdot \frac{1}{a}$ (Comm. and assoc. axs. for mult.)
6. $= 1 \cdot \frac{1}{b} + 1 \cdot \frac{1}{a}$ (Ax. of reciprocals)

(continued)

Additional Answers Written Exercises (continued)

7. $= \frac{1}{b} + \frac{1}{a}$
(Ident. ax. for mult.)

8. $= \frac{1}{a} + \frac{1}{b}$
(Comm. ax. for add.)

12. Proof:
$a + b + [(-a) + (-b)]$
$= a + [b + (-a)] + (-b)$
(Assoc. ax. for add.)
$= a + [(-a) + b] + (-b)$
(Comm. ax. for add.)
$= [a + (-a)] + [b + (-b)]$
(Assoc. ax. for add.)
$= 0 + 0$
(Ax. of opposites)
$= 0$
(Identity ax. for add.)

Example 1 For the car on the previous page, find the total amount of the down payment and the monthly payments. Calculate the amount of interest.

Solution The total amount is the sum of the down payment ($630) and the monthly payments ($36 \times \$95 = \$3420$). Thus, the total amount is $4050. Subtracting the $3600 cash price from $4050 gives the amount of interest, $450.

Many stores, such as department stores, allow customers to purchase items on credit, that is, to "charge" them. If an item is not paid for within a specified period (often a month), the customer must pay a *finance charge* (interest) in addition to the purchase price. There are several common methods for calculating finance charges. One of the simpler methods is to take a fixed percent of the total amount that a customer owes at the end of a monthly billing period. This amount is called the *unpaid balance*.

Example 2 The previous balance of a customer's charge account is $56.32. If a payment of $10 is made, what will be the finance charge owed if the interest rate is $1\frac{1}{2}\%$ per month?

Solution The balance after the payment is $46.32. At $1\frac{1}{2}\%$ interest, there is a finance charge of $0.015 \times 46.32 = \$.69$.

Exercises

1. The previous balance of a charge account is $185. If a payment of $25 is made, what will be the finance charge if the interest rate is $1\frac{1}{2}\%$ per month? $2.40
2. If a payment of $45 is made on a charge account with a balance of $125, what will be the finance charge owed if the interest rate is 1.65%? $1.32
3. A charge account has charges totaling $60.40. If a payment of $15 is made, what finance charge will be added if the rate of interest is $1\frac{1}{2}\%$? $.68
4. If a payment of $30 is made on the account in Exercise 3, what is the finance charge? $.46

Find the total amount paid on each of the cars below. Then find the amount of interest the buyer would be paying.

5. $3420; $420

ONLY $3000 USED CAR

⋮

just $600 down and $117.50 per month over the next two years.

6. $5940; $594

ONLY $5346 USED CAR

⋮

just $540 down and $150 per month for the next 36 months.

Self-Test 3

Vocabulary theorem (p. 126) proof (p. 126)

1. Kay is 5 years younger than Sid. Make a chart showing their ages now, 2 years ago, and 3 years from now. **Obj. 3-6, p. 118**

2. At the beginning of the year, Marcia had 3 times as much money in her savings account as Dora. During the year Dora saved \$1400 more, while Marcia increased her savings by \$860. At the end of the year, Marcia had twice as much money in her account as Dora. Not including interest earned during the year, how much was in each account at the end of the year? Marcia, \$6680; Dora, \$3340

3. Will has 4 times as many dimes as quarters and twice as many nickels as dimes. In all he has \$25.20. How many dimes has he? 96 **Obj. 3-7, p. 122**

4. Write the missing reasons. **Obj. 3-8, p. 126**

1.	$-a + (a + b) = (-a + a) + b$	1. ? Associative ax. for add.
2.	$= 0 + b$	2. ? Ax. of opposites
3.	$= b$	3. ? Identity ax. for add.

Check your answers with those at the back of the book.

Chapter Summary

1. The addition, subtraction, multiplication, and division properties of equality guarantee that:
   a. Adding the same real number to, or subtracting the same real number from, equal numbers gives equal results.
   b. Multiplying or dividing equal numbers by the same nonzero number gives equal results.
2. Transforming an equation by substitution, or by addition or subtraction, or by multiplication or division (not by zero) produces an equivalent equation. These transformations are used in solving equations.
3. Inverse operations are used in solving equations.
4. Equations can be used to solve word problems. Organizing the facts of a word problem in a chart is often helpful. Charts can be used to solve problems about ages, costs, and values.
5. The structure of algebra is built up of axioms and definitions and of theorems proved by using the axioms and definitions in a logical development.

Additional Answer Self-Test 3

1.

	Age now	Age 2 y ago	Age 3 y from now
Kay	$x - 5$	$x - 7$	$x - 2$
Sid	x	$x - 2$	$x + 3$

Quick Quiz

1. Marty is 3 years older than Kay. Make a chart showing their ages now, last year, and 4 years from now.

	Age now	Age last year	Age in 4 years
Marty	$x + 3$	$x + 2$	$x + 7$
Kay	x	$x - 1$	$x + 4$

2. Paula began the year with 4 times as many stamps in her collection as Jim. During the year Paula added 30 stamps, while Jim added 16. At the end of the year Paula had 3 times as many stamps as Jim. How many stamps did each have at the end of the year? Paula had 102 stamps and Jim had 34 stamps.

3. Kate has saved \$21.60 in coins. She has twice as many quarters as dimes, and 3 times as many nickels as quarters. How many nickels has she? Kate has 144 nickels.

(continued)

Quick Quiz (continued)

4. Write the missing reasons.
   a. $-b + (a + b) = (a + b) + (-b)$
      Comm. prop. for add.
   b. $= a + [b + (-b)]$
      Assoc. prop. for add.
   c. $= a + 0$
      Axiom of opposites
   d. $= a$
      Identity ax. for add.

Chapter Review

Give the letter of the correct answer.

1. Solve $15 = 17 + x$. 3-1
   (a.) -2 b. -32 c. 32 d. 2
2. Solve $f - 17 = |6 - 25|$.
   a. 14 b. 2 c. 48 (d.) 36
3. Solve $\frac{1}{7}x = 3$. 3-2
   a. $2\frac{6}{7}$ b. $\frac{3}{7}$ (c.) 21 d. $3\frac{1}{7}$
4. Solve $-1 = 3k$.
   a. 4 b. 2 c. -3 (d.) $-\frac{1}{3}$
5. Solve $\frac{x}{3} - 3 = -3$. 3-3
   (a.) 0 b. -18 c. 18 d. 2
6. Solve $b - 3b = 24$.
   a. -8 (b.) -12 c. 12 d. -6
7. During an 8-hour day, a veterinarian spent twice as much time tending animals at her clinic as she did making house calls. If she spent one hour of the day eating lunch, how many hours did she spend making house calls? 3-4
   a. $3\frac{1}{2}$ hours b. $2\frac{2}{3}$ hours c. 2 hours (d.) $2\frac{1}{3}$ hours
8. Solve the equation $2m = 1 - m$. 3-5
   (a.) $\frac{1}{3}$ b. 2 c. 1 d. 3
9. Solve the equation $3w - 13 = \frac{1}{4}(52 - 12w)$.
   (a.) $4\frac{1}{3}$ b. -1 c. no solution d. identity
10. Courtney is four years older than Naomi. Fourteen years ago she was twice as old as Naomi. How old is Courtney now? 3-6
    a. 18 years old b. 16 years old (c.) 22 years old d. 20 years old
11. Chase worked a total of 10 hours last week. He was paid $4.50 an hour to do yardwork and $5.50 an hour to work at a local supermarket. If he earned a total of $51, how many hours did he spend doing yardwork? 3-7
    a. 6 hours (b.) 4 hours c. 9.6 hours d. 5 hours
12. Which of the following axioms should be given as the reason for the statement $a(bc) = a(cb)$? 3-8
    a. Distributive axiom b. Associative axiom for multiplication
    c. Axiom of opposites (d.) Commutative axiom for multiplication

Chapter Test

Alternate Test p. T12

Solve.

1. $a - 65 = -17$ 48 | 2. $-73 = 13 - h$ 86 | 3-1
3. $c + 51 = |-38|$ -13 | 4. $87 - k = -64$ 151

Solve.

5. $9 = \frac{c}{-18}$ -162 | 6. $-19v = -114$ 6 | 3-2
7. $-144 = 16e$ -9 | 8. $-\frac{1}{11}x = -99$ 1089

Solve.

9. $13z - 65z = 0$ 0 | 10. $110 = -7 + 9t$ 13 | 3-3
11. $\frac{3}{5}x + 90 = 0$ -150 | 12. $-\frac{7}{8}(w - 16) = 70$ -64

13. Erica's teacher gave 4.5 points for each question answered correctly on a test. Erica received 15 points for correctly answering a bonus question. If she received a score of 87 points on the test, how many questions, not including the bonus question, did Erica answer correctly? 16 | 3-4

13-17-18

Solve each equation. If the equation is an identity or if it has no root, state that fact.

14. $7(a - 6) = -3 + 6a$ 39 | 15. $6(m - 1) = 6(m + 3)$ No solution | 3-5

16. Twice a number increased by 51 is the same as the opposite of the number. Find the number. -17

17. Marlowe is half as old as Jean. Eight years from now he will be $\frac{3}{4}$ as old as Jean. How old is each now? Marlowe, 4; Jean, 8 | 3-6

18. After delivering her newspapers, Vanessa noticed that she had 5 fewer quarters than dimes. Her dimes and quarters totaled \$1.55. How many quarters did she have? 3 | 3-7

19. Write the missing reasons. | 3-8

	Statement	Reason
1.	$0 = 0 + 0$	1. ? Identity ax. for add.
2.	$a \cdot 0 = a(0 + 0)$	2. ? Mult. prop. of =
3.	$a \cdot 0 = a \cdot 0 + a \cdot 0$	3. ? Distributive ax.
4.	But $a \cdot 0 = a \cdot 0 + 0$	4. Identity axiom for addition
5.	$\therefore a \cdot 0 + a \cdot 0 = a \cdot 0 + 0$	5. ? Transitive prop. of =
6.	$a \cdot 0 = 0$	6. ? Subtraction prop. of =
7.	$0 \cdot a = 0$	7. ? Comm. ax. for mult.

Cumulative Review p. T22

Cumulative Review (Chapters 1–3)

Simplify.

1. $34 - 3(22 \div 2)$ 1
2. $\frac{56 \div 7}{16}$ $\frac{1}{2}$
3. $48 \div (9 + 3)$ 4
4. $|-21| - |-14|$ 7
5. $51 - [25 \div 5]$ 46
6. $48 \div 3 + 7(3)$ 37
7. $-55 - (-42 + 7)$ -20
8. $-22 + 31 + (-44) + 50$ 15
9. $5\frac{3}{5} - 2\frac{3}{4} + 14\frac{2}{5}$ $17\frac{1}{4}$
10. $-3.8 + 2.9 - 11.7$ -12.6
11. $9 + x - (5 - x) - 6$ $2x - 2$
12. $4(x + 3y) - 3(x - 4y)$
13. $-5(42)\left(-\frac{2}{5}\right)\left(-\frac{1}{3}\right)$ -28
14. $-5(-a - b) + 5(a + b)$ $10a + 10b$
15. $\frac{144xy}{6x}$, $x \neq 0$ $24y$

12. $x + 24y$

Evaluate each expression if $p = -3$, $q = 1$, $r = 0$, and $s = \frac{1}{2}$.

16. $r - |p - q|$ -4
17. $-\frac{p - q}{s}$ 8
18. $-3(p + q)$ 6
19. $\frac{-p + 2r - q}{r - 2s}$ -2

State the coordinate of the given point.

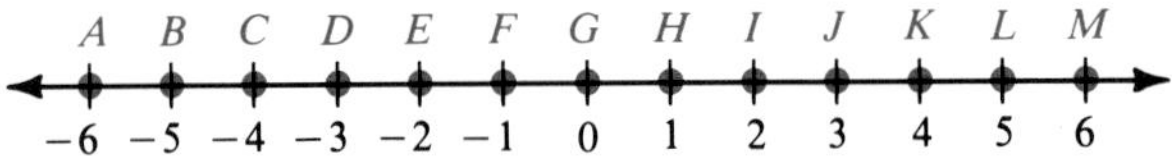

20. G 0
21. B -5
22. L 5
23. C -4
24. E -2
25. H 1

Solve. If the equation is an identity or has no solution, state that fact.

26. $|x| = 5$ $\{-5, 5\}$
27. $|y| + 5 = 3$ No solution
28. $x + 7 = 12$ 5
29. $z + 1 = -3$ -4
30. $t + 4 = |-11|$ 7
31. $(x - 3) + 17 = 30$ 16
32. $-\frac{a}{3} = 14$ -42
33. $9 = \frac{1}{2}q$ 18
34. $2a + 5 = -1$ -3
35. $\frac{1}{2}y - 3 = 9$ 24
36. $16 = \frac{3}{4}k + 1$ 20
37. $5(z - 3) = 40$ 11
38. $5y - 2 = 7y + 8$ -5
39. $9(2 - b) = b$ $\frac{9}{5}$
40. $6(3 - 4t) = -12\left(2t - \frac{3}{2}\right)$ Identity

Solve.

41. Grace is 3 years younger than $\frac{1}{4}$ of her father's age. The total of their ages is 42. How old is Grace's father? 36 years old
42. Find three consecutive integers whose sum is 72. 23, 24, and 25
43. Myron has 60 quarters and dimes. He has four times as many dimes as quarters. How much money does he have? \$7.80
44. Leslie has 20 quarters and dimes. If she had as many dimes as she has quarters and as many quarters as she has dimes, she would have 30 cents less. How many of each coin does she have? 11 quarters and 9 dimes

41-42-43-44

Maintaining Skills

Express each fraction as a mixed number.

Example 1 $\frac{35}{13}$ ***Solution*** $13\overline{)35}$ quotient 2; 26; remainder 9 $\frac{35}{13} = 2\frac{9}{13}$

1. $\frac{25}{12}$ $2\frac{1}{12}$
2. $\frac{45}{6}$ $7\frac{1}{2}$
3. $\frac{78}{15}$ $5\frac{1}{5}$
4. $\frac{86}{20}$ $4\frac{3}{10}$
5. $\frac{91}{12}$ $7\frac{7}{12}$
6. $\frac{83}{7}$ $11\frac{6}{7}$
7. $\frac{111}{12}$ $9\frac{1}{4}$
8. $\frac{115}{13}$ $8\frac{11}{13}$

Express each mixed number as a fraction.

Example 2 $5\frac{2}{5}$ ***Solution*** $5\frac{2}{5} = 5 + \frac{2}{5} = \frac{25}{5} + \frac{2}{5} = \frac{27}{5}$

9. $4\frac{1}{6}$ $\frac{25}{6}$
10. $8\frac{3}{5}$ $\frac{43}{5}$
11. $2\frac{7}{9}$ $\frac{25}{9}$
12. $12\frac{3}{4}$ $\frac{51}{4}$
13. $3\frac{8}{13}$ $\frac{47}{13}$
14. $17\frac{1}{3}$ $\frac{52}{3}$
15. $9\frac{11}{12}$ $\frac{119}{12}$
16. $10\frac{7}{8}$ $\frac{87}{8}$

Perform the indicated operations. Express the answers in simplest form.

Example 3 $8\frac{2}{3} + 7\frac{5}{6}$ ***Solution*** $8\frac{2}{3} + 7\frac{5}{6} = \frac{26}{3} + \frac{47}{6}$

$$= \frac{52}{6} + \frac{47}{6} = \frac{99}{6} = \frac{33}{2}, \text{ or } 16\frac{1}{2}$$

Example 4 $3\frac{1}{3} \div 7\frac{1}{2}$ ***Solution*** $3\frac{1}{3} \div 7\frac{1}{2} = \frac{10}{3} \div \frac{15}{2}$

$$= \frac{\overset{2}{\cancel{10}}}{3} \times \frac{2}{\underset{3}{\cancel{15}}} = \frac{4}{9}$$

17. $8\frac{7}{15} + 9\frac{11}{15}$ $18\frac{1}{5}$
18. $5\frac{7}{9} - 6\frac{4}{9}$ $-\frac{2}{3}$
19. $7\frac{1}{3} \times \left(-\frac{1}{7}\right)$ $-1\frac{1}{21}$
20. $4\frac{2}{5} \div 2\frac{1}{5}$
21. $10\frac{1}{5} \div 3\frac{2}{5}$ 3
22. $20\frac{5}{13} + 8\frac{4}{5}$ $29\frac{12}{65}$
23. $6\frac{5}{8} - 3\frac{2}{5}$ $3\frac{9}{40}$
24. $6\frac{3}{5} \div 2\frac{3}{4}$
25. $12\frac{9}{10} - 8\frac{3}{5}$ $4\frac{3}{10}$
26. $-9\frac{1}{2} + \left(-13\frac{2}{5}\right)$ $-22\frac{9}{10}$
27. $11\frac{4}{7} + 10\frac{1}{5}$ $21\frac{27}{35}$
28. $8\frac{5}{6} \div 6\frac{5}{8}$
29. $4\frac{10}{11} - 7\frac{1}{2}$ $-2\frac{13}{22}$
30. $12\frac{3}{20} \times 1\frac{5}{9}$ $18\frac{9}{10}$
31. $9\frac{5}{9} - 8\frac{1}{4}$ $1\frac{11}{36}$
32. $3\frac{9}{10} \times 7\frac{1}{13}$
33. $-5\frac{2}{3} \div 3\frac{1}{2}$ $-1\frac{13}{21}$
34. $5\frac{5}{9} \times 4\frac{1}{2}$ 25
35. $17\frac{3}{4} + 8\frac{1}{3}$ $26\frac{1}{12}$
36. $10\frac{5}{6} \times 3\frac{4}{5}$

Additional Answers Maintaining Skills

20. 2
24. $2\frac{2}{5}$
28. $1\frac{1}{3}$
32. $27\frac{3}{5}$
36. $41\frac{1}{6}$

Supplementary Materials

Practice Masters 15–17
Test 11
Resource Book, pp. 13–18, 77–78, 133–134, 149–150

Extra Practice

Skills, pp. 611–613
Problems, pp. 634–636

About the Photo

Houston, Texas, one of the largest cities in the United States, has gone through a period of rapid and sustained population growth since the discovery of oil in the early part of this century and the completion of its deepwater harbor in the 1920's. As might be expected, this rapid expansion has been accompanied by growing pains, such as traffic congestion.

City planners must cope with the problems that accompany population growth. To do so, they utilize population projections formulated by demographers, who use statistical measurements and mathematical methods to study such characteristics as the size, composition, distribution, and migration of a population. Although many subtle social and economic changes and unpredictable environmental factors can affect population growth, demographers can use equations such as $P_t = P_0b^t$, where P_t is the population at time t, P_0 is the original population, and b is the rate of increase or decrease (based on birth, mortality, and migration rates), to estimate a city's future population.

4 Polynomials

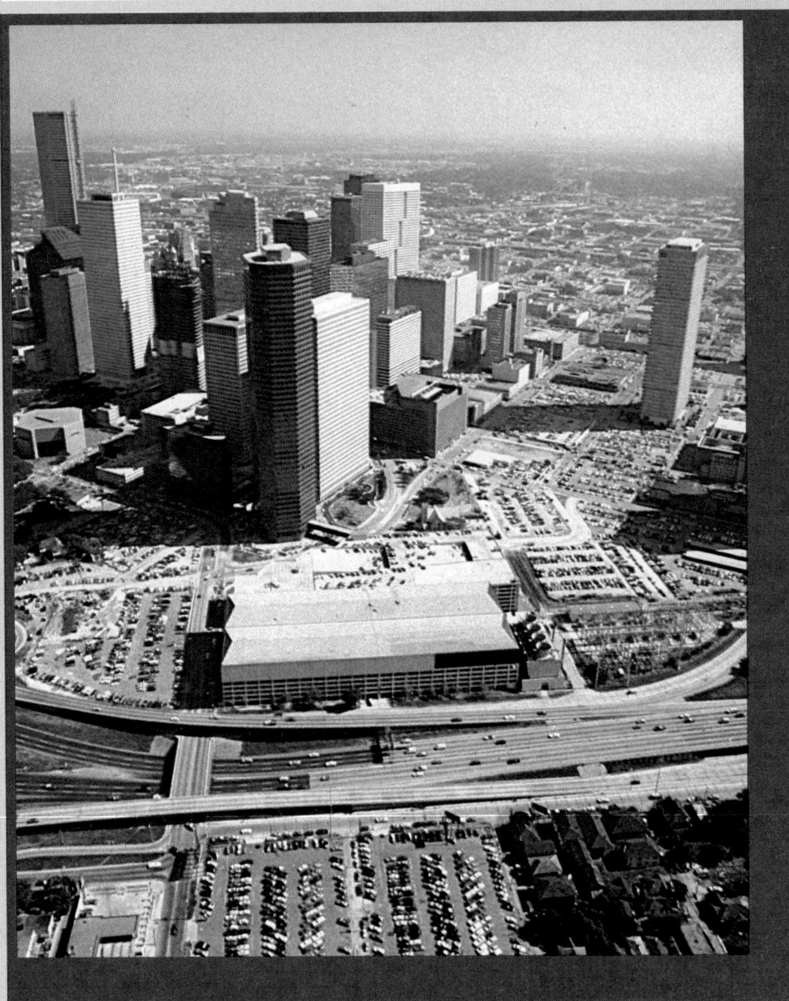

City planners use equations that contain exponents to project population growth in rapidly growing cities like Houston, Texas.

Addition and Subtraction

4-1 Exponents

Objective To write and simplify exponential expressions.

The number 9 can be written as

$$3 \times 3 \quad \text{or} \quad 3^2$$

(read "three to the second power" or "three squared"), and is called a *power* of 3. The numbers 27 and 81 are also powers of 3, since 27 can be written as

$$3 \times 3 \times 3 \quad \text{or} \quad 3^3$$

(read "three to the third power" or "three cubed"), and 81 can be written as

$$3 \times 3 \times 3 \times 3 \quad \text{or} \quad 3^4$$

(read "three to the fourth power").

In general, if b is any real number and n is any positive integer, the **nth power of b** is written b^n and is defined as follows:

$$b^n = \underbrace{b \cdot b \cdot b \cdot \ldots \cdot b}_{n \text{ factors}}$$

In b^n, b is called the **base** and the small raised symbol ^{n} is called the **exponent.**

Exponent → b^n = the nth power of b ← Base

The exponent indicates the number of times the base occurs as a factor.

Example 1 Express each of the following using exponents.

a. $5 \times 5 \times 5 \times 5 \times 5 \times 5 \times 5$

b. $8 \times 8 \times 8 \times 8 \times 8 \times 8 \times 8 \times 8 \times 8$

c. $11 \times 11 \times 11 \times 11 \times 11 \times 11 \times 11 \times 11 \times 11 \times 11$

Solution **a.** 5^7 **b.** 8^9 **c.** 11^{10}

Teaching References

Lesson Commentary, pp. T88–T92

Assignment Guide, pp. T59–T60

Supplementary Materials
- Practice Masters 18–23
- Tests 12–15
- Resource Book
  - Practice Exercises, pp. 79–83
  - Tests, pp. 19–22
  - Enrichment Activity, p. 151
  - Practice in Problem Solving/Word Problems, pp. 165–170
- Algebra Action

Extra Practice
- Skills, pp. 613–614
- Problems, pp. 636–637

Alternate Test, p. T13

Problem Solving Strategies

Looking for a Pattern
By examining number patterns, students are led to the definition of power and to rules for exponents (pp. 137, 148, 151).

Using a Formula
Using a standard formula may be the secret to solving a problem. Students are given practice in solving problems of this type in Section 4-7.

Using a Chart
Charts are particularly useful in solving distance-rate-time problems (p. 163). Diagrams can also help with these problems and with area problems (p. 168).

Recognizing No Solution
An important problem-solving skill is the ability to recognize when a problem has no solution. This topic is discussed in Section 4-10.

Teaching Suggestions p. T88

Suggested Extensions p. T88

Chalkboard Examples

Write each expression in exponential form.

1. $7 \cdot a \cdot a \cdot a \cdot a$ $7a^4$
2. $(-3)(b)(b)(b)$ $-3b^3$

Evaluate each expression if $m = -2$.

3. $2m^3$
   $2(-2)^3 = 2(-8) = -16$
4. $-2m^3$
   $-2(-2)^3 = -2(-8) = 16$
5. $(2m)^3$
   $[2(-2)]^3 = (-4)^3 = -64$
6. $(-2m)^3$
   $[(-2)(-2)]^3 = 4^3 = 64$

Simplify.

7. $2 + 3^3$
   $2 + 27 = 29$
8. $(2 + 3)^3$
   $5^3 = 125$
9. $7 - 3^2$
   $7 - 9 = -2$
10. $(7 - 3)^2$
    $4^2 = 16$

Common Error

Some students are tempted to express 2^3, for example, as 6; 3^3, as 9; 5^3, as 15; and so on. Remind these students that, in general, $b^n \neq nb$; emphasize the definition of b^n on page 137.

Powers of b can be written in **factored form** or in **exponential form** as shown below:

	Factored form	Exponential form	
First power of b:	b	b^1	(read "b to the first power." The exponent 1 is usually not written.)
Second power of b:	$b \cdot b$	b^2	(read "b to the second power" or "b squared," or "the square of b")
Third power of b:	$b \cdot b \cdot b$	b^3	(read "b to the third power" or "b cubed," or "the cube of b")
Fourth power of b:	$b \cdot b \cdot b \cdot b$	b^4	(read "b to the fourth power" or "b to the fourth")

Example 2 Evaluate x^3 if $x = -2$.

Solution Replace x with -2, and simplify the result.

$$x^3 = (-2)^3 = (-2)(-2)(-2) = -8$$

The following examples show that you must use care when an expression contains both parentheses and exponents.

$2x^3$ means $2(x \cdot x \cdot x)$. 3 is the exponent of the base x.
$(2x)^3$ means $(2x)(2x)(2x)$. 3 is the exponent of the base $2x$.

-3^4 means $-(3 \cdot 3 \cdot 3 \cdot 3)$, or -81. 4 is the exponent of the base 3.
$(-3)^4$ means $(-3)(-3)(-3)(-3)$, or 81. 4 is the exponent of the base (-3).

$(1 + 6)^2$ means $(1 + 6)(1 + 6)$, or 49. 2 is the exponent of the base $(1 + 6)$.
$1 + 6^2$ means $1 + 6 \cdot 6$, or 37. 2 is the exponent of the base 6.

The following steps are used to simplify numerical expressions that contain powers.

Summary of Order of Operations

1. First simplify expressions within grouping symbols.
2. Then simplify powers.
3. Then simplify products and quotients in order from left to right.
4. Then simplify sums and differences in order from left to right.

Example 3 Evaluate $\frac{(x+1)^3}{9} + 5(x-8)^2 - 1$ if $x = 2$.

Solution Replace x with 2 and simplify the result.

$$\begin{aligned}\frac{(x+1)^3}{9} + 5(x-8)^2 - 1 &= \frac{(2+1)^3}{9} + 5(2-8)^2 - 1 \\ &= \frac{3^3}{9} + 5(-6)^2 - 1 \\ &= \frac{27}{9} + 5(36) - 1 \\ &= 3 + 180 - 1 \\ &= 182\end{aligned}$$

Oral Exercises

Simplify.

1. 5^2 25
2. 5^3 125
3. $4 \cdot 5^2$ 100
4. $(4 \cdot 5)^2$ 400
5. $(1+5)^2$ 36
6. $1 + 5^2$ 26
7. $(-2)^4$ 16
8. -2^4 -16
9. An even power of a negative number is a __?__ number. positive
10. An odd power of a negative number is a __?__ number. negative

Write each expression in exponential form.

11. $y \cdot y \cdot y \cdot y$ y^4
12. $x \cdot x \cdot x \cdot x \cdot x$ x^5
13. $a \cdot a \cdot b$ a^2b
14. $a \cdot b \cdot a$ a^2b
15. $3 \cdot y \cdot 2 \cdot y$ $6y^2$
16. $y \cdot 3 \cdot 2 \cdot y$ $6y^2$
17. $-p \cdot p$ $-p^2$
18. $(-p)(-p)$ p^2
19. $z \cdot z \cdot z \cdot a \cdot a$ a^2z^3
20. $(-3)(-5) \cdot x \cdot x$ $15x^2$
21. $c \cdot 4 \cdot c \cdot 3 \cdot d$ $12c^2d$
22. $a \cdot y \cdot y \cdot a \cdot y \cdot c$ a^2cy^3

Evaluate if $a = 2$ and $b = 3$.

23. ab^2 18
24. $(ab)^2$ 36
25. $(a+b)^2$ 25
26. $a + b^2$ 11
27. $a - b^3$ -25
28. $(a-b)^3$ -1
29. $a^4 - b^4$ -65
30. $(a-b)^4$ 1
31. $a^2 - b^2$ -5
32. $(a-b)^2$ 1
33. $a^3 + b^3$ 35
34. $(a+b)^3$ 125
35. Study the figures below. Explain why the second and third powers of b are called "b squared" and "b cubed."

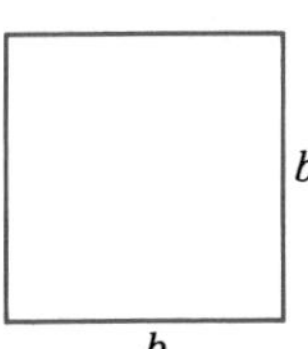

Area = __?__ b^2

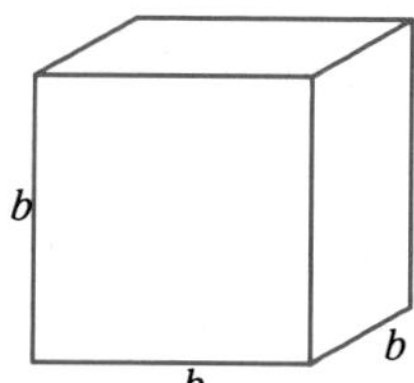

Volume = __?__ b^3

Suggested Assignments

Minimum
140/1–33 odd

Average
140/1–39 odd

Maximum
140/1–41 odd

Additional Answer Oral Exercises

35. b to the second power is called "b squared" because the area of a square with side b is b to the second power. Similarly, the volume of a cube with edge b is b to the third power, so "b cubed" is a natural term for b^3.

Additional A Exercises

Write each expression in exponential form.

1. $7 \cdot m \cdot m \cdot m \cdot 7 \cdot m$ 7^2m^4, or $49m^4$
2. Twice the square of the sum of a and b $2(a + b)^2$

Simplify.

3. a. -3^4 -81
   b. $(-3)^4$ 81
4. a. $-8 \cdot 2^2$ -32
   b. $-(8 \cdot 2)^2$ -256
5. a. $19 - 4^2$ 3
   b. $(19 - 4)^2$ 225
6. a. $2 \cdot 6 - 3^3$ -15
   b. $(2 \cdot 6 - 3)^3$ 729

Mixed Review Exercises

Solve.

1. $-7(x + 8) = 63$ -17
2. $7m = 3(m - 8)$ -6

Simplify.

3. $\frac{-27}{2} + \frac{21}{2} + 5$ 2
4. $y + (-9) - [y + (-18)]$ 9

Written Exercises

Write each expression in exponential form.

A

1. $a \cdot a \cdot a \cdot a \cdot a$ a^5
2. $x \cdot x \cdot x \cdot x \cdot x \cdot x$ x^6
3. $5 \cdot y \cdot y \cdot y$ $5y^3$
4. $4 \cdot y \cdot y \cdot 4$ 4^2y^2, or $16y^2$
5. $-8 \cdot x \cdot x$ $-8x^2$
6. $x(-8)x$ $-8x^2$
7. $(-7)(x)(x)$ $-7x^2$
8. $x(-7)x$ $-7x^2$
9. x plus the square of y $x + y^2$
10. The cube of $-4y$ $(-4y)^3$
11. The quantity $(x + y)$ squared $(x + y)^2$
12. -4 times the cube of y $-4y^3$
13. One half the sixth power of t $\frac{1}{2}t^6$
14. The sixth power of one half of t $\left(\frac{1}{2}t\right)^6$
15. The square of one third of r $\left(\frac{1}{3}r\right)^2$
16. One third the square of r $\frac{1}{3}r^2$

Simplify.

17. a. -5^2 -25
    b. $(-5)^2$ 25
18. a. -2^4 -16
    b. $(-2)^4$ 16
19. a. $-5 \cdot 2^3$ -40
    b. $-(5 \cdot 2)^3$ -1000
20. a. $-6^2 \cdot 2$ -72
    b. $(-6 \cdot 2)^2$ 144
21. a. $8 + 2^3$ 16
    b. $(8 + 2)^3$ 1000
22. a. $5 - 2^4$ -11
    b. $(5 - 2)^4$ 81
23. a. $6 - 4^2$ -10
    b. $(6 - 4)^2$ 4
24. a. $3 \cdot 5 - 4^2$ -1
    b. $(3 \cdot 5 - 4)^2$ 121

B

25. $6^3 \div [5^2 - 3^2 - (-2)^2]$ 18
26. $(6^2 - 3 \times 2^2 + 1) \div [0 + (-5)^2]$ 1
27. $6(3^2 - 2^2) \div 3 + 4 \div (-4)$ 9
28. $7(3^2 - 1) + 2^4 \times 3 \div (-3)2^2$ -8
29. $8 \times (-1)^3 - 7(-1)^2 + 2(-1) + 4$ -13
30. $15(-2)^4 - 6(-2)^3 + 5(-2)^2 + 1$ 309

Evaluate if $x = 4$ and $y = -2$.

31. a. $2x + y^2$ 12
    b. $(2x + y)^2$ 36
32. a. $8 + xy^2$ 24
    b. $(8 + xy)^2$ 0
33. a. $2x - y^3$ 16
    b. $(2x - y)^3$ 1000
34. a. $\frac{-3x}{y^2}$ -3
    b. $\left(\frac{-3x}{y}\right)^2$ 36
35. $\frac{(x + 2y)^2}{x - 2y}$ 0
36. $\frac{x^3 + y^3}{x + y}$ 28
37. $\left(\frac{8 - xy}{x}\right)^4$ 256
38. $\left(\frac{4y}{4 - xy}\right)^2$ $\frac{4}{9}$

Evaluate each expression for the given value of x.

C

39. $(x^2 + 4x - 5)(2x^2 - 7x + 1)$, $x = -5$ 0
40. $(3x^2 + 8x - 1)(x^2 + x - 6)$, $x = -2$ 20
41. $2(x - 1)^3 - 11(x - 1)^2 + 12(x - 1) + 9$, $x = 3$ 5
42. $4(x + 1)^3 - 2(x + 1)^2 - 8(x + 1) + 6$, $x = \frac{1}{2}$ 3

Computer Exercises

For students with some programming experience

1. Write a BASIC program that uses a FOR . . . NEXT loop to print out the value of n^n for $n = 1, 2, 3, 4, 5$. 1, 4, 27, 256, 3125

2. The symbol 4! is read "4 factorial," and its value is $1 \cdot 2 \cdot 3 \cdot 4 = 24$. Similarly, $6! = 1 \cdot 2 \cdot 3 \cdot 4 \cdot 5 \cdot 6 = 720$. Write a BASIC program that uses a FOR . . . NEXT loop to print out the value of $n!$ for $n = 1, 2, 3, 4, 5$. 1, 2, 6, 24, 120

3. Study the data in Exercises 1 and 2. For a given value of n, which appears to be larger, $n!$ or n^n? Can you explain why?

Computer Key-In

In computing wages in the program on page 117, you INPUT the employee ID numbers and pay per hour as well as the numbers of hours worked. Most likely, the first two items would be read from files. This situation can be represented by using READ and DATA statements in the program as explained below. In this case, the number of employees also becomes part of the stored data. (See line 5 below.)

Compare this program with the one given on page 117. Notice that lines 30, 70, and 90–140 have not been changed.

```
5  LET T=3
10  PRINT "THIS PROGRAM HAS DATA FOR"
20  PRINT T;" EMPLOYEES."
30  PRINT "FOR EACH EMPLOYEE:"
40  DATA 1234,11.5
50  DATA 3412,10
60  DATA 4321,12
70  FOR I=1 TO T
72  READ N,R
74  PRINT "HOURS FOR ";N;
80  INPUT H
90  LET W=R*H
100  IF H <= 40 THEN 120
110  LET W=W+.5*R*(H-40)
120  PRINT " ","WAGES = ";W
130  NEXT I
140  END
```

DATA statements may be placed anywhere in the program. You may prefer to put them at the end.

Line 72 READs the DATA in lines 40–60 in order, two at a time, into the variables N and R. Then, when the number of hours is INPUT, the computation proceeds as before.

Exercises

1. RUN the program given above, using the numbers of hours given on page 117 as INPUT. \$425.50; \$400; \$516
2. Revise this program by changing T to 4 and adding a line of DATA as line 65. RUN the program again. Answers will vary.

Additional Answer Computer Exercises

3. For values of $n > 1$, $n^n > n!$; however, for $n = 1$, $n^n = n! = 1$; for $n > 1$, n^n, which is the product of n factors each having a value of n, is always greater than $n!$, which is the product of n factors, each except the first having a value less than n.

Computer Key-In Commentary

Data statements are read as a list. The programmer could have included the value of T at the beginning of the data statement or all of the data could have been placed in one statement without the program's output being affected.

To change a line, use the text editor on your computer or retype the entire line. See your user's manual for instructions.

Additional Answers
Reading Algebra

2. monomial, constant monomial, constant, polynomial, binomials, trinomials, coefficient, numerical coefficient, similar, like, simplified, simplest form, degree of a monomial in a variable, degree of a monomial, degree of a polynomial
3. an expression that is either a numeral, a variable, or a product of a numeral and one or more variables; a sum of monomials

Reading Algebra / *Independent Study*

When you read an algebra textbook, it is helpful to know what you hope to achieve before you begin a lesson. The title of the lesson and the objective for the lesson, which appears directly below the title, will give you a good idea of what you should know when you have finished reading. You may find it useful to skim the lesson first. Notice any words or phrases that stand out; they are meant to attract your attention. **Heavy type** indicates new words or phrases that you must understand in order to understand the lesson. It is usually very helpful to learn the definitions of these words or phrases before you begin a slow and careful reading of the lesson. When you do start to read the lesson, pay particular attention to the important information set off in boxes or in italic type. If you come across any words whose meaning you do not understand, look them up in the glossary at the back of the book or in a dictionary. You may also find additional information by checking references from the index. Be sure to work through all the examples that are included in the lesson discussions. Try doing these examples on your own before reading the solutions that are given following the examples. If you do not understand a concept, and rereading does not seem to help, make a note of the concept so that you can discuss it with your teacher.

When you have finished reading a lesson and feel that you understand what you have read, try some of the Oral and Written Exercises. They will help you determine whether you have achieved the goal set forth in the objective. Doing the Self-Tests and checking your answers with those at the back of the book will help you to see whether you have understood a group of lessons. The Chapter Reviews, Chapter Tests, Cumulative Reviews, and Mixed Reviews will also give you a good idea of your progress.

Exercises

Skim through Sections 4-2 and 4-3 and answer the following questions.

1. What should you be able to do when you have finished reading the text of these sections? Add and subtract polynomials, multiply monomials
2. What new words or phrases are introduced?
3. What is a monomial? a polynomial? Find the definitions of these words in your book.
4. State the Rule of Exponents for Multiplication. For all positive integers m and n, $a^m \cdot a^n = a^{m+n}$.
5. Look at Example 1 on page 143. Then simplify $8x^2 + 3x - 7 + 2x - 5x^2 + 3$. $3x^2 + 5x - 4$
6. Suppose that you had forgotten the definition of the term variable. Where could you look it up? On what page of your textbook is this word first used? Glossary; page 1
7. Section 4-2 covers adding and subtracting polynomials. Where could you find information about addition and subtraction in general? Index and/or Table of Contents

4-2 Adding and Subtracting Polynomials

Objective To add and subtract polynomials.

Each of the expressions below is a *monomial.*

$$7 \qquad h \qquad \frac{1}{2}c \qquad -8x^2y$$

A **monomial** is an expression that is either a numeral, a variable, or a product of a numeral and one or more variables. A numeral, such as 7, is also called a **constant monomial,** or a **constant.**

A sum of monomials is called a **polynomial.** A polynomial such as $x^2 + (-3x) + (-2)$ is usually written as $x^2 - 3x - 2$. Some polynomials have special names:

Binomials (two terms): $4x + 9$ $\qquad 6b^2 - 7a$

Trinomials (three terms): $x^2 - 3x - 2$ $\qquad 5b^2 + 3ab - a^2$

A monomial is considered to be a polynomial of one term.

In the monomial $-8x^2y$, the number -8 is called the **coefficient,** or **numerical coefficient.** Two monomials that are exactly alike or that differ only in their numerical coefficients are called **similar,** or **like.** The following monomials are all similar:

$$-8x^2y, \quad 5yx^2, \quad x^2y, \quad \text{and} \quad \frac{1}{2}x^2y.$$

The following monomials are not similar: $-2xy^2$ and $-2x^2y$.

A polynomial is **simplified,** or **in simplest form,** when no two of its terms are similar. You may use the distributive property to add similar terms.

Example 1 Simplify $-4x^3 + 5x^2 + 3x^2 + 4x^3 - 7$.

Solution

$$\begin{aligned} \underline{-4x^3} + \underline{\underline{5x^2}} + \underline{\underline{3x^2}} + \underline{4x^3} - 7 &= (-4 + 4)x^3 + (5 + 3)x^2 - 7 \\ &= 0x^3 + 8x^2 - 7 \\ &= 8x^2 - 7 \end{aligned}$$

The **degree of a monomial in a variable** is the number of times that variable occurs as a factor in the monomial. For example,

$$-3xy^2z^3 \text{ is of degree } \begin{cases} 1 \text{ in } x, \\ 2 \text{ in } y, \\ 3 \text{ in } z. \end{cases}$$

The **degree of a monomial** is the total number of times its variables occur as factors. Thus, the degree of $-3xy^2z^3$ is $1 + 2 + 3$, or 6. The degree of any nonzero constant monomial is 0.

Teaching Suggestions p. T88

Suggested Extensions p. T89

Chalkboard Examples

Simplify each polynomial. Then state the number of terms and the degree of the resulting polynomial.

1. $4a^2 + 2a + 3 + 4a$
   $4a^2 + 6a + 3$; three terms; degree two
2. $m^2 + 3mn^2 + 2m^2 + 2mn^2$
   $3m^2 + 5mn^2$; two terms; degree three
3. $2x^3 + 3x^2 - x^3 + 9$
   $x^3 + 3x^2 + 9$; three terms; degree three
4. Add $2a^2 + ab + 2b$ and $4a^2 - 3ab + 9$.
   $$\begin{array}{r} 2a^2 + ab + 2b \\ \underline{4a^2 - 3ab + 9} \\ 6a^2 - 2ab + 2b + 9 \end{array}$$
5. Subtract $2x^2 - y^2$ from $5x^2 + 7xy + 2y^2$.
   $$\begin{array}{r} 5x^2 + 7xy + 2y^2 \\ \underline{-(2x^2 - y^2)} \\ 3x^2 + 7xy + 3y^2 \end{array}$$
6. Solve: $(3a - 2) - (1 - 2a) = 9 + 2a$
   $$\begin{aligned} 3a - 2 - 1 + 2a &= 9 + 2a \\ 5a - 3 &= 9 + 2a \\ 3a &= 12 \\ a &= 4 \end{aligned}$$

Common Errors

Students sometimes add the exponents as well as the coefficients of like terms. Point out that this is incorrect and that when you add inches to inches, for example, you get inches, not $(\text{inches})^2$.

When subtracting one polynomial from another, students may change the sign of the first term only of the polynomial that is being subtracted. Remind your students that they must add the opposite of *each* term of the polynomial that they are subtracting.

Supplementary Materials

Practice Master 18
Resource Book, p. 79

Suggested Assignments

Minimum
Day 1: 145/2–24 even
146/*P*: 2, 4
Day 2: 146/26–42 even,
P: 5–8
149/1–10
Day 2 finishes Sec. 4-2 and starts Sec. 4-3.

Average
Day 1: 145/2–46 even
146/*P*: 2, 4
Day 2: 146/39–47 odd,
P: 6, 7, 9, 10
R 147/*Self-Test 1*

Maximum
Day 1: 145/2–48 even
146/*P*: 6–9
S 140/40, 42
Day 2: 146/35–39 odd,
P: 10–13
R 147/*Self-Test 1*

Additional Answers Oral Exercises

12. $5x - 8y$
15. $-2n^2 - 2n - 7$
19. $-4a - 7; -a - 9$

The **degree of a polynomial** is the greatest of the degrees of its terms *after it has been simplified.* Since the polynomial

$$-4x^3 + 5x^2 + 3x^2 + 4x^3 - 7,$$

in Example 1, can be simplified to $8x^2 - 7$, the degree of the polynomial is 2, *not* 3.

To add two polynomials, you write the sum and simplify by adding similar terms.

Example 2 Add $5x^2y + 3x^2 - 8$ and $4x^2y + 2x^2 - 3xy^2 + 9$.

Solution 1 $(5x^2y + 3x^2 - 8) + (4x^2y + 2x^2 - 3xy^2 + 9) =$
$(5 + 4)x^2y + (3 + 2)x^2 - 3xy^2 + (-8 + 9) = 9x^2y + 5x^2 - 3xy^2 + 1$

Solution 2 You can also arrange similar terms vertically and add:

$$\begin{array}{l} 5x^2y + 3x^2 \qquad\qquad - 8 \\ \underline{4x^2y + 2x^2 - 3xy^2 + 9} \\ 9x^2y + 5x^2 - 3xy^2 + 1 \end{array}$$

Subtracting polynomials is very much like subtracting real numbers. To subtract a number you add the opposite of that number. To subtract a polynomial, you add the opposite of *each* term of the polynomial that you are subtracting and then simplify.

Example 3 Subtract $-5a^2 + 2ab + 3b^2 - 4$ from $7a^2 + 6ab - b^2 - 9$

Solution 1 $(7a^2 + 6ab - b^2 - 9) - (-5a^2 + 2ab + 3b^2 - 4) =$
$7a^2 + 6ab - b^2 - 9 + 5a^2 - 2ab - 3b^2 + 4 =$
$(7 + 5)a^2 + (6 - 2)ab + (-1 - 3)b^2 + (-9 + 4) = 12a^2 + 4ab - 4b^2 - 5$

Solution 2

$$\begin{array}{l} 7a^2 + 6ab - b^2 - 9 \\ \underline{-5a^2 + 2ab + 3b^2 - 4} \end{array} \rightarrow \left\{\begin{array}{l}\text{change to the} \\ \text{opposite and add}\end{array}\right\} \rightarrow \begin{array}{l} 7a^2 + 6ab - b^2 - 9 \\ \underline{+5a^2 - 2ab - 3b^2 + 4} \\ 12a^2 + 4ab - 4b^2 - 5 \end{array}$$

Oral Exercises

1. a. State the degree of the monomial $8x^2yz^4$ in each variable. degree 2 in x, 1 in y, 4 in z
   b. What is the degree of the monomial? 7

State the degree of each polynomial. If the polynomial is a binomial or a trinomial, state this fact.

2. $5x^2 - 7x - 4$ 2; trinomial
3. $x^2 + 3x^3 + 7 + 4x$ 3
4. $x^4 + y^3$ 4; binomial
5. $ab + ab^2 + ab^3 + ab^4$ 5
6. $r^3t^2 - r^2t$ 5; binomial
7. $5y^3 - 7y^2x + 6x^2$ 3; trinomial

Name the similar monomials.

8. $5x, 3xy, 4y, -xy, 7y, 2x$
$5x$ and $2x$; $3xy$ and $-xy$; $4y$ and $7y$

9. $3x^3y^2, 4x^2y^3, 5x^3y^2, 3xy, -x^2y^3$
$3x^3y^2$ and $5x^3y^2$; $4x^2y^3$ and $-x^2y^3$

Add.

10. $3a - 2$
$4a + 7$ — $7a + 5$

11. $4a + 9b$
$5a - b$ — $9a + 8b$

12. $7x - 3y$
$-2x - 5y$

13. $4x^2 - 3x - 7$
$2x^2 + 5x + 9$ — $6x^2 + 2x + 2$

14. $y^2 - 7y - 2$
$3y^2 + 8$ — $4y^2 - 7y + 6$

15. $2n^2 - 5n - 7$
$-4n^2 + 3n$

16. $r^2 - 2rs + 3s^2$
$2r^2 + 5rs - s^2$ — $3r^2 + 3rs + 2s^2$

17. $-3a - 2b + 5c$
$-4a + 2b - 7c$ — $-7a - 2c$

18. $5 - 3x$
$8 - 7x + 4x^2$ — $13 - 10x + 4x^2$

19–27. In Exercises 10–18, state the opposite of the lower polynomial. Then, subtract by adding that opposite to the upper polynomial.

Simplify.

28. $(5x - 3y + 7) + (2x - 5y - 8)$ — $7x - 8y - 1$

29. $(4a - 3) - (a + 7)$ — $3a - 10$

30. $(8a - 4b) - (5a - 2b)$ — $3a - 2b$

31. $(5x - 3y - 2) - (4x - 5)$ — $x - 3y + 3$

Written Exercises

Copy each polynomial and underline similar terms in the same way as in Example 1 on page 143. Then simplify the polynomial.

A

1. $2a - 3b + 4a + 7b$ — $6a + 4b$

2. $7x - 5y - 3y + 4x$ — $11x - 8y$

3. $7x^2 - 3xy + 5xy - 4x^2$ — $3x^2 + 2xy$

4. $5mn + m^2n - 4mn + 2m^2n$ — $mn + 3m^2n$

5. $x^2y + xy^2 - 3x^2y + xy$ — $-2x^2y + xy^2 + xy$

6. $3a^3 - 7a^2b + a^3 - ab^2 - 4a^3$ — $-7a^2b - ab^2$

Add.

7. $3a - 2$
$5a + 7$ — $8a + 5$

8. $5n + 3$
$-2n - 7$ — $3n - 4$

9. $3x - 4y + 2$
$-3x + 7y + 3$ — $3y + 5$

10. $8n - 4p + 7$
$-5n + 8p - 1$ — $3n + 4p + 6$

11. $3a^2 - 5a - 7$
$4a^2 - 2a + 9$ — $7a^2 - 7a + 2$

12. $7x^2 - 3xy + 4y^2$
$2x^2 - xy - y^2$ — $9x^2 - 4xy + 3y^2$

13. $3a^2 - 2ab - 7b$
$-5a^2 - b$ — $-2a^2 - 2ab - 8b$

14. $4c^2 - 5cd$
$-3c^2 + 6cd - d^2$ — $c^2 + cd - d^2$

15. $5x - 3y - 4z + 2$
$2x - y + 3z$
$2y - 5z + 6$ — $7x - 2y - 6z + 8$

16. $8a - 3b + 7$
$4a - 5c - 3$
$-a - b + 8c + 5$ — $11a - 4b + 3c + 9$

17–24. In Exercises 7–14, subtract the lower polynomial from the upper one.

20. $-5a + b$; $-a + 10b$
21. $2x + 5y$; $9x + 2y$
22. $-2x^2 - 5x - 9$; $2x^2 - 8x - 16$
23. $-3y^2 - 8$; $-2y^2 - 7y - 10$
24. $4n^2 - 3n$; $6n^2 - 8n - 7$
25. $-2r^2 - 5rs + s^2$; $-r^2 - 7rs + 4s^2$
26. $4a - 2b + 7c$; $a - 4b + 12c$
27. $-8 + 7x - 4x^2$; $-3 + 4x - 4x^2$

Additional A Exercises

1. Simplify: $6m - 2mn + 7mn - 3m + 18mn$
$3m + 23mn$

2. Add: $17x^3 - 4x^2 + 3x$
$4x^3 + 5x^2 - 2x$
$21x^3 + x^2 + x$

3. Subtract:
$12a - 3c + 4d$
$5c - 6d$
$12a - 8c + 10d$

Simplify.

4. $(12x + 5) + (3x - 7)$
$15x - 2$

5. $(7m^2n - 3mn + 8n^2) + (6mn - 7n^2 - 7m^2n)$
$3mn + n^2$

6. $(6a - 2b) - (3a + 4b)$
$3a - 6b$

7. $(13z^2 + 6z - 5) - (7z^2 + 15z - 9)$
$6z^2 - 9z + 4$

Additional Answers Written Exercises

17. $-2a - 9$
18. $7n + 10$
19. $6x - 11y - 1$
20. $13n - 12p + 8$
21. $-a^2 - 3a - 16$
22. $5x^2 - 2xy + 5y^2$
23. $8a^2 - 2ab - 6b$
24. $7c^2 - 11cd + d^2$

Additional Answers
Written Exercises

27. $8a^2 + 2a - 8$
28. $4x^2 - 3x + 7$
30. $a^2b + 2ab^2 - 7ab^3$
36. $2a^2 + 3a - 14$

Mixed Review Exercises

1. Simplify: $\dfrac{\frac{-84}{-7}}{9}$ 108
2. Solve: $9m = -27$ $m = -3$
3. Sean has $3.19 in pennies and dimes. He has the same number of each type of coin. How many dimes does he have? 29
4. Which axiom allows us to say that $\frac{1}{7}(84 + 63) = 12 + 9$? Distributive

Simplify.

25. $(5a - 3b + 2) + (7a - 6b - 3)$ $12a - 9b - 1$
26. $(x - 5y - 7) + (4x - 3y - 8)$ $5x - 8y - 15$
27. $(3a^2 + 4a - 7) + (5a^2 - 2a - 1)$
28. $(5x^2 - 7x + 2) + (-x^2 + 4x + 5)$
29. $(xy^2 - 3xy^2 + y^3) + (2xy^2 - y^3 + xy^2)$ xy^2
30. $(a^2b - 3ab^2 - ab^3) + (5ab^2 - 6ab^3)$
31. $(3a - 5) - (a + 2)$ $2a - 7$
32. $(6n - 3) - (4n + 1)$ $2n - 4$
33. $(4x - 7y) - (3x - 5y)$ $x - 2y$
34. $(8a - 7b) - (a - 4b)$ $7a - 3b$
35. $(3x^2 - 5x - 2) - (-x^2 - 5x + 9)$ $4x^2 - 11$
36. $(a^2 - 5a - 7) - (-a^2 - 8a + 7)$
37. $(2n^2 - 3m^2) - (n^2 + 6m^2 - mn)$ $n^2 + mn - 9m^2$
38. $(3c^2 - 4cd) - (cd + c^2 - d^2)$ $2c^2 - 5cd + d^2$

Solve.

B

39. $8x - (2x - 6) = 12$ 1
40. $y - (6y - 4) = 9$ -1
41. $(2a - 5) - (5a + 4) = 7 - 7a$ 4
42. $(3x - 2) - (11x - 5) = 19$ -2
43. $(5n - 3) - (6 - 8n) = 5(3 - n)$ $1\frac{1}{3}$
44. $9a - (3a - 8) = 2(6a - 5)$ 3
45. $8(5 - x) = (x - 10) - (3x - 2)$ 8
46. $3(4a - 6) = 2(4a - 3) - (a - 8)$ 4
47. $(y^2 + 3y + 1) - (y^2 + 5y + 3) = 4$ -3
48. $5 - (a^2 - 2a - 9) = 10 - (2a + a^2)$ -1

C

49. $7 + x(x + 5) = x^2 - (7 - 5x)$ No solution
50. $3x(x - 2) - 4 = 3x - (9x - 3x^2 + 4)$ {all the real numbers}

Problems

Solve.

A

1. Find two consecutive integers whose sum is 51. 25, 26
2. Find three consecutive integers whose sum is -171. $-58, -57, -56$
3. Find four consecutive even integers whose sum is 244. 58, 60, 62, 64
4. Find four consecutive odd integers whose sum is 0. $-3, -1, 1, 3$
5. The sum of the least and greatest of three consecutive integers is 44. What is the middle integer? 22
6. The sum of the least and greatest of three consecutive odd integers is 166. What are the integers? 81, 83, 85
7. The greater of two consecutive integers is 7 less than twice the lesser. Find the integers. 8, 9
8. The greater of two consecutive odd integers is 13 less than twice the lesser. Find the integers. 15, 17

B

9. Find three consecutive odd integers such that the sum of the greatest and twice the least is 25. 7, 9, 11
10. Find four consecutive integers such that the sum of the two greatest subtracted from twice the sum of the two least is 15. 9, 10, 11, 12

11. Find four consecutive integers such that five times the third decreased by twice the fourth is 55. 17, 18, 19, 20

12. Find four consecutive odd integers such that the third is the sum of the fourth and twice the second. −3, −1, 1, 3

13. The measures in meters of two adjacent sides of a rectangle are consecutive odd integers. The perimeter is 96 m. What are the dimensions of the rectangle? 23 m by 25 m

Computer Exercises

For students with some programming experience

Given the polynomial $3x^3 + x^2 - 6x - 2$:

1. Write a BASIC program to find the value of this polynomial for a given value of x that is entered with an INPUT statement.

2. Use the program you wrote in Exercise 1 to find a value of x for which the value of the polynomial is between −0.01 and 0.01.
$1.4136 \le x \le 1.4148$, $-1.4153 \le x \le -1.4132$, or $-0.3350 \le x \le -0.3316$

Self-Test 1

Vocabulary

power (p. 137)
base (p. 137)
exponent (p. 137)
factored form (p. 138)
exponential form (p. 138)
monomial (p. 143)
constant (p. 143)
polynomial (p. 143)
binomial (p. 143)
trinomial (p. 143)
coefficient (p. 143)
similar terms (p. 143)
polynomial in simplest form (p. 143)
degree of a monomial (p. 143)
degree of a polynomial (p. 144)

Write in exponential form.

1. $a \cdot a \cdot a$ a^3

2. The cube of the product of x and y $(xy)^3$

Obj. 4-1, p. 137

Simplify.

3. $(-1)^4$ 1

4. $(4 - 6)^3$ −8

a. Add the polynomials.
b. Subtract the lower polynomial from the upper one.

5. $$\begin{array}{r} 5x^2 + 6x - 8 \\ \underline{x^2 - 6x - 4} \end{array}$$

6. $$\begin{array}{r} x^2y - 3xy^2 + 7 \\ \underline{-9x^2y + 3xy^2 - 4} \end{array}$$

5. a. $6x^2 - 12$
b. $4x^2 + 12x - 4$

6. a. $-8x^2y + 3$
b. $10x^2y - 6xy^2 + 11$

Obj. 4-2, p. 143

7. Find three consecutive odd integers such that the greatest is 15 less than twice the smallest. 19, 21, 23

Check your answers with those at the back of the book.

Additional Answers Computer Exercises

1–2. Note: If X↑3 is used instead of X*X*X, the program will not accept negative values of X as input.

Quick Quiz

Write in exponential form.

1. $x \cdot x \cdot x \cdot x$ x^4

2. The square of the sum of a and b. $(a + b)^2$

Evaluate.

3. $(-3)^3$ −27

4. $(4 - 5)^4$ 1

a. Add the polynomials.
b. Subtract the lower polynomial from the upper one.

5. $$\begin{array}{r} 6x^2 - 3x + 2 \\ \underline{2x^2 + 4x + 5} \end{array}$$
a. $8x^2 + x + 7$
b. $4x^2 - 7x - 3$

6. $$\begin{array}{r} 3a^2b - ab^2 + 4 \\ \underline{-a^2b + ab^2 + 6} \end{array}$$
a. $2a^2b + 10$
b. $4a^2b - 2ab^2 - 2$

7. Find three consecutive odd integers such that the sum of the greatest and twice the least is 19. 5, 7, 9

Teaching Suggestions p. T89

Suggested Extensions p. T89

Chalkboard Examples

1. a. How many factors of x are there in x^3? 3
   b. How many factors of x are there in x^7? 7
   c. Simplify $x^3 \cdot x^7$.
   $x^3 \cdot x^7 = x^{3+7} = x^{10}$

Simplify.

2. $(4x^2y^5z^3)(7xy^4z^2)$
   $4 \cdot 7 \cdot x^{2+1}y^{5+4}z^{3+2} =$
   $28x^3y^9z^5$
3. $(2y^2)(5y^4) - (3y)(y^5)$
   $2 \cdot 5 \cdot y^{2+4} - 3 \cdot 1 \cdot y^{1+5} =$
   $10y^6 - 3y^6 = 7y^6$
4. $a^{n+1} \cdot a^{2n} \cdot a^5$
   $a^{n+1+2n+5} = a^{3n+6}$
5. $(-m)^2(-m)^3(-m)^4$
   $-1 \cdot m^2 \cdot m^3 \cdot m^4 =$
   $-1 \cdot m^{2+3+4} = -m^9$
6. $(2ab^2)(6a^4b^2) + (a^2b)(2a^3b^3)$
   $2 \cdot 6 \cdot a^{1+4}b^{2+2} +$
   $1 \cdot 2 \cdot a^{2+3}b^{1+3} =$
   $12a^5b^4 + 2a^5b^4 = 14a^5b^4$

Common Errors

Students tend to multiply the exponents when they multiply monomials. If your students write $a^3 \cdot a^2 = a^6$, for example, have them write $a^3 \cdot a^2 = (a \cdot a \cdot a) \cdot (a \cdot a)$ so they can see that it equals a^5.

Students may also have problems simplifying expressions such as Oral Exercise 9. Some students may think that $4^x \cdot 4 = 4^x$. Point out that this is not reasonable since $4 \neq 1$; remind them that $4 = 4^1$.

Multiplication

4-3 Multiplying Monomials

Objective To multiply monomials.

When you multiply two powers having the same base, you add the exponents as shown below.

$$x^2 \cdot x^5 = x^{2+5} = x^7$$
$$y^9 \cdot y^3 = y^{9+3} = y^{12}$$

You can understand why you add exponents if you remember that an exponent indicates the number of times the base is used as a factor.

$$x^2 \cdot x^5 = \underbrace{\overbrace{(x \cdot x)}^{\text{2 factors}} \cdot \overbrace{(x \cdot x \cdot x \cdot x \cdot x)}^{\text{5 factors}}}_{\text{7 factors}} = x^7$$

$$a^m \cdot a^n = \underbrace{\overbrace{(a \cdot a \cdot \cdots \cdot a)}^{m\text{ factors}} \cdot \overbrace{(a \cdot a \cdot \cdots \cdot a)}^{n\text{ factors}}}_{m+n\text{ factors}} = a^{m+n}$$

The following general rule applies when two powers to be multiplied have the same base.

Rule of Exponents for Multiplication

For all positive integers m and n,

$$\mathbf{a^m \cdot a^n = a^{m+n}}$$

When you multiply two monomials, you use the rule of exponents along with the commutative and associative axioms for multiplication.

Example 1 $(3x^3y^4)(-7xy^5) = [3 \cdot (-7)](x^3 \cdot x)(y^4 \cdot y^5)$ Commutative and associative axioms for multiplication

$= -21x^4y^9$ Rule of exponents for multiplication

Example 2 $(2a^5b)(-4ab^3) + (3a^3b^2)(a^3b^2) = -8a^6b^4 + 3a^6b^4$
$= -5a^6b^4$

Oral Exercises

Simplify.

1. $a^3 \cdot a^5$ a^8
2. $b^3 \cdot b^7$ b^{10}
3. $x^6 \cdot x \cdot x^2$ x^9
4. $y^4 \cdot y^2 \cdot y$
5. $a^n \cdot a^n$ a^{2n}
6. $b^n \cdot b^{3n}$ b^{4n}
7. $5^a \cdot 5^b$ 5^{a+b}
8. $3^x \cdot 3^2$
9. $4^x \cdot 4$ 4^{x+1}
10. $6^3 \cdot 6^y$ 6^{3+y}
11. $(2c)(3c)$ $6c^2$
12. $(5n)(2n)$
13. $(4n^4)(7n^7)$ $28n^{11}$
14. $(3a^3)(5a^5)$ $15a^8$
15. $(-2x^7)(-3x)$ $6x^8$
16. $(4c^2)(-2c^3)$
17. $(x^2y)(2xy^3)$ $2x^3y^4$
18. $(a^2b^2)(3ab^4)$ $3a^3b^6$
19. $(-2rst)(-4r^2s)$ $8r^3s^2t$
20. $-x^2 \cdot (-x)^2$

Written Exercises

Simplify.

A

1. $b^5 \cdot b^3 \cdot b^2$ b^{10}
2. $a^4 \cdot a^7 \cdot a$ a^{12}
3. $(3a^3)(5a^5)$ $15a^8$
4. $(6x^6)(3x^3)$ $18x^9$
5. $(-2x^2y)(-3xy^2)$ $6x^3y^3$
6. $(4a^3b)(-2ab^2)$
7. $(4ab)(2a^2b)(3b^2)$ $24a^3b^4$
8. $(7x^3y)(2xy^2)(3x^2)$ $42x^6y^3$
9. $(4cd^5)(-2c^3)(3cd^2)$
10. $(5r^4s^2)(-3rt^2)(-2st^3)$ $30r^5s^3t^5$
11. $\left(\frac{9}{4}a^4b\right)\left(\frac{8ab^8}{3}\right)$ $6a^5b^9$
12. $\left(\frac{14x^3y}{5}\right)\left(\frac{-15y^3x^2}{7}\right)$
13. $(7x^3)\left(\frac{1}{7}x^3\right)$ x^6
14. $(6a)\left(\frac{2}{3}a^3\right)$ $4a^4$
15. $(5y^2)\left(\frac{4}{5}y^2\right)\left(\frac{1}{2}y\right)$ $2y^5$
16. $(8n^2 - a)\left(-\frac{1}{4}an^2\right)$
17. $(3p^2r)(6p^3)\left(\frac{2}{9}r^2\right)$ $4p^5r^3$
18. $(-ab^2)(-bc^2)(-ac^2)$ $-a^2b^3c^4$
19. $b^n \cdot b^3$ b^{n+3}
20. $x^4 \cdot x^a$ x^{4+a}
21. $2^k \cdot 2^{4-k} \cdot 2$ 32
22. $3^p \cdot 3^{p+1} \cdot 3^2$ 3^{2p+3}
23. $(ay^7)(7y^a)$ $7ay^{7+a}$
24. $(cx^4)(4x^c)$ $4cx^{4+c}$

B

25. Evaluate $(-x)^3(-x)^4$ and $(-x^3)(-x^4)$ if $x = 2$. -128; 128
26. Evaluate $(-x)^4(-x)^7$ and $(-x^4)(-x^7)$ if $x = -1$. 1; -1

Simplify.

27. $(2a)(3a^3) + (4a^2)(5a^2)$ $26a^4$
28. $(3b^2)(4b^3) + 7b^3 \cdot b^2$ $19b^5$
29. $(3x^7)(2x^2) - (5x^3)(4x^6)$ $-14x^9$
30. $(4y^4)(2y^6) - (4y)(2y^9)$ 0
31. $(3x^2y)(4xy^2) - (7x^2)(2xy^3)$ $-2x^3y^3$
32. $(3ab^5)(5ab) - (3a^2b)(2b^5)$ $9a^2b^6$
33. $(5x^2y^6)(2x^3) - (-2x^4y^4)(-xy^2)$ $8x^5y^6$
34. $(7r^2s^3)(-3rs^4) - (-2r^2s)(5rs^6)$ $-11r^3s^7$

Suggested Assignments

Minimum
149/11–30
R 147/*Self-Test 1*

Day 2 of Sec. 4-2 finishes Sec. 4-2 and starts Sec. 4-3.

Average
149/1–37 odd
S 147/*P*: 11

Maximum
149/1–43 odd

Additional Answers Oral Exercises

4. y^7
8. 3^{x+2}
12. $10n^2$
16. $-8c^5$
20. $-x^4$

Additional A Exercises

Simplify.

1. $n^2 \cdot n^4 \cdot n^7$ n^{13}
2. $(3m^2)(-2m^3)$ $-6m^5$
3. $(6a^2b^3)(-4ab)(-2a^3)$ $48a^6b^4$
4. $\left(\frac{12}{5}x^2y\right)\left(\frac{15}{4}xy^5\right)$ $9x^3y^6$
5. $(16pqr^2)\left(-\frac{3}{4}p^2qr\right) \times \left(-\frac{5}{2}pq^2r^4\right)$ $30p^4q^4r^7$
6. $6^m \cdot 6^{m-2} \cdot 6$ 6^{2m-1}

Additional Answers Written Exercises

6. $-8a^4b^3$
9. $-24c^5d^7$
12. $-6x^5y^4$
16. $-2an^4 + \frac{1}{4}a^2n^2$

Mixed Review Exercises

1. Use the facts to write an equation: Marla spent twice as long doing her chemistry experiment as she did doing her math homework. It took her $4\frac{1}{2}$ h to complete both assignments. How long did the experiment take? 3 h
2. Solve: $2x - 15 = 23$ 19
3. The sum of the first and the last of four consecutive integers is 43. Find the integers. 20, 21, 22, 23
4. Express "the cube of xy^2" in exponential form. $(xy^2)^3$

Find the perimeter and area of each shaded region.

(Area of rectangle = length × width.)

35. 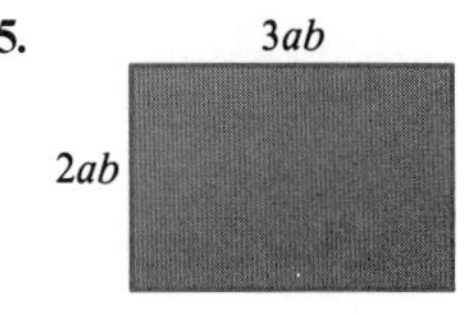

$P = 10ab;\ A = 6a^2b^2$

36. 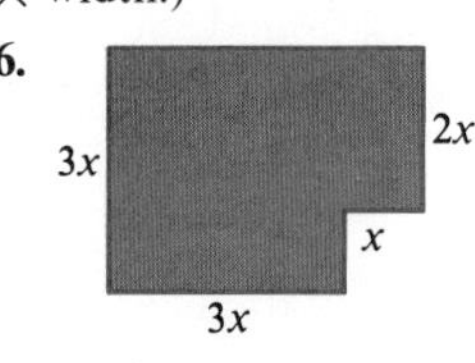

$P = 14x;\ A = 11x^2$

37. 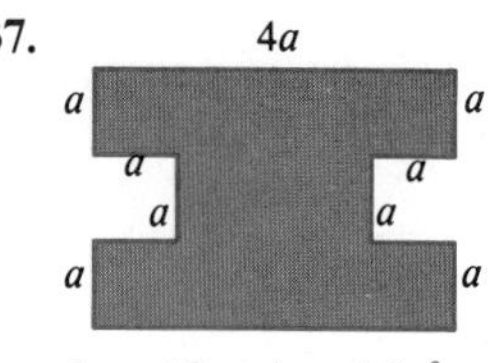

$P = 18a;\ A = 10a^2$

Find the total surface area of each solid.

(The total surface area of a solid is the sum of the areas of all its faces.)

C **38.** 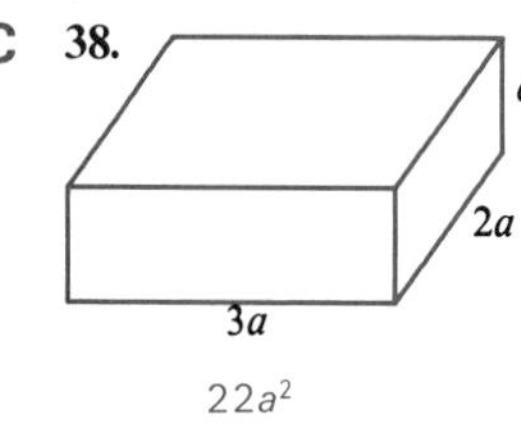

$22a^2$

39. 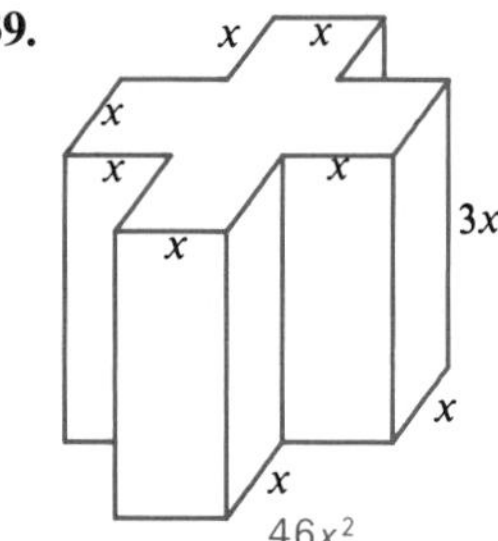

$46x^2$

40. 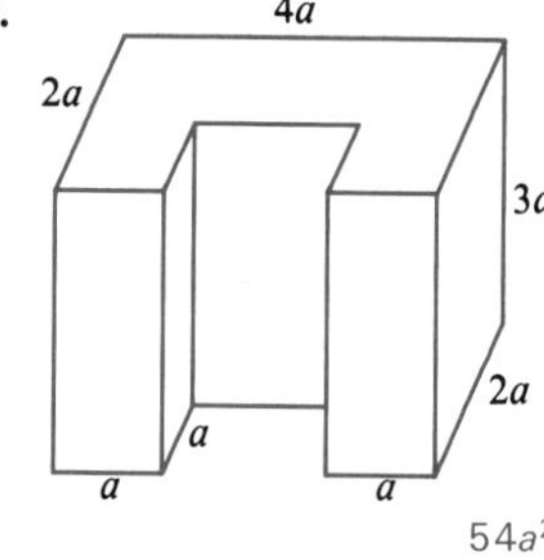

$54a^2$

41-43. Find the volume of each solid above. (The volume can be found by multiplying the area of the bottom or top of the solid by the height.) 41. $6a^3$ 42. $15x^3$ 43. $18a^3$

Career Note / *Electrical Engineer*

People use many electronic products every day such as computers, stereos, televisions, and telephones. Electrical engineers are employed in the development of components for these products. Some engineers work in research and some in development, and still others in quality assurance.

Electrical engineers work closely with physicists, chemists, metallurgists, mathematicians, and statisticians. A bachelor's degree or master's degree is often a necessity because most engineers specialize in highly technical areas. Electrical engineers must constantly keep informed of new developments in their field of engineering. Therefore, their education often continues beyond graduation.

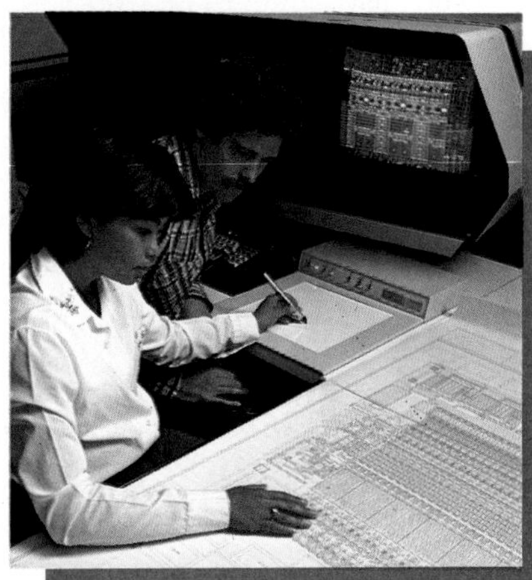

4-4 Powers of Monomials

Objective To find powers of a monomial.

To find a power of a monomial that is itself a power, you can apply the definition of a power and the rule of exponents for multiplication.

Example 1 $(x^3)^2 = x^3 \cdot x^3 = x^{3+3} = x^6$

Note that $(x^3)^2 = x^6$, or $x^{3\times 2}$. In general:

$$(a^m)^n = \overbrace{(a^m)(a^m)\cdots(a^m)}^{a^m \text{ is a factor } n \text{ times}} = a^{\overbrace{m+m+\cdots+m}^{n \text{ terms}}} = a^{mn}$$

Thus, *to find a power of a power, you multiply the exponents.*

Rule of Exponents for a Power of a Power

For all positive integers m and n,

$$(a^m)^n = a^{mn}.$$

Example 2 $(y^5)^4 = y^{20}$ ***Example 3*** $[(-a)^4]^5 = (-a)^{20} = a^{20}$

To find a power of a product, you can apply the definition of a power and the commutative and associative axioms for multiplication.

Example 4 $(3x)^2 = 3x \cdot 3x = 3 \cdot 3 \cdot x \cdot x = 3^2 \cdot x^2 = 9x^2$

Note that *both* the 3 and the x are squared when the product $3x$ is squared. In general:

$$(ab)^m = \overbrace{(ab)(ab)\cdots(ab)}^{ab \text{ is a factor } m \text{ times}} = \overbrace{(a \cdot a \cdot \cdots \cdot a)}^{m \text{ factors}}\overbrace{(b \cdot b \cdot \cdots \cdot b)}^{m \text{ factors}} = a^m b^m$$

Thus, *to find a power of a product, you find the power of each factor and then multiply.*

Rule of Exponents for a Power of a Product

For every positive integer m,

$$(ab)^m = a^m b^m.$$

Teaching Suggestions p. T89

Suggested Extensions p. T90

Chalkboard Examples

Simplify.

1. $(m^5)^3$ $m^{5\cdot 3} = m^{15}$
2. $(2x)^4$ $2^4 \cdot x^4 = 16x^4$
3. $(-3mn)^3$ $(-3)^3m^3n^3 = -27m^3n^3$
4. $(4a^3b^2)^4$ $4^4a^{3\cdot 4}b^{2\cdot 4} = 256a^{12}b^8$
5. $(2k)^3(2k)^4$ $(2^3 \cdot k^3)(2^4 \cdot k^4) = 2^{3+4}k^{3+4} = 2^7k^7 = 128k^7$
6. $(xy^2)^3 + (2xy)^2(xy^4)$ $x^3y^{2\cdot 3} + (2^2x^2y^2)(xy^4) = x^3y^6 + (4x^2y^2)(xy^4) = x^3y^6 + 4x^3y^6 = 5x^3y^6$

Evaluate if $x = 2$ and $y = -3$.

7. $3x^3$; $(3x)^3$; $3^3 \cdot x^3$ $3 \cdot 2^3 = 3 \cdot 8 = 24$ $(3 \cdot 2)^3 = 6^3 = 216$ $3^3 \cdot 2^3 = 27 \cdot 8 = 216$
8. $-xy^2$; $(-xy)^2$; $-x^2y^2$ $-2(-3)^2 = (-2)(9) = -18$; $(-2 \cdot -3)^2 = 6^2 = 36$; $-(2^2)(-3)^2 = -(4 \cdot 9) = -36$

Common Errors

Some students will write $(3a^2)^3 = 3a^6$, for example; some will write, for example, $3 \cdot 2^2 = 9 \cdot 4 = 36$. Point out that $(3a^2)^3 = 3 \cdot 3 \cdot 3 \cdot a^2 \cdot a^2 \cdot a^2 = 27a^6$ and that $3 \cdot 2^2 = 3 \cdot 2 \cdot 2 = 12$.

Supplementary Materials

Practice Master 19
Resource Book, p. 80

Example 5 $(5b)^4 = 5^4 \cdot b^4 = 625b^4$

Example 6 $(-3y)^3 = (-3)^3 \cdot y^3 = -27y^3$

Both rules of exponents for powers are applied in the following example.

Example 7 $(-3x^5y^3)^3 = (-3)^3 \cdot (x^5)^3 \cdot (y^3)^3 = -27x^{15}y^9$

Oral Exercises

Simplify. 23. a. $x^{2n}y^{2m}$ 16. $-27a^{18}$ 20. $8a^3b^{12}$

1. $(x^4)^2$ x^8
2. $(y^3)^5$ y^{15}
3. $(a^2)^6$ a^{12}
4. $(b^4)^4$ b^{16}
5. a. $(c^3)^2$ c^6 b. $c^3 \cdot c^2$ c^5
6. a. $(d^5)^3$ d^{15} b. $d^5 \cdot d^3$ d^8
7. a. $(t^4)^3$ t^{12} b. $t^4 \cdot t^3$ t^7
8. a. $s^5 \cdot s^4$ s^9 b. $(s^5)^4$ s^{20}
9. $(3a^3)^2$ $9a^6$
10. $(5a^4)^2$ $25a^8$
11. $(2x^5)^3$ $8x^{15}$
12. $(3y^2)^3$ $27y^6$
13. $(-x^3)^2$ x^6
14. $(-y^4)^3$ $-y^{12}$
15. $(-3a^6)^2$ $9a^{12}$
16. $(-3a^6)^3$
17. $[(-1)^3]^5$ -1
18. $[(-x)^5]^2$ x^{10}
19. $(x^3y^6)^2$ x^6y^{12}
20. $(2ab^4)^3$
21. a. $(b^x)^2$ b^{2x} b. $b^x \cdot b^x$ b^{2x}
22. a. $(a^y)^3$ a^{3y} b. $a^y \cdot a^y \cdot a^y$ a^{3y}
23. a. $(x^ny^m)^2$ b. $(x^ny^m)(x^ny^m)$ $x^{2n}y^{2m}$
24. a. $-(b^2)y$ $-b^2y$ b. $[(-b)^2]y$ b^2y
25. Evaluate $(ab)^2$ and a^2b^2 if $a = 2$ and $b = 3$. 36; 36
26. Evaluate $3x^2$ and $(3x)^2$ if $x = 2$. 12; 36

Written Exercises

Simplify.

A

1. a. $(x^4)^3$ x^{12} b. $(x^3)^4$ x^{12} c. $x^3 \cdot x^4$ x^7
2. a. $(a^7)^2$ a^{14} b. $(a^2)^7$ a^{14} c. $a^2 \cdot a^7$ a^9
3. a. $a^n \cdot a^n$ a^{2n} b. $(a^n)^2$ a^{2n} c. $a^2 \cdot a^n$ a^{2+n}
4. a. $b^t \cdot b^t \cdot b^t$ b^{3t} b. $(b^t)^3$ b^{3t} c. $b^t \cdot b^3$ b^{t+3}

Evaluate if $x = 2$ and $y = 3$.

5. a. $4x^2$ 16 b. $(4x)^2$ 64 c. $4^2 \cdot x^2$ 64
6. a. $5x^3$ 40 b. $(5x)^3$ 1000 c. $5^3 \cdot x^3$ 1000
7. a. xy^2 18 b. $(xy)^2$ 36 c. x^2y^2 36
8. a. yx^3 24 b. $(yx)^3$ 216 c. y^3x^3 216

Simplify.

9. $(8n)^2$ $64n^2$
10. $(3a)^3$ $27a^3$
11. $(2x)^5$ $32x^5$
12. $(6a)^4$ $1296a^4$
13. $(3n^2)^4$ $81n^8$
14. $(8b^6)^2$ $64b^{12}$
15. $\left(\frac{1}{10}x^{10}\right)^3$ $\frac{1}{1000}x^{30}$
16. $\left(\frac{1}{2}x^3\right)^4$ $\frac{1}{16}x^{12}$
17. $(2ab^2)^4$ $16a^4b^8$
18. $(3x^2y)^3$ $27x^6y^3$
19. $(2a^2b^6)^3$ $8a^6b^{18}$
20. $(5x^4y^2)^3$ $125x^{12}y^6$

Suggested Assignments

Minimum
Day 1: 152/1–20
S 146/P: 9, 10
Day 2: 153/21–33
155/2–14 even
Day 2 finishes Sec. 4-4 and starts Sec. 4-5.

Average
152/1–23 odd, 25–38
S 149/28, 30, 32

Maximum
152/1–23 odd, 25–41
S 150/38, 40, 42

Additional A Exercises

Simplify.

1. a. $(m^4)^2$ m^8
   b. $(m^2)^4$ m^8
   c. m^2m^4 m^6
2. a. $t^3 \cdot t^3 \cdot t^3 \cdot t^3$ t^{12}
   b. $(t^3)^4$ t^{12} c. t^3t^4 t^7
3. $(4m)^6$ $4096m^6$
4. $\left(\frac{1}{3}y^5\right)^3$ $\frac{1}{27}y^{15}$
5. $(4m^2n^3)^4$ $256m^8n^{12}$
6. a. $(-2a^4)^6$ $64a^{24}$
   b. $-(2a^4)^6$ $-64a^{24}$

21. a. $(-3x^5)^2$ $9x^{10}$ b. $-(3x^5)^2$ $-9x^{10}$ 22. a. $(-2n^6)^4$ $16n^{24}$ b. $-(2n^6)^4$ $-16n^{24}$

23. a. $(-3x^5)^3$ $-27x^{15}$ b. $-(3x^5)^3$ $-27x^{15}$ 24. a. $(-2n^6)^5$ $-32n^{30}$ b. $-(2n^6)^5$ $-32n^{30}$

B 25. $(2a)^2(2a)^3$ $32a^5$ 26. $(10x)^2(10x)^4$ $1{,}000{,}000x^6$ 27. $(5b)^4(2b)^4$ $10{,}000b^8$ 28. $(4n)^3\left(\frac{5}{2}n\right)^3$ $1000n^6$

29. $(3x^2y)^3 \cdot 4xy^3$ $108x^7y^6$ 30. $(2a^2b)^3(-4ab^2)^2$ $128a^8b^7$ 31. $(-2c^3d)^5\left(\frac{1}{4}d\right)^3$ $-\frac{1}{2}c^{15}d^8$ 32. $\left(\frac{1}{2}a^4\right)^3(-4a)^3$ $-8a^{15}$

33. $(2a^n)^3(3a^n)^2$ $72a^{5n}$ 34. $(x^n)^5(2x^n)^3$ $8x^{8n}$ 35. $(y^m)^n \cdot 2y^{mn}$ $2y^{2mn}$ 36. $(b^x)^y \cdot (b^y)^x$ b^{2xy}

37. $x^2(xy^3)^2 + y^2(x^2y^2)^2$ $2x^4y^6$ 38. $x^3(xy^2)^2 + x(-xy)^4$ $2x^5y^4$

39. $(2c)^3(cd)^2 + (2cd)^2(-c)^3$ $4c^5d^2$ 40. $(2a^2b^3)^2 - a(ab^2)^3$ $3a^4b^6$

C 41. a. Find the volumes of the two cubes shown. $8x^3$, $64x^3$

b. How many times larger is the volume of the bigger cube than that of the smaller cube? 8

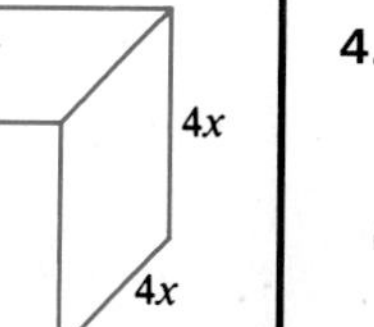

42. If $a = (3^3)^3$ and $b = 3^{(3^3)}$, is a larger or is b? How many times larger is it? b; 3^{18}

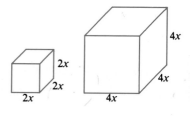

43. Show that $16^x \cdot (4^x)^2 = 2^{8x}$.
$16^x \cdot (4^x)^2 = (2^4)^x \cdot [(2^2)^x]^2 = 2^{4x} \cdot (2^{2x})^2 = 2^{4x} \cdot 2^{4x} = 2^{8x}$

Computer Exercises

For students with some programming experience

1. Write a BASIC program using READ . . . DATA statements to evaluate the expression $\frac{x^2}{2^x}$ for the following values of x: 1, 2, 3, 4, 5, 10, 50, 100, 1000, 2000. What appears to be happening to this expression as x becomes larger?
2. Repeat Exercise 1, this time using the program to evaluate the expression $\left(1 + \frac{1}{x}\right)^x$ for the given values of x.

Challenge

What is wrong with the following "proof" that 2 = 1?

$$r = s$$
$$r^2 = rs$$
$$r^2 - s^2 = rs - s^2$$
$$(r + s)(r - s) = s(r - s)$$
$$r + s = s$$
$$s + s = s$$
$$2s = s$$
$$2 = 1$$

In step 4, the equation is divided by $r - s$. If $r = s$, $r - s = 0$. You cannot divide by 0.

Mixed Review Exercises

1. On a number line, P has coordinate -7. What is the coordinate of the point 3 units to the left of P? -10
2. Simplify: $-8 + (-9.1) + 8.1$ -9
3. Solve: $m - 21 = |-22|$ 43
4. Add: $\begin{array}{r} 12x^2 - 3x - 1 \\ 5x^2 - 6x + 9 \\ \hline 17x^2 - 9x + 8 \end{array}$

Additional Answers
Computer Exercises

Answers may vary slightly.

1. 0.5, 1.0, 1.125, 1, 0.78125, 0.0976563, $2.22044605 \times 10^{-12}$, $7.88860907 \times 10^{-27}$, and when $x = 1000$ and when $x = 2000$ the computer's ability to calculate is exceeded; as x becomes very large, the value of the expression becomes very small (close to zero).
2. 2, 2.25, 2.37037038, 2.44140625, 2.48832, 2.59374248, 2.69158811, 2.70481379, 2.71692484, 2.71760456; as x increases in value, the value of the expression approaches 2.718.

Teaching Suggestions p. T90

Suggested Extensions p. T90

Chalkboard Examples

Multiply.

1. $-2a^2(3a^2 - 4a + 6)$
   $-6a^4 + 8a^3 - 12a^2$
2. $4x^2y(5x^2 + 2xy + y^2)$
   $20x^4y + 8x^3y^2 + 4x^2y^3$
3. $ab^3 - 3a^2b^2 + 2a^3b$
   $\underline{-2ab}$
   $-2a^2b^4 + 6a^3b^3 - 4a^4b^2$
4. Simplify:
   $3 - 4[5a - 2(9 - 4a)]$
   $3 - 4[5a - 18 + 8a] =$
   $3 - 20a + 72 - 32a =$
   $75 - 52a$

Solve.

5. $6(m - 2) + 3 = 2m + 7$
   $6m - 12 + 3 = 2m + 7$
   $6m - 9 = 2m + 7$
   $4m = 16$
   $m = 4$
6. $\frac{1}{2}(10x - 6) =$
   $2[x - (9 - 2x)]$
   $5x - 3 = 2[x - 9 + 2x]$
   $5x - 3 = 2[3x - 9]$
   $5x - 3 = 6x - 18$
   $15 = x$

Suggested Assignments

Minimum
155/16–36 even
S 150/35–37

Day 2 of Sec. 4-4 finishes Sec. 4-4 and starts Sec. 4-5.

Average
155/2–28 even, 33–39, 41
S 153/39, 40, 41

Maximum
155/2–38 even, 39–45
S 153/42, 43

4-5 Multiplying a Polynomial by a Monomial

Objective To multiply a polynomial by a monomial.

The distributive axiom and the rules of exponents enable you to multiply any polynomial by a monomial. For example:

$$4a(3a^2 - 4a + 3) = 4a(3a^2) + 4a(-4a) + 4a(3) = 12a^3 - 16a^2 + 12a$$

You may multiply either horizontally or vertically:

$$-3xy(3xy + 5x - y) = -9x^2y^2 - 15x^2y + 3xy^2 \quad \text{or} \quad \begin{array}{r} 3xy + 5x - y \\ -3xy \\ \hline -9x^2y^2 - 15x^2y + 3xy^2 \end{array}$$

Recall that to simplify an expression containing more than one grouping symbol, you work with the expression within the innermost grouping symbol first.

Example 1 Simplify $20 - 5[3x + 2(1 - 6x)]$.

Solution

$20 - 5[3x + 2(1 - 6x)]$ ⟵ Simplify $2(1 - 6x)$ first.
$20 - 5[3x + 2 - 12x]$ ⟵ Then simplify $5[3x + 2 - 12x]$.
$20 - 15x - 10 + 60x$
$10 + 45x$

Example 2 Solve $20x^2 - 2[4x - 2x(1 - 5x)] = 8$.

Solution

$$\begin{aligned} 20x^2 - 2[4x - 2x(1 - 5x)] &= 8 \\ 20x^2 - 2[4x - 2x + 10x^2] &= 8 \\ 20x^2 - 8x + 4x - 20x^2 &= 8 \\ -4x &= 8 \\ x &= -2 \end{aligned}$$

The check is left for you.

∴ the solution is -2. ***Answer***

Oral Exercises

4. $14a - 21$
8. $xy + xz$

Multiply.

1. $2(x + 3)$ $2x + 6$
2. $4(a - 5)$ $4a - 20$
3. $5(3y + 4)$ $15y + 20$
4. $7(2a - 3)$
5. $x(x + 8)$ $x^2 + 8x$
6. $y(2 - y)$ $2y - y^2$
7. $-a(a - 8)$ $-a^2 + 8a$
8. $x(y + z)$
9. $3a(a^2 - 5a)$ $3a^3 - 15a^2$
10. $-ab(a^2 - b^2)$ $-a^3b + ab^3$
11. $2a^2(a^3 - 3a^2 - 5a + 4)$ $2a^5 - 6a^4 - 10a^3 + 8a^2$

Written Exercises

Multiply.

A

1. $5(a + 2)$ $5a + 10$
2. $6(n - 5)$ $6n - 30$
3. $-8(a - 3)$ $-8a + 24$
4. $-5(1 + 3n)$ $-5 - 15n$
5. $4x(x + 2)$ $4x^2 + 8x$
6. $7y(3y - 5)$
7. $-3b(2 - 5b)$
8. $-4c(5c + 2)$
9. $5x(x^2 - 2x - 3)$ $5x^3 - 10x^2 - 15x$
10. $4y(2y^2 - 3y - 7)$ $8y^3 - 12y^2 - 28y$
11. $-8x^2(2x^2 - 3x + 4)$ $-16x^4 + 24x^3 - 32x^2$
12. $-3a^3(2a^2 - 5a - 4)$ $-6a^5 + 15a^4 + 12a^3$
13. $\frac{1}{2}a(4a^2 - 2ab + 8b^2)$ $2a^3 - a^2b + 4ab^2$
14. $\frac{1}{3}xy^2(9x^2 - 6xy + y^2)$ $3x^3y^2 - 2x^2y^3 + \frac{1}{3}xy^4$
15. $\begin{array}{r} 2b^2 - 5b - 9 \\ \underline{3b \qquad\qquad} \end{array}$ $6b^3 - 15b^2 - 27b$
16. $\begin{array}{r} 4a^2 - 7a - 8 \\ \underline{5a \qquad\qquad} \end{array}$ $20a^3 - 35a^2 - 40a$
17. $\begin{array}{r} 3n^2 - 4n - 6 \\ \underline{-2n^2 \qquad\qquad} \end{array}$ $-6n^4 + 8n^3 + 12n^2$
18. $\begin{array}{r} x^2y - 3xy^2 + y^3 \\ \underline{-2xy \qquad\qquad} \end{array}$ $-2x^3y^2 + 6x^2y^3 - 2xy^4$

Simplify.

19. $3x(x - 5) + 2x(4x + 3)$ $11x^2 - 9x$
20. $5a(3a - 5) + 7a(1 - 5a)$ $-20a^2 - 18a$
21. $4y^2(2y - 3) - y(6y^2 - 12y)$ $2y^3$
22. $3n^3(2n - 6) - 2n^2(2n^2 - 9n)$ $2n^4$
23. $3x(5x^2 - 4x) - (x + 2)x^2$ $14x^3 - 14x^2$
24. $4b^2(b - 3) - (2b - 5)b^2$ $2b^3 - 7b^2$
25. $-[3x - 2(5x - 3)]$ $7x - 6$
26. $-4[8a - 3(7 - 4a)]$ $-80a + 84$

Solve.

27. $3(a - 1) + 2 = 8$ 3
28. $2(y - 2) + 1 = 7$ 5
29. $4 - 5(n - 2) = 19$ -1
30. $4(x - 9) + 18 = 6$ 6
31. $\frac{1}{3}(6n - 3) - 4(3n + 6) = 0$ $-\frac{5}{2}$
32. $\frac{2}{5}(5a - 10) - 3(1 - a) = 3$ 2

B

33. $2(5x - 4) - 3(x - 5) = 8(2x - 7)$ 7
34. $\frac{1}{2}(6n + 4) - \frac{2}{3}(9 - 3n) = 2\left(n + \frac{5}{2}\right)$ 3
35. $3x\left(5 - \frac{1}{3}x\right) - (15 - x^2) = 0$ 1
36. $4(a - 7) - 2(1 - 3a)a = 6a^2$ 14
37. $2x - 5[3x - 4(1 - x)] = -2$ $\frac{2}{3}$
38. $4 - [8(x - 3) - 5(2x + 9)] = 13$ -30
39. A hockey team gets 2 points for every game won and 1 point for every game tied. No points are given for a game lost. Complete the table.

Games played	50	50	50	60	G
Games won	30	30	W	W	W
Games lost	16	L	L	L	L
Total points	?	?	?	?	?

64; $80 - L$; $W - L + 50$; $W - L + 60$; $G + W - L$

Additional A Exercises

Multiply.

1. $3(y - 2)$ $3y - 6$
2. $6x(4x - 3)$ $24x^2 - 18x$
3. $-\frac{1}{3}z(9z^2 - 27z - 12)$ $-3z^3 + 9z^2 + 4z$

Simplify.

4. $9n(6n - 3) - 2n(5 - n)$ $56n^2 - 37n$
5. $2a^2(a^2 - 3a) + (3a^3 + a^2)a$ $5a^4 - 5a^3$

Solve.

6. $5n - 3(4n - 1) = -11$ $n = 2$

Additional Answers Written Exercises

6. $21y^2 - 35y$
7. $-6b + 15b^2$
8. $-20c^2 - 8c$

Mixed Review Exercises

1. Jenna is two years older than Len and six years younger than Ken. Two years ago, the sum of their ages was 28. How old is each now? Jenna, 10; Len, 8; Ken, 16
2. The sum of twice the number x and 16 is 54. What is x? 19

Simplify.

3. $-18m^2(-2mn^2)$ $36m^3n^2$
4. $(3x^2y)^3$ $27x^6y^3$

40. There are 60 multiple-choice questions on a standardized mathematics test. Each person taking the test is given 200 points at the start of the test. For each correct answer 10 points are added; for each incorrect answer 2.5 points are subtracted. No points are gained or lost for answers that are omitted.

Number of questions answered	60	50	50	a	a
Number correct	56	42	r	40	r
Test score	?	?	?	?	?

750; 600; $75 + 12.5r$; $700 - 2.5a$; $200 + 12.5r - 2.5a$

Find the area of each shaded region.

41.

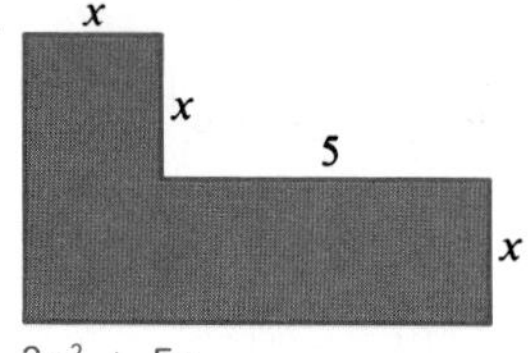

$2x^2 + 5x$

42.

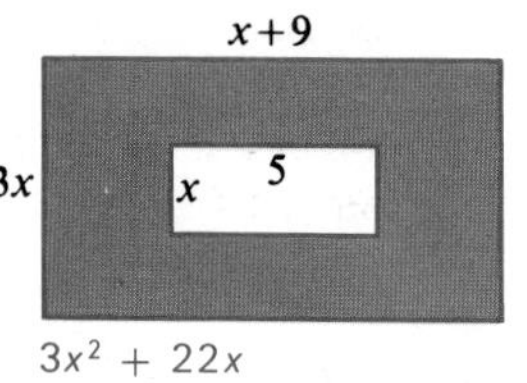

$3x^2 + 22x$

43. $2x^2 + 8x + 8$

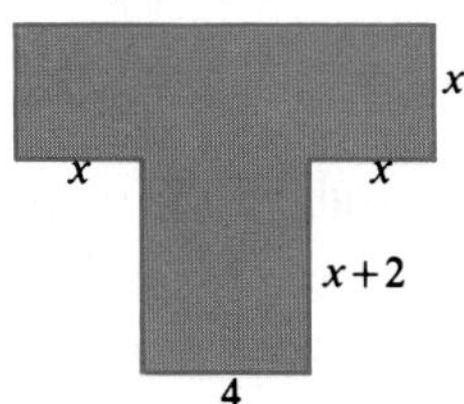

C **44.** Find the total surface area and the volume of the solid shown.

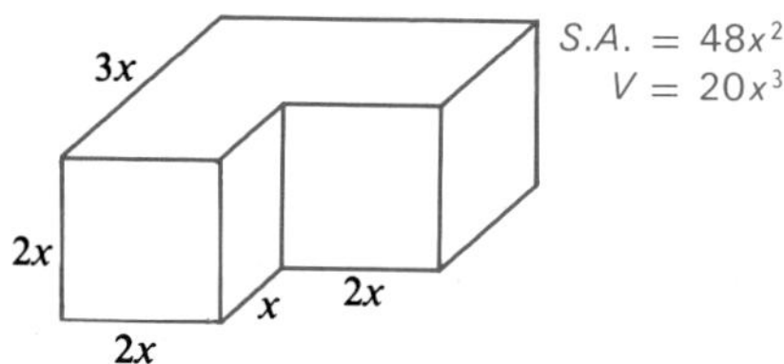

$S.A. = 48x^2$
$V = 20x^3$

Simplify. Each variable in an exponent represents a positive integer.

45. $x^n(2x^n - 3x + 4)$ $2x^{2n} - 3x^{n+1} + 4x^n$

46. $a^{n+1}(a^n + a)$ $a^{2n+1} + a^{n+2}$

47. $(2b^{n+1} + 3b^2)b^{n+1}$ $2b^{2n+2} + 3b^{n+3}$

48. $(-s)^{2n}(s^{2n} - 1)$ $s^{4n} - s^{2n}$

Challenge

Find the value of x such that the sum of the expressions is the same in each row, column, or diagonal. 12

x	5	$x - 2$
$x - 5$	9	11
8	$x + 1$	$x - 6$

4-6 Multiplying Two Polynomials

Objective To multiply polynomials.

You have learned to use the distributive axiom to multiply a polynomial by a monomial:

$$(4x + 3)(3x) = 4x(3x) + 3(3x)$$

If you replace $3x$ in the example above by the polynomial $3x + 4$, the distributive axiom can still be applied:

$$\begin{aligned}(4x + 3)(3x + 4) &= 4x(3x + 4) + 3(3x + 4)\\ &= 12x^2 + 16x + 9x + 12\\ &= 12x^2 + 25x + 12\end{aligned}$$

Here is another example in which a polynomial is multiplied by a polynomial, but the work is done in vertical form.

Step 1 Multiply by $3a$.

$$\begin{array}{r}5a^2 - 3a - 7\\ 3a + 2\\ \hline 15a^3 - 9a^2 - 21a\end{array}$$

Step 2 Multiply by 2.

$$\begin{array}{r}5a^2 - 3a - 7\\ 3a + 2\\ \hline 15a^3 - 9a^2 - 21a\\ 10a^2 - 6a - 14\\ \hline\end{array}$$

Step 3 Add.

$$\begin{array}{r}5a^2 - 3a - 7\\ 3a + 2\\ \hline 15a^3 - 9a^2 - 21a\\ 10a^2 - 6a - 14\\ \hline 15a^3 + a^2 - 27a - 14\end{array}$$

It is often helpful to rearrange the terms of a polynomial so that their degrees in a particular variable are in either decreasing or increasing order.

In order of decreasing degree in x: $5x^4 + 5x^3 - 2x + 4$

In order of increasing degree in x: $4 - 2x + 5x^3 + 5x^4$

In order of decreasing degree in a and increasing degree in b: $-7a^3 + a^2b + 2ab^2 + 3b^3$

To see the advantage of rearranging terms, first multiply the polynomials at the left below. Then compare your work with that shown at the right, where the terms of both polynomials have been rearranged.

$$\begin{array}{l}a^3 - ab^2 + 3b^3 + 2a^2b\\ b + a\\ \hline\end{array}$$

Rearrange in order of decreasing degree in a.

$$\begin{array}{r}a^3 + 2a^2b - ab^2 + 3b^3\\ a + b\\ \hline a^4 + 2a^3b - a^2b^2 + 3ab^3\\ a^3b + 2a^2b^2 - ab^3 + 3b^4\\ \hline a^4 + 3a^3b + a^2b^2 + 2ab^3 + 3b^4\end{array}$$

Teaching Suggestions p. T90

Suggested Extensions p. T91

Chalkboard Examples

Multiply.

1. $(3x + 2)(x - 5)$
   $3x^2 - 15x + 2x - 10 =$
   $3x^2 - 13x - 10$
2. $(5t - 1)(2t + 6)$
   $10t^2 + 30t - 2t - 6 =$
   $10t^2 + 28t - 6$
3. $(2y + 1)(3y^2 - y + 5)$
   $6y^3 - 2y^2 + 10y +$
   $3y^2 - y + 5 =$
   $6y^3 + y^2 + 9y + 5$
4. $(3 - n)(2 - 3n + 4n^2)$
   $6 - 9n + 12n^2$
   $- 2n + 3n^2 - 4n^3 =$
   $6 - 11n + 15n^2 - 4n^3$
5. $$\begin{array}{r}2m^2 - 3m + 4\\ 3m - 1\\ \hline 6m^3 - 9m^2 + 12m\\ - 2m^2 + 3m - 4\\ \hline 6m^3 - 11m^2 + 15m - 4\end{array}$$
6. $$\begin{array}{r}x^2 + 2xy + 2y^2\\ x - 3y\\ \hline x^3 + 2x^2y + 2xy^2\\ - 3x^2y - 6xy^2 - 6y^3\\ \hline x^3 - x^2y - 4xy^2 - 6y^3\end{array}$$

Supplementary Materials

Practice Master 20
Test 12
Resource Book, p. 81

Suggested Assignments

Minimum

Day 1: 158/1–25 odd
S 155/33, 35, 37

Day 2: 159/27–41 odd
R 160/*Self-Test 2*

Average

158/1–45 odd
R 160/*Self-Test 2*

Maximum

158/1–47 odd
S 146/49, 50

Additional A Exercises

Multiply. Use the horizontal form.

1. $(n + 6)(n + 3)$
$n^2 + 9n + 18$
2. $(3a - 1)(a - 5)$
$3a^2 - 16a + 5$
3. $(5b - 6)(2b + 4)$
$10b^2 + 8b - 24$
4. $(4 - x)(7 - 2x + 5x^2)$
$28 - 15x + 22x^2 - 5x^3$
5. $(5c - 4)(5c^2 - 4c - 3)$
$25c^3 - 40c^2 + c + 12$

Multiply. Use the vertical form.

6. $9x^2 - 3x + 5$
$4x + 6$
$36x^3 + 42x^2 + 2x + 30$

Additional Answers Written Exercises

5. $2a^2 + 9a - 18$
6. $10n^2 - 11n + 3$
7. $12t^2 + 7t - 10$
8. $20y^2 + 9y - 18$
9. $x^3 + 5x^2 + 10x + 8$
10. $2y^3 + 3y^2 + y - 6$
11. $2a^3 + 5a^2 + 11a - 7$
12. $14n^3 - 31n^2 - 3n + 2$
16. $2a^2 + 17a + 21$
17. $6n^2 + 3n - 45$
18. $4x^3 + 25x^2 + x - 30$
19. $16y^3 - 34y^2 + 11y + 6$

Oral Exercises

Arrange in order of decreasing degree in the variable indicated in color.

1. $2x + x^2 + 5$; x $x^2 + 2x + 5$
2. $5x^2 - 3x^3 - 4 + 7x$; x $-3x^3 + 5x^2 + 7x - 4$
3. $a^2b + 2a^3 - ab^2 + 4b^3$; a $2a^3 + a^2b - ab^2 + 4b^3$
4. $a^2b + 2a^3 - ab^2 + 4b^3$; b $4b^3 - ab^2 + a^2b + 2a^3$

Arrange in order of increasing degree in the variable indicated in color.

5. $5y^3 - 3y^2 + y^4 + 7$; y $7 - 3y^2 + 5y^3 + y^4$
6. $s + s^2t^2 + 3s^3t - s^3t^3$; t $s + 3s^3t + s^2t^2 - s^3t^3$

Complete.

7. $(5x + 3)(2x + 1) = 5x(\underline{?}) + 3(\underline{?})$ $2x + 1$; $2x + 1$
8. $(8a - 7)(3a + 2) = 8a(\underline{?}) - 7(\underline{?})$ $3a + 2$; $3a + 2$
9. $(4z + 2)(z^2 + z - 5) = 4z(\underline{?}) + 2(\underline{?})$ $z^2 + z - 5$; $z^2 + z - 5$
10. $(2t + 3)(t^2 + 5t + 1) = 2t(\underline{?}) + (\underline{?})(\underline{?})$ $t^2 + 5t + 1$; 3; $t^2 + 5t + 1$
11. $(2y + 5)(y + 1) = 2y(y + 1) + 5(y + 1) = (\underline{?})y^2 + (\underline{?})y + (\underline{?})$ 2; 7; 5
12. $(3x + 4)(x - 1) = 3x(x - 1) + 4(x - 1) = (\underline{?})x^2 + (\underline{?})x + (\underline{?})$ 3; 1; -4

Written Exercises

Multiply. Use the horizontal form.

A

1. $(a + 3)(a + 5)$ $a^2 + 8a + 15$
2. $(b + 4)(b + 7)$ $b^2 + 11b + 28$
3. $(c + 2)(c - 5)$ $c^2 - 3c - 10$
4. $(x - 4)(x + 9)$ $x^2 + 5x - 36$
5. $(2a - 3)(a + 6)$
6. $(5n - 3)(2n - 1)$
7. $(3t - 2)(4t + 5)$
8. $(5y + 6)(4y - 3)$
9. $(x + 2)(x^2 + 3x + 4)$
10. $(y - 1)(2y^2 + 5y + 6)$
11. $(2a - 1)(a^2 + 3a + 7)$
12. $(7n + 2)(2n^2 - 5n + 1)$
13. $(8x - 5)(3x^2 - x + 4)$ $24x^3 - 23x^2 + 37x - 20$
14. $(2b - 5)(3b^2 - 6b - 4)$ $6b^3 - 27b^2 + 22b + 20$
15. $(2 - t)(4 + 2t + 3t^2)$ $8 + 4t^2 - 3t^3$

Multiply. Use the vertical form.

16. $2a + 3$
$a + 7$
17. $3n + 9$
$2n - 5$
18. $4x^2 + x - 5$
$x + 6$
19. $8y^2 - 5y - 2$
$2y - 3$
20. $4x - 7y$
$5x - 2y$
21. $3c - 7d$
$2c + d$
22. $a^2 + ab + b^2$
$a + b$
23. $2x^2 - 3xy + y^2$
$2x + y$

24. A rectangular region is subdivided into four smaller regions with dimensions shown.
    a. Find the areas of these four regions. See right.
    b. Show that the sum of the areas of the four small regions equals the product of the length and width of the original rectangle.

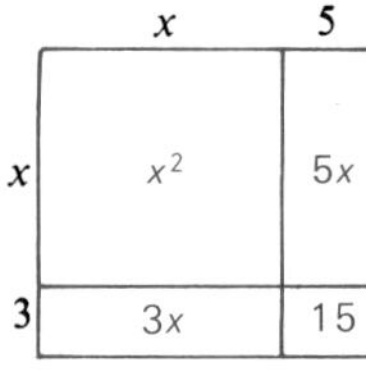

25. Use the figure at the right.
  a. Find the areas of these four regions. See right.
  b. Show that the sum of the areas of the four small regions equals the product of the length and width of the original rectangle.

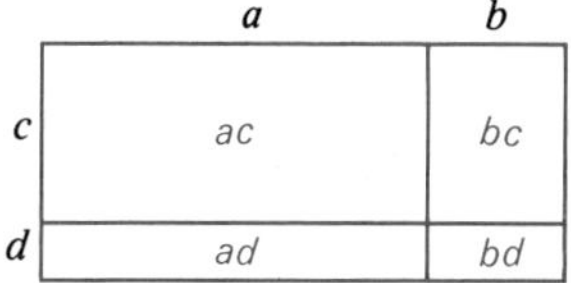

Multiply using either the horizontal or the vertical form. Arrange the terms in each factor in order of decreasing or increasing degree in some variable.

B **26.** $(3x + 5)(2x^2 + 7 - 3x)$

27. $(4n + 2)(6 - 5n + 4n^2)$

28. $(4a - 5)(3a + 6 - a^2)$

29. $(7 - 5y)(4y^2 + 2 - 9y)$

30. $(2x - 3y)(x^2 + y^2 - 4xy)$

31. $(c - 7d)(8c^2 - d^2 + cd)$

32. $(5a + 4b)(2ab - b^2 + a^2)$

33. $(8x - 4y)(2xy - y^2 + 3x^2)$

34. $(4a^2 - 3a + 2)^2$ $16a^4 - 24a^3 + 25a^2 - 12a + 4$

35. $(2y^2 - 3yz + z^2)(y^2 + yz + 2z^2)$ $2y^4 - y^3z + 2y^2z^2 - 5yz^3 + 2z^4$

Solve.

36. $(x - 3)(x + 2) = (x + 1)(x + 5)$ $\frac{-11}{7}$

37. $(3n - 1)(2n + 1) - n(6n - 2) = 0$ $\frac{1}{3}$

38. $(3r - 2)(r - 2) - (r + 1)(3r - 1) = 0$ $\frac{1}{2}$

39. $(a + 7)(a + 4) - a(a + 3) = 68$ 5

40. $(x - 5)(x^2 - 3x + 4) = x(x^2 - 8x + 6)$ $\frac{20}{13}$

41. $(2y - 4)(y^2 - 3y) - y(2y^2 - 10y + 2) = 46$ $\frac{23}{5}$

42. Find the square of $4a^2 - 3a + 2$. Express as a polynomial. $16a^4 - 24a^3 + 25a^2 - 12a + 4$

43. Find the cube of $x + 3$. Express as a polynomial. $x^3 + 9x^2 + 27x + 27$

44. Suppose you know that $(2 + y)^3 = 8 + 12y + 6y^2 + y^3$. Find $(2 + y)^4$.

45. Subtract the product of $2x + y$ and $3x - y$ from $x^2 + y^2$. $-5x^2 - xy + 2y^2$

46. When a certain polynomial is divided by $x + 2$, the quotient is $x^2 - 5x + 4$. Find the polynomial. $x^3 - 3x^2 - 6x + 8$

C **47.** **a.** Multiply:
(1) $(x + 1)(x^2 - x + 1)$ $x^3 + 1$
(2) $(x + 1)(x^3 - x^2 + x - 1)$ $x^4 - 1$
(3) $(x + 1)(x^4 - x^3 + x^2 - x + 1)$ $x^5 + 1$

b. Using your answers to part (a), predict answers for these products. $x^6 - 1$
(4) $(x + 1)(x^5 - x^4 + x^3 - x^2 + x - 1)$
(5) $(x + 1)(x^6 - x^5 + x^4 - x^3 + x^2 - x + 1)$ $x^7 + 1$

Computer Exercises

For students with some programming experience

Write a BASIC program to add and subtract two polynomials. The coefficients of each polynomial should be entered with INPUT statements in order from least to greatest degree. Each set of coefficients should be stored in an array. Use the program to find the sum and the difference of each of the following pairs of polynomials.

1. $3 + 4x + 5x^2$ and $1 + 7x - 2x^2$

2. $-5 - 6x^2$ and $2x^2 + x^4$

3. $4x + 9x^2$ and $5x^3$

4. $7 + 2x + x^3$ and $-3 + 4x + x^2$

20. $20x^2 - 43xy + 14y^2$

21. $6c^2 - 11cd - 7d^2$

22. $a^3 + 2a^2b + 2ab^2 + b^3$

23. $4x^3 - 4x^2y - xy^2 + y^3$

24. b. Total of areas of 4 regions: $x^2 + 5x + 3x + 15 = x^2 + 8x + 15$ Area of orig. rectangle: $(x + 3)(x + 5) = x^2 + 8x + 15$

25. b. The sum of the 4 regions is $ac + bc + ad + bd$. The product of the length and width of the original rectangle $= (a + b)(c + d) = ac + bc + ad + bd$.

26. $6x^3 + x^2 + 6x + 35$

27. $16n^3 - 12n^2 + 14n + 12$

28. $-4a^3 + 17a^2 + 9a - 30$

29. $-20y^3 + 73y^2 - 73y + 14$

30. $2x^3 - 11x^2y + 14xy^2 - 3y^3$

31. $8c^3 - 55c^2d - 8cd^2 + 7d^3$

32. $5a^3 + 14a^2b + 3ab^2 - 4b^3$

33. $24x^3 + 4x^2y - 16xy^2 + 4y^3$

44. $y^4 + 8y^3 + 24y^2 + 32y + 16$

Additional Answers Computer Exercises

1. $4 + 11x + 3x^2$; $2 - 3x + 7x^2$
2. $-5 - 4x^2 + x^4$; $-5 - 8x^2 - x^4$
3. $4x + 9x^2 + 5x^3$; $4x + 9x^2 - 5x^3$
4. $4 + 6x + x^2 + x^3$; $10 - 2x - x^2 + x^3$

Mixed Review Exercises

1. Find the average of the numbers $-18, 22, 41, -6, 11$. 10

Simplify.

2. $5 + 6(14 - 3)$ 71
3. $5m^2(m - 3) - 4m(m - 6)$ $5m^3 - 19m^2 + 24m$
4. What property enables us to transform $x - 7 = 14$ into $x = 21$? Addition Prop. of =

Quick Quiz

Simplify.

1. $-5a^2a^3$ $-5a^5$
2. $\left(\frac{1}{4}m\right)(-8m^5)(-2m)$ $4m^7$
3. $84x\left(\frac{1}{3}x^2\right)\left(-\frac{1}{4}x\right)$ $-7x^4$
4. $3^3 \cdot 3^{x-3} \cdot 3^x$ 3^{2x}
5. $(-3y^2)^3$ $-27y^6$
6. $-(3y^2z)^3$ $-27y^6z^3$
7. $-(3y^3z)^2$ $-9y^6z^2$
8. $(-3y^3)^2$ $9y^6$
9. $-5n(3 - n)$ $-15n + 5n^2$
10. $\frac{1}{5}a^2b(25a^2 + 10ab - b^2)$ $5a^4b + 2a^3b^2 - \frac{1}{5}a^2b^3$
11. Solve. $7 - \frac{3}{4}(8b - 12) = -14$ $b = 5$

Multiply.

12. $(5c - 3)(c - 7)$ $5c^2 - 38c + 21$
13. $(2 - 5d)(4 + 7d - 2d^2)$ $8 - 6d - 39d^2 + 10d^3$

Self-Test 2

Simplify.

1. $-2x^3x^4$ $-2x^7$
2. $(-6a^7)(-9a)\left(\frac{1}{3}a\right)$ $18a^9$ **Obj. 4-3, p. 148**
3. $126a\left(-\frac{1}{7}a\right)\left(\frac{1}{9}a^3\right)$ $-2a^5$
4. $4^2 \cdot 4^x \cdot 4^{x-2}$ 4^{2x}
5. $(-2x^4)^3$ $-8x^{12}$
6. $-(2x^4y)^3$ $-8x^{12}y^3$ **Obj. 4-4, p. 151**
7. $-(2x^3y)^4$ $-16x^{12}y^4$
8. $(-2x^3)^4$ $16x^{12}$
9. $-4c(8 - c)$ $-32c + 4c^2$
10. $\frac{1}{7}xy^2(56x^2 - 49xy + y^2)$ $8x^3y^2 - 7x^2y^3 + \frac{1}{7}xy^4$ **Obj. 4-5, p. 154**
11. Solve $4 - \frac{2}{3}(6a - 15) = -38$. 13

Multiply.

12. $(7a - 6)(a - 8)$ $7a^2 - 62a + 48$
13. $(9 - 7t)(7 - 6t + 8t^2)$ $-56t^3 + 114t^2 - 103t + 63$ **Obj. 4-6, p. 157**

Check your answers with those at the back of the book.

Biographical Note / *Hypatia*

Because so little is known about women mathematicians who may have lived before Hypatia (A.D. 370–415), she is generally regarded as the first woman mathematician. She was born in Alexandria, Egypt, at a time when that city was one of the greatest centers of learning in the world. Hypatia studied mathematics, science, art, literature, and philosophy. Highly regarded as a mathematician and as an astronomer, Hypatia became a professor of mathematics and philosophy at the university in Alexandria, where she lectured on Plato, Aristotle, astronomy, geometry, Diophantine algebra, and the conics of Appollonius. She wrote several mathematical commentaries and has been credited by some with the invention of the astrolabe and the planisphere, two instruments used in the study of astronomy. Hypatia also invented apparatus for distilling water, measuring the level of water, and determining the specific gravity of liquids.

After her death in A.D. 415, no significant progress in the mathematics taught by Hypatia was made for centuries. Unfortunately, most of her work has either been lost or destroyed. Except for a portion of one of her papers that was found in the fifteenth century, our knowledge of Hypatia is based on the letters of her contemporaries and students.

Problem Solving

4-7 Transforming Formulas

Objective To transform formulas.

Many applications of mathematics require the use of known formulas. In using a formula, it is often desirable to transform the formula to express a particular variable in terms of the other variables.

Example 1 The formula $A = \frac{1}{2}h(a + b)$ gives the area of a trapezoid with bases a units and b units long and with height h units. Use this formula to solve for the variable a in terms of A, h, and b.

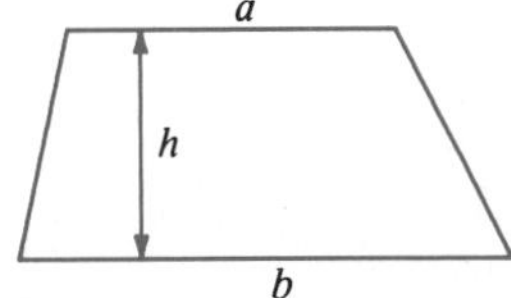

Solution

$$A = \frac{1}{2}h(a + b)$$
$$2A = h(a + b)$$
$$\frac{2A}{h} = a + b$$
$$\therefore a = \frac{2A}{h} - b \quad \textit{Answer}$$

Example 2 To compute the total piston displacement, P, in an automobile engine, a mechanic used the formula $P = 0.7854d^2sn$, where d is the diameter of each cylinder, s is the length of the stroke, and n is the number of cylinders. Use this formula to solve for the variable s in terms of P, d, and n.

Solution $P = 0.7854d^2sn$
Dividing both sides of the formula by $0.7854d^2n$, you obtain

$$s = \frac{P}{0.7854d^2n}. \quad \textit{Answer}$$

Note that the formula for s obtained in Example 2 is meaningful only if $d \neq 0$ and $n \neq 0$. Of course, neither d nor n will be zero since the engine must have cylinders and each cylinder must have a diameter.

Teaching Suggestions p. T91

Suggested Extensions p. T91

Chalkboard Examples

Solve each equation for the variable given. State the restrictions, if any, for the formula obtained to be meaningful.

1. $i = Prt$; P
   $P = \frac{i}{rt}$; $r \neq 0$; $t \neq 0$
2. $S = \frac{1}{2}n(a + 1)$; n
   $n = \frac{2S}{a + 1}$; $a \neq -1$
3. $P = 2l + 2w$; w
   $w = \frac{P - 2l}{2}$
4. $b - y = 3y$; y
   $y = \frac{b}{4}$
5. $S = \frac{1}{2}at^2$; a
   $a = \frac{2S}{t^2}$; $t \neq 0$
6. $v^2 = u^2 + 2as$; s
   $s = \frac{v^2 - u^2}{2a}$; $a \neq 0$

Suggested Assignments

Minimum
162/1–15
S 159/36, 38, 40

Average
162/1–23 odd

Maximum
162/1–29 odd
R 160/*Self-Test 2*

Additional A Exercises

Solve for the given variable. State the restrictions, if any, for the formula obtained to be meaningful.

1. $F = ma$; m $m = \frac{F}{a}$, $a \neq 0$
2. $A = \frac{1}{2}bh$; h $h = \frac{2A}{b}$, $b \neq 0$
3. $p = 2(l + w)$; l $l = \frac{p - 2w}{2}$
4. $A = \frac{1}{2}h(b + c)$; c $c = \frac{2A}{h} - b$, $h \neq 0$
5. $E = mc^2$; m $m = \frac{E}{c^2}$, $c \neq 0$
6. $V = lwh$; h $h = \frac{V}{lw}$, $l \neq 0$, $w \neq 0$

Mixed Review Exercises

1. Evaluate $\frac{ab}{c}$ if $a = 15$, $b = 21$, and $c = 3$. 105
2. Find the solution over the set of real numbers: $|x| = 3.76$ $\{\pm 3.76\}$
3. Tom bought some tapes at \$7 each and some LP's at \$6 each. He bought ten items and spent \$67. How many tapes did he buy? 7

Oral Exercises

Solve each equation for *x*.

1. $x - a = b$ $x = a + b$
2. $ax = b$ $x = \frac{b}{a}$
3. $y = kx$ $x = \frac{y}{k}$
4. $ax + b = c$ $x = \frac{c - b}{a}$

Solve each equation for the variable shown in color.

5. $P = a + b + c$; b $b = P - a - c$
6. $V = Bh$; B $B = \frac{V}{h}$
7. $A = \frac{1}{2}bh$; h $h = \frac{2A}{b}$
8. $d = rt$; t $t = \frac{d}{r}$
9. $I = Prt$; r $r = \frac{I}{Pt}$
10. $V = \pi r^2 h$; h $h = \frac{V}{\pi r^2}$
11. $R = \frac{kl}{d^2}$; l $l = \frac{Rd^2}{k}$
12. $C = \frac{mv^2}{r}$; r $r = \frac{mv^2}{C}$

Written Exercises

Solve for the variable shown in color. State the restrictions, if any, for the formula obtained to be meaningful.

A

1. $C = 2\pi r$; r $r = \frac{C}{2\pi}$
2. $F = ma$; a $a = \frac{F}{m}$; $m \neq 0$
3. $s = \frac{gt^2}{2}$; g $g = \frac{2s}{t^2}$; $t \neq 0$
4. $V = \frac{b^2h}{3}$; h $h = \frac{3V}{b^2}$; $b \neq 0$
5. $2a - z = a$; z $z = a$
6. $2b + y = b$; y $y = -b$
7. $A = \frac{1}{2}h(b + c)$; h $h = \frac{2A}{b + c}$; $b \neq -c$
8. $s = vt + 16t^2$; v $v = \frac{s - 16t^2}{t}$; $t \neq 0$
9. $C = \frac{5}{9}(F - 32)$; F $F = \frac{9}{5}C + 32$
10. $S = \frac{n}{2}(a + 50)$; a $a = \frac{2S}{n} - 50$; $n \neq 0$
11. $A = P + Prt$; t $t = \frac{A - P}{Pr}$; $P \neq 0$, $r \neq 0$
12. $A = 2(l + w)$; w $w = \frac{A}{2} - l$

B

13. $A = \frac{a + b + c + d}{4}$; d $d = 4A - a - b - c$
14. $v^2 = u^2 + 2as$; a $a = \frac{v^2 - u^2}{2s}$; $s \neq 0$
15. $2ax + 1 = ax + 5$; x $x = \frac{4}{a}$; $a \neq 0$
16. $3by - 2 = 2by + 1$; y $y = \frac{3}{b}$; $b \neq 0$
17. $3aw + 1 = aw - 7$; w $w = \frac{-4}{a}$; $a \neq 0$
18. $6bct - 1 = 4bct + 1$; t $t = \frac{1}{bc}$; $b \neq 0$, $c \neq 0$
19. $s = \frac{1}{2}n(a + l)$; l $l = \frac{2s}{n} - a$; $n \neq 0$
20. $l = a + (n - 1)d$; n $n = \frac{l - a}{d} + 1$; $d \neq 0$
21. $a = \frac{180(n - 2)}{n}$; n $n = \frac{360}{180 - a}$; $a \neq 180$
22. $A = P(1 + rt)$; r $r = \frac{A - P}{Pt}$; $P \neq 0$, $t \neq 0$
23. $(a + b)(u - 2) = (u + 2)(b - a)$; u $u = \frac{2b}{a}$; $a \neq 0$
24. $(2x + b)(2x - b) = 4x(x - 1)$; x $x = \frac{b^2}{4}$
25. $s = \frac{rL - a}{r - 1}$; L $L = \frac{s(r - 1) + a}{r}$; $r \neq 0$
26. $G = \frac{v(P - r)}{f - r}$; P $P = \frac{G(f - r)}{v} + r$; $v \neq 0$

C

27. $A = P + Prt$; P $P = \frac{A}{1 + rt}$; $r \neq \frac{-1}{t}$
28. $R = \frac{r}{1 - r}$; r $r = \frac{R}{R + 1}$; $R \neq -1$
29. $C = K\frac{Rr}{R - r}$; R $R = \frac{Cr}{C - Kr}$; $C \neq Kr$
30. $F = \frac{ef}{e + f - d}$; f $f = \frac{Fe - Fd}{e - F}$; $e \neq F$

4-8 Distance-Rate-Time Problems

Objective To solve some problems involving uniform motion.

An object is said to be in **uniform motion** when it moves without changing its speed, or rate. The three examples that follow illustrate three types of problems involving uniform motion. Each is solved using a chart, a sketch, and the formula:

$$\text{distance} = \text{rate} \times \text{time}$$

$$d = rt$$

In your work use the symbols s for seconds, min for minutes, and h for hours.

Example 1 (Motion in opposite directions)
Two planes leave Chicago's O'Hare Airport at the same time, one traveling east and the other west. The average speed of the eastbound plane is 60 km/h more than the speed of the westbound plane. After 2.5 h of flying time, the planes are 4150 km apart. What are their speeds?

Solution

Step 1 The problem asks for the speeds of the two planes. Make a sketch.

Step 2 Let x = speed of the westbound plane. Make a chart of the given facts and use it to label your sketch.

	Rate	× Time =	Distance
Westbound	x	2.5	$2.5x$
Eastbound	$x + 60$	2.5	$2.5(x + 60)$

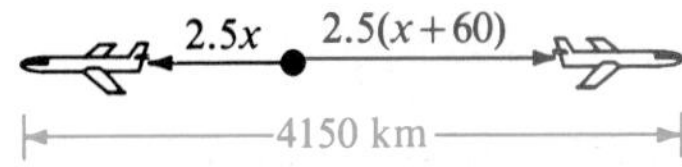

Step 3 The sketch will help you write the equation.

Step 4
$$\begin{aligned} 2.5x + 2.5(x + 60) &= 4150 \\ 2.5x + 2.5x + 150 &= 4150 \\ 5x + 150 &= 4150 \\ 5x &= 4000 \\ x &= 800 \\ x + 60 &= 860 \end{aligned}$$

Step 5 *Check:* In 2.5 h, the westbound plane flies $2.5 \cdot 800 = 2000$ km.
In 2.5 h, the eastbound plane flies $2.5 \cdot 860 = 2150$ km.
$2000 + 2150 = 4150$ km ✓

$\therefore$ the planes fly at 800 km/h and 860 km/h, respectively. ***Answer***

Teaching Suggestions p. T91

Chalkboard Examples

1. What is the distance traveled in 6 h at 60 km/h?
$d = rt = 60 \cdot 6 =$ 360 km
2. What is the average rate of speed if 275 km are traveled in 5.5 h?
$r = \frac{d}{t} = \frac{275}{5.5} =$ 50 km/h
3. How long does it take to travel 288 km at an average rate of 72 km/h?
$t = \frac{d}{r} = \frac{288}{72} = 4$ h
4. Mary Beth and Michael leave school traveling in opposite directions. Michael is walking and Mary Beth is biking, averaging 6 km/h more than Michael. If they are 18 km apart after 1.5 h, what is the rate of each?
M's dist. + MB's dist. = total distance. Let r = Michael's rate.
$1.5r + 1.5(r + 6) = 18$
$1.5r + 1.5r + 9 = 18$
$3r = 9$
Michael: 3 km/h; Mary Beth: 9 km/h
5. Carla begins biking south to the park at 20 km/h at noon. Dean leaves from the same point 15 min later to catch her. If Dean is biking at 24 km/h, how long will it take him to catch Carla?
Dean's dist. = Carla's dist. Let t = Dean's time.
$24t = 20\left(t + \frac{1}{4}\right)$
(continued)

Chalkboard Examples
(continued)

$$24t = 20t + 5$$
$$4t = 5$$
$$t = 1\frac{1}{4}$$

$\therefore$ it will take Dean $1\frac{1}{4}$ h.

6. Mark drove his car to the garage at 48 km/h and then walked back home at 8 km/h. The drive took 10 min less than the walk home. How far did Mark walk and for how long? dist. out = dist. back. Let t = time walking.

$$48\left(t - \frac{1}{6}\right) = 8t$$
$$48t - 8 = 8t$$
$$40t = 8$$
$$t = \frac{8}{40} = \frac{1}{5}$$

$\therefore$ Mark took $\frac{1}{5}$ h, or 12 min, to walk 1.6 km.

Common Error

Problem 12, for example, may be difficult for some students. Because Luke left one-half hour later than George, some students will represent the time George cycled in hours by x and the time Luke cycled in hours by $x + \frac{1}{2}$. Point out that if Luke leaves *later* than George, then he cycles for a *shorter* time than George. Therefore, if George's time in hours is represented by x, then Luke's time in hours must be represented by $x - \frac{1}{2}$.

Supplementary Materials

Practice Master 21
Resource Book, pp. 82, 165–168

Example 2 (Motion in the same direction)
Exactly 12 minutes after the Costanzas head north on the expressway, the Carrs set out from the same point to overtake them. The Costanzas travel at a steady 45 mph (miles per hour); the Carrs travel at 54 mph. How long does it take the Carrs to overtake the Costanzas?

Solution

Step 1 The problem asks for the Carrs' driving time. Make a sketch.

Step 2 Let x = the Carrs' time. Make a chart of the given facts and use it to label your sketch. Remember that 12 minutes must be written as $\frac{1}{5}$ *hour* because the speeds are given in miles per *hour*.

	Rate $\times$	Time	= Distance
Costanzas	45	$x + \frac{1}{5}$	$45\left(x + \frac{1}{5}\right)$
Carrs	54	x	$54x$

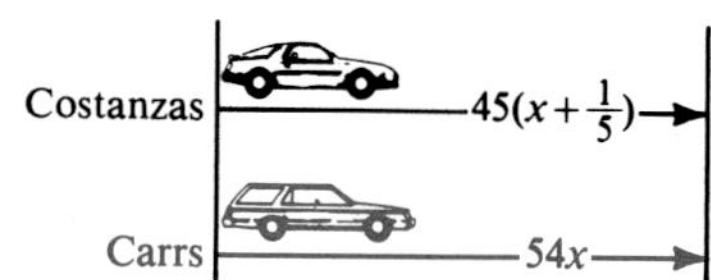

Step 3 When the Carrs overtake the Costanzas, the distances will be equal. This fact gives us the equation

$$45\left(x + \frac{1}{5}\right) = 54x.$$

Step 4

$$45x + 9 = 54x$$
$$9 = 9x$$
$$1 = x$$

Step 5 *Check:* In 1 hour, the Carrs travel $54 \cdot 1 = 54$ miles. In $\left(1 + \frac{1}{5}\right)$ hours, the Costanzas travel $45\left(1 + \frac{1}{5}\right) = 54$ miles.

$\therefore$ the Carrs overtake the Costanzas in 1 hour. ***Answer***

Example 3 (Round trip)
Gregory jogs to baseball practice at 10 km/h and gets a ride back home at 60 km/h. The ride home took 15 min less than his jogging. How far did he jog and for how long?

Solution

Step 1 The problem asks for the jogging distance and time. Make a sketch.

Step 2 Let x = the jogging time. Then $10x$ = jogging distance. Make a chart of the given facts and use it to label your sketch. Remember 15 min is 0.25 h.

	Rate ×	Time =	Distance
Jog	10	x	$10x$
Ride	60	$x - 0.25$	$60(x - 0.25)$

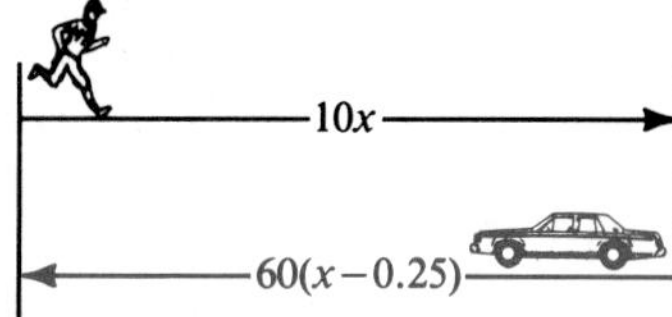

Step 3 In round-trip problems, the two distances are equal.

$$60(x - 0.25) = 10x$$

Step 4

$$60x - 15 = 10x$$
$$50x = 15$$
$$x = \frac{15}{50} = \frac{3}{10}$$
$$x = 0.3$$
$$10x = 3$$

Step 5 The check is left to you.

∴ Gregory jogs 0.3 h, or 18 min, for a distance of 3 km. ***Answer***

Notice in Examples 2 and 3 that the time, originally given in *minutes,* was changed to *hours*. This was done in order to make the units of time compatible with the speeds, which were given in terms of miles per *hour* and kilometers per *hour*.

Oral Exercises

Classify each problem as (1) a problem with motion in opposite directions, (2) a problem with motion in the same direction, or (3) a round-trip problem. Then complete the chart and give an equation.

1. Maria can average 30 km/h on her 10-speed racing bike, but Cooper cannot go that fast on his 3-speed bike. When Maria finished a race from Boston to Worcester, 90 km away, Cooper was still 18 km from the finish line. What is Cooper's average speed?

	Rate ×	Time =	Distance
Maria	?30	? 3	? 90
Cooper	x	? 3	? 72

same direction; $3x = 72$

2. Rip skates across a frozen lake at 10 mph and returns at 5 mph. If his total skating time is one hour, how wide is the lake?

	Rate	× Time	= Distance
Going	? 10	x	? $10x$
Returning	? 5	? $1 - x$	? $5(1 - x)$

round trip; $5(1 - x) = 10x$

3. Ann leaves Avon at noon biking to Batavia at 16 km/h. At 1 P.M. Bill leaves Batavia and bikes toward Avon at 20 km/h. If the distance between Avon and Batavia is 70 km, at what time do Ann and Bill meet?

	Rate	× Time	= Distance
Ann	? 16	x	? $16x$
Bill	? 20	? $x - 1$	? $20(x - 1)$

opposite direction; $16x + 20(x - 1) = 70$

4. Tracy leaves for work at 8 A.M. traveling at 36 mph. Sarah finds that Tracy has forgotten her briefcase, so she leaves at 8:05 chasing after her at 50 mph. At what time will Sarah catch Tracy?

	Rate	× Time	= Distance
Tracy	? 36	x	? $36x$
Sarah	? 50	? $x - \frac{1}{12}$	? $50\left(x - \frac{1}{12}\right)$

same direction; $36x = 50\left(x - \frac{1}{12}\right)$

Problems

1. 24 km/h 2. $3\frac{1}{3}$ mi wide 3. 2:30 P.M. 4. approx. 8:18 A.M.

A 1-4. Complete the solutions of Oral Exercises 1-4.

5. Two jets leave St. Louis at 2 P.M., one traveling north at 850 km/h and the other south at 750 km/h. At what time will they be 4000 km apart? 4:30 P.M.

6. Lisa can bike 6 km/h faster than Wendy. At noon, each girl leaves her house, traveling toward the other. If the distance between their houses is 20 km and they meet in 0.5 h, what is each girl's rate? Wendy, 17 km/h; Lisa, 23 km/h

7. It takes a train 90 min longer to go from Farmington to Allentown at 60 km/h than it does to return at 80 km/h. What is the distance between these towns? 360 km

Suggested Assignments

Minimum
Day 1: 166/*P*: 1–5, 7
S 162/16–18
Day 2: 166/*P*: 6, 8, 9
169/*P*: 1, 2, 4, 5
Day 2 finishes Sec. 4-8 and starts Sec. 4-9.

Average
Day 1: 166/*P*: 1–5, 7, 9
S 162/24–27
Day 2: 166/*P*: 6, 8, 11, 12, 13
S 159/38–46 even

Maximum
Day 1: 166/*P*: 1–10
S 162/26, 28, 30
Day 2: 167/*P*: 11–15
169/*P*: 1, 2, 4
Day 2 finishes Sec. 4-8 and starts Sec. 4-9.

Additional A Exercises

1. Two trains leave Mill City at the same time, one traveling north, the other, south. The average speed of the northbound train is 12 km/h more than the speed of the southbound train. After 3 hours, the trains are 396 km apart. What are their speeds? northbound, 72 km/h; southbound, 60 km/h
2. Kay and Janet leave Samantha's house, traveling in opposite directions toward their homes. Kay walks twice as fast as Janet and they both reach home in 15 min. If their homes are 1 km apart, what are their walking speeds?

Janet, $\frac{4}{3}$ km/h; Kay, $\frac{8}{3}$ km/h

8. A car travels 418 km in 6 h. One hour of the trip is in the city, where its average speed is just half of what the car averaged on the turnpike for the rest of the trip. What was the car's average city speed? 38 km/h

B 9. Kelly rode her bike from home to the repair shop and then walked home. She spent 10 min riding, 5 min talking to the attendant, and 20 min walking. If Kelly's walking speed is 12 km/h less than her biking speed, find the distance from her house to the repair shop. 4 km

10. Because Chip can run 1 m/s faster than Dean, he is able to run across a field in 20 s, a full 2.5 s quicker than Dean. How fast can Chip run? 9 m/sec

11. Laura can run at 8 m/s and Mary at 7.5 m/s. On a race track, Mary is given a 25 m head start and the race ends in a tie. How long is the track? 400 m

12. At 1:30 P.M., George left Exeter for Portsmouth, cycling at 20 km/h. At 2:00 P.M., Luke left Portsmouth for Exeter, cycling at 24 km/h. If the distance from Exeter to Portsmouth is 32 km, at what time did the boys meet? 2:30 P.M.

13. At 2:00 P.M., a small plane had been flying 1 h when a change of wind direction doubled its average ground speed. If the entire trip of 860 km took 2.5 h, how far did the plane travel in the first hour? 215 km

14. A ship must average 22 knots (nautical miles per hour) to make its 10-hour run on schedule. During the first four hours, bad weather caused it to reduce its average speed to 16 knots. What should its average speed be for the rest of the trip to maintain its schedule? 26 knots

C 15. A boy walking r km/h has a head start of b km on his friend who is walking at the rate of s km/h ($r < s$). How long will it take the second boy to overtake the first? $\left(\frac{b}{s - r}\right)$ hours

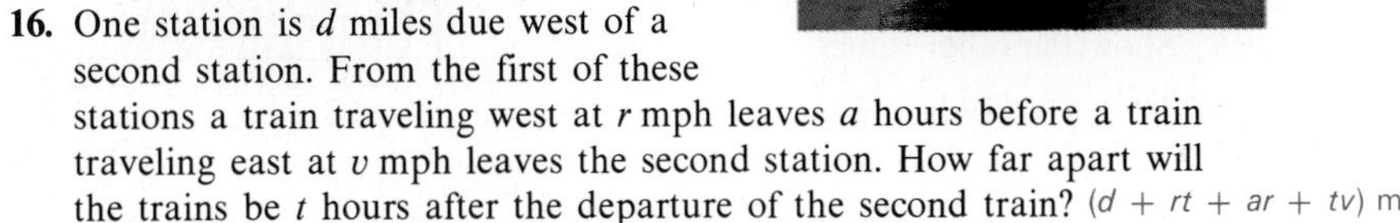

16. One station is d miles due west of a second station. From the first of these stations a train traveling west at r mph leaves a hours before a train traveling east at v mph leaves the second station. How far apart will the trains be t hours after the departure of the second train? $(d + rt + ar + tv)$ mi

17. It usually takes a bus 20 min to travel the 12 miles from City Hall to the airport. However, from 4:00 P.M. to 6:00 P.M., the bus will travel only 10 miles in the same length of time. If a bus leaves City Hall on the hour and every 15 min after that, and if it takes 20 min to get from a bus to an airplane, what is the last bus Sam can take from City Hall to get on a plane leaving at 5:50 P.M.? 5:00 P.M.

3. Twenty minutes after Jack started on his bike trip, his brother Don decided to join him. Jack was traveling 15 km/h, Don, 20 km/h. How long did Don travel before he caught up to Jack? 1 h

4. Robin rides her bike to the repair shop at 10 mi/h and walks back home at 4 mi/h. If her total traveling time is 42 min, how far is it from the repair shop to her home? 2 mi

Mixed Review Exercises

1. Diane has 24 yards of ribbon. She wants to make 18 bows. How many yards of ribbon will be in each bow? $1\frac{1}{3}$ yd

2. Simplify: $13x + 9 - (12x - 5)$ $x + 14$

Solve.

3. $3x + 22 = \frac{1}{2}(26 - 4x)$ $\frac{-9}{5}$

4. $D = rt$ for t. $t = \frac{D}{r}$

Teaching Suggestions p. T92

Suggested Extensions p. T92

Chalkboard Examples

1. A rectangle is 3 times as long as it is wide. If the length is increased by 6 and the width by 8, the area is increased by 108. Find the original dimensions.
   Step 2 Let w = width. Then $3w$ = length.
   Step 3
   $(3w + 6)(w + 8) = 3w^2 + 108$
   Step 4
   $3w^2 + 30w + 48 = 3w^2 + 108$
   $30w = 60$
   $w = 2$
   ∴ the width was 2 and the length was 6.
2. A rectangular placemat is 8 cm longer than it is wide. A 1-cm border is crocheted around the placemat. If the area of the border is 100 cm², find the dimensions of the placemat without the border.
   Step 2 Let w = width in centimeters. Then $w + 8$ = length.
   Step 3
   $(w + 10)(w + 2) - (w + 8)w = 100$
   Step 4 $w^2 + 12w + 20 - w^2 - 8w = 100$
   $4w + 20 = 100$
   $4w = 80$
   $w = 20$
   ∴ the width is 20 cm and the length is 28 cm.

Supplementary Material

Resource Book, pp. 169–170

4-9 Area Problems

Objective To solve some problems involving area.

To solve some problems involving area, you will need to multiply and add or subtract polynomials. Sketches are especially helpful in solving such problems.

The metric units of square measure that you will use most often are square centimeters (cm²) and square meters (m²).

A photograph 8 cm wide and 10 cm long is surrounded by a border 3 cm wide. To find the area of the border, you subtract the areas of the two rectangles.

Area of border
$= \text{Area of outer rectangle} - \text{Area of inner rectangle}$
$= (10 + 6)(8 + 6) - 10 \cdot 8$
$= (16)(14) - 80 = 144$

Thus, the area of the border is 144 cm².

Example A photograph is twice as long as it is wide. It is mounted so that a border 3 cm wide completely surrounds the photograph. Find the dimensions of the photograph if the area of the border is 216 cm².

Solution

Step 1 The problem asks for the dimensions of the photograph. Make a sketch.

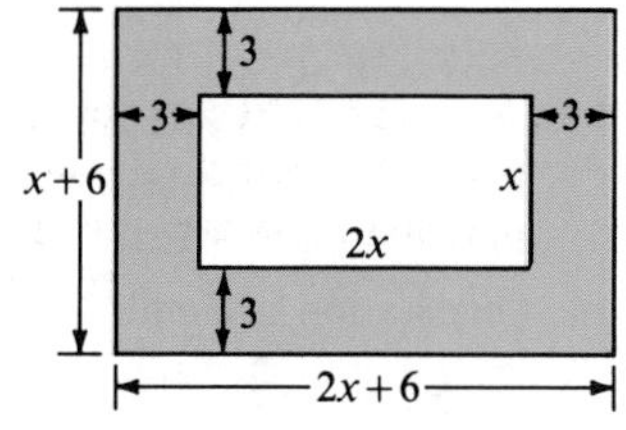

Step 2 Let x = width of the photograph. Show the other dimensions on the sketch.

Step 3

Area of border = Area of photograph and border − Area of photograph

$216 = (2x + 6)(x + 6) - (2x)(x)$

Step 4
$216 = 2x^2 + 18x + 36 - 2x^2$
$216 = 18x + 36$
$180 = 18x$
$10 = x$

Step 5 *Check:* Area of photograph and border

$$= (2x + 6)(x + 6) = (26)(16) = 416$$
$$\text{Area of photograph} = (2x)(x) = (20)(10) = 200$$
$$\text{Area of border} = 416 - 200 = 216 \quad \checkmark$$

$\therefore$ the dimensions of the photograph are 20 cm and 10 cm. ***Answer***

Problems

	Length × Width = Area		
First rectangle	$5 + x$?	x x	$x(5 + x)$?
New rectangle	$6 + x$?	$x + 1$?	?

$(6 + x)(x + 1)$

A **1.** A rectangle is 5 m longer than it is wide. If its length is increased by 1 m and its width is increased by 1 m, the area is increased by 14 m². Find the original dimensions. 4 m by 9 m

2. A rectangle is twice as long as it is wide. If the length and width are both increased by 3, the area of the rectangle is increased by 45. Make a chart like the one in Exercise 1 and find the dimensions of the original rectangle. 4 by 8

3. A baker has two pans with the same area. One is a square and the other is a rectangle 5 cm longer than the square but 4 cm less wide than the square. Find the total area of each pan. 400 cm²

4. A photo is 10 cm longer than it is wide. It is mounted in a frame 2 cm wide. The area of the frame is 112 cm². Find the dimensions of the photo. 7 cm by 17 cm

5. A poster is 20 cm longer than it is wide. It is mounted on a piece of cardboard so that there is a 10 cm border on all sides. If the area of the border is 2800 cm², what is the area of the poster? 3500 cm²

6. A brick patio is twice as long as it is wide. It is bordered on all sides by a garden one meter wide. If the area of the garden is 40 m², find the dimensions of the patio. 6 m by 12 m

7. A rectangular swimming pool is 5 m longer than it is wide. If a concrete walk 2 m wide is placed around the pool, the area covered by the pool and the walk is 156 m² greater than the area covered by the pool alone. What are the dimensions of the pool? 15 m by 20 m

Suggested Assignments

Minimum
169/*P*: 3, 6, 9
172/*P*: 1, 3, 4, 7

Day 2 of Sec. 4-8 finishes Sec. 4-8 and starts Sec. 4-9. This assignment finishes Sec. 4-9 and covers Sec. 4-10.

Average
Day 1: 169/*P*: 1, 2, 4, 5, 8
S 150/39, 40
Day 2: 169/*P*: 3, 6, 7, 9
S 167/*P*: 10, 14

Maximum
169/*P*: 5, 7–10
S 159/42, 44, 46

Day 2 of Sec. 4-8 finishes Sec. 4-8 and starts Sec. 4-9.

Additional A Exercises

1. A rectangle is 10 cm longer than it is wide. If its length is increased by 5 cm and its width is increased by 2 cm, its area is increased by 100 cm². Find the dimensions of the original rectangle. 10 cm by 20 cm
2. A rectangle is three times as long as it is wide. If the length and width are each decreased by 4, the area is decreased by 176. What are the original dimensions? 12 by 36
3. A quilting square is put in a frame 2 in. wide. The area of the frame is 136 in.². What is the length of a side of the square? 15 in.

(continued)

Additional A Exercises (continued)

4. The graduation picture of Grant High School's senior class is featured in the yearbook. The picture is on a page that is 5 cm longer than it is wide, and the picture has a 3 cm border around it. If the area of the border is 270 cm^2, how large is the picture? 17 cm by 22 cm

Mixed Review Exercises

1. Express "the square of $a - b$" in exponential form. $(a - b)^2$
2. Multiply: $(m - 9)(m + 10)$ $m^2 + m - 90$
3. Kelly can ride her bike (at 10 km/h) from her home to school in 20 min less than the time it takes her to walk the same route (at 4 km/h). How far is it from her home to her school? $2\frac{2}{9}$ km
4. Solve: $-16 = \frac{1}{6}k$ $k = -96$

B **8. a.** If a circle has radius r, then its area A is given by the formula $A = \pi r^2$. Use this formula to find a formula for the area of the shaded region in the figure at the right.

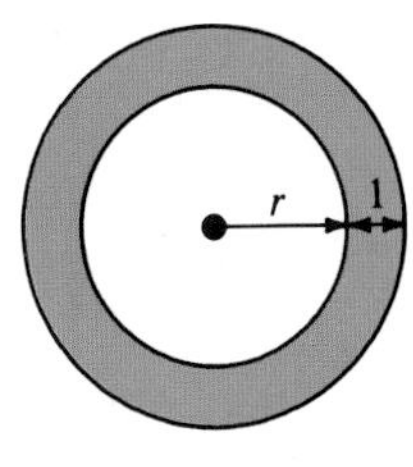

b. If the area of the shaded region is 11 cm^2, find the radius r. (Use $\frac{22}{7}$ as an approximation for π.)

a. $A = \pi(2r + 1)$ b. $r = \frac{5}{4}$ cm

9. A circular swimming pool is surrounded by a walkway 2 m wide. Find the radius of the pool if the area of the walkway is 88 m^2. (*Hint:* See Exercise 8a.) $r \approx 6$ m

C **10.** A running track 4 m wide goes around a rectangular soccer field that is twice as long as it is wide. At each end of the soccer field the track is a semicircle with radius r. Find a formula for the area of the track in terms of r. $A = 32r + 8\pi r + 16\pi$ m^2

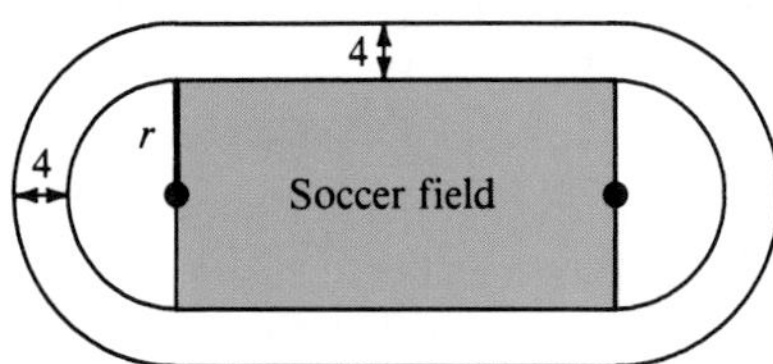

11. a. Suppose you plan to run once around the track described in Exercise 10. If you run staying 0.5 m from the inside edge of the track, find a formula for the distance that you would run. (*Hint:* The circumference of a circle is $C = 2\pi r$. Your answer will be in terms of π and r.) distance $= (8 + 2\pi)r + \pi$ m

b. Suppose a friend runs staying 0.5 m from the outer edge of the track. How much farther does your friend run than you? 6π m

Computer Key-In

It is very useful to include descriptive statements, called REMARK statements, in your programs. Such statements begin with the letters REM. The computer prints these statements in a LISTing but ignores them in a RUN. Thus, additional information about the program can be given, as shown in the program on the next page.

This program will find the cost of a number of items, the prices of which are stored on a file. Again, we use READ and DATA statements to represent this situation. The READ statement in line 130 READs the entire set of DATA. In order to READ through a second time as in line 220, a RESTORE statement (line 200) must be given to tell the computer to start back at the beginning.

The value of N and the dimension statement DIM S(N) are also used in the program. S(N) represents an *array,* or list, of numbers. In this program, lines 120–160 allow values of S(1), S(2), S(3), and S(4) to be INPUT. The dimension statement is not needed unless you wish to use more than 10 values.

```
10  REM: DATA ON FILE                                  Stored
20  REM: ITEM ID NO., PRICE                            data
30  DATA 2341,8.25
40  DATA 7204,10.95
50  DATA 3475,9.68
60  DATA 5068,11.49
70  REM---N = NUMBER OF ITEMS
80  REM---S(N) IS ARRAY OF NO.
90  REM---OF EACH ITEM SOLD
100  LET N=4
105  DIM S(4)  (not needed here—see text)
110  PRINT "INPUT NO. SOLD:"                           INPUT
120  FOR I=1 TO N                                      data
130  READ T,P
140  PRINT T;", HOW MANY SOLD";
150  INPUT S(I)
160  NEXT I
170  PRINT                                             Computation
180  PRINT "SUMMARY"                                   and
190  PRINT "ITEM";TAB(7);"NO. SOLD";                   OUTPUT
195  PRINT TAB(17);"PRICE";TAB(24);"COST"
200  RESTORE
210  FOR I=1 TO N
220  READ T,P
230  PRINT T;TAB(7);S(I);TAB(17);P;
235  PRINT TAB(24);S(I)*P
240  NEXT I
250  END
```

This program prints the OUTPUT as a table, using TAB statements as shown in lines 190, 195, 230, and 235. The TAB statement tells the computer in which column to print the OUTPUT. To see how TAB works, observe the positions of the OUTPUT.

Exercises

1. RUN the given program. Use 7, 4, 12, and 15 as the numbers of items. See above.

1.

ITEM	NO. SOLD	PRICE	COST
2341	7	8.25	57.75
7204	4	10.95	43.80
3475	12	9.68	116.16
5068	15	11.49	172.35

2. Modify the program to compute the total cost. RUN the program to find the total cost of the items in Exercise 1. $390.06

Computer Key-In Commentary

An array can represent a list of numbers or strings. If students are having difficulty understanding arrays, it may help to illustrate the concept with a list of strings, say, a grocery list:
List G$
1. lettuce
2. fish
3. asparagus
4. beets

The first item in the list, lettuce, is G$ (1). This has a different value than G$ (2), fish. It is not the same as the variable, G$.

If your computer prints columns in which the positive numbers do not align with column headings, this is because your machine prints a space in front of all numbers to allow for a possible negative sign.

Teaching Suggestions p. T92

Chalkboard Examples

Solve each problem if it has a solution. If a problem has no solution, explain why.

1. Find two consecutive even integers whose sum is 29. No solution; the sum of two even integers is an even integer.
2. For the senior play, twice as many adult tickets as student tickets were sold. If $420 was collected, how many student tickets were sold? No solution; the cost of each type of ticket is needed.
3. Chris has 127 stamps in her stamp collection. She has 4 less than 3 times as many foreign stamps as domestic stamps. How many foreign stamps does she have?
   Step 2 Let x = no. of domestic stamps. Then $3x - 4$ = no. of foreign stamps.
   Step 3
   $x + (3x - 4) = 127$
   Step 4 $4x - 4 = 127$
   $4x = 131$
   $x = 32\frac{3}{4}$
   No solution, since x is not an integer.

Supplementary Materials

Practice Master 22
Test 13
Resource Book, p. 83

4-10 Problems without Solutions

Objective To recognize problems that do not have solutions.

Does every problem have a solution? Consider the following situation.

Example At Green's Country Restaurant, a shrimp salad cost as much as a roast beef sandwich and a glass of milk together. What was the price of each item if the sandwich cost three times as much as the milk and the salad cost one dollar less than four times as much as the milk?

Solution

Step 1 The problem asks for the price of each item: the sandwich, the glass of milk, and the shrimp salad.
The problem tells how the price of the sandwich relates to the price of the milk (*three times as much*) and how the price of the salad relates to the price of the milk (*one dollar less than four times as much*).

Step 2 Let p = price of the glass of milk in dollars.

Then $3p$ = price of the sandwich, and $4p - 1$ = price of the salad.

Step 3 $\underbrace{\text{cost of salad}}_{4p-1}$ is the same as ($=$) $\underbrace{\text{cost of milk and sandwich}}_{p+3p}$

$$4p - 1 = p + 3p$$

Step 4

$$4p - 1 = 4p$$
$$-1 = 0$$

The equation obtained in Step 3 is equivalent to the false statement $-1 = 0$ and, therefore, has no solution. This means that the facts of the problem contain a contradiction and the problem has no solution!

In reading a problem, you should be on the lookout for facts that contradict each other. You should also be alert to recognize problems in which not enough facts are given for you to obtain a definite answer. Some of the problems in the following set can be solved; others fail to have solutions either because their facts are contradictory or because they contain too few facts.

Problems

Solve each problem if it has a solution. If a problem has no solution, explain why.

A

1. Fred has just as many dimes as quarters. His quarters and dimes total $8. How many coins of each type has he? No. sol.; facts contradictory

2. Kandy buys more twenty-cent stamps than fifteen-cent stamps. How many of each of these kinds of stamps does she buy if the total cost of the stamps is $7.20? No sol.; not enough info.

3. In the course of a year, the sum of an investor's gains and losses was $1000. What were her gains that year? her losses? No sol.; not enough info.

4. Find two consecutive integers whose sum is 54. No sol.; facts contradictory

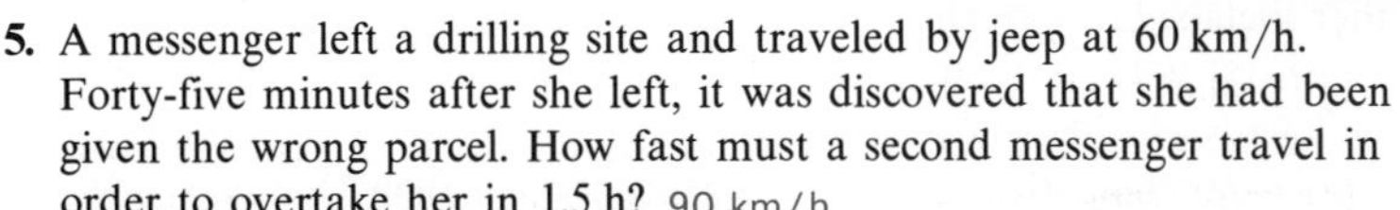

5. A messenger left a drilling site and traveled by jeep at 60 km/h. Forty-five minutes after she left, it was discovered that she had been given the wrong parcel. How fast must a second messenger travel in order to overtake her in 1.5 h? 90 km/h

6. For the first half hour of his trip, Al Martinez drove at his normal speed, but then traffic forced him to slow to three fourths of his normal speed for the rest of his journey. Still, he made the trip in 2 hours. Find his normal driving speed. No sol.; not enough info.

7. Don is three times as old as Barbara. Six years ago the sum of their ages was 8. How old was Barbara 6 years ago? No sol.; facts contradictory

8. The sponsor of a time-share vacation condominium plans to sell the permanent use of an apartment for 50 weeks of each year. Each week is designated to be either "prime" or "off-season." If each prime week sells for $7000 and each off-season week for $4000, and all weeks are sold, how many weeks must be prime in order for the sponsor to receive a total of $260,000 for the apartment? 20

9. Find three consecutive integers whose sum is 36 more than the greatest of the integers. No sol.; facts contradictory

10. A truck left town at noon and traveled at a uniform rate of 45 mph. At 1:00 P.M. the same day, a sedan set out from the same place at a uniform rate 10 mph greater. At what time did the sedan overtake the truck? 5:30 P.M.

11. In going to a medical meeting, Dr. Lloyd made a trip of 500 miles. She traveled by train for $1\frac{1}{2}$ hours and by automobile for the rest of the trip. The average speed of the train was 15 miles per hour more than that of the automobile. Find the average speed of the automobile. No sol.; not enough info.

Suggested Assignments

Minimum
The assignment for Sec. 4-9 covers Sec. 4-10.

Average
172/*P*: 1, 2, 4, 6, 7, 10, 12
R 174/*Self-Test 3*

Maximum
172/*P*: 1–11 odd, 12–16
S 170/*P*: 11
R 174/*Self-Test 3*

Additional A Exercises

Solve each problem if it has a solution. If a problem has no solution, explain why.

1. Find a combination of 20 nickels and dimes that adds up to $2.70. No sol.; 20 dimes, the max. value, only gives $2.00.
2. Find three consecutive odd integers whose sum is 72. No sol.; 3 such integers are even.
3. John is twice Don's age. 15 years ago, he was 10 years older than Don. How old is each now? No sol.; Ans. to equation is 10, but you cannot talk about a 10-yr-old's age "15 yrs ago."
4. Jackie walks from her house to school in 1 h, but can get there in 15 min by bus. How far is it from school to her house? Not enough information
5. A rectangular picture has a 3 in. frame. The area of the picture and frame is 172 in.^{2}. What are the dimensions of the picture? Not enough information

(continued)

Additional A Exercises (continued)

6. Myra bought some fourteen-cent stamps and some twenty-two-cent stamps. If she spent \$5.10 and bought 25 stamps in all, how many of each type did she buy? 5 fourteen-cent stamps, 20 twenty-two-cent stamps

Mixed Review Exercises

1. Write an equation for the sentence "19 more than the product of 6 and the number z is 15." $19 + 6z = 15$
2. Solve: $|t| - 6 = 4$ over the real numbers. ± 10
3. Simplify: $3^2 \cdot 3^5$ 3^7
4. A rectangular patio is 3 ft longer than it is wide. If both its dimensions are increased by 3 ft, the new patio will be 120 ft² larger. What are the original dimensions? width, 17 ft; length, 20 ft

Quick Quiz

1. Solve the formula $C = \frac{mv^2}{r}$ for m. $m = \frac{Cr}{v^2}$

Solve each problem. If a problem has no solution, explain why.

2. Jack and Janice leave their houses at 10:00 A.M. walking toward each other. They meet at 10:30 A.M. If their houses are 7 km apart, and Jack is walking at 8 km/h, find Janice's rate.

(continued)

B **12.** A square window is framed by two rectangular shutters. Each shutter is as long as one side of the window and the width of each shutter is 40 cm less than its length. If the area covered by one of the shutters is 4500 cm² less than the area of the window, find the dimensions of a shutter. 112.5 cm by 72.5 cm

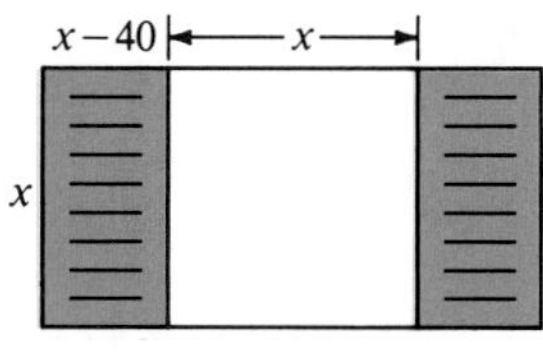

13. The edge of a certain cube is 1 cm longer then the edge of another cube. The total surface area of the first cube exceeds the total surface area of the smaller cube by 78 cm². Find the edge of the larger cube. 7 cm

14. Eighteen-karat gold contains 18 parts by mass of gold to 6 parts of other metals. Fourteen-karat gold contains 14 parts of gold and 10 parts of other metals. How much eighteen-karat gold must be mixed with fourteen-karat gold to obtain 80 kg of an alloy containing 17 parts of gold and 7 parts of other metals? 60 kg

15. Ella is 9 years older than Rick, and Rick is 8 years older than Donna. The sum of their ages 2 years ago was 10. How old is Ella? No sol.; facts contradictory

16. Jack and Jill, together, have 19 paperback books. If Jack lost 3 of his books, but Jill doubled her supply, the two of them, together, would have 40 books. How many does each have now?
No sol.; facts contradictory

Self-Test 3

Vocabulary uniform motion (p. 163)

1. Solve the formula $\frac{PV}{T} = k$ for V. $V = \frac{kT}{P}$ **Obj. 4-7, p. 161**

Solve each problem. If a problem has no solution, explain why.

2. At 9:00 A.M. two river boats are 210 km apart, and heading toward one another. At 3:00 P.M. the same day, they both pass Catfish Heights. If the northbound boat steams at a uniform rate of 15 km/h, find the rate of the southbound boat. 20 km/h **Obj. 4-8, p. 163**

3. A rectangular swimming pool is 7 ft longer than it is wide. A wooden walk 1 ft wide is placed around the pool. The area covered by the pool and the walk is 58 square feet greater than the area covered by the pool alone. What are the dimensions of the pool? 10 ft by 17 ft **Obj. 4-9, p. 168**

4. A bank teller was asked to cash a check for \$140 so as to give equal numbers of \$5 bills and \$10 bills. How many of each kind of bill did she count out? No sol.; facts contradictory **Obj. 4-10, p. 172**

Check your answers with those at the back of the book.

Chapter Summary

1. The expression b^n is an abbreviation for $\underbrace{b \cdot b \cdot b \cdot \dots \cdot b}_{n \text{ factors}}$.

   The base is b and the exponent is n.
2. To simplify expressions that contain powers, the steps listed on page 138 are followed.
3. To add (or subtract) polynomials, you add (or subtract) their similar terms. Similar terms have the same variables to the same powers.
4. Rules of Exponents

   $$a^m \cdot a^n = a^{m+n} \qquad (a^m)^n = a^{mn} \qquad (ab)^m = a^m b^m$$

5. Polynomials can be multiplied in a vertical or horizontal form by applying the distributive axiom (p. 64). Before multiplying, it is wise to rearrange the terms of each polynomial in order of increasing or decreasing degree in one variable.
6. A formula may be transformed to express a particular variable in terms of the other variables.
7. A three-column chart can be used to solve problems about distances or areas. The formulas which head these columns are:

   rate × time = distance
   length × width = area of rectangle

8. Problems may fail to have solutions due to contradictory facts or due to too few facts.

Chapter Review

Give the letter of the correct answer.

1. Express the square of $(x + y)$ in exponential form. 4-1
a. $x^2 + y^2$ **b.** x^2y^2 **c.** $2x^2y^2$ **(d.)** $(x + y)^2$

2. Evaluate $8 - 3^3$.
a. 125 **b.** -125 **c.** -1 **(d.)** -19

3. Simplify $xy^2 + 4x^2y - 6 + (5xy^2 - 5x^2y - 7)$. 4-2
a. $6xy^2 - 9x^2y - 1$ **(b.)** $6xy^2 - x^2y - 13$
c. $5xy^2 - 13$ **d.** $6xy^2 - x^2y - 1$

4. Solve $x - (15x - 6) = 104$.
(a.) -7 **b.** $-6\frac{1}{8}$ **c.** $-6\frac{7}{8}$ **d.** 7

5. Simplify $8x^5\left(-\frac{1}{8}x^5\right)$. 4-3
a. $-64x^5$ **b.** $-x^5$ **c.** $-x^{25}$ **(d.)** $-x^{10}$

Step 2 Let r = Janice's rate.
Step 3 $8\left(\frac{1}{2}\right) + r\left(\frac{1}{2}\right) = 7$
Step 4 $4 + \frac{1}{2}r = 7$
$\frac{1}{2}r = 3$
$r = 6$
∴ Janice is walking at a rate of 6 km/h.

3. A rectangle is 4 cm longer than it is wide. If the length and width are each increased by 3 cm, the new area is 63 cm^2 greater than the original area. Find the dimensions of the original rectangle.
Step 2 Let w = width in centimeters. Then $w + 4$ = length.
Step 3 $(w + 7)(w + 3) = (w + 4)w + 63$
Step 4 $w^2 + 10w + 21 = w^2 + 4w + 63$
$6w = 42$
$w = 7$
∴ the width was 7 cm and the length 11 cm.

4. Robert sold boxes of greeting cards costing \$1 and \$2 for a fund-raising drive. If he sold the same number of \$1 boxes as \$2 boxes, and collected \$52 in all, how many \$1 boxes did he sell?
Step 2 Let x = the number of boxes of each kind sold.
Step 3 $1x + 2x = 52$
Step 4 $3x = 52$
$x = 17\frac{1}{3}$
No solution, since x is not an integer.

6. Evaluate $x^5 \cdot x^6$ if $x = -1$.
a. 30 b. -30 (c.) -1 d. 1

7. Simplify $(-3x^2y^4)^3$. 4-4
a. $9x^5y^7$ b. $-9x^5y^7$ c. $27x^6y^{12}$ (d.) $-27x^6y^{12}$

8. Simplify $8n^3\left(\frac{1}{2}n\right)^4$.
a. $32n^7$ (b.) $\frac{1}{2}n^7$ c. $4n^{12}$ d. $32n^{12}$

9. Simplify $-6[16a - 8(2a - 2)]$. 4-5
a. 12 b. $-96a$ c. 0 (d.) -96

10. Solve $6 - 2(n - 3) = 12$.
(a.) 0 b. 6 c. -6 d. $-4\frac{1}{2}$

11. Multiply $(3c - 1)(3c + 1)$. 4-6
a. $6c^2 - 6c - 2$ (b.) $9c^2 - 1$ c. $9c^2 - 6c - 1$ d. $6c^2 - 2$

12. Multiply $(c - 6)(c - 7)$.
a. $2c + 42$ b. $c^2 - c + 42$ (c.) $c^2 - 13c + 42$ d. $c^2 - 42c - 13$

13. Multiply $(a - b)(a^2 + ab + b^2)$.
(a.) $a^3 - b^3$ b. $a^3 + a^2b + ab^2$
c. $a - a^2b - ab^2 - b^3$ d. $a^3 + 2a^2b + 2ab^2 - b^3$

14. Solve for b in the equation $ax + b = c$. 4-7
a. $b = \frac{c - x}{a}$ b. $b = ax - c$ c. $b = c + ax$ (d.) $b = c - ax$

15. Solve for y in the equation $\frac{xy + z}{2} = a$.
a. $y = \frac{2a + z}{x}$ (b.) $y = \frac{2a - z}{x}$
c. $y = 2ax - zx$ d. $y = 2ax + zx$

16. Erin ran a certain distance at 0.4 km/min and returned to her starting point at 0.3 km/min. If her total running time was 21 min, how far did she run in all? 4-8
a. 9 km b. 18 km (c.) 3.6 km d. 7.2 km

17. A rug is 1 m longer than it is wide. It is centered in a room so that it is surrounded by a border of hardwood floor 0.5 m wide. Find the dimensions of the room if the area of the border is 8 m². 4-9
a. 3 m by 4 m (b.) 4 m by 5 m
c. 5 m by 6 m d. 7 m by 8 m

18. Esteban has 16 coins that total $3.00. If he has only nickels and quarters, how many quarters does he have? 4-10
a. no solution—not enough facts b. no solution—facts contradict
c. 5 (d.) 11

Chapter Test

Alternate Test p. T13

Rewrite each expression in exponential form.

1. The quantity xy squared. $(xy)^2$ 4-1
2. The sum of the squares of x and y. $x^2 + y^2$
3. Simplify $(4^2 - 3 \times 1 - 3^2) \div [0 - (-2)^2]$. -1

In Exercises 4 and 5:
a. Add the polynomials.
b. Subtract the lower polynomial from the upper one.

4. $\begin{array}{r} 6x^2 - 5x - 1 \\ -6x^2 + 5x + 1 \\ \hline \end{array}$ a. 0 b. $12x^2 - 10x - 2$

5. $\begin{array}{r} x^2 + 2xy + 3y^2 \\ 5x^2 - xy - y^2 \\ \hline \end{array}$ a. $6x^2 + xy + 2y^2$ b. $-4x^2 + 3xy + 4y^2$ 4-2

Simplify.

6. $-15c^2(-7cd)$ $105c^3d$
7. $(12a^2)\left(\frac{2}{3}a^3\right)$ $8a^5$
8. $7^2 \cdot 7^a$ 7^{2+a} 4-3

Simplify.

9. $(2a^2)^6$ $64a^{12}$
10. 3^4x^4 $81x^4$
11. $4n^3\left(\frac{1}{2}n\right)^4$ $\frac{1}{4}n^7$ 4-4

Multiply.

12. $-5(16 - 9n)$ $-80 + 45n$
13. $-3xy(7x^2 - 8xy + 9y^2)$ $-21x^3y + 24x^2y^2 - 27xy^3$ 4-5
14. Solve $\frac{5}{6}(12x - 6) - 4(3x - 1) = 0$. $-\frac{1}{2}$

Multiply.

15. $(a - 1)(2a^2 - 5a - 1)$ $2a^3 - 7a^2 + 4a + 1$
16. $(2c + d)(9c^2 - 8cd + d^2)$ $18c^3 - 7c^2d - 6cd^2 + d^3$ 4-6

Solve for the variable shown in color.

17. $F = \frac{9}{5}C + 32$; C $C = \frac{5}{9}(F - 32)$
18. $D = \frac{a}{2}(2t - 1)$; a $a = \frac{2D}{2t - 1}$ 4-7

19. Lynn swims at an average speed of 3.6 km/h. If Becky swims 2.25 km in the same time Lynn swims 1.8 km, what is Becky's average speed? 4.5 km/h 4-8

20. Elrod is mowing a rectangular lawn. The lawn is 5 m shorter than it is long. If Elrod mows a strip 0.5 m wide around the outside, the area of this border will be 28 m. Find the dimensions of the uncut lawn. 16 m by 11 m 4-9

21. Solve the following problem if it has a solution. If it does not, explain why. 4-10

    Dirk is twice as old as Meghan. If Meghan is 8 years old, in how many years will their ages be 4 years apart? No sol.; facts contradictory

Additional Answers
Cumulative Review

6. $10\frac{3}{4}$ 9. $8z - 5$

12. $15z^2 - 10z + 20$

Cumulative Review (Chapters 1–4)

Simplify.

1. $-4|3 - 21|$ -72

2. $\frac{1}{2}(101 - 43)$ 29

3. $-2.2 + 3.8 - 5.6 + 4$ 0

4. $15s - (2s - 9)$ $13s + 9$

5. $-29 - (-45) \div 3$ -14

6. $-\frac{3}{5} + 4\frac{5}{8} - \frac{2}{5} + 7\frac{1}{8}$

7. $3^3 + 42 \div 3 + 4$ 45

8. $(9a - 5) + (4a + 7)$ $13a + 2$

9. $(12z - 2) - (4z + 3)$

10. $(6x^6)(4x^4) - 5(3x^3)(x^7)$ $9x^{10}$

11. $(4a^n)^3(5a^n)^2$ $1600a^{5n}$

12. $5(3z^2 - 2z + 4)$

13. $-4x^2(3x^2 - 2x - 5)$ $-12x^4 + 8x^3 + 20x^2$

14. $(4a - 1)(2a + 3)$ $8a^2 + 10a - 3$

15. $(5 - 4x)(3 + 2x)$ $15 - 2x - 8x^2$

Evaluate each expression if $a = -2$, $b = -1$, $c = 2$, and $d = \frac{1}{4}$.

16. $d(3a + c)$ -1

17. $d(ab - c)$ 0

18. $(ac + b)^3$ -125

19. $(4 + a^2b)^2$ 0

Solve. If the equation is an identity or has no solution, state that fact.

20. $|-t| = 5$ -5 or 5

21. $|y - 1| + 4 = 0$ No sol.

22. $|x| + 5 = 5$ 0

23. $c - (-4) = -8$ -12

24. $\frac{1}{5}x = 90$ 450

25. $42z = -42$ -1

26. $\frac{1}{3}t + 2 = 0$ -6

27. $4z + 2 = -10$ -3

28. $7y - 4 = 6y + 6$ 10

29. $(7y - 5) + (6 - 5y) = 23$ 11

30. $(11x - 3) - (4 + 2x) = 11$ 2

31. $(2n + 9) + (5n - 4) = 6n + 9$ 4

32. $5(2 - 3z) = -4(4z + 9)$ -46

33. $-3(m + 7) - 5 = 4$ -10

34. $(2x - 3)(3x + 1) = (3x - 4)(2x + 2)$ 1

35. Solve for m: $am - bn = c$ $m = \frac{c + bn}{a}$

Solve.

36. One third of the sum of two consecutive odd integers is 5 less than the smaller integer. Find both integers. 17, 19

37. Frank has 24 dimes and nickels. Rick has $\frac{2}{3}$ as many nickels and $1\frac{1}{2}$ times as many dimes as Frank has. If Rick and Frank have the same amount of money, how much does each of them have? \$1.50

38. Jessica and Amy left school at the same time and began walking in opposite directions. Jessica walked at a rate of 3.6 km/h and Amy walked at a rate of 4.2 km/h. How far apart were they after 10 min? 1.3 km

39. A rectangular piece of cardboard is trimmed to make a square by cutting a 4-cm strip off the top and a 2-cm strip off one side. If the area of the original piece is 74 cm² greater than the area of the square, find the dimensions of the rectangle. 15 cm by 13 cm

Maintaining Skills

Simplify.

Example 1 $614 - (821 - 911)$

Solution $614 - (821 - 911) = 614 - (-90) = 614 + 90 = 704$

1. $1921 + (-876)$ 1045

2. $181 + 97 - 64$ 214

3. $(55 - 82) + (91 - 108)$ -44

4. $-78 - 84 - (-92)$ -70

5. $(28 - 86) - (46 - 81)$ -23

6. $284 - (93 - 165)$ 356

7. $35 - (58 + 62)$ -85

8. $-325 + (-726) + 922$ -129

9. $\frac{7}{8} - \left(-\frac{1}{4} + \frac{1}{2}\right)$ $\frac{5}{8}$

10. $\left(\frac{3}{5} - \frac{2}{3}\right) - \frac{5}{9}$ $-\frac{28}{45}$

11. $17.6 - (8.05 - 9.6)$ 19.15

12. $112.72 + (92.04 - 87.6)$ 117.16

Example 2 $-53(28) + 27(-40)$

Solution

$$\begin{aligned} -53(28) + 27(-40) &= -1484 + (-1080) \\ &= -2564 \end{aligned}$$

Example 3 $(-814 + 776) \div (-19)$

Solution

$$\begin{aligned} (-814 + 776) \div (-19) &= -38 \div (-19) \\ &= 2 \end{aligned}$$

13. $-12(-16) + 5(-24)$ 72

14. $27(20) - 60(48)$ -2340

15. $-65 - (412 - 385)$ -92

16. $-4(-50) + 8(25)$ 400

17. $9.25(-2.3)$ -21.275

18. $-6.06(-5.4)$ 32.724

19. $-82.05 \div (-25)$ 3.282

20. $-\frac{24}{35} \div \frac{9}{14}$ $-\frac{16}{15}$

21. $7.24 \div (-0.25)$ -28.96

22. $-\frac{12}{25} \times \left(-\frac{35}{42}\right)$

23. $-\frac{18}{35} \times \frac{49}{54}$ $-\frac{7}{15}$

24. $-\frac{15}{64} \times \left(-\frac{40}{27}\right)$ $\frac{25}{72}$

25. $-2\frac{3}{8} \div \left(-2\frac{1}{8}\right)$

22. $\frac{2}{5}$

25. $\frac{19}{17}$

Example 4 $82 + (-14)^2 \div 7 + 6$

Solution

$$\begin{aligned} 82 + (-14)^2 \div 7 + 6 &= 82 + 196 \div 7 + 6 \\ &= 82 + 28 + 6 \\ &= 116 \end{aligned}$$

26. $7 \times 8^2 - 6 \times 3 - 12 \div 2$ 424

27. $(29 + 7) \div 3^2 + 13 - 2^2$ 13

28. $(0.6)^2 - 1.2^2 \div 8 + 0.27 \div 0.3$ 1.08

29. $-2(0.35 + 0.55)^2 \div 1.8 \div 2$ -0.45

30. $1\frac{4}{5} \div 9 \times \frac{1}{2} - \left(\frac{1}{3} + \frac{1}{2}\right)^2$ $-\frac{107}{180}$

31. $-\frac{5}{7}\left[-\left(1\frac{1}{3} - \frac{3}{4}\right)\right] + \frac{1}{3} \div 4$ $\frac{1}{2}$

Additional Answer Mixed Review

21. Note: $b_1 \neq -b_2$; but since b_1 and b_2 are positive, this restriction is not applicable.

Supplementary Materials

Practice Master 23
Tests 14–15
Resource Book, pp. 19–22, 151

Extra Practice

Skills, pp. 613–614
Problems, pp. 636–637

Mixed Review

Skills and Problem Solving

Solve. If the equation is an identity or has no solution, state that fact.

1. $3n - 1 = 11$ 4

2. $(2y - 2)(y + 1) = 2(y - 3)(y + 4)$ 11

3. $|b| = \frac{20 - 5^2}{3}$ No solution

4. $\frac{1}{2}(q + 3) = 10$ 17

Simplify.

5. $(x + 3)(2x - 4)$ $2x^2 + 2x - 12$

6. $(x + 3) - (2x - 4)$ $-x + 7$

7. $(x + 3) + (2x - 4)$ $3x - 1$

8. $(x^2 + 3^2) - (x + 3)^2$ $-6x$

9. Brian is 8 years older than Maura and Maura is 8 years older than Pete. The sum of their ages is 27. How old is Pete? 1 year old

10. Solve $|x - 2| - 2 = 2$ if $x \in \{-3, -2, -1, 0, 1, 2, 3, 4, 5, 6, 7\}$. $\{-2, 6\}$

Write the axiom illustrated in each of the following statements.

11. $6 \cdot \frac{2}{2} = 6$ Identity axiom for $\times$

12. $(7 + 4) + 3 = 3 + (7 + 4)$ Commutative axiom for $+$

13. $(8a)c = 8(ac)$ Associative axiom for $\times$

14. $3(m + 2) = 3m + 6$ Distributive axiom

15. $(5z + 3) + 0 = 5z + 3$ Ident. ax. for $+$

16. If $x = -2$, then $x + 11 = 9$. Addition Prop. of $=$

17. Evaluate $(-ab^2c)^2 - (ab)^2c$ if $a = -2$, $b = -1$, and $c = 2$. 8

18. Write the numbers $-\left(\frac{1}{2}\right)^2$, -2, 3, $\left(-\frac{1}{3}\right)^2$, -1, $|-2|$ in order from least to greatest. $-2, -1, -\left(\frac{1}{2}\right)^2, \left(-\frac{1}{3}\right)^2, |-2|, 3$

19. Sarah finished second in a 10-km road race. If she could have increased her average speed by 1.25 km/h, she would have won with a time of 30 min. What was her average speed? 18.75 km/h

20. A bag contains 44 nickels, dimes, and quarters. There are twice as many dimes as nickels and 8 more quarters than nickels. How much money is in the bag? \$6.50

21. The area of a trapezoid is given by the formula $A = \frac{1}{2}h(b_1 + b_2)$, where h is the height and b_1 and b_2 are the lengths of the bases. Solve this equation for h. State the restrictions, if any, for the new formula to be meaningful. $h = \frac{2A}{b_1 + b_2}$

22. Write an inequality for the following. The opposite of the sum of negative two and a is greater than the difference of a and the opposite of four. $-(-2 + a) > [a - (-4)]$

23. Four consecutive odd integers are such that the product of the second and fourth minus the product of the first and third is 48. Find the integers. 9, 11, 13, 15

Preparing for College Entrance Exams

Strategy for Success

If you cannot solve a problem within a short period of time, leave that problem and go on to others that may be easier for you. If time permits, you can return and attempt the problem again. Also, you may get an idea while working the other problems and your success on those may help you.

Decide which is the best of the choices given and write the corresponding letter on your answer sheet.

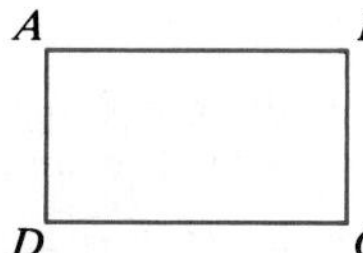

1. *ABCD* is a rectangle. Each of the longer sides is 3 cm shorter than twice a shorter side. The perimeter of the rectangle is 24 cm. Find the length of a longer side. B
(A) 11 cm **(B)** 7 cm **(C)** 5 cm **(D)** 9 cm

2. Twice the sum of two consecutive integers is 10 less than 5 times the smaller integer. Find the larger integer. C
(A) 12 **(B)** 14 **(C)** 13 **(D)** -6 **(E)** -8

3. Jess is twice as old as Phil and Phil's age is three fourths of Megan's age. Four years ago Jess's age was the same as Phil's and Megan's ages together. Find the sum of the ages of these three people now. B
(A) 48 **(B)** 52 **(C)** 60 **(D)** 44

4. The Hawks' baseball park has reserved seats and bleacher seats. There are four times as many reserved seats as bleacher seats. Reserved seats cost $4 more than bleacher seats. Which of the following is (are) sufficient to determine the amount of money collected on a sellout day? D
I. the number of bleacher seats II. the cost of a bleacher seat
III. the total number of seats
(A) I only **(B)** II only **(C)** III only **(D)** I and II only

5. Evaluate the expression $(a + b)^2 \div (2a) - b^2$ if $a = 6$ and $b = 4$. A
(A) $-\frac{23}{3}$ **(B)** -13 **(C)** -25 **(D)** $\frac{25}{16}$

6. Find $(2n^3)^2$ if $(n + 2)(n + 3) = (4 - n)(12 - n)$. C
(A) 144 **(B)** 128 **(C)** 256 **(D)** 784

7. Solve for p in the equation $q = 1 + \frac{p}{100}$. C
(A) $p = 100q - 1$ **(B)** $p = \frac{q-1}{100}$ **(C)** $p = 100(q - 1)$ **(D)** $p = 1 + \frac{q}{100}$

8. On the 16-km trip to the ball field, Lea ran for 20 min, then walked the rest of the way. Her walking speed was 18 km/h slower than her running speed. How long did the trip take? E
(A) 30 min **(B)** 40 min **(C)** 50 min **(D)** 60 min
(E) Cannot be determined from the given information

About the Photo

For centuries a display of fireworks marked a celebration of great importance. So that crowds of people could see the spectacular displays, methods were devised to project fireworks high into the sky where they would burst into thousands of smaller burning particles and light the sky.

The path that fireworks take when projected is a parabola, and the actual path taken depends on many factors. A force must be applied to give fireworks an initial velocity, b. The height, c, from which the fireworks are launched also determines how high the fireworks will go. In addition, the force of gravity bends the linear path of fireworks into a parabolic curve. This force is independent of initial velocity and launch height and affects the launch of any projectile. The equation $y = -4.9t^2 + bt + c$ gives the height of a projectile above the ground at time t.

Your students might be interested in performing the following experiment.

1. Hold a ball at table height. Release the ball and measure the time it takes for the ball to hit the floor.
2. Place the same ball on the table and near the edge of the table. Give the ball a push off the table and measure the time it takes to hit the floor.
3. Repeat the experiment in part 2 many times.
4. Compare the times measured. They should be equal.

5 Factoring Polynomials

Fireworks produce spectacular displays of light, noise, and smoke. The curved path of fireworks at a given time (t) can be represented by a polynomial in the form $at^2 + bt + c$.

Quotients and Factoring

5-1 Factoring Integers

Objective To factor integers.

When you write

$$72 = 9 \cdot 8 \quad \text{or} \quad 72 = (2)(36),$$

you have *factored* 72. In the first case the factors are 9 and 8; in the second case they are 2 and 36. You could also write $72 = (\frac{1}{2})(144)$ and call $\frac{1}{2}$ and 144 factors of 72. Usually, however, you are interested only in factors drawn from a specified set. The given number is then said to be **factored** over the given set, called the **factor set.** In this text, *integers will be factored over the set of integers* unless some other set is specified. Such factors are called *integral* factors.

You can find factors by dividing. If the remainder is zero, the divisor is a factor. For example,

$$-5 \text{ is a factor of } 110 \text{ because } 110 \div (-5) = -22$$

$$\text{but } \; 8 \text{ is not a factor of } 110 \text{ because } 110 \div 8 = 13 \text{ R}6.$$

You can find the *positive factors* of a positive integer by dividing it by the positive integers in succession until a previous factor is repeated. Thus:

$$72 = (1)(72) = (2)(36) = (3)(24) = (4)(18) = (6)(12) = (8)(9)$$

A set of numbers useful in factoring is the set of *prime numbers,* or *primes.* A **prime number,** or **prime,** is an integer *greater than* 1 that has no positive integral factor other than itself and 1. The first ten prime numbers are:

$$2, 3, 5, 7, 11, 13, 17, 19, 23, 29$$

A systematic way to find the prime factors of positive integers is to try the primes, in order, as divisors. You divide by each prime as many times as possible before going on to the next. This technique is illustrated at the right. The final result is

$$\begin{aligned} 588 &= 2 \cdot 294 \\ &= 2 \cdot 2 \cdot 147 \\ &= 2 \cdot 2 \cdot 3 \cdot 49 \\ &= 2 \cdot 2 \cdot 3 \cdot 7 \cdot 7 \\ &= 2^2 \cdot 3 \cdot 7^2 \end{aligned}$$

$$588 = 2^2 \cdot 3 \cdot 7^2.$$

This factorization shows that the prime factors of 588 are 2, 3, and 7. The expression of a positive integer as a product of prime factors is called the **prime factorization** of the integer.

Teaching References

Lesson Commentary, pp. T93–T99

Assignment Guide, pp. T60–T62

Supplementary Materials

Practice Masters 24–32

Tests 16–19

Resource Book

Practice Exercises, pp. 84–88

Tests, pp. 23–26

Enrichment Activity, p. 152

Algebra Action

Extra Practice

Skills, pp. 615–617

Problems, p. 638

Alternate Test, p. T14

Problem Solving Strategies

Making an Organized List
The listing of factors in the examples in Section 5-1 and the tree diagrams help students count prime factors of a number in an orderly and reliable way.

Recognizing a Problem Type
In Sections 5-7 through 5-9 students learn to classify various quadratic trinomials before attempting trial and error to obtain a factorization.

Word Problem Plan
Section 5-13 provides a good opportunity to join the five-step plan with quadratic equations, diagrams, and the skill of solving by factoring presented in Section 5-12.

Teaching Suggestions p. T93

Suggested Extensions p. T93

Chalkboard Examples

1. Name the positive factors of 42. 1, 2, 3, 6, 7, 14, 21, 42

Find the prime factorization of each number.

2. 180 $2^2 \cdot 3^2 \cdot 5$
3. 47 47
4. 756 $2^2 \cdot 3^3 \cdot 7$

Find the GCF of each pair of numbers.

5. 36, 90 18
6. 35, 39 1
7. 132, 156 12
8. 252, 184 4

Common Error

Students often think that odd numbers such as 1, 51, 57, and 111, for example, are prime. Emphasize that 1 is not prime by definition (see page 183). Show that 51, 57, and 111 are each divisible by 3. To help students who are having difficulty, review divisibility rules (see Extra on page 382), and point out the last paragraph of the Historical Note on page 213.

Suggested Assignments

Minimum
185/1–39 odd
Average
185/1–45 odd
Maximum
185/1–45 odd

It can be proved by advanced methods that the prime factorization of an integer is *unique* (one and only one) except for the order in which the factors are written. (If 1 were to be considered a prime factor, the factorization would not be unique because 1 could be considered to be a factor any number of times.)

A factor of two or more integers is called a **common factor** of the integers. The greatest integer that is a factor of two or more integers is called the **greatest common factor (GCF) of the integers.**

The following example shows how you can use the prime factorization of two integers to find their greatest common factor.

Example Find the GCF of 594 and 693.

Solution First find the prime factorization of each integer. Then form the product of the smaller powers of each common prime factor.

$$594 = 2 \cdot 3^3 \cdot 11 \qquad 693 = 3^2 \cdot 7 \cdot 11$$

The common prime factors are 3 and 11.
The smaller powers of 3 and 11 are 3^2 and 11, respectively.
The greatest common factor of 594 and 693 is $3^2 \cdot 11$, or 99. ***Answer***

Oral Exercises

Give all the positive factors of each number.

1. 14 1, 2, 7, 14 **2.** 41 1, 41 **3.** 57 1, 3, 19, 57 **4.** 70 1, 2, 5, 7, 10, 14, 35, 70 **5.** 1 1 **6.** 45 1, 3, 5, 9, 15, 45

State whether or not the number is prime. Find the prime factorization of the number.

7. 32 2^5 **8.** 117 $3^2 \cdot 13$ **9.** 97 Prime **10.** 125 5^3 **11.** 121 11^2 **12.** 43 Prime

13. 36 $2^2 \cdot 3^2$ **14.** 89 Prime **15.** 59 Prime **16.** 147 $3 \cdot 7^2$ **17.** 84 $2^2 \cdot 3 \cdot 7$ **18.** 107 Prime

Find the GCF of each pair of numbers.

19. 36 and 48 12 **20.** 27 and 54 27 **21.** 22 and 35 1 **22.** 17 and 39 1

Written Exercises

List all the pairs of integral factors of each integer.

Example 50

Solution (1)(50), (2)(25), (5)(10), (−1)(−50), (−2)(−25), (−5)(−10)

A 1. 18 2. 30 3. 37 4. 63 5. 64

6. 49 7. 101 8. 68 9. 83 10. 65

11–20. List all the pairs of factors of the opposites of the integers in Exercises 1–10.

Give the prime factorization of each number.

B **21.** 99 $3^2 \cdot 11$ **22.** 120 $2^3 \cdot 3 \cdot 5$ **23.** 104 $2^3 \cdot 13$ **24.** 128 2^7 **25.** 189 $3^3 \cdot 7$

26. 250 $5^3 \cdot 2$ **27.** 476 $2^2 \cdot 7 \cdot 17$ **28.** 539 $7^2 \cdot 11$ **29.** 408 $2^3 \cdot 3 \cdot 17$ **30.** 576

31. 242 $2 \cdot 11^2$ **32.** 280 $2^3 \cdot 5 \cdot 7$ **33.** 455 $5 \cdot 7 \cdot 13$ **34.** 1024 2^{10} **35.** 600

30. $2^6 \cdot 3^2$
35. $2^3 \cdot 3 \cdot 5^2$

Give the GCF of each group of numbers.

36. 78, 90 6 **37.** 28, 182 14 **38.** 147, 275 1 **39.** 144, 180 36

40. 315, 350 35 **41.** 252, 288 36 **42.** 693, 882 63 **43.** 1925, 2100 175

44. 28, 56, 70 14 **45.** 105, 110, 132 1 **46.** 80, 96, 135 1 **47.** 65, 91, 143 13

Computer Exercises

For students with some programming experience

1. Write a BASIC program that uses the INT function to test whether an integer entered with an INPUT statement is even or odd.
2. Write a BASIC program that uses the INT function to test whether one integer is a factor of another integer. Both integers should be entered with an INPUT statement.
3. Write a BASIC program that uses the INT function to test whether two integers entered with INPUT statements have any factors in common other than 1. (Two integers whose only common factor is 1 are called *relatively prime.*)

Challenge

The Coles are racing the Browns in the annual Fourth of July canoe race across Eagle Pond and back. Sixty meters before the Browns reach the opposite shore, they meet the Coles, who have already reached the opposite shore and are on their way back. It takes the Browns 40 seconds before they reach the opposite shore and return to the point where they met the Coles. Thirty-five seconds later the Coles win the race, 195 meters ahead of the Browns. Find the speed of each canoe and the width of the pond. (Assume no time is lost on the turn around.)

Browns': 3 m/s
Coles': 4 m/s
pond: 360 m wide

Additional A Exercises

List all the pairs of positive integral factors of each integer.

1. 24 (1)(24), (2)(12), (3)(8), (4)(6)
2. 60 (1)(60), (2)(30), (3)(20), (4)(15), (5)(12), (6)(10)
3. 39 (1)(39), (3)(13)
4. 81 (1)(81), (3)(27), (9)(9)
5. 53 (1)(53)
6. 144 (1)(144), (2)(72), (3)(48), (4)(36), (6)(24), (8)(18), (9)(16), (12)(12)

Additional Answers Written Exercises

1. (1)(18), (2)(9), (3)(6), (−1)(−18), (−2)(−9), (−3)(−6)
2. (1)(30), (2)(15), (3)(10), (5)(6), (−1)(−30), (−2)(−15), (−3)(−10), (−5)(−6)
3. (1)(37), (−1)(−37)
4. (1)(63), (3)(21), (7)(9), (−1)(−63), (−3)(−21), (−7)(−9)
5. (1)(64), (2)(32), (4)(16), (8)(8), (−1)(−64), (−2)(−32), (−4)(−16), (−8)(−8)
6. (1)(49), (7)(7), (−1)(−49), (−7)(−7)
7. (1)(101), (−1)(−101)
8. (1)(68), (2)(34), (4)(17), (−1)(−68), (−2)(−34), (−4)(−17)
9. (1)(83), (−1)(−83)
10. (1)(65), (5)(13), (−1)(−65), (−5)(−13)

(continued)

Additional Answers
Written Exercises
(continued)

11. $(-1)(18)$, $(-2)(9)$, $(-3)(6)$, $(1)(-18)$, $(2)(-9)$, $(3)(-6)$
12. $(-1)(30)$, $(-2)(15)$, $(-3)(10)$, $(-5)(6)$, $(1)(-30)$, $(2)(-15)$, $(3)(-10)$, $(5)(-6)$
13. $(-1)(37)$, $(1)(-37)$
14. $(-1)(63)$, $(-3)(21)$, $(-7)(9)$, $(1)(-63)$, $(3)(-21)$, $(7)(-9)$
15. $(-1)(64)$, $(-2)(32)$, $(-4)(16)$, $(-8)(8)$, $(1)(-64)$, $(2)(-32)$, $(4)(-16)$, $(8)(-8)$
16. $(-1)(49)$, $(-7)(7)$, $(1)(-49)$, $(7)(-7)$
17. $(-1)(101)$, $(1)(-101)$
18. $(-1)(68)$, $(-2)(34)$, $(-4)(17)$, $(1)(-68)$, $(2)(-34)$, $(4)(-17)$
19. $(-1)(83)$, $(1)(-83)$
20. $(-1)(65)$, $(-5)(13)$, $(1)(-65)$, $(5)(-13)$

Additional Answers
Computer Key-In

1. **a.** One example is given. factors of 30: 1, 30; 2, 15; 3, 10; 5, 6; 6, 5; 10, 3; 15, 2
   b. 31, 37 **c.** 36
2. They are used to test whether W is prime. C counts the number of factors from 1 to $W/2$; if $C > 1$, then W is not prime.

Computer Key-In Commentary

A PRINT statement executed after a statement ending in a semicolon causes the output to be printed on the next line.

Computer Key-In

BASIC has a function, INT(N), that will enable you to find factors of integers. INT(N) will give the greatest integer *less than or equal to N*.

$$\text{INT}(4) = 4,\ \text{INT}(4.9) = 4,\ \text{INT}(-4.9) = -5$$

This function can be used to find factors, since

$$\text{INT}(12/3) = 12/3, \text{ but } \text{INT}(12/5) \neq 12/5.$$

The following program will PRINT pairs of factors of a positive integer. (*F* and *Q* represent the factors.)

```
 10 PRINT "TO FIND PAIRS OF FACTORS"
 20 PRINT "OF A POSITIVE INTEGER:"
 30 PRINT "WHAT IS YOUR POSITIVE INTEGER";
 40 INPUT W
 50 LET C=0
 60 FOR F=1 TO W/2
 70 LET Q=W/F
 80 IF Q <> INT(Q) THEN 110
 90 PRINT F;" AND ";Q;" ARE FACTORS OF ";W;"."
100 LET C=C+1
110 NEXT F
120 IF C>1 THEN 140
130 PRINT W;" IS PRIME,"
140 END
```

(Line 60: No additional factors will be found between $W/2$ and W.)
(Line 80: $\neq$ is written <> in BASIC.)

Exercises

1. **a.** RUN the program for the following values of W.
   30, 31, 32, 33, 34, 35, 36, 37, 38, 39, 40
   b. Which of the numbers in part (a) are prime?
   c. Which number has a pair of equal factors?
2. Explain the purpose of lines 50, 100, and 120.
3. Insert these lines into the program and RUN it for $W = 36$.

```
91 FOR I = 1 TO F
92 FOR J = 1 TO Q
93 PRINT "*";
94 NEXT J
95 PRINT
96 NEXT I
```

Notice that the J-loop is inside the I-loop, which is inside the F-loop. Such loops are called *nested loops*.

Note: The program above can be used to do Exercises 1–10 on page 185.

5-2 Dividing Monomials

Objective To divide and factor monomials.

There are three basic rules that are used to simplify fractions and quotients of monomials. The property of quotients (proved in Exercise 45 on page 190) enables you to express a fraction as a product.

Property of Quotients

If c, d, x, and y are any real numbers, $d \neq 0$, and $y \neq 0$, then

$$\frac{cx}{dy} = \frac{c}{d} \cdot \frac{x}{y}.$$

Example 1 $\frac{14}{45} = \frac{2 \cdot 7}{9 \cdot 5} = \frac{2}{9} \cdot \frac{7}{5}$

If you let $d = c$ in the quotient rule, you derive the cancellation rule stated below. (This rule is proved in Exercise 46 on page 190.)

Cancellation Rule for Fractions

If c, x, and y are any real numbers, $c \neq 0$, and $y \neq 0$, then

$$\frac{cx}{cy} = \frac{x}{y}.$$

The cancellation rule enables you to divide the numerator and denominator of a fraction by the same nonzero number. In the following examples, assume that no denominator equals 0.

Example 2 $\frac{3xy}{15x} = \frac{\cancel{3x} \cdot y}{\cancel{3x} \cdot 5} = \frac{y}{5}$ — The red marks indicate that both the numerator and the denominator are divided by $3x$.

The cancellation rule can be used to simplify a quotient of two powers of the same number.

Example 3 Simplify: **a.** $\frac{y^8}{y^5}$ **b.** $\frac{z}{z^7}$ **c.** $\frac{x^4}{x^4}$

Solution **a.** $\frac{y^8}{y^5} = \frac{\cancel{y^5} \cdot y^3}{\cancel{y^5}} = y^3$ **b.** $\frac{z}{z^7} = \frac{\cancel{z}}{\cancel{z} \cdot z^6} = \frac{1}{z^6}$ **c.** $\frac{x^4}{x^4} = x^4 \cdot \frac{1}{x^4} = 1$

Teaching Suggestions p. T93

Chalkboard Examples

Simplify each expression, assuming no denominator equals zero.

1. $\frac{15r^6s^4}{18r^3s^2}$ $\frac{5r^3s^2}{6}$
2. $\frac{-21x^3y}{6x^5y^3}$ $\frac{-7}{2x^2y^2}$
3. $\frac{(2ab^2)^4}{2a^2b^4}$ $8a^2b^4$
4. $\frac{(u^3v^2)^2}{(-u^2v)^3}$ $-v$

Find the missing factor.

5. $28r^2s^5 = (-4rs)(\underline{?})$ $-7rs^4$
6. $24x^3y^5z = (-6xy^2)(\underline{?})$ $-4x^2y^3z$
7. $144a^4b^6c^3 = (18a^2b^2c^2)(\underline{?})$ $8a^2b^4c$
8. Find the greatest monomial factor of $24xy^3z^2$, $16x^2y^4z$, and $36xy^2z^4$. $4xy^2z$

Common Error

When students divide monomials they often divide the exponents as well. Have students who make this error write out the factors of the numerator and denominator and simplify as shown in the examples on page 187.

Supplementary Material

Practice Master 24

Example 3 illustrates the following rule of exponents for division.

Rule of Exponents for Division

When m and n are positive integers and a is a real number not equal to 0:

If $m > n$:	If $n > m$:	If $n = m$:
$\frac{a^m}{a^n} = a^{m-n}$	$\frac{a^m}{a^n} = \frac{1}{a^{n-m}}$	$\frac{a^m}{a^n} = 1$

In short, the rule above says that when you divide powers you subtract the smaller exponent from the larger exponent if the exponents are different. You have already seen that when you multiply powers you add the exponents.

A quotient of monomials is said to be *simplified* when each base appears only once, when there are no powers of powers, and when all fractions have been expressed in simplest form. Examples 4 and 5 show that all three rules presented in this section may be needed to simplify quotients of monomials.

Example 4 $\frac{18t^5}{-3t^6} = \frac{18}{-3} \cdot \frac{t^5}{t^6} = -6 \cdot \frac{1}{t} = -\frac{6}{t}, \ (t \neq 0)$

Example 5 $\frac{21ab^{10}}{49a^7b^9c} = \frac{21}{49} \cdot \frac{1}{a^{7-1}} \cdot b^{10-9} \cdot \frac{1}{c}$

$= \frac{3}{7} \cdot \frac{1}{a^6} \cdot b \cdot \frac{1}{c} = \frac{3b}{7a^6c}, \ (a \neq 0, \ b \neq 0, \ c \neq 0)$

The **greatest common factor of two or more monomials** is defined to be the common factor that has the greatest coefficient and the greatest degree in each variable. Example 6 shows how to find the greatest common factor of two monomials.

Example 6 Find the greatest common factor of $30xz^4$ and $100x^3y^2z^8$.

Solution Form the product of the GCF of the numerical coefficients and the smaller power of each variable that appears in *both* monomials.

GCF of 30 and 100: 10 — Smaller power of x: x

Smaller power of z: z^4 — y is not a common factor.

The greatest common monomial factor of $30xz^4$ and $100x^3y^2z^8$ is $10xz^4$. ***Answer***

Oral Exercises

Simplify each expression, assuming that no denominator equals zero.

5. $-4x^2$
10. $\frac{1}{(a-b)^{11}}$

1. $\frac{3x}{x}$ 3
2. $\frac{8a^2}{2a}$ $4a$
3. $\frac{5bc}{10b^6}$ $\frac{c}{2b^5}$
4. $\frac{3c^2d^5}{cd^3}$ $3cd^2$
5. $\frac{-8x^3}{2x}$
6. $\frac{3^{10}}{3^8}$ 9
7. $\frac{a^8b^4}{a^3b^4}$ a^5
8. $-\frac{12t^7}{9t^9}$ $-\frac{4}{3t^2}$
9. $\frac{(st)^7}{(st)^5}$ s^2t^2
10. $\frac{a-b}{(a-b)^{12}}$
11. $\frac{4.8 \times 10^5}{2.4 \times 10^2}$ 2×10^3
12. $\frac{6x^{12}y^2}{2x^8y}$ $3x^4y$
13. $\frac{7r^3s^2}{49r^3s}$ $\frac{s}{7}$
14. $\frac{2u^4v^{10}}{-u^5v^5}$ $-\frac{2v^5}{u}$
15. $\frac{-12c^{12}}{-4c^4}$ $3c^8$

Find the greatest common factor of the given monomials.

16. $8x$, $2xy$ $2x$
17. $3a^2$, $6a$ $3a$
18. $5x^2y$, $10xy^2$ $5xy$
19. $12u^3v^2$, $5uv^3$ uv^2
20. $14s^5t^2$, $21s^3t^3$ $7s^3t^2$
21. $36x^2y^4$, $15x^3y^5$ $3x^2y^4$
22. $2a^2b$, ab^2c ab
23. $4r^6s^7$, $6r^6s^4$ $2r^6s^4$

Written Exercises

Simplify each expression, assuming that no denominator equals zero.

8. $\frac{2xz^2}{5y^2}$

A

1. $\frac{9a^4}{3a}$ $3a^3$
2. $\frac{-18r^3t}{12rt^5}$ $-\frac{3r^2}{2t^4}$
3. $\frac{-8xy}{-24xy^3}$ $\frac{1}{3y^2}$
4. $\frac{13a^4b^9}{26a^2b^2}$ $\frac{a^2b^7}{2}$
5. $\frac{6(xy)^5}{8(xy)^3}$ $\frac{3x^2y^2}{4}$
6. $\frac{-36u^5v^4}{27uv^6}$ $-\frac{4u^4}{3v^2}$
7. $\frac{-16a^5b^3}{-24a^5b^7}$ $\frac{2}{3b^4}$
8. $\frac{14x^2yz^3}{35xy^3z}$
9. $\frac{(x^2)^4}{(x^3)^3}$ $\frac{1}{x}$
10. $\frac{(3a)^3}{3a^3}$ 9
11. $\frac{(3y)^2}{(3y)^3}$ $\frac{1}{3y}$
12. $\frac{5k^3}{(5k)^3}$ $\frac{1}{25}$
13. $\frac{(2x)^4}{2x^4}$ 8
14. $\frac{(-x)^8}{-x^6}$ $-x^2$
15. $\frac{(-2y)^3}{(y^2)^3}$ $-\frac{8}{y^3}$
16. $\frac{(a^5)^3}{(a^4)^4}$ $\frac{1}{a}$
17. $\frac{(4ab^2)^3}{(2a^2b)^4}$ $\frac{4b^2}{a^5}$
18. $\frac{(3a^5)(2a^4)}{(6a^3)^2}$ $\frac{a^3}{6}$
19. $\frac{(13c^4d)^2}{(13cd^2)^3}$ $\frac{c^5}{13d^4}$
20. $\frac{-(8x^2y)^4}{(8x^2y)^5}$ $-\frac{1}{8x^2y}$

Find the missing factor.

Example $36a^5b^8 = (12a^3b^2)(\underline{\ ?\ })$

Solution $\frac{36a^5b^8}{12a^3b^2} = 3a^2b^6$ ***Answer***

21. $9a^5 = (3a)(\underline{\ ?\ })$ $3a^4$
22. $12a^2b = (3a)(\underline{\ ?\ })$ $4ab$
23. $-4c^3d^3 = (2cd^2)(\underline{\ ?\ })$ $-2c^2d$
24. $35u^5v^6 = (7uv)(\underline{\ ?\ })$ $5u^4v^5$
25. $24x^6y^4 = (-3x^2y^2)(\underline{\ ?\ })$ $-8x^4y^2$
26. $-18x^3y^5 = (-9x^2y)(\underline{\ ?\ })$ $2xy^4$
27. $98a^7b^4 = (\underline{\ ?\ })(14a^7b)$ $7b^3$
28. $156k^3z^5n = (-13k^2z)(\underline{\ ?\ })$ $-12kz^4n$

B

29. $(a^2b)^6 = (a^2b)^4(\underline{\ ?\ })$ a^4b^2
30. $(3xy)^5 = (3xy)^4(\underline{\ ?\ })$ $3xy$
31. $144x^6y^3 = (-12xy)^2(\underline{\ ?\ })$ x^4y
32. $42x^4y^5 = (3x^2y)(2xy)(\underline{\ ?\ })$ $7xy^3$
33. $36a^8b^5 = (6ab^2)(3a^4b)(\underline{\ ?\ })$ $2a^3b^2$
34. $72x^5y^8 = (3xy^2)^2(2y^3)(\underline{\ ?\ })$ $4x^3y$

Suggested Assignments

Minimum
Day 1: 189/1–25
S 185/44, 45, 46
Day 2: 189/26–38 even
192/1–21 odd
Day 2 finishes Sec. 5-2 and starts Sec. 5-3.

Average
Day 1: 189/2–42 even
Day 2: 189/29–41 odd
192/1–21 odd, 27–31
Day 2 finishes Sec. 5-2 and starts Sec. 5-3.

Maximum
189/2–34 even, 35–42
S 185/46, 47

Additional A Exercises

Simplify each expression, assuming that no denominator equals zero.

1. $\frac{-72m^2n^3}{-9mn^3}$ $8m$
2. $\frac{-4(xy)^2}{4xy^2}$ $-x$
3. $\frac{(-3m)^4}{(m^2)^5}$ $\frac{81}{m^6}$
4. $\frac{(6t^2s^3)^2}{(2t^5s)^4}$ $\frac{9s^2}{4t^{16}}$

Find the missing factor.

5. $52ab^2c = (4ab)(\underline{\ ?\ })$ $13bc$
6. $-21m^2n^4 = (-mn)^2(\underline{\ ?\ })$ $-21n^2$

Mixed Review Exercises

1. Solve $5x^2 = 90$ if $x \in \{0, 1, 2, 3, 4, 5\}$. ∅
2. Simplify: $-7 - (-6) - [-3 - (-2)]$ 0
3. Solve: $-132 = 11m$ -12
4. In 1970, Jack was half as old as Jill, but by 1974 he was $\frac{2}{3}$ as old as Jill. How old were they in 1970? Jack was 4, Jill was 8.

Find the greatest common factor of the given monomials.

35. $16rs^2t^3$, $40r^3s^3t^2$ $8rs^2t^2$
36. $18k^2m^4n$, $27km^2n$ $9km^2n$
37. $25ab^2$, $15ab^2$, $36a^2b^2$ ab^2
38. $21m^3n^2$, $14m^2n^3$; $35m^4n$ $7m^2n$
39. $(x + y)(x - y)^3$, $2(x + y)^4$ $x + y$
40. $4r^8(r + 1)^7$, $9r^2(r - 1)$ r^2

Simplify each expression, assuming that $x \neq 0$, $y \neq 0$, and n is a positive integer.

C **41.** $\frac{152x^n}{133x}$ $\frac{8x^{n-1}}{7}$
42. $\frac{162y^{2n+2}}{54y^{2n+3}}$ $\frac{3}{y}$
43. $\frac{x^{3n}y^{n+1}}{-x^ny}$ $-x^{2n}y^n$
44. $\frac{667x^{5n+2}y^{2n}}{460(xy)^{2n}}$ $\frac{29}{20}x^{3n+2}$

Give a reason for each step in the proofs of the property of quotients and the cancellation rule for fractions. Assume that c, d, x, and y are real numbers, $c \neq 0$, $d \neq 0$, and $y \neq 0$. Once you prove the property of quotients, you may use it in the proof of the cancellation rule.

45. Property of quotients: $\frac{cx}{dy} = \frac{c}{d} \cdot \frac{x}{y}$

$\frac{cx}{dy} = cx\left(\frac{1}{dy}\right)$ (1) ? Def. of div.

$= cx\left(\frac{1}{d} \cdot \frac{1}{y}\right)$ (2) ? Prop. of the reciprocal of a product

$= \left(c \cdot \frac{1}{d}\right)\left(x \cdot \frac{1}{y}\right)$ (3) ?; ? Comm. ax. for ×; Assoc. ax. for ×

$= \frac{c}{d} \cdot \frac{x}{y}$ (4) ? Def. of div.

46. Cancellation rule for fractions: $\frac{cx}{cy} = \frac{x}{y}$

$\frac{cx}{cy} = \frac{c}{c} \cdot \frac{x}{y}$ (1) ? Prop. of quotients

$= \left(c \cdot \frac{1}{c}\right) \cdot \frac{x}{y}$ (2) ? Def. of div.

$= 1 \cdot \frac{x}{y}$ (3) ? Ax. of reciprocals

$= \frac{x}{y}$ (4) ? Identity ax. for mult.

Calculator Key-In

When you use a calculator to divide one number by another, the remainder, if any, is always given as a decimal. You can see what the remainder is and what fraction the decimal represents by using the following method.

1. Subtract the whole number part of the quotient from the entire quotient.
2. Multiply the decimal that remains from the subtraction by the divisor and round to the nearest integer.

The number that results from Step 2 is the remainder. Using this number as the numerator and the divisor as the denominator gives the value of the decimal as a fraction. On some calculators, because of rounding error, the answers will not be exact.

Find the remainder. Then give the value of the decimal as a fraction.

1. $354 \div 13$ 3; $\frac{3}{13}$
2. $621 \div 7$ 5; $\frac{5}{7}$
3. $753 \div 11$ 5; $\frac{5}{11}$
4. $1258 \div 15$ 13; $\frac{13}{15}$
5. $3698 \div 36$ 26; $\frac{13}{18}$
6. $5829 \div 45$ 24; $\frac{8}{15}$

5-3 Monomial Factors of Polynomials

Objective To divide a polynomial by a monomial and to find a monomial factor of a polynomial.

The following result was proved earlier (see page 83):
If a, b, and c are real numbers and $c \neq 0$,

$$\frac{a+b}{c} = \frac{a}{c} + \frac{b}{c}.$$

This result is also true when a, b, and c are monomials and $c \neq 0$. It suggests a technique for dividing a polynomial by a monomial.

To divide a polynomial by a monomial, divide each term of the polynomial by the monomial, and then add the quotients.

The examples below illustrate this technique. In these examples assume that no denominator equals 0.

Example 1 $$\frac{4x^4 + 8x^3y - 12x^2y^2}{4x^2} = \frac{4x^4}{4x^2} + \frac{8x^3y}{4x^2} - \frac{12x^2y^2}{4x^2}$$
$$= x^2 + 2xy - 3y^2$$

Example 2 $$\frac{x^2y^2 + x - y}{xy} = \frac{x^2y^2}{xy} + \frac{x}{xy} - \frac{y}{xy}$$
$$= xy + \frac{1}{y} - \frac{1}{x}$$

One polynomial is said to be **evenly divisible,** or simply **divisible,** by another polynomial if the quotient is also a polynomial. Example 1 shows that $4x^4 + 8x^3y - 12x^2y^2$ is evenly divisible by $4x^2$. Example 2 shows that $x^2y^2 + x - y$ is not evenly divisible by xy, since $\frac{1}{y}$ and $\frac{1}{x}$ are not polynomials.

You *factor* a polynomial by expressing it as a product of other polynomials. Unless otherwise stated, the *factor set for a polynomial having integral coefficients is the set of all polynomials having integral coefficients.*

You can use division to test for factors of a polynomial. Example 1 shows that you can factor $4x^4 + 8x^3y - 12x^2y^2$ as $4x^2(x^2 + 2xy - 3y^2)$. Notice that 4, x^2, and $4x^2$ are all factors of $4x^4 + 8x^3y - 12x^2y^2$. In general, you find the greatest monomial factor of a polynomial. The **greatest monomial factor of a polynomial** is the greatest common monomial factor of its terms. This process is illustrated in Examples 3 and 4 on the following page.

Teaching Suggestions p. T94

Suggested Extensions p. T94

Chalkboard Examples

Divide. Assume that no denominator is zero.

1. $\frac{8t^2 + 10}{2}$ $4t^2 + 5$
2. $\frac{12z^3 + 16z^2 - 8z}{4z}$
$3z^2 + 4z - 2$
3. $\frac{6r^3s - 18r^2s^2 + 3r}{-3r}$
$-2r^2s + 6rs^2 - 1$

Express each polynomial as the product of its greatest monomial factor and another polynomial.

4. $15m^2 - 9$ $3(5m^2 - 3)$
5. $28a^5 - 12a^3 + 20a^2$
$4a^2(7a^3 - 3a + 5)$
6. $-21s^3t + 15st^2 + 33s^2t^2$
$3st(-7s^2 + 5t + 11st)$

Common Errors

Some students divide only the *first* term of a polynomial by a monomial divisor. Remind them that *each* term must be divided by the monomial. It may be helpful to use a numerical example such as $\frac{24 + 6}{3}$ to show your students that this is reasonable.

Some students may forget to write terms that are equal to one for exercises such as Written Exercises 4, 6, 8, and 27. Encourage these students to check their answers by multiplying factors.

Also point out that if a polynomial factor can be divided by a monomial, then the monomial factor is not the *greatest* monomial factor.

Example 3 Factor $4a^3b^2c - 12b^2c^3$.

Solution

1. The greatest monomial factor of $4a^3b^2c - 12b^2c^3$ is $4b^2c$.
2. Divide: $\dfrac{4a^3b^2c - 12b^2c^3}{4b^2c} = \dfrac{4a^3b^2c}{4b^2c} - \dfrac{12b^2c^3}{4b^2c} = a^3 - 3c^2$
3. $4a^3b^2c - 12b^2c^3 = 4b^2c(a^3 - 3c^2)$ ***Answer***

Example 4 Factor $30x^5 + 45x^3 - 10x$.

Solution

1. The greatest monomial factor of $30x^5 + 45x^3 - 10x$ is $5x$.
2. Divide: $\dfrac{30x^5 + 45x^3 - 10x}{5x} = \dfrac{30x^5}{5x} + \dfrac{45x^3}{5x} - \dfrac{10x}{5x} = 6x^4 + 9x^2 - 2$
3. $30x^5 + 45x^3 - 10x = 5x(6x^4 + 9x^2 - 2)$ ***Answer***

You should check your factorizations by multiplying the resulting factors. The checks for Examples 3 and 4 are left for you.

Oral Exercises

9. $3; 3(3ab - 2)$ 10. $4a; 4a(2a + 1)$ 11. $4y; 4y(4x + 3z)$

Divide. Assume that no denominator equals zero.

1. $\dfrac{6a + 12}{6}$ $a + 2$
2. $\dfrac{9x - 6y}{3}$ $3x - 2y$
3. $\dfrac{6c - 18}{6}$ $c - 3$
4. $\dfrac{33ab - 22b}{11b}$ $3a - 2$
5. $\dfrac{27a - 18b + 9c}{9}$ $3a - 2b + c$
6. $\dfrac{4a^3 - 10a^2 + 6a}{2a}$ $2a^2 - 5a + 3$
7. $\dfrac{6x^2y - 4xy^2}{2xy}$ $3x - 2y$
8. $\dfrac{9a^3b - 12ab^4}{3ab}$ $3a^2 - 4b^3$

Find the greatest monomial factor. Then factor the polynomial.

9. $9ab - 6$
10. $8a^2 + 4a$
11. $16xy + 12yz$
12. $14ab - 21bc$ $7b; 7b(2a - 3c)$
13. $3a^3 - 9ac$ $3a; 3a(a^2 - 3c)$
14. $\pi r^2 + 2\pi r$ $\pi r; \pi r(r + 2)$
15. $x^2yz - wyz^2$ $yz; yz(x^2 - wz)$
16. $5cd - 15ce$ $5c; 5c(d - 3e)$

Written Exercises

Divide. Assume that no denominator equals zero.

A

1. $\dfrac{3a + 6}{3}$ $a + 2$
2. $\dfrac{18a - 12}{6}$ $3a - 2$
3. $\dfrac{30x - 15}{5}$ $6x - 3$
4. $\dfrac{9a + 6b + 3}{3}$ $3a + 2b + 1$
5. $\dfrac{4x - 8y + 12}{4}$ $x - 2y + 3$
6. $\dfrac{x^3 + 4x^2 + x}{x}$ $x^2 + 4x + 1$
7. $\dfrac{10xy - 15x^2}{5x}$ $2y - 3x$
8. $\dfrac{6a - 12a^2 - 18a^3}{6a}$ $1 - 2a - 3a^2$
9. $\dfrac{14y - 21y^2 - 7y^3}{7y}$ $2 - 3y - y^2$
10. $\dfrac{9a^2b - 6ab^2}{3ab}$ $3a - 2b$
11. $\dfrac{24cd^3 - 18c^2d - 12c}{-6c}$ $-4d^3 + 3cd + 2$
12. $\dfrac{25x^4y^3 - 15x^2y^5}{5xy}$ $5x^3y^2 - 3xy^4$

Supplementary Material

Resource Book, p. 84

Suggested Assignments

Minimum
193/27–36, 45–48
194/*P*: 1–3, 5
Day 2 of Sec. 5-2 finishes Sec. 5-2 and starts Sec. 5-3.

Average
193/33–49 odd
194/*P*: 2, 5, 6
R 195/*Self-Test 1*
Day 2 of Sec. 5-2 finishes Sec. 5-2 and starts Sec. 5-3.

Maximum
192/1–49 odd
194/*P*: 2–10 even

Additional A Exercises

Divide. Assume that no denominator equals zero.

1. $\dfrac{50j - 30}{10}$ $5j - 3$
2. $\dfrac{42m - 14m^2 + 77m^3}{7m}$ $11m^2 - 2m + 6$
3. $\dfrac{39x^4y^5 - 13x^2y^3 + 78x^3y^6}{13x^2y^3}$ $3x^2y^2 - 1 + 6xy^3$

Evaluate by factoring.

4. $23 \times 14 - 14 \times 21$ $14(23 - 21) = 28$

Express each polynomial as the product of its greatest monomial factor and another polynomial.

5. $16mn^3 - 4m^2n^2 + 12m^3n$ $4mn(4n^2 - mn + 3m^2)$
6. $21f^4e - 49fe + 63$ $7(3f^4e - 7fe + 9)$

13. $\frac{42s^4t^4 - 35st^2}{7st^2}$ $6s^3t^2 - 5$

14. $\frac{8yz^2 - 24y^3z - 32yz}{-8yz}$ $-z + 3y^2 + 4$

15. $\frac{45d^4k^2 - 75d^3k + 30d^4}{15d^2}$ $3d^2k^2 - 5dk + 2d^2$

16. $\frac{32k^4z^2 - 96k^2z^4 - 48k^6z^2}{16k^2z^2}$ $2k^2 - 6z^2 - 3k^4$

Evaluate by factoring.

Example 1 $4 \times 21 + 4 \times 79 = 4(21 + 79)$
$= 4(100) = 400$

17. $3 \times 78 + 7 \times 78$ 780
18. $28 \times 43 - 18 \times 43$ 430
19. $13 \times 19 + 4 \times 19 + 3 \times 19$ 380
20. $9 \times 11^2 - 9 \times 11$ 990
21. $81^2 + 81 \times 19$ 8100
22. $(18)^2 - 4 \times 9$ 288
23. $32 \times 17 + 17^2 + 17$ 850
24. $216 + 2 \times 36 + 5 \times 6$ 318
25. $22 \times 14 \times 25 - 11 \times 21 \times 30$ 770
26. $39 \times 21 \times 2 - 26 \times 7 \times 4$ 910

Express each polynomial as the product of its greatest monomial factor and another polynomial.

27. $9p - 6q + 3$ $3(3p - 2q + 1)$
28. $4x - 8y + 16$ $4(x - 2y + 4)$
29. $15a^2 - 9a$ $3a(5a - 3)$
30. $6x^2 + 12$ $6(x^2 + 2)$
31. $4a^3 + 8a^2$ $4a^2(a + 2)$
32. $12x^3 - 6x^2 + 24x$ $6x(2x^2 - x + 4)$
33. $10y^3 - 5y^2 + 15y$ $5y(2y^2 - y + 3)$
34. $\pi r^2h + 2\pi r^2$ $\pi r^2(h + 2)$
35. $\frac{1}{2}bh - \frac{1}{2}ah$ $\frac{1}{2}h(b - a)$
36. $14s^2 + 7st$ $7s(2s + t)$

B 37. $24a^4x - 18a^3x + 12a^2x^2$ $6a^2x(4a^2 - 3a + 2x)$
38. $7s^2y - 21xy^2$ $7y(s^2 - 3xy)$
39. $8a^2b - 16ab - 24a$ $8a(ab - 2b - 3)$
40. $25c^3d - 15c^2d^2 + 5cd^3$
41. $-40r^8s^6 - 16r^9s^5$ $-8r^8s^5(5s + 2r)$
42. $21e^3k - 49e^2k^2 + 84k^3$
43. $126w^2x^3yz + 210w^3y^4z^2$ $42w^2yz(3x^3 + 5wy^3z)$
44. $231a^4b^3c^2d - 143ab^2c^3$ $11ab^2c^2(21a^3bd - 13c)$

40. $5cd(5c^2 - 3cd + d^2)$
42. $7k(3e^3 - 7e^2k + 12k^2)$

Simplify.

Example 2 $\frac{5x - 10}{5} - \frac{12x - 9}{3} = (x - 2) - (4x - 3)$
$= x - 2 - 4x + 3$
$= -3x + 1$

45. $\frac{3x - 6}{3} - \frac{4 - 8x}{2}$ $5x - 4$
46. $\frac{15a - 5}{5} - \frac{9a - 12}{3}$ 3
47. $\frac{24x - 18}{6} + \frac{14x + 7}{7}$ $6x - 2$
48. $\frac{12a^2b - 6ab^2}{3ab} + \frac{4a^2 + 10ab}{2a}$ $6a + 3b$
49. $\frac{a^2b + 2a^2b^2}{ab} - \frac{2a^3 - 6a^2b}{2a}$ $a + 5ab - a^2$
50. $\frac{a^4b^3 - b^2a^3}{a^3b} + \frac{b^3c - ab^3c}{bc}$ $b^2 - b$

Mixed Review Exercises

Simplify.

1. $8z - 3(7z - 5)$ $-13z + 15$
2. $9m^3\left(\frac{1}{3}m\right)^4$ $\frac{m^7}{9}$
3. Name the axiom or property illustrated: $(x + y)z = z(x + y)$ Comm. ax. for mult.
4. Solve: $\frac{4}{5}(20x - 25) - 3(2x - 10) = 0$ $x = -1$

LONG DIV.
PAGE 263

Problems

Write an expression in factored form for the area A of each shaded region.

Example

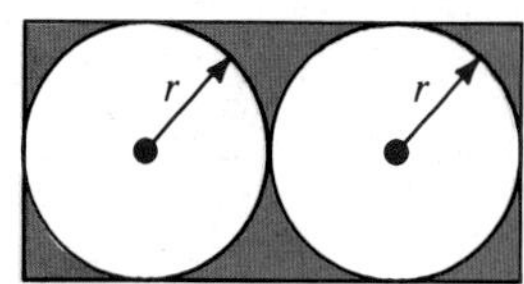

Solution

A = Area of rectangle − 2 · area of circle
$= (4r \cdot 2r) - 2\pi r^2$
$= 2r^2(4 - \pi)$ ***Answer***

A

1.

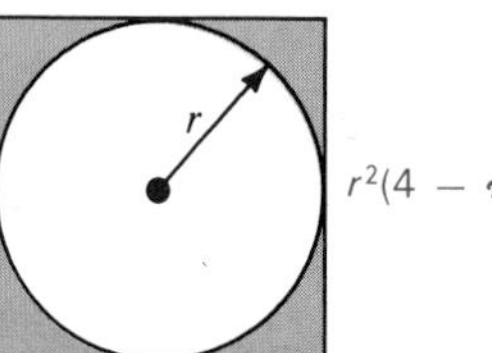

$r^2(4 - \pi)$

2.

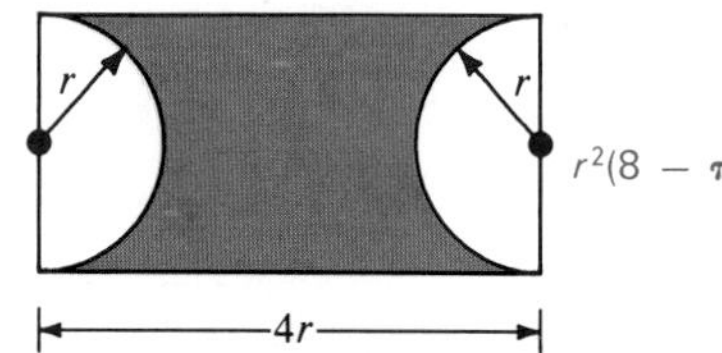

$r^2(8 - \pi)$

3.

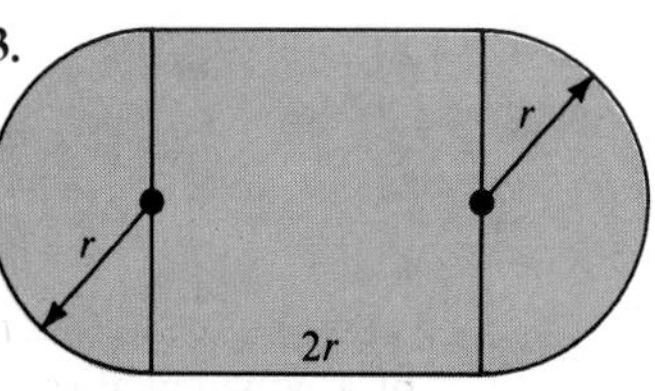

$r^2(4 + \pi)$

4.

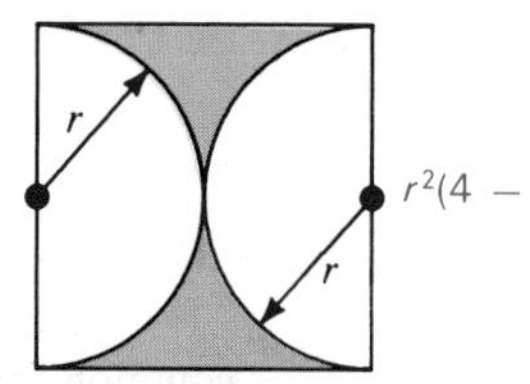

$r^2(4 - \pi)$

5.

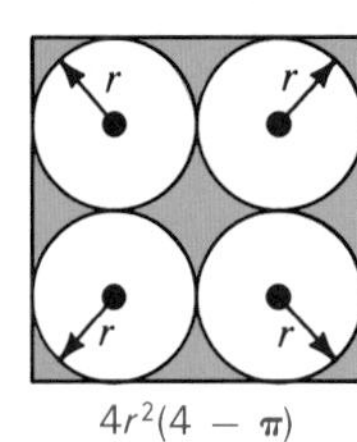

$4r^2(4 - \pi)$

B

6.

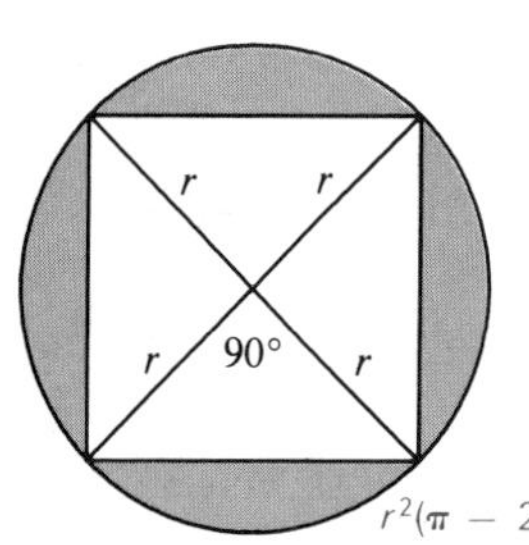

$r^2(\pi - 2)$

7.

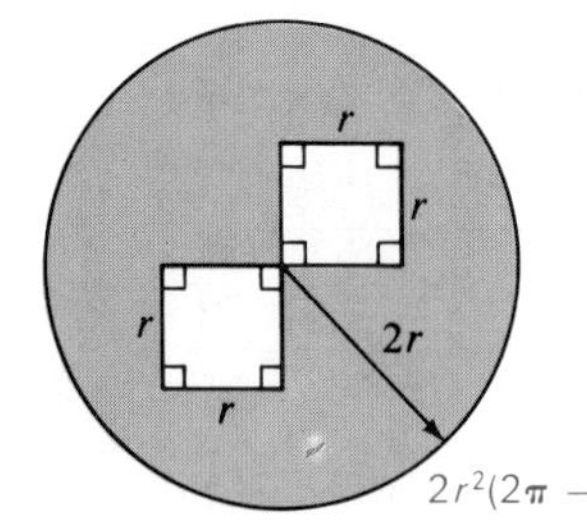

$2r^2(2\pi - 1)$

8.

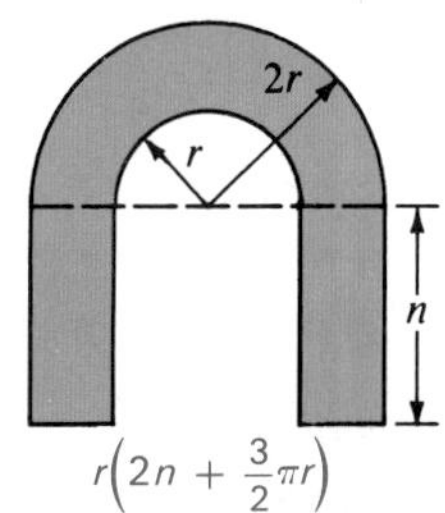

$r\left(2n + \frac{3}{2}\pi r\right)$

9.

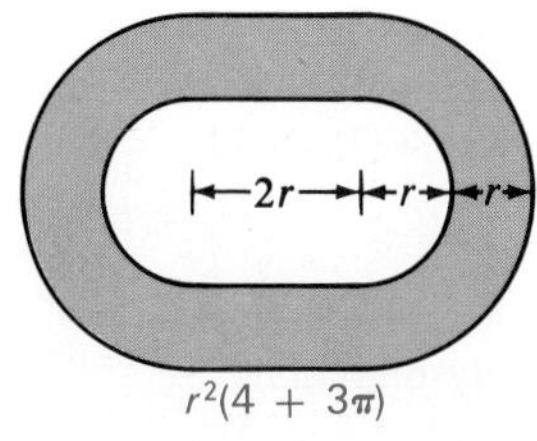

$r^2(4 + 3\pi)$

10.

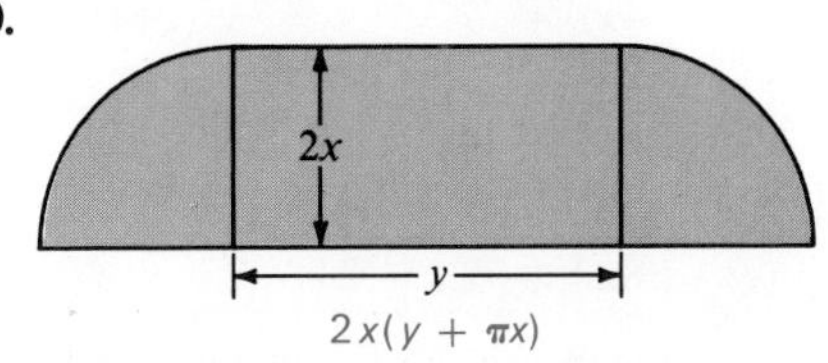

$2x(y + \pi x)$

Self-Test 1

Vocabulary

factored (p. 183)
factor set (p. 183)
prime number (p. 183)
prime factorization (p. 183)
common factor (p. 184)
greatest common factor of integers (p. 184)
greatest common factor of monomials (p. 188)
divisible (p. 191)
greatest monomial factor of a polynomial (p. 191)

1. Find the prime factorization of 72. $2^3 \cdot 3^2$ **Obj. 5-1, p. 183**
2. Find all pairs of integral factors of 44. (1)(44), (2)(22), (4)(11), (−1)(−44), (−2)(−22), (−4)(−11)
3. Find the greatest common factor of 72 and 44. 4

Simplify, assuming that no denominator equals zero.

4. $-\frac{21x^2y^5}{7xy^6}$ $-\frac{3x}{y}$
5. $\frac{8k^2m^7}{32k^3m^3}$ $\frac{m^4}{4k}$ **Obj. 5-2, p. 187**

Find the missing factor.

6. $-84t^3 = -7t(\underline{\ ?\ })$ $12t^2$
7. $-35a^2b^5 = (7ab)(\underline{\ ?\ })$ $-5ab^4$
8. Simplify $\frac{21t^4 + 15t^3 - 9t^2}{3t^2}$, $(t \neq 0)$. $7t^2 + 5t - 3$ **Obj. 5-3, p. 191**
9. Factor $4x^4y^3 - 8x^2y^2 + 6xy^2$. $2xy^2(2x^3y - 4x + 3)$

Check your answers with those at the back of the book.

Quick Quiz

1. Find the greatest common factor of 66 and 81. 3
2. Simplify, assuming that the denominator does not equal 0. $\frac{5x^2y^6}{-15x^2y^3z}$ $-\frac{y^3}{3z}$
3. Simplify $\frac{21y^5 - 42y^4 + 49y^3}{7y^3}$ $(y \neq 0)$. $3y^2 - 6y + 7$
4. Factor $15a^3b - 6a^2b^2 + 18a^3b^3$. $3a^2b(5a - 2b + 6ab^2)$

Teaching Suggestions p. T94

Chalkboard Examples

Write each product as a trinomial.

1. $(x + 5)(x - 4)$
   $x^2 + x - 20$
2. $(t - 2)(t - 5)$
   $t^2 - 7t + 10$
3. $(3z - 1)(2z + 2)$
   $6z^2 + 4z - 2$
4. $(5k - 3)(2k + 3)$
   $10k^2 + 9k - 9$
5. $(a^2 - 3b)(3a^2 + b)$
   $3a^4 - 8a^2b - 3b^2$
6. $(4y^2 - 3)(2y^2 + 1)$
   $8y^4 - 2y^2 - 3$

Common Error

Because multiplication and addition are involved in multiplying binomials, you may initially have to remind some students that $x \cdot x = x^2$ rather than $2x$. Students may also need to review the rules for addition on page 54.

Supplementary Materials

Practice Master 25
Test 16

Suggested Assignments

Minimum
Day 1: 197/1–15
R 195/*Self-Test 1*
Day 2: 197/16–30
S 193/37–41

Average
197/1–41 odd
S 195/*P*: 8

Maximum
197/1–41 odd
S 190/43–46
R 195/*Self-Test 1*

Products and Factors

5-4 Multiplying Binomials Mentally

Objective To find the product of two binomials mentally.

Study the multiplication below and notice how the three terms of the product are formed. Do you see where the distributive axiom is used?

$$\begin{array}{r} 4x + 7 \\ 2x - 3 \\ \hline 8x^2 + 14x \\ -12x - 21 \\ \hline 8x^2 + 2x - 21 \end{array}$$

$$\begin{aligned}(4x + 7)(2x - 3) &= (4x + 7)2x - (4x + 7)3 \\ &= 8x^2 + 14x - 12x - 21 \\ &= 8x^2 + 2x - 21\end{aligned}$$

You can use the following short method to multiply binomials.

Think: $8x^2$ -21
$(4x + 7)(2x - 3)$
$14x$
$-12x$

Write the product: $8x^2 + 2x - 21$

To find the terms in the trinomial product of two binomials $(ax + b)(cx + d)$:

1. Multiply the first terms of the binomials.
2. Multiply the first term of each polynomial by the last term of the other and add these products.
3. Multiply the last terms of the binomials.

Each term of a trinomial like $8x^2 + 2x - 21$ has a standard name. A **quadratic term** is a term of degree two. A **linear term** is a term of degree one. As defined earlier, a *constant term* is a numerical term with no variable factor. The trinomial itself is called a **quadratic polynomial** since its term of greatest degree is quadratic.

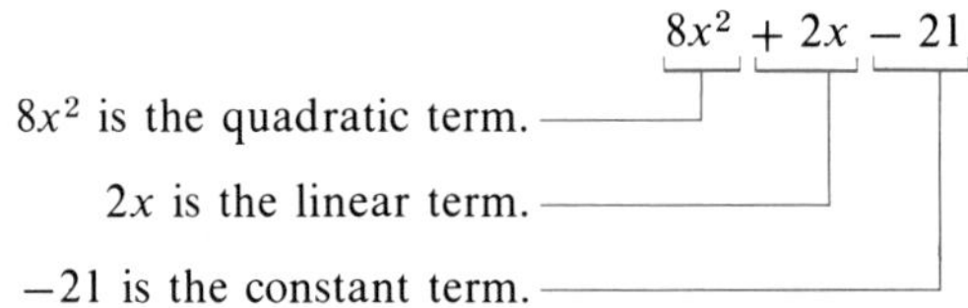

$8x^2 + 2x - 21$
$8x^2$ is the quadratic term.
$2x$ is the linear term.
-21 is the constant term.

Oral Exercises

State the two terms of the product that form the linear term. Then state the linear term, the quadratic term, the constant term, and the product.

Example $(k-9)(k+8)$

Solution $8k$ and $-9k$; linear term, $-k$; quadratic term, k^2; constant term, -72; product, k^2-k-72

1. $(x+1)(x+3)$ **2.** $(y+4)(y+2)$ **3.** $(z-3)(z-4)$ **4.** $(a-5)(a-1)$
5. $(b-4)(b-6)$ **6.** $(c-9)(c-2)$ **7.** $(r+4)(r-2)$ **8.** $(s-6)(s+1)$
9. $(t+3)(t-4)$ **10.** $(g+8)(g-2)$ **11.** $(h-5)(h+3)$ **12.** $(k-1)(k+7)$
13. $(a+5)(2a+1)$ **14.** $(3a+1)(a+2)$ **15.** $(y-1)(2y-1)$ **16.** $(x-3)(2x-5)$

Written Exercises

Write each product as a trinomial.

A
1. $(x+7)(x+2)$ **2.** $(y+3)(y+2)$ **3.** $(a-4)(a-5)$
4. $(b-7)(b-6)$ **5.** $(c+3)(c+7)$ **6.** $(k-3)(k-11)$
7. $(a-5)(a-9)$ **8.** $(1+x)(2+x)$ **9.** $(2a+1)(a+5)$
10. $(4x+3)(x+5)$ **11.** $(2a+9)(a-3)$ **12.** $(3a-1)(2a-1)$
13. $(x-9)(x+7)$ **14.** $(a-5)(a+7)$ **15.** $(b-3)(b+8)$
16. $(c-7)(c+8)$ **17.** $(3k+1)(2k+5)$ **18.** $(4a-5)(2a-3)$
19. $a(7a-5)(5a-7)$ **20.** $b(3b+2)(7b+8)$ **21.** $2x(2x-5)(3x+1)$
22. $n(4n-7)(3n+6)$ **23.** $k(2k-5)(7k+4)$ **24.** $3n(n-3)(2n+7)$

Express each product as a trinomial.

Example $(5x+2y)(4x-3y)$

Solution $20x^2+(-15xy+8xy)-6y^2=20x^2-7xy-6y^2$

B
25. $(2x+4y)(3x+2y)$ **26.** $(3x-2y)(4x+y)$ **27.** $(9a-2b)(3a-5b)$
28. $(x^2+y^2)(x^2+3y^2)$ **29.** $(a^2-3)(2a^2+7)$ **30.** $(r^2-2s)(3r^2+s)$
31. $(x^4+7x^2)(x^2-3)$ **32.** $(x^3-2y)(3x^3+4y)$ **33.** $(3a^4-5b^2)(a^4-2b^2)$

Solve and check.

34. $(x+5)(x-3)=(x-4)(x+9)$ 7 **35.** $(a-4)(a+4)=(a+7)(a-6)$ 26
36. $(6y-5)(6y+5)=(4y+3)(9y-7)$ 4 **37.** $(y+1)(2y-1)=(y-1)^2+(y+1)^2$ 3

Additional Answers
Oral Exercises

1. x and $3x$; $4x$; x^2; 3; x^2+4x+3
2. $4y$ and $2y$; $6y$; y^2; 8; y^2+6y+8
3. $-3z$ and $-4z$; $-7z$; z^2; 12; $z^2-7z+12$
4. $-5a$ and $-a$; $-6a$; a^2; 5; a^2-6a+5
5. $-4b$ and $-6b$; $-10b$; b^2; 24; $b^2-10b+24$
6. $-9c$ and $-2c$; $-11c$; c^2; 18; $c^2-11c+18$
7. $4r$ and $-2r$; $2r$; r^2; -8; r^2+2r-8
8. $-6s$ and s; $-5s$; s^2; -6; s^2-5s-6
9. $3t$ and $-4t$; $-t$; t^2; -12; t^2-t-12
10. $8g$ and $-2g$; $6g$; g^2; -16; $g^2+6g-16$
11. $-5h$ and $3h$; $-2h$; h^2; -15; $h^2-2h-15$
12. $-k$ and $7k$; $6k$; k^2; -7; k^2+6k-7
13. $10a$ and a; $11a$; $2a^2$; 5; $2a^2+11a+5$
14. a and $6a$; $7a$; $3a^2$; 2; $3a^2+7a+2$
15. $-2y$ and $-y$; $-3y$; $2y^2$; 1; $2y^2-3y+1$
16. $-6x$ and $-5x$; $-11x$; $2x^2$; 15; $2x^2-11x+15$

Additional Answers
Written Exercises

1. $x^2+9x+14$
2. y^2+5y+6
3. $a^2-9a+20$
4. $b^2-13b+42$
5. $c^2+10c+21$
6. $k^2-14k+33$

(continued)

Additional Answers Written Exercises

7. $a^2 - 14a + 45$
8. $x^2 + 3x + 2$
9. $2a^2 + 11a + 5$
10. $4x^2 + 23x + 15$
11. $2a^2 + 3a - 27$
12. $6a^2 - 5a + 1$
13. $x^2 - 2x - 63$
14. $a^2 + 2a - 35$
15. $b^2 + 5b - 24$
16. $c^2 + c - 56$
17. $6k^2 + 17k + 5$
18. $8a^2 - 22a + 15$
19. $35a^3 - 74a^2 + 35a$
20. $21b^3 + 38b^2 + 16b$
21. $12x^3 - 26x^2 - 10x$
22. $12n^3 + 3n^2 - 42n$
23. $14k^3 - 27k^2 - 20k$
24. $6n^3 + 3n^2 - 63n$
25. $6x^2 + 16xy + 8y^2$
26. $12x^2 - 5xy - 2y^2$
27. $27a^2 - 51ab + 10b^2$
28. $x^4 + 4x^2y^2 + 3y^4$
29. $2a^4 + a^2 - 21$
30. $3r^4 - 5r^2s - 2s^2$
31. $x^6 + 4x^4 - 21x^2$
32. $3x^6 - 2x^3y - 8y^2$
33. $3a^8 - 11a^4b^2 + 10b^4$

Additional A Exercises

Write each product as a trinomial.

1. $(x + 5)(x + 4)$
   $x^2 + 9x + 20$
2. $(z - 6)(z - 8)$
   $z^2 - 14z + 48$
3. $(15 + y)(2 - y)$
   $-y^2 - 13y + 30$
4. $(9a - 2)(6a - 5)$
   $54a^2 - 57a + 10$
5. $(7x - 3)(2x + 4)$
   $14x^2 + 22x - 12$
6. $n(10n + 3)(3n + 10)$
   $30n^3 + 109n^2 + 30n$

Solve and check.

38. $(3a - 4)(4a + 5) = (6a - 2)(2a + 10)$ 0
39. $2(x + 1)(2x + 5) = (x + 3)(4x + 3)$ 1
40. Show that $(ax + by)(cx + dy) = acx^2 + (ad + bc)xy + bdy^2$.
41. If $(ax + b)(2x - 3) = 18x^2 - 23x + c$, find the values of a, b, and c.
    $a = 9,\ b = 2,\ c = -6$

Write each product as a trinomial, assuming that n represents a positive integer.

C 42. $(x^n + 2y^n)(x^n - y^n)$ $x^{2n} + x^ny^n - 2y^{2n}$
43. $(x^n + 4y^n)(x^n - 4y^n)$ $x^{2n} - 16y^{2n}$
44. Show that the square of an odd integer is odd.

Computer Exercises

For students with some programming experience

Write a BASIC program to find the product of $(AX + B)(CX + D)$, where A, B, C, and D are entered with INPUT statements. Use the program to find the following products. Check the computer's answers by multiplying the binomials mentally.

1. $(x + 3)(x + 5)$ $x^2 + 8x + 15$
2. $(x - 4)(2x + 1)$ $2x^2 - 7x - 4$
3. $(4x + 3)(2x - 5)$ $8x^2 - 14x - 15$
4. $(2x + 7)^2$ $4x^2 + 28x + 49$
5. $(3x - 2)(3x + 2)$ $9x^2 - 4$
6. $(6x - 7)(6x - 7)$ $36x^2 - 84x + 49$

Calculator Key-In

You can use a calculator to evaluate a polynomial for a given value of the variable. One way is to evaluate the polynomial term by using the calculator's memory to store the partial sums.

Another way is to express the polynomial in a form that suggests a sequence of steps on the calculator. For example, to evaluate $5x^2 - 3x + 6$ you could first rewrite it as follows:

$$5x^2 - 3x + 6 = (5x - 3)x + 6$$

To evaluate the polynomial for a particular value, you can just work through the rewritten expression from left to right substituting the appropriate value for x.

Evaluate the polynomial for the given value of the variable.

1. $4x^2 + 5x - 7;\ 3$ 44
2. $6z^2 + 8z - 9;\ 4$ 119
3. $2x^2 + 4x + 5;\ -31$ 1
4. $y^2 - 4y - 3;\ 2.5$ -6.75
5. $9k^2 - 35k + 50;\ 10$ 600
6. $40y^2 - 25y + 70;\ 14$ 7560
7. $18x^2 - 15x - 10;\ -6$ 728
8. $4y^2 + 4y - 5;\ 0.4$ -2.76
9. $20z^2 - 15z + 5;\ -0.5$ 17.5

5-5 Differences of Squares

Objective To simplify products of the form $(a + b)(a - b)$ and to factor differences of squares.

Observe what happens when you simplify the product $(a + b)(a - b)$.

$$\begin{array}{r} a + b \\ a - b \\ \hline a^2 + ab \\ - ab - b^2 \\ \hline a^2 - b^2 \end{array}$$

Two of the terms are opposites, so the product is just a difference of two squares. This result is so useful that you should remember it in either of the following forms.

$$(a + b)(a - b) = a^2 - b^2$$

$$\begin{bmatrix}\text{Sum of two} \\ \text{numbers}\end{bmatrix} \cdot \begin{bmatrix}\text{Difference of} \\ \text{the numbers}\end{bmatrix} = [\text{First number}]^2 - [\text{Second number}]^2$$

Example 1 Express each product as a binomial.

a. $(a + 4)(a - 4)$ **b.** $(2x + 7)(2x - 7)$ **c.** $\left(\frac{1}{2}r^2 - 3s\right)\left(\frac{1}{2}r^2 + 3s\right)$

Solution

a. $(a + 4)(a - 4) = a^2 - 16$

b. $(2x + 7)(2x - 7) = (2x)^2 - 7^2 = 4x^2 - 49$

c. $\left(\frac{1}{2}r^2 - 3s\right)\left(\frac{1}{2}r^2 + 3s\right) = \left(\frac{1}{2}r^2\right)^2 - (3s)^2 = \frac{1}{4}r^4 - 9s^2$

You can use the symmetric property of equality to write the statement $(a + b)(a - b) = a^2 - b^2$ in a form useful for factoring the difference of two squares.

$$a^2 - b^2 = (a + b)(a - b)$$

Example 2 Factor. **a.** $t^2 - 100$ **b.** $25a^2 - 121b^2$

Solution

a. $t^2 - 100 = (t + 10)(t - 10)$

b. $25a^2 - 121b^2 = (5a)^2 - (11b)^2 = (5a + 11b)(5a - 11b)$

In Example 2(b) it was important to recognize that both monomials were *squares*. A monomial is a *square* if the exponents of all powers in it are even and the numerical coefficient is the square of an integer. You can

Teaching Suggestions p. T95

Suggested Extensions p. T95

Chalkboard Examples

Express each product as a binomial.

1. $(t - 1)(t + 1)$ $t^2 - 1$
2. $(6 - z)(6 + z)$ $36 - z^2$
3. $(4n - 5)(4n + 5)$ $16n^2 - 25$

Factor.

4. $y^2 - 49$ $(y + 7)(y - 7)$
5. $25t^2 - 4y^2$ $(5t + 2y)(5t - 2y)$
6. $121m^4 - 9$ $(11m^2 + 3)(11m^2 - 3)$
7. $x^2y^2 - 100z^2$ $(xy + 10z)(xy - 10z)$
8. $-x^6 + 81y^4$ $(9y^2 + x^3)(9y^2 - x^3)$

Suggested Assignments

Minimum
Day 1: 200/1–12, 21–28
S 197/34, 35
Day 2: 201/29–34, 41–44
205/1–8
Day 2 finishes Sec. 5-5 and starts Sec. 5-6.

Average
200/2–50 even
S 198/38, 43

Maximum
200/2–56 even
S 198/42–44

TABLE PAGE 649

use the table of squares at the back of the book or a calculator to determine whether or not an integer is a square. For example, the table shows that 625 is the square of 25.

Example 3 Factor $81y^4 - 625$.

Solution
$$81y^4 - 625 = (9y^2)^2 - 25^2 = (9y^2 + 25)(9y^2 - 25) = (9y^2 + 25)(3y + 5)(3y - 5)$$

Example 3 shows that you should continue factoring until the polynomial is factored completely.

Oral Exercises

Square each monomial.

Example $-4k^2$ ***Solution*** $(-4k^2)^2 = 16k^4$

1. $3x$ $9x^2$
2. $-4z$ $16z^2$
3. $6m^4$ $36m^8$
4. $-2r^2$ $4r^4$
5. $7x^2y$ $49x^4y^2$
6. $-\frac{1}{5}a^2b^3$ $\frac{1}{25}a^4b^6$

Express each product as a binomial.

7. $(x + 2)(x - 2)$ $x^2 - 4$
8. $(a + 5)(a - 5)$ $a^2 - 25$
9. $(s - t)(s + t)$ $s^2 - t^2$
10. $(4b + 3)(4b - 3)$ $16b^2 - 9$
11. $(2n - 3)(2n + 3)$ $4n^2 - 9$
12. $(5x - 7)(5x + 7)$ $25x^2 - 49$

Tell whether or not each binomial is the difference of two squares. If it is, factor it.

13. $x^2 - 16$ Yes; $(x - 4)(x + 4)$
14. $a^2 - 10$ No
15. $k^3 - 4$ No
16. $t^8 + 64$ No
17. $4y^2 - 81$ Yes; $(2y - 9)(2y + 9)$
18. $a^4 - 1$ Yes; $(a^2 - 1)(a^2 + 1) = (a - 1)(a + 1)(a^2 + 1)$
19. $b^2 + 9$ No
20. $c^6 - 25d^2$ Yes; $(c^3 - 5d)(c^3 + 5d)$

Written Exercises

Express each product as a binomial.

A

1. $(a - 3)(a + 3)$ $a^2 - 9$
2. $(2 - x)(2 + x)$ $4 - x^2$
3. $(3b - 5)(3b + 5)$ $9b^2 - 25$
4. $(7x - y)(7x + y)$ $49x^2 - y^2$
5. $(9a - 7)(9a + 7)$ $81a^2 - 49$
6. $(8 + 3x)(8 - 3x)$ $64 - 9x^2$
7. $(8a - 5b)(8a + 5b)$ $64a^2 - 25b^2$
8. $(x^2 - 5)(x^2 + 5)$ $x^4 - 25$
9. $(3u^2 + v)(3u^2 - v)$ $9u^4 - v^2$
10. $(2a^2 - 5b^2)(2a^2 + 5b^2)$ $4a^4 - 25b^4$
11. $(rs + t^2)(rs - t^2)$ $r^2s^2 - t^4$
12. $(a^7 - b^4)(a^7 + b^4)$ $a^{14} - b^8$

Additional A Exercises

Express each product as a binomial.

1. $(4 - j)(4 + j)$ $16 - j^2$
2. $(m^2 - n^2)(m^2 + n^2)$ $m^4 - n^4$

Multiply using the form $(a + b)(a - b)$.

3. 26×34 $(30 - 4)(30 + 4) = 884$

Factor.

4. $81m^2 - 1$ $(9m - 1)(9m + 1)$
5. $196p^2 - s^4t^4$ $(14p - s^2t^2)(14p + s^2t^2)$
6. $k^{10} - 625$ $(k^5 - 25)(k^5 + 25)$

Multiply using the form $(a + b)(a - b)$.

Example 1 $83 \times 77 = (80 + 3)(80 - 3) = 6400 - 9 = 6391$

13. 17×23 391	**14.** 28×32 896	**15.** 62×58 3596	**16.** 45×55 2475
17. 51×49 2499	**18.** 102×98 9996	**19.** 204×196 39,984	**20.** 70×130 9100

Factor. Use the table of squares.

$(5y - 3)(5y + 3)$ **21.** $25y^2 - 9$	$(7a - 4)(7a + 4)$ **22.** $49a^2 - 16$	$(12 - x)(12 + x)$ **23.** $144 - x^2$	$(13b - 7c)(13b + 7c)$ **24.** $169b^2 - 49c^2$
25. $9a^2 - b^2c^2$	**26.** $121 - 400r^2$	**27.** $x^6 - y^6$	**28.** $a^4 - 100$
29. $-144 + 25t^6$ $(5t^3 - 12)(5t^3 + 12)$	**30.** $-361 + 4x^4$ $(2x^2 - 19)(2x^2 + 19)$	**31.** $225 - a^2b^4$ $(15 - ab^2)(15 + ab^2)$	**32.** $16x^4 - 3721$ $(4x^2 - 61)(4x^2 + 61)$
B **33.** $a^4b^4 - c^8$	**34.** $x^8 - 256$	**35.** $a^{16} - 1$	**36.** $81k^8 - n^8$

Factor each expression as the difference of two squares. Simplify.

Example 2
$$(y + 3)^2 - y^2 = [(y + 3) - y][(y + 3) + y] = 3(2y + 3)$$

37. $(x + 3)^2 - x^2$ $3(2x + 3)$

38. $y^2 - (y - 1)^2$ $2y - 1$

39. $(a + 1)^2 - (a - 1)^2$ $4a$

40. $9(x + 1)^2 - 4(x - 1)^2$ $(x + 5)(5x + 1)$

Factor completely.

Example 3
$$3x^3 - 75x = 3x(x^2 - 25) = 3x(x + 5)(x - 5)$$

48. $3x(3x - 11y)(3x + 11y)$

$9(2x - 3y)(2x + 3y)$ **41.** $36x^2 - 81y^2$	$2x(x - 3)(x + 3)$ **42.** $2x^3 - 18x$	$2xy(1 - 6x)(1 + 6x)$ **43.** $2xy - 72x^3y$	$4(3 - k)(3 + k)(9 + k^2)$ **44.** $324 - 4k^4$
45. $81t^9 - 9t$ $9t(3t^4 - 1)(3t^4 + 1)$	**46.** $16r^2 - r^6$ $r^2(2 - r)(2 + r)(4 + r^2)$	**47.** $450a^5 - 8a$ $2a(15a^2 - 2)(15a^2 + 2)$	**48.** $27x^3 - 363xy^2$

Factor, assuming that n is a positive integer.

Example 4
$$x^{2n} - y^2 = (x^n)^2 - y^2 = (x^n - y)(x^n + y)$$

$(x^n - y^n)(x^n + y^n)$ C **49.** $x^{2n} - y^{2n}$	$(a^n - 3)(a^n + 3)$ **50.** $a^{2n} - 9$	$(b^n - c^{2n})(b^n + c^{2n})$ **51.** $b^{2n} - c^{4n}$	$2(x^n - 7)(x^n + 7)$ **52.** $2x^{2n} - 98$
53. $a^{4n} - b^{6n}$ $(a^{2n} - b^{3n})(a^{2n} + b^{3n})$	**54.** $x^{2n+1} - x$ $x(x^n - 1)(x^n + 1)$	**55.** $y^{2n+3} - y^3$ $y^3(y^n - 1)(y^n + 1)$	**56.** $ab^{4n} - a$ $a(b^n - 1)(b^n + 1)(b^{2n} + 1)$

57. Show that the absolute value of the difference of the squares of two consecutive integers is equal to the absolute value of the sum of the integers.

58. Show that the absolute value of the difference of the squares of two consecutive even integers is equal to twice the absolute value of the sum of the integers.

Additional Answers Written Exercises

25. $(3a - bc)(3a + bc)$

26. $(11 - 20r)(11 + 20r)$

27. $(x^3 - y^3)(x^3 + y^3)$

28. $(a^2 - 10)(a^2 + 10)$

33. $(ab - c^2)(ab + c^2)(a^2b^2 + c^4)$

34. $(x - 2)(x + 2) \cdot (x^2 + 4)(x^4 + 16)$

35. $(a - 1)(a + 1)(a^2 + 1) \cdot (a^4 + 1)(a^8 + 1)$

36. $(3k^2 - n^2)(3k^2 + n^2) \cdot (9k^4 + n^4)$

57. Let n and $n + 1$ be the integers. $|(n + 1)^2 - n^2| = |n^2 + 2n + 1 - n^2| = |2n + 1| = |n + (n + 1)|$

58. Let n and $n + 2$ be the integers. $|(n + 2)^2 - n^2| = |n^2 + 4n + 4 - n^2| = |4n + 4| = 2|2n + 2| = 2|n + (n + 2)|$

Mixed Review Exercises

1. Write "the quantity $z - y$ squared" in exponential form. $(z - y)^2$

2. If Q is a point on the number line with coordinate 5, what is the coordinate of the point $8\frac{1}{2}$ units to the left of Q? $-3\frac{1}{2}$

Simplify.

3. $17 + m + n + 5 + 6n$ $22 + m + 7n$

4. $(-8)^m(-8)^n$ $(-8)^{m+n}$

Extra / Sums and Differences of Cubes

Both sums and differences of cubes can be factored, as shown by the factoring patterns below.

$$x^3 + y^3 = (x + y)(x^2 - xy + y^2)$$
$$x^3 - y^3 = (x - y)(x^2 + xy + y^2)$$

Example Factor $m^3 - 27$.

Solution $(m - 3)(m^2 + 3m + 9)$

Exercises

1. Verify the factoring pattern for the sum of two cubes by multiplying $(x + y)(x^2 - xy + y^2)$.
2. Verify the factoring pattern for the difference of two cubes by multiplying $(x - y)(x^2 + xy + y^2)$.

Factor.

3. $w^3 + 8$ **4.** $a^3 - 64$ **5.** $n^3 + 125$ **6.** $27 - 216e^3$

7. a. Factor $z^6 - 1$ as a difference of cubes to show that
$$z^6 - 1 = (z - 1)(z + 1)(z^4 + z^2 + 1).$$
b. Factor $z^6 - 1$ as a difference of squares to show that
$$z^6 - 1 = (z - 1)(z + 1)(z^2 + z + 1)(z^2 - z + 1).$$
c. Show that the factorizations given in parts (a) and (b) are equivalent by writing
$$z^4 + z^2 + 1 = (z^4 + 2z^2 + 1) - z^2$$
and then factoring the difference of squares on the right.

Challenge

According to the legend, the inventor of the game of chess asked to be rewarded by having one grain of wheat put on the first square of a chessboard, two grains on the second, four grains on the third, eight grains on the fourth, and so on. The total number of grains would be $2^{64} - 1$, which is several thousand times the world's annual wheat yield.

1. To find out how large 2^{64} is approximately, you could enter the number 2 on the calculator and press the squaring button a number of times. How many times? 6
2. Factor $2^{64} - 1$ as a difference of squares to show that it is divisible by 3, 5, and 17.

Additional Answers Extra

1. $(x + y)(x^2 - xy + y^2) = x^3 - x^2y + xy^2 + yx^2 - xy^2 + y^3 = x^3 + y^3$
2. $(x - y)(x^2 + xy + y^2) = x^3 + x^2y + xy^2 - yx^2 - xy^2 - y^3 = x^3 - y^3$
3. $(w + 2)(w^2 - 2w + 4)$
4. $(a - 4)(a^2 + 4a + 16)$
5. $(n + 5)(n^2 - 5n + 25)$
6. $27(1 - 2e)\cdot(1 + 2e + 4e^2)$
7. **a.** $z^6 - 1 = (z^2)^3 - (1)^3 = (z^2 - 1)\cdot(z^4 + z^2 + 1) = (z - 1)\cdot(z + 1)(z^4 + z^2 + 1)$
b. $z^6 - 1 = (z^3)^2 - (1)^2 = (z^3 - 1)(z^3 + 1) = (z - 1)(z^2 + z + 1)\cdot(z + 1)(z^2 - z + 1) = (z - 1)(z + 1)\cdot(z^2 + z + 1)(z^2 - z + 1)$
c. $z^4 + z^2 + 1 = (z^4 + 2z^2 + 1) - z^2 = (z^2 + 1)^2 - z^2 = (z^2 + 1 - z)(z^2 + 1 + z) = (z^2 - z + 1)(z^2 + z + 1)$

Additional Answer Challenge

2. $(2^{64} - 1) = (2^{32} - 1)\cdot(2^{32} + 1) = (2^{16} - 1)\cdot(2^{16} + 1)(2^{32} + 1) = (2^8 - 1)(2^8 + 1)(2^{16} + 1)\cdot(2^{32} + 1) = (2^4 - 1)\cdot(2^4 + 1)(2^8 + 1)(2^{16} + 1)\cdot(2^{32} + 1) = (2^2 - 1)(2^2 + 1)(2^4 + 1)(2^8 + 1)(2^{16} + 1)\cdot(2^{32} + 1) = (2 - 1)(2 + 1)\cdot(2^2 + 1)(2^4 + 1)(2^8 + 1)\cdot(2^{16} + 1)(2^{32} + 1)$. Hence, $(2 - 1), (2 + 1), \ldots, (2^{32} + 1)$ are the factors of $2^{64} - 1$; but $(2 + 1) = 3$, $(2^2 + 1) = 5$, and $(2^4 + 1) = 17$, so 3, 5, and 17 are factors of $2^{64} - 1$.

5-6 Squares of Binomials

Objective To find squares of binomials and to factor trinomial squares.

Note what happens when you square the binomial $a + b$.

$$\begin{array}{r} a + b \\ a + b \\ \hline a^2 + ab \quad \\ ab + b^2 \\ \hline a^2 + 2ab + b^2 \end{array}$$

1. Square of the first term.
2. Twice the product of the two terms.
3. Square of the last term.

When you square the binomial difference $a - b$, the middle term in the product is preceded by a minus sign.

$$\begin{array}{r} a - b \\ a - b \\ \hline a^2 - ab \quad \\ - ab + b^2 \\ \hline a^2 - 2ab + b^2 \end{array}$$

1. Square of the first term.
2. Twice the product of the two terms.
3. Square of the last term.

These results may be expressed as these two useful formulas.

$$(a + b)^2 = a^2 + 2ab + b^2$$
$$(a - b)^2 = a^2 - 2ab + b^2$$

These formulas can be used to write squares of binomials as trinomials.

Example 1 $(x + 5)^2 = x^2 + 2 \cdot x \cdot 5 + 5^2 = x^2 + 10x + 25$

Example 2 $(2m - 1)^2 = (2m)^2 - 2 \cdot 2m \cdot 1 + 1^2 = 4m^2 - 4m + 1$

Example 3 $(7s - 4t)^2 = 49s^2 - 2(28st) + 16t^2 = 49s^2 - 56st + 16t^2$

Example 4 $(6x^2 - y^3)^2 = 36x^4 - 12x^2y^3 + y^6$

Teaching Suggestions p. T95

Suggested Extensions p. T95

Chalkboard Examples

Express each square as a trinomial.

1. $(t - 2)^2$ $t^2 - 4t + 4$
2. $(b - 7)^2$ $b^2 - 14b + 49$
3. $(y + 3)^2$ $y^2 + 6y + 9$
4. $(3z - 1)^2$ $9z^2 - 6z + 1$

Factor completely.

5. $x^2 - 18x + 81$ $(x - 9)^2$
6. $25b^2 + 10b + 1$ $(5b + 1)^2$
7. $4t^2 - 12t + 9$ $(2t - 3)^2$
8. $9m^3 - 12m^2 + 4m$ $m(3m - 2)^2$

Common Error

Some students may still get "doubling" and "squaring" confused. Students may need to be reminded and shown that squaring a binomial results in a trinomial rather than a binomial. Some students may square only part of a term, writing "$2x^2$" instead of "$4x^2$," for example, to represent $(2x)^2$.

Supplementary Materials

Practice Master 26
Resource Book, p. 85

Suggested Assignments

Minimum

205/9–19 odd, 21–29, 42, 43, 44

Day 2 of Sec. 5-5 finishes Sec. 5-5 and starts Sec. 5-6.

Average

Day 1: 205/2–20 even, 21–49 odd

S 185/44, 46, 47

Day 2: 205/42–60 even

R 207/*Self-Test 2*

Maximum

205/2–60 even

R 207/*Self-Test 2*

The symmetric property of equality enables you to rewrite the formulas for squaring a binomial in a form useful for factoring.

$$a^2 + 2ab + b^2 = (a + b)^2$$
$$a^2 - 2ab + b^2 = (a - b)^2$$

The expressions on the left sides of the two equations above are called **trinomial squares,** since each expression has three terms and is the square of a binomial.

To determine whether or not a trinomial is a trinomial square, ask the three questions illustrated in the next examples.

Example 5 Is $81x^2 - 36x + 4$ a trinomial square?

Solution

1. Is the first term a square? Yes, $81x^2 = (9x)^2$
2. Is the last term a square? Yes, $4 = 2^2$
3. Is the middle term, neglecting the sign, twice the product of $9x$ and 2? Yes, $36x = 2(9x \cdot 2)$

Thus, $81x^2 - 36x + 4$ is a trinomial square and $81x^2 - 36x + 4 = (9x - 2)^2$. ***Answer***

Example 6 Is $100c^2 + 30cd + 9d^2$ a trinomial square?

Solution

1. Is the first term a square? Yes, $100c^2 = (10c)^2$
2. Is the last term a square? Yes, $9d^2 = (3d)^2$
3. Is the middle term twice the product of $10c$ and $3d$? No, $30cd \neq 2(10c \cdot 3d)$

Thus, $100c^2 + 30cd + 9d^2$ is not a trinomial square. ***Answer***
(It would be a trinomial square if the linear term were $60cd$.)

Oral Exercises

Express each square as a trinomial.

1. $(k - 5)^2$ $k^2 - 10k + 25$
2. $(x - y)^2$ $x^2 - 2xy + y^2$
3. $(a + 6)^2$ $a^2 + 12a + 36$
4. $(b - 8)^2$ $b^2 - 16b + 64$
5. $(3x + 1)^2$ $9x^2 + 6x + 1$
6. $(2k + 1)^2$ $4k^2 + 4k + 1$
7. $(d^2 + 3)^2$ $d^4 + 6d^2 + 9$
8. $(5z^2 - 3)^2$ $25z^4 - 30z^2 + 9$

Decide whether or not each polynomial is a trinomial square. If so, factor it.

9. $x^2 + 14x + 49$ $(x + 7)^2$
10. $a^2 - 6a + 9$ $(a - 3)^2$
11. $b^2 - 8b + 16$ $(b - 4)^2$
12. $y^2 + 2y + 4$ No
13. $9n^2 - 12n + 4$ $(3n - 2)^2$
14. $25x^2 - 10xy + 4y^2$ No
15. $v^2 + vt + t^2$ No
16. $h^2 - 4h + 2$ No
17. $j^4 - 2j^2 + 1$ $(j^2 - 1)^2$
18. Find the square of 31 by thinking of it as $(30 + 1)^2$. 961
19. Find the square of 49 by thinking of it as $(50 - 1)^2$. 2401

Additional A Exercises

Express each square as a trinomial.

1. $(a - 7)^2$ $a^2 - 14a + 49$
2. $(y + 5)^2$ $y^2 + 10y + 25$
3. $(3t - 2)^2$ $9t^2 - 12t + 4$
4. $(m^2 + 4)^2$ $m^4 + 8m^2 + 16$

Factor each trinomial as the square of a binomial if possible. If it is not possible, write "not factorable."

5. $z^2 + 12z + 36$ $(z + 6)^2$
6. $x^2 + x + 1$ not factorable

Written Exercises

Express each square as a trinomial.

A

1. $(x + 2)^2$ 2. $(y - 3)^2$ 3. $(a - 4)^2$ 4. $(b + 9)^2$
5. $(2x + 3)^2$ 6. $(3y + 8)^2$ 7. $(4k - 5)^2$ 8. $(7k - 2)^2$
9. $(4p + 3q)^2$ 10. $(8x - 5y)^2$ 11. $(3x + 7y)^2$ 12. $(2a - 9b)^2$
13. $(ab - 5)^2$ 14. $(x^2 + 4)^2$ 15. $(2st - 7)^2$ 16. $(2x^2 - y^2)^2$
17. $(-3 + 5a)^2$ 18. $(-7 - 6b)^2$ 19. $(-8x^2 + 1)^2$ 20. $(-11a^2 - b^2)^2$

Factor each trinomial as the square of a binomial if possible. If it is not possible, write "not factorable." (N.F. = not factorable)

21. $n^2 - 2n + 1$ $(n - 1)^2$ 22. $k^2 + 6k + 9$ $(k + 3)^2$ 23. $r^2 - 4r + 4$ $(r - 2)^2$
24. $a^2 + 12a + 24$ N.F. 25. $81 - 18b + b^2$ $(9 - b)^2$ 26. $49 - 7k + k^2$ N.F.
27. $4x^2 + 4x + 1$ $(2x + 1)^2$ 28. $9 + 12y + 4y^2$ $(3 + 2y)^2$ 29. $36 - 60a + 25a^2$ $(6 - 5a)^2$
30. $25d^2 - 50d + 100$ N.F. 31. $64x^2 - 16xy + y^2$ $(8x - y)^2$ 32. $81n^2 + nt + 9t^2$ N.F.

B

33. $x^4 + 2x^2 + 1$ $(x^2 + 1)^2$ 34. $y^4 + 10y^2 + 25$ $(y^2 + 5)^2$ 35. $a^2b^2 - 12ab + 36$ $(ab - 6)^2$
36. $25t^2 + 55t + 121$ N.F. 37. $a^4 - 24a^2 + 144$ $(a^2 - 12)^2$ 38. $(x + 1)^2 + 2(x + 1) + 1$ $(x + 2)^2$
39. a. Express $(5x - 2)^2$ and $(2 - 5x)^2$ as trinomials.
    b. Explain why $(5x - 2)^2 = (2 - 5x)^2$ although $5x - 2 \neq 2 - 5x$.
40. Show that $a^4 - 8a^2 + 16$ can be factored as $(a - 2)^2(a + 2)^2$.
41. Show that $x^4 - 18x^2 + 81$ can be factored as $(x - 3)^2(x + 3)^2$.

Factor completely.

Example 1 $12x^3 + 36x^2 + 27x = 3x(4x^2 + 12x + 9) = 3x(2x + 3)^2$

42. $6x^2 + 12x + 6$ $6(x + 1)^2$ 43. $3z^2 + 18z + 27$ $3(z + 3)^2$ 44. $a^3 - 10a^2 + 25a$ $a(a - 5)^2$
45. $18y^2 - 12y + 2$ $2(3y - 1)^2$ 46. $24b - 24b^2 + 6b^3$ 47. $20x^4 + 60x^2 + 45$
48. $2a^6 - 24a^4 + 72a^2$ $2a^2(a^2 - 6)^2$ 49. $16k^5 - 48k^3 + 36k$ $4k(2k^2 - 3)^2$ 50. $3v^8 - 48v^5 + 192v^2$ $3v^2(v^3 - 8)^2$

Example 2 $x^2 - 4x + 4 - y^2 = (x - 2)^2 - y^2 = [(x - 2) + y][(x - 2) - y]$
$= (x + y - 2)(x - y - 2)$

51. $w^2 + 6w + 9 - 4q^2$ $(w + 3 - 2q)(w + 3 + 2q)$ 52. $s^2t^2 - 2st + 1 - z^2$ $(st - 1 - z)(st - 1 + z)$ 53. $25c^2 - 4d^2 - 4d - 1$ $(5c - 2d - 1)(5c + 2d + 1)$

Solve and check.

54. $(x + 3)(x + 5) = (x + 1)^2 + 13x$ 2
55. $(2x + 1)^2 - (2x - 1)^2 = (x + 6)^2 - x^2$ -9
56. $(2x - 1)^2 - (4x - 3)(x + 2) = 1 - 7x$ 3
57. $(5x + 4)^2 - (3x + 2)^2 = (4x + 4)(4x - 4)$ -1

Additional Answers
Written Exercises

1. $x^2 + 4x + 4$
2. $y^2 - 6y + 9$
3. $a^2 - 8a + 16$
4. $b^2 + 18b + 81$
5. $4x^2 + 12x + 9$
6. $9y^2 + 48y + 64$
7. $16k^2 - 40k + 25$
8. $49k^2 - 28k + 4$
9. $16p^2 + 24pq + 9q^2$
10. $64x^2 - 80xy + 25y^2$
11. $9x^2 + 42xy + 49y^2$
12. $4a^2 - 36ab + 81b^2$
13. $a^2b^2 - 10ab + 25$
14. $x^4 + 8x^2 + 16$
15. $4s^2t^2 - 28st + 49$
16. $4x^4 - 4x^2y^2 + y^4$
17. $9 - 30a + 25a^2$
18. $49 + 84b + 36b^2$
19. $64x^4 - 16x^2 + 1$
20. $121a^4 + 22a^2b^2 + b^4$
39. a. $25x^2 - 20x + 4$; $4 - 20x + 25x^2$
    b. $5x - 2$ and $2 - 5x$ are opposites and the squares of opposites are equal.
40. $a^4 - 8a^2 + 16 = (a^2 - 4)^2 = [(a - 2)(a + 2)]^2 = (a - 2)^2(a + 2)^2$
41. $x^4 - 18x^2 + 81 = (x^2 - 9)^2 = [(x - 3)(x + 3)]^2 = (x - 3)^2(x + 3)^2$
46. $6b(2 - b)^2$
47. $5(2x^2 + 3)^2$

Additional Answers Written Exercises

60.

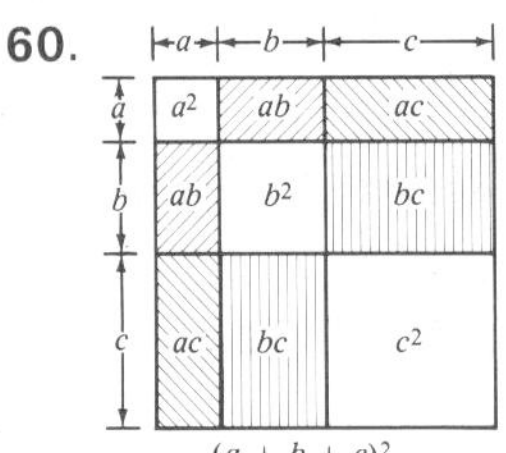

61.

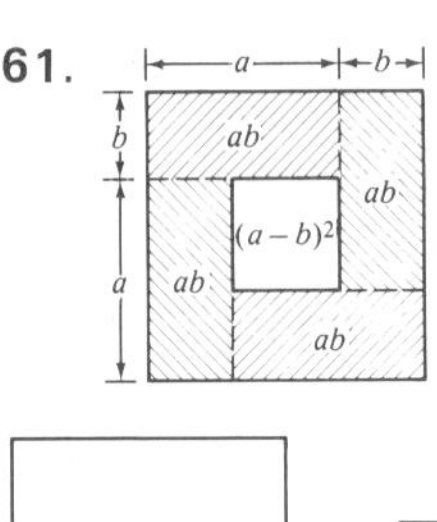

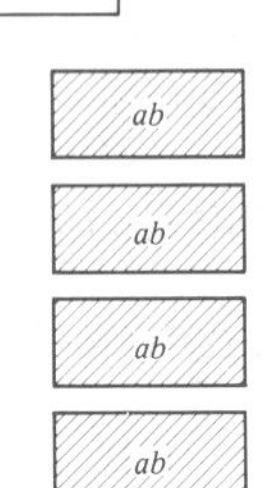

62.

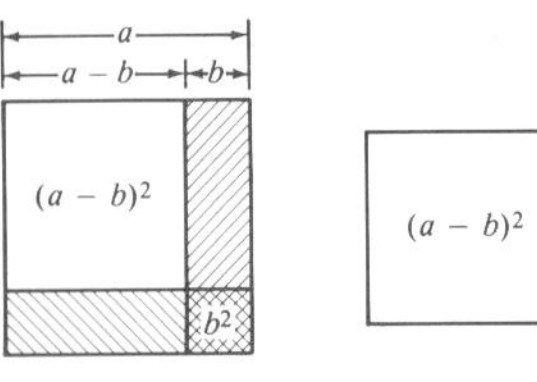

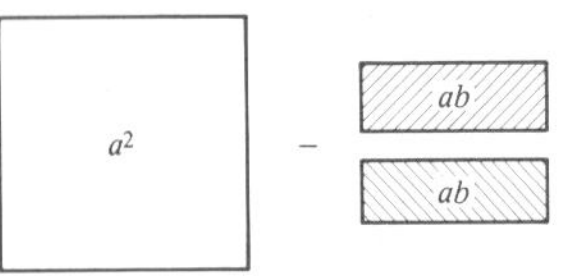

58. The length of a rectangular flower garden is four times its width. If the width is increased by 4 m and the length is decreased by 4 m, the area will be increased by 32 m^2. Find the dimensions of the original garden. 4 m by 16 m

59. The sum of the squares of three consecutive integers is 22 less than three times the product of the two greater integers. Find the integers. 7, 8, 9

Show that each diagram illustrates the statement below it.

Example 3

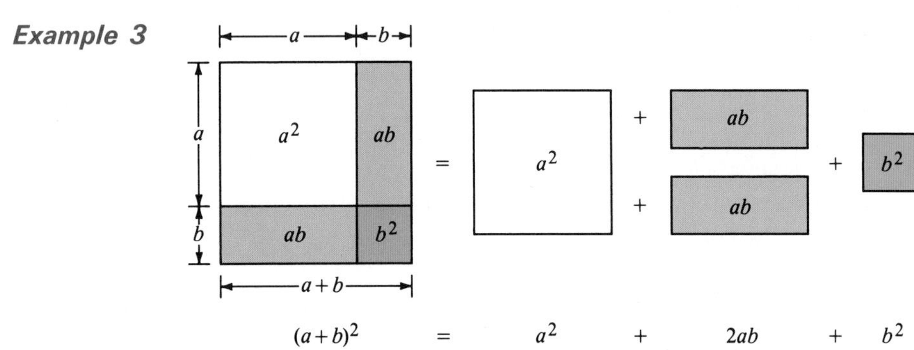

$(a+b)^2 = a^2 + 2ab + b^2$

60.

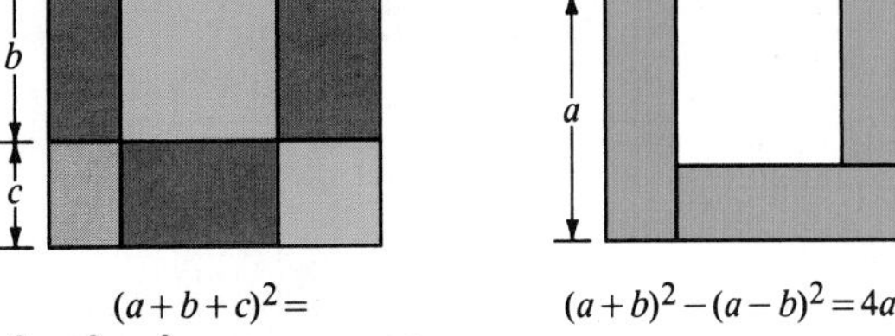

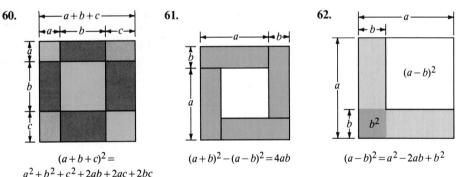

$(a+b+c)^2 = a^2+b^2+c^2+2ab+2ac+2bc$

61.

$(a+b)^2-(a-b)^2=4ab$

62.

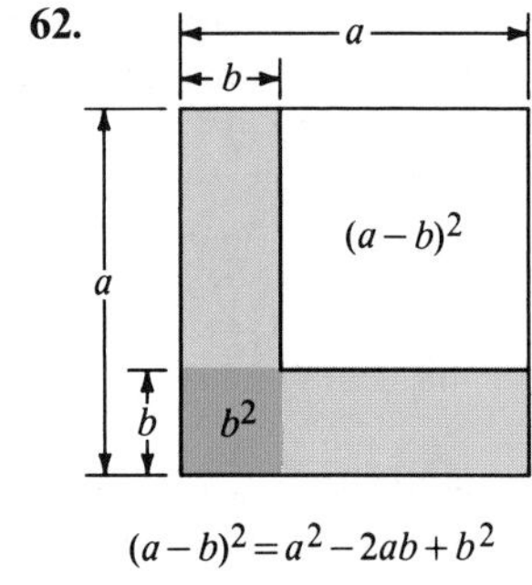

$(a-b)^2=a^2-2ab+b^2$

C **63.** The square of a two-digit number ending in 5 always ends in 25. The digits before the 25 are found by multiplying the tens digit by one more than the tens digit, as shown at the right.

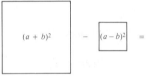

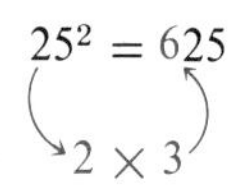

a. Use this rule to find the squares of 35, 55, and 85. 1225, 3025, 7225

b. Prove the rule works by letting $10t + 5$ represent a two-digit number ending in 5. Square this number and show that the result equals $[t(t+1) \times 100] + 25$.

Self-Test 2

Vocabulary quadratic term (p. 196) linear term (p. 196) quadratic polynomial (p. 196) trinomial square (p. 204)

Express each product as a polynomial.

1. $(3y + 5)(2y - 6)$ $6y^2 - 8y - 30$

2. $2x(x - 4)(3x - 2)$ $6x^3 - 28x^2 + 16x$ **Obj. 5-4, p. 196**

3. $(x - 7)(x + 7)$ $x^2 - 49$

4. $(9a + 2b)(9a - 2b)$ $81a^2 - 4b^2$ **Obj. 5-5, p. 199**

Factor.

5. $4x^2 - 49$ $(2x - 7)(2x + 7)$

6. $36x^4 - 81$ $9(2x^2 - 3)(2x^2 + 3)$

Express each square as a trinomial.

7. $(2y + 5)^2$ $4y^2 + 20y + 25$

8. $(3z - 5k)^2$ $9z^2 - 30zk + 25k^2$ **Obj. 5-6, p. 203**

Factor.

9. $9a^2 + 12a + 4$ $(3a + 2)^2$

10. $16m^2 - 24mn + 9n^2$ $(4m - 3n)^2$

Check your answers with those at the back of the book.

Career Note / Nutritionist

Schools, hospitals, and other large institutions rely on nutritionists to plan for groups and individuals in their organizations. Sometimes nutritionists are needed to plan special menus for individuals in need of a salt-free, a low-cholesterol, or a high-protein diet. A nutritionist must plan appealing meals that supply the nutrients needed to maintain good health. Once a menu has been planned, a nutritionist may also be involved with the preparation and serving of the food.

Nutritionists may need to teach people about sound nutritional practices. Thus, they should be able to work well with people. The minimum requirement for a career as a nutritionist is a bachelor's degree with coursework in physiology, food and nutrition, bacteriology, and chemistry. A scientific aptitude is also helpful. Nutritionists often continue their training after graduation with an internship in a hospital.

63. **b.** $(10t + 5)^2 =$
$100t^2 + 100t + 25 =$
$100t(t + 1) + 25 =$
$[t(t + 1) \times 100] + 25$

Mixed Review Exercises

Simplify.

1. "22 decreased by −18."
$22 - (-18) = 40$
2. $(-75xy + 30)\left(\frac{-4}{15}\right)$
$20xy - 8$
3. $\frac{64xy^2 - 56x^2y^5}{8xy}$
$8y - 7xy^4$
4. Solve: $28 = 92 + x$
$x = -64$

Quick Quiz

Express each product as a polynomial.

1. $(4n - 3)(2n + 5)$
$8n^2 + 14n - 15$
2. $3t(2t - 5)(t + 2)$
$6t^3 - 3t^2 - 30t$
3. $(k - 11)(k + 11)$
$k^2 - 121$
4. $(6y - 5t)(6y + 5t)$
$36y^2 - 25t^2$

Factor.

5. $9t^6 - 16$
$(3t^3 + 4)(3t^3 - 4)$
6. $25x^2 + 20x + 4$
$(5x + 2)^2$
7. $9y^2 - 42yz + 49z^2$
$(3y - 7z)^2$

Teaching Suggestions p. T96

Suggested Extensions p. T96

Chalkboard Examples

Factor. If not factorable, write "prime."

1. $x^2 + 16x + 28$
   $(x + 2)(x + 14)$
2. $y^2 - 9y + 8$
   $(y - 8)(y - 1)$
3. $s^2 + 8st + 12t^2$
   $(s + 2t)(s + 6t)$
4. $m^2 - 3m + 5$ prime
5. $k^2 + 9k + 20$
   $(k + 4)(k + 5)$
6. $t^2 - 15t + 26$
   $(t - 13)(t - 2)$

Common Error

Students seem to make more mistakes when factoring trinomials of this type when b is negative. Remind students that when c is positive, the factors of c must *each* have the *same sign* as b and that the *sum*, not the difference, of the factors of c must equal b. Encourage students to check their factorizations by multiplying.

Suggested Assignments

Minimum
209/1–33 odd
R 207/*Self-Test 2*

Average
209/1–45 odd

Maximum
209/1–49 odd
S 206/61–63

5-7 Factoring Pattern for $x^2 + bx + c$, c positive

Objective To factor quadratic trinomials whose quadratic coefficient is 1 and whose constant term is positive.

In this section you will study trinomials that can be factored as a product of the form $(x + r)(x + s)$ where r and s are both positive or both negative. First look at some products of this form to see what clues they give you for factoring the trinomial.

Example 1 $(x + 4)(x + 3) = x^2 + 7x + 12$

sum of 4 and 3 (→ 7); product of 4 and 3 (→ 12)

Example 2 $(x - 5)(x - 6) = x^2 - 11x + 30$

sum of −5 and −6 (→ −11); product of −5 and −6 (→ 30)

Example 3 $(x + r)(x + s) = x^2 + (r + s)x + rs$

Example 3 suggests the following technique for factoring polynomials with quadratic coefficient 1 and positive constant term.

1. List the pairs of factors that have a product equal to the constant term.
2. Find the pair of factors in the list that have a sum equal to the coefficient of the linear term.

Examples 1 and 2 suggest that in Step 1 you can just look at the factors with the same sign as the linear term.

Example 4 Factor $a^2 + 13a + 30$.

Solution

1. Since the coefficient of the linear term is 13, which is positive, list the pairs of positive factors of 30.
2. Find the factors that have a sum of 13: 3 and 10
3. $a^2 + 13a + 30 = (a + 10)(a + 3)$ ***Answer***

30	
1	30
2	15
3	10
5	6

As you gain experience with factoring, you will learn to review the factors of the constant term mentally instead of writing them down.

Example 5 Factor $z^2 - 16z + 28$.

Solution

1. Since $-16 < 0$, think of the negative factors of 28.
2. Select the factors of 28 with sum -16: -2 and -14
3. $z^2 - 16z + 28 = (z - 14)(z - 2)$ ***Answer***

A polynomial that cannot be rewritten as a product of polynomials of lower degree is called **irreducible.** An irreducible polynomial whose greatest monomial factor is 1 is a **prime polynomial.**

Example 6 Factor $x^2 - x + 10$.

Solution
1. List the pairs of negative factors of 10: $-1, -10; -2, -5$
2. Neither of these pairs of factors has a sum of -1.
3. Thus, $x^2 - x + 10$ cannot be factored. It is irreducible and prime. ***Answer***

Oral Exercises

Find two integers with the given sum and product.

	1.	2.	3.	4.	5.	6.	7.	8.
sum	5	−6	−5	−7	11	19	−9	9
product	4	9	6	6	18	18	18	18

For each trinomial, tell which two factors of the constant term have a sum equal to the coefficient of the linear term.

Example $x^2 - 10x + 21$ ***Solution*** $(-3)(-7) = 21$ and $-3 + (-7) = -10$; -3 and -7

9. $x^2 + 10x + 9$ 9, 1
10. $y^2 - 5y + 4$ −4, −1
11. $z^2 - 4z + 4$ −2, −2
12. $t^2 + 7t + 10$ 5, 2
13. $a^2 - 3a + 2$ −2, −1
14. $b^2 - 9b + 14$
15. $c^2 + 2c + 1$ 1, 1
16. $d^2 + 17d + 16$ 16, 1
17. $v^2 - 21v + 20$
18. $h^2 + 9h + 20$ 5, 4
19. $j^2 - 12j + 20$ −10, −2
20. $k^2 + 12k + 20$ 10, 2

Written Exercises

Factor. Check by multiplying the factors. If the polynomial is not factorable, write "prime."

A

1. $x^2 + 6x + 5$
2. $y^2 + 7y + 6$
3. $a^2 - 4a + 3$
4. $b^2 - 10b + 16$
5. $r^2 + 9r + 18$
6. $v^2 - 20v + 51$
7. $k^2 - 11k + 28$
8. $x^2 - 13x + 22$
9. $z^2 - 13z + 42$
10. $y^2 + 15y + 44$
11. $a^2 - 17a + 50$
12. $b^2 - 14b + 45$
13. $y^2 + 16y + 55$
14. $d^2 - 14d + 32$
15. $p^2 - 17p + 72$
16. $72 - 38z + z^2$
17. $20 - 12c + c^2$
18. $40 - 15a + a^2$

Additional A Exercises

Factor. Check by multiplying the factors.

1. $x^2 + 14x + 13$
   $(x + 13)(x + 1)$
2. $b^2 - 9b + 20$
   $(b - 4)(b - 5)$
3. $d^2 + 19d + 48$
   $(d + 16)(d + 3)$
4. $56 - 18a + a^2$
   $(14 - a)(4 - a)$
5. $m^2 + 20mn + 64n^2$
   $(m + 16n)(m + 4n)$
6. $a^2 - 20ab + 75b^2$
   $(a - 15b)(a - 5b)$

Additional Answers Oral Exercises

1. 4, 1
2. −3, −3
3. −2, −3
4. −6, −1
5. 9, 2
6. 18, 1
7. −6, −3
8. 6, 3
14. −7, −2
17. −20, −1

Additional Answers Written Exercises

1. $(x + 5)(x + 1)$
2. $(y + 6)(y + 1)$
3. $(a - 3)(a - 1)$
4. $(b - 8)(b - 2)$
5. $(r + 6)(r + 3)$
6. $(v - 17)(v - 3)$
7. $(k - 4)(k - 7)$
8. $(x - 11)(x - 2)$
9. $(z - 6)(z - 7)$
10. $(y + 11)(y + 4)$
11. prime
12. $(b - 9)(b - 5)$
13. $(y + 11)(y + 5)$
14. prime
15. $(p - 9)(p - 8)$
16. $(36 - z)(2 - z)$
17. $(10 - c)(2 - c)$
18. prime

Additional Answers Written Exercises

19. $(x - 7y)(x - 5y)$
20. $(a - 8b)(a - 3b)$
21. $(s - 5t)(s - 6t)$
22. $(c - 16d)(c - 3d)$
23. $(b + 8c)(b + 5c)$
24. $(x + 10y)(x + 5y)$
25. $(s - 6t)(s - 7t)$
26. $(a + 5b)^2$
27. prime
28. $(y - 7z)^2$
29. $(d + 9e)(d + 3e)$
30. $(y - 3z)(y - 25z)$
31. $(a - 8)(a - 15)$
32. $(y + 16)(y + 6)$
33. $(9 - a)(12 - a)$
34. $(36 - b)(5 - b)$
35. $(7n - x)(14n - x)$
36. $(8y - z)(14y - z)$

Mixed Review Exercises

1. Twice a number n, decreased by 5, is 17. What is the number? 11
2. Subtract: $6x - 3y + 5$ from...
$$\begin{array}{r} 6x - 3y + 5 \\ -7x - 5y + 6 \\ \hline 13x + 2y - 1 \end{array}$$

Express as a polynomial.

3. $(3z - 2y)(4z + y)$ $12z^2 - 5yz - 2y^2$
4. $(7 - 2y)(7 + 2y)$ $49 - 4y^2$

Example 1 $a^2 - 8ab + 12b^2$

Solution $a^2 - 8ab + 12b^2 = (a - \quad)(a - \quad)$
$= (a - 2b)(a - 6b)$ ***Answer***

19. $x^2 - 12xy + 35y^2$
20. $a^2 - 11ab + 24b^2$
21. $s^2 - 11st + 30t^2$
22. $c^2 - 19cd + 48d^2$
23. $b^2 + 13bc + 40c^2$
24. $x^2 + 15xy + 50y^2$
25. $s^2 - 13st + 42t^2$
26. $a^2 + 10ab + 25b^2$
27. $k^2 - 18ka + 36a^2$
28. $y^2 - 14yz + 49z^2$
29. $d^2 + 12de + 27e^2$
30. $y^2 - 28yz + 75z^2$

B

31. $a^2 - 23a + 120$
32. $y^2 + 22y + 96$
33. $108 - 21a + a^2$
34. $180 - 41b + b^2$
35. $98n^2 - 21nx + x^2$
36. $112y^2 - 22yz + z^2$

Determine all integral values for k for which the trinomial can be factored.

Example 2 $x^2 + kx + 35$

Solution 35 can be factored as a product of two integers in these ways:

$1 \cdot 35 \qquad 5 \cdot 7 \qquad (-1)(-35) \qquad (-5)(-7)$

The corresponding values of k are 36, 12, -36, -12. ***Answer***

37. $x^2 + kx + 10$ 11, 7, -11, -7
38. $y^2 + ky + 4$ 5, 4, -5, -4
39. $z^2 + kz + 15$ 16, 8, -16, -8
40. $u^2 + ku + 21$ 22, 10, -22, -10
41. $r^2 + kr + 12$ 13, 8, 7, -13, -8, -7
42. $n^2 + kn + 18$ 19, 11, 9, -19, -11, -9

Factor. Check by multiplying the factors.

C

43. $(x + 2)^2 + 5(x + 2) + 4$ $(x + 6)(x + 3)$
44. $(y - 2)^2 + 7(y - 2) + 10$ $y(y + 3)$
45. $(a + b)^2 - 6(a + b) + 8$ $(a + b - 4)(a + b - 2)$
46. $(z + 4)^2 - 8(z + 4) + 16$ z^2
47. $a^4 - 10a^2 + 9$ $(a - 3)(a + 3)(a - 1)(a + 1)$
48. $b^4 - 26b^2 + 25$
49. $c^4 - 12c^2 + 27$ $(c - 3)(c + 3)(c^2 - 3)$
50. $x^5 - 13x^3 + 36x$
51. Factor $x^{2n} - 42x^ny^{2n} + 437y^{4n}$, where n is a positive integer. $(x^n - 19y^{2n})(x^n - 23y^{2n})$

48. $(b - 5)(b + 5)(b - 1)(b + 1)$
50. $x(x - 3)(x + 3)(x - 2)(x + 2)$

Computer Exercises

For students with some programming experience

Write a BASIC program to test whether a monomial entered with an INPUT statement is a perfect square. (*Note:* In BASIC, the function SQR(N) gives the square root of the number N.) Use the program to test whether each of the following monomials is a perfect square.

1. 36 yes
2. $4x^2$ yes
3. $16y$ no
4. m^2n^4 yes
5. $2xy^6$ no
6. $25w^9$ no

5-8 Factoring Pattern for $x^2 + bx + c$, c negative

Objective To factor quadratic trinomials whose quadratic coefficient is 1 and whose constant term is negative.

The factoring that you did in the last section had this form:

$$x^2 + bx + c = (x + r)(x + s)$$

c: positive; r and s both positive or both negative

By contrast, the factoring that you will do in this section has the following form:

$$x^2 + bx + c = (x + r)(x + s)$$

c: negative; r and s have opposite signs

The procedure that you will use in this section is the same as before. You find two numbers r and s whose product is c and whose sum is b.

If a quadratic polynomial of the form $x^2 + bx + c$ (c negative) can be factored, its factors will be of the form

$$(x + r)(x + s)$$

where one of r and s, say r, is negative and s is positive.

Example 1 Factor $a^2 - a - 12$.

Solution
1. List the factors of -12.
2. Find the pair of factors with a sum of -1: -4 and 3
3. $a^2 - a - 12 = (a - 4)(a + 3)$ ***Answer***

You should check by multiplying $a - 4$ and $a + 3$.

-12	
1	-12
-1	12
2	-6
-2	6
3	-4
-3	4

It is usually faster to review the factors of the constant term mentally.

Example 2 Factor $b^2 + 31bc - 32c^2$.

Solution
1. The factoring pattern is $(b + \quad)(b - \quad)$.
2. Find the pair of factors of -32 with a sum of 31: 32 and -1.
3. $b^2 + 31bc - 32c^2 = (b + 32c)(b - c)$ ***Answer***

Teaching Suggestions p. T96

Suggested Extensions p. T96

Chalkboard Examples

Factor. If not factorable, write "prime."

1. $k^2 - 7k - 44$
   $(k + 4)(k - 11)$
2. $z^2 - 2z - 35$
   $(z + 5)(z - 7)$
3. $b^2 + b - 42$
   $(b - 6)(b + 7)$
4. $y^2 - 6y - 55$
   $(y - 11)(y + 5)$
5. $m^2 - 7m - 51$ prime
6. $n^2 - 4n - 32$
   $(n - 8)(n + 4)$

Common Error

When factoring trinomials of this type, some students think that because c is negative, both factors of c must be negative (especially if b is negative). Remind and show them that this is not the case. Again, encourage students to check their factorizations by multiplying.

Supplementary Material

Practice Master 27

Suggested Assignments

Minimum
212/2–32 even
S 210/20–30 even

Average
212/2–40 even, 43
S 210/20–38 even

Maximum
212/2–48 even

Additional Answers
Oral Exercises

1. $-2, 1$
2. $6, -2$
3. $-20, 1$
4. $-5, 4$
5. $10, -2$
6. $-4, 4$
7. $-2, 8$
8. $-16, 1$

Additional Answers
Written Exercises

1. $(a + 5)(a - 1)$
2. $(x - 3)(x + 1)$
3. $(y - 6)(y + 1)$
4. $(b + 5)(b - 3)$
5. prime
6. prime
7. prime
8. $(y - 12)(y + 2)$
9. $(a + 7)(a - 5)$
10. prime
11. $(z + 9)(z - 4)$
12. $(r - 8)(r + 5)$
13. $(p - 7)(p + 3)$
14. $(a + 9)(a - 6)$
15. prime
16. $(z - 9)(z + 8)$
17. $(a - 6b)(a + 5b)$
18. $(y - 3z)(y + z)$
19. $(p - 10q)(p + 5q)$
20. $(a - 11b)(a + 7b)$
21. $(k - 15d)(k + 4d)$
22. $(s + 18t)(s - 4t)$
23. $(x - 11y)(x + 2y)$
24. $(p - 9q)(p + 8q)$
25. $(1 - 10ab)(1 + 2ab)$
26. $(1 - 12pq)(1 + 5pq)$
27. $(1 - 8ab)(1 + 7ab)$
28. $(n + 16m)(n - 3m)$
29. $(r - 24)(r + 6)$
30. $(a + 25)(a - 6)$
31. $(40 + b)(20 - b)$
32. $(a + 18)(a - 15)$
33. $(40 + x)(8 - x)$

Oral Exercises

Find two integers with the given sum and product.

	1.	2.	3.	4.	5.	6.	7.	8.
sum	-1	4	-19	-1	8	0	6	-15
product	-2	-12	-20	-20	-20	-16	-16	-16

For each trinomial, tell which two factors of the constant term have a sum equal to the coefficient of the linear term.

Example $x^2 - 7x - 8$

Solution $(1)(-8) = -8$ and $1 + (-8) = -7$; 1 and -8

9. $a^2 + 3a - 4$ 4, -1
10. $x^2 + 2x - 3$ 3, -1
11. $t^2 + 5t - 6$ 6, -1
12. $y^2 + y - 6$ 3, -2
13. $y^2 - y - 6$ -3, 2
14. $b^2 - 8b - 9$
15. $b^2 + 8b - 9$ 9, -1
16. $u^2 - 3u - 10$ -5, 2
17. $r^2 + 5r - 14$

14. -9, 1
17. 7, -2

Written Exercises

Factor. Check by multiplying the factors. If the polynomial is not factorable, write "prime."

A

1. $a^2 + 4a - 5$
2. $x^2 - 2x - 3$
3. $y^2 - 5y - 6$
4. $b^2 + 2b - 15$
5. $c^2 - 11c - 10$
6. $r^2 + 16r - 28$
7. $x^2 - 6x - 18$
8. $y^2 - 10y - 24$
9. $a^2 + 2a - 35$
10. $k^2 - 2k - 20$
11. $z^2 + 5z - 36$
12. $r^2 - 3r - 40$
13. $p^2 - 4p - 21$
14. $a^2 + 3a - 54$
15. $y^2 - 5y - 30$
16. $z^2 - z - 72$
17. $a^2 - ab - 30b^2$
18. $y^2 - 2yz - 3z^2$
19. $p^2 - 5pq - 50q^2$
20. $a^2 - 4ab - 77b^2$
21. $k^2 - 11kd - 60d^2$
22. $s^2 + 14st - 72t^2$
23. $x^2 - 9xy - 22y^2$
24. $p^2 - pq - 72q^2$

B

25. $1 - 8ab - 20a^2b^2$
26. $1 - 7pq - 60p^2q^2$
27. $1 - ab - 56a^2b^2$
28. $n^2 + 13nm - 48m^2$
29. $r^2 - 18r - 144$
30. $a^2 + 19a - 150$
31. $800 - 20b - b^2$
32. $a^2 + 3a - 270$
33. $320 - 32x - x^2$

Find all the integral values of *k* for which the given polynomial can be factored.

34. $x^2 + kx - 45$
44, 12, 4, -44, -12, -4
35. $y^2 + ky - 28$
27, 12, 3, -27, -12, -3
36. $15 - kz - z^2$
14, 2, -14, -2

Find two negative values for k for which the given trinomial can be factored. (There are many possible values.) Answers may vary.

C **37.** $x^2 - 3x + k$ $-18, -10$ **38.** $y^2 + 2y + k$ $-8, -63$ **39.** $z^2 + 4z + k$ $-140, -96$

40. $k - 6x - x^2$ $-8, -9$ **41.** $n^2 + 11n + k$ $-26, -60$ **42.** $k + 4m - m^2$ $-4, -3$

Factor.

43. $(x + 1)^2 - 2(x + 1) - 15$ $(x - 4)(x + 4)$

44. $(a + b)^2 - 3(a + b) - 70$ $(a + b - 10)(a + b + 7)$

45. $(2x - y)^2 + 4(2x - y) - 60$

46. $4(a^2 - 1) - x^2(a^2 - 1)$

47. $x^4 - 8x^2 - 9$ $(x - 3)(x + 3)(x^2 + 1)$

48. $2x^4 - 30x^2 - 32$

49. $3a^4 - 63a^2 - 300$ $3(a^2 + 4)(a - 5)(a + 5)$

50. $(3a + b)^4 - (a + b)^4$

45. $(2x - y + 10)(2x - y - 6)$

46. $(a - 1)(a + 1)(2 - x)(2 + x)$

48. $2(x - 4)(x + 4)(x^2 + 1)$

50. $8a(2a + b)(5a^2 + 4ab + b^2)$

Historical Note / *The Sieve of Eratosthenes*

Although Eratosthenes (276–194 B.C.) is best known for determining the diameter and circumference of Earth, one of his greatest contributions to mathematics was his sieve, a method of "sifting out" the primes from the set of positive integers.

The sieve of Eratosthenes can be used as follows. First, write a given number of consecutive integers greater than 1. Then, circle 2 and cross out all numbers in the list that are multiples of 2. Next, circle 3 and cross out every number that is a multiple of 3. Continue in this manner until only the circled numbers remain. These are the prime numbers.

	(2)	(3)	~~4~~	(5)	~~6~~	(7)	~~8~~	~~9~~	~~10~~
(11)	~~12~~	(13)	~~14~~	~~15~~	~~16~~	(17)	~~18~~	(19)	~~20~~
~~21~~	~~22~~	(23)	~~24~~	~~25~~	~~26~~	~~27~~	~~28~~	(29)	~~30~~
(31)	~~32~~	~~33~~	~~34~~	~~35~~	~~36~~	(37)	~~38~~	~~39~~	~~40~~
(41)	~~42~~	(43)	~~44~~	~~45~~	~~46~~	(47)	~~48~~	~~49~~	~~50~~
~~51~~	~~52~~	(53)	~~54~~	~~55~~	~~56~~	~~57~~	~~58~~	(59)	~~60~~
(61)	~~62~~	~~63~~	~~64~~	~~65~~	~~66~~	(67)	~~68~~	~~69~~	~~70~~
(71)	~~72~~	(73)	~~74~~	~~75~~	~~76~~	~~77~~	~~78~~	(79)	~~80~~
~~81~~	~~82~~	(83)	~~84~~	~~85~~	~~86~~	~~87~~	~~88~~	(89)	~~90~~
~~91~~	~~92~~	~~93~~	~~94~~	~~95~~	~~96~~	(97)	~~98~~	~~99~~	~~100~~

You may find it helpful to know that a number is prime if it is not divisible by any prime number less than or equal to its square root. For example, to find out if 101 is a prime number, check to see if 101 is divisible by each prime number less than or equal to $\sqrt{101}$, that is, each prime number less than 10. If 101 is not divisible by 2, 3, 5, or 7, then it is prime.

Additional A Exercises

Factor. Check by multiplying the factors.

1. $a^2 + 18a - 63$
   $(a + 21)(a - 3)$
2. $m^2 - 24m - 25$
   $(m - 25)(m + 1)$
3. $k^2 + 8k - 33$
   $(k + 11)(k - 3)$
4. $b^2 + 4b - 45$
   $(b + 9)(b - 5)$
5. $r^2 - 2r - 99$
   $(r - 11)(r + 9)$
6. $j^2 - jk - 132k^2$
   $(j - 12k)(j + 11k)$

Mixed Review Exercises

1. Simplify: $(47 - 3) \times 9$
   396
2. Write an equation for the word sentence, "The sum of a number, its double, and its triple is 996."
   $n + 2n + 3n = 996$
3. Solve:
   $4a - 3 = 3(2a - 5)$
   $a = 6$
4. Express $(2a + 6b)^2$ as a polynomial.
   $4a^2 + 24ab + 36b^2$

Teaching Suggestions p. T96

Suggested Extensions p. T97

Chalkboard Examples

Factor. If not factorable, write "prime."

1. $2b^2 + 13b - 24$
   $(2b - 3)(b + 8)$
2. $5z^2 + 13z - 6$
   $(5z - 2)(z + 3)$
3. $3t^2 - 8t - 35$
   $(3t + 7)(t - 5)$
4. $6n^2 + 7n - 3$
   $(3n - 1)(2n + 3)$
5. $2y^2 + 3y + 5$ prime
6. $12t^2 + 7t - 12$
   $(4t - 3)(3t + 4)$

Supplementary Materials

Test 17
Resource Book, p. 86

5-9 Factoring Pattern for $ax^2 + bx + c$

Objective To factor quadratic trinomials when the coefficient of the quadratic term is an integer greater than 1.

If $ax^2 + bx + c$ $(a > 1)$ can be factored, the factors will have the pattern

$$(px + r)(qx + s).$$

Example 1 Factor $3x^2 + x - 4$.

Solution

First clue: Because the trinomial has a negative constant term, one of r and s will be negative and the other will be positive.

Second clue: You can determine the possible factors of the quadratic term, $3x^2$, and the constant term, -4, as shown at the right.

Factors of $3x^2$
$3x$ and x

Factors of -4	
$1, -4$	$-1, 4$
$2, -2$	$-2, 2$
$4, -1$	$-4, 1$

Test the possibilities to see which produces the correct linear term, x.

Possible factors	Linear term	Possible factors	Linear term
$(3x + 1)(x - 4)$	$(-12 + 1)x = -11x$	$(3x - 1)(x + 4)$	$(12 - 1)x = 11x$
$(3x + 2)(x - 2)$	$(-6 + 2)x = -4x$	$(3x - 2)(x + 2)$	$(6 - 2)x = 4x$
$(3x + 4)(x - 1)$	$(-3 + 4)x = x$	$(3x - 4)(x + 1)$	$(3 - 4)x = -x$

Since $(3x + 4)(x - 1)$ yields the correct linear term,

$$3x^2 + x - 4 = (3x + 4)(x - 1).$$ ***Answer***

Example 2 Factor $10d^2 - 37d + 7$.

Solution

First clue: Because the trinomial has a positive constant term and a negative linear term, both r and s will be negative.

Second clue: Consider the possible factors of the quadratic term, $10d^2$, and the possible *negative* factors of the constant term, 7.

Factors of $10d^2$	
$10d, d$	$5d, 2d$

Negative factors of 7	
$-7, -1$	$-1, -7$

Test the possibilities to see which produces the correct linear term, $-37d$.

Possible factors	Linear term	Possible factors	Linear term
$(10d - 7)(d - 1)$	$(-10 - 7)d = -17d$	$(5d - 7)(2d - 1)$	$(-5 - 14)d = -19d$
$(10d - 1)(d - 7)$	$(-70 - 1)d = -71d$	$(5d - 1)(2d - 7)$	$(-35 - 2)d = -37d$

The last possibility gives the correct linear term.

$$10d^2 - 37d + 7 = (5d - 1)(2d - 7)$$ ***Answer***

As you practice factoring, you will become able to select the correct factors without writing all the possibilities.

Example 3 Factor $7x^2 - 16xy - 15y^2$.

Solution

$$\begin{aligned} 7x^2 - 16xy - 15y^2 &= (7x \quad\;)(x \quad\;) \\ &= (7x + \quad)(x - \quad) \\ &= (7x + 5y)(x - 3y) \quad \textbf{\textit{Answer}} \end{aligned}$$

Note: If you had written $(7x - \quad)(x + \quad)$ as the second step, you would have found that no such combination of factors would produce the desired term, $-16xy$.

When the coefficient of the quadratic term is negative, it may be helpful to begin by factoring -1 from each term.

Example 4 Factor $5 + 7s - 6s^2$.

Solution First, rearrange the polynomial in order of decreasing degree.

$5 + 7s - 6s^2 = -6s^2 + 7s + 5$

Then factor -1 from each term.

$-6s^2 + 7s + 5 = -(6s^2 - 7s - 5)$

Now factor $6s^2 - 7s - 5$.

$6s^2 - 7s - 5 = (3s - 5)(2s + 1)$

$\therefore 5 + 7s - 6s^2 = -(6s^2 - 7s - 5) = -(3s - 5)(2s + 1)$ ***Answer***

Note: If you had factored $5 + 7s - 6s^2$ directly, you would have found $(5 - 3s)(1 + 2s)$. Since both $(5 - 3s)(1 + 2s)$ and $-(3s - 5)(2s + 1)$ equal $5 + 7s - 6s^2$, the two answers are equivalent.

Oral Exercises

For each quadratic polynomial, tell whether its factorization will have the form

$$(px + r)(qx + s), \quad (px + r)(qx - s), \quad \text{or} \quad (px - r)(qx - s),$$

where p, q, r, and s represent positive integers.

1. $3x^2 - 22x + 7$ −, −
2. $3x^2 + 4x - 7$ +, −
3. $3x^2 + 10x + 7$ +, +

4. $5x^2 + 19x - 4$ +, −
5. $5x^2 - x - 4$ +, −
6. $4x^2 - 12x + 4$

7. $6x^2 + x - 2$ +, −
8. $6x^2 + 13x + 2$ +, +
9. $6x^2 - 7x + 2$

6. −, − 9. −, −

Suggested Assignments

Minimum
Day 1: 216/1–15
R 216/*Self-Test 3*
Day 2: 216/16–26
219/1–6
Day 2 finishes Sec. 5-9 and covers Sec. 5-10.

Average
216/1–39 odd
S 212/17–29 odd

Maximum
216/1–43 odd
R 216/*Self-Test 3*

Additional A Exercises

Factor. Check by multiplying the factors.

1. $2a^2 + 7a + 5$ $(2a + 5)(a + 1)$
2. $12b^2 - 8b + 1$ $(6b - 1)(2b - 1)$
3. $24z^2 - 10z - 1$ $(12z + 1)(2z - 1)$
4. $15m^2 + 4m - 3$ $(3m - 1)(5m + 3)$

Additional Answers Written Exercises

1. $(2x + 3)(x + 1)$
2. $(2n + 1)(n + 3)$
3. $(5a + 1)(a + 1)$
4. $(4n + 1)(2n + 1)$
5. $(7n - 1)(n - 1)$
6. $(7k - 1)(2k - 1)$
7. $(5y - 1)(y - 3)$
8. $(7y - 4)(y - 2)$
9. prime
10. $(3z - 2)(z + 1)$
11. $(2t + 3)(t - 2)$
12. $(3a + 5)(a - 1)$
13. $(8y - 9)(y + 1)$
14. $(3a - 1)(3a + 2)$
15. $(k + 3)(7k - 2)$
16. prime
17. prime
18. prime
19. $-(2y - 5)(y + 2)$
20. $-(4a - 1)(a + 6)$
21. $(a + 2b)(a - b)$
22. $(x - 8y)(x + 7y)$
23. $(9r + 2s)(r - 3s)$
24. $(3a + 4b)(a - 3b)$
25. $(5a - b)(5a + 3b)$
26. $(9d - 8)(4d + 3)$
27. $(3x - 2y)(4x + 9y)$
28. $(4k - 1)(5k + 8)$
29. $-(2x - 3)(6x + 7)$

Written Exercises

Factor. Check by multiplying the factors. If the polynomial is not factorable, write "prime."

A

1. $2x^2 + 5x + 3$ **2.** $2n^2 + 7n + 3$ **3.** $5a^2 + 6a + 1$

4. $8n^2 + 6n + 1$ **5.** $7n^2 - 8n + 1$ **6.** $14k^2 - 9k + 1$

7. $5y^2 - 16y + 3$ **8.** $7y^2 - 18y + 8$ **9.** $3k^2 - 5k + 1$

10. $3z^2 + z - 2$ **11.** $2t^2 - t - 6$ **12.** $3a^2 + 2a - 5$

13. $8y^2 - y - 9$ **14.** $9a^2 + 3a - 2$ **15.** $7k^2 + 19k - 6$

16. $3x^2 - 7x + 6$ **17.** $3 + b - 6b^2$ **18.** $10 + 3y - 2y^2$

19. $10 + y - 2y^2$ **20.** $6 - 23a - 4a^2$ **21.** $a^2 + ab - 2b^2$

22. $x^2 - xy - 56y^2$ **23.** $9r^2 - 25rs - 6s^2$ **24.** $3a^2 - 5ab - 12b^2$

B

25. $25a^2 + 10ab - 3b^2$ **26.** $36d^2 - 5d - 24$ **27.** $12x^2 + 19xy - 18y^2$

28. $20k^2 + 27k - 8$ **29.** $21 + 4x - 12x^2$ **30.** $15 - 31a - 24a^2$

31. $-48c^2 + 29c + 15$ **32.** $-21b^2 + 4b + 12$ **33.** $108x^2 + 15x - 7$

34. $6x^2 - 17x - 45$ **35.** $42y^2 + 41y + 9$ **36.** $40a^2 - 7a - 21$

C

37. $2(y + 4)^2 - (y + 4) - 3$ $(2y + 5)(y + 5)$ **38.** $3(a + b)^2 - 17(a + b) - 6$ $(3a + 3b + 1)(a + b - 6)$

39. $(x^2 - 1)^2 - 14(x^2 - 1) - 15$ **40.** $(x^2 - 5x - 1)^2 - 25$

41. $10(a - b)^2 - 11(a - b) - 6$ $(5a - 5b + 2)(2a - 2b - 3)$ **42.** $14(2 - x)^2 - 15(2 - x) - 11$ $(5 - 2x)(3 - 7x)$

43. Show that the product of $6x^2 - 13x - 5$, $15x^2 - 16x - 7$, and $10x^2 - 39x + 35$ is a *perfect square* by showing that it is the square of another polynomial.

44. Factor $60a^{4n+2}b + 25a^{2n+2}b^{4n+1} - 360a^2b^{8n+1}$, where n is a positive integer. $5a^2b(3a^{2n} + 8b^{4n})(2a^n - 3b^{2n})(2a^n + 3b^{2n})$

Self-Test 3

Vocabulary irreducible polynomial (p. 209) prime polynomial (p. 209)

Factor.

1. $y^2 + 8y + 15$ $(y + 5)(y + 3)$ **2.** $x^2 - 10x + 16$ $(x - 8)(x - 2)$ **Obj. 5-7, p. 208**

3. $n^2 - 3n - 28$ $(n - 7)(n + 4)$ **4.** $v^2 + 9vt - 36t^2$ $(v + 12t)(v - 3t)$ **Obj. 5-8, p. 211**

5. $6x^2 - 19x + 15$ $(2x - 3)(3x - 5)$ **6.** $3x^2 + 10xy - 8y^2$ $(3x - 2y)(x + 4y)$ **Obj. 5-9, p. 214**

Check your answers with those at the back of the book.

Computer Key-In

In order to factor a quadratic trinomial of the form

$$Ax^2 + Bx + C,$$

you need to find positive and negative factors of the integer C, including 1, C, -1, and $-C$.

The program given below will find the positive and negative factors of any integer N. Since the values of F in line 40 must increase, you need to use the absolute value of N. In BASIC this is written ABS(N). Line 70 will stop the loop after a pair of equal factors (if any) have been passed. This avoids duplications.

If N is negative, then Q will be negative. Lines 100 and 110 will give the opposite pairs of factors.

This program uses a *subroutine* for the OUTPUT. Line 90 GOSUB 160 sends the execution of the program to line 160. Line 170 RETURN ends the subroutine and sends the execution back to line 100. Line 120 also sends the program to the subroutine, although this time line 170 returns it to line 130.

```
10  PRINT "TO FACTOR AN INTEGER (ABS(N)>1):"
20  PRINT "WHAT IS YOUR INTEGER";
30  INPUT N
40  FOR F=1 TO ABS(N)/2
50  LET Q=N/F
60  IF Q <> INT(Q) THEN 130
70  IF ABS(Q)<ABS(F) THEN 180
80  LET F1=F
90  GOSUB 160
100  LET F1=-F
110  LET Q=-Q
120  GOSUB 160
130  NEXT F
140  GOTO 180
150  REM---SUBROUTINE
160  PRINT F1;" AND ";Q;" ARE FACTORS OF ";N
170  RETURN
180  END
```

Exercises

1. RUN the program for 36 and -36.
2. RUN the program for 120 and -120.
3. RUN the program for 87 and -87.

30. $-(8a - 3)(3a + 5)$
31. $-(3c + 1)(16c - 15)$
32. $-(7b - 6)(3b + 2)$
33. $(3x + 1)(36x - 7)$
34. $(2x - 9)(3x + 5)$
35. $(14y + 9)(3y + 1)$
36. prime
39. $x^2(x - 4)(x + 4)$
40. $(x - 6)(x + 1) \times (x - 1)(x - 4)$
43. $(6x^2 - 13x - 5) \times (15x^2 - 16x - 7) \times (10x^2 - 39x + 35) = [(3x + 1)(2x - 5)] \times [(3x + 1)(5x - 7)] \times [(5x - 7)(2x - 5)] = (3x + 1)^2(2x - 5)^2 \times (5x - 7)^2 = [(3x + 1) \times (2x - 5)(5x - 7)]^2$

Additional Answers Computer Key-In

1. factors of 36: 1, 36; -1, -36; 2, 18; -2, -18; 3, 12; -3, -12; 4, 9; -4, -9; 6, 6; -6, -6
factors of -36: 1, -36; -1, 36; 2, -18; -2, 18; 3, -12; -3, 12; 4, -9; -4, 9; 6, -6; -6, 6

Quick Quiz

Factor.

1. $y^2 + 11y + 24$
   $(y + 3)(y + 8)$
2. $z^2 - 12z + 32$
   $(z - 4)(z - 8)$
3. $x^2 + 2x - 15$
   $(x + 5)(x - 3)$
4. $x^2 + 9x - 22$
   $(x + 11)(x - 2)$
5. $2t^2 - 19t - 10$
   $(2t + 1)(t - 10)$
6. $20k^2 - 16k + 3$
   $(2k - 1)(10k - 3)$

Teaching Suggestions p. T97

Suggested Extensions p. T97

Chalkboard Examples

Factor.

1. $x(y - z) - 3(y - z)$
   $(x - 3)(y - z)$
2. $5(t - 2) - s(t - 2)$
   $(5 - s)(t - 2)$
3. $yz - y + 2z - 2$
   $(y + 2)(z - 1)$
4. $mx - m - 3x + 3$
   $(m - 3)(x - 1)$

Common Error

Sometimes students who are factoring by grouping get confused about whether a number or variable is a factor or a term. For example, some students may incorrectly factor Oral Exercise 1 as: $(x + y) + 5w$ or $(x + y) + (5 + w)$. You can use the distributive axiom to show that these expressions are not equal to the original expression and that the correct factorization, $(x + y)(5 + w)$, is.

Supplementary Material

Practice Master 28

Suggested Assignments

Minimum
The assignment for Day 2 of Sec. 5-9 finishes Sec. 5-9 and covers Sec. 5-10.

Average
Day 1: 219/2–34 even
R 216/*Self-Test 3*
Day 2: 219/35–53 odd
S 206/59, 61, 62

Maximum
219/2–50 even
S 216/38–44 even

General Factoring and Its Application

5-10 Factoring by Grouping

Objective To factor a polynomial by grouping terms.

One of the key tools in factoring is the distributive axiom:

$$ab + ac = a(b + c).$$

This axiom holds not only when a represents a monomial, but also when a represents any polynomial. If $a = 5 + x$,

$$(5 + x)b + (5 + x)c = (5 + x)(b + c).$$

If $a = p - 4q + r$,

$$(p - 4q + r)b + (p - 4q + r)c = (p - 4q + r)(b + c).$$

It will help you in factoring if you learn to recognize factors that are opposites of each other.

Factor	Opposite
$a - b$	$-(a - b)$, or $-a + b$, or $b - a$
$4z - y$	$-(4z - y)$, or $-4z + y$, or $y - 4z$
$5 - p - 2q$	$-(5 - p - 2q)$, or $-5 + p + 2q$, or $p + 2q - 5$

Example 1 Factor $7(r - 4) - 3r(4 - r)$.

Solution Notice that $r - 4$ and $4 - r$ are opposites.

$$\begin{aligned} 7(r - 4) - 3r(4 - r) &= 7(r - 4) - 3r[-(r - 4)] \\ &= 7(r - 4) + 3r(r - 4) \\ &= (7 + 3r)(r - 4) \\ &= (3r + 7)(r - 4) \quad \textit{Answer} \end{aligned}$$

In Example 2, you first group terms and then factor each group of terms.

Example 2 Factor $rq - 2rp + 5q - 10p$.

Solution 1

$(rq - 2rp) + (5q - 10p) =$

$r(q - 2p) + 5(q - 2p) =$

$(r + 5)(q - 2p)$

Solution 2

$(rq + 5q) - (2rp + 10p) =$

$q(r + 5) - 2p(r + 5) =$

$(q - 2p)(r + 5)$

Example 3 applies what you know about factoring trinomial squares and differences of squares.

Example 3 Factor $16j^2 - 81k^2 + 18k - 1$.

Solution
$$16j^2 - 81k^2 + 18k - 1 = 16j^2 - (81k^2 - 18k + 1)$$
$$= (4j)^2 - (9k - 1)^2$$
$$= (4j + 9k - 1)[4j - (9k - 1)]$$
$$= (4j + 9k - 1)(4j - 9k + 1) \quad \textit{Answer}$$

Oral Exercises

Factor.

1. $5(x + y) + w(x + y)$ $(x + y)(5 + w)$
2. $6(a - 2b) - 4(a - 2b)$ $2(a - 2b)$
3. $r(p - 2q) - (p - 2q)$ $(p - 2q)(r - 1)$
4. $7k(k - 6) + 4(6 - k)$ $(k - 6)(7k - 4)$
5. $z(z - 5) + 5(5 - z)$ $(z - 5)^2$
6. $9(2u + v) + 5(v + 2u)$ $14(2u + v)$
7. $(3r - s) - t(s - 3r)$ $(3r - s)(1 + t)$
8. $(m^2 - m) + (m - 1)$ $(m + 1)(m - 1)$
9. $(ab - ac) + (b - c)$ $(a + 1)(b - c)$

Written Exercises

Factor. Check by multiplying the factors.

A

1. $2t(n - 3) - (3 - n)$
2. $(c + 3d) - e(3d + c)$
3. $2(x + y) - y(y + x) + (x + y)$
4. $(s - r) - 3(r - s) + q(r - s)$
5. $x^2(2d - e + f) + (f - e + 2d)$
6. $(2a - b + 3c) + x(b - 2a - 3c)$
7. $(gz - g) + (hz - h)$
8. $(gz + hz) - (g + h)$
9. $(2x - 2y + 4z) + (x^2 - xy + 2xz)$
10. $(j^2 - 4j^2p) + (k - 4kp)$
11. $(2mp - 8mr) - (4nr - np)$
12. $(4x - 4xr) - (ry - y)$
13. $(2wz^2 - 12w) + (6 - z^2)$
14. $(6a - 3ay) + (7y - 14)$
15. $(2rs - 12r) - (30 - 5s)$
16. $(x^2 + xy) + (xz + yz)$
17. $2p + ap + 2q + aq$
18. $y^2 - 3y + yz - 3z$
19. $pq + 2qr + 2r^2 + pr$
20. $6x - 3y + 2zx - yz$
21. $ab - 2b + ac - 2c$
22. $x^3 - 2x^2 + 3x - 6$
23. $2x^3 + x^2 + 8x + 4$
24. $2ac - 6bc - 3a + 9b$
25. $4x^2 - 8xy - 3x + 6y$
26. $3rs - s + 12r - 4$
27. $4y^2 + 8ay - y - 2a$
28. $2a^3 - a^2 - 10a + 5$
29. $4x^2 - 2xy - 7yz + 14xz$
30. $2x^3 - 6x^2 - 5x + 15$

Factor each expression as a difference of two squares.

B

31. $a^2 - (2b + 3c)^2$ $(a - 2b - 3c)(a + 2b + 3c)$
32. $(p - q)^2 - r^2$ $(p - q - r)(p - q + r)$
33. $36k^2 - (2a - c)^2$ $(6k - 2a + c)(6k + 2a - c)$
34. $25 - (5x - y)^2$ $(5 - 5x + y)(5 + 5x - y)$
35. $(x - 4y)^2 - 9$ $(x - 4y - 3)(x - 4y + 3)$
36. $(a + b)^2 - (c + d)^2$ $(a + b + c + d)(a + b - c - d)$

Additional A Exercises

Factor. Check by multiplying the factors.

1. $3x(m - n) - (n - m)$ $(m - n)(3x + 1)$
2. $12(z + e) + (z + e)$ $13(z + e)$
3. $(tp - t) + (jp - j)$ $(p - 1)(t + j)$
4. $l + 3m + 5l + 15m$ $6(l + 3m)$

Additional Answers Written Exercises

1. $(n - 3)(2t + 1)$
2. $(c + 3d)(1 - e)$
3. $(x + y)(3 - y)$
4. $(s - r)(4 - q)$
5. $(x^2 + 1)(2d - e + f)$
6. $(1 - x)(2a - b + 3c)$
7. $(g + h)(z - 1)$
8. $(z - 1)(g + h)$
9. $(2 + x)(x - y + 2z)$
10. $(j^2 + k)(1 - 4p)$
11. $(2m + n)(p - 4r)$
12. $(4x + y)(1 - r)$
13. $(2w - 1)(z^2 - 6)$
14. $(3a - 7)(2 - y)$
15. $(2r + 5)(s - 6)$
16. $(x + z)(x + y)$
17. $(p + q)(2 + a)$
18. $(y - 3)(y + z)$
19. $(q + r)(p + 2r)$
20. $(3 + z)(2x - y)$
21. $(b + c)(a - 2)$
22. $(x - 2)(x^2 + 3)$
23. $(x^2 + 4)(2x + 1)$
24. $(2c - 3)(a - 3b)$
25. $(4x - 3)(x - 2y)$
26. $(s + 4)(3r - 1)$
27. $(4y - 1)(y + 2a)$
28. $(a^2 - 5)(2a - 1)$
29. $(2x + 7z)(2x - y)$
30. $(2x^2 - 5)(x - 3)$

Additional Answers Written Exercises

37. $(x + 3 - y) \cdot (x + 3 + y)$
38. $(p - q - 2) \cdot (p - q + 2)$
39. $(h - 6 - k) \cdot (h - 6 + k)$
40. $(a - x - 1) \cdot (a + x + 1)$
41. $(5 - a - 2b) \cdot (5 + a + 2b)$
42. $(7k - 2a + 1) \cdot (7k + 2a - 1)$
43. $(4y + 1 - 4z) \cdot (4y + 1 + 4z)$
44. $(k + t + n + 4) \cdot (k + t - n - 4)$
45. $(a - 2b + 2) \cdot (a + 2b - 2)$
46. $(x - 3 - 4y) \cdot (x - 3 + 4y)$
47. $(a - b - 5c) \cdot (a + b + 5c)$
48. $(x - 2y + 2z) \cdot (x + 2y - 2z)$
49. $9(a - b - c) \cdot (a - b + c)$
50. $(x^2 - 4 - 4y) \cdot (x^2 - 4 + 4y)$
51. $(a - b)(a - b - 3)$
52. $(x + 4y)(x - 4y + 2)$

Factor each expression as a difference of two squares.

37. $x^2 + 6x + 9 - y^2$ **38.** $p^2 - 2pq + q^2 - 4$ **39.** $h^2 - 12h + 36 - k^2$

40. $a^2 - x^2 - 2x - 1$ **41.** $25 - a^2 - 4ab - 4b^2$ **42.** $4a - 4a^2 + 49k^2 - 1$

43. $16y^2 + 8y + 1 - 16z^2$ **44.** $k^2 + 2kt + t^2 - n^2 - 8n - 16$

Factor.

45. $8b - 4 + a^2 - 4b^2$ **46.** $x^2 - 16y^2 - 6x + 9$

47. $a^2 - b^2 - 10bc - 25c^2$ **48.** $8yz - 4y^2 - 4z^2 + x^2$

49. $9a^2 + 9b^2 - 9c^2 - 18ab$ **50.** $x^4 - 8x^2 + 16 - 16y^2$

51. $a^2 - 2ab + b^2 - 3a + 3b$ **52.** $x^2 - 16y^2 + 2x + 8y$

C **53.** Factor $4x^4 + 1$ by writing it as $4x^4 + 4x^2 + 1 - 4x^2$, a difference of two squares. $(2x^2 - 2x + 1)(2x^2 + 2x + 1)$

54. Factor $64y^4 + 1$. $(8y^2 - 4y + 1)(8y^2 + 4y + 1)$

55. Factor $a^{3n+1} + 2b^{2n+1} - ab - 2a^{3n}b^{2n}$, where n is a positive integer. $(a - 2b^{2n})(a^{3n} - b)$

Biographical Note / *Hsien Wu*

Hsien Wu was born in Foochow, China, in 1893. He received his formal schooling in China and in 1911 came to the United States to attend the Massachusetts Institute of Technology. Upon graduation, he enrolled at Harvard University, where he received his Ph.D. in biochemistry in 1917.

While at Harvard, Wu developed techniques that permitted small samples of blood to be analyzed for use in testing and research. This was a major breakthrough as previous methods required large samples, a procedure that was not very advantageous for either the patient or the doctor.

Upon completion of his work at Harvard, Wu returned to China where in 1924 he was appointed to head the biochemistry department at Peking Union Medical College. While there, Wu conducted numerous studies in nutrition, eating habits and health, and food composition. His more than 150 research papers made Wu the foremost nutrition scientist in China, as well as a leading scientific figure worldwide. He was appointed to a number of international scientific committees and was made director of the Nutrition Institute of China.

5-11 Using More than One Method of Factoring

Objective To factor polynomials completely.

A polynomial is said to be **factored completely** when it is expressed as the product of prime polynomials and a monomial. The following guidelines will help you factor polynomials completely.

Guidelines for Factoring

1. Factor out the greatest monomial factor first.
2. Look for a difference of squares.
3. Look for a trinomial square.
4. If a trinomial is not a square, look for a pair of binomial factors.
5. If a polynomial has four or more terms, look for a way to group the terms in pairs or in a group of three terms that is a binomial square.
6. Make sure that each factor is prime. Check your work by multiplying the factors.

In each of the following examples the given polynomial is factored completely.

Example 1 Factor $30x^3 + 51x^2 + 9x$.

Solution

1. Factor out the greatest monomial factor, $3x$. $\quad 3x(10x^2 + 17x + 3)$
2. Find the binomial factors of $10x^2 + 17x + 3$. $\quad 3x(5x + 1)(2x + 3)$

Example 2 Factor $25y^4 - 100y^2$.

Solution

1. Factor out the greatest monomial factor, $25y^2$. $\quad 25y^2(y^2 - 4)$
2. Factor $y^2 - 4$ as the difference of squares. $\quad 25y^2(y + 2)(y - 2)$

Example 3 Factor $12rs - 3s^2 - 12r^2$.

Solution

1. Factor out -3 to give a positive quadratic coefficient. $\quad -3(4r^2 - 4rs + s^2)$
2. Notice that $4r^2 - 4rs + s^2$ is a trinomial square. $\quad -3(2r - s)^2$

Teaching Suggestions p. T98

Chalkboard Examples

Factor.

1. $3x^2 + 3x - 6$
   $3(x + 2)(x - 1)$
2. $9ay^2 - 4a$
   $a(3y + 2)(3y - 2)$
3. $2x^2 + 12x + 18$
   $2(x + 3)^2$
4. $x^2 + 4xy + 4y^2 - 1$
   $(x + 2y + 1)(x + 2y - 1)$
5. $16y^4 - 72y^2 + 81$
   $[(2y + 3)(2y - 3)]^2$
6. $x^3 - x + 5x^2 - 5$
   $(x + 5)(x + 1)(x - 1)$

Common Errors

Students sometimes forget to factor out the greatest monomial factor. Point out that checking for the greatest monomial factor first prevents this and makes it easier to factor further when possible.

Sometimes students factor binomials like Written Exercises 11 and 13–15 incorrectly because they think the sum of two squares is factorable. You may have to remind them that $(a + b)^2 = a^2 + 2ab + b^2$.

Supplementary Material

Resource Book, p. 87

Suggested Assignments

Minimum
222/1–8, 10–15, 19–24

Average
222/8–40 even
S 216/37, 40, 41

Maximum
Day 1: 222/8–50 even
Day 2: 222/35–51 odd, 52–57
S 220/51–55

Additional A Exercises

Factor completely.

1. $6a^2 + 18ab + 12b^2$
   $6(a + 2b)(a + b)$
2. $3x^4 - 48$
   $3(x^2 + 4)(x - 2)(x + 2)$
3. $nm^2 - 4n + 3m^2 - 12$
   $(n + 3)(m - 2)(m + 2)$
4. $bx^3 - 9by^2x$
   $bx(x - 3y)(x + 3y)$
5. $c^4 - 8c^2 + 16$
   $(c - 2)^2(c + 2)^2$
6. $y^4 + 2y^2 - 3$
   $(y^2 + 3)(y - 1)(y + 1)$

Mixed Review Exercises

1. Simplify: $(5m^3)^3$ $125\ m^9$
2. Solve:
   $\frac{4}{5}(10x - 25) - \frac{3}{2}(2x - 10) = 0$
   $x = 1$
3. Solve the problem or explain why it cannot be solved. Mike is $\frac{1}{2}$ as old as Sue, and 12 years ago he was 10 years younger than Sue. How old are they now?
   The equation leads to Mike being -2 years old twelve years ago, which is impossible. Therefore, there is no solution.
4. Factor:
   $12x^2 + 7x - 12$
   $(4x - 3)(3x + 4)$

Additional Answers Written Exercises

(See page 226.)

Oral Exercises

State the greatest monomial factor of each polynomial.

1. $5a^2 + 10ab + 5b^2$ 5 **2.** $-x^3 + 9xy^2$ x **3.** $-14z^3 + 21z + 35z^2$ $7z$

4. $32r^4 - 48r^3 + 18r^2$ $2r^2$ **5.** $56x^2 + 40x^3 - 16x$ $8x$ **6.** $6(m + 1)^2 - 24$ 6

Factor completely.

7. $3ab^2 - 27a^3$
$3a(b - 3a)(b + 3a)$

8. $-a + 4a^3$
$a(2a - 1)(2a + 1)$

9. $-8x + 8x^2 - 2$
$2(4x^2 - 4x - 1)$

Written Exercises

A **1–6.** Factor the polynomials in Oral Exercises 1–6 completely.

Factor completely.

7. $t^4 - 3t^2 - 2t^3$ **8.** $175 - 140w + 28w^2$ **9.** $xy + 5y - 2x - 10$

10. $24y - 9y^2 - 64$ **11.** $144z^3 - 36zq^2$ **12.** $40j^2k - 76jk^2 + 24k^3$

13. $x^4 - y^4$ **14.** $a^3x - 4ax^3$ **15.** $2x^4 - 162$

16. $a^2b - 9b + 3a^2 - 27$ **17.** $a^2 - 1 - 4b^2 - 4b$ **18.** $9a^2 - b^2 - 4b - 4$

19. $y^4 - 5y^2 + 4$ **20.** $x^4 - 26x^2 + 25$ **21.** $b^4 - 18b^2 + 81$

22. $2x^4 - 6x^2 - 8$ **23.** $10k^3 - 25k - 15k^2$ **24.** $-x^2 + 6xy - 9y^2$

B **25.** $2x^2 - 8y^2 + 16y - 8$ **26.** $x^2 - 9y^2 - 2x + 6y$ **27.** $4(a - 3)^2 - 4$

28. $x^8 - y^8$ **29.** $x^3 - x^2 - 4x + 4$ **30.** $a^3 + 2a^2 - 9a - 18$

31. $m^2 + m - k^2 - k$ **32.** $2pa + 2pr + r^2 - a^2$ **33.** $a^2c - 4abc - 9c^3 + 4b^2c$

34. $n(n + 1)(n + 2) - 3n(n + 1)$ **35.** $a(x^2 - a^2) + x(a - x)$

36. $2x^2(x + 1)(x + 3) - 6x^2$ **37.** $a^2(b - 3c) + 9b^2(3c - b)$

38. $(a - b)^3 + 4(b - a)$ **39.** $2 - 2y^2 - 8x^2 - 8xy$

40. $a^2 - 2ab + b^2 - 3a + 3b$ **41.** $x(x^2 - 1) - 2(x + 1)$

42. $x(x - 5)(x - 2) + 6(x - 2)$ **43.** $ax + 2ay - 3x^2 + 12y^2$

44. $2c^{16} - 2d^{16}$ **45.** $2p(p + 1)(p - 6) + 16(p + 1)$

46. $4a^2(2a - 1) - 4a(2a - 1) + (2a - 1)$ **47.** $p^2 - 4pq + 4q^2 - r^2 + 4sr - 4s^2$

48. $16a^2 - 16b^2 - 64bc - 64c^2$ **49.** $45x^2 - 177xy - 12y^2$

C **50.** $(a^2 - 4)^2 - (a - 2)^2$ **51.** $4b^2c^2 - (b^2 + c^2 - a^2)^2$

52. $(a^2 - 9)^2 - (3 - a)^2$ **53.** $(a + 3b)^2 - (a^2 - 9b^2)^2$

54. $x^2(x^2 - 4) + 4x(x^2 - 4) + 4(x^2 - 4)$ **55.** $x^2 + 4x^2y^2 + y^2 + 2xy - x^4 - 4y^4$

56. $t^3 + t^2 - t - 1$ **57.** $x^3 - x^2 - 4x + 4$

5-12 Solving Equations by Factoring

Objective To solve polynomial equations by factoring.

The **converse** of a statement in if-then form is obtained by interchanging the "if" and "then" parts of the statement. The converse of a true statement is not necessarily true.

By the multiplicative property of zero you know that for any two real numbers a and b:

If $a = 0$ or $b = 0$, then $ab = 0$.

You can show (see Exercise 52 on page 225) that the converse of the statement above is also true.

If $ab = 0$, then $a = 0$ or $b = 0$.

You can use the words *if and only if* to combine a statement and its converse. The *zero-product property* below combines the multiplicative property of zero and its converse into a single statement.

Zero-Product Property

For all real numbers a and b,

$ab = 0$ if and only if $a = 0$ or $b = 0$.

The zero-product property is true for any number of factors. *A product of factors is equal to zero if and only if one or more of the factors is zero.* This property can be used to solve certain equations.

Example 1 Solve $(x + 3)(x - 7) = 0$.

Solution One of the factors on the left side must equal zero. Thus,

$$x + 3 = 0 \quad \text{or} \quad x - 7 = 0$$
$$x = -3 \quad \text{or} \quad x = 7$$

Of course, you might have seen without writing the equations that when $x = -3$ or $x = 7$ one of the factors will be 0. Either method gives the solution set $\{-3, 7\}$. ***Answer***

A **polynomial equation** is an equation whose sides are both polynomials. Polynomial equations may be named by the term of highest degree. When $a \neq 0$:

$ax + b = 0$ is a **linear equation.**

$ax^2 + bx + c = 0$ is a **quadratic equation.**

$ax^3 + bx^2 + cx + d = 0$ is a **cubic equation.**

Teaching Suggestions p. T98

Suggested Extensions p. T98

Chalkboard Examples

Solve.

1. $(z - 11)(z + 7) = 0$
   $\{11, -7\}$
2. $4x^2 - 25 = 0$
   $(2x + 5)(2x - 5) = 0;$
   $\left\{-\frac{5}{2}, \frac{5}{2}\right\}$
3. $x^2 - 5x + 4 = 0$
   $(x - 4)(x - 1) = 0;$
   $\{4, 1\}$
4. $5z^2 = 80$
   $5z^2 - 80 = 0;$
   $z^2 - 16 = 0;$
   $(z + 4)(z - 4) = 0;$
   $\{-4, 4\}$
5. $6n^2 + 11n = 10$
   $6n^2 + 11n - 10 = 0;$
   $(3n - 2)(2n + 5);$
   $\left\{\frac{2}{3}, -\frac{5}{2}\right\}$
6. $6y^2 + 22y - 8 = 0$
   $3y^2 + 11y - 4 = 0;$
   $(3y - 1)(y + 4) = 0;$
   $\left\{\frac{1}{3}, -4\right\}$

Common Errors

Some students may have trouble solving equations such as Written Exercises 16, 49, and 50 because they think incorrectly that if ab = any constant, a = that constant or b = that constant. Point out that the Zero-Product Property applies only when the product of two or more numbers is *zero*.

Students may also try to transform an equation by dividing both sides by an expression containing a variable (see **Caution!** at the bottom of page 224).

Supplementary Material

Practice Master 29

Suggested Assignments

Minimum
Day 1: 225/1–14
S 216/27–32
Day 2: 225/15–41 odd

Average
Day 1: 225/1–15 odd, 16–28
Day 2: 225/29–39 odd, 40–51
S 222/41–51 odd

Maximum
Day 1: 225/1–51 odd
Day 2: 226/36–50 even
229/*P*: 4, 5, 9, 10, 12, 13
Day 2 finishes Sec. 5-12 and starts Sec. 5-13.

Many polynomial equations can be solved by factoring and then applying the zero-product property. Often, the first step in solving such an equation is to transform it into **standard form** in which one side is 0 and the other side is a simplified polynomial arranged in descending powers of the variable.

Example 2 Solve the quadratic equation $3x^2 + 2x = 8$.

Solution

1. Transform the equation into standard form. $\quad 3x^2 + 2x - 8 = 0$
2. Factor the left side. $\quad (3x - 4)(x + 2) = 0$
3. Set each factor equal to zero and solve. $\quad 3x - 4 = 0$ or $x + 2 = 0$; $3x = 4$, $x = \frac{4}{3}$ | $x = -2$
4. Check the solutions in the original equation $3x^2 + 2x = 8$, as shown below.

$$3\left(\frac{4}{3}\right)^2 + 2\left(\frac{4}{3}\right) \stackrel{?}{=} 8$$
$$3\left(\frac{16}{9}\right) + \frac{8}{3} \stackrel{?}{=} 8$$
$$\frac{16}{3} + \frac{8}{3} = \frac{24}{3} = 8 \quad \checkmark$$

$$3(-2)^2 + 2(-2) \stackrel{?}{=} 8$$
$$3(4) + (-4) = 12 + (-4) = 8 \quad \checkmark$$

$\therefore$ the solution set is $\left\{\frac{4}{3}, -2\right\}$. ***Answer***

Example 3 Solve the cubic equation $27x^3 + 3x + 18x^2 = 0$.

Solution

1. Transform the equation into standard form. $\quad 27x^3 + 18x^2 + 3x = 0$
2. Factor completely. $\quad 3x(9x^2 + 6x + 1) = 0$; $\quad 3x(3x + 1)(3x + 1) = 0$
3. Solve by inspection or by equating each factor to zero. $\quad x = 0$ or $x = -\frac{1}{3}$ or $x = -\frac{1}{3}$
4. The check is left for you.

$\therefore$ the solution set is $\left\{0, -\frac{1}{3}\right\}$. ***Answer***

The factorization in Example 3 produced two identical factors. Since the factor $3x + 1$ occurs twice in the factored form of the equation, $-\frac{1}{3}$ is a **double** or **multiple root.** Note, however, that $-\frac{1}{3}$ is listed only once in the solution set.

Caution! Never transform an equation by dividing by an expression containing a variable. Notice that in Example 3, the solution 0 would have been lost if both sides of $3x(9x^2 + 6x + 1) = 0$ had been divided by $3x$.

Oral Exercises

Solve each equation by inspection or by setting each factor equal to 0.

1. $a(a-7)=0$ $\{0, 7\}$
2. $3b(b+2)=0$ $\{0, -2\}$
3. $(c+8)(c-7)=0$ $\{-8, 7\}$
4. $-5d(4d-1)=0$ $\left\{0, \frac{1}{4}\right\}$
5. $(6e+1)(3e-2)=0$ $\left\{-\frac{1}{6}, \frac{2}{3}\right\}$
6. $(f+5)(2f+9)=0$ $\left\{-5, -\frac{9}{2}\right\}$
7. Describe how you would solve the equation $2x^3+9x^2=5x$.
   Write the equation in standard form. Factor the left side.
   Set each factor equal to zero and solve. $\left\{0, \frac{1}{2}, -5\right\}$

Written Exercises

Solve.

A

1. $(n+17)(n+7)=0$ $\{-17, -7\}$
2. $(y-15)(y-100)=0$ $\{15, 100\}$
3. $35n(n-35)=0$ $\{0, 35\}$
4. $(3x-1)(2x+5)=0$
5. $(4k+2)(k-3)=0$ $\left\{-\frac{1}{2}, 3\right\}$
6. $(4z+5)5z=0$ $\left\{-\frac{5}{4}, 0\right\}$
7. $3n(n-4)(2n+7)=0$
8. $2x(2x-5)(5x+2)=0$
9. $m(3m-8)(3m+1)=0$
10. $x^2-13x+36=0$ $\{9, 4\}$
11. $y^2+2y-63=0$ $\{-9, 7\}$
12. $z^2+2z-8=0$ $\{-4, 2\}$
13. $x^2-5x+6=0$ $\{3, 2\}$
14. $x^2-x-6=0$ $\{3, -2\}$
15. $x^2+25=10x$ $\{5\}$
16. $n^2-5n=24$ $\{8, -3\}$
17. $k^2+9=10k$ $\{9, 1\}$
18. $y^2-16y=0$ $\{0, 16\}$
19. $y^2-16=0$ $\{-4, 4\}$
20. $4x^2-9=0$ $\left\{\frac{3}{2}, -\frac{3}{2}\right\}$
21. $a^2-4a+4=0$ $\{2\}$
22. $3x^2+2x-1=0$ $\left\{\frac{1}{3}, -1\right\}$
23. $a^3-a=0$ $\{0, 1, -1\}$
24. $n^3-4n=0$ $\{0, 2, -2\}$
25. $x^2-x-30=0$ $\{6, -5\}$
26. $2x^2-5x-3=0$ $\left\{-\frac{1}{2}, 3\right\}$
27. $y^3-10y^2+25y=0$
28. $n^2=36$ $\{6, -6\}$
29. $4x^2=8x+5$ $\left\{-\frac{1}{2}, \frac{5}{2}\right\}$
30. $3y^2+2y=1$ $\left\{\frac{1}{3}, -1\right\}$
31. $a^2=24-5a$ $\{-8, 3\}$
32. $4a^2=8a$ $\{0, 2\}$
33. $6x^2=x+1$ $\left\{-\frac{1}{3}, \frac{1}{2}\right\}$
34. $6x^2+x=77$ $\left\{-\frac{11}{3}, \frac{7}{2}\right\}$
35. $3x^2-6x=9$ $\{3, -1\}$
36. $6x^2+17x+12=0$
37. $4y^2+7=29y$ $\left\{\frac{1}{4}, 7\right\}$
38. $6y^2=22y+40$ $\left\{-\frac{4}{3}, 5\right\}$
39. $6z^2+11z=72$ $\left\{\frac{8}{3}, -\frac{9}{2}\right\}$

B

40. $x^3-12x^2+32x=0$ $\{0, 8, 4\}$
41. $y^3+49y=14y^2$ $\{0, 7\}$
42. $y^4-13y^2+36=0$ $\{3, -3, 2, -2\}$
43. $t^3+t^2=4t+4$ $\{-1, 2, -2\}$
44. $a^4-2a^2+1=0$ $\{1, -1\}$
45. $2x^4-20x^2+18=0$
46. $9t^3-9t^2-9t+9=0$
47. $y^3+45y=14y^2$ $\{0, 5, 9\}$
48. $y^5=25y^3$ $\{0, 5, -5\}$
49. $(x-2)(x+3)=6$ $\{-4, 3\}$
50. $(a-5)(a-2)=28$ $\{-2, 9\}$
51. $4x^4=64$ $\{2, -2\}$

C

52. Give the missing reasons in the proof of the statement: If $ab=0$, then $a=0$ or $b=0$.
    If $a=0$, then there is nothing to prove.
    If $a \neq 0$:

$ab=0$	(1) Given	$\frac{1}{a}(ab)=0$	(4) ? Mult. prop. of 0
There is a unique real number $\frac{1}{a}$.	(2) ? Ax. of reciprocals	$\left(\frac{1}{a}\cdot a\right)b=0$	(5) ? Assoc. ax.
$\frac{1}{a}(ab)=\frac{1}{a}(0)$	(3) ? Mult. prop. of equality	$(1)b=0$	(6) ? Ax. of reciprocals
		$b=0$	(7) ? Ident. ax. for mult.

Additional A Exercises

Solve.

1. $(z-3)(z+5)=0$
   $z=3, -5$
2. $n(2n-15)(3n+2)=0$
   $n=0, 7\frac{1}{2}, \frac{-2}{3}$
3. $t^2-7t+6=0$
   $t=6, 1$
4. $j^2+5j=36$
   $j=-9, 4$
5. $p^3-16p=0$
   $p=0, \pm 4$
6. $7x^2=4x+3$
   $x=1, \frac{-3}{7}$

Mixed Review Exercises

Factor.

1. $121m^4-n^2$
   $(11m^2-n)(11m^2+n)$
2. $x^2+14xy+49y^2$
   $(x+7y)^2$
3. $t^2-13t+36$
   $(t-9)(t-4)$
4. $n^2-6n-72$
   $(n-12)(n+6)$

Additional Answers Written Exercises

4. $\left\{\frac{1}{3}, -\frac{5}{2}\right\}$
7. $\left\{0, 4, -\frac{7}{2}\right\}$
8. $\left\{0, \frac{5}{2}, -\frac{2}{5}\right\}$
9. $\left\{0, \frac{8}{3}, -\frac{1}{3}\right\}$
27. $\{0, 5\}$
36. $\left\{-\frac{4}{3}, -\frac{3}{2}\right\}$
45. $\{-3, 3, -1, 1\}$
46. $\{1, -1\}$

Additional Answers
Written Exercises (p. 222)

1. $5(a + b)^2$
2. $x(3y - x)(3y + x)$
3. $-7z(2z + 1)(z - 3)$
4. $2r^2(4r - 3)^2$
5. $8x(5x^2 + 7x - 2)$
6. $6(m - 1)(m + 3)$
7. $t^2(t - 3)(t + 1)$
8. $7(5 - 2w)^2$
9. $(x + 5)(y - 2)$
10. prime
11. $36z(2z - q)(2z + q)$
12. $4k(5j - 2k)(2j - 3k)$
13. $(x - y)(x + y)(x^2 + y^2)$
14. $ax(a - 2x)(a + 2x)$
15. $2(x - 3)(x + 3) \cdot (x^2 + 9)$
16. $(a - 3)(a + 3)(b + 3)$
17. $(a - 2b - 1) \cdot (a + 2b + 1)$
18. $(3a - b - 2) \cdot (3a + b + 2)$
19. $(y - 2)(y + 2)(y - 1) \cdot (y + 1)$
20. $(x - 5)(x + 5)(x - 1) \cdot (x + 1)$
21. $(b - 3)^2(b + 3)^2$
22. $2(x - 2)(x + 2) \cdot (x^2 + 1)$
23. $5k(2k - 5)(k + 1)$
24. $-(x - 3y)^2$
25. $2(x - 2y + 2) \cdot (x + 2y - 2)$
26. $(x - 3y)(x + 3y - 2)$
27. $4(a - 4)(a - 2)$
28. $(x - y)(x + y) \cdot (x^2 + y^2)(x^4 + y^4)$
29. $(x - 1)(x - 2)(x + 2)$
30. $(a + 2)(a - 3)(a + 3)$
31. $(m - k)(m + k + 1)$
32. $(r + a)(2p + r - a)$
33. $c(a - 2b - 3c) \cdot (a - 2b + 3c)$
34. $n(n + 1)(n - 1)$

Computer Key-In

A quadratic trinomial $Ax^2 + Bx + C$ can be thought of as

$$(A1 \times A2)x^2 + [(A1 \times C2) + (A2 \times C1)]x + (C1 \times C2)$$

where $A1$ and $A2$ are factors of A and $C1$ and $C2$ are factors of C.

A chart of the program is shown at the right.

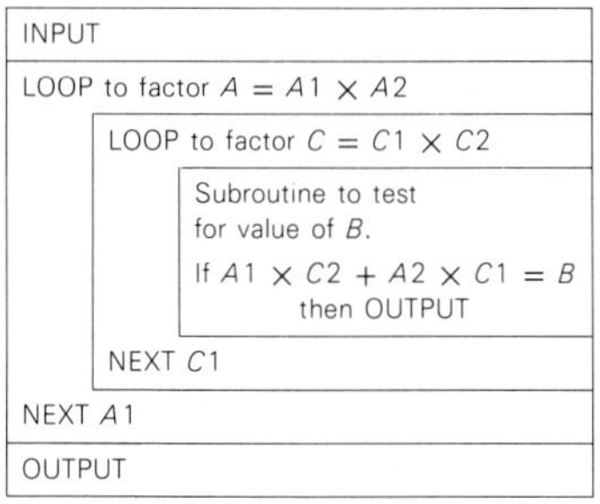

- INPUT
- LOOP to factor $A = A1 \times A2$
  - LOOP to factor $C = C1 \times C2$
    - Subroutine to test for value of B. If $A1 \times C2 + A2 \times C1 = B$ then OUTPUT
  - NEXT $C1$
- NEXT $A1$
- OUTPUT

In BASIC, an exponent is expressed by using an upward arrow or some similar symbol. For example,

x^2 is written X↑2.

The factors of C will need to be tested in both orders. This is done in lines 360–380.

```
10  PRINT "TO FIND FACTORS OF"
15  PRINT
20  PRINT "AX↑2 + BX + C:"
25  PRINT
30  PRINT "INPUT A (>0),B,C (<>0)";
40  INPUT A,B,C
50  IF A <= 0 THEN 30
60  PRINT
70  REM---FIND THE FACTORS
80  REM---OF A WHERE
90  REM---A IS THE
100  REM---COEFFICIENT
110  REM---OF X↑2
120  FOR A1=1 TO A
130  LET A2=A/A1
140  IF A2 <> INT(A2) THEN 410
150  IF A2<A1 THEN 540
160  PRINT
170  PRINT "A1 = ";A1,"A2 = ";A2
180  PRINT
190  REM---FIND THE FACTORS
200  REM---OF C WHERE
210  REM---C IS THE
220  REM---CONSTANT TERM
230  REM---OF THE TRINOMIAL
240  FOR C1=1 TO ABS(C)
250  LET C2=C/C1
260  IF C2 <> INT(C2) THEN 400
270  IF ABS(C2)<ABS(C1) THEN 410
```

```
280  LET K=0
290  LET C3=C1
300  GOSUB 460
310  LET C3=-C3
320  LET C2=-C2
330  GOSUB 460
340  IF K=1 THEN 400
350  LET K=1
360  LET T=C2
370  LET C2=C3
380  LET C3=T
390  GOTO 300
400  NEXT C1
410  NEXT A1
420  GOTO 540
430  REM---SUBROUTINE
440  REM---COMPUTE AND PRINT
450  REM---POSSIBLE MIDDLE TERMS
460  PRINT A1;" X ";C2;" + ";
470  PRINT A2;" X ";C3;" = ";
480  LET M=A1*C2+A2*C3
490  PRINT M;" B = ";B
500  IF M=B THEN 560
510  PRINT
520  RETURN
530  REM---OUTPUT
540  PRINT "PRIME"
550  GOTO 580
560  PRINT "(";A1;"X + (";C3;"))";
570  PRINT "(";A2;"X + (";C2;"))"
580  END
```

Exercises

1. Explain the use of the temporary variable T in lines 360 and 380.

2. If you can print out a copy of the program, use colored pencils to mark the loops for factoring A and C. A-loop: 70–410 C-loop: 180–400

RUN the program to factor the following trinomials.

3. $x^2 + 11x + 28$ $(x + 7)(x + 4)$ **4.** $x^2 - x + 10$ prime **5.** $4x^2 + 20x + 21$ $(2x + 7)(2x + 3)$

6. $7x^2 - 16x - 15$ $(7x + 5)(x - 3)$ **7.** $6x^2 - 7x - 5$ $(3x - 5)(2x + 1)$ **8.** $35x^2 + 12x - 36$ $(7x - 6)(5x + 6)$

9. When does the program give duplicate values of M?

10. Which lines would you need to change or delete in order to print just the answer? 170, 460, 470, 490

Note: The program above can be used to do Exercises 1–36 on page 216.

35. $(x - a)(ax + a^2 - x)$
36. $2x^3(x + 4)$
37. $(b - 3c)(a - 3b) \cdot (a + 3b)$
38. $(a - b)(a - b - 2) \cdot (a - b + 2)$
39. $2(1 - 2x - y) \cdot (1 + 2x + y)$
40. $(a - b)(a - b - 3)$
41. $(x + 1)^2(x - 2)$
42. $(x - 2)^2(x - 3)$
43. $(x + 2y)(a - 3x + 6y)$
44. $2(c - d)(c + d) \cdot (c^2 + d^2)(c^4 + d^4) \cdot (c^8 + d^8)$
45. $2(p + 1)(p - 4) \cdot (p - 2)$
46. $(2a - 1)^3$
47. $(p - 2q - r + 2s) \cdot (p - 2q + r - 2s)$
48. $16(a - b - 2c) \cdot (a + b + 2c)$
49. $3(15x + y)(x - 4y)$
50. $(a - 2)^2(a + 1)(a + 3)$
51. $-(b - c - a) \cdot (b - c + a)(b + c - a) \cdot (b + c + a)$
52. $(a - 3)^2(a + 2)(a + 4)$
53. $(a + 3b)^2(1 - a + 3b) \cdot (1 + a - 3b)$
54. $(x + 2)^3(x - 2)$
55. $(x + y - x^2 + 2y^2) \cdot (x + y + x^2 - 2y^2)$
56. $(t + 1)^2(t - 1)$
57. $(x - 1)(x - 2)(x + 2)$

Additional Answers Computer Key-In

1. T allows the values of $C3$ and $C2$ to be switched.

9. when the factors are in reverse order

Teaching Suggestions p. T98

Suggested Extensions p. T99

Chalkboard Examples

Solve.

1. Find two consecutive odd integers whose product is 143.
   Step 2 Let x = the first integer. Then $x + 2$ = second integer.
   Step 3 $x(x + 2) = 143$
   Step 4 $x^2 + 2x = 143$
   $x^2 + 2x - 143 = 0$
   $(x + 13)(x - 11) = 0$
   $x = -13$ or $x = 11$
   $\therefore$ the integers are -13 and -11 or 11 and 13.
2. The length of a rectangle is 3 cm more than twice the width. The area of the rectangle is 90 cm^2. Find the dimensions of the rectangle.
   Step 2 Let w = width in centimeters. Then $2w + 3$ = length.
   Step 3 $w(2w + 3) = 90$
   Step 4 $2w^2 + 3w = 90$
   $2w^2 + 3w - 90 = 0$
   $(2w + 15)(w - 6) = 0$
   $w = -\frac{15}{2}$ or $w = 6$
   Reject $w = -\frac{15}{2}$.
   $w = 6$; $2w + 3 = 15$.
   $\therefore$ the rectangle is 15 cm by 6 cm.

228

5-13 Solving Problems by Factoring

Objective To solve problems involving quadratic equations.

The problems in this section all lead to polynomial equations that can be solved by factoring. Sometimes a solution of the equation may not satisfy some of the conditions of the problem. For example, a negative number could not be a length or a width. You simply discard solutions that do not make sense for the problem.

Example 1 A pool is surrounded by a deck of uniform width. The area of the pool is 180 m^2. If the dimensions of the pool plus the deck are 16 m by 24 m, find the width of the deck.

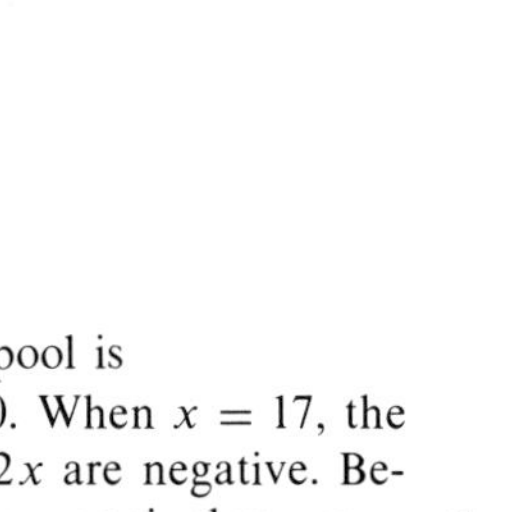

Solution

Step 1 The problem asks for the width of the deck.

Step 2 Let x = width of the deck (in meters). Then the length of the pool $= 24 - 2x$ and the width of the pool $= 16 - 2x$.

Step 3 Area of the pool = 180.
$(16 - 2x)(24 - 2x) = 180$

Step 4
$$384 - 80x + 4x^2 = 180$$
$$4x^2 - 80x + 204 = 0$$
$$x^2 - 20x + 51 = 0$$
$$(x - 3)(x - 17) = 0$$

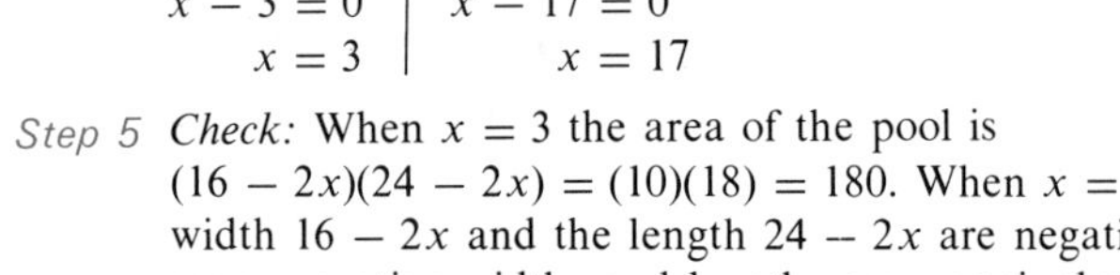

$x - 3 = 0$ | $x - 17 = 0$
$x = 3$ | $x = 17$

Step 5 *Check:* When $x = 3$ the area of the pool is $(16 - 2x)(24 - 2x) = (10)(18) = 180$. When $x = 17$, the width $16 - 2x$ and the length $24 - 2x$ are negative. Because negative widths and lengths are meaningless, we must reject $x = 17$ as an answer.

$\therefore$ the width of the deck is 3 m. ***Answer***

You may wonder how the equation in Step 3 can produce a solution, 17, that does not check. The reason is that the equation in Step 3 gives only one of the requirements of the problem. The requirements that the pool have a positive width $(16 - 2x > 0)$ and a positive length $(24 - 2x > 0)$ were not written down. Usually, it is easier to write only the equation and then check its solutions against the other conditions stated in the problem.

In the next example, both solutions of the equation satisfy the conditions of the problem.

You can use the formula $h = rt - 4.9t^2$ to obtain a good approximation of the height h in meters that an object will reach in t seconds when it is projected upward with an initial speed of r meters per second (m/s).

Example 2

A ball is thrown upward with an initial speed of 19.6 m/s. When is it directly opposite a balcony that is 14.7 m high?

Solution

Step 1 The problem asks for the time when the ball is opposite the balcony.

Step 2 Let t = number of seconds after being thrown that the ball is opposite the balcony,
h = height of ball = 14.7 (meters),
and r = initial speed = 19.6 (meters per second).

Step 3

$$h = rt - 4.9t^2$$
$$14.7 = 19.6t - 4.9t^2$$
$$\frac{14.7}{4.9} = \frac{19.6t}{4.9} - \frac{4.9t^2}{4.9}$$

Step 4

$$3 = 4t - t^2$$
$$t^2 - 4t + 3 = 0$$
$$(t - 3)(t - 1) = 0$$

Completing the solution and checking the values is left to you.

$\therefore$ the ball is opposite the balcony both 1 s and 3 s after being thrown. ***Answer***

Problems

Solve.

A **1.** The sum of a number and its square is 72. Find the number. -9 or 8

2. The sum of a positive number and its square is 90. Find the number. 9

3. A negative number is 42 less than its square. Find the number. -6

4. Find two consecutive negative integers whose product is 110. -11, -10

Common Errors

Because negative solutions must frequently be discarded, students sometimes reject negative solutions without checking to see if it is reasonable to do so. Encourage careful rereading of the problem in Step 5 of the five-step plan.

Students may confuse "sum of the squares" with "square of the sum" (see Problems 6, 12, and 14), so you may wish to discuss how these two phrases differ.

Supplementary Materials

Practice Master 30
Test 18
Resource Book, p. 88

Suggested Assignments

Minimum
229/*P*: 2–14 even
R 232/*Self-Test 4*

Average
Day 1: 229/*P*: 2–14 even, 20, 22
Day 2: 230/*P*: 15–18, 21, 23, 25
R 232/*Self-Test 4*

Maximum
230/*P*: 15, 16, 17–27 odd
R 232/*Self-Test 4*

Day 2 of Sec. 5–12 finishes Sec. 5–12 and starts Sec. 5–13.

Additional A Exercises

Solve.

1. The sum of a number and its square is 132. Find the number. 11 or −12
2. Find two consecutive odd integers whose product is 255. 15, 17
3. The square of a number is 75 more than 10 times the number. Find the number. −5 or 15
4. The sum of the squares of two consecutive integers is 221. Find the integers. 10 and 11 or −10 and −11
5. A rectangle has perimeter 34 and area 60. Find its dimensions. 5 by 12
6. Find two numbers whose sum is 25 and the sum of whose squares is 325. 10 and 15

Mixed Review Exercises

Factor.

1. $9x^2 - 3x - 6$
   $3(3x + 2)(x - 1)$
2. $a^2 + ax - 2a - 2x$
   $(a - 2)(a + x)$
3. Factor $m^3n - mn^3$ completely.
   $mn(m - n)(m + n)$
4. Solve:
   $x^3 - 16x^2 + 63x = 0$
   $x = 0, 7, 9$

5. The square of a number is 20 more than 8 times the number. Find the number. 10 or −2
6. The squares of two consecutive positive even integers total 100. Find the integers. 6, 8
7. The length of a rectangle is 9 cm more than its width. Its area is 112 cm^2. Find the dimensions of the rectangle. 7 cm by 16 cm
8. The length of a rectangle is 4 cm more than twice its width. If the area of the rectangle is 160 cm^2, find its dimensions. 8 cm by 20 cm
9. A rectangle has perimeter 42 m and area 104 m^2. Find the dimensions of the rectangle. (*Hint:* If the width is w, the length is $21 - w$.) 8 m by 13 m
10. The dimensions of a rectangle were 5 cm by 9 cm. When both dimensions were increased by equal amounts, the area of the rectangle increased by 120 cm^2. Find the dimensions of the new rectangle. 11 cm by 15 cm
11. A square field has 4 m added to its length and 2 m added to its width, thereby creating a field with an area of 195 m^2. Find the dimensions of the original field. 11 m by 11 m
12. The sum of two numbers is 20, and the sum of their squares is 218. Find the numbers. (*Hint:* If one number is x, the other will be $20 - x$.) 7, 13
13. Find two numbers that total 13 and whose squares total 229. 15, −2
14. I am thinking of three consecutive integers. The square of the largest one equals the sum of the squares of the other two. Find the integers. −1, 0, 1 or 3, 4, 5

In Problems 15–19, use the formula $h = rt - 4.9t^2$. Notice that all numbers appearing are integral multiples of 4.9.

15. A ball is thrown upward with an initial speed of 24.5 m/s. When is it 29.4 m high? (Two answers) after 2 s and after 3 s
16. A projectile is fired upward with an initial speed of 2940 m/s. After how many minutes does it hit the ground? 10 min

B 17. A signal flare is fired upward with an initial speed of 245 m/s. A stationary balloonist at a height of 1960 m sees the flare pass on its way up. How long will it be before the flare passes the balloonist again on its way down? 30 s

18. A ball is thrown upward from the top of a 98 m tower with an initial speed of 39.2 m/s. When does it hit the ground? (*Hint:* If h is the height of the ball above the top of the tower, then $h = -98$ when the ball hits the ground.) 10 s

19. A ball is thrown upward with an initial speed of 29.4 m/s.
   a. When is the ball 44.1 m high? after 3 s
   b. Explain why 44.1 m is the greatest height attained by the ball.

b. There is only one time when the ball is 44.1 m high.

20. The height of a box is 8 cm and the total surface area of the box is 114 cm^2. Find the length of a side of the base of the box if the base is a square. 3 cm

21. The bottom of a box is a rectangle with dimensions in centimeters of x and $x + 2$. The height of the box is 5 cm and its total surface area is 236 cm^2. Find x. 6 cm

22. A rug placed in a room 12 m long and 9 m wide covers half the floor area and leaves a uniform strip of bare floor around the edges. What are the dimensions of the rug? 6 m by 9 m

23. A garden plot 4 m by 12 m has one side along a fence as shown below. The area of the garden is to be doubled by digging up a border of uniform width on the other three sides. What should be the width of the border? 2 m

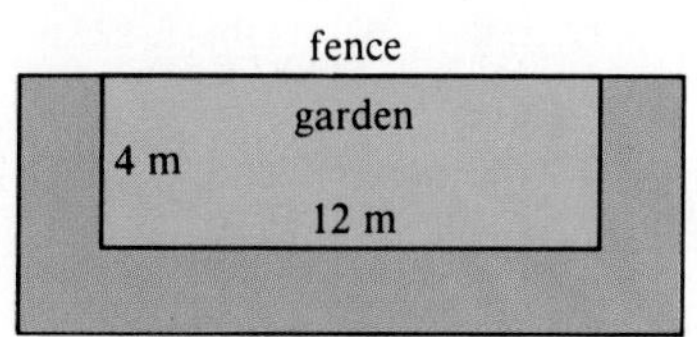

Ex. 23

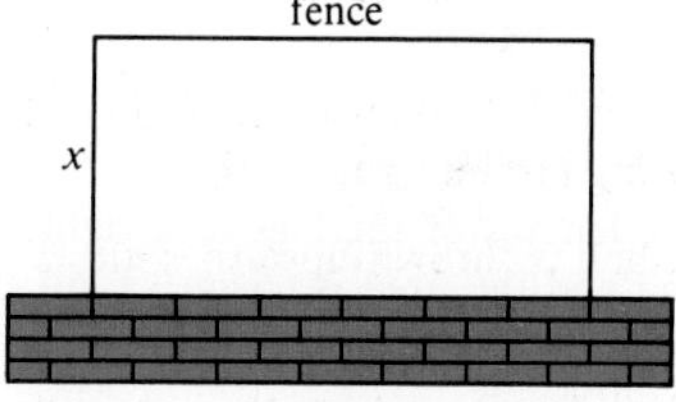

Ex. 24

24. The diagram above shows a rectangular enclosure formed by a wall and 20 m of fencing. If the area of the enclosure is 48 m^2, find its dimensions. 4 m by 12 m or 6 m by 8 m

25. A rectangular garden 40 m by 30 m has two paths crossing through it as shown. If the width of each path in meters is x and the area covered by the paths is 325 m^2, find x. 5 m

26. The side of one cube is 2 cm more than the side of another cube. The volumes of the cubes differ by 152 cm^3. Find the lengths of the sides of each cube. 4 cm, 6 cm

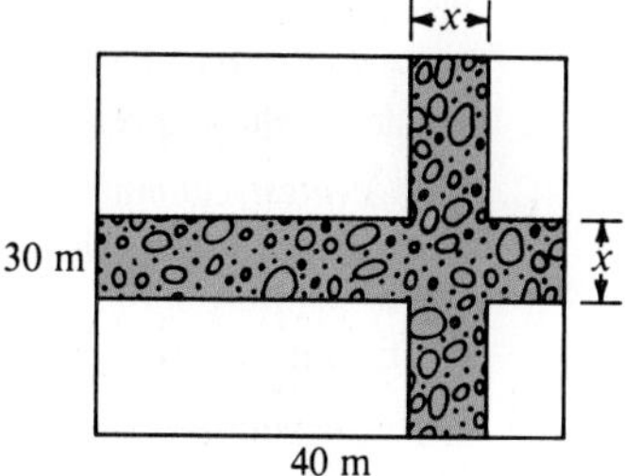

Ex. 25

C 27. A rectangular piece of cardboard is 20 cm longer than it is wide. Squares, 10 cm on a side, are cut from the corners of the cardboard, and the sides are folded up to make an open box whose volume is 8 L. Find the dimensions of the original piece of cardboard. (*Remember:* 1 L = 1000 cm^3) 60 cm by 40 cm

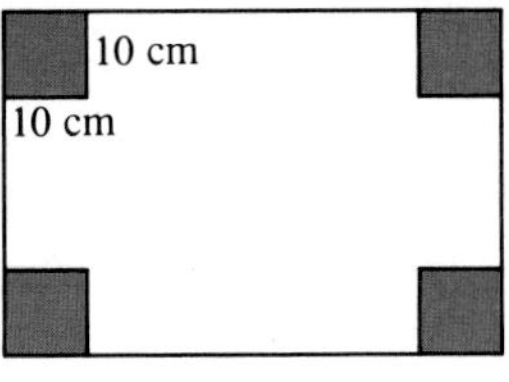

Ex. 27

Quick Quiz

Factor.

1. $zy - 3z + 4y - 12$ $(z + 4)(y - 3)$
2. $6x^2 + 15x - 9$ $3(2x - 1)(x + 3)$
3. $x^3 - 3x^2 - 4x + 12$ $(x - 3)(x + 2)(x - 2)$

Solve.

4. $(y - 3)(y + 22) = 0$ $\{3, -22\}$
5. $x^2 + 49 = 14x$ $\{7\}$
6. The sum of a number and its square is 56. Find the number. 7 or -8

Self-Test 4

Vocabulary

factor completely (p. 221)
converse (p. 223)
polynomial equation (p. 223)
linear equation (p. 223)
quadratic equation (p. 223)
cubic equation (p. 223)
standard form of a polynomial equation (p. 224)

Factor completely.

1. $5a - 2ac + 5b - 2bc$ $(a + b)(5 - 2c)$
2. $n^2 - 2n + 1 - 100t^4$ $(n - 1 - 10t^2)(n - 1 + 10t^2)$ **Obj. 5-10, p. 218**
3. $18a^3 - 12a^2 + 2a$ $2a(3a - 1)^2$
4. $21xy - 18x^2 - 6y^2$ $-3(2x - y)(3x - 2y)$ **Obj. 5-11, p. 221**

Solve.

5. $k^2 - 4k = 32$ $\{8, -4\}$
6. $3g^2 + 12g + 12 = 0$ $\{-2\}$ **Obj. 5-12, p. 223**
7. $w^3 = 121w$ $\{0, 11, -11\}$
8. $z^3 = z^2 + 30z$ $\{0, 6, -5\}$
9. The lengths of the legs of a right triangle are consecutive integers and the area is 66 cm^2. Find the length of the shorter leg. 11 cm **Obj. 5-13, p. 228**

Check your answers with those at the back of the book.

Chapter Summary

1. Prime factors of positive integers can be found systematically by using the primes in order as divisors. The *prime factorization* of a positive integer is the expression of the integer as a product of prime factors.
2. The *greatest common factor (GCF) of two or more integers* is the greatest integer that divides all of them evenly. The *greatest common factor of two or more monomials* is the common factor that has the greatest coefficient and the greatest degree in each variable.
3. The *cancellation rule for fractions* (page 187) and the *rule of exponents for division* (page 188) can be used to simplify quotients of monomials.
4. A method for *multiplying binomials mentally* is given on page 196.

5. The following factoring patterns are useful in factoring polynomials:

$$a^2 + 2ab + b^2 = (a + b)^2 \qquad a^2 - b^2 = (a + b)(a - b)$$
$$a^2 - 2ab + b^2 = (a - b)^2$$

6. Guidelines for *factoring polynomials completely* are given on page 221.
7. The *zero-product property* (page 223) is useful in solving *polynomial equations.*

Chapter Review

Give the letter of the correct answer.

1. List all the pairs of integral factors of -111. 5-1
a. $(-1)(-111)$, $(-3)(-37)$ **b.** $(-1)(111)$, $(-3)(37)$
c. $(-1)(111)$, $(1)(-111)$, $(3)(-37)$, $(-3)(37)$ **d.** $(1)(111)$, $(-1)(-111)$, $(3)(37)$, $(-3)(-37)$

2. Give the prime factorization of 72.
a. $1 \cdot 2^3 \cdot 3^2$ **b.** $2^2 \cdot 3 \cdot 6$ **c.** $2^2 \cdot 3^3$ **d.** $2^3 \cdot 3^2$

3. Give the GCF of 12 and 36.
a. 2 **b.** 6 **c.** 12 **d.** 36

4. Simplify $\frac{(-4a)^3}{-4a^3}$. 5-2
a. 1 **b.** -1 **c.** 3 **d.** 16

5. Find the missing factor: $-105x^3y^6 = (7xy^2)(\underline{\ ?\ })$
a. $-112x^3y^3$ **b.** $-15x^3y^3$ **c.** $-15x^2y^4$ **d.** $-25x^2y^4$

6. Divide: $\frac{24a^2 - 48a + 8}{8}$ 5-3
a. $3a^2 - 6a$ **b.** $6a^2 - 7a + 1$ **c.** $3a^2 - 6a + 1$ **d.** 3

7. Express $18x^3 - 63x^2 + 9x$ as the product of its greatest monomial factor and another polynomial.
a. $9(2x^3 - 7x^2 + x)$ **b.** $9x(2x^2 - 7x)$
c. $9x(2x^2 - 7x + x)$ **d.** $9x(2x^2 - 7x + 1)$

8. Express $(k - 1)(k - 1)$ as a polynomial. 5-4
a. $k^2 + 1$ **b.** $2k + 1$ **c.** $k^2 - 2k + 1$ **d.** $k^2 + 2k + 1$

9. Express $(7x + 3y)(x + 3y)$ as a polynomial.
a. $7x^2 + 6y^2$ **b.** $7x^2 + 9y^2$
c. $7x^2 + 24xy + 6y^2$ **d.** $7x^2 + 24xy + 9y^2$

10. Express $(x^3 + 1)(x^3 - 1)$ as a polynomial. 5-5
a. $x^6 - 1$ **b.** $x^9 - 1$ **c.** $2x^3 - 1$ **d.** $x^6 - 2x - 1$

11. Factor $196 - x^{16}$.
a. $(x^4 + 14)(x^4 - 14)$ **b.** $(14 + x^8)(14 - x^8)$
c. $(x^8 + 14)(x^8 - 14)$ **d.** $(14 - x^4)(14 + x^4)$

12. Express $(4a - 7b)^2$ as a polynomial. 5-6

a. $16a^2 + 49b^2$
b. $16a^2 - 49b^2$
c. $16a^2 + 56ab - 49b^2$
(d.) $16a^2 - 56ab + 49b^2$

13. Factor $a^2 - 2a + 1$.

a. not possible
(b.) $(a - 1)^2$
c. $(a + 1)^2$
d. $(a - 2)^2$

14. Factor $a^2 + ab + b^2$.

(a.) not possible
b. $(a + b)^2$
c. $(a - b)^2$
d. $(a + b)(a - b)$

15. Factor $m^2 - 5m + 6$. 5-7

a. not possible
b. $(m - 6)(m - 1)$
c. $(m + 1)(m - 6)$
(d.) $(m - 2)(m - 3)$

16. Factor $x^2 + 16x + 48$.

a. $(x + 6)(x + 8)$
b. $(x + 3)(x + 16)$
c. $(x + 2)(x + 24)$
(d.) $(x + 4)(x + 12)$

17. Factor $x^2 + 14x - 32$. 5-8

a. $(x - 8)(x + 4)$
b. $(x + 8)(x - 4)$
(c.) $(x + 16)(x - 2)$
d. $(x - 16)(x + 2)$

18. Factor $x^2 - 14x - 48$.

(a.) not possible
b. $(x - 6)(x - 8)$
c. $(x - 16)(x + 2)$
d. $(x + 4)(x - 12)$

19. Factor $6x^2 - 19x + 3$. 5-9

a. $(2x - 3)(3x - 1)$
(b.) $(6x - 1)(x - 3)$
c. $(x - 1)(6x - 3)$
d. $(3x - 3)(2x - 1)$

20. Factor $6x^2 - 5x - 6$.

a. $(3x + 2)(3x - 3)$
b. $(3x - 2)(2x + 3)$
c. $(3x - 1)(2x + 6)$
(d.) $(2x - 3)(3x + 2)$

21. Factor $7t(n - 4) - (4 - n)$. 5-10

a. $7t(n - 4)$
(b.) $(n - 4)(7t + 1)$
c. $7t(2n - 8)$
d. $(n - 4)(7t - 1)$

22. Factor $4t^2 + 36$ completely. 5-11

a. $(2t + 6)^2$
(b.) $4(t^2 + 9)$
c. $4(t + 3)^2$
d. $4(t + 3)(t - 3)$

23. Solve $3x(2x - 1)(3x + 2) = 0$. 5-12

(a.) $\left\{0, \frac{1}{2}, -\frac{2}{3}\right\}$
b. $\left\{0, 2, -\frac{2}{3}\right\}$
c. $\left\{0, 2, -\frac{3}{2}\right\}$
d. $\left\{0, \frac{1}{2}, -\frac{3}{2}\right\}$

24. I am thinking of four consecutive integers. The sum of the squares of the second and third is 61. Find the integers. 5-13

a. $\{4, 5, 6, 7\}$
b. $\{-10, -9, -8, -7\}$
(c.) $\{-4, -5, -6, -7\}$ or $\{4, 5, 6, 7\}$
d. no solution

Chapter Test

List all the pairs of integral factors of each integer.

1. 91 (1)(91), (7)(13), (−1)(−91), (−7)(−13) **2.** −87 (−1)(87), (−87)(1), (−3)(29), (−29)(3) 5-1

Give the prime factorization of each number.

3. 168 $2^3 \cdot 3 \cdot 7$ **4.** 420 $2^2 \cdot 3 \cdot 5 \cdot 7$

Simplify each expression assuming that no denominator equals zero.

5. $\dfrac{-80ux^6}{-48ux^8}$ $\dfrac{5}{3x^2}$ **6.** $\dfrac{(-2y)^4}{-36y}$ $-\dfrac{4y^3}{9}$ 5-2

7. $\dfrac{49ab^2 - 56ab^8}{7ab^2}$ $7 - 8b^6$ **8.** $\dfrac{-65r^6 + 78r^4 - 52r^2}{-13r^2}$ $5r^4 - 6r^2 + 4$ 5-3

Evaluate by factoring.

9. $79 \times 15 - 79 \times 8$ 553 **10.** $64^2 - 64 \times 56$ 512

Express each product as a polynomial.

11. $(6a - 1)(7a - 6)$ $42a^2 - 43a + 6$ **12.** $(6a - b)(9a + 8b)$ $54a^2 + 39ab - 8b^2$ 5-4

13. $(8 + 9x)(8 - 9x)$ $64 - 81x^2$ **14.** $(a^5 - b^3)(a^5 + b^3)$ $a^{10} - b^6$ 5-5

15. $(a - 16)^2$ $a^2 - 32a + 256$ **16.** $(5p - 7q)^2$ $25p^2 - 70pq + 49q^2$ 5-6

Factor each trinomial as the square of a binomial, if possible. If it is not possible, write "not factorable."

17. $k^2 + 14k - 49$ not factorable **18.** $16x^2 - 8x + 1$ $(4x - 1)^2$ **19.** $a^2 - 9ab + 81b^2$ not factorable

Factor completely. If the polynomial is not factorable, write "prime."

20. $b^2 - 3b + 2$ **21.** $x^2 - 2x + 4$ **22.** $a^2 - 6ab + 8b^2$ 5-7

23. $a^2 - 6a - 40$ **24.** $z^2 + z - 3$ **25.** $x^2 + 22xy - 48y^2$ 5-8

26. $4a^2 - a - 5$ **27.** $6y^2 + y - 15$ **28.** $7 - 23r + 6r^2$ 5-9

29. $2r - 6 - 6r + 18$ $-4(r - 3)$ **30.** $ax + 2x + a + 2$ $(x + 1)(a + 2)$ 5-10

31. $x^4 - 1$ $(x - 1)(x + 1)(x^2 + 1)$ **32.** $x^2y - y^3$ $x(x - y)(x + y)$ 5-11

33. $9x^3 - 63x^2 + 108x$ $9x(x - 3)(x - 4)$ **34.** $x^2 + x + xy + y$ $(x + y)(x + 1)$

Solve.

35. $3x^2 - 41x = -60$ $\left\{\frac{5}{3}, 12\right\}$ **36.** $3a^2 = 57a$ $\{0, 19\}$ **37.** $4a^2 = 1$ $\left\{\frac{1}{2}, -\frac{1}{2}\right\}$ 5-12

38. A rectangle has perimeter 34 cm and area 60 cm². Find the dimensions of the rectangle. 5 cm by 12 cm 5-13

Additional Answers Chapter Test

20. $(b - 2)(b - 1)$
21. prime
22. $(a - 4b)(a - 2b)$
23. $(a - 10)(a + 4)$
24. prime
25. $(x + 24y)(x - 2y)$
26. $(4a - 5)(a + 1)$
27. $(2y - 3)(3y + 5)$
28. $(7 - 2r)(1 - 3r)$

Alternate Test p. T14

Additional Answers Cumulative Review

17. $2p^2(3p - pr^2 + 4r^3st)$
18. $7t(2z - 1)(2z + 1)$
19. $(2a + 3b)^2$
20. $(d + 11)(d + 2)$
21. $(m - 6)(m - 3)$
22. $(t - 5)(t + 4)$
23. $(3y - 1)(2y + 5)$
24. $(x + 2y - 4) \cdot (x + 2y + 4)$
25. $(a + b)^2(a - b)$

Cumulative Review (Chapters 1–5)

Simplify. Assume that no denominator equals zero.

1. $-2.1 + (-31.4) + 20.8$ -12.7

2. $-\frac{3}{5}\left(-\frac{9}{17}\right) + \frac{8}{5}\left(-\frac{9}{17}\right)$ $-\frac{9}{17}$

3. $\frac{-180t}{36}$ $-5t$

4. $(-4)^2 \div 2 + 2 - 8$ 2

5. $(2z - 3) + (3z - 4)$ $5z - 7$

6. $(2z - 3) - (3z - 4)$ $-z + 1$

7. $(2a^2b)^3(3a^2b)^3$ $216a^{12}b^6$

8. $\frac{-35x^2yz^3}{21xyz}$ $-\frac{5xz^2}{3}$

9. $\frac{27x^3y^2 - 9x^2y + 8xy}{9xy}$ $3x^2y - x + \frac{8}{9}$

10. $(7ab - 9c)(7ab + 9)$ $49a^2b^2 - 63abc + 63ab - 81c$

11. $(5y + 6)^2$ $25y^2 + 60y + 36$

12. $-t(3t + 5)(2t - 5)$ $-6t^3 + 5t^2 + 25t$

Evaluate if $a = -\frac{1}{2}$, $b = 2$, $c = 0$, and $d = -3$.

13. $\frac{(d - 2a) - b}{-c + 1}$ -4

14. $\frac{1}{a}(bc - d)$ -6

15. $(2b + d)^b$ 1

16. Find the prime factorizations of 90 and 756 and then find their GCF. $90 = 2 \cdot 3^2 \cdot 5$; $756 = 2^2 \cdot 3^3 \cdot 7$; GCF = 18

Factor completely. If the polynomial cannot be factored write "prime."

17. $6p^3 - 2p^3r^2 + 8p^2r^3st$

18. $28z^2t - 7t$

19. $4a^2 + 12ab + 9b^2$

20. $d^2 + 13d + 22$

21. $m^2 - 9m + 18$

22. $t^2 - t - 20$

23. $6y^2 + 13y - 5$

24. $x^2 + 4xy + 4y^2 - 16$

25. $a^3 + a^2b - ab^2 - b^3$

Solve. If the equation is an identity or has no solution, state that fact.

26. $5t - 3 = 12$ 3

27. $|t| - 4 = 2$ 6 or -6

28. $\frac{3}{4}y = 21$ 28

29. $7(x - 1) = 4x + 5$ 4

30. $\frac{1}{4}x = -3$ -12

31. $9 - b = -1$ 10

32. $3m - 2 = \frac{1}{2}(8m + 6) - (m + 5)$ identity

33. $4y^2 - 36 = 0$ $\{3, -3\}$

34. $(x + 7)(x + 1) = (x + 2)^2 + 5x$ $\{3\}$

35. $x^2 - 6x + 15 = 6$ $\{3\}$

36. $x^3 - 9x^2 + 20x = 0$ $\{0, 4, 5\}$

37. $8b^2 - 10b = 3$ $\left\{-\frac{1}{4}, \frac{3}{2}\right\}$

38. I have 20 dimes and nickels. I have $1\frac{1}{2}$ times as many nickels as I do dimes. How many nickels and how many dimes do I have? 12 nickels, 8 dimes

39. The 42 km drive from Fairview to Middletown usually takes 28 min. Because of highway construction and a reduced speed limit, the trip now takes 14 min longer. Find the reduced speed limit in kilometers per hour. 60 km/h

40. The sum of the squares of two consecutive integers is 9 greater than 8 times the smaller integer. Find the integers. 4 and 5 or -1 and 0

41. The length of a rectangle is 5 greater than 3 times its width. The area of the rectangle is 22 cm². Find the length and width of the rectangle. 2 cm wide by 11 cm long

Maintaining Skills

Express each fraction as a decimal to the nearest hundredth.

Example 1 $\frac{11}{13}$ ***Solution*** $13\overline{)11.000}$ (quotient 0.846) $\frac{11}{13} \approx 0.85$

1. $\frac{23}{25}$ 0.92 **2.** $\frac{35}{20}$ 1.75 **3.** $\frac{10}{4}$ 2.5 **4.** $\frac{49}{50}$ 0.98 **5.** $\frac{81}{25}$ 3.24 **6.** $\frac{5}{3}$ 1.67

7. $\frac{51}{30}$ 1.7 **8.** $\frac{7}{8}$ 0.88 **9.** $\frac{14}{6}$ 2.33 **10.** $\frac{41}{24}$ 1.71 **11.** $\frac{15}{22}$ 0.68 **12.** $\frac{21}{17}$ 1.24

Express each percent as a fraction in simplest form.

Example 2 4.8% ***Solution*** $\frac{4.8}{100} = \frac{48}{1000} = \frac{6}{125}$

13. 62% $\frac{31}{50}$ **14.** 12% $\frac{3}{25}$ **15.** 85% $\frac{17}{20}$ **16.** 0.5% $\frac{1}{200}$ **17.** 0.03% $\frac{3}{10{,}000}$ **18.** 9.2% $\frac{23}{250}$

Express each decimal as a percent.

Example 3 0.73 ***Solutions*** (1) $0.73 = \frac{73}{100} = 73\%$ (2) 0.73 = 73%

19. 0.91 91% **20.** 0.07 7% **21.** 0.8 80% **22.** 12 1200% **23.** 0.032 3.2% **24.** 1.23 123%

Find each number.

Example 4 24% of 35 ***Solution*** $0.24 \times 35 = 8.4$

25. 32% of 85 27.2 **26.** 12% of 80 9.6 **27.** 0.2% of 40 0.08

28. 15.6% of 50 7.8 **29.** 130% of 40 52 **30.** 312% of 20 62.4

Find the value of each variable.

Example 5 35% of $x = 7$ ***Solution*** $0.35x = 7;\ x = \frac{7}{0.35} = \frac{700}{35} = 20$

Example 6 n% of $75 = 33$ ***Solution*** $\frac{n}{100} \times 75 = 33;\ \frac{n}{100} = \frac{33}{75};\ n = 44$

31. 30% of $z = 21$ 70 **32.** 15% of $m = 6$ 40 **33.** 5% of $y = 0.6$ 12

34. 52% of $x = 39$ 75 **35.** 24% of $t = 108$ 450 **36.** 45% of $b = 81$ 180

37. p% of $50 = 30$ 60 **38.** a% *of* $45 = 18$ 40 **39.** t% of $105 = 21$ 20

40. $28 = n$% of 112 25 **41.** $51 = x$% of 150 34 **42.** j% of $35 = 14$ 40

Supplementary Materials

Practice Masters 31–32
Test 19
Resource Book, pp. 23–26, 152

Extra Practice

Skills, pp. 615–617
Problems, p. 638

About the Photo

The temperature of the atmosphere surrounding Earth up to a height of 8 to 18 km is generally lower at higher altitudes. As a result, many mountains remain snow covered even in summer.

The decrease in temperature at higher altitudes in the troposphere, the layer of atmosphere closest to the surface of Earth, also affects cloud formation. Clouds form when rising warm air containing water vapor expands under decreasing air pressure. This expansion is accompanied by adiabatic cooling (no heat exchange with the surrounding air), and the air becomes saturated with water vapor. The water vapor then adheres to nuclei such as dust particles, exhaust products, and salt. These droplets then grow in size to form larger cloud droplets.

Your students may be interested in investigating why the temperature of clouds is of great concern to pilots.

6 Fractions

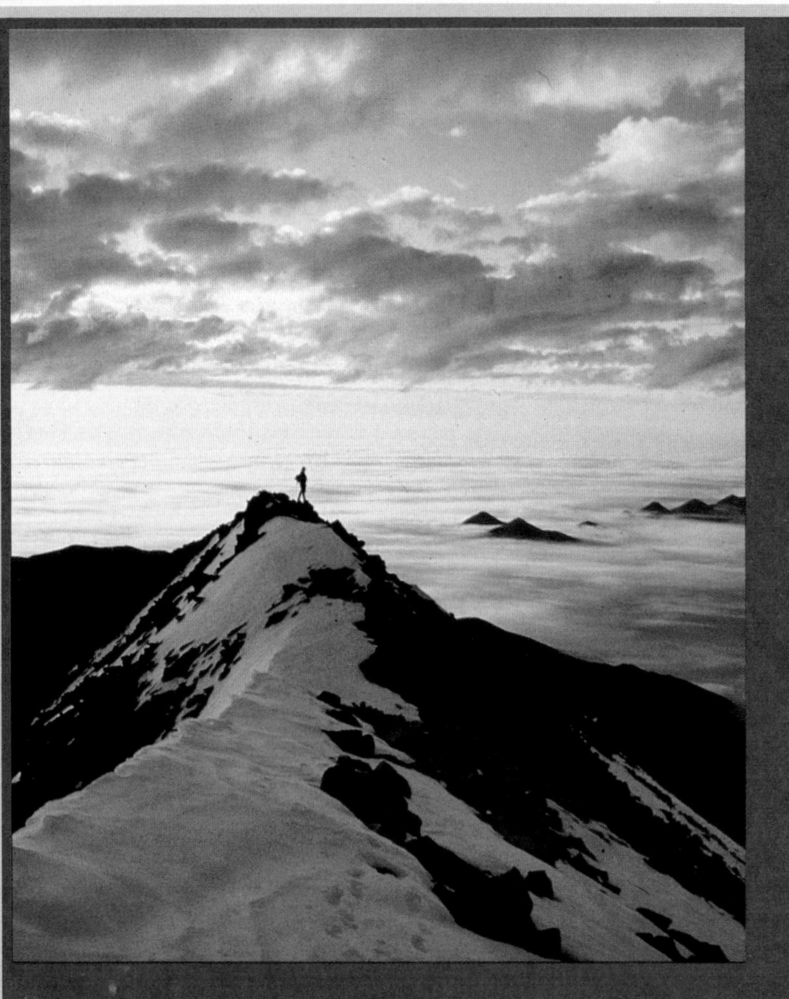

The temperature, T, in degrees Celsius, at a height of h meters is given by the equation $T = t - \frac{h}{100}$, where t is the ground surface temperature in degrees Celsius.

Algebraic Fractions

6-1 Simplifying Fractions

Objective To simplify algebraic fractions.

The procedure for simplifying a quotient of polynomials is the same procedure you learned for simplifying a quotient of monomials. Just factor the numerator and denominator and apply the cancellation rule for fractions. When the numerator and denominator have no common factor other than 1 and -1, the quotient is said to be in *simplest form.*

Example 1 Express $\frac{4a^2 - b^2}{4a^2 - 4ab + b^2}$ in simplest form.

Solution

$$\frac{4a^2 - b^2}{4a^2 - 4ab + b^2} = \frac{(2a + b)\cancel{(2a - b)}}{(2a - b)\cancel{(2a - b)}} = \frac{2a + b}{2a - b} \quad (2a \neq b)$$

Recall that you cannot divide by zero. Thus, you must restrict the variables in a denominator so that the denominator does not equal zero. In Example 1, $2a$ cannot equal b.

The next example shows that you must be alert to factors that have the same value, but whose terms are written in a different order.

Example 2 Express $\frac{12x^2 + 34x + 24}{(2x + 10)(3 + 2x)}$ in simplest form.

Solution

$$\frac{12x^2 + 34x + 24}{(2x + 10)(3 + 2x)} = \frac{2(2x + 3)(3x + 4)}{2(x + 5)(3 + 2x)} \quad \begin{cases} 2x + 3 \text{ and } 3 + 2x \\ \text{have the same value.} \end{cases}$$

$$= \frac{\cancel{2}\cancel{(2x + 3)}(3x + 4)}{\cancel{2}(x + 5)\cancel{(3 + 2x)}} = \frac{3x + 4}{x + 5} \quad \left(x \neq -5, x \neq -\frac{3}{2}\right)$$

Example 3 shows that you must be alert to factors that are opposites of each other.

Example 3 Express $\frac{2x^2 + x - 15}{20 - 3x - 2x^2}$ in simplest form.

Solution

$$\frac{2x^2 + x - 15}{20 - 3x - 2x^2} = \frac{(2x - 5)(x + 3)}{(5 - 2x)(4 + x)} \quad \{2x - 5 \text{ and } 5 - 2x \text{ are opposites.}$$

$$= \frac{-\cancel{(5 - 2x)}(x + 3)}{\cancel{(5 - 2x)}(x + 4)}$$

$$= \frac{-(x + 3)}{x + 4} = -\frac{x + 3}{x + 4} \quad \left(x \neq -4, x \neq \frac{5}{2}\right)$$

Teaching References

Lesson Commentary, pp. T99–T102

Assignment Guide, pp. T61–T62

Supplementary Materials

- Practice Masters 33–39
- Tests 20–23
- Resource Book
  - Practice Exercises, pp. 89–96
  - Tests, pp. 27–35
  - Enrichment Activity, p. 153
  - Mixed Review, pp. 135–137
- Algebra Action

Extra Practice

- Skills, pp. 617–619

Alternate Test, p. T15

Cumulative Review, p. T24

Problem Solving Strategies

Generalizing from Specific
Throughout the chapter students see algebraic patterns suggested by numerical patterns. See, for example, pages 248, 251–252, 260, and 263.

Drawing a Diagram
Students might find a tree diagram useful in solving the Challenge that follows Section 6-3.

Looking for a Pattern
Students look for a general pattern in a sum in the Computer Exercises following Section 6-4 and in a product in Exercise 46 in Section 6-6.

Teaching Suggestions p. T99

Chalkboard Examples

Express in simplest form, noting any restrictions on the variables.

1. $\frac{2t+6}{5t+15}$ $\frac{2(t+3)}{5(t+3)} = \frac{2}{5}$; $t \neq -3$

2. $\frac{3p+3}{3p-3}$ $\frac{3(p+1)}{3(p-1)} = \frac{p+1}{p-1}$; $p \neq 1$

3. $\frac{3st}{s^2t - st^2}$ $\frac{3st}{st(s-t)} = \frac{3}{s-t}$; $s \neq 0,\ t \neq 0,\ s \neq t$

4. $\frac{2t+2}{t^2-1}$ $\frac{2(t+1)}{(t+1)(t-1)} = \frac{2}{t-1}$; $t \neq 1,\ t \neq -1$

Common Error

Students often think that they can simplify algebraic fractions such as $\frac{2a+1}{2a-3}$ because $\frac{2a}{2a} = 1$. Point out that $2a$ is a term rather than a factor of both the numerator and denominator of the algebraic fraction above. It may help to substitute several values for a to show that this fraction does not always simplify to $-\frac{1}{3}$.

Suggested Assignments

Minimum
Day 1: 240/1–17
Day 2: 240/22–35, 40, 41

Average
Day 1: 240/1–21
Day 2: 240/22–35, 39, 40, 43–50

Maximum
240/1–53 odd

Oral Exercises

Express in simplest form, noting any restrictions on the variable.

1. $\frac{a^2-1}{a-1}$ $a+1$; $a \neq 1$
2. $\frac{b^2-4}{b+2}$ $b-2$; $b \neq -2$
3. $\frac{x^2-2x+1}{x-1}$ $x-1$; $x \neq 1$
4. $\frac{x+6}{36-x^2}$ $\frac{1}{6-x}$; $x \neq 6,\ x \neq -6$
5. $\frac{2b+4}{b+2}$ 2; $b \neq -2$
6. $\frac{3x-6}{4x-8}$ $\frac{3}{4}$; $x \neq 2$
7. $\frac{2c-2d}{2c+2d}$ $\frac{c-d}{c+d}$; $c \neq -d$
8. $\frac{(2y-8)^2}{(2y-8)^3}$ $\frac{1}{2y-8}$; $y \neq 4$
9. $\frac{a-7}{7-a}$ -1; $a \neq 7$
10. $\frac{(x-2)(x+3)}{3+x}$ $x-2$; $x \neq -3$
11. $\frac{9-3c}{c-3}$ -3; $c \neq 3$
12. $\frac{(4-x)(x^2-9)}{(x-4)(x-3)}$ $-(x+3)$; $x \neq 4,\ x \neq 3$

Which of the following fractions *cannot* be simplified? 14 and 16

13. $\frac{4x-6y}{4x+6y}$ $\frac{2x-3y}{2x+3y}$
14. $\frac{4x-7y}{4x+7y}$
15. $\frac{4x^2-y^2}{2x-y}$ $2x+y$
16. $\frac{4x^2+y^2}{2x+y}$

Written Exercises

Express in simplest form, noting any restrictions on the variable.

A

1. $\frac{3a-6}{a-2}$
2. $\frac{4n+12}{n+3}$
3. $\frac{3n+1}{9n+3}$
4. $\frac{6x-6y}{6x+6y}$
5. $\frac{2x-2}{x^2-1}$
6. $\frac{2y+14}{49-y^2}$
7. $\frac{2xy}{x^2y-y^2x}$
8. $\frac{4p^3}{4p^2-8p}$
9. $\frac{a^2+8a+16}{16-a^2}$
10. $\frac{b^2-25}{b^2-12b+35}$
11. $\frac{4y+20}{4y^2-100}$
12. $\frac{6x+8y}{16y^2+9x^2}$
13. $\frac{2-y}{y^2-4y+4}$
14. $\frac{(a-5)^2}{25-a^2}$
15. $\frac{(2x-y)^3}{(y-2x)^4}$
16. $\frac{(4n-3)^5}{(3-4n)^5}$
17. $\frac{x^2+xy}{x^2-xy}$
18. $\frac{2ab+2ac+4a^2}{4b+4c+8a}$
19. $\frac{(x-2)(2x+5)}{(5+2x)(x+2)}$
20. $\frac{(3r+7)^2(2r-1)}{(1-2r)(7+3r)}$
21. $\frac{2n^2-5n-3}{4n^2-8n-5}$
22. $\frac{2z^2+z-6}{2z+4}$
23. $\frac{3x^2-15x}{3x^2-16x+5}$
24. $\frac{4n^2-6n}{4n^2+8n-21}$
25. $\frac{10-7a+a^2}{a^2-4}$
26. $\frac{2y^2-9y+4}{2y^2-8y}$
27. $\frac{x^2-y^2}{x^2+2xy-3y^2}$
28. $\frac{a^2-b^2}{a^2+5ab+4b^2}$

Solve for x. Use the following steps. Assume no denominator is 0.

Step 1 Collect all terms with x on one side of the equation and all other terms on the other side.

Step 2 Factor both sides of the equation.

Step 3 Divide both sides of the equation by the coefficient of x.

B

29. $cx + dx = c^2 - d^2$ $x = c - d$
30. $ax + bx = a^2 + 2ab + b^2$ $x = a + b$
31. $ax - a^2 = bx - b^2$ $x = a + b$
32. $2ax + 1 = 4a^2 + x$ $x = 2a + 1$

33. $5kx - x = 25k^2 - 10k + 1$ $x = 5k - 1$

34. $4x - 4 = b^2 + 5b - bx$ $x = b + 1$

35. $cx - dx = c^2 - 3cd + 2d^2$ $x = c - 2d$

36. $x + 4p = 3p^2 + 3px + 1$ $x = 1 - p$

37. $a(x - a) + 6(x + 6) = 0$ $x = a - 6$

38. $2n(x - n) = x - 5n + 2$ $x = n - 2$

39. To evaluate $\frac{9x^2 - 4y^2}{3x - 2y}$ when $x = 4$ and $y = 5$, Stan first simplifies the fraction to $3x + 2y$. Then he substitutes $x = 4$ and $y = 5$, getting 22 for his answer. To evaluate $\frac{9x^2 - 4y^2}{3x - 2y}$ when $x = 4$ and $y = 6$, Stan substitutes these values in the simplified form $3x + 2y$, getting 24. One of his answers is correct and the other is not. Give the correct answer. Explain why the other answer is not correct. The first answer is correct. The second is incorrect because the values $x = 4$ and $y = 6$ make the denominator of the original fraction zero.

If the given values of the variables make the denominator zero, indicate that the fraction cannot be evaluated. Otherwise, evaluate the fraction by first simplifying it, and then substituting the given values of the variables.

40. $\frac{4x^2 - y^2}{2x + y}$ **a.** $x = 4, y = -8$ cannot be eval. **b.** $x = 4, y = 8$ 0 **c.** $x = -\frac{1}{4}, y = \frac{1}{2}$ cannot be eval.

41. $\frac{x^3y - xy^3}{x^2y + xy^2}$ **a.** $x = 3, y = 3$ 0 **b.** $x = 53, y = 49$ 4 **c.** $x = 8, y = -8$ cannot be eval.

42. $\frac{n^2 - 9m^2}{n^2 - 5nm + 6m^2}$ **a.** $n = 8, m = -4$ $-\frac{1}{4}$ **b.** $n = 6, m = 3$ cannot be eval. **c.** $n = 9, m = -3$ 0

Simplify.

43. $\frac{16x^2 - 49y^2}{16x^2 - 56xy + 49y^2}$

44. $\frac{4x^2 + 16xy + 15y^2}{2x^2 + xy - 10y^2}$

45. $\frac{6a^3 + 10a^2}{36a^3 - 100a}$

46. $\frac{8a^2 + 6ab - 5b^2}{16a^2 - 25b^2}$

47. $\frac{a - b + x(a - b)}{a - b}$

48. $\frac{a^4 - 4}{a^2(a + 2) + 2(a + 2)}$

C 49. $\frac{2x^3 - 13x^2 + 15x}{15x - 7x^2 - 2x^3}$

50. $\frac{x^4 - 10x^2 + 9}{3 - 2x - x^2}$

51. $\frac{a^2 - 9b^2 - 2a + 6b}{(a + 3b)^2 - 4}$

52. $\frac{x^3 + 6x^2 - 4x - 24}{x^3 - 2x^2 - 36x + 72}$

53. $\frac{a^2 - 6ab + 9b^2 - 9}{3a - 9b - 9}$

54. $\frac{(a - b)^3 + 4(b - a)}{(a - b)^2 + 4(b - a) + 4}$

For which value(s) of x do the given fractions equal zero? (*Hint:* A fraction is equal to zero only if its numerator equals zero.)

55. $\frac{x^2 - 3x}{x^2 - 2x - 3}$ 0

56. $\frac{x^2 - 2x - 8}{x^2 - 4x}$ -2

57. $\frac{x^2 - 2x - 15}{x^2 + 3x - 40}$ -3

58. $\frac{x^4 - x^2}{x^3 + x^2 - 2x}$ -1

59. $\frac{2x^3 - x^2 - 10x}{x^3 - 2x^2 - 8x}$ $\frac{5}{2}$

60. $\frac{3x^4 + 27x^3 + 60x^2}{6x^2 + 6x - 72}$ $0, -5$

Additional A Exercises

Express in simplest form, noting any restrictions on the variable.

1. $\frac{6n - 24}{n - 4}$ $6, n \neq 4$
2. $\frac{3a - 2}{9a^2 - 4}$ $\frac{1}{3a + 2}$, $a \neq \pm\frac{2}{3}$
3. $\frac{5b - 25}{b^2 - 25}$ $\frac{5}{b + 5}$, $b \neq \pm 5$
4. $\frac{(z - 6)^2}{z^2 - 36}$ $\frac{z - 6}{z + 6}$, $z \neq \pm 6$

Additional Answers Written Exercises

1. $3; a \neq 2$
2. $4; n \neq -3$
3. $\frac{1}{3}; n \neq -\frac{1}{3}$
4. $\frac{x - y}{x + y}; x \neq -y$
5. $\frac{2}{x + 1}; x \neq 1, x \neq -1$
6. $\frac{2}{7 - y}; y \neq 7, y \neq -7$
7. $\frac{2}{x - y}; x \neq y, x \neq 0, y \neq 0$
8. $\frac{p^2}{p - 2}; p \neq 0, p \neq 2$
9. $\frac{a + 4}{4 - a}; a \neq 4, a \neq -4$
10. $\frac{b + 5}{b - 7}; b \neq 7, b \neq 5$
11. $\frac{1}{y - 5}; y \neq 5, y \neq -5$
12. cannot be simplified
13. $-\frac{1}{y - 2}; y \neq 2$
14. $\frac{5 - a}{5 + a}; a \neq 5, a \neq -5$
15. $\frac{1}{2x - y}; y \neq 2x$
16. $-1; n \neq \frac{3}{4}$

(continued)

Additional Answers Written Exercises

17. $\frac{x+y}{x-y}$; $x \neq 0$, $x \neq y$

18. $\frac{a}{2}$; $a \neq \frac{-b-c}{2}$

19. $\frac{x-2}{x+2}$; $x \neq -2$, $x \neq -\frac{5}{2}$

20. $-3r-7$; $r \neq \frac{1}{2}$, $r \neq -\frac{7}{3}$

21. $\frac{n-3}{2n-5}$; $n \neq -\frac{1}{2}$, $n \neq \frac{5}{2}$

22. $\frac{2z-3}{2}$; $z \neq -2$

23. $\frac{3x}{3x-1}$; $x \neq \frac{1}{3}$, $x \neq 5$

24. $\frac{2n}{2n+7}$; $n \neq \frac{3}{2}$, $n \neq -\frac{7}{2}$

25. $\frac{a-5}{a+2}$; $a \neq 2$, $a \neq -2$

26. $\frac{2y-1}{2y}$; $y \neq 0$, $y \neq 4$

27. $\frac{x+y}{x+3y}$; $x \neq -3y$, $x \neq y$

28. $\frac{a-b}{a+4b}$; $a \neq -4b$, $a \neq -b$

43. $\frac{4x+7y}{4x-7y}\left(x \neq \frac{7y}{4}\right)$

44. $\frac{2x+3y}{x-2y}\left(x \neq -\frac{5y}{2}, x \neq 2y\right)$

45. $\frac{a}{2(3a-5)}$ $\left(a \neq 0, a \neq \frac{5}{3}, a \neq -\frac{5}{3}\right)$

46. $\frac{2a-b}{4a-5b}\left(a \neq \frac{5b}{4}, a \neq -\frac{5b}{4}\right)$

Computer Exercises

For students with some programming experience

1. a. Write a BASIC program to evaluate each of the following algebraic fractions for $x = 10, 20, 30, 40, 50$.

(1) $\frac{3x+4}{4x^3+x}$ (2) $\frac{5x^2+2x}{2x^2-9}$ (3) $\frac{3-2x^4}{x^3+x^2}$

b. As the value of x increases, what happens to the value of each of these algebraic fractions? Can you explain why?

2. a. Write a BASIC program that uses READ . . . DATA statements to evaluate the algebraic fraction $\frac{x^5+1}{x^4-x^3+x^2-x+1}$ for the following values of x: 2, 13, 22, 50, 99. 3, 14, 23, 51, 100

b. On the basis of your results in part (a), guess a general formula $\frac{x^5+1}{x^4-x^3+x^2-x+1} = \underline{\ ?\ }$ for all values of x. $x + 1$

Application / Energy Consumption

Power is associated with the flow of electricity in a circuit. Electrical power is measured in watts (W). The amount of power that is used depends on the number of volts of the source of electricity and on the current. Current is the rate of flow of electrical charge. It is measured in amperes.

When P watts of power are used for t hours, the energy consumed, measured in watt-hours (W•h), is $e = Pt$.

Electric companies base their bills on a larger unit, the kilowatt-hour (kW•h), that is equal to one thousand watt-hours.

Example 1 An air conditioner uses 1330 W in 6 hours.

a. How much energy is consumed?

b. If electricity costs 7.3 cents per kilowatt-hour, find the cost of operating the air conditioner.

Solution **a.** Use the formula $e = Pt$.

$$e = 1330 \times 6 = 7980$$

∴ the amount of energy consumed is 7980 W•h, or 7.98 kW•h.

b. Cost $= 7.3 \times 7.98 = 58.254$

∴ the cost of energy is about 58 cents.

It has been estimated that appliances account for as much as two fifths of total home energy consumption. Thus, consumers can save money by using energy-efficient appliances. Some appliances have a tag that shows the estimated yearly energy cost. Such tags make it easy for consumers to compare the energy efficiency of different models.

If you know the annual cost (c) as given on the energy cost tag and the expected lifetime (l) of the appliance, you can estimate the energy cost for the life of the machine. For example, suppose the appliance whose tag is shown is expected to last 15 years. The lifetime operating cost of this appliance is

$$c \cdot l = \$91 \cdot 15 = \$1365.$$

The total cost of an appliance is the sum of the purchase price and the cost of energy for the lifetime of the machine.

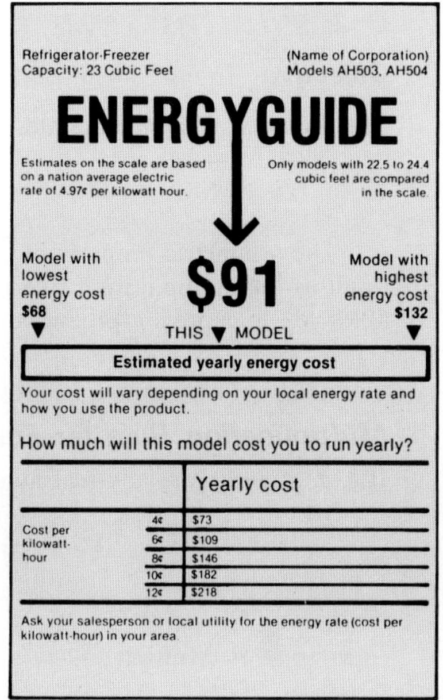

Refrigerator-Freezer
Capacity: 23 Cubic Feet
(Name of Corporation)
Models AH503, AH504
ENERGYGUIDE
Estimates on the scale are based on a nation average electric rate of 4.97¢ per kilowatt hour.
Only models with 22.5 to 24.4 cubic feet are compared in the scale.
Model with lowest energy cost $68
$91
Model with highest energy cost $132
THIS MODEL
Estimated yearly energy cost
Your cost will vary depending on your local energy rate and how you use the product.
How much will this model cost you to run yearly?
Yearly cost
Cost per kilowatt-hour
4¢ $73
6¢ $109
8¢ $146
10¢ $182
12¢ $218
Ask your salesperson or local utility for the energy rate (cost per kilowatt-hour) in your area.

Example 2 Television A can be purchased for \$225 and costs \$58 per year to operate. Television B can be purchased for \$275 and costs \$45 per year to operate. If both have an expected lifetime of eight years, calculate the lifetime operating cost for each. Which is the least expensive?

Solution Use the formula to find the operating costs.

Television A	**Television B**
$c \cdot l = \$58 \cdot 8 = \$464$	$c \cdot l = \$45 \cdot 8 = \$360$
Total cost to consumer:	Total cost to consumer:
$\$225 + \$464 = \$689$	$\$275 + \$360 = \$635$

Television B costs less to operate over the eight-year lifetime.

Exercises

1. A television uses 200 W per hour. If electricity costs 7.3¢ per kW • h, how much does it cost to watch a three-hour movie? about 4¢
2. An oven uses 12,200 W per hour. At 7.3¢ per kW • h, how much does it cost to roast a turkey for five hours? \$4.45
3. How many kilowatt-hours does a dishwasher use in a year if it costs \$31 per year to operate at a cost of 8¢ per kilowatt-hour? What is the cost of energy over the lifetime of the dishwasher if its operating lifetime is 12 years? 387.5 kW·h; \$372
4. Room air conditioner A can be purchased for \$225 and costs \$109 per year to operate. Room air conditioner B can be purchased for \$350 and costs \$95 per year to operate. Each is expected to last nine years. Which is the least expensive appliance over the length of the expected lifetime? B

47. $1 + x \ (a \neq b)$

48. $\frac{a^2 - 2}{a + 2} \ (a \neq -2)$

49. $\frac{5 - x}{5 + x}$ $\left(x \neq 0, x \neq -5, x \neq \frac{3}{2}\right)$

50. $(3 - x)(1 + x)$ $(x \neq -3, x \neq 1)$

51. $\frac{a - 3b}{a + 3b + 2}$ $(a \neq 2 - 3b, a \neq -2 - 3b)$

52. $\frac{x + 2}{x - 6}$ $(x \neq 2, x \neq 6, x \neq -6)$

53. $\frac{a - 3b + 3}{3}$ $(a \neq 3b + 3)$

54. $\frac{(a - b)(a - b + 2)}{a - b - 2}$ $(a \neq b + 2)$

Additional Answers Computer Exercises

Answers to Ex. **1a** may vary slightly.

1. a. (1) 0.0084788, 0.0019988, 0.0008701, 0.0004843, 0.000308
(2) 2.7225131, 2.5790139, 2.5460637, 2.5321216, 2.5245442
(3) −18.179091, −38.094881, −58.064409, −78.048735, −98.039192

b. (1) The value decreases toward 0.
(2) The value decreases toward 2.5.
(3) The value decreases toward negative infinity.

Teaching Suggestions
p. T99

Suggested Extensions
p. T100

Chalkboard Examples

Express each product as a fraction in simplest form.

1. $\frac{3}{5} \cdot \frac{20}{7} \cdot \frac{14}{16}$ $\frac{3}{2}$

2. $\left(\frac{-2}{3}\right)^3 \cdot \left(\frac{3}{4}\right)^2$
$-\frac{8}{27} \cdot \frac{9}{16} = -\frac{1}{6}$

$\left(\frac{4y}{z^2}\right)^3 \cdot \left(\frac{2z}{y}\right)^2$
$\frac{64y^3}{z^6} \cdot \frac{4z^2}{y^2} = \frac{256y}{z^4}$

4. $\frac{y-3}{y^2} \cdot \frac{y}{3-y}$ $-\frac{1}{y}$

5. $\frac{(3-z)^2}{12} \cdot \frac{8}{(z-3)^3}$
$\frac{2}{3(z-3)}$

6. $\frac{a}{a^2-25} \cdot (a^2 + 10a + 25)$
$\frac{a}{(a+5)(a-5)} \cdot (a+5)^2 =$
$\frac{a(a+5)}{a-5}$

6-2 Multiplying Fractions

Objective To multiply algebraic fractions.

The property of quotients states that

$$\frac{cx}{dy} = \frac{c}{d} \cdot \frac{x}{y}.$$

The symmetric property of equality makes it possible to rewrite this result as the multiplication rule for fractions, shown below. This rule enables you to express a product of two fractions as a quotient.

Multiplication Rule for Fractions

If c, d, x, and y are any real numbers such that $d \neq 0$ and $y \neq 0$, then

$$\frac{c}{d} \cdot \frac{x}{y} = \frac{cx}{dy}.$$

Example 1 Multiply: $\frac{3x}{4} \cdot \frac{6}{2y}$

Solution 1 $\frac{3x}{4} \cdot \frac{6}{2y} = \frac{3x \cdot 6}{4 \cdot 2y} = \frac{\overset{9}{\cancel{18}}x}{\underset{4}{\cancel{8}}y} = \frac{9x}{4y}$ $(y \neq 0)$

Solution 2 $\frac{3x}{\underset{2}{\cancel{4}}} \cdot \frac{\overset{3}{\cancel{6}}}{2y} = \frac{9x}{4y}$

Example 2 Multiply: $\frac{x^2 + 2x - 8}{x^2 + 3x} \cdot \frac{x^2 - 9}{x + 4}$

Solution

$$\frac{x^2 + 2x - 8}{x^2 + 3x} \cdot \frac{x^2 - 9}{x + 4} = \frac{(x-2)(x+4)}{x(x+3)} \cdot \frac{(x-3)(x+3)}{(x+4)}$$ Factor the numerators and denominators.

$$= \frac{(x-2)\cancel{(x+4)}}{x\cancel{(x+3)}} \cdot \frac{(x-3)\cancel{(x+3)}}{\cancel{(x+4)}}$$ Divide by common factors.

$$= \frac{(x-2)(x-3)}{x}$$ $(x \neq 0, x \neq -3, x \neq -4)$ ***Answer***

Another way to write the answer to Example 2 is $\frac{x^2 - 5x + 6}{x}$. The factored form of the answer, as shown in Example 2, is the one you should use unless otherwise directed.

If you study the denominators in the first step in Example 2, you will see that there will be a zero denominator when x equals 0, -3, or -4. Thus the answer is restricted to values of x other than 0, -3, and -4.

Hereafter, it will be assumed that the domains of the variables include no value for which any denominator is zero. Hence, it will not be necessary to show the excluded values of the variables.

In Chapter 4, you learned the rule of exponents for a power of a product:

For every positive integer m, $(ab)^m = a^m b^m$.

The rule of exponents for a power of a quotient is similar.

Common Error

In using the cancellation rule for fractions, students sometimes forget to write a simplified fractional factor or do not include all factors in their answers. Encourage students who make such errors to take their time and use enough space to show their work.

Supplementary Materials

Practice Master 33
Resource Book, p. 89

Rule of Exponents for a Power of a Quotient

For every positive integer m,

$$\left(\frac{a}{b}\right)^m = \frac{a^m}{b^m}.$$

Example 3 $\left(\frac{c}{4}\right)^3 = \frac{c^3}{4^3} = \frac{c^3}{64}$

Example 4 Simplify $\left(\frac{x}{3}\right)^2 \cdot \frac{9}{8x}$.

Solution $\left(\frac{x}{3}\right)^2 \cdot \frac{9}{8x} = \frac{x^2}{9} \cdot \frac{9}{8x} = \frac{x}{8}$ ***Answer***

Power of a quotient

Oral Exercises

Express each product as a fraction in simplest form.

1. $\frac{2}{5} \cdot \frac{3}{8}$ $\frac{3}{20}$
2. $\frac{4}{7} \cdot \frac{14}{5}$ $\frac{8}{5}$
3. $\frac{-3}{4} \cdot \frac{8}{9}$ $-\frac{2}{3}$
4. $\frac{a}{b} \cdot \frac{b}{a}$ 1
5. $\frac{3}{x} \cdot \frac{x}{6}$ $\frac{1}{2}$
6. $\frac{n}{2} \cdot \frac{8}{n}$ 4
7. $\frac{5y^2}{3} \cdot \frac{6}{y^2}$ 10
8. $\frac{2a}{3} \cdot \frac{a}{4}$ $\frac{a^2}{6}$
9. $(2x)^2 \cdot \frac{1}{x}$ $4x$
10. $\frac{a}{b} \cdot \frac{b^2}{c}$ $\frac{ab}{c}$
11. $\frac{(x-1)^2}{8} \cdot \frac{4}{x-1}$ $\frac{x-1}{2}$
12. $\frac{3n-2}{n^2} \cdot \frac{n^4}{2-3n}$ $-n^2$

Complete.

13. $\frac{x^2}{9y^2} = \left(\frac{?}{?}\right)^2$ $\frac{x}{3y}$
14. $\left(\frac{5a}{b}\right)^2 = \frac{?}{?}$ $\frac{25a^2}{b^2}$
15. $\left(\frac{n}{2s}\right)^3 = \frac{?}{?}$ $\frac{n^3}{8s^3}$

Suggested Assignments

Minimum
246/1–40
S 240/18–21

Average
246/1, 4, 6, 7, 13, 14, 15–33 odd, 35–44

Maximum
246/8–50 even
S 241/55, 56

Additional A Exercises

Express each product as a fraction in simplest form.

1. $\frac{5}{6} \cdot \frac{18}{25}$ $\frac{3}{5}$

2. $\frac{8}{7} \cdot \frac{2}{5} \cdot \frac{7}{16}$ $\frac{1}{5}$

3. $\frac{5}{6}\left(\frac{3}{5}\right)^2\left(\frac{2}{5}\right)$ $\frac{3}{25}$

4. $\frac{3a^2x}{5c^3} \cdot \frac{20c^2}{15a^2}$ $\frac{4x}{5c}$

Simplify, using the rules of exponents for the power of a product and the power of a quotient.

5. $\left(\frac{x}{4}\right)^3$ $\frac{x^3}{64}$

6. $\left(\frac{6m^2}{7}\right)^2$ $\frac{36m^4}{49}$

Written Exercises

Express each product as a fraction in simplest form.

A

1. $\frac{4}{7} \cdot \frac{21}{8}$ $\frac{3}{2}$
2. $\frac{4}{9} \cdot \frac{3}{16}$ $\frac{1}{12}$
3. $\frac{15}{2} \cdot \frac{6}{25}$ $\frac{9}{5}$
4. $\frac{-3}{14} \cdot \frac{35}{6}$ $-\frac{5}{4}$
5. $\frac{3}{5} \cdot \frac{5}{7} \cdot \frac{7}{9}$ $\frac{1}{3}$
6. $\frac{9}{5} \cdot \frac{2}{3} \cdot \frac{15}{18}$ 1
7. $\left(\frac{-3}{4}\right)^2 \cdot \frac{8}{27}$ $\frac{1}{6}$
8. $\left(\frac{-3}{5}\right)^3 \cdot \frac{-25}{27}$ $\frac{1}{5}$
9. $\frac{4}{x} \cdot \frac{x^2}{8}$ $\frac{x}{2}$
10. $\frac{3y}{2} \cdot \frac{6}{5y}$ $\frac{9}{5}$
11. $\frac{a}{b} \cdot \frac{b}{c} \cdot \frac{c}{d}$ $\frac{a}{d}$
12. $\frac{4}{x^2} \cdot \frac{7x}{8}$ $\frac{7}{2x}$
13. $\frac{p^2}{2q} \cdot \frac{q^2}{2p}$ $\frac{pq}{4}$
14. $\frac{5ac^2}{3b^2} \cdot \frac{6b}{15a^2}$ $\frac{2c^2}{3ab}$
15. $\frac{4d^2e}{9ef} \cdot \frac{f^2}{6d}$ $\frac{2df}{27}$
16. $\frac{2rs^2}{3t} \cdot \frac{9t^2}{4rs}$ $\frac{3st}{2}$

Simplify, using the rules of exponents for the power of a product and the power of a quotient.

24. $-\frac{25b^8}{36}$

17. $(3a^5)^2$ $9a^{10}$
18. $(5n^2)^3$ $125n^6$
19. $\left(\frac{a}{6}\right)^2$ $\frac{a^2}{36}$
20. $\left(\frac{4x}{3}\right)^2$ $\frac{16x^2}{9}$
21. $\left(\frac{5a}{3b^2}\right)^3$ $\frac{125a^3}{27b^6}$
22. $\left(\frac{3n^2}{4}\right)^3$ $\frac{27n^6}{64}$
23. $\left(\frac{-x^2}{10}\right)^4$ $\frac{x^8}{10{,}000}$
24. $-\left(\frac{5b^4}{6}\right)^2$
25. $\left(\frac{a}{b}\right)^2 \cdot \frac{b}{a}$ $\frac{a}{b}$
26. $\left(\frac{3x}{y}\right)^3 \cdot \frac{y^2}{9}$ $\frac{3x^3}{y}$
27. $\left(\frac{2x}{5}\right)^3 \cdot \frac{75}{x^2}$ $\frac{24x}{5}$
28. $\left(\frac{5a}{b}\right)^2 \cdot \frac{2ab}{15}$ $\frac{10a^3}{3b}$
29. Find the area of a square if each side has length $\frac{2x}{7}$ in. $\frac{4x^2}{49}$ in.^{2}
30. Find the volume of a cube if each edge has length $\frac{4n}{5}$ in. $\frac{64n^3}{125}$ in.^{3}
31. A rectangle has length $\frac{5x}{4}$ and width $\frac{2x}{15}$. What is the area? $\frac{x^2}{6}$
32. If you travel for $\frac{9h}{2}$ hours at $\frac{80r}{3}$ mph, how far have you gone? $120rh$ mi

B

33. Find the total dollar cost of $\frac{4y}{3}$ eggs if they cost d dollars per dozen. $\frac{dy}{9}$ dollars
34. Find the total dollar cost of n dozen pencils if each pencil costs $\frac{2c}{3}$ cents. $\frac{2nc}{25}$ dollars

Simplify.

40. $(2a + 1)(a - 5)$

35. $\frac{y+3}{y} \cdot \frac{y^2}{y^2 - 9}$ $\frac{y}{y-3}$
36. $\frac{a+b}{a-b} \cdot \frac{a^2 - b^2}{2a + 2b}$ $\frac{a+b}{2}$
37. $\frac{a^2 - x^2}{a^2} \cdot \frac{a}{3x - 3a}$ $-\frac{a+x}{3a}$
38. $\frac{(1-x)^3}{5} \cdot \frac{10}{(x-1)^2}$ $2(1-x)$
39. $\frac{x^2 - 4}{x^2 + 4x} \cdot \frac{x^2 - 16}{x^2 + 2x}$ $\frac{(x-2)(x-4)}{x^2}$
40. $\frac{2a+1}{3a^2 + 15a} \cdot 3a^3 - 75a$
41. $\frac{3x - xy}{6x^2y} \cdot \frac{3}{9 - y^2}$ $\frac{1}{2xy(3+y)}$
42. $\left(\frac{x-2}{2}\right)^2 \cdot \left(\frac{2}{2-x}\right)^3$ $\frac{2}{2-x}$
43. $\left(\frac{2n-1}{3}\right)^4 \cdot \left(\frac{9}{1-2n}\right)^2$ $(2n-1)^2$
44. $\frac{x^2 + 4x - 21}{x^2 - 6x - 16} \cdot \frac{x^2 - 8x + 15}{x^2 + 9x + 14}$ $\frac{(x-5)(x-3)^2}{(x-8)(x+2)^2}$
45. $\frac{4x^2 - 2ax}{x^2 - 4ax + 4a^2} \cdot \frac{(2a - x)^3}{2x - a}$ $2x(2a-x)$

46. $\dfrac{n^2 - 3n + 2}{n^2 + 3n + 2} \cdot \dfrac{8n + 8}{4n - 8}$ $\dfrac{2(n-1)}{n+2}$

47. $\dfrac{3c^2 - 9c + 6}{2c^2 - 10c + 12} \cdot \dfrac{6 - 2c}{3 - 3c}$ 1

48. $\left(\dfrac{x - y}{x + y}\right)^2 \cdot \dfrac{x^2 + y^2}{x^2 - y^2}$ $\dfrac{(x - y)(x^2 + y^2)}{(x + y)^3}$

49. $\dfrac{4a^2 - b^2}{4c^2 - d^2} \cdot \left(\dfrac{d - 2c}{b - 2a}\right)^2$ $\dfrac{(2a + b)(d - 2c)}{(b - 2a)(2c + d)}$

C 50. $\dfrac{4z^2 - 4}{1 + z^2} \cdot \dfrac{1 - z}{2z} \cdot \dfrac{1 - 2z^2 + z^4}{2 + 2z}$

51. $\dfrac{x^2 - x - 2}{x^2} \cdot \dfrac{x^2 + x - 2}{9x} \cdot \dfrac{54x^3}{x^4 - 5x^2 + 4}$

52. $\dfrac{x^3 + 3x^2 - 4x - 12}{2x^2 - 18} \cdot \dfrac{x^3 - 3x^2 + 3x - 9}{3x^3 - 12x}$

53. $\dfrac{a^2 - (b - c)^2}{2a - 2b + 2c} \cdot \dfrac{6a - 6b + 6c}{b^2 - (a - c)^2}$

54. Use the multiplication rule for fractions to derive the rule of exponents for the power of a quotient.

Computer Key-In

To find the prime numbers less than a given number N, you look for numbers that *do not* have factors other than 1 and N. Compare line 80 in the program given below with line 80 in the program given on page 186.

```
10  PRINT "TO FIND PRIME NUMBERS"
20  PRINT "LESS THAN N:"
30  PRINT "INPUT N";
40  INPUT N
45  PRINT "2 ";
50  FOR W=2 TO N
60  FOR F=2 TO W/2
70  LET Q=W/F
80  IF Q=INT(Q) THEN 140
110  NEXT F
130  PRINT W;" ";
140  NEXT W
150  END
```

Exercises

1. Why does the loop in the program above begin with 2 instead of 1? 1 is a factor of every integer.
2. Use the program to print the prime numbers less than 100, 500, and 1000.
3. FOR-NEXT loops can use numbers other than 1 as increments by specifying a STEP. Copy and RUN the following program, which will print the odd numbers from 1 to 25.

```
10  FOR N=1 TO 25 STEP 2
20  PRINT N;" ";
30  NEXT N
40  END
```

Additional Answers Written Exercises

50. $\dfrac{-(1 - z)^4(1 + z)^2}{z(1 + z^2)}$

51. 6

52. $\dfrac{x^2 + 3}{6x}$

53. $\dfrac{3(a - b + c)}{(b - a + c)}$

54. $\left(\dfrac{a}{b}\right)^n = \underbrace{\dfrac{a}{b} \times \dfrac{a}{b} \times \dfrac{a}{b} \times \cdots \times \dfrac{a}{b}}_{n \text{ factors}} =$

n factors

$\dfrac{\overbrace{a \times a \times a \times \cdots \times a}^{n \text{ factors}}}{\underbrace{b \times b \times b \times \cdots \times b}_{n \text{ factors}}} = \dfrac{a^n}{b^n}$

Mixed Review Exercises

1. The sum of the squares of two consecutive even integers is 340. Name the integers. -14 and -12 or 12 and 14
2. Cathy has a square garden with a 2 ft wide walk around it. The area of the walk is 136 ft^2. What are the dimensions of the garden? 15 ft by 15 ft
3. Solve: $-\dfrac{1}{7}m = -22$ $m = 154$
4. Express $\dfrac{10m^2 - 10n^2}{5m + 5n}$ in simplest form. $2(m - n)$

Teaching Suggestions
p. T100

Chalkboard Examples

Express in simplest form.

1. $\frac{5}{8} \div \frac{25}{24}$

   $\frac{\cancel{5}}{\cancel{8}} \cdot \frac{\overset{3}{\cancel{24}}}{\underset{5}{\cancel{25}}} = \frac{3}{5}$

2. $\frac{y^5}{21} \div \frac{y^3}{3}$

   $\frac{y^5}{\underset{7}{\cancel{21}}} \cdot \frac{\cancel{3}}{y^3} = \frac{y^2}{7}$

3. $\frac{5t - 10}{t - 5} \div \frac{t - 2}{10}$

   $\frac{5\cancel{(t-2)}}{t-5} \cdot \frac{10}{\cancel{t-2}} = \frac{50}{t-5}$

4. $\frac{y + 3}{2} \div \frac{y^2 - 9}{4}$

   $\frac{\cancel{y+3}}{\cancel{2}} \cdot \frac{\overset{2}{\cancel{4}}}{\cancel{(y+3)}(y-3)} = \frac{2}{y-3}$

5. $\frac{a^2}{b} \cdot \frac{2a}{b} \div \left(\frac{a}{b}\right)^3$

   $\frac{\cancel{a^2}}{\cancel{b}} \cdot \frac{2\cancel{a}}{\cancel{b}} \cdot \frac{\overset{b}{\cancel{b^3}}}{\cancel{a^3}} = 2b$

Supplementary Material

Test 20

6-3 Dividing Fractions

Objective To divide algebraic fractions.

The rule for division of real numbers states that to divide by a real number, you multiply by its reciprocal. For example,

$$\frac{5}{8} \div \frac{2}{9} = \frac{5}{8} \cdot \frac{9}{2} = \frac{45}{16}.$$

In algebra, division by fractions obeys the same rule.

Division Rule for Fractions

$$\frac{a}{b} \div \frac{c}{d} = \frac{a}{b} \cdot \frac{d}{c}$$

Example 1 Divide: $\frac{x^2 + 3x - 10}{2x + 6} \div \frac{x^2 - 4}{x^2 - x - 12}$

Solution

$$\frac{x^2 + 3x - 10}{2x + 6} \div \frac{x^2 - 4}{x^2 - x - 12} = \frac{x^2 + 3x - 10}{2x + 6} \cdot \frac{x^2 - x - 12}{x^2 - 4} \quad \text{Multiply by the reciprocal.}$$

$$= \frac{(x + 5)(x - 2)}{2(x + 3)} \cdot \frac{(x + 3)(x - 4)}{(x - 2)(x + 2)} \quad \text{Factor.}$$

$$= \frac{(x + 5)\cancel{(x - 2)}}{2\cancel{(x + 3)}} \cdot \frac{\cancel{(x + 3)}(x - 4)}{\cancel{(x - 2)}(x + 2)} \quad \text{Divide by common factors.}$$

$$= \frac{(x + 5)(x - 4)}{2(x + 2)}$$

When simplifying an expression that involves both multiplication and division, do the operations in order from left to right, unless parentheses indicate a different order. Remember that you can change each division sign to a multiplication sign if you replace the fraction immediately following the division sign by its reciprocal.

Example 2 Simplify $\frac{z}{z + 3} \div \frac{3z^2}{3z + 9} \cdot \frac{z^2 + 4z + 3}{z^2 - 9}$.

Solution

$$\frac{z}{z + 3} \div \frac{3z^2}{3z + 9} \cdot \frac{z^2 + 4z + 3}{z^2 - 9} = \frac{z}{z + 3} \cdot \frac{3z + 9}{3z^2} \cdot \frac{z^2 + 4z + 3}{z^2 - 9}$$

$$= \frac{\cancel{z}}{\cancel{z + 3}} \cdot \frac{\cancel{3}\cancel{(z + 3)}}{\cancel{3} \cdot \cancel{z} \cdot z} \cdot \frac{(z + 1)\cancel{(z + 3)}}{(z - 3)\cancel{(z + 3)}}$$

$$= \frac{z + 1}{z(z - 3)}$$

Oral Exercises

Simplify.

1. $\frac{2}{5} \div \frac{3}{5}$ $\quad \frac{2}{3}$
2. $\frac{2}{3} \div \frac{1}{4}$ $\quad \frac{8}{3}$
3. $\frac{1}{4} \div \frac{2}{3}$ $\quad \frac{3}{8}$
4. $-\frac{4}{7} \div \frac{2}{5}$ $\quad -\frac{10}{7}$
5. $\frac{a}{b} \div \frac{c}{d}$ $\quad \frac{ad}{bc}$
6. $\frac{x}{y} \div \frac{y}{x}$ $\quad \frac{x^2}{y^2}$
7. $2a \div \frac{a}{b}$ $\quad 2b$
8. $\frac{1}{bc} \div \frac{1}{b+c}$
9. $\frac{y^2}{3} \div \frac{y}{6}$ $\quad 2y$
10. $-\frac{x}{2} \div \frac{1}{x^2}$ $\quad -\frac{x^3}{2}$
11. $\frac{1}{2} \cdot \frac{1}{3} \div \frac{1}{4}$ $\quad \frac{2}{3}$
12. $\frac{a}{b} \div \frac{c}{d} \cdot \frac{e}{f}$

8. $\frac{b+c}{bc}$

12. $\frac{ade}{bcf}$

Written Exercises

8. $\frac{1}{ab}$

12. $\frac{n^3}{2}$

Divide. Express the answers in simplest form.

A

1. $\frac{5}{8} \div \frac{3}{4}$ $\quad \frac{5}{6}$
2. $\frac{2}{9} \div \frac{4}{3}$ $\quad \frac{1}{6}$
3. $\frac{a}{6} \div \frac{a}{3}$ $\quad \frac{1}{2}$
4. $\frac{x^2}{5} \div \frac{x}{15}$ $\quad 3x$
5. $\frac{ab}{3} \div \frac{b}{a}$ $\quad \frac{a^2}{3}$
6. $\frac{x}{2y} \div \frac{xy}{4}$ $\quad \frac{2}{y^2}$
7. $\frac{3n^2}{5} \div \frac{9n}{10}$ $\quad \frac{2n}{3}$
8. $\frac{a}{b^2} \div \frac{a^2}{b}$
9. $\frac{4x^2}{3y} \div (2x)$ $\quad \frac{2x}{3y}$
10. $\frac{9a^2}{2b} \div (6ab)$ $\quad \frac{3a}{4b^2}$
11. $1 \div \left(\frac{3x}{5}\right)^2$ $\quad \frac{25}{9x^2}$
12. $4 \div \left(\frac{2}{n}\right)^3$
13. $\frac{a+b}{3} \div \frac{2a+2b}{6}$ $\quad 1$
14. $\frac{x^2-1}{2} \div \frac{x-1}{4}$ $\quad 2(x+1)$
15. $\frac{2n-5}{4} \div \frac{6n-15}{8}$ $\quad \frac{2}{3}$
16. $\frac{a^2-b^2}{a^2+b^2} \div (a+b)$ $\quad \frac{a-b}{a^2+b^2}$
17. $\frac{a-b}{cd^2} \div \frac{ab}{c^2d}$ $\quad \frac{c(a-b)}{dab}$
18. $\frac{1}{8-2a} \div \frac{1}{3a-12}$ $\quad -\frac{3}{2}$
19. $\frac{3-3x}{3+3x} \div (x^2-1)$ $\quad \frac{-1}{(x+1)^2}$
20. $\frac{2x+2y}{x^2} \div \frac{x^2-y^2}{4x}$ $\quad \frac{8}{x(x-y)}$
21. $\frac{a^2+b^2}{c+d} \div \frac{5a+5b}{5c+5d}$
22. $\frac{3}{n^2-9} \div \frac{3n-9}{n+3}$ $\quad \frac{1}{(n-3)^2}$
23. $\frac{3-3n}{n^2+2n-3} \div (2n-2)$ $\quad -\frac{3}{2(n+3)(n-1)}$
24. $\frac{x^2-4}{x^2-x-6} \div (2-x)$

21. $\frac{a^2+b^2}{a+b}$ $\quad$ 24. $-\frac{1}{x-3}$

Simplify.

25. a. $\frac{1}{2} \div \frac{1}{5} \cdot \frac{3}{4}$ $\quad \frac{15}{8}$
    b. $\frac{1}{2} \div \left(\frac{1}{5} \cdot \frac{3}{4}\right)$ $\quad \frac{10}{3}$
    c. $\frac{r}{5} \div \frac{t}{r} \cdot \frac{5}{t^2}$ $\quad \frac{r^2}{t^3}$
26. a. $\frac{3}{8} \cdot \left(\frac{2}{3} \div \frac{1}{4}\right)$ $\quad 1$
    b. $\frac{3}{8} \cdot \frac{2}{3} \div \frac{1}{4}$ $\quad 1$
    c. $\frac{x}{y^2} \cdot \frac{2}{x^2} \div \frac{x}{y}$ $\quad \frac{2}{x^2y}$
27. a. $\left(\frac{n}{2}\right)^2 \div \frac{n}{4} \cdot \frac{n}{3}$ $\quad \frac{n^2}{3}$
    b. $\left(\frac{n}{2}\right)^2 \div \left(\frac{n}{4} \cdot \frac{n}{3}\right)$ $\quad 3$
    c. $\left(\frac{n}{2}\right)^2 \div \left(\frac{n}{4}\right)^2$ $\quad 4$
28. a. $\left(\frac{x}{y}\right)^3 \div \frac{x}{2y} \cdot \frac{x}{4y}$ $\quad \frac{x^3}{2y^3}$
    b. $\left(\frac{x}{y}\right)^3 \div \left(\frac{x}{2y} \cdot \frac{x}{4y}\right)$ $\quad \frac{8x}{y}$
    c. $\left(\frac{x}{y}\right)^3 \div \left(\frac{x}{2y}\right)^3$ $\quad 8$

B

29. $2a^2 \div 3a^3 \div 4a^4$ $\quad \frac{1}{6a^5}$
30. $\frac{6n}{6n-14} \div \frac{21}{9n-21} \div \frac{n^2}{35}$ $\quad \frac{15}{n}$

Suggested Assignments

Minimum
Day 1: 249/1–27 odd
S 246/41–44
Day 2: 249/2–20 even, 29–32
R 250/*Self-Test 1*

Average
249/1–37 odd
S 247/46–48
R 250/*Self-Test 1*

Maximum
249/5–41 odd
R 250/*Self-Test 1*

Additional A Exercises

Divide. Express the answers in simplest form.

1. $\frac{4}{5} \div \frac{8}{25}$ $\quad \frac{5}{2}$
2. $\frac{8m^3}{n^2} \div 4m^2$ $\quad \frac{2m}{n^2}$
3. $\frac{c+d}{ab^3} \div \frac{c^2-d^2}{a^2b}$ $\quad \frac{a}{b^2(c-d)}$
4. $\frac{3x-3y}{2x^2} \div \frac{x^2-2xy+y^2}{4x^3}$ $\quad \frac{6x}{x-y}$
5. $\frac{6-2n}{6+n-n^2} \div (n+2)$ $\quad \frac{2}{(n+2)^2}$

Simplify.

6. a. $\frac{4}{5} \div \left(\frac{1}{4} \cdot \frac{2}{3}\right)$ $\quad \frac{24}{5}$
   b. $\frac{4}{5} \div \frac{1}{4} \cdot \frac{2}{3}$ $\quad \frac{32}{15}$
   c. $\frac{a}{b} \div \frac{1}{b} \cdot \frac{b}{c}$ $\quad \frac{ab}{c}$

Mixed Review Exercises

Express in simplest form.

1. $\frac{-9}{5} - \frac{3}{5} + 3$ $\frac{3}{5}$
2. $(-14x + 10) + (14x - 3)$ 7
3. $\frac{(4a)^3}{6b^2}\left(\frac{b}{a}\right)^2$ $\frac{32a}{3}$
4. Jim sold both \$3 adult and \$2 student tickets to the Senior Follies. He sold 20 tickets altogether and collected \$45. How many of each kind did he sell? 5 adult, 15 student

Quick Quiz

Express in simplest form.

1. $\frac{y^2 - 4}{y^2 + 5y + 6}$ $\frac{y - 2}{y + 3}$
2. $\frac{k^2 + 6k + 5}{k^2 + 3k + 2}$ $\frac{k + 5}{k + 2}$
3. $\frac{s^2 - t^2}{3s^2} \cdot \frac{(st)^2}{st^2 + t^3}$ $\frac{s - t}{3}$
4. $\frac{k^2 + 3k + 2}{k + 3} \cdot \frac{k^2 + 4k + 3}{k^2 + 2k + 1}$ $k + 2$
5. $\frac{m^2 - 9}{m + 1} \div \frac{m^2 - 6m + 9}{m^2 - 2m - 3}$ $m + 3$
6. $\frac{x^2 - y^2}{3 - x} \div \frac{x^4 - y^4}{x^2 - 6x + 9}$ $\frac{3 - x}{x^2 + y^2}$

Simplify.

31. $\frac{4x^2 - 25}{x^2 - 16} \div \frac{12x + 30}{2x^2 + 8x}$ $\frac{x(2x - 5)}{3(x - 4)}$

32. $\frac{2x - y}{2y - x} \div \frac{4x^2 - y^2}{4y^2 - x^2}$ $\frac{2y + x}{2x + y}$

33. $\frac{a^4 - b^4}{3a - 3b} \div \frac{a^2 + b^2}{3}$ $a + b$

34. $\frac{8 - 2x^4}{3x^4} \div \frac{2 + x^2}{6x^2}$ $\frac{4(2 - x^2)}{x^2}$

35. $\frac{c - d}{c + 2d} \cdot \frac{2d + c}{d + c} \div \frac{d - c}{d + c}$ -1

36. $\frac{r^2}{r^2 - s^2} \cdot \frac{r - s}{r + s} \div \left(\frac{r}{r + s}\right)^2$ 1

37. $\left(\frac{3n - 5}{4}\right)^3 \div \left(\frac{5 - 3n}{2}\right)^4$ $-\frac{1}{4(5 - 3n)}$

38. $\frac{4a - 6}{9} \div \left(\frac{3 - 2a}{3}\right)^2$ $-\frac{2}{3 - 2a}$

C 39. $\frac{s^2 - 2s}{s^2 - 3s - 4} \cdot \frac{s^2 - 25}{s^2 - 4s - 5} \div \frac{s^2 + 5s}{5s^2 + 10s + 5}$ $\frac{5(s - 2)}{s - 4}$

40. $\frac{b^2 + 6b - 7}{6b^2 - 7b - 20} \cdot \frac{2b^2 + b - 15}{b^2 + 2b - 3} \div \frac{b^2 + 5b - 14}{3b^2 - 2b - 8}$ 1

41. $\frac{a^3 + 5a^2 - 9a - 45}{2a^2 - 9a + 9} \div \frac{a^2 + 10a + 25}{12 - 14a + 4a^2} \cdot \frac{a + 5}{a^2 - 4a + 4}$ $\frac{2(a + 3)}{a - 2}$

42. $\frac{x^2 - 6xy + 9y^2 - 9}{x^4 - 81y^4} \cdot \frac{3x - 9y}{3x - 9y + 9} \div \frac{x - 3y - 3}{3x^2 + 27y^2}$ $\frac{3}{x + 3y}$

Self-Test 1

Express in simplest form, noting any restrictions on the variable.

1. $\frac{-3a^2 + 6a}{a^2 - 2a}$ $-3;\ a \neq 0,\ a \neq 2$

2. $\frac{4a^2 - 9}{6a^2 + 13a + 6}$ $\frac{2a - 3}{3a + 2};\ a \neq -\frac{3}{2},\ a \neq -\frac{2}{3}$

Obj. 6-1, p. 239

Express in simplest form.

3. $\frac{-3b}{4a^2c} \cdot \frac{-5a}{45b^3}$ $\frac{1}{12ab^2c}$

4. $\left(\frac{2x}{3}\right)^3 \cdot \frac{27}{48x}$ $\frac{x^2}{6}$

Obj. 6-2, p. 244

5. $\frac{1}{56 - 8a} \div \frac{1}{4a - 28}$ $-\frac{1}{2}$

6. $\frac{2}{15}\left(\frac{1}{4r} \div \frac{r}{10}\right)$ $\frac{1}{3r^2}$

Obj. 6-3, p. 248

Check your answers with those at the back of the book.

Challenge

The following problem is from the Egyptian Rhind papyrus:

There are seven houses; in each are seven cats. Each cat kills seven mice. Each mouse would have eaten seven ears of spelt [wheat]. Each ear of spelt will produce seven hekats of grain. What is the total of these? [That is, how much grain was saved?] 7^5, or 16,807, hekats of grain

Adding and Subtracting Fractions

6-4 Least Common Denominators

Objective To express two or more fractions with their least common denominator.

The cancellation rule for fractions states that if $c \neq 0$

$$\frac{cx}{cy} = \frac{x}{y}.$$

This rule enables you to express a fraction in simpler form by dividing its numerator and denominator by the same nonzero number. Using the symmetric property of equality you can rewrite this rule as

$$\frac{x}{y} = \frac{cx}{cy} \quad (c \neq 0).$$

In this form, it enables you to express a fraction in a different form by multiplying its numerator and denominator by the same number.

Example 1 $\frac{5}{8} = \frac{?}{24}$ ← 8 must be multiplied by 3 to get 24.

$\frac{5}{8} = \frac{5 \cdot 3}{8 \cdot 3} = \frac{15}{24}$ ← Therefore, multiply 5 by 3 to get 15.

Example 2 $\frac{7}{3c} = \frac{?}{12c^2}$ ← $3c$ must be multiplied by $4c$ to get $12c^2$.

$\frac{7}{3c} = \frac{28c}{12c^2}$ ← Therefore, multiply 7 by $4c$ to get $28c$.

Example 3 $\frac{5}{x-7} = \frac{?}{(x-7)(x+3)}$ ← $(x - 7)$ must be multiplied by $(x + 3)$ to get $(x - 7)(x + 3)$.

$\frac{5}{x-7} = \frac{5(x+3)}{(x-7)(x+3)}$ ← Therefore, multiply 5 by $(x + 3)$.

The technique shown in the examples above is used to rewrite two or more fractions so that they have equal denominators. For example, you can express $\frac{1}{4}$ and $\frac{5}{6}$ as fractions having a common denominator of 12, 24, 36, or any other positive *multiple* of 12. (The product of a number and an integer is called a **multiple** of the number.) Usually, it is convenient to use the **least common denominator (LCD)** of the fractions. To determine the least common denominator of several fractions, find the **least common multiple** of the denominators.

Teaching Suggestions
p. T100

Suggested Extensions
p. T101

Chalkboard Examples

Find the missing numerator.

1. $\frac{3}{8} = \frac{?}{32}$ 12

2. $\frac{x+1}{3} = \frac{?}{15}$ $5x + 5$

3. $\frac{t}{3-t} = \frac{?}{t^2-9}$ $-t^2 - 3t$

Find the LCD for each group of fractions.

4. $\frac{3}{5}, \frac{5}{8}, \frac{5}{12}$ 120

5. $\frac{2k-1}{15}, \frac{k-3}{12}$ 60

6. $\frac{3}{a^2b}, \frac{5}{6ab^3}, \frac{1}{10ab}$ $30a^2b^3$

7. $\frac{a}{3a+9b}, \frac{ab}{a^2-9b^2}$ $3a + 9b = 3(a + 3b)$; $a^2 - 9b^2 = (a + 3b) \cdot (a - 3b)$; LCD is $3(a + 3b)(a - 3b) = 3a^2 - 27b^2$.

Common Error

Some students think that the LCD of a group of fractions is the product of the denominators of the fractions. Emphasize that it frequently is not and that they should factor denominators such as $x^2 - 1$ before trying to decide on the LCD.

Supplementary Materials

Practice Master 34
Resource Book, p. 90

Finding the Least Common Denominator

1. Factor each denominator into primes.
2. Form the product of the greatest power of each prime factor occurring in the denominators.

Example 4 What is the LCD of the fractions $\frac{3}{25}$, $\frac{11}{30}$, and $\frac{7}{40}$?

Solution

1. Factor each denominator into primes.

$$25 = 5^2 \qquad 30 = 2 \cdot 3 \cdot 5 \qquad 40 = 2^3 \cdot 5$$

2. Greatest power of 2: 2^3
   Greatest power of 3: 3^1
   Greatest power of 5: 5^2

$$2^3 \cdot 3^1 \cdot 5^2 = 600$$

$\therefore$ the LCD is 600. ***Answer***

When the denominators of the fractions contain variables, the LCD will be the simplest of the common multiples of the denominators.

Example 5 What is the LCD of $\frac{3}{5x - 20}$ and $\frac{8}{9x - 36}$?

Solution

1. Factor each denominator completely.

$$5x - 20 = 5(x - 4)$$
$$9x - 36 = 3^2(x - 4)$$

2. Form the product of the greatest power of each prime factor.

$$3^2 \cdot 5(x - 4) = 45(x - 4)$$

$\therefore$ the LCD is $45(x - 4)$. ***Answer***

Example 6 Express $\frac{5}{c^2 + 2c - 15}$ and $\frac{9}{c^2 - 6c + 9}$ with their least common denominator.

Solution Since $c^2 + 2c - 15 = (c + 5)(c - 3)$ and $c^2 - 6c + 9 = (c - 3)^2$, the LCD is $(c + 5)(c - 3)^2$.

$$\frac{5}{c^2 + 2c - 15} = \frac{5}{(c + 5)(c - 3)} = \frac{5(c - 3)}{(c + 5)(c - 3)(c - 3)} = \frac{5(c - 3)}{(c + 5)(c - 3)^2}$$

$$\frac{9}{c^2 - 6c + 9} = \frac{9}{(c - 3)^2} = \frac{9(c + 5)}{(c - 3)^2(c + 5)} = \frac{9(c + 5)}{(c + 5)(c - 3)^2}$$

Oral Exercises

Find the missing numerator.

1. $\frac{2}{5} = \frac{?}{10}$ 4
2. $\frac{3}{8} = \frac{?}{40}$ 15
3. $\frac{x}{7} = \frac{?}{21}$ 3x
4. $\frac{a}{3} = \frac{?}{12}$ 4a
5. $\frac{2x}{3} = \frac{?}{9}$ 6x
6. $\frac{a}{b} = \frac{?}{b^2}$ ab
7. $\frac{5}{2n} = \frac{?}{6n^2}$ 15n
8. $\frac{1}{ab} = \frac{?}{a^2b^3}$ ab^2
9. $\frac{3}{x-1} = \frac{?}{(x-1)(x+2)}$ 3(x + 2)
10. $\frac{4}{n+2} = \frac{?}{n^2-4}$ 4(n − 2)

Find the LCD for each group of fractions.

11. $\frac{1}{4}, \frac{5}{6}$ 12
12. $\frac{3}{8}, \frac{4}{7}$ 56
13. $\frac{5}{18}, \frac{5}{12}$ 36
14. $\frac{1}{2}, \frac{1}{3}, \frac{1}{4}$ 12
15. $\frac{2}{x}, \frac{3}{xy}$ xy
16. $\frac{4}{ab}, \frac{3}{a^2}$ a^2b
17. $\frac{1}{n-2}, \frac{3}{2-n}$ n − 2
18. $\frac{2}{3a-b}, \frac{5}{6a-2b}$ 2(3a − b)
19. $\frac{4}{x^2-1}, \frac{3}{x+1}, \frac{7}{x-1}$ (x − 1)(x + 1)
20. $\frac{2y}{(y-3)^2}, \frac{y^2}{5(y-3)(y+1)}$ $5(y-3)^2(y+1)$

Written Exercises

4. 12a
8. 5(2x − y)

Find the missing numerator.

A

1. $\frac{3}{7} = \frac{?}{35}$ 15
2. $\frac{4}{9} = \frac{?}{27}$ 12
3. $\frac{2x}{5} = \frac{?}{15}$ 6x
4. $\frac{4a}{13} = \frac{?}{39}$
5. $\frac{x-3}{4} = \frac{?}{12}$ 3(x − 3)
6. $\frac{2n-5}{5} = \frac{?}{25}$ 5(2n − 5)
7. $\frac{4-a}{4} = \frac{?}{20}$ 5(4 − a)
8. $\frac{2x-y}{9} = \frac{?}{45}$
9. $\frac{a}{b} = \frac{?}{a^2b}$ a^3
10. $\frac{x}{2y} = \frac{?}{6xy}$ $3x^2$
11. $\frac{2n}{3m} = \frac{?}{6m^2n}$ $4mn^2$
12. $\frac{7}{2a} = \frac{?}{8a^3}$ $28a^2$
13. $\frac{5}{2n-3} = \frac{?}{(2n-3)^2}$ 5(2n − 3)
14. $\frac{4}{a-1} = \frac{?}{2a-2}$ 8
15. $\frac{4}{a-1} = \frac{?}{1-a}$ −4
16. $\frac{6}{2x-5} = \frac{?}{10-4x}$ −12
17. $\frac{2}{x+1} = \frac{?}{x^2-1}$ 2(x − 1)
18. $\frac{5}{n-3} = \frac{?}{n^2-9}$ 5(n + 3)
19. $\frac{3}{y-2} = \frac{?}{y^2-2y}$ 3y
20. $\frac{x}{x+5} = \frac{?}{x^2+5x}$ x^2
21. $\frac{6}{x+1} = \frac{?}{x^2+3x+2}$ 6(x + 2)
22. $\frac{7}{a+b} = \frac{?}{a^2+2ab+b^2}$ 7(a + b)
23. $\frac{1}{x-5} = \frac{?}{2x^2-50}$ 2(x + 5)
24. $\frac{3}{2-a} = \frac{?}{8-2a^2}$ 6(2 + a)

Find the LCD for each group of fractions.

25. $\frac{1}{6}, \frac{5}{9}$ 18
26. $\frac{3}{8}, \frac{2}{5}, \frac{4}{3}$ 120
27. $\frac{1}{3}, \frac{2}{9}, \frac{3}{4}$ 36
28. $\frac{2}{5}, \frac{3}{7}, \frac{1}{10}$ 70
29. $\frac{1}{2}, \frac{2}{3}, \frac{3}{4}$ 12
30. $\frac{n-3}{20}, \frac{n+4}{15}$ 60

Suggested Assignments

Minimum
253/2–36 even

Average
253/2–44 even
S 250/32–38 even

Maximum
253/6–32 even, 34–37
S 250/40, 42

Additional A Exercises

Find the missing numerator.

1. $\frac{7a}{8} = \frac{?}{16}$ 14a
2. $\frac{4y-z}{12} = \frac{?}{36}$ 12y − 3z
3. $\frac{9}{z+4} = \frac{?}{3z+12}$ 27
4. $\frac{10}{m+6} = \frac{?}{m^2-36}$ 10m − 60
5. $\frac{j}{j-8} = \frac{?}{10j-80}$ 10j

Find the LCD.

6. $\frac{a-6}{36}, \frac{a+3}{42}$ 252

Mixed Review Exercises

1. Solve $x^2 - 3 = 22$ if $x \in \{5, 6, 7, 8, 9, 10\}$. {5}
2. Simplify: 25 × 75 × 4 7500
3. Solve for *s*: $\frac{1}{3}qst^2 = R$ $s = \frac{3R}{qt^2}$
4. List all pairs of integral factors of 124. 1, 124; 2, 62; 4, 31; −1, −124; −2, −62; −4, −31

Find the LCD for each group of fractions.

39. $2(x-1)(x+1)$
42. $2(x-2)(x+2)$

31. $\frac{3x+2}{8}, \frac{x-4}{12}$ 24

32. $\frac{2a-b}{4}, \frac{2a+b}{6}$ 12

33. $\frac{2-y}{20}, \frac{y+3}{25}$ 100

B 34. $\frac{1}{3n^2m}, \frac{2}{nm^2}$ $3n^2m^2$

35. $\frac{1}{x-2}, \frac{-3}{6-3x}$ $3(x-2)$

36. $\frac{3}{4x-2y}, \frac{5}{y-2x}$ $2(2x-y)$

37. $\frac{5}{8x^2}, \frac{4}{3xy}, \frac{1}{16y^3}$ $48x^2y^3$

38. $\frac{9}{a+b}, \frac{4}{a}, \frac{3}{b}$ $ab(a+b)$

39. $\frac{1}{x-1}, \frac{2}{x+1}, \frac{3}{2x^2-2}$

40. $\frac{1}{2xy}, \frac{3}{x^2}$ $2x^2y$

41. $\frac{3}{4a^2b}, \frac{5}{8b^2}$ $8a^2b^2$

42. $\frac{3x}{2x-4}, \frac{1}{x^2-4}$

43. $\frac{1}{y^2-3y}, \frac{1}{y^2+3y}$ $y(y-3)(y+3)$

44. $\frac{3}{x^2-x-2}, \frac{1}{x^2-4}$ $(x-2)(x+1)(x+2)$

45. $\frac{a^2}{a-1}, \frac{a}{a+1}, \frac{1}{a^2-1}$ $(a-1)(a+1)$

C 46. $\frac{1}{16a^4-16b^4}, \frac{y+3}{(2a-2b)^2}$ $2^4(a-b)^2(a+b)(a^2+b^2)$

47. $\frac{y+3}{y^2+6y+8}, \frac{-5}{3y^2+21y+36}, \frac{7y}{4y+12}$ $12(y+2)(y+3)(y+4)$

48. The product of the first n positive integers, denoted by $n!$, is called ***n* factorial.**
   a. Find 4!, 5!, and 6!. 24; 120; 720
   b. What is the LCD of the fractions $\frac{1}{4!}, \frac{1}{5!}$, and $\frac{1}{6!}$? 6!
   c. What is the LCD of the fractions $\frac{1}{n!}$ and $\frac{1}{(n+1)!}$? $(n+1)!$
   d. True or false? $(n!)^2 = (n^2)!$ false

Computer Exercises

For students with some programming experience

In the Computer Exercises on pages 140–141, you wrote a BASIC program to compute $n!$ for a value of n entered with an INPUT statement.

1. Write a BASIC program to find the following.

Answers may vary slightly.

$1 + \frac{1}{1!} + \frac{1}{2!}$ 2.5

$1 + \frac{1}{1!} + \frac{1}{2!} + \frac{1}{3!}$ 2.6666667

$1 + \frac{1}{1!} + \frac{1}{2!} + \frac{1}{3!} + \frac{1}{4!}$ 2.7083333

$1 + \frac{1}{1!} + \frac{1}{2!} + \frac{1}{3!} + \frac{1}{4!} + \frac{1}{5!}$ 2.7166667

$1 + \frac{1}{1!} + \frac{1}{2!} + \frac{1}{3!} + \frac{1}{4!} + \frac{1}{5!} + \frac{1}{6!}$ 2.7180556

$1 + \frac{1}{1!} + \frac{1}{2!} + \frac{1}{3!} + \frac{1}{4!} + \frac{1}{5!} + \frac{1}{6!} + \frac{1}{7!}$ 2.718254

2. Based upon your results from Exercise 1 guess what happens to the sum $1 + \frac{1}{1!} + \frac{1}{2!} + \frac{1}{3!} + \cdots + \frac{1}{n!}$ as n becomes larger and larger.
approaches 2.7182818

6-5 Adding and Subtracting Fractions

Objective To add and subtract algebraic fractions.

The results proved in Exercises 30 and 31 on page 83 can be used to show how to add and subtract fractions with the same denominator. Rewriting those results using the symmetric property of equality gives the following rules.

Addition Rule for Fractions

$$\frac{a}{c} + \frac{b}{c} = \frac{a + b}{c}$$

Subtraction Rule for Fractions

$$\frac{a}{c} - \frac{b}{c} = \frac{a - b}{c}$$

To add fractions with the same denominator, you add their numerators. To subtract fractions with the same denominator, you subtract their numerators.

Example 1 $\frac{5a}{7} + \frac{3a}{7} = \frac{5a + 3a}{7} = \frac{8a}{7}$

Example 2 $\frac{5x + 7}{9} - \frac{2x - 5}{9} + \frac{11x}{9} = \frac{(5x + 7) - (2x - 5) + 11x}{9}$

$$= \frac{5x + 7 - 2x + 5 + 11x}{9}$$

$$= \frac{14x + 12}{9} = \frac{2(7x + 6)}{9}$$

To add or subtract fractions with different denominators, you must first express the fractions with a common denominator.

Example 3 $\frac{2x - 3}{16} - \frac{2 - x}{8} + \frac{3x}{4} = \frac{2x - 3}{16} - \frac{2(2 - x)}{16} + \frac{12x}{16}$

$$= \frac{(2x - 3) - 2(2 - x) + 12x}{16}$$

$$= \frac{2x - 3 - 4 + 2x + 12x}{16}$$

$$= \frac{16x - 7}{16}$$

Teaching Suggestions
p. T101

Suggested Extensions
p. T101

Chalkboard Examples

Simplify.

1. $\frac{8}{3b} - \frac{5}{3b} + \frac{9}{3b}$ $\frac{4}{b}$

2. $\frac{6t - 1}{8} - \frac{5t + 4}{8}$ $\frac{t - 5}{8}$

3. $\frac{4y - 2}{y - 5} - \frac{3y + 1}{5 - y}$
$\frac{4y - 2}{y - 5} + \frac{3y + 1}{y - 5} =$
$\frac{7y - 1}{y - 5}$

4. $\frac{3}{z + 1} + \frac{z - 3}{z^2 - 1}$
$\frac{3(z - 1)}{(z + 1)(z - 1)} +$
$\frac{z - 3}{(z + 1)(z - 1)} =$
$\frac{3z - 3 + z - 3}{(z + 1)(z - 1)} =$
$\frac{4z - 6}{(z + 1)(z - 1)} =$
$\frac{2(2z - 3)}{(z + 1)(z - 1)}$

5. $\frac{n}{n + 3} + \frac{n + 1}{n^2 + 8n + 15}$
$\frac{n(n + 5)}{(n + 3)(n + 5)} +$
$\frac{n + 1}{(n + 3)(n + 5)} =$
$\frac{n^2 + 5n + n + 1}{(n + 3)(n + 5)} =$
$\frac{n^2 + 6n + 1}{(n + 3)(n + 5)}$

Common Error

Many students make errors when subtracting algebraic expressions because they think of $-\frac{2-x}{8}$, for example, as $\frac{-2-x}{8}$. Remind them that the fraction bar is a grouping symbol. Thus, $-\frac{2-x}{8} = \frac{-(2-x)}{8} = \frac{-2+x}{8}$.

Suggested Assignments

Minimum
Day 1: 256/1–25 odd
S 254/31–41 odd
Day 2: 257/28, 29, 32–41
R 258/*Self-Test 2*

Average
Day 1: 256/1–35 odd
S 241/51, 52, 55
Day 2: 257/18, 20, 22, 38–50

Maximum
Day 1: 256/1–35 odd
S 241/52–54
Day 2: 258/38–54
R 258/*Self-Test 2*

Additional A Exercises

Simplify.

1. $\frac{6}{b} - \frac{4}{b} + \frac{13}{b}$ $\frac{15}{b}$
2. $\frac{d}{d-4} + \frac{6}{d-4} - \frac{7-d}{d-4}$ $\frac{2d-1}{d-4}$
3. $\frac{4}{k-3} - \frac{6}{3-k}$ $\frac{10}{k-3}$
4. $\frac{12}{mn^3} + \frac{11}{m^2n}$ $\frac{12m+11n^2}{m^2n^3}$
5. $\frac{3x-4}{4x^3} + \frac{6}{x^2}$ $\frac{27x-4}{4x^3}$
6. $\frac{6n-3}{15} - \frac{4n+3}{10}$ $\frac{-1}{2}$

To simplify an expression involving fractions means to express it as a fraction in simplest form.

Example 4 Simplify $\frac{a+10}{a^2-2a} + \frac{2}{a} - \frac{6}{a-2}$.

Solution

$$\frac{a+10}{a^2-2a} + \frac{2}{a} - \frac{6}{a-2} = \frac{a+10}{a(a-2)} + \frac{2}{a} - \frac{6}{a-2}$$
$$= \frac{a+10}{a(a-2)} + \frac{2(a-2)}{a(a-2)} - \frac{6a}{a(a-2)}$$
$$= \frac{(a+10) + 2(a-2) - 6a}{a(a-2)}$$
$$= \frac{a+10+2a-4-6a}{a(a-2)}$$
$$= \frac{-3a+6}{a(a-2)} = \frac{-3\cancel{(a-2)}}{a\cancel{(a-2)}} = -\frac{3}{a}$$

Oral Exercises

Simplify.

1. $\frac{4}{5} + \frac{3}{5}$ $\frac{7}{5}$
2. $\frac{7}{9} - \frac{4}{9}$ $\frac{1}{3}$
3. $\frac{x}{6} + \frac{2x}{6}$ $\frac{x}{2}$
4. $\frac{5a}{8} - \frac{a}{8}$ $\frac{a}{2}$
5. $\frac{4}{x} - \frac{1}{x}$ $\frac{3}{x}$
6. $\frac{7}{2x} + \frac{3}{2x}$ $\frac{5}{x}$
7. $\frac{4}{1+x} + \frac{x}{1+x}$
8. $\frac{n}{n-2} - \frac{1}{n-2}$
9. $\frac{3}{x-5} - \frac{1}{5-x}$
10. $\frac{4}{a-b} + \frac{1}{b-a}$
11. $\frac{1}{a} + \frac{1}{a^2}$ $\frac{a+1}{a^2}$
12. $\frac{3}{n^3} - \frac{1}{n}$ $\frac{3-n^2}{n^3}$
13. $\frac{x}{2} + \frac{x}{8}$ $\frac{5x}{8}$
14. $\frac{2x}{2} - \frac{x+1}{2}$ $\frac{x-1}{2}$
15. $\frac{4y}{3} - \frac{2y-5}{3}$ $\frac{2y+5}{3}$
16. $\frac{n^2}{5} - \frac{n^2-3n+2}{5}$ $\frac{3n-2}{5}$

Written Exercises

Simplify.

A

1. $\frac{2}{n} + \frac{3}{n} - \frac{4}{n}$ $\frac{1}{n}$
2. $\frac{5}{3x} + \frac{9}{3x} - \frac{2}{3x}$ $\frac{4}{x}$
3. $\frac{8}{2a} - \frac{9}{2a} + \frac{3}{2a}$ $\frac{1}{a}$
4. $\frac{a}{5} - \frac{2a+3}{5}$ $\frac{-a-3}{5}$
5. $\frac{2x}{3} - \frac{x-1}{3}$ $\frac{x+1}{3}$
6. $\frac{y-3}{4} - \frac{3y-5}{4}$ $\frac{1-y}{2}$
7. $\frac{x+4}{2} - \frac{3x+6}{2}$ $-x-1$
8. $\frac{x}{x-5} + \frac{1}{x-5} - \frac{10-x}{x-5}$ $\frac{2x-9}{x-5}$
9. $\frac{1}{n-2} - \frac{3n-2}{n-2} + \frac{n}{n-2}$ $\frac{3-2n}{n-2}$
10. $\frac{3}{x-5} - \frac{2}{5-x}$ $\frac{5}{x-5}$
11. $\frac{4}{2y-7} - \frac{1}{7-2y}$ $\frac{5}{2y-7}$
12. $\frac{4a}{a-b} + \frac{4b}{b-a}$ 4

18. $\frac{4+5x}{5(x+1)}$ 24. $\frac{2x-1}{15}$

13. $\frac{2}{x}+\frac{3}{x^2}$ $\frac{2x+3}{x^2}$

14. $\frac{5}{ab}-\frac{3}{ab^2}$ $\frac{5b-3}{ab^2}$

15. $\frac{4}{3x}-\frac{1}{6x^2}$ $\frac{8x-1}{6x^2}$

16. $\frac{1}{2ab}-\frac{5}{6a}$ $\frac{3-5b}{6ab}$

17. $\frac{2n-1}{2n^3}+\frac{5}{n^2}$ $\frac{12n-1}{2n^3}$

18. $\frac{4}{5(x+1)}+\frac{x}{x+1}$

19. $\frac{x-1}{2}+\frac{2x-3}{6}$ $\frac{5x-6}{6}$

20. $\frac{2b-3}{4}+\frac{b-5}{6}$ $\frac{8b-19}{12}$

21. $\frac{3y-2}{6}-\frac{y-3}{9}$ $\frac{7y}{18}$

22. $\frac{a-6}{15}-\frac{4-a}{10}$ $\frac{5a-24}{30}$

23. $\frac{2x+4}{5}-\frac{x}{6}+\frac{3x-2}{10}$ $\frac{8x+9}{15}$

24. $\frac{x-3}{5}-\frac{x+2}{15}+\frac{2}{3}$

25. $\frac{5n-2}{12}-\frac{3(n-3)}{8}$ $\frac{n+23}{24}$

26. $\frac{3(a-b)}{20}-\frac{5(a+b)}{12}$ $\frac{-8a-17b}{30}$

27. $\frac{2a-b}{3}-\frac{b}{6}-\frac{2b-3a}{4}$ $\frac{17a-12b}{12}$

Find the perimeter and the area of each figure.

B 28.

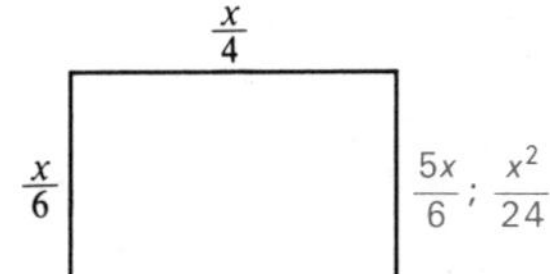

$\frac{5x}{6}$; $\frac{x^2}{24}$

29.

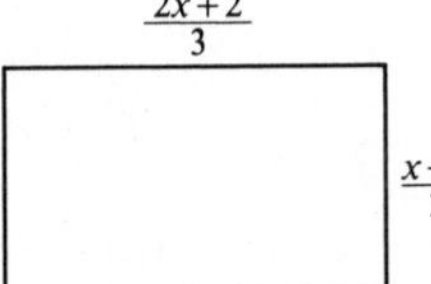

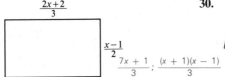

$\frac{7x+1}{3}$; $\frac{(x+1)(x-1)}{3}$

30.

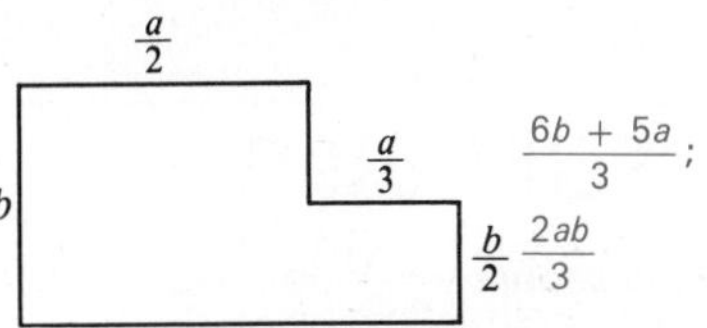

$\frac{6b+5a}{3}$; $\frac{2ab}{3}$

31.

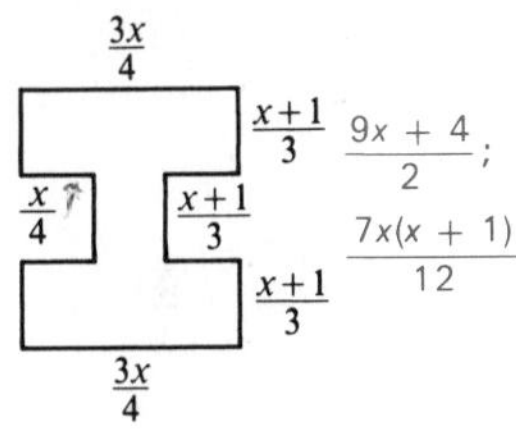

$\frac{9x+4}{2}$; $\frac{7x(x+1)}{12}$

Simplify.

34. $\frac{4a+7}{(a-2)(a+1)}$ 37. $-\frac{y(y+3)}{(y-5)(y+5)}$

32. $\frac{1}{x-1}+\frac{1}{x}$ $\frac{2x-1}{x(x-1)}$

33. $\frac{2}{x-3}+\frac{4}{x+3}$ $\frac{6(x-1)}{(x-3)(x+3)}$

34. $\frac{5}{a-2}-\frac{1}{a+1}$

35. $\frac{4}{x+1}-\frac{1}{x-2}$ $\frac{3(x-3)}{(x+1)(x-2)}$

36. $\frac{x}{x^2-1}+\frac{4}{x+1}$ $\frac{5x-4}{(x-1)(x+1)}$

37. $\frac{2y}{y^2-25}-\frac{y}{y-5}$

Mixed Review Exercises

Express in simplest form.

1. $\frac{5a^2}{3b}\div 25a^3b^2$ $\frac{1}{15ab^3}$

2. $\frac{m^2-n^2}{5m+5n}\div(n-m)$ $\frac{-1}{5}$

3. Factor: $px^2+x^3+pt+xt$ $(x^2+t)(p+x)$

4. Find the missing numerator:
$\frac{3}{a+b}=\frac{?}{a^2+2ab+b^2}$
$3(a+b)$, or $3a+3b$

Additional Answers
Oral Exercises

7. $\frac{4+x}{1+x}$

8. $\frac{n-1}{n-2}$

9. $\frac{4}{x-5}$

10. $\frac{3}{a-b}$

EXAMPLE

$\frac{1}{3X-6}+\frac{1}{6X}-\frac{1}{2X+4}$

ANSWER

$\frac{5X-2}{3X(X-2)(X+2)}$

Additional Answers
Written Exercises

43. $\frac{z^2 + z - 1}{z(1 - z)(1 + z)}$

44. $\frac{n^2 + 25}{n(n + 5)^3}$

45. $\frac{a + b}{ab}$

46. $\frac{2a}{(a + 2)^2(a - 2)}$

47. $\frac{4}{(n - 5)(n + 5)}$

48. $-\frac{2}{(b + 3)(b - 3)}$

49. $\frac{3(3c + 2)}{(c + 2)^2(c + 1)}$

51. $\frac{2x - 1}{2x + 1}$

53. $-\frac{2x^2 + 15x + 9}{3(x - 3)(x + 3)}$

55. $-\frac{3}{cd}$

57. $-\frac{4}{(y - 1)^2(y + 1)^2}$

58. a. $4 \cdot 9! + 6 \cdot 9! = 9!(4 + 6) = 9! \cdot 10 = 10!$

b. $\frac{9!}{3!6!} + \frac{9!}{4!5!} = \frac{(9!)(4)}{4!6!} + \frac{(9!)(6)}{4!6!} = \frac{9!(4) + (9!)(6)}{4!6!} = \frac{9!(4 + 6)}{4!6!} = \frac{10!}{4!6!}$

Simplify.

38. $\frac{a + 1}{a} - \frac{a}{a + 1}$ $\frac{2a + 1}{a(a + 1)}$

39. $\frac{x}{x + y} + \frac{y}{x - y}$ $\frac{x^2 + y^2}{(x + y)(x - y)}$

40. $\frac{y}{2y - 4} + \frac{8}{4 - y^2}$ $\frac{y^2 + 2y - 16}{2(y - 2)(y + 2)}$

41. $\frac{x}{x - 5} + \frac{5}{5 - x}$ 1

42. $\frac{3a}{a - 2b} + \frac{6b}{2b - a}$ 3

43. $\frac{z}{z - z^2} - \frac{1}{z - z^3}$

44. $\frac{1}{n(n + 5)} - \frac{10}{(n + 5)^3}$

45. $\frac{a}{ab - b^2} - \frac{b}{a^2 - ab}$

46. $\frac{1}{a^2 + 4a + 4} + \frac{1}{a^2 - 4}$

47. $\frac{2n}{n^3 - 5n^2} + \frac{2}{n^2 + 5n}$

48. $\frac{b + 2}{b^2 + 3b} - \frac{b - 2}{b^2 - 3b}$

49. $\frac{3c}{c^2 + 3c + 2} - \frac{3c - 6}{c^2 + 4c + 4}$

C 50. $\frac{x^2 + 1}{x^2 - 1} + \frac{1}{x + 1} + \frac{1}{x - 1}$ $\frac{x + 1}{x - 1}$

51. $\frac{x}{2x - 1} + \frac{x - 1}{2x + 1} - \frac{2x}{4x^2 - 1}$

52. $\frac{a + 2}{a^2 + 5a + 6} - \frac{2 + a}{4 - a^2} + \frac{2 - a}{a^2 + a - 6}$ $\frac{1}{a - 2}$

53. $\frac{x - 3}{2x + 6} - \frac{x + 3}{3x - 9} - \frac{5x^2 + 27}{6x^2 - 54}$

54. $\frac{b + 1}{(b - 1)^2} + \frac{2 - 2b}{(b - 1)^3} + \frac{1}{b - 1}$ $\frac{2}{b - 1}$

55. $\frac{4}{c^2 - 4cd} - \frac{1}{cd - 4d^2} - \frac{2}{cd}$

56. $\frac{1}{(a - b)(a - c)} + \frac{1}{(b - c)(b - a)} + \frac{1}{(c - a)(c - b)}$ 0

57. $\frac{2}{y^2 - 1} - \frac{1}{(y + 1)^2} - \frac{1}{(1 - y)^2}$

58. Show that the following are true. (*Hint:* See Exercise 48, page 254.)

a. $4 \cdot 9! + 6 \cdot 9! = 10!$ b. $\frac{9!}{3!6!} + \frac{9!}{4!5!} = \frac{10!}{4!6!}$

Self-Test 2

Vocabulary multiple (p. 251) least common multiple (p. 251) least common denominator (p. 251)

Find the missing numerators.

1. $\frac{5a}{28b} = \frac{?}{84ab^3}$ $15a^2b^2$

2. $\frac{5}{1 - a} = \frac{?}{a^2 - a}$ $-5a$

Obj. 6-4, p. 251

Express each group of fractions with their LCD.

3. $\frac{3}{4x - 8y}, \frac{-12}{2y - x}$ $\frac{3}{4(x - 2y)}, \frac{48}{4(x - 2y)}$

4. $\frac{2}{x}, \frac{3}{y}, \frac{5}{x + y}$ $\frac{2y(x + y)}{xy(x + y)}, \frac{3x(x + y)}{xy(x + y)}, \frac{5xy}{xy(x + y)}$

Simplify.

5. $\frac{25a + 1}{5a} - \frac{5a - 4}{5a}$ $\frac{4a + 1}{a}$

6. $\frac{4}{3ab} - \frac{8}{7ab^2}$ $\frac{4(7b - 6)}{21ab^2}$

Obj. 6-5, p. 255

7. $\frac{x}{x - y} + \frac{y}{y - x}$ 1

8. $\frac{x}{x - 1} - \frac{1}{9(x - 1)}$ $\frac{9x - 1}{9(x - 1)}$

Check your answers with those at the back of the book.

Historical Note / *Broken Numbers*

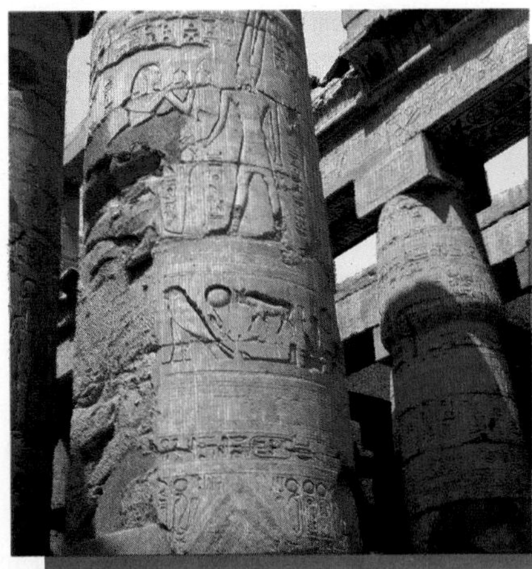

The word "fraction" comes from the Latin verb *frangere,* meaning "to break." A fraction is thus a "broken number," or a part of a number.

The Babylonians used special symbols to represent commonly used fractions such as $\frac{1}{2}$, $\frac{1}{3}$, and $\frac{2}{3}$. However, sexagesimals, fractions having denominators of base sixty, were used consistently in astronomical calculations and in mathematical texts. Because the denominators of the fractions were restricted to a certain base, a positional notation was used to represent these fractions. Thus, ≪ intended as a fraction meant $\frac{20}{60}$. These sexagesimals were arranged in tables that expressed the reciprocals of counting numbers as sexagesimal fractions. (The denominators were understood.) For instance, in these tables "igi 2 gál-bi 30" stood for "the reciprocal of 2 is $\frac{30}{60}$." The numerous integer divisors of sixty made it easier to simplify fractional computations. Sexagesimal fractions were also used by the ancient Greeks. In fact, they were used in Europe until the sixteenth century, when they were replaced by decimals.

Like the Babylonians the Egyptians had special symbols for commonly used fractions. In hieroglyphics the elliptical symbol ⬭ was placed over the symbol for a whole number to express its reciprocal. This symbol was replaced by a dot in cursive hieratic writing and was later adopted by the English who wrote $\dot{2}$ for $\frac{1}{2}$. The Egyptians attempted to avoid computational difficulties by expressing fractions in terms of unit fractions, that is, fractions having a numerator of one. Like the Babylonians, the Egyptians found it necessary to construct lengthy tables. The Egyptians expressed fractions as sums of unit fractions. There were numerous rules for forming unit fractions, but no one rule was used consistently. Thus, $\frac{2}{43}$ might have been expressed in any of the following ways:

$$\frac{1}{24} + \frac{1}{258} + \frac{1}{1032}$$

$$\frac{1}{30} + \frac{1}{86} + \frac{1}{645}$$

$$\frac{1}{36} + \frac{1}{86} + \frac{1}{645} + \frac{1}{172} + \frac{1}{774}$$

$$\frac{1}{40} + \frac{1}{860} + \frac{1}{1720}$$

$$\frac{1}{42} + \frac{1}{86} + \frac{1}{129} + \frac{1}{301}$$

These unit fractions, also used by the ancient Greeks, became known as simple fractions during the Middle Ages and were used as late as the seventeenth century.

Quick Quiz

1. Find the LCD of $\frac{5}{3y}$, $\frac{y}{y+1}$, and $\frac{y+1}{2y^2}$.
   $6y^2(y+1)$

Simplify.

2. $\frac{z}{2z-1} + \frac{2z+1}{2z-1} - \frac{z^2}{2z-1}$ $\quad \frac{-z^2+3z+1}{2z-1}$
3. $\frac{5a}{2bc} - \frac{3}{a^2b}$ $\quad \frac{5a^3-6c}{2a^2bc}$
4. $\frac{b-4b}{5b^2-5} + \frac{3}{2b-2} - \frac{2}{3b+3}$
   $\frac{7b+65}{30(b+1)(b-1)}$

Polynomial Division

6-6 Mixed Expressions

Objective To write mixed expressions as fractions in simplest form.

A mixed number like $4\frac{2}{5}$ denotes the sum of an integer and a fraction. Recall that $4\frac{2}{5}$ may be expressed as a fraction as follows:

$$4\frac{2}{5} = \frac{4}{1} + \frac{2}{5} = \frac{20}{5} + \frac{2}{5} = \frac{22}{5}$$

A sum or difference of a polynomial and a fraction is called a **mixed expression.** The following example shows that a mixed expression may be expressed as a fraction in simplest form.

Example Express as a fraction in simplest form.

a. $b + \frac{4}{b}$ **b.** $3 - \frac{n-4}{n+1}$

Solution **a.** $b + \frac{4}{b} = \frac{b}{1} + \frac{4}{b} = \frac{b^2}{b} + \frac{4}{b} = \frac{b^2+4}{b}$

b. $3 - \frac{n-4}{n+1} = \frac{3}{1} - \frac{n-4}{n+1}$

$= \frac{3(n+1)}{n+1} - \frac{n-4}{n+1}$

$= \frac{3n+3-n+4}{n+1}$

$= \frac{2n+7}{n+1}$

Oral Exercises

State each expression as a fraction in simplest form.

1. $2\frac{1}{8}$ $\frac{17}{8}$
2. $5\frac{2}{3}$ $\frac{17}{3}$
3. $-3\frac{4}{7}$ $-\frac{25}{7}$
4. $-8\frac{3}{4}$ $-\frac{35}{4}$
5. $1 + \frac{1}{x}$ $\frac{x+1}{x}$
6. $2 + \frac{4}{a}$ $\frac{2(a+2)}{a}$
7. $n + \frac{2}{n}$ $\frac{n^2+2}{n}$
8. $4 - \frac{1}{y}$
9. $2 - \frac{a}{b}$ $\frac{2b-a}{b}$
10. $3 - \frac{1}{x+1}$ $\frac{3x+2}{x+1}$
11. $\frac{3x}{x+2} - 1$ $\frac{2x-2}{x+2}$
12. $\frac{b}{2b-3} + 2$
13. $2 + \frac{3}{x+1}$ $\frac{2x+5}{x+1}$
14. $4 - \frac{1}{y+3}$ $\frac{4y+11}{y+3}$
15. $\frac{2n}{2n+1} - 1$ $-\frac{1}{2n+1}$
16. $\frac{5a}{a-3} + 2$

Teaching Suggestions
p. T102

Suggested Extensions
p. T102

Chalkboard Examples

Write as a fraction in simplest form.

1. $3t - \frac{2}{t}$

$\frac{3t}{1} - \frac{2}{t} = \frac{3t^2}{t} - \frac{2}{t} = \frac{3t^2-2}{t}$

2. $\frac{x}{x-1} - 5$

$\frac{x}{x-1} - \frac{5}{1} = \frac{x}{x-1} - \frac{5x-5}{x-1} = \frac{-4x+5}{x-1}$

Supplementary Materials

Practice Master 35
Resource Book, p. 91

Suggested Assignments

Minimum
Day 1: 261/1–18
S 258/42, 43
Day 2: 261/19–26
265/1–6
Day 2 finishes Sec. 6-6 and starts Sec. 6-7.

Average
Day 1: 261/1–37 odd
S 258/51–53
Day 2: 261/22–42 even
265/1–6
Day 2 finishes Sec. 6-6 and starts Sec. 6-7.

Maximum
261/1–45 odd
S 258/56, 57

Written Exercises

Write each expression as a fraction in simplest form.

A

1. $4\frac{1}{5}$ $\frac{21}{5}$
2. $2\frac{3}{8}$ $\frac{19}{8}$
3. $6 + \frac{1}{x}$ $\frac{6x + 1}{x}$
4. $5 + \frac{2}{a}$ $\frac{5a + 2}{a}$
5. $3a - \frac{2}{a}$ $\frac{3a^2 - 2}{a}$
6. $5x - \frac{3}{x}$ $\frac{5x^2 - 3}{x}$
7. $\frac{a}{b} + 2$ $\frac{a + 2b}{b}$
8. $\frac{c}{d} - 7$
9. $5 - \frac{4}{x + 2}$
10. $8 + \frac{y}{y - 1}$
11. $\frac{x}{x + 3} - 5$
12. $\frac{a + 2}{a} - 4$
13. $6x - \frac{x}{x + 1}$
14. $4y + \frac{y}{2y - 5}$
15. $3 - \frac{n + 2}{n^2 - 1}$
16. $8k - \frac{3k - 2}{3k + 2}$
17. $n - \frac{2}{n + 1}$
18. $a + \frac{a - 5}{2a + 3}$
19. $a + \frac{3a + 2}{a + 2}$
20. $2y - \frac{y - 4}{y + 4}$

B

21. $x - \frac{8}{x + 1} - \frac{6x - 2}{x + 1}$
22. $y - \frac{4(y + 1)}{y + 2} - \frac{4}{y + 2}$
23. $\frac{x}{x + 1} - \frac{x + 1}{x} + 2$
24. $\frac{a}{a + 3} + \frac{a}{a - 3} - 2$
25. $4 - \frac{1}{x + 1} - \frac{3}{x + 1}$
26. $\frac{y}{x + y} + \frac{x}{y - x} + 1$
27. $a + 1 - \frac{a^2 - a - 18}{a - 3}$
28. $5a + b - \frac{5a^2 - b^2}{5a - b}$
29. $3x - \frac{x^2}{2x + 3} - 2$
30. $(x + 4)\left(\frac{4}{x} - 1\right)$
31. $\left(a + \frac{2}{a}\right)\left(a - \frac{4}{a}\right)$
32. $\left(2x - \frac{1}{x}\right)\left(x - \frac{3}{x}\right)$
33. $\left(\frac{a + b}{a} - 1\right)\left(\frac{a}{b} + 1\right)$
34. $\left(y - \frac{2}{y + 1}\right)\left(1 - \frac{1}{y + 2}\right)$
35. $\left(a - \frac{b^2}{a}\right) \div \left(1 + \frac{b}{a}\right)$
36. $\left(4 - \frac{1}{c^2}\right) \div (2c + 1)$
37. $\left(1 - \frac{2}{a}\right) \div \left(1 - \frac{4}{a^2}\right)$
38. $1 + \frac{2x}{2x - 1} - \frac{8x^2}{4x^2 - 1}$
39. As an algebra exercise, Sue, Bob, and Julie were asked to simplify $1 - \frac{8x}{x^2 - x} - \frac{2x}{1 - x}$. Sue used a common denominator of $x(x - 1)(1 - x)$. Bob used $x(x - 1)$. Julie showed that the exercise could be done with a common denominator of $x - 1$. Explain why all three denominators could be used.
40. Jim bought n baseballs for a total of \$30. He then sold all but 2 of them for \$1 more per ball than he paid. How much did he receive for the balls that he sold? (*Hint:* Make a chart. Answer in terms of n.)
41. It took Roz y hours to drive 200 km. If she had increased her speed by 10 km/h and driven for 2 h less, how far could she have gone? (*Hint:* Make a chart. Answer in terms of y.)

Additional A Exercises

Write each expression as a fraction in simplest form.

1. $7\frac{7}{8}$ $\frac{63}{8}$
2. $6 - \frac{3}{b}$ $\frac{6b - 3}{b}$
3. $7 - \frac{3}{m - 4}$ $\frac{7m - 31}{m - 4}$

Additional Answers Oral Exercises

8. $\frac{4y - 1}{y}$
12. $\frac{5b - 6}{2b - 3}$
16. $\frac{7a - 6}{a - 3}$

Additional Answers Written Exercises

8. $\frac{c - 7d}{d}$
9. $\frac{5x + 6}{x + 2}$
10. $\frac{9y - 8}{y - 1}$
11. $\frac{-4x - 15}{x + 3}$
12. $\frac{-3a + 2}{a}$
13. $\frac{6x^2 + 5x}{x + 1}$
14. $\frac{8y^2 - 19y}{2y - 5}$
15. $\frac{3n^2 - n - 5}{n^2 - 1}$
16. $\frac{24k^2 + 13k + 2}{3k + 2}$
17. $\frac{(n + 2)(n - 1)}{n + 1}$
18. $\frac{2a^2 + 4a - 5}{2a + 3}$
19. $\frac{a^2 + 5a + 2}{a + 2}$
20. $\frac{2y^2 + 7y + 4}{y + 4}$

(continued)

Additional Answers
Written Exercises

21. $x - 6$

22. $y - 4$

23. $\frac{2x^2 - 1}{x(x + 1)}$

24. $\frac{18}{(a + 3)(a - 3)}$

25. $\frac{4x}{x + 1}$

26. $\frac{2y^2}{(y + x)(y - x)}$

27. $\frac{-a + 15}{a - 3}$

28. $\frac{20a^2}{5a - b}$

29. $\frac{5x^2 + 5x - 6}{2x + 3}$

30. $\frac{16 - x^2}{x}$

31. $\frac{a^4 - 2a^2 - 8}{a^2}$

32. $\frac{2x^4 - 7x^2 + 3}{x^2}$

33. $\frac{a + b}{a}$

34. $y - 1$

35. $a - b$

36. $\frac{2c - 1}{c^2}$

37. $\frac{a}{a + 2}$

38. $\frac{1}{2x + 1}$

39. $\frac{8x}{x^2 - x}$ can be reduced to $\frac{8}{x - 1}$. Thus, $x - 1$ is the LCD. $x(x - 1) \cdot (1 - x)$ and $x(x - 1)$ could be used because they are multiples of $x - 1$.

40. $\frac{n^2 + 28n - 60}{n}$ dollars

41. $\frac{10y^2 + 180y - 400}{y}$ km

Write the expression as a fraction in simplest form.

C **42.** $\left(1 - \frac{b^2 + c^2 - a^2}{2bc}\right) \div \left(1 - \frac{a^2 + b^2 - c^2}{2ab}\right)$ $\frac{a(a + b - c)}{c(c - a + b)}$

43. $\left(2 - \frac{n}{n + 1} + \frac{n}{1 - n}\right) \div \left(\frac{1}{n - 1} - \frac{1}{n + 1}\right)$ -1

44. Find constants A and B such that $\frac{4}{x^2 - 4} = \frac{A}{x + 2} + \frac{B}{x - 2}$. $A = -1$, $B = 1$

45. Find constants C and D such that $\frac{6x}{x^2 - x - 2} = \frac{C}{x - 2} + \frac{D}{x + 1}$. $C = 4$, $D = 2$

46. Simplify: $\left(1 - \frac{1}{2}\right)\left(1 - \frac{1}{3}\right)\left(1 - \frac{1}{4}\right)\left(1 - \frac{1}{5}\right) \cdots \left(1 - \frac{1}{n}\right)$ $\frac{1}{n}$

Computer Key-In

The following program will find the LCD for two denominators.

```
10  PRINT "TO FIND THE LEAST"
20  PRINT "COMMON DENOMINATOR;"
30  PRINT "INPUT D1, D2:";
40  INPUT D1,D2
50  FOR M=1 TO D1
60  LET Q=D2*M/D1
70  IF Q=INT(Q) THEN 90
80  NEXT M
90  PRINT "LCD(";D1;",";D2;") = ";
100  PRINT D2;" X ";M;" = ";D2*M
110  END
```

Exercises

RUN this program for the following denominators.

1. $D1 = 24$, $D2 = 36$ 72

2. $D1 = 36$, $D2 = 24$ 72

3. $D1 = 13$, $D2 = 15$ 195

4. $D1 = 15$, $D2 = 13$ 195

5–8. In order to see how the program works, insert

```
65 PRINT D2*M;"/";D1;"=";D2*M/D1
```

and RUN the program again for the data in Exercises 1–4.

9. Compare the RUNs when you put the smaller denominator first and then second. Which requires fewer steps of computation? smaller denominator first

10. Explain how to find the least common denominator for the three denominators 27, 36, and 30. Find LCD (27, 36) = 108. Then find LCD (108, 30) = 540.

Note: The program above can be used to do Exercises 25–33 on pages 253–254.

6-7 Polynomial Long Division

Objective To divide polynomials.

Division of one polynomial by another is very much like ordinary long division. Compare the long division and the polynomial division shown below.

Long Division

Step 1
$$31\overline{)688} \quad \text{quotient } 2$$
$$\begin{array}{r} 688 \\ \underline{62} \\ 68 \end{array}$$

Step 2
$$31\overline{)688} \quad \text{quotient } 22$$
$$\begin{array}{r} 688 \\ \underline{62} \\ 68 \\ \underline{62} \\ 6 \end{array}$$

Check:
$$688 \stackrel{?}{=} 22 \cdot 31 + 6$$
$$688 \stackrel{?}{=} 682 + 6$$
$$688 = 688 \checkmark$$

$$\therefore \frac{688}{31} = 22\frac{6}{31}$$

Polynomial Division

Step 1
$$3x + 1\overline{)6x^2 + 8x + 8} \quad \text{quotient } 2x$$
$$\begin{array}{r} 6x^2 + 8x + 8 \\ \underline{6x^2 + 2x\phantom{{}+8}} \\ 6x + 8 \end{array}$$

Step 2
$$3x + 1\overline{)6x^2 + 8x + 8} \quad \text{quotient } 2x + 2$$
$$\begin{array}{r} 6x^2 + 8x + 8 \\ \underline{6x^2 + 2x\phantom{{}+8}} \\ 6x + 8 \\ \underline{6x + 2} \\ 6 \end{array}$$

Check:
$$6x^2 + 8x + 8 \stackrel{?}{=} (2x + 2)(3x + 1) + 6$$
$$6x^2 + 8x + 8 \stackrel{?}{=} (6x^2 + 8x + 2) + 6$$
$$6x^2 + 8x + 8 = 6x^2 + 8x + 8 \checkmark$$

$$\therefore \frac{6x^2 + 8x + 8}{3x + 1} = (2x + 2) + \frac{6}{3x + 1}$$

In both divisions above, the answer was expressed in the following form:

$$\frac{\text{Dividend}}{\text{Divisor}} = \text{Quotient} + \frac{\text{Remainder}}{\text{Divisor}}$$

The following identity was used to check both divisions:

$$\text{Dividend} = \text{Quotient} \times \text{Divisor} + \text{Remainder}$$

When you divide polynomials, always make sure that the terms in each polynomial are arranged in order of decreasing degree in the variable.

Teaching Suggestions
p. T102

Suggested Extensions
p. T102

Chalkboard Examples

Divide.

1. $\dfrac{12x^2 + 19x - 21}{4x - 3}$

$$4x - 3\overline{)12x^2 + 19x - 21} \quad \text{quotient } 3x + 7$$
$$\begin{array}{r} 12x^2 + 19x - 21 \\ \underline{12x^2 - 9x\phantom{{}-21}} \\ 28x - 21 \\ \underline{28x - 21} \\ 0 \end{array}$$

2. $\dfrac{15t^2 - 2t + 6}{3t + 2}$

$$3t + 2\overline{)15t^2 - 2t + 6} \quad \text{quotient } 5t - 4$$
$$\begin{array}{r} 15t^2 - 2t + 6 \\ \underline{15t^2 + 10t\phantom{{}+6}} \\ -12t + 6 \\ \underline{-12t - 8} \\ 14 \end{array}$$

3. $\dfrac{21y^2 + 32y - 1}{3y + 5}$

$$3y + 5\overline{)21y^2 + 32y - 1} \quad \text{quotient } 7y - 1$$
$$\begin{array}{r} 21y^2 + 32y - 1 \\ \underline{21y^2 + 35y\phantom{{}-1}} \\ -3y - 1 \\ \underline{-3y - 5} \\ 4 \end{array}$$

Common Error

Students often make errors in polynomial division because they get confused about whether a particular term is positive or negative when they subtract. Suggest to students who are having trouble that they change the signs of each term of the polynomial being subtracted by writing the new sign above the old one and circling it.

Supplementary Materials

Practice Master 36
Test 21
Resource Book, p. 92

Suggested Assignments

Minimum
265/7–23 odd
R 266/*Self-Test 3*
Day 2 of Sec. 6-6 finishes Sec. 6-6 and starts Sec. 6-7.

Average
265/9–37 odd
R 266/*Self-Test 3*
Day 2 of Sec. 6-6 finishes Sec. 6-6 and starts Sec. 6-7.

Maximum
Day 1: 265/1–23 odd
S 261/34–46 even
Day 2: 265/25–39 odd
R 266/*Self-Test 3*

Additional A Exercises

Divide. Write your answer as a polynomial or mixed expression.

1. $\frac{m^2 + 4m - 5}{m + 5}$ $m - 1$
2. $\frac{k^2 - 7k + 13}{k - 3}$ $k - 4 + \frac{1}{k - 3}$
3. $\frac{t^2 + 9}{t - 3}$ $t + 3 + \frac{18}{t - 3}$
4. $\frac{6 + 7x^2}{7x + 3}$ $x + \frac{-3x + 6}{7x + 3}$
5. $\frac{9n^2 - 58n + 24}{9n - 4}$ $n - 6$
6. $\frac{p^3 - 13p - 2}{p + 3}$ $p^2 - 3p - 4 + \frac{10}{p + 3}$

Example 1 Divide $13x - 35 + 12x^2$ by $4x - 5$.

Solution First rewrite $13x - 35 + 12x^2$ as $12x^2 + 13x - 35$.

$$\begin{array}{r} 3x \quad + 7 \\ 4x - 5 \overline{) 12x^2 + 13x - 35} \\ \underline{12x^2 - 15x} \\ 28x - 35 \\ \underline{28x - 35} \\ 0 \end{array}$$

Check: $(3x + 7)(4x - 5) \stackrel{?}{=} 12x^2 + 13x - 35$

$$(3x + 7)(4x - 5) = 12x^2 - 15x + 28x - 35$$
$$= 12x^2 + 13x - 35 \ \checkmark$$

$\therefore \frac{12x^2 + 13x - 35}{4x - 5} = 3x + 7$ ***Answer***

Notice that in Example 1 the remainder is 0. Thus, both $4x - 5$ and $3x + 7$ are factors of $12x^2 + 13x - 35$.

Example 2 Divide: $\frac{3a^3 + 5}{a - 2}$. Write the answer as a mixed expression.

Solution Rewrite $3a^3 + 5$ in order of decreasing degree in a, inserting terms with 0 coefficients as shown below.

$$\begin{array}{r} 3a^2 + 6a \quad + 12 \\ a - 2 \overline{) 3a^3 + 0a^2 + 0a + 5} \\ \underline{3a^3 - 6a^2} \\ 6a^2 + 0a \\ \underline{6a^2 - 12a} \\ 12a + 5 \\ \underline{12a - 24} \\ 29 \end{array}$$

Check: $(3a^2 + 6a + 12)(a - 2) + 29 \stackrel{?}{=} 3a^3 + 5$

$$(3a^2 + 6a + 12)(a - 2) + 29 = 3a^3 + 6a^2 + 12a - 6a^2 - 12a - 24 + 29$$
$$= 3a^3 + (6a^2 - 6a^2) + (12a - 12a) - 24 + 29$$
$$= 3a^3 + 5 \ \checkmark$$

$\therefore \frac{3a^3 + 5}{a - 2} = 3a^2 + 6a + 12 + \frac{29}{a - 2}$ ***Answer***

The division process ends when the remainder is either 0 or of lesser degree than the divisor.

Oral Exercises

Show how you would arrange the divisor and dividend before actually doing the long division. Do not divide.

1. Divide $x^2 + 3x^3 + 5x - 2$ by $x + 1$. $3x^3 + x^2 + 5x - 2,\ x + 1$
2. Divide $x^3 + 8$ by $x + 2$. $x^3 + 0x^2 + 0x + 8,\ x + 2$
3. Divide $5 + 4x^3 - 17x$ by $2x - 5$. $4x^3 + 0x^2 - 17x + 5,\ 2x - 5$

Use the given information to find the dividend.

4. divisor = 4; quotient = 7; remainder = 3 — 31
5. divisor $= x - 2$; quotient $= x$; remainder $= 5$ — $x^2 - 2x + 5$
6. divisor $= x^2 + 1$; quotient $= 2x$; remainder $= 7x + 5$ — $2x^3 + 9x + 5$
7. When $x^3 - x - 6$ is divided by $x - 2$, the quotient is $x^2 + 2x + 3$ and the remainder is 0.
   This means that __?__ and __?__ are factors of __?__.
   $x - 2$ $\quad x^2 + 2x + 3$ $\quad x^3 - x - 6$

Written Exercises

Divide. Write your answer as a polynomial or mixed expression.

A

1. $\dfrac{x^2 + 8x + 15}{x + 3}$
2. $\dfrac{x^2 - 5x - 36}{x - 4}$
3. $\dfrac{n^2 - 3n - 54}{n - 9}$
4. $\dfrac{n^2 - 11n - 26}{n + 2}$
5. $\dfrac{y^2 + 6y + 10}{y + 2}$
6. $\dfrac{a^2 - 4a - 6}{a + 2}$
7. $\dfrac{x^2 - 3x - 9}{x - 3}$
8. $\dfrac{z^2 - 8z - 12}{z + 4}$
9. $\dfrac{8 + n^2 - 3n}{n - 5}$
10. $\dfrac{s^2 + 6 - 4s}{s + 4}$
11. $\dfrac{x^2 + 4}{x + 2}$
12. $\dfrac{y^2 - 9}{y + 9}$
13. $\dfrac{2x^2 - 7x + 5}{2x - 1}$
14. $\dfrac{3a^2 + 8a + 5}{3a + 2}$
15. $\dfrac{8 + 4x^2}{2x + 1}$
16. $\dfrac{9y^2 + 6}{3y - 1}$
17. $\dfrac{n^3 + n^2 - n - 1}{n - 1}$
18. $\dfrac{a^3 - 4a^2 + a + 6}{a - 2}$
19. $\dfrac{a^3 + 8}{a + 2}$
20. $\dfrac{n^3 - 1}{n - 1}$
21. $\dfrac{24x^3 + 2x^2 - 15}{3x - 2}$
22. $\dfrac{6n^3 + 5n^2 - 13n + 10}{3n - 5}$

B

23. $\dfrac{a^3 + 7a^2b + 3ab^2 - 14b^3}{a + 2b}$ $\quad a^2 + 5ab - 7b^2$
24. $\dfrac{3x^3 + 5x^2y - xy^2}{3x + 2y}$ $\quad x^2 + xy - y^2 + \dfrac{2y^3}{3x + 2y}$
25. $\dfrac{4x^4 - 8x^3 - 3x^2 + 13x - 6}{2x - 3}$ $\quad 2x^3 - x^2 - 3x + 2$
26. $\dfrac{6x^4 - 2x^3 + 6x^2 - 5x + 3}{3x - 1}$ $\quad 2x^3 + 2x - 1 + \dfrac{2}{3x - 1}$
27. $\dfrac{2n^4 - n^3 - 2n + 1}{2n - 1}$ $\quad n^3 - 1$
28. $\dfrac{z^4 + 16}{z + 2}$ $\quad z^3 - 2z^2 + 4z - 8 + \dfrac{32}{z + 2}$
29. $\dfrac{n^4 + 3n^3 + 3n^2 - 3n - 4}{n^2 - 1}$ $\quad n^2 + 3n + 4$
30. $\dfrac{3x^3 - 4x^2 + 2x + 4}{x^2 - 2x + 2}$ $\quad 3x + 2$

Additional Answers
Written Exercises

1. $x + 5$
2. $x - 1 - \dfrac{40}{x - 4}$
3. $n + 6$
4. $n - 13$
5. $y + 4 + \dfrac{2}{y + 2}$
6. $a - 6 + \dfrac{6}{a + 2}$
7. $x - \dfrac{9}{x - 3}$
8. $z - 12 + \dfrac{36}{z + 4}$
9. $n + 2 + \dfrac{18}{n - 5}$
10. $s - 8 + \dfrac{38}{s + 4}$
11. $x - 2 + \dfrac{8}{x + 2}$
12. $y - 9 + \dfrac{72}{y + 9}$
13. $x - 3 + \dfrac{2}{2x - 1}$
14. $a + 2 + \dfrac{1}{3a + 2}$
15. $2x - 1 + \dfrac{9}{2x + 1}$
16. $3y + 1 + \dfrac{7}{3y - 1}$
17. $n^2 + 2n + 1$
18. $a^2 - 2a - 3$
19. $a^2 - 2a + 4$
20. $n^2 + n + 1$
21. $8x^2 + 6x + 4 - \dfrac{7}{3x - 2}$
22. $2n^2 + 5n + 4 + \dfrac{30}{3n - 5}$

Additional Answers Written Exercises

32. a. $a^3 + 2a^2 + 5a + 10$
b. $(a + 2)(a^2 + 5)$
c. $(a + 2)(a^2 + 5) = a^3 + 2a^2 + 5a + 10$

33. $(3n + 2)(n - 1)(n - 2)$

34. $(x - 1)(x + 2)(x + 3)$

41. a. $x^{99} + x^{98} + x^{97} + \cdots + x^2 + x + 1$
b. $x^{n-1} + x^{n-2} + \cdots + x + 1$

42. a. $x^{99} - x^{98} + x^{97} - \cdots - x^2 + x - 1 + \frac{2}{x + 1}$
b. $x^{n-1} - x^{n-2} + x^{n-3} - x^{n-4} + \cdots + x^3 - x^2 + x - 1 + \frac{2}{x + 1}$

43. a. $x^{100} - x^{99} + x^{98} - x^{97} + \cdots + x^2 - x + 1$
b. $x^{n-1} - x^{n-2} + x^{n-3} - x^{n-4} + \cdots + x^2 - x + 1$

Mixed Review Exercises

1. State the reciprocal of $-\frac{9}{5}$. $-\frac{5}{9}$

Simplify.

2. $-|6 - (-2.4)|$ -8.4

3. $\frac{6}{x - y} - \frac{3x}{y - x}$ $\frac{6 + 3x}{x - y}$

4. Express $3 - \frac{7n^2}{m^2 + n^2}$ as a fraction in simplest form. $\frac{3m^2 - 4n^2}{m^2 + n^2}$

31. The volume of a rectangular solid is $12n^3 + 8n^2 - 3n - 2$. The length of the solid is $2n + 1$ and the width is $2n - 1$. Find the height. $3n + 2$

32. Divide $a^4 + a^2 - 20$ by $a - 2$.
   a. Use long division.
   b. Factor $a^4 + a^2 - 20$ first. Then divide by $a - 2$.
   c. Show that your answers to parts (a) and (b) are the same.

33. Factor $3n^3 - 7n^2 + 4$ completely given that $3n + 2$ is one of its factors.

34. Factor $x^3 + 4x^2 + x - 6$ given that $x - 1$ is one of its factors.

35. Factor $4x^3 - 12x^2 - 37x - 15$ given that $2x + 1$ is a factor. $(2x + 1)(2x + 3)(x - 5)$

36. Factor $2x^3 - 7x^2 + 4x + 4$ given that $(x - 2)^2$ is a factor. $(x - 2)^2(2x + 1)$

C

37. Find the value of k for which $2x + 3$ is a factor of $6x^2 + 5x + k$. -6

38. Find the value of k for which $x + 3$ is a factor of $2x^3 + 11x^2 + 13x + k$. -6

39. Find the value of k for which $y - 2$ is a factor of $y^3 - 4y^2 + ky + 6$. 1

40. When $6x^4 - 5x^3 - 37x^2 + 46x + n$ is divided by $2x - 5$, the remainder is 5. Find the value of n. -35

41. **a.** Divide $x^{100} - 1$ by $x - 1$. **b.** Divide $x^n - 1$ by $x - 1$.

42. **a.** Divide $x^{100} + 1$ by $x + 1$. **b.** Divide $x^n + 1$ by $x + 1$, where n is even.

43. **a.** Divide $x^{101} + 1$ by $x + 1$. **b.** Divide $x^n + 1$ by $x + 1$, where n is odd.

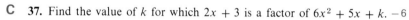

Self-Test 3

Vocabulary mixed expression (p. 260)

Write each expression as a fraction in simplest form.

1. $9 + \frac{a}{b}$ $\frac{9b + a}{b}$ **2.** $4x - \frac{1}{x}$ $\frac{4x^2 - 1}{x}$ **3.** $a - \frac{a - 1}{a + 1}$ $\frac{a^2 + 1}{a + 1}$ **Obj. 6-6, p. 260**

Divide. Write your answer as a polynomial or mixed expression.

4. $\frac{-20 + 2x^2 + 3x}{x + 4}$ $2x - 5$ **5.** $\frac{2b^3 + b^2 + b + 16}{b + 2}$ $2b^2 - 3b + 7 + \frac{2}{b + 2}$ **Obj. 6-7, p. 263**

Check your answers with those at the back of the book.

Extra / *Complex Fractions*

A complex fraction is a fraction whose numerator or denominator contains one or more fractions. To express a complex fraction as a simple fraction, use one of the methods below.

Method 1: Simplify the numerator and denominator. Express the fraction as a quotient using the ÷ sign. Multiply by the reciprocal of the divisor.

Method 2: Find the LCD of all the simple fractions. Multiply the numerator and the denominator of the complex fraction by the LCD.

Example Simplify $\dfrac{\frac{1}{a}+\frac{1}{b}}{\frac{b}{2a}-\frac{a}{2b}}$.

Solution *Method 1:*

$$\frac{\frac{1}{a}+\frac{1}{b}}{\frac{b}{2a}-\frac{a}{2b}} = \frac{\frac{b+a}{ab}}{\frac{b^2-a^2}{2ab}}$$

$$= \frac{b+a}{ab} \div \frac{b^2-a^2}{2ab}$$

$$= \frac{\cancel{b+a}}{\cancel{ab}} \cdot \frac{2\cancel{ab}}{\cancel{(b+a)}(b-a)}$$

$$= \frac{2}{b-a}$$

Method 2:

The LCD of all the simple fractions is $2ab$.

$$\frac{\frac{1}{a}+\frac{1}{b}}{\frac{b}{2a}-\frac{a}{2b}} = \frac{\left(\frac{1}{a}+\frac{1}{b}\right)2ab}{\left(\frac{b}{2a}-\frac{a}{2b}\right)2ab}$$

$$= \frac{2b+2a}{b^2-a^2}$$

$$= \frac{2\cancel{(b+a)}}{\cancel{(b+a)}(b-a)} = \frac{2}{b-a}$$

Exercises

In the following exercises you can use either Method 1 or Method 2 to simplify the fractions. Most people find Method 2 preferable, especially when simplifying more involved complex fractions.

Simplify.

12. $\dfrac{2wx+6x}{5wx-45}$

A

1. $\dfrac{\frac{m}{8}}{\frac{5m}{8}}$ $\frac{1}{5}$
2. $\dfrac{\frac{3a}{4}}{\frac{15a}{12}}$ $\frac{3}{5}$
3. $\dfrac{\frac{u}{v^2}}{\frac{u}{v}}$ $\frac{1}{v}$
4. $\dfrac{\frac{6e}{3}}{7e}$ $14e^2$
5. $\dfrac{\frac{1}{4}+\frac{1}{8}}{\frac{1}{4}-\frac{1}{8}}$ 3
6. $\dfrac{\frac{1}{6}+\frac{1}{3}}{\frac{1}{2}+\frac{1}{5}}$ $\frac{5}{7}$
7. $\dfrac{\frac{5}{6}-\frac{5}{7}}{\frac{5}{6}+\frac{5}{7}}$ $\frac{1}{13}$
8. $\dfrac{\frac{3}{x}}{\frac{1}{x}-\frac{1}{3x}}$ $\frac{9}{2}$
9. $\dfrac{\frac{9c^2}{5d^4}}{\frac{3c^2}{10d^3}}$ $\frac{6}{d}$
10. $\dfrac{\frac{n^2-25}{n}}{n-5}$ $\frac{n+5}{n}$
11. $\dfrac{\frac{r}{s}+2}{1-\frac{r}{s}}$ $\frac{r+2s}{s-r}$
12. $\dfrac{\frac{2w}{3}+2}{\frac{5w}{3}-\frac{15}{x}}$

Quick Quiz

1. Express $\dfrac{3y}{5y-1}+y$ as a fraction in simplest form. $\dfrac{5y^2+2y}{5y-1}$

Divide. Write your answer as a polynomial or as a mixed expression.

2. $\dfrac{6y^2+y-40}{2y-5}$ $3y+8$
3. $\dfrac{5m^2-34m-18}{m-7}$ $5m+1-\dfrac{11}{m-7}$
4. $\dfrac{2y^3+9y^2-27}{y+3}$ $2y^2+3y-9$

Additional Answers
Extra

23. $\frac{\text{total distance}}{\text{total time}} = \frac{2d}{\frac{d}{50} + \frac{d}{30}} = \frac{2d}{\frac{3d + 5d}{150}} = \frac{2d}{\frac{8d}{150}} = 2d \cdot \frac{150}{8d} = \frac{150}{4} =$ 37.5. Thus, Sam's average speed is 37.5 km/h.

26. $a + b = \frac{1 - c}{1 + c} + b = \frac{1 - \frac{1 + b}{1 - b}}{1 + \frac{1 + b}{1 - b}} + b = \frac{1 - b - (1 + b)}{1 - b + 1 + b} + b = \frac{-2b}{2} + b = -b + b = 0$

27. $\frac{w + 6}{3(w - 2)}$

28. $\frac{2}{x^2 - 2x}$

29. $n^2 + 1$

30. $\frac{c - d}{2(c + d)}$

31. $\frac{54e^2 - e - 29}{6(3e - 1)(3e + 1)}$

32. $-\frac{u^2 + v^2}{4uv}$

33. $\frac{1}{2s}$

34. $\frac{2x + y}{3(x + y)}$

35. $-\frac{1}{c - 3}$

36. $\frac{3a^2 + 4a + 3}{(a + 1)^2}$

Simplify.

B

13. $\frac{z - \frac{5z}{z + 5}}{z + \frac{5z}{z - 5}}$ *Ans.* $\frac{z - 5}{z + 5}$

14. $\frac{1 - \frac{6}{s^2 + 2}}{\frac{4s + 2}{s^2 + 2} + 1}$ *Ans.* $\frac{s - 2}{s + 2}$

15. $\frac{k + \frac{k - 3}{k + 1}}{k - \frac{2}{k + 1}}$ *Ans.* $\frac{k + 3}{k + 2}$

16. $\frac{\frac{1}{c} - \frac{1}{3 - 3c}}{\frac{1}{1 - c} - \frac{3}{c}}$ *Ans.* $-\frac{1}{3}$

17. $\frac{\frac{e}{e - f} - \frac{f}{e + f}}{\frac{f}{e - f} + \frac{e}{e + f}}$ *Ans.* 1

18. $\frac{1 - 2u}{1 + \frac{1}{2u}} \div \frac{1 + 2u}{1 - \frac{1}{2u}}$ *Ans.* $-\frac{(1 - 2u)^2}{(1 + 2u)^2}$

19. $\frac{\frac{2}{z + 1} - 2}{\frac{2 - z}{z^2 - 1} - 2}$ *Ans.* $\frac{2z^2 - 2z}{2z^2 + z - 4}$

20. $\frac{\frac{m - n}{m + n} + \frac{n}{m}}{\frac{m}{n} - \frac{m - n}{m + n}}$ *Ans.* $\frac{n}{m}$

21. If $x = \frac{y - 1}{y + 1}$ and $y = \frac{1}{1 - z}$, express x in terms of z. *Ans.* $x = \frac{z}{2 - z}$

22. If $a = \frac{b - c}{1 + bc}$ and $b = \frac{1}{z - 1}$ and $c = \frac{1}{z + 1}$, find a in terms of z. *Ans.* $a = \frac{2}{z^2}$

23. Sam drives d km at 50 km/h and returns the same distance at 30 km/h. Show that the average speed is 37.5 km/h. (*Hint:* Average speed = total distance divided by total time.)

24. A cyclist travels 12 km on a level road at x km/h and then goes 9 km on a downhill road at $2x$ km/h. Find her average speed in terms of x. (See Hint for Exercise 23.) *Ans.* $\frac{14x}{11}$ km/h

25. If n items can be purchased for 50 cents, how many items can be purchased for 50 cents after the price per item is decreased by 10 cents? *Ans.* $\frac{5n}{5 - n}$

26. If $a = \frac{1 - c}{1 + c}$ and $c = \frac{1 + b}{1 - b}$, show that $a + b = 0$.

Simplify.

27. $\left(\frac{w}{6} - \frac{6}{w}\right) \div \left(\frac{6}{w} - 4 + \frac{w}{2}\right)$

28. $\left(\frac{x}{4 - x^2} + \frac{1}{x - 2}\right) \div \left(1 - \frac{2}{2 + x}\right)$

29. $\left(\frac{1}{n - n^2} - \frac{1}{n^2 + n}\right) \div \left(\frac{1}{n^2 + 1} - \frac{1}{n^2 - 1}\right)$

30. $\left(\frac{c^2 + d^2}{cd} - 2\right) \div \left(\frac{4c^2 - 4d^2}{2cd}\right)$

31. $\left(\frac{9e^2 - 5}{e - 1} - \frac{1}{6}\right) \div \left(1 - \frac{e - 9e^2}{e - 1}\right)$

32. $\left(\frac{u^2 + v^2}{u^2 - v^2}\right) \div \left(\frac{u - v}{u + v} - \frac{u + v}{u - v}\right)$

C

33. $\frac{r}{2}\left(\frac{r^2 - s^2}{r^2s + rs^2}\right)\left(\frac{1}{r - s}\right)\left(\frac{1}{r + s}\right) \div \frac{1}{r + s}$

34. $\left(\frac{4x^2 - y^2}{3xy}\right) \div \left(\frac{2x^2 - y^2}{xy} + 1\right)$

35. $1 - \frac{1}{1 - \frac{1}{c - 2}}$

36. $2 + \frac{1}{1 + \frac{2}{a + \frac{1}{a}}}$

Chapter Summary

1. A fraction can be simplified by factoring its numerator and its denominator and dividing each by their common factors.
2. The *rule of exponents for a power of a quotient* (page 245) is often useful in simplifying fractions.
3. The following rules are used for combining fractions.

Multiplication Rule

$$\frac{c}{d} \cdot \frac{x}{y} = \frac{cx}{dy}$$

Division Rule

$$\frac{a}{b} \div \frac{c}{d} = \frac{a}{b} \cdot \frac{d}{c}$$

Addition Rule

$$\frac{a}{c} + \frac{b}{c} = \frac{a+b}{c}$$

Subtraction Rule

$$\frac{a}{c} - \frac{b}{c} = \frac{a-b}{c}$$

4. When adding or subtracting fractions with different denominators, rewrite the fractions using their *least common denominator* (*LCD*). Then apply the appropriate rule. (See the method and the examples on pages 255–256.)
5. A sum or difference of a polynomial and a fraction is called a *mixed expression.* A mixed expression can be expressed as a fraction in simplest form.
6. When dividing polynomials, arrange the terms of the *divisor* and *dividend* in order of decreasing degree in a variable. Insert zero coefficients where the dividend is missing a power.

Supplementary Materials

Practice Masters 37–39
Tests 22–23
Resource Book,
pp. 27–35, 93–96, 135–137, 153

Extra Practice

Skills, pp. 617–619

Chapter Review

Give the letter of the correct answer.

1. Express $\frac{9x^2 - 9}{x^2 + 1}$ in simplest form. **6-1**

a. 0 **b.** -9

(c.) $\frac{9(x+1)(x-1)}{x^2+1}$ **d.** $\frac{9(x-1)}{x+1}$

2. Express $\frac{8xy}{12x^2y - xy^2}$ in simplest form.

a. $\frac{2}{3(x-y)}$ **(b.)** $\frac{8}{12x-y}$ **c.** $\frac{3}{2(x-y)}$ **d.** $\frac{8}{11y}$

3. Express $\left(-\frac{3}{4}\right)^3\left(-\frac{16}{9}\right)$ in simplest form. **6-2**

(a.) $\frac{3}{4}$ **b.** $-\frac{4}{3}$ **c.** $-\frac{3}{4}$ **d.** $\frac{4}{3}$

4. Express $\frac{5xy}{12} \cdot \frac{32}{3xy^2}$ in simplest form.

a. $\frac{40}{3y}$ b. $\frac{40}{3y^2}$ (c.) $\frac{40}{9y}$ d. $40y$

5. Express $5ab^2 \div \frac{10a}{b}$ in simplest form. 6-3

a. $\frac{1}{2}b$ (b.) $\frac{b^3}{2}$ c. $\frac{50a^2}{b}$ d. $2b^3$

6. Express $\frac{x^2 - 16}{4x + 16} \div (4 - x)$ in simplest form.

a. -4 b. 4 c. $\frac{1}{4}$ (d.) $-\frac{1}{4}$

7. Find the missing numerator in $\frac{2}{x - y} = \frac{?}{x^2 - 2xy + y^2}$. 6-4

a. 2 b. $2(x + y)$ c. $2xy$ (d.) $2(x - y)$

8. Find the LCD for $\frac{4n}{9n - 6}$ and $\frac{2n}{15(3n - 2)^2}$.

a. $15(3n - 2)$ b. $45(3n - 2)^2$
(c.) $15(3n - 2)^2$ d. $5(3n - 2)$

9. Simplify $\frac{5a}{a - 1} + \frac{5}{1 - a}$. 6-5

(a.) 5 b. $\frac{5a + 5}{a - 1}$ c. -5 d. $\frac{5a - 5}{1 - a}$

10. Simplify $\frac{n - 9}{36} - \frac{n - 35}{108}$.

a. $\frac{n - 2}{27}$ (b.) $\frac{n + 4}{54}$ c. $2n + 8$ d. $\frac{n - 31}{54}$

11. Write $3 - \frac{a + 1}{a - 1}$ as a fraction in simplest form. 6-6

a. 2 b. $\frac{2a}{a - 1}$ c. $\frac{a - 2}{a - 1}$ (d.) $\frac{2a - 4}{a - 1}$

12. Simplify $z + 3 + \frac{1}{z - 3}$.

(a.) $\frac{z^2 - 8}{z - 3}$ b. $\frac{z + 4}{z - 3}$ c. $\frac{z^2 - 8}{z^2 - 9}$ d. $\frac{z^2 - 10}{z - 3}$

13. When $x^3 - 3x^2 + 3x + 4$ is divided by $x - 2$, what is the remainder? 6-7

a. 2 b. 4 (c.) 6 d. 8

14. Divide $\frac{8x^3 + 27}{2x + 3}$. Write your answer as a polynomial or mixed expression.

a. $4x^2 + 9$ b. $4x^2 + 6x - 9 + \frac{54}{2x + 3}$
(c.) $4x^2 - 6x + 9$ d. $4x^2 + 6x + 9$

Chapter Test

Alternate Test p. T15

Express in simplest form, noting any restrictions on the variable.

6-1

1. $\dfrac{4x - 32}{64 - x^2}$ $-\dfrac{4}{x+8}$; $x \neq 8$, $x \neq -8$
2. $\dfrac{49 - a^2}{a^2 - 14a + 49}$ $\dfrac{7+a}{7-a}$; $a \neq 7$
3. $\dfrac{3x^2 - 6x - 24}{3x^2 + 2x - 8}$ $\dfrac{3(x-4)}{3x-4}$; $x \neq \dfrac{4}{3}$, $x \neq -2$
4. $\dfrac{15y^2 - 30y - 45}{5y^2 + 10y - 15}$ $\dfrac{3(y-3)(y+1)}{(y+3)(y-1)}$; $y \neq -3$, $y \neq 1$

Express in simplest form.

6-2

5. $\left(-\dfrac{x^2}{5}\right)^3$ $-\dfrac{x^6}{125}$
6. $\dfrac{(2x)^3}{6} \cdot \dfrac{x^3}{6}$ $\dfrac{2x^6}{9}$
7. $\left(\dfrac{3a}{b}\right)^3 \cdot \dfrac{7ab}{54}$ $\dfrac{7a^4}{2b^2}$

6-3

8. $\dfrac{5}{9} \div \dfrac{5}{9}$ 1
9. $\dfrac{7}{8} \div \dfrac{8}{7}$ $\dfrac{49}{64}$
10. $\dfrac{3a^2}{8b} \div 24ab$ $\dfrac{a}{64b^2}$
11. $18 \div \left(\dfrac{3n}{2}\right)^3$ $\dfrac{16}{3n^3}$
12. $\dfrac{6a + 36}{6a} \div \dfrac{a^2 - 36}{a^2}$ $\dfrac{a}{a-6}$
13. $\dfrac{y}{2x^3} \div \left(\dfrac{y}{2x}\right)^3$ $\dfrac{4}{y^2}$

Find the missing numerator.

6-4

14. $\dfrac{7n}{16m} = \dfrac{?}{144m^2n}$ $63n^2m$
15. $\dfrac{3}{x+5} = \dfrac{?}{3x^2 - 75}$ $9(x-5)$

Express each group of fractions with their LCD.

16. $\dfrac{2}{7x^2}, \dfrac{3}{14xy}, \dfrac{7}{8y^2}$ $\dfrac{16y^2}{56x^2y^2}, \dfrac{12xy}{56x^2y^2}, \dfrac{49x^2}{56x^2y^2}$
17. $\dfrac{2-y}{16}, \dfrac{y+1}{18}$ $\dfrac{9(2-y)}{144}, \dfrac{8(y+1)}{144}$

Simplify.

6-5

18. $\dfrac{x}{x-9} + \dfrac{1}{x-9} - \dfrac{19-x}{x-9}$ 2
19. $\dfrac{x-1}{3} + \dfrac{3-2x}{6}$ $\dfrac{1}{6}$
20. $\dfrac{2}{y^2 - 2y} - \dfrac{3}{y^2 - y - 2}$ $-\dfrac{1}{y(y+1)}$
21. $\dfrac{4a}{a-2b} + \dfrac{8b}{2b-a}$ 4

Write each expression as a fraction in simplest form.

6-6

22. $\dfrac{a}{b} - 6$ $\dfrac{a-6b}{b}$
23. $5y + \dfrac{3-y}{y-3}$ $5y - 1$
24. $\dfrac{3}{4-x} - 2$ $\dfrac{2x-5}{4-x}$
25. $\dfrac{x}{x+2} + \dfrac{2}{x-2} + 1$ $\dfrac{2x^2}{(x-2)(x+2)}$

Divide. Write your answer as a polynomial or mixed expression.

6-7

26. $\dfrac{45 - 13n + n^2}{n-5}$ $n - 8 + \dfrac{5}{n-5}$
27. $\dfrac{2x^3 - x^2 - 5x - 2}{2x+1}$ $x^2 - x - 2$
28. Use long division to decide whether or not $x - 2$ is a factor of $x^3 + 6x^2 - x - 30$. $x - 2$ is a factor.

Cumulative Review p. T24

Additional Answers Cumulative Review

5. $20x^2 + 3x - 9$
6. $-8x^4 + 6x^3 - 18x$
13. $a^2b(6a + 5ab - 3b)$
18. $(t - 11)(t - 2)$
31. $\frac{1}{a + 4}$
32. $\frac{3x^2 + 2x + 10}{5(x - 2)(x - 1)}$
33. $\frac{a - b}{cd^2}$
34. $-\frac{a^2 + a + 12}{(a + 3)^2(a - 3)}$
35. $3b^2 - 2b + 1 - \frac{8}{2b - 3}$
36. $\frac{2x^4 + x^2y^2 - 2x^2y - y^3}{x^2}$

Cumulative Review (Chapters 1–6)

Perform the indicated operations. Express the answers in simplest form. Assume that no denominator is zero.

1. $0.6(-0.8)^2 + 0.4(-0.8)^2$ 0.64
2. $\frac{45x^3y^2z^5}{-30(xyz)^2}$ $-\frac{3xz^3}{2}$
3. $(-3a^2b^3c^4)^3$ $-27a^6b^9c^{12}$
4. $(3m - 9n) + (2m + 11n)$ $5m + 2n$
5. $(5x - 3)(4x + 3)$
6. $-2x(4x^3 - 3x^2 + 9)$
7. $(-13t + 6s) - (4t + 9s)$ $-17t - 3s$
8. $(-2b + 7c)^2$ $4b^2 - 28bc + 49c^2$
9. $(4t^2s - 9)(4t^2s + 9)$ $16t^4s^2 - 81$

Evaluate if $a = -1$, $b = 1$, $c = -2$, and $d = 3$.

10. $\frac{a + b}{c} - cd$ 6
11. $(a + b)^2 \div (c^2 + d)$ 0
12. $(a^2 + b^2) \div c^2 + d$ $\frac{7}{2}$

Factor completely. If the polynomial cannot be factored, write "prime."

13. $6a^3b + 5a^3b^2 - 3a^2b^2$
14. $81x^2 + 18xy + y^2$ $(9x + y)^2$
15. $8t^3 - 56t^2 + 98t$ $2t(2t - 7)^2$
16. $z^4 + 11z^3 + 18z^2$ $z^2(z + 2)(z + 9)$
17. $m^2 + 12m + 30$ prime
18. $t^2 - 13t + 22$
19. $y^3 + 4y^2 - 32y$ $y(y + 8)(y - 4)$
20. $10z^2 + 16z - 8$ $2(5z - 2)(z + 2)$
21. $4x^2 - y^2 + 2y - 1$ $(2x - y + 1)(2x + y - 1)$

Solve. If the equation is an identity or has no solution, state that fact.

22. $8z - 1 = 23$ 3
23. $\frac{1}{3}y - 5 = 7$ 36
24. $6 - \frac{3}{4}d = -3$ 12
25. $(n + 2)^2 = (n + 4)(n - 2)$ -6
26. $10m^2 - m^3 = 25m$ $\{0, 5\}$
27. $18c^2 - 32 = 0$ $\left\{-\frac{4}{3}, \frac{4}{3}\right\}$
28. $t^2 + 12t + 15 = -5$ $\{-2, -10\}$
29. $x^2 - 6x = 7$ $\{7, -1\}$
30. $6y^3 + 13y^2 - 5y = 0$ $\left\{0, \frac{1}{3}, -\frac{5}{2}\right\}$

Perform the indicated operations. Express the answers in simplest form. Assume that no denominator is zero.

31. $\frac{2a^2 + 9a + 4}{2a^2 + 3a + 1} \cdot \frac{a + 1}{a^2 + 8a + 16}$
32. $\frac{3x}{5x - 10} + \frac{x + 2}{x^2 - 3x + 2}$
33. $\frac{a^2 - b^2}{(cd)^3} \div \frac{a + b}{c^2d}$
34. $\frac{3}{a^2 + 6a + 9} - \frac{a + 1}{a^2 - 9}$
35. $\frac{6b^3 - 13b^2 + 8b - 11}{2b - 3}$
36. $\left(x - \frac{y}{x}\right)\left(2x + \frac{y^2}{x}\right)$

37. Ted and Tina are twins. Their mother was 24 years old when they were born. Eight years ago she was 4 times their age. How old are all three now? Tina and Ted are 16; their mother is 40.
38. Maggie has 24 quarters and half dollars. If she had twice as many half dollars and half as many quarters, she would have \$2 more. How much money does she have? \$8
39. It took Len 25 min to ride his bicycle to the repair shop and 1 h 15 min to walk back home. If Len can ride his bicycle 8 km/h faster than he can walk, how far is the repair shop from his house? 5 km
40. Find two numbers whose sum is 15 and whose squares total 113. 7 and 8

Maintaining Skills

Review the five-step problem-solving method described in Section 1-6.

Example The length of a rectangle is 28 cm less than 5 times the width. If the perimeter is 1.12 m, find the dimensions.

Solution

Step 1 Read the problem carefully a few times. It asks for the length and width of the rectangle. Make a sketch.

Step 2 Choose a variable and use it with the given facts to represent the numbers described in the problem.
Let w = the width.
Then $5w - 28$ = the length.

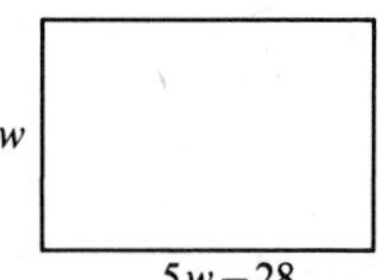

Step 3 Write an open sentence based on the given facts:

The perimeter is 1.12 m.

$$2w + 2(5w - 28) = 112 \qquad (1.12 \text{ m} = 112 \text{ cm})$$

Step 4 Solve the open sentence and find the required numbers:

$$12w - 56 = 112$$
$$12w = 168$$
$$w = 14;\ 5w - 28 = 5(14) - 28 = 42$$

Step 5 Check your results with the words of the problem. Give the answer. The check is left to you.

∴ the length is 42 cm and the width is 14 cm. ***Answer***

Use the five-step plan to solve each problem.

1. The length of a rectangle is 10 cm greater than twice its width. The area of the rectangle is 28 cm^2. Find the dimensions of the rectangle. 2 cm by 14 cm
2. Three consecutive integers are such that the square of the greatest is 32 less than the sum of the squares of the other two. Find the integers. 7, 8, 9 or −5, −4, −3
3. The bottom of a box is a rectangle with length 3 cm more than the width. The height of the box is 6 cm and its volume is 324 cm^3. Find the dimensions of the bottom of the box. 6 cm wide, 9 cm long, 6 cm high
4. A painting is 10 cm longer than it is wide. The painting is to be surrounded by a mat that is 3 cm wide and covered by a piece of glass with area 816 cm^2. Find the dimensions of the painting. 18 cm by 28 cm
5. Cynthia and George paddled a canoe downstream from a boat landing to a picnic area and back. They averaged 24 km/h downstream and 16 km/h less upstream. The whole trip took 50 min. How far was it from the boat landing to the picnic area? 5 km

Additional Answer
Mixed Review

3. 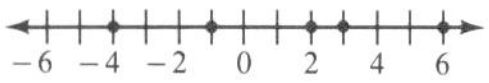

Mixed Review

Skills and Problem Solving

1. The length of a rectangle is 1 cm longer than 3 times the width. If both dimensions of the rectangle are increased by 3 cm, the area is increased by 36 cm^2. Find the dimensions of the original rectangle. 2 cm by 7 cm
2. Factor the polynomial $128r^2s^8 - 2r^2t^4$ completely. $2r^2(8s^4 - t^2)(8s^4 + t^2)$
3. Choose a point on a number line and label it "0." Then graph the numbers −4, 6, 2, −1, and 3.

Solve. Assume that no denominator is zero. If the equation is an identity or has no solution, state that fact.

4. $\frac{(n+1)^2}{3} \div \frac{n+1}{n} = n + 1$ 3
5. $-\frac{1}{2}|x - 1| = 6$ no solution
6. $15b^2 + 7b - 2 = 0$ $\frac{1}{5}, -\frac{2}{3}$
7. $(z + 1)^2 - (z + 2)^2 = 3$ −3
8. Write $\frac{2x - 2y}{x^2 - y^2} + \frac{4}{x^2 + 2x + y^2} + \frac{1}{x + y}$ as a fraction in simplest form. $\frac{3x + 3y + 4}{(x + y)^2}$
9. The home team scored 50 points more than half the number scored by the visitors. Their scores totaled 194 points. Who won the game and by how many points? The home team won by 2 points.

Express the answers in simplest form. Assume that no denominator is zero.

10. $-\frac{1}{5}(140x)\left(\frac{3x}{4} + \frac{5x}{7}\right)$ $-41x^2$
11. $(2a + b)^2 - (a - 2b)^2$ $3a^2 + 8ab - 3b^2$
12. $\frac{c - d}{c + d} \div \frac{d}{c - d}$ $\frac{(c - d)^2}{d(c + d)}$
13. $-\left|-108 \div \left(\frac{15}{4^2 - 11}\right)^2\right|$ −12
14. Divide $6x^3 + 9x^2 - 7x + 16$ by $2x + 5$. Write the answer as a polynomial or a mixed expression. $3x^2 - 3x + 4 - \frac{4}{2x + 5}$
15. Express $x^2 + 5x - (1 - 3x^2) + 4 + 3x$ as the product of two binomials. $(2x + 1)(2x + 3)$
16. Solve the equation $x^3 + 3x^2 - 9x = 27$ if $x \in \{-5, -4, -3, -2, -1, 0, 1, 2, 3, 4, 5\}$. $\{3, -3\}$
17. Find two numbers whose sum is 2 and whose squares total 164. 10, −8
18. A bag contains $9.75 in quarters and half dollars. The number of half dollars is 8 less than twice the number of quarters. How many coins of each type are in the bag? 11 quarters and 14 half dollars

Evaluate if $q = -7$, $r = -4$, $s = -0.75$, $t = 2$, and $u = 3$.

19. $2rs - qt^2$ 34
20. $(2q + rt + 1) \div q$ 3
21. $2r^2 \div 4 + 3rt$ −16

Preparing for College Entrance Exams

Strategy for Success

In some types of problems, especially those involving length and width, area, perimeter, or relative position, it may be helpful to draw a sketch. Use any available space in the test booklet. Be careful to make no assumptions in drawing the figure. Use only the information specifically given in the problem.

Decide which is the best of the choices given and write the corresponding letter on your answer sheet.

1. How many integral values of k are there for which $x^2 + kx + 24$ is factorable? E

(A) 0 **(B)** 2 **(C)** 4 **(D)** 6 **(E)** 8

2. Which of the polynomials is prime? B

(A) $35x^2 + 76x + 33$ **(B)** $4x^2 - 26x + 13$
(C) $121y^2 + 176$ **(D)** $21x^2 + 40x - 21$

3. How many distinct roots does the equation $10x^3 - 7x^2 - 12x = 0$ have? D

(A) none **(B)** one **(C)** two **(D)** three

4. A rectangular pool is to be built in a rectangular yard 12 m by 16 m. The pool will be positioned so that a uniform strip of land will be left around the pool. If the pool will take up half the area of the yard, find the perimeter of the pool. D

(A) 20 m **(B)** 22 m **(C)** 24 m **(D)** 40 m **(E)** 44 m

5. Express $\frac{4t + v}{t + v} - \frac{4t^2 - v^2}{t^2 - v^2}$ in simplest form. Assume that no denominator is zero. D

(A) $\frac{2tv}{t^2 - v^2}$ **(B)** $\frac{8tv + 2v^2}{v^2 - t^2}$ **(C)** $\frac{5tv}{t^2 - v^2}$ **(D)** $\frac{3tv}{v^2 - t^2}$

6. Which of the following are factors of $6x^3 + 29x^2 - 7x - 10$?
I. $3x - 1$ II. $2x + 2$ III. $x + 5$ C

(A) I only **(B)** II only **(C)** III only **(D)** I and III only
(E) II and III only

7. Express $\frac{(3n - 5)^4}{(2n + 1)^2} \div \frac{(5 - 3n)^4}{2n^2 + 7n + 3}$ in simplest form. Assume that no denominator is zero. B

(A) $\frac{(3n - 5)^4(n + 3)}{(5 - 3n)^4(2n + 1)}$ **(B)** $\frac{n + 3}{2n + 1}$ **(C)** $\frac{2n + 1}{n + 3}$

(D) $\frac{(3n - 5)^4(2n + 1)}{(5 - 3n)^4(n + 3)}$ **(E)** $n + 3$

About the Photo

Io is one of the four Galilean satellites of Jupiter, so named after the Italian astronomer Galileo, who discovered them in 1610. Io is about the size of Earth's moon, but the diameter of Jupiter is about eleven times that of Earth.

Unlike Earth's moon, Io is geologically active. Lava flows from at least eight active volcanoes, and sulfur compounds released by volcanic eruption produce brilliant colors around Io, ranging from bright yellow-orange to red. Because its surface is continuously changing, geologists and astronomers consider Io to be one of the most fascinating moons in the solar system to study.

Most of what is known about Io and the other moons of Jupiter comes from photographs and data collected by the Voyager spacecrafts in 1979 and 1980 when they flew past Jupiter, which is an average of 7.78×10^8 km from the sun. Voyager 1 continued on a journey past Saturn, which is about 1.43×10^9 km from the sun, and transmitted valuable information about Saturn's rings back to Earth. Astronomers are optimistic that Voyager 2 will provide us with even more valuable information about our solar system.

7 Applying Fractions

Io is the third largest of the known moons of Jupiter. Astronomical distances are often expressed in scientific notation and can be compared by using ratios.

Ratio and Proportion

7-1 Ratios

Objective To solve problems involving ratios.

The distance from Earth to the moon is approximately 240,000 miles. The distance from Jupiter to one of its moons, Io, is approximately 260,000 miles. Although these distances differ by 20,000 miles, they are approximately the same. This relationship is indicated by the quotient, or ratio, of the distances:

$$\frac{240{,}000}{260{,}000} = \frac{12}{13}$$

The **ratio** of one number to another is the quotient of the first number divided by the second. You can express the ratio of 7 to 4 as:

1. an indicated quotient using the division sign $\div$ — $7 \div 4$
2. an indicated quotient using the ratio sign : — $7:4$
3. a fraction — $\frac{7}{4}$
4. a decimal — 1.75

When working with ratios, you must be certain that all distances, masses, and other measures are *expressed in the same units.* For example, if you wish to find the ratio of the height of a 4 m tree to the height of a 50 cm sapling, you express 4 m as 400 cm and divide to find the ratio

$$\frac{400}{50} \text{ or } 8:1.$$

To find the ratio of two quantities of the same kind:

1. Express the measures in the same unit.
2. Then divide them.

The ratio $\frac{9}{6}$ can be expressed in simplest form as $\frac{3}{2}$. When solving certain problems involving ratios, you need to express a ratio in a different form. If you know that two numbers are in the ratio 3:2, you can represent the numbers as $3x$ and $2x$ for some nonzero x because the cancellation rule for fractions gives

$$\frac{3x}{2x} = \frac{3}{2}.$$

Teaching References

Lesson Commentary, pp. T103–T108

Assignment Guide, pp. T62–T64

Supplementary Materials
- Practice Masters 40–45
- Tests 24–26
- Resource Book
  - Practice Exercises, pp. 97–101
  - Tests, pp. 36–39
  - Enrichment Activity, p. 154
  - Practice in Problem Solving/Word Problems, pp. 171–175
- Algebra Action

Extra Practice
- Skills, pp. 617–619
- Problems, pp. 638–642

Alternate Test, p. T16

Problem Solving Strategies

Word Problem Plan
The five-step plan is used throughout the chapter to solve word problems that lead to equations involving fractions or involving equations with fractions.

Recognizing Problem Types
Students learn to recognize and differentiate among various types of problems. Among these types of problems are ratio, proportion, percent, mixture, and work.

Using a Chart
In Sections 7-6, 7-7, and 7-8 students might find it useful to arrange information and unknowns in an organized chart.

Teaching Suggestions
p. T103

Suggested Extensions
p. T103

Chalkboard Examples

State each ratio in simplest form.

1. 5 days to 18 hours 20:3
2. 720 mL to 3 L 6:25
3. 18 min to 3 h 1:10
4. If $34y = 18x$, find the ratio of x to y.
   $\frac{34}{18}y = x$; $\frac{x}{y} = \frac{34}{18} = \frac{17}{9}$
5. Two numbers are in the ratio 8:5 and their sum is 65. Find the numbers.
   Step 2: Let $8x$ and $5x$ be the numbers.
   Step 3: $8x + 5x = 65$
   Step 4: $13x = 65$
   $x = 5$
   $8x = 40$
   $5x = 25$
   Step 5: The numbers are 40 and 25.

Common Errors

Students sometimes express ratios such as 4 h:20 min, for example, as $\frac{4}{20}$, or $\frac{1}{5}$, instead of as $\frac{240}{20}$, or $\frac{12}{1}$. Emphasize that the two quantities in the quotient must be expressed in the same units.

Because some students express each ratio as the quotient of the two numbers given in a problem, caution students to read the exercises and problems carefully.

Example

A farmer plants alfalfa and wheat in the ratio 3:5. How many acres of the 160-acre farm are planted with alfalfa and how many acres with wheat?

Solution

Step 1 The problem asks for the number of acres of alfalfa and the number of acres of wheat.

Step 2 Let $3x$ = the number of acres of alfalfa and $5x$ = the number of acres of wheat.

Step 3 $3x + 5x = 160$

Step 4 $8x = 160$
$x = 20$

Number of acres of alfalfa $= 3x = 3 \cdot 20 = 60$
Number of acres of wheat $= 5x = 5 \cdot 20 = 100$

Step 5 The check is left to you.

$\therefore$ there are 60 acres of alfalfa and 100 acres of wheat. ***Answer***

Saying that three numbers are in the ratio 3:7:11 means that the ratio of the first to the second is 3:7 and the ratio of the second to the third is 7:11.

Oral Exercises

State each ratio in simplest form.

1. 5:15 1:3
2. 18:24 3:4
3. 75:50 3:2
4. 8:24:16 1:3:2
5. $4x:6x$ 2:3
6. $20t:35t$ 4:7
7. $4a^2:8a$ $a:2$
8. $20n:30n:15n$ 4:6:3
9. $\frac{4a^2b}{12ab^2}$ $\frac{a}{3b}$
10. $\frac{(3n)^2}{9n^2}$ 1
11. $\frac{(8x)^2}{8x^2}$ 8
12. $\frac{1}{2}:\frac{3}{4}$ $\frac{2}{3}$
13. 45 min to 2 h 3:8
14. 3 m to 60 cm 5:1
15. 4 h to 20 min 12:1
16. 10 cm to 2 m 1:20
17. 8 wk to 16 d 7:2
18. 1 kg to 50 g 20:1
19. If a problem states that two numbers are in the ratio 5:6, how would you represent those numbers using a variable? $5x$, $6x$

Written Exercises

State each ratio in simplest form.

A 1. 20 min:2 h 1 : 6 2. 6 m:120 cm 5 : 1 3. 4 cm:4 m 1 : 100

4. 150 g:3 kg 1 : 20 5. 6 wk:3 d 14 : 1 6. 5 km:450 cm 10,000 : 9

7. The student-teacher ratio in a school with 3300 students and 150 teachers. 22 : 1

8. The ratio of rainy days to rainless days in a year having 365 days of which 245 are rainless. 24 : 49

9. The ratio of new airplanes to old airplanes in a fleet of 720 planes of which 240 are old. 2 : 1

10. The ratio of seniors taking a math course to seniors not taking a math course if 105 out of 270 seniors are taking math. 7 : 11

11. The ratio of wins to losses to ties for a hockey team that played 48 games, winning 24 and tying 6. 4 : 3 : 1

12. The ratio of whole-wheat flour to milk to nuts in a recipe calling for $2\frac{1}{4}$ cups of flour, 1 cup of milk, and $1\frac{1}{2}$ cups of nuts. 9 : 4 : 6

Find the ratio of (a) the perimeters and (b) the areas of each pair of figures.

13. A rectangle with sides 8 cm and 6 cm and one with sides 10 cm and 9 cm. a. 14 : 19 b. 8 : 15

14. A rectangle with length 12 cm and perimeter 30 cm and one with length 10 cm and perimeter 30 cm. a. 1 : 1 b. 18 : 25

15. A rectangle with sides 4 m and 80 cm and one with sides 3 m and 80 cm. a. 24 : 19 b. 4 : 3

16. A rectangle with sides 50 cm and 1.5 m and a similar rectangle whose sides are 3 times as long. a. 1 : 3 b. 1 : 9

Find the ratio of x to y determined by each equation.

Example $3x = 7y$

Solution

$$3x = 7y$$

$$x = \frac{7}{3}y$$

$$\frac{x}{y} = \frac{7}{3} \text{ or } x:y = 7:3 \quad \textit{Answer}$$

B 17. $8x = 5y$ 5 : 8 18. $14x = 12y$ 6 : 7 19. $18y = 9x$ 2 : 1

20. $ax = by$ $b : a$ 21. $4(x + y) = 8(x - y)$ 3 : 1 22. $8(2x - 3y) = 6(x + y)$ 3 : 1

23. $8x - 4y = 2cx - cy$ 1 : 2 24. $ax + by = cx + dy$ $(d - b) : (a - c)$ 25. $ax - a^2y = bx - b^2y$ $(a + b) : 1$

(*Hint:* In Exercises 23–25, collect x terms on one side and y terms on the other. Then factor.)

Suggested Assignments

Minimum
Day 1: 279/2–20 even
280/*P*: 1, 3, 5
Day 2: 280/*P*: 2–8 even
284/1–15 odd
Day 2 finishes Sec. 7-1 and starts Sec. 7-2.

Average
Day 1: 279/2–22 even
280/*P*: 1, 3, 5, 6
Day 2: 280/*P*: 2, 9–13
284/1–23 odd
Day 2 finishes Sec. 7-1 and starts Sec. 7-2.

Maximum
279/2–28 even
280/*P*: 2–8 even, 9–13

Additional A Exercises

State each ratio in simplest form.

1. 7 min: 25 s 84:5
2. 7 days:20 h 42:5
3. Ratio of men to women in an audience if 135 out of 400 are women 53:27
4. Ratio of children to adults at a play where 425 out of the 700 tickets sold were adult tickets 11:17

Find the ratio of (a) the perimeters and (b) the areas of the figures.

5. A rectangle with sides 6 and 9 to one with sides 8 and 12
a. 3:4 b. 9:16

Mixed Review Exercises

1. Give the prime factorization of 990. $2 \cdot 3^2 \cdot 5 \cdot 11$
2. Evaluate $82 \times 17 - 82 \times 7$ by factoring. $82(17 - 7) = 82 \times 10 = 820$
3. Express $(9 - 6x)(9 + 6x)$ as a polynomial. $81 - 36x^2$
4. Express $\frac{6x^2 - 6}{3x + 3}$ in simplest form. $2x - 2 (x \neq -1)$

Find the ratio of x to y determined by each equation.

C **26.** $x^2 + 2y^2 = 2xy + y^2$ 1 : 1 **27.** $x^2 - 4xy + 4y^2 = 0$ 2 : 1 **28.** $25x^2 + 36y^2 = 60xy$ 6 : 5

(*Hint:* In Exercises 26–28, collect terms on one side of the equation. Then factor the resulting polynomial.)

Problems

A

1. Two numbers are in the ratio 3:8 and their sum is 66. What are the numbers? 18, 48

2. There are a total of 180 players and coaches in the town soccer league. If the player-coach ratio is 9:1, how many players are there? 162

3. The freshman class of 700 students has a boy to girl ratio of 17:18. How many girls are there? 360

4. The perimeter of a rectangle is 96 cm. Find the length and width if their ratio is 7:5. 28 cm by 20 cm

5. Three numbers are in the ratio 5:6:7 and their total is 720. Find the numbers. 200, 240, 280

6. The measures of the angles of a triangle are in the ratio 1:2:3. Find these measures. (*Hint:* The measures of the angles of a triangle total 180°.) 30, 60, 90

7. Concrete can be made by mixing cement, sand, and gravel in the ratio 3:6:8. How many cubic meters of each ingredient are needed to make 850 m^3 of concrete? 150 m^3 cement, 300 m^3 sand, 400 m^3 gravel

8. A new alloy is made by mixing 8 parts of iron with 3 parts of zinc and 1 part of tungsten. How much of each metal is needed to make 420 m^3 of the alloy? 280 m^3 iron, 105 m^3 zinc, 35 m^3 tungsten

B

9. Two cars leave from the same place at the same time, traveling in opposite directions at speeds that are in the ratio 4:3. After 2 h, the cars are 308 km apart. What are their speeds? (*Hint:* Make a rate-time-distance chart.) 88 km/h, 66 km/h

10. The ratio of Alex's cycling speed to Bart's cycling speed is 6:5. Bart leaves school at 3 P.M. and Alex leaves at 3:10 P.M. By 3:30, Alex is only 2 km behind Bart. How fast is each boy going? Alex, 24 km/h; Bart, 20 km/h

11. In a collection of dimes and nickels worth $3.20, the ratio of the number of dimes to the number of nickels is 3:2. Find the number of each type of coin. (*Hint:* Make a coin value chart.) 16 nickels, 24 dimes

12. In a collection of nickels, dimes, and quarters worth $20.30, the ratio of the numbers of nickels, dimes, and quarters is 5:4:9. Find the number of each type of coin. 35 nickels, 28 dimes, 63 quarters

13. The College Bookstore purchased a supply of mechanical pencils and ball-point pens. The ratio of pencils to pens is 5:9. If the pencils cost \$1 each, the pens 25 cents each, and the total bill was \$290, find the number of pencils purchased. (*Hint:* Make a number-price-cost chart.) 200

14. The ratio of Sue's age to her father's age is 2:7. In three years, their ages will total 60. How old is each now? Sue, 12; her father, 42

C 15. There are 2820 cars in Farmington. The ratio of intermediates to compacts is 7:5 and the ratio of compacts to full-size cars is 8:9. How many full-size cars are there? 900

16. Find two numbers such that their sum, their difference, and their product have the ratio 3:2:5. 2, 10

Biographical Note / *Juan de la Cierva*

Juan de la Cierva was born in Murcia, Spain, in 1895. He attended school in Murcia and Madrid and later graduated from the Special Technical College in Madrid.

Juan de la Cierva was interested from childhood in the design and building of aircraft. In 1912, at the age of seventeen, de la Cierva and two friends assembled a biplane using the wreckage from a French aircraft. This airplane became the first Spanish-built plane to fly. De la Cierva later designed and built a monoplane, as well as the world's second trimotor, a plane powered by three engines.

It was the crash of the trimotor that started de la Cierva on the road to designing a new type of aircraft, the autogiro. This aircraft resembled a cross between a helicopter and an airplane, although the large rotor at the top of the plane was not powered, but moved due to the passage of air over the blades. De la Cierva hoped that this design would eliminate a major problem of airplanes of his day, that of crashes caused by engines stalling at low speeds. He constructed a number of autogiros from 1920 to 1922, continually refining the concept until in 1923 a successful autogiro took to the air. By 1928 the design had been perfected to the point that de la Cierva was able to fly an autogiro across the English Channel, a feat that brought him numerous honors. The concept of the autogiro reached its high point in 1933 with the model C.30, a craft that could take off in a space of six yards and was capable of a speed of 100 miles per hour. At the time of his death in 1936, Juan de la Cierva was recognized, along with the Wright brothers, as one of the creative forces in modern aviation.

Teaching Suggestions
p. T103

Suggested Extensions
p. T103

Chalkboard Examples

Solve.

1. $\frac{x}{3} = \frac{5}{12}$
$12x = 15$
$x = \frac{15}{12} = \frac{5}{4}$

2. $\frac{3}{2y} = \frac{9}{32}$
$18y = 96$
$y = \frac{96}{18} = \frac{16}{3}$

3. $\frac{3x + 1}{5} = \frac{x}{2}$
$2(3x + 1) = 5x$
$6x + 2 = 5x$
$x = -2$

4. $\frac{x - 5}{12} = \frac{x + 2}{5}$
$5(x - 5) = 12(x + 2)$
$5x - 25 = 12x + 24$
$-49 = 7x$
$x = -7$

5. An investment of $1200 paid interest of $102. How much interest would $1600 invested at the same rate for the same amount of time pay?
$\frac{1200}{102} = \frac{1600}{x}$
$1200x = 102 \cdot 1600$
$x = \frac{102 \cdot 1600}{1200}$
$x = 136$; $136

7-2 Proportion

Objective To solve problems involving proportion.

An equation that states that two ratios are equal is called a **proportion.** You can write proportions in several different ways.

$2:3 = 4:6$ read, "2 is to 3 as 4 is to 6."

$\frac{x}{12} = \frac{9}{4}$ read, "x divided by 12 equals 9 divided by 4."

In the proportion

$$a:b = c:d \quad \text{or} \quad \frac{a}{b} = \frac{c}{d},$$

a and d are called the **extremes** and b and c are called the **means.** You can use the multiplication property of equality to show that in any proportion *the product of the extremes equals the product of the means.* (See Oral Exercise 9.) Thus, if $a:b = c:d$, you have $ad = bc$ (and by the commutative axiom for multiplication, $da = cb$). This fact can be used to solve proportions.

Example 1 Solve: $\frac{3}{x} = \frac{5}{4}$

Solution

$\frac{3}{x} = \frac{5}{4}$
$3 \cdot 4 = 5x$
$12 = 5x$
$\frac{12}{5} = x$

$\therefore$ the solution is $\frac{12}{5}$. ***Answer***

Example 2 Solve: $\frac{2n - 3}{5} = \frac{n + 2}{6}$

Solution

$\frac{2n - 3}{5} = \frac{n + 2}{6}$
$6(2n - 3) = 5(n + 2)$
$12n - 18 = 5n + 10$
$7n = 28$
$n = 4$

$\therefore$ the solution is 4. ***Answer***

Example 3 Solve the formula $I = \frac{E}{R}$ for R.

Solution Rewrite the formula as the proportion $\frac{I}{1} = \frac{E}{R}$.

$\frac{I}{1} = \frac{E}{R}$
$IR = E$
$R = \frac{E}{I}$ ***Answer***

The following examples illustrate two of the many types of problems that can be solved by proportions.

Example 4 A recipe for making 30 bran muffins requires 1200 g of flour. If you have only 1000 g of flour, how many muffins can you make?

Solution

Step 1 The problem asks for the number of muffins.

Step 2 Let x = the number of muffins.

Step 3 1200 g makes 30 muffins.
1000 g makes x muffins.

$$\frac{1200}{1000} = \frac{30}{x}$$

Step 4 Solve.

$$\frac{12}{10} = \frac{30}{x}$$

$$12x = 300$$

$$x = 25$$

Step 5 The check is left to you.

∴ you can make 25 bran muffins. ***Answer***

Example 5 Nick Massey drove 352 miles on 11 gallons of gas. How many additional miles can he drive on the 4 gallons remaining in his car's gas tank?

Solution

Step 1 The problem asks for the number of additional miles he can drive.

Step 2 Let x = the number of additional miles.

Step 3 352 miles on 11 gallons
x miles on 4 gallons

$$\frac{352}{11} = \frac{x}{4}$$

Step 4 Solve.

$$\frac{352}{11} = \frac{x}{4}$$

$$352 \cdot 4 = 11x$$

$$128 = x$$

Step 5 The check is left to you.

∴ he can drive 128 additional miles. ***Answer***

6. A typist types an essay of 1260 words in 15 min. At that rate, how long would it take to type an essay of 2100 words?

$$\frac{y}{2100} = \frac{15}{1260}$$

$$1260y = 15 \cdot 2100$$

$$y = \frac{15 \cdot 2100}{1260}$$

$$y = 25;\ 25 \text{ min}$$

Common Error

Students sometimes solve proportions incorrectly because they try to reduce fractions by "cancelling" a factor from the numerator of the fraction on one side of the equation with the same factor from the denominator of the fraction on the other side of the equation. Use an example such as $\frac{12a}{16} = \frac{8}{18}$ to point out that this is unreasonable and to review the cancellation rule for fractions.

Supplementary Materials

Practice Master 40
Resource Book, p. 97

Suggested Assignments

Minimum
284/16–26
285/*P*: 1–6
S 279/11, 13, 15
Day 2 of Sec. 7-1 finishes Sec. 7-1 and starts Sec. 7-2.

Average
284/25–35
285/*P*: 1, 5–9
S 279/23–25
Day 2 of Sec. 7-1 finishes Sec. 7-1 and starts Sec. 7-2.

Maximum
284/1–43 odd
285/*P*: 3–7 odd, 8–11

Additional A Exercises

Solve.

1. $\frac{a}{6} = \frac{15}{18}$ 5
2. $\frac{4}{7} = \frac{12}{3x}$ 7
3. $\frac{14y}{35} = \frac{16}{40}$ 1
4. $\frac{16}{5n} = -2$ $-\frac{8}{5}$
5. $\frac{3k+4}{4} = \frac{5}{2}$ 2
6. $\frac{4n-9}{5} = \frac{n+3}{3}$ 6

Oral Exercises

State the equation that results when you equate the product of the extremes and the product of the means in the following proportions.

1. $\frac{5}{3} = \frac{2}{x}$ $5x = 6$
2. $\frac{3}{y} = \frac{7}{8}$ $24 = 7y$
3. $\frac{2x}{7} = \frac{3}{5}$ $10x = 21$
4. $\frac{-3}{2n} = \frac{5}{-6}$ $18 = 10n$
5. $\frac{y-3}{4} = \frac{5}{2}$ $2(y-3) = 20$
6. $\frac{4}{9} = \frac{a-2}{3}$ $12 = 9(a-2)$
7. $\frac{2}{2d-1} = \frac{4}{7}$ $14 = 4(2d-1)$
8. $\frac{3}{x-5} = \frac{4}{x+5}$ $3(x+5) = 4(x-5)$
9. If you multiply both sides of the proportion $\frac{a}{b} = \frac{c}{d}$ by bd, what equation do you get? $ad = bc$

Written Exercises

Solve.

A

1. $\frac{x}{5} = \frac{3}{4}$ $\frac{15}{4}$
2. $\frac{y}{3} = \frac{4}{7}$ $\frac{12}{7}$
3. $\frac{9}{2x} = \frac{6}{4}$ 3
4. $\frac{2}{3} = \frac{8}{2n}$ 6
5. $\frac{3n}{7} = \frac{4}{5}$ $\frac{28}{15}$
6. $\frac{8}{5k} = \frac{2}{5}$ 4
7. $\frac{9}{4} = \frac{3a}{5}$ $\frac{15}{4}$
8. $\frac{4}{3} = \frac{12}{7k}$ $\frac{9}{7}$
9. $\frac{18x}{13} = \frac{36}{39}$ $\frac{2}{3}$
10. $\frac{15x}{64} = \frac{45}{32}$ 6
11. $\frac{81}{49} = \frac{27y}{14}$ $\frac{6}{7}$
12. $\frac{25}{17a} = \frac{125}{51}$ $\frac{3}{5}$
13. $\frac{15a}{36} = \frac{45}{12}$ 9
14. $\frac{81}{64} = \frac{27n}{40}$ $\frac{15}{8}$
15. $\frac{17}{25b} = \frac{34}{75}$ $\frac{3}{2}$
16. $\frac{36}{24} = \frac{12x}{36}$ $\frac{9}{2}$
17. $\frac{4}{x} = 5$ $\frac{4}{5}$
18. $\frac{5}{2n} = 3$ $\frac{5}{6}$
19. $\frac{3r}{7} = -6$ -14
20. $-2 = \frac{4y}{5}$ $-\frac{5}{2}$
21. $\frac{x-5}{4} = \frac{3}{2}$ 11
22. $\frac{y-3}{8} = \frac{3}{4}$ 9
23. $\frac{2n-1}{5} = 7$ 18
24. $\frac{1-4n}{5} = 9$ -11
25. $\frac{5n-3}{4} = \frac{5n+3}{6}$ 3
26. $\frac{6x-2}{7} = \frac{5x+7}{8}$ 5
27. $\frac{4y-3}{7} = \frac{2y-1}{3}$ -1
28. $\frac{3n-11}{5} = \frac{1+5n}{18}$ 7
29. $\frac{4x}{5} = \frac{2x}{7}$ 0
30. $\frac{4x+12}{8} = \frac{x+3}{2}$ {all the real numbers}

B

31. $\frac{25(x-3)}{28} = \frac{75}{14}$ 9
32. $\frac{36}{2x-3} = \frac{72}{2x+3}$ $\frac{9}{2}$
33. $\frac{15}{x+7} = \frac{45}{x+21}$ 0

Find the ratio of x to y.

34. $\frac{3x+2y}{5} = \frac{4x-7y}{6}$ $\frac{47}{2}$
35. $\frac{8x-y}{4} = \frac{x+y}{3}$ $\frac{7}{20}$
36. $\frac{x-2y}{17} = \frac{x+2y}{34}$ $\frac{6}{1}$
37. $\frac{cy}{d-c} = \frac{dx}{d^2-c^2}$ (Give your answer in terms of c and d.) $\frac{c(d+c)}{d}$

38. Solve the formula $\frac{F}{m} = a$ for F. Then solve for m. $F = ma$; $m = \frac{F}{a}$

39. Solve the formula $F = \frac{mr^2}{r}$ for m. Then solve for r. $m = \frac{Fr}{r^2}$; $r = \frac{F}{m}$

40. Solve $\frac{p}{t} = \frac{P}{T}$ for P. Then solve for T. $P = \frac{pT}{t}$; $T = \frac{tP}{p}$

41. Solve $\frac{PV}{T} = K$ for V. Then solve for T. $V = \frac{TK}{P}$; $T = \frac{PV}{K}$

When the means of a proportion are the same, the mean is called the **mean proportional** between the two extremes. For example, since $4:6 = 6:9$, 6 is the mean proportional between 4 and 9.

Find the mean proportional between the following.

C 42. 3 and 27 9

43. 4 and 64 16

44. a and b, if both are positive $\sqrt{ab}$

Problems

A 1. Three cans of tuna cost \$3.51. How much will five cans cost? \$5.85

2. A plane can fly 1800 km in 2 h. How far can it fly in 3 h? 2700 km

3. A truck uses 8 L of gasoline to go 120 km. How much will it use to go 300 km? 20 L

4. A car that sold for \$7200 had a sales tax of \$240. How much is the tax on a car that sells for \$9000? \$300

5. A recipe for $2\frac{1}{2}$ dozen whole-wheat muffins requires 600 g of flour. How many muffins can be made with 900 g of flour? 45

6. A pump can fill a 2400-liter water tank in 50 min. How much water can it pump in half an hour? 1440 L

7. An advertisement claims that in a recent poll, three out of four dentists recommended brushing with Cleanteeth toothpaste. If there were 92 dentists polled, how many favored Cleanteeth? 69

B 8. In a town with 18,000 homes, a survey was taken to determine the number with cable television. Of the 360 homes surveyed, 135 had cable television. Estimate the number of homes in the town that have cable television. 6750

9. A 25-acre field yields 550 bushels of wheat annually. How many additional acres should be planted so that the annual yield will be 660 bushels? 5 acres

Mixed Review Exercises

1. Simplify: $\frac{(-6xy)^3}{(-2x^2y)^2}$
$\frac{-54y}{x}$ $(x \neq 0, y \neq 0)$

Express as a polynomial.

2. $(7b - 2)(8b + 3)$
$56b^2 + 5b - 6$

3. $(n + 15)^2$
$n^2 + 30n + 225$

4. Express in simplest form: $\frac{9m^2 + m}{m^2 - n^2} \div \frac{mn}{m + n}$
$\frac{9m + 1}{n(m - n)}$
$(m \neq 0, n \neq 0, m \neq \pm n)$

10. A photograph 20 cm by 15 cm is enlarged so that its length becomes 28 cm. **a.** What does the width become? **b.** Find these ratios:

$$\frac{\text{new length}}{\text{old length}}, \quad \frac{\text{new perimeter}}{\text{old perimeter}}, \quad \frac{\text{new area}}{\text{old area}}$$

a. 21 cm
b. $\frac{7}{5}, \frac{7}{5}, \frac{49}{25}$

11. On a map, 1 cm represents 10 km, and Wyoming is a rectangle 44.5 cm by 59.1 cm. Find the area of Wyoming in square kilometers. 262,995 km^2

C 12. Mahogany weighs 33.94 pounds per cubic foot, whereas pine weighs 23.45 pounds per cubic foot. Which weighs more: a mahogany board with dimensions $5\frac{1}{2}$ in. by 1 in. by 6 ft or a pine board with dimensions $3\frac{1}{2}$ in. by $1\frac{1}{2}$ in. by 8 ft? the mahogany board

Quick Quiz

State each ratio in simplest form.

1. 25 g to 4 kg 1:160
2. 16 wk to 12 d 28:3
3. Two numbers are in the ratio of 6 : 7 and their sum is 78. Find the numbers. 36 and 42

Solve.

4. $\frac{13}{x} = \frac{39}{21}$ 7
5. $\frac{7z}{45} = \frac{42}{18}$ 15
6. $\frac{3x+3}{7} = \frac{5x-3}{9}$ 6

Self-Test 1

Vocabulary ratio (p. 277) proportion (p. 282) means (p. 282) extremes (p. 282)

Express each ratio in simplest form.

1. 36 min : 1 h 3 : 5
2. 2 dollars : 5 cents 40 : 1

Obj. 7-1, p. 277

3. The ratio of the number of questions Tony answered correctly on a test to the total number of questions on the test was 9 : 11. If the test consisted of 77 questions, how many questions did Tony answer correctly? 63

Solve.

4. $\frac{x}{150} = \frac{9}{25}$ 54
5. $\frac{3}{4r} = 12$ $\frac{1}{16}$
6. $\frac{x+2}{4} = \frac{x-5}{3}$ 26

Obj. 7-2, p. 282

Check your answers with those at the back of the book.

Computer Exercises

For students with some programming experience

1. Write a BASIC program that converts the ratio of two integers entered with INPUT statements to a decimal number. Use the program to convert the following ratios to decimal form.

   a. $\frac{2}{3}$ 0.666667 **b.** $\frac{15}{6}$ 2.5 **c.** $\frac{5}{11}$ 0.454545 **d.** $\frac{5}{37}$ 0.135135

2. Write a BASIC program that converts a repeating decimal number to the ratio of two integers. Use the program to convert the following decimal numbers to ratios.

   a. $0.\overline{4}$ $\frac{4}{9}$ **b.** $0.\overline{03}$ $\frac{3}{99}$ **c.** $0.\overline{9}$ $\frac{9}{9} = 1$ **d.** $0.\overline{123}$ $\frac{123}{999}$

Computer Key-In

The following program will print out several ratios equal to $\frac{A}{B}$.

```
10  PRINT "TO PRINT OUT EQUAL RATIOS:"
20  PRINT "INPUT A,B";
30  INPUT A,B
40  PRINT
50  FOR I=1 TO 10
60  PRINT I*A
70  PRINT "-----"
80  PRINT I*B
90  PRINT
100  NEXT I
110  END
```

Exercises

RUN the program for the following.

1. $A = 3, B = 5$ **2.** $A = 5, B = 7$

Make these changes in the program.

```
10  PRINT "TO PRINT PROPORTIONAL RECTANGLES:"
50  FOR I=1 TO 5
55  PRINT "RECTANGLE ";I
60  FOR J=1 TO I*A
65  FOR K=1 TO I*B
70  PRINT "*";
75  NEXT K
80  PRINT
85  NEXT J
```

RUN the revised program for the following.

3. $A = 3, B = 5$ **4.** $A = 2, B = 6$

Let the number of asterisks represent the area of each rectangle.

5. What is the area of each of the five rectangles?

What is the ratio of the following?

6. The area of rectangle 2 to the area of rectangle 1.

7. The area of rectangle 5 to the area of rectangle 1.

8. If you can print out the results of Exercises 3 and 4, draw lines to mark off rectangles equivalent to rectangle 1 on each of the other rectangles.

Additional Answers
Computer Key-In

1. $\frac{3}{5}, \frac{6}{10}, \frac{9}{15}, \frac{12}{20}, \frac{15}{25}, \frac{18}{30}, \frac{21}{35}, \frac{24}{40}, \frac{27}{45}, \frac{30}{50}$

2. $\frac{5}{7}, \frac{10}{14}, \frac{15}{21}, \frac{20}{28}, \frac{25}{35}, \frac{30}{42}, \frac{35}{49}, \frac{40}{56}, \frac{45}{63}, \frac{50}{70}$

5. For $A = 3$, $B = 5$: 15, 60, 135, 240, 375
For $A = 2$, $B = 6$: 12, 48, 108, 192, 300

6. For $A = 3$, $B = 5$, ratio is 4 : 1
For $A = 2$, $B = 6$, ratio is 4 : 1

7. For $A = 3$, $B = 5$, ratio is 25 : 1
For $A = 2$, $B = 6$, ratio is 25 : 1

Computer Key-In Commentary

Most BASICs allow messages in INPUT statements. Lines 20 and 30 could be incorporated into:20 INPUT ''A, B''; A, B. The message must be in quotation marks.

Fractional Equations

7-3 Equations with Fractional Coefficients

Objective To solve equations with fractional coefficients.

You can solve equations with fractional coefficients by using the least common denominator of all the fractions in the equation. Transform the equation by multiplying both sides by the least common denominator. Then solve the transformed equation.

Example Solve: $\frac{n+1}{10} - \frac{n}{3} = \frac{19}{15}$

Solution The LCD of the fractions is 30.

$$30\left[\left(\frac{n+1}{10}\right) - \left(\frac{n}{3}\right)\right] = 30\left[\frac{19}{15}\right]$$

$$30\left(\frac{n+1}{10}\right) - 30\left(\frac{n}{3}\right) = 30\left[\frac{19}{15}\right]$$

$$3(n+1) - 10n = 2[19]$$

$$3n + 3 - 10n = 38$$

$$-7n + 3 = 38$$

$$-7n = 35$$

$$n = -5$$

$\therefore$ the solution is -5. ***Answer***

Oral Exercises

State the least common denominator of the fractions in each equation. Then state the equation that results when both sides are multiplied by the LCD.

1. $\frac{x}{3} + \frac{x}{2} = 1$ **2.** $\frac{3y}{8} + \frac{y}{4} = 10$ **3.** $\frac{n}{2} + \frac{n}{3} = \frac{20}{6}$

4. $\frac{3a}{5} - \frac{a}{2} = \frac{1}{20}$ **5.** $\frac{x+1}{6} + \frac{x+5}{4} = 1$ **6.** $\frac{y}{2} - \frac{y+5}{3} = 0$

7. $\frac{x}{4} - \frac{2x-1}{3} = -3$ **8.** $\frac{1}{4}(n+2) - \frac{1}{6}(n-2) = \frac{3}{2}$ **9.** $\frac{3(x+1)}{2} - \frac{5(x+1)}{4} = \frac{1}{2}$

Teaching Suggestions
p. T104

Suggested Extensions
p. T104

Chalkboard Examples

Solve.

1. $\frac{n}{5} + \frac{3n}{10} = \frac{3}{2}$
   The LCD is 10.
   $10\left(\frac{n}{5}\right) + 10\left(\frac{3n}{10}\right) = 10\left(\frac{3}{2}\right)$
   $2n + 3n = 15$
   $n = 3$

2. $\frac{n}{4} + \frac{n}{3} = \frac{7}{4}$
   The LCD is 12.
   $12\left(\frac{n}{4}\right) + 12\left(\frac{n}{3}\right) = 12\left(\frac{7}{4}\right)$
   $3n + 4n = 21$
   $n = 3$

3. $\frac{y-1}{3} - \frac{y+1}{5} = 2$
   The LCD is 15.
   $15\left(\frac{y-1}{3}\right) - 15\left(\frac{y+1}{5}\right) = 15(2)$
   $5y - 5 - 3y - 3 = 30$
   $2y = 38$
   $y = 19$

Additional Answers
Oral Exercises

1. 6; $2x + 3x = 6$
2. 8; $3y + 2y = 80$
3. 6; $3n + 2n = 20$
4. 20; $12a - 10a = 1$
5. 12; $2(x+1) + 3(x+5) = 12$
6. 6; $3y - 2(y+5) = 0$
7. 12; $3x - 4(2x-1) = -36$
8. 12; $3(n+2) - 2(n-2) = 18$
9. 4; $6(x+1) - 5(x+1) = 2$

Written Exercises

1. $\frac{6}{5}$ 2. 16 3. 4 4. $\frac{1}{2}$ 5. −1 6. 10 7. 8 8. 8 9. 1

A **1–9.** Solve the equations in Oral Exercises 1–9.

Solve.

18. $\frac{1}{2}$

10. $\frac{5n}{18} - \frac{4n}{9} = \frac{1}{12}$ $-\frac{1}{2}$

11. $2a + \frac{a}{3} = \frac{a}{4} + 5$ $\frac{12}{5}$

12. $x + \frac{x}{4} = 14 - \frac{x}{2}$ 8

13. $\frac{x-2}{3} = \frac{x+1}{4}$ 11

14. $\frac{17x}{25} = \frac{51}{50}$ $\frac{3}{2}$

15. $x + \frac{x+2}{4} = 0$ $-\frac{2}{5}$

16. $\frac{y+2}{3} + \frac{y-1}{6} = 5$ 9

17. $\frac{4y+1}{3} - \frac{2y+1}{5} = \frac{3}{5}$ $\frac{1}{2}$

18. $\frac{x+2}{15} - \frac{x-3}{5} = \frac{2}{3}$

19. $\frac{5y}{3} = \frac{y}{6}$ 0

20. $\frac{3y-9}{6} = \frac{2y-6}{4}$ {all the real numbers}

21. $\frac{n+3}{3} - \frac{n}{4} = \frac{n-2}{5}$ 12

B **22.** $\frac{2}{3}(x-1) - \frac{1}{5}(x-2) = \frac{x+2}{3}$ 7

23. $\frac{1}{4}(y-1) - \frac{1}{6}(y-3) = \frac{2}{3}$ 5

24. $\frac{x+2}{4} - \frac{x+3}{3} + \frac{2x-3}{6} = 0$ 4

25. $\frac{2}{3}(x-1) - \frac{1}{5}(2x-3) = 1$ 4

26. $\frac{6b-4}{3} - 2 = \frac{18-4b}{3} + b$ 4

27. $2 - \frac{7c-1}{6} = 3c - \frac{19c+3}{4}$ −5

28. $\frac{3}{4}(x+4) - \frac{2}{5}(x+5) = x+1$ 0

29. $\frac{1}{3}(x+6) - 1 = \frac{1}{6}(9-x)$ 1

C **30.** $\frac{1}{4}\left(y - \frac{1}{3}\right) - \frac{1}{6}(y-3) = \frac{2}{3}$ 3

31. $\frac{1}{2}\left(x + \frac{2}{3}\right) - \frac{1}{6}\left(7x - \frac{1}{3}\right) = \frac{1}{6}$ $\frac{1}{3}$

32. $\frac{1}{5}(2x-3) - \frac{2}{3}\left(x - \frac{1}{2}\right) = \frac{7}{15}$ $-\frac{11}{4}$

33. $\frac{3}{4}(x-2) - \frac{2}{3}\left(x - \frac{1}{2}\right) = \frac{x+1}{2}$ −4

Solve for *x* in terms of the other variable.

34. $\frac{x+3a}{10} - \frac{x-a}{2} = \frac{x}{5}$ $\frac{4}{3}a$

35. $\frac{x-n}{5} - \frac{7x-n}{10} = \frac{2n-x}{15}$ $-\frac{7n}{13}$

36. $\frac{1}{5}(2x-3c) - \frac{1}{3}\left(x - \frac{c}{2}\right) - \frac{x}{6} = 0$ $-\frac{13c}{3}$

37. $\frac{a^2+6a+9}{x} = a^2 + 3a$ $\frac{a+3}{a}$

Problems

A **1.** One third of a number is 10 more than one eighth of the number. Find the number. 48

2. One fourth of a number is 4 less than one third of the number. Find the number. 48

3. Two numbers are in the ratio 5:2. One half of their sum is $10\frac{1}{2}$. Find the numbers. 15, 6

Suggested Assignments

Minimum
Day 1: 289/1–27 odd; *P*: 1, 3, 4
R 286/*Self-Test 1*
Day 2: 289/*P*: 2, 5, 7, 8
292/1–6, 7–17 odd
Day 2 finishes Sec. 7-3 and starts Sec. 7-4.

Average
Day 1: 289/1–33 odd; *P*: 1, 3, 4
R 286/*Self-Test 1*
Day 2: 290/*P*: 4–12 even
292/7–29 odd
Day 2 finishes Sec. 7-3 and starts Sec. 7-4.

Maximum
289/1–33 odd
290/*P*: 4–8 even, 9, 11
R 286/*Self-Test 1*

Additional A Exercises

Solve.

1. $\frac{y}{4} + \frac{y}{3} = 1$ $y = \frac{12}{7}$

2. $\frac{x+5}{8} - \frac{x-3}{4} = 0$ $x = 11$

3. $\frac{1}{6}(y+4) - \frac{1}{2}(y-2) = \frac{5}{12}$ $y = \frac{15}{4}$

4. $5s + \frac{s}{5} = \frac{s}{3} + 2$ $s = \frac{30}{73}$

5. $n + \frac{n+7}{6} = 1$ $n = -\frac{1}{7}$

6. $\frac{y+5}{2} - \frac{y}{4} = \frac{y+6}{3}$ $y = 6$

Common Error

Sometimes students forget to multiply both sides of fractional equations by the LCD or they "cancel" the LCD with the denominator of one term on one side of the equation, essentially using the distributive axiom incorrectly. Encourage students who make such errors to write out their work as shown in the first two steps of the solution to the example given on page 288.

Mixed Review Exercises

Factor.

1. $x^2 - 7x - 60$
   $(x - 12)(x + 5)$
2. $ab + a^2 - b - a$
   $(a + b)(a - 1)$
3. Solve: $6x^2 - x = 15$
   $x = \frac{5}{3}, \frac{-3}{2}$
4. Divide to decide whether or not $x + 3$ is a factor of $x^3 + 2x^2 + 9x + 6$.
   It is not.

4. Three numbers are in the ratio 2:3:4. One fourth of their sum is 5 more than the smallest number. Find the numbers. 40, 60, 80

5. Jack is 3 years older than Jill. Three years ago Jill's age was four fifths of Jack's age. How old is each now? Jack, 18; Jill, 15

6. Tom is two years older than Jerry. Next year Tom will be one and a half times as old as Jerry. How old is each now? Jerry, 3; Tom, 5

7. A rectangle is 9 cm longer than it is wide. The width is one seventh of the perimeter. Find the length and width. length, 15 cm; width, 6 cm

8. The lengths of the sides of a triangle are consecutive integers. Half of the perimeter is 14 more than the length of the longest side. Find the perimeter. 90

B **9.** Erica hiked up a mountain trail at 3 km/h and returned at 4 km/h. The entire trip took 5 h 10 min, including the half hour she spent at the top. How long was the trail? 8 km

10. Consuela walks from her house to the recreation center at 6 km/h, stays for 45 min, and then gets a ride back home at 48 km/h. If she arrives home 1.5 h after she started out, find the distance from her home to the recreation center. 4 km

11. Three fourths of a pile of coins are quarters and the rest are dimes. If the total value is \$6.80, how many of each type of coin are there? 8 dimes, 24 quarters

12. Two thirds of a pile of coins are nickels, one fourth are dimes, and the rest are quarters. If the total value is \$4.75, how many of each type of coin are there? 40 nickels, 15 dimes, 5 quarters

13. Liann bought several apples at the rate of 3 apples for 35 cents. She sold nine tenths of them at 25 cents each, making a profit of \$6.50. How many apples did Liann fail to sell? 6 apples

C **14.** Diophantus was a famous Greek mathematician, who lived and worked in Alexandria, Egypt, probably in the third century A.D. After he died, someone described his life in this puzzle:

> He was a boy for $\frac{1}{6}$ of his life.
>
> After $\frac{1}{12}$ more, he acquired a beard.
>
> After another $\frac{1}{7}$, he married.
>
> In the fifth year after his marriage
> his son was born.
> The son lived half as many years as
> his father.
> Diophantus died 4 years after his son.

How old was Diophantus when he died? 84 years old

7-4 Fractional Equations

Objective To solve fractional equations.

An equation that has a variable in the denominator of one or more terms is called a **fractional equation.** You can use the multiplication property of equality to solve fractional equations.

Example Solve: $1 + \frac{2}{b - 1} = \frac{2}{b^2 - b}$

Solution 1. Factor all the denominators to determine the LCD.

$$1 + \frac{2}{b - 1} = \frac{2}{b(b - 1)}$$

The LCD is $b(b - 1)$; note that $b \neq 0$ or 1.

2. Multiply both sides of the equation by the LCD.

$$b(b - 1)\left[1 + \frac{2}{b - 1}\right] = b(b - 1)\left[\frac{2}{b(b - 1)}\right]$$

$$\begin{aligned} b(b - 1) + 2b &= 2 \\ b^2 - b + 2b &= 2 \\ b^2 + b - 2 &= 0 \\ (b - 1)(b + 2) &= 0 \\ b = 1 \quad \text{or} \quad b &= -2 \end{aligned}$$

3. Recall that 1 is not permissible as a solution to the original equation. Check -2 in the original equation.

$$1 + \frac{2}{-2 - 1} \stackrel{?}{=} \frac{2}{(-2)^2 - (-2)}$$

$$1 + \left(-\frac{2}{3}\right) \stackrel{?}{=} \frac{2}{6}$$

$$\frac{1}{3} = \frac{1}{3} \quad \checkmark$$

$\therefore$ the solution is -2. ***Answer***

In the preceding example you saw that 1 was not a solution of the original equation even though it satisfied the transformed equation. Notice that multiplying the equation by $b(b - 1)$ led to an equation that was *not equivalent* to the given one. This new equation had the extra root 1, a number for which the multiplier $b(b - 1)$ represents *zero.*

In general, multiplying both sides of an equation by a variable expression that can represent zero may produce an equation that is not equivalent to the original equation. Therefore, *you must check each root of the resulting equation to see that it satisfies the original equation.*

Teaching Suggestions
p. T104

Suggested Extensions
p. T104

Chalkboard Examples

Solve.

1. $\frac{3}{t} - \frac{1}{2} = \frac{1}{10}$

Value not permitted: 0

The LCD is $10t$.

$10t\left(\frac{3}{t}\right) - 10t\left(\frac{1}{2}\right) = 10t\left(\frac{1}{10}\right)$

$$\begin{aligned} 30 - 5t &= t \\ 6t &= 30 \\ t &= 5 \end{aligned}$$

The solution is 5.

2. $\frac{x - 4}{x - 2} = \frac{4}{5}$

Value not permitted: 2

The LCD is $5(x - 2)$.

$5(x - 2)\left(\frac{x - 4}{x - 2}\right) = 5(x - 2)\left(\frac{4}{5}\right)$

$$\begin{aligned} 5x - 20 &= 4x - 8 \\ x &= 12 \end{aligned}$$

The solution is 12.

3. $\frac{n + 1}{n + 2} - \frac{10}{n^2 - 4} = 0$

Values not permitted: 2, -2

The LCD is $(n + 2)(n - 2)$.

$(n + 2)(n - 2)\left(\frac{n + 1}{n + 2}\right) - (n + 2)(n - 2) \cdot \left[\frac{10}{(n + 2)(n - 2)}\right] = 0$

$$\begin{aligned} n^2 - n - 2 - 10 &= 0 \\ n^2 - n - 12 &= 0 \\ (n - 4)(n + 3) &= 0 \\ n = 4 \text{ or } n &= -3 \end{aligned}$$

The solutions are 4 and -3.

Common Errors

Some students forget to multiply constant terms of fractional equations by the LCD. Encourage such students to write out their work as shown in Step 2 of the solution to the example given on page 291.

Some students may think that the LCD of a fraction that has a denominator such as $a - 1$ and a fraction that has a denominator such as $3a - 1$, for example, is $3a - 1$, rather than $(3a - 1)(a - 1)$. Remind them that $3a - 1 \neq 3(a - 1)$.

Students may also include extraneous roots that are not solutions in their answers. Be sure to emphasize the last two paragraphs of page 291.

Supplementary Materials

Practice Master 41
Resource Book, p. 98

Suggested Assignments

Minimum
292/18–25
293/*P*: 1–6
S 284/27, 28, 31
Day 2 of Sec. 7-3 finishes Sec. 7-3 and starts Sec. 7-4.

Average
292/22, 26, 28–38
293/*P*: 4, 6, 7, 9

Maximum
Day 1: 292/7–41 odd
293/*P*: 3, 7, 8
S 281/15
Day 2: 292/36–42 even
293/*P*: 9, 11, 12
S 290/*P*: 7, 10, 13

Oral Exercises

State the least common denominator of the fractions in each equation. Then state the equation that results when both sides are multiplied by the LCD.

1. $\frac{1}{4} + \frac{2}{x} = \frac{3}{4}$ $4x;\ x + 8 = 3x$
2. $\frac{3}{x} + \frac{1}{2} = 1$ $2x;\ 6 + x = 2x$
3. $\frac{3}{y} - \frac{1}{4} = \frac{1}{12}$ $12y;\ 36 - 3y = y$
4. $\frac{1}{a} + \frac{3}{2a} = \frac{1}{6}$ $6a;\ 6 + 9 = a$
5. $\frac{n}{n-2} = \frac{6}{5}$ $5(n-2);\ 5n = 6(n-2)$
6. $\frac{1+b}{1-b} = \frac{4}{3}$ $3(1-b);\ 3(1+b) = 4(1-b)$

Written Exercises

1. 4 2. 6 3. 9 4. 15 5. 12 6. $\frac{1}{7}$

A 1–6. Solve the equations in Oral Exercises 1–6.

Solve and check. If the equation has no solution, write "no solution."

7. $\frac{3}{4n} + \frac{1}{n} = \frac{7}{8}$ 2
8. $\frac{2}{3n} + \frac{4}{n} = \frac{7}{9}$ 6
9. $\frac{6-x}{4-x} = \frac{3}{5}$ 9
10. $\frac{9}{4+3x} = \frac{5}{3-3x}$ $\frac{1}{6}$
11. $\frac{2x-5}{8x-5} = \frac{1}{4}$ No sol.
12. $\frac{n-3}{6n-18} = \frac{1}{6}$ all reals except $n = 3$
13. $\frac{x-4}{x-2} = 2$ 0
14. $\frac{2x-4}{x-2} = 2$ all reals except $x = 2$
15. $\frac{2x-4}{x-2} = 3$ No sol.
16. $\frac{y-6}{y-2} = 3$ 0
17. $\frac{3y-6}{y-2} = 3$ all reals except $y = 2$
18. $\frac{3y-6}{y-2} = 2$ No sol.
19. $\frac{1+y}{3y} = \frac{1}{y}$ 2
20. $\frac{a-5}{2} = \frac{3}{a}$ -1
21. $\frac{1}{x} - \frac{2x}{x+1} = 0$ $\left\{-\frac{1}{2}, 1\right\}$
22. $\frac{3}{2a+1} - \frac{3}{2a-1} = 0$ No sol.
23. $\frac{3}{2n+1} - \frac{6}{4n+2} = 0$ all reals except $n = -\frac{1}{2}$
24. $\frac{3}{2x-1} = \frac{7}{4x-2}$ No sol.

B

25. $\frac{3x+5}{6} - \frac{10}{x} = \frac{x}{2}$ 12
26. $\frac{4}{x+1} - \frac{1}{x} = 1$ 1
27. $\frac{5}{1+y} - \frac{3}{1-y} = 2$ $\{0, 4\}$
28. $\frac{2}{a+1} - \frac{1}{1-a} = 1$ $\{0, 3\}$
29. $\frac{1}{y-3} = \frac{6}{y^2-9}$ No sol.
30. $\frac{4}{a^2-4a} + \frac{1}{4-a} = 0$ No sol.
31. $\frac{n+1}{3n-1} + \frac{n}{n-1} = \frac{4}{3}$ $\frac{7}{13}$
32. $\frac{y+2}{y-3} - \frac{y-3}{y+2} = \frac{5}{6}$ $\{0, 13\}$
33. $\frac{n-2}{n} - \frac{n-3}{n-6} = \frac{1}{n}$ 3
34. $\frac{5}{y-5} - \frac{3}{y+5} = \frac{2}{y}$ $-\frac{5}{4}$
35. $\frac{1}{2x-1} - \frac{3}{4x^2-1} = 0$ 1
36. $\frac{1}{y^2-y} + \frac{1}{1-y} = \frac{1}{2}$ -2
37. $\frac{1}{x-4} + \frac{2}{x^2-16} = \frac{3}{x+4}$ 9
38. $\frac{3a}{a-1} - \frac{4}{a+1} = \frac{4}{a^2-1}$ $\left\{0, \frac{1}{3}\right\}$
39. $\frac{8}{b-1} + \frac{30}{1-b^2} = \frac{6}{b+1}$ 8
40. $\frac{1}{y} - \frac{2}{1-y} = \frac{8}{y^2-y}$ 3

C **41.** $\frac{x-2}{x^2-x-6} = \frac{1}{x^2-4} + \frac{3}{2x+4}$ {1, 4}

42. $\frac{x}{x+1} - \frac{x+1}{x-4} = \frac{5}{x^2-3x-4}$ No sol.

43. $\frac{n-4}{2n^2+5n-3} + \frac{2n+7}{8n^2-2n-1} = \frac{4n-1}{4n^2+13n+3}$ {4, −2}

44. $\frac{2x^2}{1-x^2} = \frac{x}{x-1} - \frac{x}{x+1} - 3$ 3

Problems

A **1.** The sum of a number and its reciprocal is $\frac{13}{6}$. Find the number. $\frac{2}{3}$ or $\frac{3}{2}$

2. The sum of the reciprocals of two consecutive even integers is $\frac{11}{60}$. Find the integers. 10, 12

3. The numerator of a fraction is 1 more than the denominator. If the numerator and the denominator are both increased by 2, the new fraction will be $\frac{1}{4}$ less than the original fraction. Find the original fraction. $\frac{3}{2}$

4. The denominator of a fraction is 4 more than the numerator. The sum of the fraction and its reciprocal is $\frac{5}{2}$. Find the fraction. $\frac{4}{8}$

5. The sum of two numbers is 40. If twice the larger number is divided by the smaller, the quotient is 3 and the remainder is 10. Find the numbers. 14, 26

6. Two numbers differ by 20. If the larger number is divided by the smaller, the quotient is 2 and the remainder is 5. Find the numbers. 15, 35

B **7.** Dale hikes 15 km up a mountain trail. Her return trip along the same trail takes 30 min less because she is able to increase her speed by 1 km/h. How long does it take her to climb up and down the mountain? 5.5 h

	Rate × Time = Distance		
Up	x	$\frac{15}{x}$	15
Down	? $x+1$	? $\frac{15}{x} - \frac{1}{2}$	? 15

8. If I increase my usual driving speed by 10 km/h, I can drive the 255 km trip to Nashville in 24 min less than usual. How fast do I usually drive? 75 km/h

9. The cost of a bus excursion was $180. This amount was to have been shared equally by all those who said they wished to go. However, 6 people failed to show up so that those who did go each had to pay $1.50 more. How many people actually went on the trip? 24 people

	Number × Price = Cost		
Original plan	x	$\frac{180}{x}$	180
Later plan	? $x-6$	? $\frac{180}{x-6}$	? 180

10. The $75 cost for a party was to be shared equally by all those attending. Since 5 more people attended than was expected, the price per person dropped by 50 cents. How many people attended the party? 30 people

Additional A Exercises

Solve and check. If the equation has no solution, write "no solution."

1. $\frac{1}{6} + \frac{5}{x} = \frac{5}{6}$ $x = \frac{15}{2}$
2. $\frac{z}{z+5} = \frac{9}{4}$ $z = -9$
3. $\frac{5x+2}{4x-2} = \frac{1}{3}$ $x = \frac{-8}{11}$
4. $\frac{2+z}{3z} = \frac{1}{z}$ $z = 1$
5. $\frac{1}{m} - \frac{4m}{m+3} = 0$ $m = 1, \frac{-3}{4}$
6. $\frac{4}{3a+1} - \frac{6}{6a+2} = 0$ no solution

Mixed Review Exercises

1. Factor $14 + 29y - 15y^2$. $(7-3y)(2+5y)$
2. The width of a rectangle is 5 less than its length. The area is 336. Find the dimensions. width, 16; length, 21
3. Simplify: $\frac{z}{z-6} + \frac{z-1}{6-z}$ $\frac{1}{z-6}$ $(z \neq 6)$
4. State the ratio 4 yd : 2 ft in simplest form. 6 : 1

11. Fifteen minutes after Cindy and Dave leave the dock to canoe downstream, Tammy leaves by motor boat with the supplies. Since the motor boat goes twice as fast as the canoe, it catches up with the canoe 3 km from the dock. How fast does the motor boat go? 12 km/h

12. A plumber made \$600 for working on a certain job. His apprentice who makes \$3 per hour less, also made \$600, but he worked 10 hours more than the plumber. How much does the plumber make per hour? \$15/h

Computer Exercises

For students with some programming experience

Write a BASIC program to find the least common denominator for a pair of integers that are entered through INPUT statements. Use the program to find the LCD for each of the following pairs of denominators.

1. 12 and 15 60 **2.** 31 and 17 527 **3.** 5 and 50 50 **4.** 252 and 98 1764

Self-Test 2

Vocabulary fractional equation (p. 291)

Solve.

1. $\frac{5n}{48} - \frac{2n}{9} = \frac{17}{18}$ −8 **2.** $x + \frac{x-2}{8} = 20$ 18 **Obj. 7-3, p. 288**

3. $\frac{5a+2}{3} = \frac{a-1}{2}$ −1 **4.** $\frac{n+6}{6} - \frac{n}{9} = \frac{2}{3}$ −6

Solve and check. If the equation has no solution, write "no solution."

5. $\frac{3x-1}{x+1} = 4$ −5 **6.** $\frac{2}{x-3} - \frac{1}{2x-6} = 0$ No sol. **Obj. 7-4, p. 291**

7. Find two consecutive integers such that the sum of their reciprocals is $\frac{5}{6}$. 2, 3

Check your answers with those at the back of the book.

Quick Quiz

Solve.

1. $\frac{7}{8}y - \frac{3}{5}y = \frac{11}{2}$ 20
2. $\frac{2t-1}{3} - \frac{3t-1}{7} = 6$ 26
3. $\frac{15}{n} = 3 + \frac{n-1}{4}$ −15 or 4
4. $\frac{x+1}{x+4} = \frac{x-3}{x} + \frac{1}{8}$ −12 or 8

Percent Problems

7-5 Percents

Objective To work with percents.

The ratio of one number to another can be expressed as a percent. The word **percent** (usually denoted %) means "hundredths" or "divided by 100." For example,

$\frac{29}{100}$ is called "29 percent" and written 29%.

Example 1 Express each number as a percent.

a. $\frac{3}{5}$ b. $\frac{1}{3}$ c. 4.7

Solution

a. $\frac{x}{100} = \frac{3}{5}$
$5x = 300$
$x = 60$
$\therefore \frac{3}{5} = 60\%$

b. $\frac{x}{100} = \frac{1}{3}$
$3x = 100$
$x = 33\frac{1}{3}$
$\therefore \frac{1}{3} = 33\frac{1}{3}\%$

c. $\frac{x}{100} = 4.7$
$x = 470$
$\therefore 4.7 = 470\%$

In problems involving percent, the word "of" indicates multiplication and the word "is" indicates equality. The next three examples illustrate these ideas.

Example 2 15% of 180 is what number?

Solution $\frac{15}{100} \cdot 180 = x$

$27 = x$

$\therefore$ 15% of 180 is 27. ***Answer***

When finding a percent of a number, it is often convenient to express the percent as a decimal and then multiply. Example 2 can be worked as follows:

$15\% = 0.15 \qquad 15\% \text{ of } 180 = 0.15 \times 180 = 27$

Teaching Suggestions
p. T105

Suggested Extensions
p. T105

Chalkboard Examples

Express as a fraction in simplest form.

1. 36% $\frac{36}{100} = \frac{9}{25}$
2. 15% $\frac{15}{100} = \frac{3}{20}$
3. $\frac{3}{4}\%$
$\frac{3}{4} \div 100 = \frac{3}{4} \cdot \frac{1}{100} = \frac{3}{400}$
4. 180% $\frac{180}{100} = \frac{9}{5}$
5. What is 48% of 125?
$0.48(125) = 60$
6. 9 is 36% of what number?
$9 = 0.36n$
$n = \frac{9}{0.36} = 25$
7. What percent of 225 is 99?
$\frac{x}{100} \cdot 225 = 99$
$225x = 9900$
$x = 44$
44%
8. The Booster Club has raised $825 toward its goal of $1500. What percent of the goal is that?
$\frac{x}{100} \cdot 1500 = 825$
$1500x = 82{,}500$
$x = 55$
55%

Common Error

Students may have trouble with exercises such as Oral Exercises 14 and 15 and Written Exercises 3, 6, 7, and 10. Be sure to point out, for example, that $2\frac{1}{2}\%$ does not equal either $\frac{5}{2}$ or a fraction greater than 200. Emphasize that $2\frac{1}{2}\%$ may be thought of as $\frac{5}{2}$ of $1\% = \frac{5}{2} \cdot \frac{1}{100} = \frac{1}{40}$ or as $2\frac{1}{2} \div 100 = \frac{5}{2} \div 100 = \frac{5}{2} \cdot \frac{1}{100} = \frac{1}{40}$. Encourage students to consider the reasonableness of their answers. For example $2\frac{1}{2}\%$ must be a little larger than 2%, or $\frac{2}{100} = \frac{1}{50}$. Remind students who think that $2\frac{1}{2}\%$ is greater than 200 that any number greater than 1 would represent more than 100%.

Supplementary Material

Test 24

Additional Answers Oral Exercises

26. 10; $3x = 12 + 23x$
27. 100; $8x = 150(8 - x)$
28. 1000; $4500x - 20 = 75(100 - x)$
29. 10; $152(1000 - x) = 28$
30. 1000; $100x - 10x = 1$
31. 1000; $125x = 7000$

Example 3 23 is 25% of what number?

Solution

$$23 = \frac{25}{100} \cdot x$$
$$2300 = 25x$$
$$92 = x$$

$\therefore$ 23 is 25% of 92. ***Answer***

Example 4 What percent of 64 is 48?

Solution

$$\frac{x}{100} \cdot 64 = 48$$
$$64x = 4800$$
$$x = 75$$

$\therefore$ 75% of 64 is 48. ***Answer***

When solving an equation containing coefficients expressed as decimals, it is helpful to multiply both sides of the equation by a power of 10 to obtain an equivalent equation with integral coefficients.

Example 5 Solve: $1.2x = 36 + 0.4x$

Solution

$$10(1.2x) = 10(36 + 0.4x)$$ (Multiply both sides by 10 to eliminate decimals.)
$$12x = 360 + 4x$$
$$8x = 360$$
$$x = 45$$ ***Answer***

Example 6 Solve: $94 = 0.15x + 0.08(1000 - x)$

Solution

$$100 \cdot [94] = 100[0.15x + 0.08(1000 - x)]$$ (Multiply both sides by 100 to eliminate decimals.)
$$9400 = 15x + 8(1000 - x)$$
$$9400 = 15x + 8000 - 8x$$
$$1400 = 7x$$
$$200 = x$$ ***Answer***

Oral Exercises

Express as a percent.

1. 0.83 83%
2. 0.07 7%
3. 1.50 150%
4. 0.085 8.5%
5. 0.003 0.3%
6. $\frac{1}{2}$ 50%
7. $\frac{3}{4}$ 75%
8. $\frac{2}{5}$ 40%
9. $1\frac{1}{4}$ 125%
10. $\frac{9}{50}$ 18%

Express as a fraction in simplest form.

11. 10% $\frac{1}{10}$ **12.** 30% $\frac{3}{10}$ **13.** 6% $\frac{3}{50}$ **14.** $\frac{1}{2}$% $\frac{1}{200}$ **15.** $37\frac{1}{2}$% $\frac{3}{8}$

Express as a mixed number and then as a fraction.

16. 150% $1\frac{1}{2}$; $\frac{3}{2}$ **17.** 250% $2\frac{1}{2}$; $\frac{5}{2}$ **18.** 175% $1\frac{3}{4}$; $\frac{7}{4}$ **19.** 325% $3\frac{1}{4}$; $\frac{13}{4}$ **20.** 360% $3\frac{3}{5}$; $\frac{18}{5}$

Express as a decimal.

21. 35% 0.35 **22.** 4% 0.04 **23.** 115% 1.15 **24.** 0.4% 0.004 **25.** $9\frac{1}{2}$% 0.095

Tell whether you would multiply by 10, 100, or 1000 to eliminate the decimals in each equation. Then give the equation that would result if you did the multiplication.

26. $0.3x = 1.2 + 2.3x$ **27.** $0.08x = 1.5(8 - x)$ **28.** $4.5x - 0.02 = 0.075(100 - x)$

29. $15.2(1000 - x) = 2.8$ **30.** $0.1x - 0.01x = .001$ **31.** $0.125x = 7$

Written Exercises

Express as a fraction in simplest form.

A **1.** 25% $\frac{1}{4}$ **2.** 40% $\frac{2}{5}$ **3.** $33\frac{1}{3}$% $\frac{1}{3}$ **4.** 75% $\frac{3}{4}$

5. 60% $\frac{3}{5}$ **6.** $66\frac{2}{3}$% $\frac{2}{3}$ **7.** $12\frac{1}{2}$% $\frac{1}{8}$ **8.** 80% $\frac{4}{5}$

9. 4% $\frac{1}{25}$ **10.** $2\frac{1}{2}$% $\frac{1}{40}$ **11.** 125% $\frac{5}{4}$ **12.** 240% $\frac{12}{5}$

Evaluate.

13. 32% of 300 96 **14.** 6% of 145 8.7 **15.** $9\frac{1}{2}$% of 2000 190 **16.** $8\frac{1}{4}$% of 4000 330

17. $\frac{1}{2}$% of 12 0.06 **18.** 9.2% of 180 16.56 **19.** 17.8% of 500 89 **20.** 35% of 84 29.4

21. 28% of 483 + 72% of 483 483 **22.** $7\frac{1}{2}$% of 15,500 + $12\frac{1}{2}$% of 15,500 3100

23. $33\frac{1}{3}$% of 6200 + $33\frac{1}{3}$% of 2800 3000 **24.** $66\frac{2}{3}$% of 7650 − $66\frac{2}{3}$% of 1650 4000

25. 8 is 20% of what number? 40 **26.** 15 is 25% of what number? 60

27. 27 is 15% of what number? 180 **28.** 78 is 15% of what number? 520

29. 4.2 is 75% of what number? 5.6 **30.** 32.4 is 45% of what number? 72

31. What percent of 75 is 60? 80% **32.** What percent of 48 is 12? 25%

33. What percent of 150 is 3? 2% **34.** What percent of 36 is 45? 125%

35. What percent of 63 is 21? $33\frac{1}{3}$% **36.** What percent of 800 is 120? 15%

Suggested Assignments

Minimum
Day 1: 297/1–35 odd, 37–40
R 294/*Self-Test 2*
Day 2: 298/45–59 odd, 60–65
299/*P*: 1–4
S 293/*P*: 7, 9

Average
297/1–65 odd
299/*P*: 3–5, 10, 12, 15
R 294/*Self-Test 2*

Maximum
297/1–65 odd
299/*P*: 3–5, 10, 12, 15
R 294/*Self-Test 2*

Additional A Exercises

1. Express $11\frac{1}{9}$% as a fraction in simplest form. $\frac{1}{9}$

Evaluate.

2. 5.2% of 600 31.2
3. $66\frac{2}{3}$% of 33 22
4. 9 is 50% of what number? 18
5. 80 is $16\frac{2}{3}$% of what number? 480
6. What percent of 150 is 60? 40%
7. What percent of 56 is 7? $12\frac{1}{2}$%
8. If there is a 15% discount on a price of $150, what is the price decrease? What is the new price? $22.50; $127.50

Mixed Review Exercises

1. Factor $2x^2 + 16x + 32$ completely. $2(x + 4)^2$

2. Express $\left(\frac{9x}{5y}\right)^2 \cdot \frac{2xy}{3x^3}$ in simplest form. $\frac{54}{25y}$

3. Find the LCD for $\frac{9}{x}$, $\frac{3x+1}{x^2+x}$, $\frac{4x}{x^2-1}$. $x(x+1)(x-1)$

4. Solve: $\frac{22}{x} = \frac{24}{36}$ 33

Complete the tables.

	Original Price	% Discount	Price Decrease	New Price
37.	\$ 12	25%	? \$3	? \$9
38.	\$ 18	20%	? \$3.60	? \$14.40
39.	\$160	15%	? \$24	? \$136
40.	\$120	$33\frac{1}{3}\%$	? \$40	? \$80

	Original Price	% Markup	Price Increase	New Price
41.	\$ 44	25%	? \$11	? \$55
42.	\$ 85	20%	? \$17	? \$102
43.	\$180	$66\frac{2}{3}\%$	? \$120	? \$300
44.	\$ 15	40%	? \$6	? \$21

Solve.

B

45. $1.8x = 36$ 20

46. $0.06x = 120$ 2000

47. $0.4n = 7.2 - 0.5n$ 8

48. $0.4n = 1.2(8 - n)$ 6

49. $0.75y + 1.3y = 41$ 20

50. $0.05a + 0.5a = 4.4$ 8

51. $0.025x + 0.05 = 0.3$ 10

52. $0.06y - 0.035y = 9$ 360

53. $90 - x = 0.04(180 - x)$

54. $0.4x + 0.24(x - 5) = 0.08$ 2

55. $0.025y - 0.05(20 - 2y) = 0.2$

56. $0.08x + 0.09(6000 - x) = 530$ 1000

57. $0.06(1000 - x) + 0.05x = 700$

58. $0.1x - 0.01(10 - x) + 0.01(100 - x) = 19$ 181

59. $\frac{0.3x - 1}{5} = 0.12x + 3.2$ $-\frac{170}{3}$

53. 86.25
55. 9.6
57. −64,000

Complete the table below in which interest rates are given as decimals.

	Principal	× Annual interest rate	= One year's interest
60.	\$ 5000	0.085	? \$425
61.	\$12,000	0.1025	? \$1230
62.	\$ 1000	? 0.105	\$105
63.	\$ 2500	? 0.11	\$275
64.	? \$900	0.15	\$135
65.	? \$2000	0.09	\$180

Problems

A 1. The Chess Club has a goal of 25 new members. So far, they have 15. What percent of the club's goal have they achieved? 60%

2. Laura makes an 8% commission on each of her sales. How much does she make when she sells a $180 camera? $14.40

3. The fund drive has raised $18,700. That is 22% of its goal. What is its goal? $85,000

4. Because an item is slightly damaged a storekeeper reduces the price by $6. This represents a 30% reduction. What was the original price? $20

5. Roger Carlson makes a 2% commission on each of his sales. When he sold a new car, he made $190. How much did the car cost? $9500

6. A weed killer is to be diluted with water so that the weed killer is just 1% of the solution. How much water should be mixed with 5 cm³ of weed killer? 495 cm³

7. Where Sondra lives, there is a 3% state sales tax, a $1\frac{1}{2}$% county sales tax, and a 1% municipal sales tax. How much tax would Sondra pay if she bought a $340 bicycle? $18.70

8. Molly Pritchard invests $4000 in bonds paying $11\frac{1}{2}$% simple interest and $5000 in bank accounts paying 9.1% simple interest. Which investment yields more interest in one year? How much more? bond; $5 per year

B 9. A $52 sweater is marked down 25%. What is the new price? $39

10. A sporting goods dealer estimates that an $85 tennis racket will cost 6% more next year. What will be the new price? $90.10

11. A $160 pair of skis is on sale at a 25% discount. If there is a 5% sales tax, how much will the skis cost? $126

12. A dealer buys a new car for $8400. How much do you have to pay for the car if the dealer makes a 20% profit and there is a 5% sales tax? $10,584

13. In a nation of 221 million people, the urban population is 2.25 times the rural population. Find the rural and urban populations. rural, 68,000,000; urban, 153,000,000

14. Sam Goddard is 112 lb heavier than his daughter. He also figures that he is 2.4 times as heavy as she is. How much does each person weigh? Sam, 192 lb; daughter, 80 lb

15. For lunch Roberto had a sandwich and two glasses of milk for a total of 660 calories. The sandwich had 2.4 times as many calories as a glass of milk. How many calories were in the sandwich? 360 calories

Teaching Suggestions
p. T105

Suggested Extensions
p. T105

Chalkboard Examples

Complete the table.

	Orig. Price	Sale Price	% Decr.
1.	\$60	\$51	? 15%
2.	? \$56	\$42	25%
3.	\$75	? \$63	16%

Solve.

4. The Fergusons' real estate taxes went from \$1560 to \$1638. Find the percent of increase.
$$\frac{x}{100} = \frac{1638 - 1560}{1560}$$
$$\frac{x}{100} = \frac{1}{20}$$
$$20x = 100$$
$$x = 5$$
The percent increase is 5%.

5. The number of registered voters in Franklin increased by 14% over last year. There are now 9633 registered voters. How many were there last year?
$$\frac{14}{100} = \frac{9633 - x}{x}$$
$$14x = 963{,}300 - 100x$$
$$114x = 963{,}300$$
$$x = 8450$$
There were 8450 registered voters last year.

Supplementary Materials

Practice Master 42
Resource Book, p. 99

7-6 Percent Problems

Objective: To solve problems involving percents.

Whenever a price increases or decreases, the percent change is based on the original price and is given by the following formula.

$$\frac{\text{percent change}}{100} = \frac{\text{change in price}}{\text{original price}}$$

Example 1 The annual membership fee in the Film Club increased from \$25 to \$27. What was the percent increase?

Solution

Step 1 The problem asks for the percent increase.

Step 2 Let x = the percent increase.

Step 3
$$\frac{\text{percent change}}{100} = \frac{\text{change in price}}{\text{original price}}$$
$$\frac{x}{100} = \frac{27 - 25}{25}$$

Step 4
$$\frac{x}{100} = \frac{2}{25}$$
$$25x = 200$$
$$x = 8$$

Step 5 The check is left to you.

∴ there was an 8% increase. ***Answer***

Example 2

Ricardo pays \$76.50 for ice skates that are on sale at a 15% discount. What was the original price of the skates?

Solution

Step 1 The problem asks for the original price.

Step 2 Let x = the original price.

Step 3
$$\frac{\text{percent change}}{100} = \frac{\text{change in price}}{\text{original price}}$$
$$\frac{15}{100} = \frac{x - 76.50}{x}$$

Step 4 $15x = 100x - 7650$
$7650 = 85x$
$90 = x$

Step 5 The check is left to you.

$\therefore$ the original price was \$90. ***Answer***

In the last example, the 15% discount was written as the fraction $\frac{15}{100}$, but it also could have been written as the decimal 0.15. In the next example the percents are expressed as decimals. Example 3 uses the following formula.

Principal $\times$ Annual Interest Rate $=$ Annual Simple Interest

Example 3 Selma Peterson invests part of her \$6000 in bank accounts that pay 7% annual simple interest and the rest in bonds that pay 13% annual simple interest. Her total annual income from these investments is \$540. How much money is invested in bank accounts and how much money in bonds?

Solution

Step 1 The problem asks for the amounts invested in bank accounts and in bonds.

Step 2 Let $x =$ amount invested in bank accounts. Then $6000 - x =$ amount invested in bonds.

	Principal $\times$	Rate $=$	Interest
Bank Accounts	x	0.07	$0.07x$
Bonds	$6000 - x$	0.13	$0.13(6000 - x)$

Step 3 Since the total interest is \$540, we have:

$$0.07x + 0.13(6000 - x) = 540$$

Step 4 $100[0.07x + 0.13(6000 - x)] = 100(540)$ {Multiply both sides by 100 to eliminate decimals.

$$7x + 13(6000 - x) = 54{,}000$$
$$7x + 78{,}000 - 13x = 54{,}000$$
$$-6x = -24{,}000$$
$$x = 4000$$
$$6000 - x = 2000$$

Step 5 The check is left to you.

$\therefore$ she invested \$4000 in bank accounts and \$2000 in bonds. ***Answer***

Suggested Assignments

Minimum
302/1–21 odd
303/*P*: 1–13 odd
R 305/*Self-Test 3*

Average
302/1–21 odd
303/*P*: 1–7 odd, 10, 11, 13, 14
R 305/*Self-Test 3*

Maximum
302/1–21 odd
303/*P*: 1–11 odd, 13–16
S 293/41, 44
R 305/*Self-Test 3*

Additional A Exercises

Complete the tables.

Item	Orig. Price	New Price	Percent Increase
Sweater	$40	$44	? 10%
Gallon of gas	$1.20	? $1.26	5%
Refrigerator	? $370	$407	10%

Item	Orig. Price	Sale Price	Percent Decrease
Skillet	$25	$20	? 20%
T-shirt	? $5	$4	20%
Basketball	$44	? $33	25%

Oral Exercises

Complete each table.

	Item	Original price	New price	Price increase	Percent increase
1.	Jeans	$25.00	$30.00	? $5	? 20%
2.	School lunch	$ 1.60	$ 2.00	? $.40	? 25%
3.	Shirt	$14.00	$15.40	? $1.40	? 10%
4.	Sandwich	$ 2.00	$ 2.10	? $.10	? 5%

	Item	Original price	Sale price	Price decrease	Percent decrease
5.	Sweater	$ 60	$ 45	? $15	? 25%
6.	Fly rod	$ 20	$ 15	? $5	? 25%
7.	Hiking boots	$120	$108	? $12	? 10%
8.	Bike	$300	$210	? $90	? 30%

State the equation you would use to find x. 9. $\frac{10}{100} = \frac{88 - x}{x}$ 10. $\frac{25}{100} = \frac{75 - x}{x}$

	Original price	New price	Percent change
9.	x	$88	10% price increase
10.	x	$75	25% price increase
11.	x	$36	10% price decrease
12.	x	$72	20% price decrease

11. $\frac{10}{100} = \frac{x - 36}{x}$ 12. $\frac{20}{100} = \frac{x - 72}{x}$

Written Exercises

Complete each table.

	Item	Original price	New price	Percent increase
A **1.**	Sneakers	$ 30.00	$ 33.00	? 10%
2.	Record album	$ 12.00	$ 15.00	? 25%
3.	Hat	$ 8.00	$ 8.40	? 5%
4.	Shoes	$ 36.00	$ 37.80	? 5%

	Item	Original price	New price	Percent increase
5.	Paint	\$ 20.00	\$ 22.50	? 12.5%
6.	Skis	\$220.00	\$253.00	? 15%
7.	Movie ticket	\$ 3.50	\$? 3.64	4%
8.	Tank of gas	\$ 23.20	\$?24.36	5%
9.	Hammer	\$? 6.40	\$ 8.00	25%
10.	Saw	\$? 20	\$ 22.00	10%
11.	Airplane ticket	\$? 50	\$ 51.00	2%
12.	Paperback book	\$? 3	\$ 3.36	12%

	Item	Original price	Sale price	Percent decrease
13.	Shirt	\$ 25.00	\$ 20.00	? 20%
14.	Pants	\$ 36.00	\$ 27.00	? 25%
15.	Belt	\$ 8.00	\$ 6.80	? 15%
16.	Camera	\$240.00	\$168.00	? 30%
17.	Soccer ball	\$ 32.00	\$?25.60	20%
18.	Spaghetti sauce	\$ 2.20	\$?1.87	15%
19.	Souvenir	\$? 7	\$ 6.30	10%
20.	Shovel	\$? 18.75	\$ 15.00	20%
21.	Skates	\$? 70	\$ 59.50	15%
22.	Math book	\$? 14	\$ 13.30	5%

Problems

A

1. The population of Houston increased from 1.2 million in 1970 to 1.6 million in 1980. What was the percent increase? $33\frac{1}{3}\%$
2. Elaine Poro bought 100 shares of stock at \$25 per share and sold them at \$31 per share. What was her percent profit? 24%
3. Michael Quigley's home was reassessed at a value of \$162,000. It had previously been assessed at \$150,000. What was the percent increase in the assessment? 8%

Mixed Review Exercises

1. Sandy found jeans and tops on sale. Jeans were \$20 per pair and tops were \$12 each. She bought 6 items and spent \$96. How many tops did she buy? 3
2. Write $m + 5 + \frac{6}{m - 5}$ as a fraction in simplest form. $\frac{m^2 - 19}{m - 5} (m \neq 5)$

Solve.

3. $\frac{x}{2} + \frac{2x + 3}{3} = \frac{8}{9}$ $x = -\frac{2}{21}$
4. $\frac{2}{x - 3} + \frac{4}{x + 2} = 0$ $x = \frac{4}{3}$

4. While traveling during her last vacation, Luann noted that a \$3.25 breakfast actually cost \$3.38 because of the sales tax. What is the sales tax rate? 4%

5. A \$60 sweater is on sale for \$48. What is the percent of discount? 20%

6. The number of paid subscribers to *The Groundhog Quarterly* has declined from 3240 people to 2430 people. What is the percent of decrease? 25%

7. Yvonne Gregory paid \$11,448 for a new automobile. This amount included the 6% sales tax. What was the price of the automobile without the tax? \$10,800

8. The selling price of a house includes the 6% real-estate commission. If the Lings' house was sold for \$159,000, how much did the Lings receive and how much did the real estate broker receive? Lings, \$150,000; broker, \$9000

9. At the Runner's Shop anniversary sale, running shoes were on sale at a 15% discount. If Hector Gonzalez paid \$35.70 for a pair of running shoes, what was the original price? \$42

10. The population in Dogwood is now 115 people. This represents an 8% decline from last year. What was the population last year? 125

11. Sondra Warren invests \$6000. Some of the money is invested in stocks paying 6% a year and some in bonds paying 11% a year. She receives a total of \$580 each year from these investments. How much money is invested in stocks and how much money in bonds? stocks, \$1600; bonds, \$4400

12. Bob Cornell invested \$8000 in bank certificates and bonds. The certificates pay 7% interest and the bonds pay 10% interest. His interest income is \$725 each year. How much money was invested in bank certificates? \$2500

B 13. The Dalton Arts Fund must raise \$2500 next year by investing \$30,000 in federal notes paying 9% and in municipal bonds paying 8%. The treasurer wants to invest as much as possible in the bonds, even though they pay less, because the bonds are for projects in the Dalton area. How much should the treasurer invest in bonds? \$20,000

14. Eric Steel invested in company stock paying a $10\frac{1}{2}\%$ dividend. Marie Steel invested \$4000 more than Eric in tax-free bonds paying $7\frac{1}{2}\%$ annual simple interest. If Marie's income from the investment is \$75 more than Eric's, find how much money each invested. Eric, \$7500; Marie, \$11,500

15. Beatrice Roberts invested \$2000 more in stocks than in bonds. The bonds paid 7.2% interest and stocks paid 6%, yet the income from each was the same. How much annual interest did she receive? \$1440

16. Half of Bill Lee's money is invested at 12% interest, one third at 11%, and the rest at 9%. If the total annual income is \$1340, how much money has Bill invested? \$12,000

Computer Exercises

For students with some programming experience

1. Suppose that you deposit \$100 in a bank account that pays 6% interest per year. At the end of one year, you will have $(100 + 100 \cdot \frac{6}{100}) = \$106$. At the end of the second year, you will have $(106 + 106 \cdot \frac{6}{100})$ dollars. Write a BASIC program that will display in chart form how much money you will have at the end of 1, 2, 3, 4, . . . , 10 years.

2. Write a BASIC program that will store a set of DATA entered with INPUT statements in an array. The program should then calculate and print out the percent of increase or decrease between each consecutive pair of data. If the percent of increase (or decrease) is the same for each consecutive pair, we say that the data are growing (or decaying) exponentially. RUN the program for the following sets of data.

a.

No. of yr after 1984	Population of Muddville	
1	207	
		−3.38%
2	200	
		−3.5%
3	193	
		−3.627%
4	186	
		−3.76%
5	179	

b.

No. of hr observing a bacteria colony	No. bacteria present	
1	500	
		41%
2	705	
		41.84%
3	1000	
		41%
4	1410	
		40.99%
5	1988	

Self-Test 3

Vocabulary percent (p. 295)

Express as a fraction in simplest form.

1. 56% $\frac{14}{25}$ **2.** $87\frac{1}{2}\%$ $\frac{7}{8}$ **3.** 105% $\frac{21}{20}$ **Obj. 7-5, p. 295**

4. Find 16% of 85. 13.6 **5.** 3.75 is 60% of what number? 6.25

6. What percent of 90 is 225? 250% **7.** What percent of 300 is 75? 25%

8. Last year an accountant earned \$18,000. This year she received a 12% raise. How much was the raise? \$2160

9. A suit that sold for \$162 is now on sale for \$108. What is the percent of discount? $33\frac{1}{3}\%$ **Obj. 7-6, p. 300**

Check your answers with those at the back of the book.

Quick Quiz

Solve.

1. Express $56\frac{1}{4}\%$ as a fraction in simplest form. $\frac{9}{16}$
2. Find 64% of 225. 144
3. 65 is $62\frac{1}{2}\%$ of what number? 104
4. What percent of 220 is 143? 65%
5. A chair that originally cost \$325 is on sale for \$273. Find the percent of decrease. 16%

Mixture and Work Problems

7-7 Mixture Problems

Objective To solve mixture problems.

A merchant often mixes goods of two or more kinds in order to sell a blend at a given price. Similarly, a chemist often mixes solutions of different strengths of a chemical to obtain a solution of desired strength. Charts can be helpful in solving mixture problems.

Example 1 A convenience store owner wishes to mix together raisins and roasted peanuts to produce a high energy snack for hikers. The raisins sell for \$3.50 per kilogram and the nuts sell for \$4.75 per kilogram. How many kilograms of each should be mixed together to obtain 20 kg of this snack worth \$4.00 per kilogram?

Solution

Step 1 The problem asks for the number of kilograms of raisins and the number of kilograms of nuts.

Step 2 Let x = number of kilograms of raisins.
Then $20 - x$ = number of kilograms of nuts.

	Number $\times$ Price = Cost		
Raisins	x	3.50	$3.5x$
Nuts	$20 - x$	4.75	$4.75(20 - x)$
Mixture	20	4.00	80

Step 3 Cost of raisins + cost of nuts = cost of mixture

$$3.5x + 4.75(20 - x) = 80$$

Step 4 Multiply both sides of the equation by 100.

$$350x + 475(20 - x) = 8000$$
$$350x + 9500 - 475x = 8000$$
$$-125x = -1500$$
$$x = 12$$
$$20 - x = 8$$

Step 5 The check is left to you.

$\therefore$ 12 kg of raisins and 8 kg of nuts are needed. ***Answer***

Teaching Suggestions
p. T106

Suggested Extensions
p. T106

Chalkboard Examples

1. A grocer makes a natural breakfast cereal by mixing oat cereal costing \$2 per kilogram with dried fruits and nuts costing \$9 per kilogram. How many kilograms of each are needed to make 60 kg of cereal costing \$3.75 per kilogram?
   Step 2: Let x = no. of kg of cereal and $60 - x$ = no. of kg of dried mixture.

	No. kg	$\times$ \$/kg =	Cost
Cereal	x	2	$2x$
Dried	$60 - x$	9	$9(60 - x)$
Mix	60	3.75	225

   Step 3:
   $2x + 9(60 - x) = 225$
   Step 4:
   $2x + 540 - 9x = 225$
   $7x = 315$
   $x = 45$
   $60 - x = 15$
   45 kg of cereal; 15 kg of dried fruits and nuts

2. How many liters of water must be added to 20 L of a 24% acid solution to make a solution that is 8% acid?
   Step 2: Let x = no. of L of water.

	No. L	$\times$ % Acid =	Amt. Acid
Acid	20	24	4.8
Water	x	0	0
Mix	$20 + x$	8	$0.08(20 + x)$

Example 2 An auto mechanic has 300 g of battery acid solution that is 60% acid. He must add water to this solution in order to dilute it so that it is only 45% acid. How much water should be added?

Solution

Step 1 The problem asks for the number of grams of water to be added.

Step 2 Let x = number of grams of water to be added.

	Total amount	× % acid	= Amount of acid
Original solution	300	60%	0.60(300)
Added water	x	0%	0
New solution	$300 + x$	45%	$0.45(300 + x)$

Step 3 Original amount of acid + added acid = new amount of acid

$$0.60(300) + 0 = 0.45(300 + x)$$

Step 4 $60(300) = 45(300 + x)$ {Multiply both sides of the equation by 100.

$$18{,}000 = 13{,}500 + 45x$$
$$4500 = 45x$$
$$100 = x$$

Step 5 The check is left to you.

$\therefore$ 100 g of water should be added. ***Answer***

Although Examples 1 and 2 may at first glance appear to be quite different, they are very much alike. You can see the similarities in the charts and in Step 3 of each solution. In fact, mixture problems are very much like investment problems, coin problems, and certain distance problems. The Oral Exercises will help to point out these similarities.

Oral Exercises

Read each problem and complete each chart. Use the chart to give an equation, but do not solve the equation.

1. The owner of the Fancy Food Shoppe wishes to mix cashews selling at $8.00 per kilogram and pecans selling at $7.00 per kilogram. How much of each kind of nut should be mixed to get 8 kg worth $7.25 per kilogram?

	Number of kilograms	× Price per kilogram	= Total cost
Cashews	x	$8 ?	$8x$?
Pecans	$8 - x$?	$7 ?	$7(8 - x)$?
Mixture	8 ?	$7.25?	58 ?

$8x + 7(8 - x) = 58$

Step 3:
$0.08(20 + x) = 4.8$

Step 4: $8(20 + x) = 480$
$160 + 8x = 480$
$8x = 320$
$x = 40$

40 L of water must be added.

3. How many kilograms of water must be evaporated from 12 kg of a 5% salt solution to produce a solution that is 30% salt?

Step 2: Let x = no. of kg of water.

	No. kg	× % salt	= Amt. Salt
Original	12	5	0.6
Water	x	0	0
New	$12 - x$	30	$0.30(12 - x)$

Step 3:
$0.30(12 - x) = 0.6$

Step 4: $30(12 - x) = 60$
$360 - 30x = 60$
$300 = 30x$
$10 = x$

10 kg of water must be evaporated.

Common Error

Because up to this point they have always added two quantities to produce a mixture, some students may try to add the amount of water evaporated and the original amount of solution to produce the more concentrated salt solutions in Problems 18 and 19. Point out that when a liquid is evaporated it is taken away. Thus, to solve problems of this type, the amount of liquid evaporated must be subtracted from the amount of the original solution.

Supplementary Material

Resource Book, pp. 171–173

Suggested Assignments

Minimum
Day 1: 309/*P*: 2–16 even
S 298/46–54 even
Day 2: 309/*P*: 9–15 odd, 19
315/*P*: 1–4
Day 2 finishes Sec. 7-7 and starts Sec. 7-8.

Average
Day 1: 309/*P*: 4–6, 10, 12, 14, 18
S 293/*P*: 8, 10, 11
Day 2: 310/*P*: 13, 15, 19–22
315/*P*: 1–9 odd
S 299/*P*: 13, 14
Day 2 finishes Sec. 7-7 and starts Sec. 7-8.

Maximum
Day 1: 309/*P*: 4–6, 10, 12, 18, 20, 21
S 281/*P*: 14, 16
Day 2: 310/*P*: 22–28
315/*P*: 1–13 odd
S 289/32, 34
Day 2 finishes Sec. 7-7 and starts Sec. 7-8.

2. A chemist has 40 g of a solution that is 50% acid. How much water should she add to make a solution that is 10% acid? $20 + 0 = 0.10(40 + x)$

	Total amount	× % acid =	Amount of acid
Original solution	? 40	? 50%	? 20
Added water	x	? 0%	? 0
New solution	? $40 + x$	? 10%	? $0.1(40 + x)$

3. A chemist has 800 g of a solution that is 15% salt. How much salt should be added to make a solution that is 20% salt? $120 + x = 0.2(800 + x)$

	Total amount	× % salt =	Amount of salt
Original solution	? 800	? 15%	? 120
Added salt	x	? 100%	? x
Mixture	? $800 + x$	? 20%	? $0.2(800 + x)$

4. A chemist mixes together 20 L of a solution that is 60% acid and 30 L of a solution that is 20% acid. What is the acid percentage of the mixture?
$12 + 6 = \frac{50x}{100}$

	Total amount	× % acid =	Amount of acid
Solution *A*	20	60%	? 12
Solution *B*	? 30	? 20%	? 6
Mixture	? 50	x%	? $50\left(\frac{x}{100}\right)$

5. A grocer mixes together four pounds of peanuts costing \$2 per pound with two pounds of walnuts costing \$5 per pound. What should the price per pound of this mixture be?
$8 + 10 = 6x$

	Number of pounds	× Cost per pound	= Total cost
Peanuts	4	2	? 8
Walnuts	? 2	? 5	? 10
Mixture	? 6	x	? $6x$

6. Sam Daniels drives for 2 h at 85 km/h and then for one more hour at 70 km/h. What is his average speed? $3x = 240$

	Time	× Rate =	Distance
1st part of trip	2	? 85	? 170
2nd part of trip	? 1	? 70	? 70
Whole trip	? 3	x	? 240

7. Sally Chou has \$100 earning 10% interest and \$300 earning 14% interest. What is her average rate of return? $400x = 52$

	Principal	× Rate	= Interest
Investment A	\$100	? 0.10	? 10
Investment B	? \$300	? 0.14	? 42
Total Investments	? \$400	x	? $400x$

8. Lucy has a pile of 50 dimes and nickels worth \$4.30. How many of each coin does she have? $10x + 5(50 - x) = 430$

	Number of coins	× Value per coin	= Total value
Dimes	x	? 10	? $10x$
Nickels	? $50 - x$	? 5	? $5(50 - x)$
Mixture	50	—	? 430

Note: The bottom row of the chart in Exercise 8 is usually omitted. However, it is included here so that you will see that coin problems are another type of mixture problem. The missing middle entry in the bottom row of the chart stands for the average value per coin of the 50 coins. It is similar to the x in Exercise 7 that stands for the average rate of interest, or the x in Exercise 6 that stands for the average speed. What kinds of averages do the x's stand for in Exercises 4 and 5? 4. average % of acid
5. average cost per pound

Problems

A 1–8. Solve the problems presented in Oral Exercises 1–8.

Solve.

9. How many grams of water must be added to 50 g of a 30% acid solution in order to produce a 20% acid solution? 25 g

10. How many kilograms of water must be added to 80 kg of a 60% iodine solution in order to dilute it to a 40% iodine solution? 40 kg

11. How many kilograms of salt must be added to 30 kg of a 20% salt solution in order to increase the salt content to 25%? 2 kg

12. A grocer mixes two kinds of nuts. One kind costs \$5.00 per kilogram and the other \$5.80 per kilogram. How many kilograms of each type are needed to make 40 kg of a blend worth \$5.50 per kilogram? first type, 15 kg; second type, 25 kg

Additional A Exercises

1. A gourmet foods dealer wants to mix a type of nut worth \$8/kg, with a second type worth \$4/kg to make 40 kg of a mixture to sell for \$5/kg. How much of each type should be mixed? 10 kg of first type 30 kg of second type
2. A nurse has 60 g of a solution that is 10% salt. How much sterile water must he add to make a 6% salt solution? 40 g
3. Phillip has a 10% acid solution, but he wants to increase the strength to 20%. If he has 50 g of the solution, how much acid must he add? 6.25 g
4. The Millbergs travel 4 h at 80 km/h and 1 h at 40 km/h. What is their average speed for the whole trip? 72 km/h
5. For a party, the ninth grade bought 15 L of juice at \$.45/L and 10 L at \$.60/L. What was the average cost of a liter of the juice? \$.51/L

Additional Answers Problems

1. 2 kg of cashews, 6 kg of pecans
2. 160 g of water
3. 50 g of salt
4. 36%
5. \$3 per pound
6. 80 km/h
7. 13%
8. 36 dimes, 14 nickels

13. A health food store makes a mixture of dried fruits by mixing dried apples costing \$6.00 per kilogram with dried apricots costing \$8.00 per kilogram. How many kilograms of each are needed to produce 20 kg of a mixture worth \$7.20 per kilogram? 8 kg apples, 12 kg apricots

14. A grocer mixes two types of juice. How much should he charge if he mixes 24 L of juice worth 80 cents per liter with 16 L of juice worth \$1.00 per liter? \$.88 per liter

15. If you drive for 2 h at 80 km/h, how fast must you drive during a third hour in order to have an average speed of 75 km/h? 65 km/h

16. When Julia works overtime, she is paid $1\frac{1}{2}$ times as much per hour as she normally is. After working her usual 40 hours last week, she worked an additional 8 hours overtime. If she made \$520 last week, find her normal hourly wage. \$10 per hour

B 17. A chemist wishes to mix some pure acid with some water to produce 8 L of a solution that is 40% acid. How much pure acid and how much water should be mixed? 3.2 L acid, 4.8 L water

18. How many kilograms of water must be evaporated from 10 kg of a 40% salt solution to produce a 50% salt solution? 2 kg

19. How many kilograms of water must be evaporated from 12 kg of a 20% salt solution to produce a 60% solution? 8 kg

20. A wholesaler has 100 kg of mixed nuts that sell for \$4.00 per kilogram. In order to make the price more attractive, the wholesaler plans to mix in some cheaper nuts worth \$3.20 per kilogram. If the wholesaler wants to sell the mixture for \$3.40 per kilogram, how many kilograms of the cheaper nuts should be used? 300 kg

21. A securities broker advised a client to invest \$14,000 in bonds paying 12% interest and in certificates of deposit paying $5\frac{1}{2}\%$ interest. The annual income from these investments is \$1127.50. Find out how much is invested at each rate. \$5500 at 12%, \$8500 at $5\frac{1}{2}\%$

22. A collection of 50 coins is worth \$5.20. There are 12 more nickels than dimes and the rest of the coins are quarters. How many of each kind of coin is in the collection? 14 dimes, 26 nickels, 10 quarters

23. a. If you bike for 2 h at 30 km/h and then for 2 h at 20 km/h, what is your average speed for the whole trip? 25 km/h
    b. If you bike for 60 km at 30 km/h and then return at 20 km/h, what is your average speed for the whole trip? 24 km/h

24. The ratio of nickels to dimes to quarters is 3:8:1. If all the coins were dimes, the amount of money would be the same. Show that there are an infinite number of solutions to this problem.

Additional Answer Problems

24.

	Number ×	Value =	Total value
Nickels	$3x$	5	$15x$
Dimes	$8x$	10	$80x$
Quarters	x	25	$25x$
All dimes	$12x$	10	$120x$

$15x + 80x + 25x = 120x$; $120x = 120x$. Since this equation is an identity, there are infinitely many solutions.

Write a formula for each of the following.

25. a. The total distance traveled if you go for x hours at r km/h and $2x$ hours at s km/h. $2sx + rx$

b. The average speed for this trip. $\frac{2s + r}{3}$

26. a. The total amount of salt in a solution formed by mixing n grams of salt with 100 g of a solution that is 10% salt. $10 + n$

b. The percent of salt in the mixture. $\frac{100(10 + n)}{100 + n}$

27. a. The total annual income from investing a dollars in bank accounts that pay 5% simple interest and b dollars in bonds that pay 10% simple interest. $0.05a + 0.1b$

b. The average interest rate from these two investments. $\frac{0.05a + 0.1b}{a + b}$

28. a. The total value of a mixture of j kg of peanuts costing \$5 per kilogram with k kg of walnuts costing \$8 per kilogram. $5j + 8k$

b. The price at which the mixture should be sold to make a 25% profit. $1.25\left(\frac{5j + 8k}{j + k}\right)$

Calculator Key-In

If your calculator does not have a percent key, you can divide by 100 when entering percents. For example, you can find 9.5% of 3000 as follows:

$$9.5 \div 100 \times 3000 = 285$$

1. Find 5.24% of 18,500. 969.4
2. Find 4.4% of 6600. 290.4
3. Find 7.5% of 8500. 637.5
4. Find 11.32% of 4500. 509.4
5. Find $6\frac{1}{2}$% of 25,000. 1625
6. Find $\frac{1}{2}$% of 550. 2.75
7. Helen Fong purchased a computer at a sale offering a 15.5% discount off the original price. If the original price of the computer she bought was \$2038 and the sales tax rate was 5.5%, how much did she pay in all? \$1816.83

Challenge

Two horses approach each other along the same country road, one walking at 5.5 km/h and the other at 4.5 km/h. At the time they are 10 km apart, a horsefly leaves one horse and flies at 30 km/h to the other horse. No sooner does he reach that horse than the fly turns around (losing no time on the turn) and returns to the first horse. If the fly continues to fly back and forth between the approaching horses, how far has the fly flown when the horses meet? 30 km

Mixed Review Exercises

1. Express $38\frac{1}{2}$% as a fraction in simplest form. $\frac{77}{200}$
2. What percent of 750 is 90? 12%
3. Find 83% of 9600. 7968
4. 22 is 5% of what number? 440

Teaching Suggestions
p. T106

Suggested Extensions
p. T107

Chalkboard Examples

1. One printing press can finish a job in 8 h. The same job would take a second press 12 h. How long would it take both presses together?
Step 2: Let x = no. of hours it would take both.

	Work rate	× Time =	Work done
1st	$\frac{1}{8}$	x	$\frac{x}{8}$
2nd	$\frac{1}{12}$	x	$\frac{x}{12}$

Step 3: $\frac{x}{8} + \frac{x}{12} = 1$

Step 4: $3x + 2x = 24$

$x = 4\frac{4}{5}$

It would take $4\frac{4}{5}$ h.

2. Frank can wash the windows in 5 h. If he and Brian work together, they can finish in 2 h. How long would it take Brian working alone?
Step 2: Let r = no. of hours it would take Brian.

	Work rate	× Time =	Work done
F	$\frac{1}{5}$	2	$\frac{2}{5}$
B	$\frac{1}{r}$	2	$\frac{2}{r}$

Step 3: $\frac{2}{5} + \frac{2}{r} = 1$

Step 4: $2r + 10 = 5r$

$r = 3\frac{1}{3}$

It would take Brian $3\frac{1}{3}$ h.

7-8 Work Problems

Objective To solve work problems.

The following formula is used to solve work problems.

$$\text{work rate} \times \text{time} = \text{work done}$$
$$rt = w$$

Work rates are often expressed in terms of the job to be done. For example, if it takes you 4 days to do a job, then your rate is $\frac{1}{4}$ job per day.

Notice in the following examples that the fractional parts of a job must have a sum of 1.

Example 1 Eldridge can split a cord of wood in 4 days and his father can do it in 3 days. How long would it take them if they worked together?

Solution

Step 1 The problem asks for the number of days it will take if they both work together.

Step 2 Let x = number of days required to do the job together. Since Eldridge can do the whole job in 4 days, his work rate is $\frac{1}{4}$ job per day. Similarly, his father's work rate is $\frac{1}{3}$ job per day.

	Work rate	× Time =	Work done
Eldridge	$\frac{1}{4}$	x	$\frac{x}{4}$
Father	$\frac{1}{3}$	x	$\frac{x}{3}$

Step 3 Part of job Eldridge does + Part of job father does = Whole job

$$\frac{x}{4} + \frac{x}{3} = 1$$

Step 4

$$12\left(\frac{x}{4} + \frac{x}{3}\right) = 12(1)$$
$$3x + 4x = 12$$
$$7x = 12$$
$$x = \frac{12}{7}$$

Step 5 The check is left to you.

$\therefore$ it would take $\frac{12}{7}$, or $1\frac{5}{7}$, days to do the job together. ***Answer***

Example 2

It will take a Type A robot 6 min to weld a fender, but a Type B robot would take only $5\frac{1}{2}$ min. If the robots work together for 2 min, how long will it take the Type B robot to finish welding by itself?

Solution

Step 1 The problem asks for the time needed for a Type B robot to finish welding.

Step 2 Let x = number of minutes for a Type B robot to finish. Since a Type B robot's work rate is $\frac{1}{5\frac{1}{2}} = \frac{1}{\frac{11}{2}} = \frac{2}{11}$, we have the chart at the right.

	Work rate × Time = Work done		
Type A robot	$\frac{1}{6}$	2	$\frac{2}{6}$ or $\frac{1}{3}$
Type B robot	$\frac{2}{11}$	$2 + x$	$\frac{2}{11}(2 + x)$

Step 3 Part of job done by A + Part of job done by B = Whole job

$$\frac{1}{3} + \frac{2}{11}(2 + x) = 1$$

Step 4

$$11 + 6(2 + x) = 33$$
$$11 + 12 + 6x = 33$$
$$6x = 10$$
$$x = \frac{5}{3}$$

Step 5 The check is left to you.

∴ it will take $1\frac{2}{3}$ min for a Type B robot to finish welding. ***Answer***

The charts used for work problems look similar to the charts used for other problems. The reason is that work problems are just another type of mixture problem. The following equations will help to show the similarities between several types of problems that you have studied.

work done by A + work done by B = total work done

acid in solution A + acid in solution B = total acid in mixture

interest from banks + interest from bonds = total interest

distance traveled by bike + distance traveled by car = total distance traveled

3. An installer can carpet a room in 3 h. An assistant needs $4\frac{1}{2}$ h to do the same job. If the assistant helps for 1 h and then is called away, how long will it take the installer to finish?

Step 2: Let n = no. of hours it will take to finish.

	Work rate	× Time =	Work done
I	$\frac{1}{3}$	$n + 1$	$\frac{n+1}{3}$
A	$1 \div \frac{9}{2} = \frac{2}{9}$	1	$\frac{2}{9}$

Step 3: $\frac{n+1}{3} + \frac{2}{9} = 1$

Step 4: $3n + 3 + 2 = 9$

$3n = 4$

$n = \frac{4}{3} = 1\frac{1}{3}$

It would take the installer $1\frac{1}{3}$ h to finish.

Supplementary Materials

Practice Master 43

Resource Book, pp. 100, 174–175

Oral Exercises

State the work rate.

Example Pete can rake the lawn in 2 hours.

Solution rate $= \frac{1}{2}$ job per hour

1. Beatrice can wallpaper the room in 8 hours. $\frac{1}{8}$ job per hour
2. Mary can edit a book in 10 months. $\frac{1}{10}$ job per month
3. Sandy can tune a car in 30 minutes. $\frac{1}{30}$ job per minute or 2 jobs per hour
4. A drain pipe can empty a full tank in 3 hours. $\frac{1}{3}$ job per hour

Complete the charts. Do not solve the problems.

5. Using a ride-on lawn mower, Abby can mow the lawn in 2 hours. Her sister Carla takes 3 hours using an older mower. How long will it take them if they work together?

	Work rate	× Time	= Work done
Abby	? $\frac{1}{2}$	x	? $\frac{x}{2}$
Carla	? $\frac{1}{3}$	? x	? $\frac{x}{3}$

6. Phil can paint the garage in 12 hours and Rick can do it in 10 hours. They work together for 3 hours. How long will it take Rick to finish the job alone?

	Work rate	× Time	= Work done
Phil	? $\frac{1}{12}$	3	? $\frac{1}{4}$
Rick	? $\frac{1}{10}$	$x + 3$	? $\frac{1}{10}(x + 3)$

7. Bill usually takes 50 minutes to groom the horses. After working for 10 minutes, he was joined by Ann and they finished the grooming in 15 minutes. How long would it have taken Ann working alone?

	Work rate	× Time	= Work done
Bill	? $\frac{1}{50}$	? 25	? $\frac{1}{2}$
Ann	$\frac{1}{x}$	? 15	? $\frac{15}{x}$

Suggested Assignments

Minimum
315/*P*: 5–10
S 304/*P*: 8, 10, 12
Day 2 of Sec. 7-7 finishes Sec. 7-7 and starts Sec. 7-8.

Average
315/*P*: 11–18
R 316/*Self-Test 4*
Day 2 of Sec. 7-7 finishes Sec. 7-7 and starts Sec. 7-8.

Maximum
315/*P*: 10, 15, 16, 18, 19
R 316/*Self-Test 4*
Day 2 of Sec. 7-7 finishes Sec. 7-7 and starts Sec. 7-8.

Additional A Exercises

1. A pipe can fill a pool in 12 h. What part of the pool can it fill in 1 h? In x h? $\frac{1}{12}$; $\frac{x}{12}$
2. Billy can paint a room in 6 h; Sally can paint the same room in only 4 h. If they work together, what part of the room can they paint in 2 h? $\frac{5}{6}$
3. A file clerk needs 6 h to file an average day's papers, but, with an assistant, they can get it done in 4 h. How long would it take the assistant working alone? 12 h
4. It takes Mr. Evans $1\frac{1}{2}$ h to do the weekly grocery shopping, but it only takes Mrs. Evans 1 h. How fast can they do the shopping if they go together? 36 min

Problems

A 1. Selby takes 5 hours to type a report. What part of the typing can she do in 2 hours? in x hours? $\frac{2}{5}$; $\frac{x}{5}$

2. Lincoln can do a job in 8 hours and Dave can do it in 6 hours. What part of the job can they do by working together for 2 hours? for x hours? $\frac{7}{12}$; $\frac{7x}{24}$

3. Jake can wallpaper a room in 5 hours and Maura can do it in 6 hours. What part of the job can they do by working together for 1.5 hours? for x hours? $\frac{11}{20}$; $\frac{11x}{30}$

4. One drain pipe can empty a swimming pool in 6 hours. Another pipe takes 3 hours. If both pipes are used simultaneously to drain the pool, what part of the job is completed in 2 hours? in x hours? the whole job; $\frac{x}{2}$

5–7. Solve the problems stated in Oral Exercises 5–7. 5. $\frac{6}{5}$ h 6. $4\frac{1}{2}$ h 7. 30 min

8. It takes Ruth 60 minutes to pick the apples from her backyard tree. Bud can do it in 40 minutes. How long will it take them if they pick together? 24 min

9. It takes Gary 1 hour to milk all of the cows, and it takes Dana 1.5 hours. How long will it take to do the job together? 0.6 h, or 36 min

10. A roofing contractor estimates that he can shingle a house in 20 hours and that his assistant can do it in 30 hours. How long will it take for the two of them together to shingle the house? 12 h

11. Stan can load the truck in 40 minutes. If I help him, it takes us 15 minutes. How long will it take me alone? 24 min

12. One printing machine works twice as fast as another. When both machines are used, they can print a magazine in 3 hours. How many hours would each machine require to do this printing alone? faster machine, $4\frac{1}{2}$ h; slower machine, 9 h

B 13. Art can do a job in 30 minutes, Bob can do it in 40 minutes, and Carl can do it in 60 minutes. How long will it take them if they work together? $13\frac{1}{3}$ min

14. It takes my father 3 hours to plow our cornfield with his new tractor. Using the old tractor it takes me 5 hours. If we both plow for 1 hour before I go to school, how long will it take Dad to finish the plowing? $1\frac{2}{5}$ h

15. Ingrid can rake our lawn in 90 minutes and I can do it in 60 minutes. If Ingrid rakes for 15 minutes before I join her, how long will it take us to finish? 30 min

5. Felix takes 2 h to mow the lawn, but, if his brother helps him, they can do it in $\frac{2}{3}$ h. How long would it take his brother to mow the lawn alone? 1 h

Mixed Review Exercises

Solve or explain why there is no solution.

1. After school Karen walked to the bike shop then rode her bike home. If she walked at 6 km/h and rode at 15 km/h, and the whole trip took her $\frac{1}{2}$ h what is the distance from the bike shop to her home? $2\frac{1}{7}$ km

2. Henry ran 6 km to his brother's house and walked home. He ran twice as fast as he walked. How far is it from his house to his brother's? Not enough information

3. A certain number is multiplied by 7. The result is decreased by 10 and this difference is divided by 60. The result is 8. What is the original number? 70

4. Jack bought an $80 jacket marked on sale for 20% off. What did he pay for the jacket? $64

16. One pump can fill a water tank in 40 minutes and another pump takes 30 minutes. When the tank was empty, both pumps were turned on for 10 minutes and then the slower pump was turned off. How much longer did the faster pump have to run before the tank was filled? $12\frac{1}{2}$ min

17. A pipe can fill a swimming pool in 6 hours. After it has been filling the empty pool for 3 hours, a second pipe is also used, with the result that the pool is filled in another 2 hours. How long will it take the second pipe alone to fill the pool? 12 h

18. Vanessa can do a job in 12 days. After she has worked for 4 days, she is joined by Susan, and they finish the job together in 2 more days. How long would it have taken Susan to do the whole job herself? 4 days

19. The fill pipe for a tank can fill the tank in 4 hours, and the drain pipe can drain it in 2 hours. If both pipes are accidentally opened, how long will it take to empty a half-filled tank? 2 h

C 20. Miranda and Sally are addressing invitations to the junior class party. Miranda can address one every 30 seconds and Sally can do one every 40 seconds. How long will it take them to address 140 invitations? 40 min

21. Sam Bordner can dig his garden in 4 hours and Elsie Bordner takes the same amount of time. After working together for an hour, their son Gregory helps them finish in just half an hour. How long would it have taken Gregory to dig the garden by himself? 2 h

22. If three pipes are all opened, they can fill an empty swimming pool in 3 hours. The largest pipe alone takes one third the time that the smallest pipe takes and half the time the other pipe takes. How long will each pipe take by itself? largest, $5\frac{1}{2}$ h; other, 11 h; smallest, $16\frac{1}{2}$ h

Self-Test 4

Solve.

1. How many kilograms of water must be evaporated from 40 kg of a 10% salt solution to produce a 25% salt solution? 24 kg **Obj. 7-7, p. 306**

2. How many kilograms of raisins must be added to 1.8 kg of plain bran muffin batter to produce a batter that is 10% raisins? 0.2 kg

3. Jean can make a quilt in 9 days. If Donna helps her, they can make the quilt in 6 days. How long will it take Donna to make the quilt alone? 18 days **Obj. 7-8, p. 312**

4. The main engine on a rocket can consume the fuel supply in 60 s. The auxiliary engine can consume the fuel supply in 80 s. How long can both engines be fired together? $34\frac{2}{7}$ s

Check your answers with those at the back of the book.

Quick Quiz

1. A grocer mixes grated cheese costing $9 per kilogram with cornmeal costing $1.20 per kilogram. How many kilograms of each are needed to produce 10 kg of a mix costing $7.44 per kilogram? 8 kg of cheese, 2 kg of cornmeal
2. How many kilograms of water must be evaporated from 216 kg of a 5% salt solution to produce a solution that is 45% salt? 192 kg
3. One pipe can fill a tank in 18 h. A second pipe can fill the tank in 14 h. How long would it take both pipes together to fill the tank? $7\frac{7}{8}$ h
4. Carmen can weed the garden in 24 min. If Kim helps, they can finish in 8 min. How long would it take Kim working alone? 12 min

Problems Involving Exponents

Teaching Suggestions p. T107

Suggested Extensions p. T107

7-9 Scientific Notation

Objective To use scientific notation.

Some numbers are so large or so small that they are difficult to read or to write. For example, consider the following:

diameter of the solar system: 118,000,000,000 km

diameter of a silver atom: 0.00000000000025 km

Scientific notation makes it easier to read and to calculate with such numbers.

Scientific notation is based on positive and negative powers of 10. You are familiar with the positive powers of 10. The negative powers are defined below.

Positive Powers of 10	**Negative Powers of 10**
$10^1 = 10$	$10^{-1} = \frac{1}{10^1} = \frac{1}{10} = 0.1$
$10^2 = 100$	$10^{-2} = \frac{1}{10^2} = \frac{1}{100} = 0.01$
$10^3 = 1000$	$10^{-3} = \frac{1}{10^3} = \frac{1}{1000} = 0.001$
$10^4 = 10{,}000$	$10^{-4} = \frac{1}{10^4} = \frac{1}{10{,}000} = 0.0001$
and so on	and so on

A number is written in **scientific notation** when it is expressed as a product of a number greater than or equal to 1, but less than 10, and an integral power of 10.

118,000,000,000 (11)	$= 1.18 \times 10^{11}$	decimal point moved 11 places
4,709,000,000 (9)	$= 4.709 \times 10^{9}$	decimal point moved 9 places
0.000152 (4)	$= 1.52 \times 10^{-4}$	decimal point moved 4 places
0.00000000000025 (13)	$= 2.5 \times 10^{-13}$	decimal point moved 13 places

Chalkboard Examples

1. Rewrite 1.54×10^{-8} without using scientific notation. 0.0000000154
2. Express 0.0000072 in scientific notation. 7.2×10^{-6}
3. Express 65,208,000 in expanded notation. $6 \cdot 10^7 + 5 \cdot 10^6 + 2 \cdot 10^5 + 0 \cdot 10^4 + 8 \cdot 10^3 + 0 \cdot 10^2 + 0 \cdot 10^1 + 0 \cdot 10^0$

Simplify.

4. $\frac{9 \times 10^{12}}{3 \times 10^5}$
   $\frac{9}{3} \times \frac{10^{12}}{10^5} = 3 \times 10^7$
5. $(2.2 \times 10^5)(3.5 \times 10^8)$
   $(2.2)(3.5)(10^5 \times 10^8) = 7.7 \times 10^{13}$
6. An astronomical unit (AU) is the mean distance from the sun to Earth, 1.50×10^{11} m. The mean distance from the sun to Uranus is 2.85×10^{12} m. Find the distance in astronomical units.
   Step 2: Let x = distance in astronomical units.
   Step 3: $\frac{1}{1.50 \times 10^{11}} = \frac{x}{2.85 \times 10^{12}}$
   Step 4: $x = \frac{2.85 \times 10^{12}}{1.5 \times 10^{11}}$
   $= \frac{2.85}{1.5} \times \frac{10^{12}}{10^{11}}$
   $= 1.9 \times 10^1$
   The distance is 19 AU.

Example 1 Express each number in scientific notation.
a. 58,120,000,000 **b.** 0.00000072

Solution **a.** The decimal point must be moved 10 places to get a number between 1 and 10.

$58{,}120{,}000{,}000 = 5.812 \times 10^{10}$ (10)

b. The decimal point must be moved 7 places to get a number between 1 and 10.

$0.00000072 = 7.2 \times 10^{-7}$ (7)

Example 2 Express each number without using scientific notation.
a. 4.95×10^8 **b.** 7.63×10^{-5}

Solution **a.** The decimal point must be moved 8 places.

$4.95 \times 10^8 = 495{,}000{,}000$ (8)

b. The decimal point must be moved 5 places.

$7.63 \times 10^{-5} = 0.0000763$ (5)

Example 3 shows that it is easier to compare large or small numbers and to calculate with them if they are expressed in scientific notation.

Example 3 The distances from the sun to Pluto and from the sun to Mercury are 5.9×10^9 km and 6×10^8 km, respectively. Find the ratio of these distances.

Solution

$$\frac{\text{sun to Pluto}}{\text{sun to Mercury}} = \frac{5.9 \times 10^9}{6 \times 10^8} = \frac{59 \times 10^8}{6 \times 10^8} = \frac{59}{6} \times \frac{10^8}{10^8} = \frac{59}{6}$$

Numbers written in scientific notation can be multiplied and divided easily by using the rules of exponents. For example:

$$(3.2 \times 10^7)(2.0 \times 10^4) = (3.2 \times 2.0)(10^7 \times 10^4) = 6.4 \times 10^{11}$$ {Add exponents when multiplying.

$$\frac{3.2 \times 10^7}{2.0 \times 10^4} = \frac{3.2}{2.0} \times \frac{10^7}{10^4} = 1.6 \times 10^3$$ {Subtract exponents when dividing.

$$(2.5 \times 10^3)(6.0 \times 10^2) = (2.5 \times 6.0)(10^3 \times 10^2) = 15 \times 10^5 = 1.5 \times 10^6$$

Positive and negative powers of 10 are used in our decimal number system, as well as in scientific notation, since every digit of a number can be associated with an integral power of 10. For convenience, the zero power of 10, written 10^0, is defined as 1. The following numbers are written in **expanded notation.**

$$8572 = 8 \cdot 10^3 + 5 \cdot 10^2 + 7 \cdot 10^1 + 2 \cdot 10^0$$
$$0.3946 = 3 \cdot 10^{-1} + 9 \cdot 10^{-2} + 4 \cdot 10^{-3} + 6 \cdot 10^{-4}$$
$$25.307 = 2 \cdot 10^1 + 5 \cdot 10^0 + 3 \cdot 10^{-1} + 0 \cdot 10^{-2} + 7 \cdot 10^{-3}$$

The metric system of measurement is also based on powers of 10. Conversions from one metric unit to another simply involve multiplying by a power of 10. For example:

To convert from meters to kilometers, multiply by 10^{-3}.

To convert from kilometers to meters, multiply by 10^3.

Oral Exercises

Express each of the following numbers in scientific notation.

1. 38,500 3.85×10^4
2. 4,070,000 4.07×10^6
3. 18,050,000,000 1.805×10^{10}
4. 0.003 3.0×10^{-3}
5. 0.000028 2.8×10^{-5}
6. 0.0000000902 9.02×10^{-8}

7–12. Express each number in Exercises 1–6 in expanded notation.

Simplify each expression to a power of 10.

13. $10^3 \cdot 10^4 \cdot 10^8$ 10^{15}
14. $\frac{10^5 \cdot 10^4}{10^2}$ 10^7
15. $\frac{10^8}{10^6 \cdot 10^6}$ 10^{-4}
16. $\frac{10^5}{10^{-2}}$ 10^7
17. $\frac{10^{-4}}{10^{-6}}$ 10^2
18. $\frac{10^4 \cdot 10^{-2}}{10^{-1}}$ 10^3

Express each in scientific notation.

19. $(2 \times 10^5)(4 \times 10^6)$ 8×10^{11}
20. $\frac{6 \times 10^7}{2 \times 10^2}$ 3×10^5
21. $(4 \times 10^6)(3 \times 10^2)$ 1.2×10^9
22. $\frac{8 \times 10^6}{2 \times 10^{-3}}$ 4×10^9
23. $\frac{9 \times 10^{-5}}{3 \times 10^{-3}}$ 3×10^{-2}
24. $\frac{(4 \times 10^4)(9 \times 10^{-2})}{2 \times 10^5}$ 1.8×10^{-2}

Written Exercises

Rewrite each number without using scientific notation.

A

1. The speed of light is 3.0×10^8 m/s. 300,000,000 m/s
2. The diameter of the sun is about 1.39×10^9 m. 1,390,000,000 m

Suggested Assignments

Minimum
319/2–32 even
320/*P*: 1–3
R 316/*Self-Test 4*

Average
319/2–32 even
320/*P*: 1, 3–5
S 316/*P*: 19, 20

Maximum
319/2–32 even
320/*P*: 1–5 odd
S 316/*P*: 20–22

Additional Answers
Oral Exercises

7. $3 \cdot 10^4 + 8 \cdot 10^3 + 5 \cdot 10^2 + 0 \cdot 10^1 + 0 \cdot 10^0$
8. $4 \cdot 10^6 + 0 \cdot 10^5 + 7 \cdot 10^4 + 0 \cdot 10^3 + 0 \cdot 10^2 + 0 \cdot 10^1 + 0 \cdot 10^0$
9. $1 \cdot 10^{10} + 8 \cdot 10^9 + 0 \cdot 10^8 + 5 \cdot 10^7 + 0 \cdot 10^6 + 0 \cdot 10^5 + 0 \cdot 10^4 + 0 \cdot 10^3 + 0 \cdot 10^2 + 0 \cdot 10^1 + 0 \cdot 10^0$
10. $0 \cdot 10^{-1} + 0 \cdot 10^{-2} + 3 \cdot 10^{-3}$
11. $0 \cdot 10^{-1} + 0 \cdot 10^{-2} + 0 \cdot 10^{-3} + 0 \cdot 10^{-4} + 2 \cdot 10^{-5} + 8 \cdot 10^{-6}$
12. $0 \cdot 10^{-1} + 0 \cdot 10^{-2} + 0 \cdot 10^{-3} + 0 \cdot 10^{-4} + 0 \cdot 10^{-5} + 0 \cdot 10^{-6} + 0 \cdot 10^{-7} + 9 \cdot 10^{-8} + 0 \cdot 10^{-9} + 2 \cdot 10^{-10}$

Additional A Exercises

Rewrite each number without using scientific notation.

1. The area of the U.S. is 3.6×10^6 square miles. 3,600,000 mi^2
2. The average distance from Jupiter to the sun is 4.8×10^8 mi. 480,000,000 mi

Complete each statement by writing a power of 10.

3. a. 1 L = _?_ mL 10^3
   b. 1 mL = _?_ L 10^{-3}

Express each of the following numbers in **(a)** scientific notation and **(b)** expanded notation.

4. 7,280 a. 7.28×10^3 b. $7 \times 10^3 + 2 \times 10^2 + 8 \times 10^1 + 0 \times 10^0$
5. 19,207,000 a. 1.9207×10^7 b. $1 \times 10^7 + 9 \times 10^6 + 2 \times 10^5 + 0 \times 10^4 + 7 \times 10^3 + 0 \times 10^2 + 0 \times 10^1 + 0 \times 10^0$
6. 0.0075 a. 7.5×10^{-3} b. $0 \times 10^{-1} + 0 \times 10^{-2} + 7 \times 10^{-3} + 5 \times 10^{-4}$

Additional Answers Written Exercises

15. a. 4.7×10^3 b. $4 \cdot 10^3 + 7 \cdot 10^2 + 0 \cdot 10^1 + 0 \cdot 10^0$
16. a. 3.95×10^5 b. $3 \cdot 10^5 + 9 \cdot 10^4 + 5 \cdot 10^3 + 0 \cdot 10^2 + 0 \cdot 10^1 + 0 \cdot 10^0$
17. a. 9.081×10^8 b. $9 \cdot 10^8 + 0 \cdot 10^7 + 8 \cdot 10^6 + 1 \cdot 10^5 + 0 \cdot 10^4 + 0 \cdot 10^3 + 0 \cdot 10^2 + 0 \cdot 10^1 + 0 \cdot 10^0$

Rewrite each number without using scientific notation.

3. The mass of the sun is about 2.0×10^{30} kg. 2,000,000,000,000,000,000,000,000,000,000 kg
4. The frequency of an AM radio wave is 1.4×10^6 cycles per second. 1,400,000 cycles per second
5. The wavelength of ultraviolet light is 1.36×10^{-6} cm. 0.00000136 cm
6. The wavelength of gamma rays is 3.0×10^{-10} cm. 0.0000000003 cm
7. The diameter of the nucleus of a hydrogen atom is 5.0×10^{-17} cm. 0.00000000000000005 cm
8. The mass of an atom of helium is 6.65×10^{-24} g. 0.00000000000000000000000665 g

Complete each statement by writing a power of 10.

9. a. 1 kg = _?_ g 10^3
   b. 1 g = _?_ kg 10^{-3}
10. a. 1 m = _?_ cm 10^2
    b. 1 cm = _?_ m 10^{-2}
11. a. 1 kg = _?_ mg 10^6
    b. 1 mg = _?_ kg 10^{-6}
12. 1 mm = _?_ cm 10^{-1}
13. 1 km = _?_ mm 10^6
14. 1 g = _?_ mg 10^3

Express each of the following numbers in (a) scientific notation and (b) expanded notation.

15. 4700
16. 395,000
17. 908,100,000
18. 87,060,000
19. 0.00021
20. 0.0000039
21. 0.0000000102
22. 0.000000606
23. $99\frac{44}{100}\%$

B

24. 4.5 million
25. 17 billion
26. 108 trillion

Perform the indicated operations.

27. $\frac{6 \times 10^8}{3 \times 10^2}$ 2×10^6
28. $(1.5 \times 10^7)(3 \times 10^4)$ 4.5×10^{11}
29. $(8 \times 10^4)(2 \times 10^4)$ 1.6×10^9
30. $\frac{(5 \times 10^7)(9 \times 10^{-3})}{3 \times 10^{-2}}$ 1.5×10^7
31. $\frac{(2 \times 10^5)^2}{(8 \times 10^{-3})(5 \times 10^{12})}$ 1
32. $\frac{(4 \times 10^{-5})^3}{(2 \times 10^{-7})^2}$ 1.6

Problems

Give your answers in scientific notation.

A

1. Find the number of kilometers in a light year. A light year is the distance that light travels in one year. Light travels at the rate of 3.0×10^5 km/s. 9.4608×10^{12} km
2. The Andromeda galaxy is approximately 1.5×10^6 light years from Earth. Find the distance in kilometers. 1.41912×10^{19} km

3. The distance from Earth to the star Alpha Centauri is about 4.07×10^{13} km. Use the result of Problem 1 to find how long it takes light from this star to reach Earth. 4.3 years

4. How long does it take light from the sun to reach Earth? The sun is 1.5×10^8 km from Earth. 5×10^2 seconds

5. A sheet of paper is 0.015 cm thick. Suppose that you tear this paper in half, place the two halves together and tear them in half. Then you take the four pieces, place them together and rip them in half. If it were possible to continue this process of stacking the ripped pieces together and tearing them apart for 50 times, the stack would have 2^{50} pieces in it. How high would the stack reach? Would it be higher than your room? Higher than the tallest redwood tree (83 m)? Higher than the world's tallest building (443.18 m)? Higher than the moon (384,432 km)? Higher than the sun (1.5×10^8 km)? 1.695×10^{11} m; yes; yes; yes; yes; yes

6. The diagram shows the repetitive pattern of an electromagnetic wave. The frequency of such a wave is the number of repetitions, or cycles, per second. A typical television wave could have a frequency of 1.3×10^8 cycles per second. The wavelength, L, is the distance from the peak of one wave to the peak of the next. The frequency, F, and wavelength, L, in centimeters, are related by the following formula:

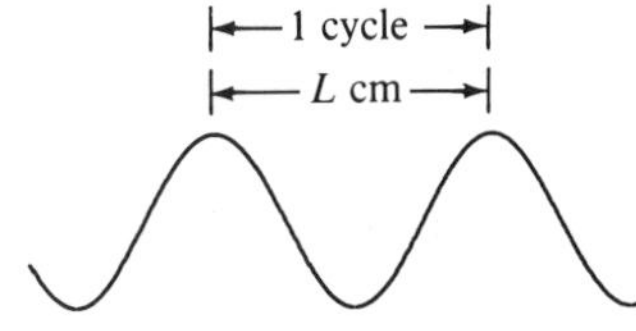

$$F \cdot L = 3.0 \times 10^{10} = \text{speed of light in cm/s}$$

Use this formula to complete the table below.

2.3×10^{18} 3×10^{21}

	Television	Red light	Violet light	x rays
Frequency F	1.3×10^8	4.0×10^{14}	?	?
Wavelength L	?	?	1.3×10^{-8}	1×10^{-11}

2.3×10^2 7.5×10^{-5}

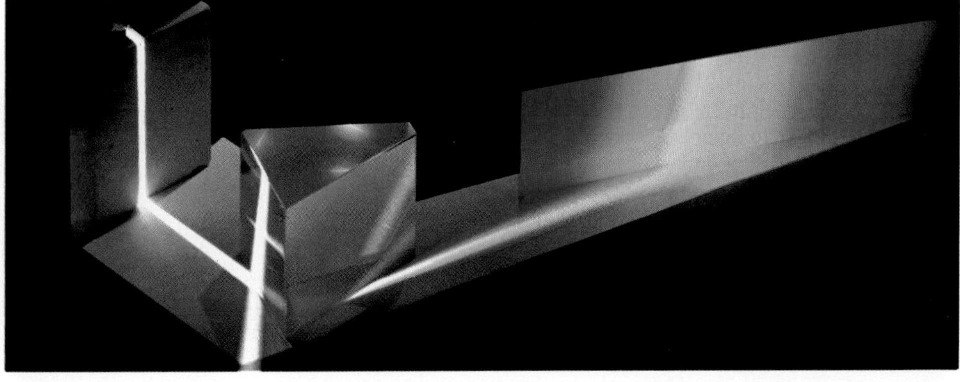

18. a. 8.706×10^7
b. $8 \cdot 10^7 + 7 \cdot 10^6 + 0 \cdot 10^5 + 6 \cdot 10^4 + 0 \cdot 10^3 + 0 \cdot 10^2 + 0 \cdot 10^1 + 0 \cdot 10^0$

19. a. 2.1×10^{-4}
b. $0 \cdot 10^{-1} + 0 \cdot 10^{-2} + 0 \cdot 10^{-3} + 2 \cdot 10^{-4} + 1 \cdot 10^{-5}$

20. a. 3.9×10^{-6}
b. $0 \cdot 10^{-1} + 0 \cdot 10^{-2} + 0 \cdot 10^{-3} + 0 \cdot 10^{-4} + 0 \cdot 10^{-5} + 3 \cdot 10^{-6} + 9 \cdot 10^{-7}$

21. a. 1.02×10^{-8}
b. $0 \cdot 10^{-1} + 0 \cdot 10^{-2} + 0 \cdot 10^{-3} + 0 \cdot 10^{-4} + 0 \cdot 10^{-5} + 0 \cdot 10^{-6} + 0 \cdot 10^{-7} + 1 \cdot 10^{-8} + 0 \cdot 10^{-9} + 2 \cdot 10^{-10}$

22. a. 6.06×10^{-7}
b. $0 \cdot 10^{-1} + 0 \cdot 10^{-2} + 0 \cdot 10^{-3} + 0 \cdot 10^{-4} + 0 \cdot 10^{-5} + 0 \cdot 10^{-6} + 6 \cdot 10^{-7} + 0 \cdot 10^{-8} + 6 \cdot 10^{-9}$

23. a. 9.944×10^{-1}
b. $9 \cdot 10^{-1} + 9 \cdot 10^{-2} + 4 \cdot 10^{-3} + 4 \cdot 10^{-4}$

24. a. 4.5×10^6
b. $4 \cdot 10^6 + 5 \cdot 10^5 + 0 \cdot 10^4 + 0 \cdot 10^3 + 0 \cdot 10^2 + 0 \cdot 10^1 + 0 \cdot 10^0$

25. a. 1.7×10^{10}
b. $1 \cdot 10^{10} + 7 \cdot 10^9 + 0 \cdot 10^8 + 0 \cdot 10^7 + 0 \cdot 10^6 + 0 \cdot 10^5 + 0 \cdot 10^4 + 0 \cdot 10^3 + 0 \cdot 10^2 + 0 \cdot 10^1 + 0 \cdot 10^0$

26. a. 1.08×10^{14}
b. $1 \cdot 10^{14} + 0 \cdot 12^{13} + 8 \cdot 10^{12} + 0 \cdot 10^{11} + 0 \cdot 10^{10} + 0 \cdot 10^9 + 0 \cdot 10^8 + 0 \cdot 10^7 + 0 \cdot 10^6 + 0 \cdot 10^5 + 0 \cdot 10^4 + 0 \cdot 10^3 + 0 \cdot 10^2 + 0 \cdot 10^1 + 0 \cdot 10^0$

Mixed Review Exercises

1. Evaluate: $12^2 - 11^2$ 23
2. Simplify: $-14m^4\left(-\frac{1}{2}m^2\right)$ $7m^6$
3. Solve: $-x + 7(x - 3) = 3$ $x = 4$
4. Elaine has 2 L of a solution which is 50% ammonia. How much water should she add to decrease the strength to 10%? 8 L

Computer Key-In Commentary

The number of digits a computer can print varies from machine to machine. Most print at least 6 digits, some as many as 15 digits, or more.

Additional Answers Calculator Key-In

Answers may vary according to calculator make and length of display. For example,
$99{,}999{,}999 \times 2 \approx 200{,}000{,}000$, or
2. 08
on one calculator. Similarly,
$99{,}999{,}999 \times 20 \approx 2{,}000{,}000{,}000$, or
2. 09
on the calculator. Finally,
$99{,}999{,}999 \times 400 \approx 40{,}000{,}000{,}000$, or
4. 10
on the calculator.

Computer Key-In

Computers are programmed to switch over to scientific notation to give approximate values for very large and very small numbers. The actual format depends on the number of digits the computer handles.

In BASIC

$\times 10^3$ is written E+03 and $\times 10^{-3}$ is written E−03.

To explore when and how your computer uses scientific notation for large numbers, RUN the program given below.

```
10  LET N=1
20  FOR I=1 TO 39
30  LET N=N*10
40  PRINT N,
50  NEXT I
60  END
```

Change line 30 to 30 LET N = N/10 to see how your computer uses scientific notation for small numbers.

Exercises

Change the program above by deleting line 30 and changing line 40 to PRINT I, N↑I. RUN the program for the following values of N.

1. 2 **2.** 5 **3.** −3 **4.** −7

5–6. In Exercises 1 and 2, find the largest power for which your computer gives an exact value. Answers will vary.

7. In the program on page 58, you used a negative number to end the loop. What kind of number can you use to end the loop if you want to add a list of positive and negative numbers? 0

Calculator Key-In

To display very large numbers, most calculators use a form of exponential notation similar to scientific notation. Try this on a calculator:

Press the 9 key until the display is filled with 9's. Next, estimate what the answer would be if you were to multiply this large number by 2. Write your estimate on paper. Now go ahead and multiply by 2 on the calculator. Compare the displayed answer with your estimate. They should be two different forms of the same number.

Enter 9's again. Predict what the calculator will display when you multiply by 20. Try it. Were you right? What will be displayed if you multiply by 400 instead of 20?

7-10 Negative Exponents

Objective To use negative exponents.

You have seen negative powers of 10 used in scientific notation. Negative powers of other numbers are defined in the same way as negative powers of 10.

$$10^{-2} = \frac{1}{10^2} = \frac{1}{100} \qquad 10^{-3} = \frac{1}{10^3} = \frac{1}{1000}$$

$$5^{-2} = \frac{1}{5^2} = \frac{1}{25} \qquad 5^{-3} = \frac{1}{5^3} = \frac{1}{125}$$

$$4^{-2} = \frac{1}{4^2} = \frac{1}{16} \qquad 4^{-3} = \frac{1}{4^3} = \frac{1}{64}$$

In general, you have the following rule.

Rule for Negative Exponents

If $a \neq 0$ and n is a positive integer,

$$a^{-n} = \frac{1}{a^n}.$$

You can understand why a^{-n} is defined as $\frac{1}{a^n}$ by considering the Rule of Exponents for Division (page 188). This rule states that for $m > n$, $\frac{a^m}{a^n} = a^{m-n}$. To apply the rule when $m < n$, that is, when $m - n$ is a negative number, we must give meaning to raising to a power when the exponent is negative. We apply this rule as follows:

$$\frac{a^7}{a^3} = a^{7-3} = a^4 \qquad \frac{a^3}{a^7} = a^{3-7} = a^{-4}$$

Since $\frac{a^7}{a^3}$ and $\frac{a^3}{a^7}$ are reciprocals, a^4 and a^{-4} must be reciprocals; that is, $a^4 = \frac{1}{a^{-4}}$ and $a^{-4} = \frac{1}{a^4}$.

In order to define a^0 we again refer to the Rule of Exponents for Division. In the first two parts of this rule $m \neq n$. However, if you were to apply these two rules to evaluate $\frac{a^m}{a^m}$, you would obtain these expressions:

$$\frac{a^m}{a^m} = a^{m-m} = a^0 \qquad \frac{a^m}{a^m} = \frac{1}{a^{m-m}} = \frac{1}{a^0}$$

Since $\frac{a^m}{a^m} = a^0$, and also, by the third part of the Exponent Rule for Division, $\frac{a^m}{a^m} = 1$, we can state the following rule for a^0.

Teaching Suggestions
p. T107

Suggested Extensions
p. T108

Chalkboard Examples

Evaluate.

1. 11^{-2} $\frac{1}{11^2} = \frac{1}{121}$
2. $(4^{-2})^{-2}$ $4^{(-2)(-2)} = 4^4 = 256$
3. $\frac{3^{-5}}{3^{-2}}$ $3^{-5-(-2)} = 3^{-3} = \frac{1}{27}$
4. $\frac{(5^{-3} \cdot 2)^2}{5^{-5}}$ $\frac{5^{-6} \cdot 4}{5^{-5}} = 4 \cdot 5^{-6-(-5)} = 4 \cdot 5^{-1} = \frac{4}{5}$

Simplify. Give answers in terms of positive exponents.

5. $(y^{-8} \cdot y^5)^4$ $y^{(-8+5)4} = (y^{-3})^4 = y^{-12} = \frac{1}{y^{12}}$
6. $\left(\frac{t^2}{t^5}\right)^{-3}$ $(t^{2-5})^{-3} = (t^{-3})^{-3} = t^{(-3)(-3)} = t^9$

Common Errors

Some students confuse negative exponents with the opposite of a number. A student may think, for example, that $5^{-1} = -5$, rather than $\frac{1}{5}$.

Some students may still confuse expressions such as $8a^{-2}$ with expressions such as $(8a)^{-2}$. Point out, for example, that $8a^{-2} = \frac{8}{a^2}$, whereas $(8a)^{-2} = \frac{1}{(8a)^2} = \frac{1}{64a^2}$.

You may have to remind students, for example, that $(2^{-1} + 2^{-2})^{-1} \neq 2^1 + 2^2$. You may wish to assign Written Exercises 25–28, which are designed to make students think about rules and conventions learned earlier in this course.

Rule for a Zero Exponent

If a is a real number not equal to zero,

$$a^0 = 1.$$

We shall not use the expression 0^0.

Since all the rules of positive exponents continue to hold for zero and negative exponents, we have the following.

Summary of Rules for Exponents

1. Multiplication: $b^m b^n = b^{m+n}$
2. Division: $b^m \div b^n = b^{m-n}$
3. Power of a Power: $(b^m)^n = b^{mn}$
4. Power of a Product: $(ab)^m = a^m b^m$
5. Power of a Quotient: $\left(\frac{a}{b}\right)^m = \frac{a^m}{b^m}$

Example 1 Simplify. Give answers in terms of positive exponents.

a. $\frac{5}{5^{-3}}$ **b.** $(b^{-1})^{-3}$ **c.** $(3x^{-1})^2$

Solution

a. $\frac{5^1}{5^{-3}} = 5^{1-(-3)} = 5^4$ (Rule 2)

b. $(b^{-1})^{-3} = b^{(-1)(-3)} = b^3$ (Rule 3)

c. $(3x^{-1})^2 = 9x^{-2}$ (Rules 4 and 3)

$= \frac{9}{x^2}$ (Definition of negative exponents)

Positive and negative exponents are often used in problems dealing with population growth, interest, or energy consumption. These quantities are said to grow exponentially when the equations that describe the growth involve exponents.

Example 2 The population of a city has been growing exponentially. It is estimated that in t years the population P will be

$$P = 2(1.03)^t \text{ million people.}$$

a. What will the population be in 2 years?
b. What is the population now?
c. What was the population last year?

Solution

a. Let $t = 2$. $P = 2(1.03)^2 = 2(1.0609)$ million $= 2{,}121{,}800$

b. Let $t = 0$. $P = 2(1.03)^0 = 2(1) = 2$ million

c. Let $t = -1$. $P = 2(1.03)^{-1} = \frac{2}{1.03}$ million $\approx 1{,}941{,}748$

Oral Exercises

Evaluate.

1. 10^{-1} $\frac{1}{10}$
2. 6^{-1} $\frac{1}{6}$
3. 7^{-1} $\frac{1}{7}$
4. 3^{-1} $\frac{1}{3}$
5. 10^{-2} $\frac{1}{100}$
6. 6^{-2} $\frac{1}{36}$
7. 7^{-2} $\frac{1}{49}$
8. 3^{-3} $\frac{1}{27}$
9. 2^{-3} $\frac{1}{8}$
10. 4^{-3} $\frac{1}{64}$
11. $3^{-4} \cdot 3^2$ $\frac{1}{9}$
12. $5^6 \cdot 5^{-8}$ $\frac{1}{25}$
13. $(3^{-1})^2$ $\frac{1}{9}$
14. $(3^{-1})^{-2}$ 9
15. $\frac{5}{5^{-1}}$ 25
16. $\frac{4^{-3}}{4^{-6}}$ 64
17. $\left(\frac{1}{2} - \frac{1}{4}\right)^{-1}$ 4
18. $\left(\frac{1}{2} \cdot \frac{1}{4}\right)^{-1}$ 8
19. $(2 + 3^{-1})^{-1}$ $\frac{3}{7}$
20. $(2 \cdot 5^{-1})^{-1}$ $\frac{5}{2}$

Simplify. Give answers in terms of positive exponents.

21. $a^{-1}b^2$ $\frac{b^2}{a}$
22. $\frac{c^{-2}}{d^{-3}}$ $\frac{d^3}{c^2}$
23. $(2x^{-1})^3$ $\frac{8}{x^3}$
24. $(3y^{-2})^{-1}$ $\frac{y^2}{3}$
25. The electrical energy consumption in a city has been increasing. In n years it is estimated that the annual electrical consumption will be $C = 1.3(1.07)^n$ billion kilowatts. What value of n should be substituted to find the value of C (a) now? (b) 10 years from now? (c) 10 years ago? a. 0 b. 10 c. −10

Written Exercises

Evaluate.

A

1. 5^{-1} $\frac{1}{5}$
2. 4^{-1} $\frac{1}{4}$
3. 5^{-2} $\frac{1}{25}$
4. 4^{-2} $\frac{1}{16}$
5. 9^{-2} $\frac{1}{81}$
6. 8^{-2} $\frac{1}{64}$
7. 9^{-3} $\frac{1}{729}$
8. 8^{-3} $\frac{1}{512}$
9. 2^{-4} $\frac{1}{16}$
10. 3^{-4} $\frac{1}{81}$
11. 2^{-5} $\frac{1}{32}$
12. 3^{-5} $\frac{1}{243}$
13. $4^{-2} \cdot 4^5$ 64
14. $3^7 \cdot 3^{-9}$ $\frac{1}{9}$
15. $(3^{-2})^{-2}$ 81
16. $(5^{-1})^{-3}$ 125
17. $\frac{3}{3^{-2}}$ 27
18. $\frac{6^{-2}}{6^{-3}}$ 6
19. $\frac{8 \cdot 8^{-2}}{8^{-3}}$ 64
20. $\frac{7^{-2} \cdot 7^5}{7^3}$ 1
21. $\left(\frac{3^{-1}}{3}\right)^2$ $\frac{1}{81}$
22. $\left(\frac{8^4}{8^{-4}}\right)^0$ 1
23. $\left(\frac{9^3 \cdot 9}{9^5}\right)^{-3}$ 729
24. $\frac{(4^{-2} \cdot 3)^3}{4^{-6}}$ 27

Supplementary Materials

Practice Master 44
Test 25
Resource Book, p. 101

Suggested Assignments

Average
325/1–49 odd
327/*P*: 2, 4
R 327/*Self-Test 5*

Maximum
325/1–57 odd
327/*P*: 2, 4, 5
R 327/*Self-Test 4*

Additional A Exercises

Evaluate.

1. 14^{-2} $\frac{1}{196}$
2. $5^{-6} \cdot 5^4$ $\frac{1}{25}$
3. $(12^{-1})^{-2}$ 144
4. $\left(\frac{8^3 \cdot 8^{-2}}{8^2}\right)^{-2}$ 64
5. $(4^{-2} - 3^0)^{-2}$ $\frac{256}{225}$
6. $(5x^{-6})^2$ $\frac{25}{x^{12}}$

Mixed Review Exercises

1. Simplify: $|-3| - |-15|$ −12
2. Millie jumped from a diving board 6 ft above the water, rose $4\frac{1}{2}$ ft into the air, then went straight to the bottom of the 12 ft pool before coming back to the surface. How far did she travel? $4\frac{1}{2} + 4\frac{1}{2} + 6 + 12 + 12 = 39$, or 39 ft
3. Which axiom should be given as the reason for $a + (b + c) = (a + b) + c$? Associative ax. for add.

Additional Answers Written Exercises

29. Because $b^{-3} = \frac{1}{b^3}$ and division by 0 is meaningless.

30. Since $b^2 \cdot b^0 = b^{2+0} = b^2$, b^0 must equal 1.

Evaluate.

25. a. $(2^{-1} + 2^{-2})^{-1}$ $\frac{4}{3}$ b. $(2^{-1} \cdot 2^{-2})^{-1}$ 8

26. a. $(2 + 3^{-1})^{-2}$ $\frac{9}{49}$ b. $(2 \cdot 3^{-1})^{-2}$ $\frac{9}{4}$

27. a. $(3^0 \cdot 2^{-2})^{-2}$ 16 b. $(3^0 - 2^{-2})^{-2}$ $\frac{16}{9}$

28. a. $(2^{-1} \div 2^{-2})^3$ 8 b. $(2^{-1} - 2^{-2})^3$ $\frac{1}{64}$

29. Why is b^{-3} not defined when $b = 0$?

30. Suppose that you did not know that $b^0 = 1$. Explain how you could deduce this fact by using the laws of exponents to simplify $b^2 \cdot b^0 = b^2$.

Simplify. Give answers in terms of positive exponents.

31. $7x^{-1}$ $\frac{7}{x}$

32. $8a^{-2}$ $\frac{8}{a^2}$

33. $x^{-1}y^2$ $\frac{y^2}{x}$

34. $a^{-2}b^{-3}$ $\frac{1}{a^2b^3}$

35. $(a^{-2})^3$ $\frac{1}{a^6}$

36. $(b^{-1})^{-3}$ b^3

37. $(3x^{-2})^3$ $\frac{27}{x^6}$

38. $(4n^{-1})^2$ $\frac{16}{n^2}$

B 39. $x^3 \cdot x^{-5}$ $\frac{1}{x^2}$

40. $y^3 \cdot y^{-3}$ 1

41. $(a^2 \cdot a^{-5})^2$ $\frac{1}{a^6}$

42. $(b^5 \cdot b^{-7})^3$ $\frac{1}{b^6}$

43. $\frac{a^5}{a^{-3}}$ a^8

44. $\frac{b^7}{b^{-7}}$ b^{14}

45. $\frac{c^{-5}}{c^2}$ $\frac{1}{c^7}$

46. $\frac{d^{-3}}{d^{-5}}$ d^2

47. $\left(\frac{x^{-2}}{x^{-4}}\right)^3$ x^6

48. $\left(\frac{a^{-1}}{a^4}\right)^2$ $\frac{1}{a^{10}}$

49. $\left(\frac{n^{-3}}{n}\right)^{-2}$ n^8

50. $\left(\frac{y^5}{y^{-2}}\right)^{-3}$ $\frac{1}{y^{21}}$

Use the table of powers of 5 to evaluate the expressions below.

Example $\frac{3125}{0.008} = \frac{5^5}{5^{-3}} = 5^8 = 390{,}625$

$5^1 = 5$	$5^{-1} = 0.2$
$5^2 = 25$	$5^{-2} = 0.04$
$5^3 = 125$	$5^{-3} = 0.008$
$5^4 = 625$	$5^{-4} = 0.0016$
$5^5 = 3125$	$5^{-5} = 0.00032$
$5^6 = 15{,}625$	$5^{-6} = 0.000064$
$5^7 = 78{,}125$	$5^{-7} = 0.0000128$
$5^8 = 390{,}625$	$5^{-8} = 0.00000256$

51. $15{,}625 \times 0.0016$ 25

52. 0.00032×3125 1

53. $(78{,}125)^{-1}$ 0.0000128

54. $(0.0016)^{-2}$ 390,625

55. $\frac{0.008}{625}$ 0.0000128

56. $\frac{125}{0.00032}$ 390,625

57. $\frac{(3125)^2}{15{,}625}$ 625

58. $(0.0000128)^3(390{,}625)^2$ 0.00032

Exponents can be fractions as well as integers. Exercises 59-63 will help you see how fractional exponents can be defined.

C 59. If Rule 1 for integral exponents were to hold for fractional exponents, then $9^{\frac{1}{2}} \cdot 9^{\frac{1}{2}} = 9^{\frac{1}{2}+\frac{1}{2}} = 9^1$.
Therefore, $9^{\frac{1}{2}}$ ought to be defined as the number _?_. 3

60. If Rule 1 for integral exponents were to hold for fractional exponents, then $16^{\frac{1}{2}} \cdot 16^{\frac{1}{2}} = 16^1$.
Therefore, $16^{\frac{1}{2}}$ ought to be defined as the number _?_. 4

61. If Rule 3 for integral exponents were to hold for fractional exponents, then $(8^{\frac{1}{3}})^3 = 8^{\frac{1}{3}\cdot 3} = 8^1$.
Therefore, $8^{\frac{1}{3}}$ ought to be defined as the number _?_. 2

62. Guess how $x^{\frac{1}{2}}$ and $x^{\frac{1}{3}}$ are defined. $x^{\frac{1}{2}} = \sqrt{x}$; $x^{\frac{1}{3}} = \sqrt[3]{x}$

63. Guess how $x^{-\frac{1}{2}}$ and $x^{-\frac{1}{3}}$ are defined. $x^{-\frac{1}{2}} = \frac{1}{\sqrt{x}}$; $x^{-\frac{1}{3}} = \frac{1}{\sqrt[3]{x}}$

Problems

A 1. If you have 1 kg of radioactive iodine, it will gradually decay (decrease in amount) so that d days later you will have 1.09^{-d} kg. Find how many kilograms you will have 4 days later and 8 days later. 0.7084252 kg 0.5018663 kg

2. The value, V, of a new $10,000 automobile y years after it is purchased is given by the formula $V = 10{,}000(1.3)^{-y}$. Copy and complete the table below.

Years	0	1	2	3	4	5
Value (V)	?	?	?	?	?	?

3. The population of a certain state t years from now is predicted to be $P = 15(1.04)^t$ million. Estimate to the nearest million the population (a) now, (b) 10 years from now, and (c) 10 years ago.

4. The cost of living in a large metropolitan area has been increasing in such a way that an item costing one dollar today will cost $(1.08)^t$ dollars in t years. (a) How much will today's one-dollar item cost in 3 years? (b) How much in 9 years? (c) How much did today's one-dollar item cost 9 years ago? a. $1.26 b. $2 c. $.50

5. A microbiologist has a bacteria culture whose growth rate can be described by $N = n(2.72)^{2t}$, where n is the original number of bacteria, and N is the number after t hours. If the number of bacteria at noon is 100 find (a) the number at 2 P.M., (b) the number at 10 A.M., (c) the number at 6 P.M., and (d) the number at 6 A.M.
a. 5474 b. 2 c. 16,399,358 d. 0

Self-Test 5

Vocabulary scientific notation (p. 317) expanded notation (p. 319)

Express each of the following numbers in scientific notation.

1. 150 million 1.5×10^8
2. 0.000000009 9×10^{-9} **Obj. 7-9, p. 317**

Evaluate.

3. $(3^0)^{-5}$ 1
4. $\frac{2^{-3}}{2^0}$ $\frac{1}{8}$
5. $-\frac{2}{2^{-3}}$ -16 **Obj. 7-10, p. 323**

Simplify. Give answers in terms of positive exponents.

6. x^{-5} $\frac{1}{x^5}$
7. $4a^{-2}$ $\frac{4}{a^2}$
8. $(3a^{-4})^2$ $\frac{9}{a^8}$

Check your answers with those at the back of the book.

Additional Answers Problems

2. 0: $10,000
1: $7692.31
2: $5917.16
3: $4551.66
4: $3501.28
5: $2693.29

3. a. 15 million
b. 22 million
c. 10 million

Quick Quiz

1. Express 120,500,000,000 in scientific notation and in expanded notation.
1.205×10^{11}; $1 \cdot 10^{11} + 2 \cdot 10^{10} + 0 \cdot 10^9 + 5 \cdot 10^8 + 0 \cdot 10^7 + 0 \cdot 10^6 + 0 \cdot 10^5 + 0 \cdot 10^4 + 0 \cdot 10^3 + 0 \cdot 10^2 + 0 \cdot 10^1 + 0 \cdot 10^0$

2. Simplify:
$\frac{(2.8 \times 10^5)(4.5 \times 10^4)}{6.3 \times 10^7}$
2.0×10^2, or 200

3. Evaluate: $\frac{3^{-2}}{3^{-1}}$ $\frac{1}{3}$

4. Express $(2x^{-3})^2$ in simplest form using positive exponents.
$\frac{4}{x^6}$

Historical Note / *The Rule of Three*

The Rule of Three was the forerunner of the statement "The product of the means equals the product of the extremes." However, because the rule was used primarily by merchants, and because the terms were not written in ratio form, its relationship to ratio and proportion was not realized until the end of the fifteenth century. Although no explanation was ever given as to why the rule worked, merchants knew the first and third terms had to be measured in the same units and that the product of the second and third terms divided by the first term gave the quantity they wanted to find.

The Rule of Three was stated in various forms. For instance, the seventh-century mathematician Brahmagupta wrote, "In the Rule of Three, Argument, Fruit, and Requisition are the names of the terms. The first and last terms must be similar. Requisition multiplied by Fruit, and divided by Argument is the Produce." In the twelfth century Bhāskara asked, "Two palas and a half of saffron are purchased for three sevenths of a niska, how many palas will be purchased for nine niskas?" Other application problems can be found in the Egyptian Rhind mathematical papyrus (1550 B.C.), the Chinese *K'iu—ch'ang Suan-shu,* or *Arithmetic in Nine Sections* (second millennium B.C.), and the *Treviso Arithmetic* published in Italy (A.D. 1478).

In the early nineteenth century the Rule of Three was listed among the requirements for admission to Harvard College and Princeton University.

Calculator Key-In

You can use a calculator to evaluate algebraic fractions for given values of their variables. First evaluate the denominator and store its value in the calculator's memory. (You may want to review the method for evaluating a polynomial given on page 198.) Then evaluate the numerator and divide by the value of the denominator.

Evaluate each fraction for the given value of the variable.

1. $\frac{9}{x+3}$; $x = 12$ 0.6

2. $\frac{2y+5}{8}$; $y = 9$ 2.875

3. $\frac{5n-16}{2n}$; $n = 5$ 0.9

4. $\frac{7a+20}{3a}$; $a = 4$ 4

5. $\frac{7x^2+4x+12}{x}$; $x = 9$ $68.\overline{3}$

6. $\frac{4z^2+11z-60}{2z+8}$; $z = -6$ -4.5

7. $\frac{a^2+8a-10}{2a}$; $a = 0.5$ -5.75

8. $\frac{5y^2-22y+30}{6y-10}$; $y = -2$ $-4.\overline{27}$

Chapter Summary

1. A *ratio* of two numbers is their quotient. The ratio 6 to 8 can be written as 6:8 or more simply as 3:4, $3 \div 4$, $\frac{3}{4}$, or 0.75. If you are told that the ratio of two numbers is 5:7, you can represent the numbers as $5x$ and $7x$.

2. A *proportion* is an equation stating that two ratios are equal. In a proportion the product of the means is equal to the product of the extremes. Thus,
$$\text{if } \frac{a}{b} = \frac{c}{d}, \text{ then } ad = bc.$$

3. You can eliminate fractions from equations with fractional coefficients and from *fractional equations* by multiplying both sides of the equation by the LCD. Similarly, you can eliminate decimals from equations by multiplying each term by a suitable power of 10.

4. *Percent* means "hundredths." Percent problems usually involve finding a percent of a number, finding what percent one number is of another, or finding a number when a percent of the number is known (see the examples on pages 295–296). When solving word problems involving percents, it is often convenient to express the percent as a decimal. For example:
$$7\frac{1}{2}\% = 7.5\% = 0.075$$

5. Many word problems are very much alike. The similarities that exist among mixture, coin, investment, work, and distance problems can be seen in the charts and equations used to solve them.

6. Expressing very large or very small numbers in *scientific notation* makes these numbers easier to read and to use in calculations.

7. Exponents can be positive, negative, or zero. The rules for positive exponents continue to hold for zero and negative exponents.

Supplementary Materials

Practice Master 45
Test 26
Resource Book, pp. 36–39, 154

Extra Practice

Skills, pp. 619–621
Problems, pp. 638–642

Chapter Review

1. State the ratio 52 wk:28 d in simplest form. 7-1

a. $\frac{13}{7}$ **b.** $\frac{7}{13}$ **c.** $\frac{12}{1}$ **(d.)** $\frac{13}{1}$

2. In a ceramics class the ratio of students making projects that they intend to give as gifts to students making projects that they intend to keep is 5:3. If there are 24 students in the class, how many of the students intend to keep the projects that they are making?

a. 3 **b.** 12 **(c.)** 9 **d.** 15

3. Solve for x: $\frac{x}{60} = \frac{45}{25}$ 7-2

(a.) 108 b. $\frac{12}{25}$ c. $\frac{25}{12}$ d. 21

4. Elena is drawing a map. If she lets 1.5 cm represent 125 km, how long should she draw a segment that represents 875 km?

a. 12 cm (b.) 10.5 cm c. 7.5 cm d. 7 cm

5. Solve for x: $x - \frac{x + 3}{3} = 0$ 7-3

a. 0 b. $-\frac{3}{2}$ c. $\frac{2}{3}$ (d.) $\frac{3}{2}$

6. Solve for a: $\frac{1}{a - 1} + \frac{3}{3a - 1} = 0$ 7-4

(a.) $\frac{2}{3}$ b. 0 c. $\frac{3}{2}$ d. no solution

7. Express $166\frac{2}{3}\%$ as a fraction in simplest form. 7-5

a. $\frac{8}{3}$ (b.) $\frac{5}{3}$ c. $\frac{20}{3}$ d. $\frac{7}{3}$

8. Find 56% of 56.

a. 1 b. 100 c. $\frac{14}{25}$ (d.) 31.36

9. 18 is 6% of what number?

a. 3 (b.) 300 c. 1.08 d. $\frac{3}{50}$

10. What percent of 36 is 27?

a. $\frac{4}{3}\%$ b. $\frac{3}{4}\%$ (c.) 75% d. 7.5%

11. A team won 63 games and lost 21. What percent did the team win?

(a.) 75% b. 3% c. 30% d. 70%

12. Monty saves 20% by buying a record on sale for \$6.36. What was the original price of the record? 7-6

(a.) \$7.95 b. \$9.54 c. \$7.99 d. \$8.48

13. A chemist has 10 cm^3 of a 20% salt solution. How many cubic centimeters of water should she add to produce a 5% salt solution? 7-7

a. 13 cm^3 b. 18 cm^3 c. 22 cm^3 (d.) 30 cm^3

14. Veronica can clean the house in 5 hours. If Eduardo helps her, they can clean the house in 3 hours. How long would it take Eduardo to clean the house alone? 7-8

a. $3\frac{3}{5}$ hours (b.) $7\frac{1}{2}$ hours c. $5\frac{1}{3}$ hours d. 6 hours

15. Express 163 million in scientific notation. 7-9

a. 1.63×10^2 b. 1.63×10^6 (c.) 1.63×10^8 d. 1.63×10^{-8}

16. Simplify $(2^{-1} - 2^0)^3$. 7-10

(a.) $-\frac{1}{8}$ b. $\frac{1}{8}$ c. 8 d. -8

Chapter Test

Alternate Test p. T16

Express each ratio in simplest form.

1. 42 min:2 h 7:20
2. 63 cm:0.9 m 7:10 — 7-1
3. The ratio of time Lionel spent writing an essay to the time he spent revising it was 3:1. If he spent a total of 2 hours writing and revising the essay, how long did it take him to write it? $1\frac{1}{2}$ h

Solve.

4. $\frac{91}{x} = \frac{7}{3}$ 39
5. $\frac{16}{3y} = \frac{12}{5}$ $2\frac{2}{9}$ — 7-2
6. $\frac{3x}{10} = \frac{5x}{6}$ 0
7. $\frac{2n-1}{3} = \frac{n-4}{5}$ -1
8. $a + \frac{a}{3} = 18 - \frac{a}{6}$ 12
9. $\frac{3y+5}{2} - \frac{3y+2}{5} = \frac{3}{10}$ -2 — 7-3
10. $\frac{1}{b} + \frac{3b}{5b-2} = 0$ $\left\{-2, \frac{1}{3}\right\}$
11. $\frac{c-1}{6c} = \frac{1}{c}$ 7 — 7-4

Express as a fraction in simplest form.

12. 35% $\frac{7}{20}$
13. $62\frac{1}{2}\%$ $\frac{5}{8}$
14. 510% $\frac{51}{10}$ — 7-5
15. Find 20% of $83\frac{1}{2}$. 16.7
16. Find 37% of 68. 25.16
17. 48 is 32% of what number? 150
18. What percent of 675 is 225? $33\frac{1}{3}\%$
19. On Saturday night the attendance at the senior play was 15% higher than it had been Friday night. If 340 people attended the play Friday night, how many people attended that play on Saturday night? 391 — 7-6
20. How many liters of apple juice must be added to 16 L of cranberry juice to produce a drink that is 36% apple juice? 9 L — 7-7
21. Working alone, Sally Jillson can correct a set of examinations in 7 hours. It would take Ellen Ryan 3 hours to correct the same set of examinations. If they work together, how long will it take them to correct the examinations? $2\frac{1}{10}$ h — 7-8
22. Express 0.000128 in scientific notation. 1.28×10^{-4} — 7-9

Evaluate.

23. $2^{-3} \cdot 2^{-2}$ $\frac{1}{32}$
24. $\frac{4^0}{4^{-2}}$ 16
25. $(3 + 2^{-1})^{-1}$ $\frac{2}{7}$ — 7-10

Simplify. Give answers in terms of positive exponents.

26. $14x^{-7}$ $\frac{14}{x^7}$
27. $(a^{-2})^{-3}$ a^6
28. $(n^{-4})^2$ $\frac{1}{n^8}$

Additional Answers
Cumulative Review

4. $-2x^3y^3 - 3x^2y^5 + 12xy^2$
7. $36t^2v^4 - 60tv^2 + 25$
8. $15b^2c^2 - 2bc - 24$
9. $2x^3 - 11x^2y + 11xy^2 - 3y^3$
18. $7st(-6s^2 + 2st + 3t^2)$
19. $(7z - 2)^2$
20. $(10t - 7y)(10t + 7y)$

Cumulative Review (Chapters 1–7)

Perform the indicated operations. Express the answers in simplest form using only positive exponents. Assume that no denominator is zero.

1. $24 \div 2 + 2^2 - 4^3 \div 2^4$ 12

2. $\frac{16}{32}\left(\frac{2}{19}\right) + \frac{1}{2}\left(\frac{2}{19}\right)$ $\frac{2}{19}$

3. $(-2m^3n^4)(8m^5n^3)$ $-16m^8n^7$

4. $xy^2(-2x^2y - 3xy^3 + 12)$

5. $(-5a^3bc^4)^2$ $25a^6b^2c^8$

6. $(10b + 9)^2$ $100b^2 + 180b + 81$

7. $(6tv^2 - 5)^2$

8. $(3bc - 4)(5bc + 6)$

9. $(2x - y)(x^2 - 5xy + 3y^2)$

10. $\frac{t^2 - 10s + 25s^2}{t - s} \cdot \frac{t^2 - s^2}{t^2 - 4ts - 5s^2}$ $t - 5s$

11. $\frac{3z - 1}{xyz^3} \div \frac{9xz^2 - x}{yz^2}$ $\frac{1}{x^2z(3z + 1)}$

12. $\frac{x}{x + 5} + \frac{x + 2}{x^2 + 4x - 6}$ $\frac{x^3 + 5x^2 + x + 10}{(x + 5)(x^2 + 4x - 6)}$

13. $\frac{10b^2 - 9b - 9}{2b - 3}$ $5b + 3$

14. $\left(\frac{y^3}{y - 4}\right)^3$ $\frac{y^9}{(y - 4)^3}$

15. $\left(\frac{x^{-7}}{x - 4}\right)^{-2}$ $x^{14}(x - 4)^2$

16. What percent of 400 is 336? 84%

17. 72 is what percent of 600? 12%

Factor completely. If the polynomial cannot be factored, write "prime."

18. $-42s^3t + 14s^2t^2 + 21st^3$

19. $49z^2 - 28z + 4$

20. $-49y^2 + 100t^2$

21. $6b^2 + 23b + 21$ $(3b + 7)(2b + 3)$

22. $18t^2 + 27t + 12$ $3(6t^2 + 9t + 4)$

23. $12x^2 + 47x - 4$ $(12x - 1)(x + 4)$

Solve. If the equation is an identity or has no solution, state that fact.

24. $8x + 9 = -39$ -6

25. $\frac{2}{3}t - 8 = 12$ 30

26. $(n + 4)^2 = (n + 2)^2 + 4(n + 3)$ identity

27. $4y^2 + 36y + 81 = 0$ $-\frac{9}{2}$

28. $m^2 + 14 + 9m = 0$ $\{-7, -2\}$

29. $y^3 - 12y^2 + 11y = 0$ $\{0, 11, 1\}$

30. $0.02(700 - x) + 0.5x = 20$ 12.5

31. $\frac{n - 2}{n + 2} + \frac{1}{n - 2} = \frac{4}{n^2 - 4}$ 1

Express in scientific notation.

32. 112 billion 1.12×10^{11}

33. 0.000074 7.4×10^{-5}

34. $(8.2 \times 10^6)(2.0 \times 10^{-3})$ 1.64×10^4

35. The product of two consecutive even integers is 32 less than the square of the greater integer. Find the integers. 14, 16

36. Three numbers are in the ratio 3:4:5 and their sum is 144. Find the numbers. 36, 48, 60

37. A video cassette recorder that normally costs $625 at Fenton's would cost an employee $550. What is the percent of the employee's discount? 12%

38. How many liters of water should be added to 15 L of a 40% acid solution to make a solution that is 10% acid? 45 L

39. One pipe can fill a tank in 2 hours. A second pipe can fill it in $1\frac{3}{4}$ hours. How long will it take to fill the tank with both pipes open? $\frac{14}{15}$ h, or 56 min

Maintaining Skills

Simplify.

Example 1 $-5(a + 3b) - 4(-2a + b) = -5a - 15b + 8a - 4b = 3a - 19b$

1. $7a^2 + 2 - 5a + 2a^2 + 6$ $9a^2 - 5a + 8$

2. $-4c + 2d - 3 - 5d + 3c - 6$ $-c - 3d - 9$

3. $(12 - 2x) + (-8x + 5x)$ $12 - 5x$

4. $(3m - 2n) - (-4m + 3n)$

5. $4(x - 3z) - 8(-x + z)$ $12x - 20z$

6. $-2(5y^2 - 2y) + 3(-3y + 1)$

7. $-2(5x + 3) + 4(3x - 2y)$ $2x - 8y - 6$

8. $-3(5x - y) + 5x(2y + 2)$

9. $\frac{3}{4}(8a - 2b) - \frac{2}{3}(9a + b)$ $-\frac{13b}{6}$

10. $\frac{2}{3}(-12j - k) + \frac{1}{6}(18j + 8k)$ $-5j + \frac{2}{3}k$

Example 2 $(-4x^2yz)(-5xy^4z^3) = [(-4)(-5)](x^2 \cdot x)(y \cdot y^4)(z \cdot z^3) = 20x^3y^5z^4$

11. $(-2a^2b^2)(3ab^2c)$ $-6a^3b^4c$

12. $(4st^2)(-s^3t)(-2s^2t^2)$ $8s^6t^5$

13. $(4m^2np)\left(-\frac{1}{4}m^3np^2\right)$ $-m^5n^2p^3$

14. $(-5a^2b^3)(2a^3b^2) + (a^4b)(6ab^4)$ $-4a^5b^5$

Example 3 $(-9a^3b^2)^3 = (-9)^3(a^3)^3(b^2)^3 = -729a^9b^6$

15. $(2x^2y^3)^4$ $16x^8y^{12}$

16. $(-11m^4n^3)^2$ $121m^8n^6$

17. $(r^3s^2t)^4(rst)^3$ $r^{15}s^{11}t^7$

18. $-9(fg^3)^2(-2f^3g)^2$ $-36f^8g^8$

19. $(2c^2d^2e)^6 + (-2c^4d^4r^2)^3$ $64c^{12}d^{12}e^6 - 8c^{12}d^{12}r^6$

20. $-ab(a^3b^2)^4 + a^3b^4(-a^2b)^5$ $-2a^{13}b^9$

Multiply.

Example 4 $5x^2y(3x^2 - 4xy + 2y^2) = 15x^4y - 20x^3y^2 + 10x^2y^3$

21. $3ab^2(a^2 - ab + b^2)$ $3a^3b^2 - 3a^2b^3 + 3ab^4$

22. $-4m^2n(3mn^2 - 2m + n^3)$ $-12m^3n^3 + 8m^3n - 4m^2n^4$

23. $c^2d^3(d^4 - 2d^2c + c^3)$ $c^2d^7 - 2c^3d^5 + c^5d^3$

24. $-xy(5x^3y^2 - 2x^2y + 7y^5)$ $-5x^4y^3 + 2x^3y^2 - 7xy^6$

Example 5 $(2r - 5s)(-3r + 2s) = 2r(-3r + 2s) - 5s(-3r + 2s)$

$$= -6r^2 + 4rs + 15rs - 10s^2$$
$$= -6r^2 + 19rs - 10s^2$$

25. $(z - 3)(z + 8)$ $z^2 + 5z - 24$

26. $(2d + 7)(7d - 2)$ $14d^2 + 45d - 14$

27. $(y - 2)(y + 10)$ $y^2 + 8y - 20$

28. $(2t - 5)(5t - 3)$

29. $(4z + 1)(3z - 3)$

30. $(3c + 4)(5c + 3)$

31. $(9d - 3)(9d + 3)$

32. $(4t + 5)^2$

33. $(x^2 - 6)(x^2 + 6)$

34. $(y - 3)(3y^2 - 4y + 1)$ $3y^3 - 13y^2 + 13y - 3$

35. $(b - 7)(-2b^2 + 5b - 2)$ $-2b^3 + 19b^2 - 37b + 14$

Additional Answers Maintaining Skills

4. $7m - 5n$
6. $-10y^2 - 5y + 3$
8. $-5x + 3y + 10xy$
28. $10t^2 - 31t + 15$
29. $12z^2 - 9z - 3$
30. $15c^2 + 29c + 12$
31. $81d^2 - 9$
32. $16t^2 + 40t + 25$
33. $x^4 - 36$

About the Photo

The coordinate plane (see pages 339–340) referred to in the caption is often called the Cartesian plane in honor of the French mathematician René Descartes, who linked algebra and geometry by associating points in a plane with ordered pairs of real numbers.

By the seventeenth century scientists had posed problems that could not be adequately handled by Euclidean geometry, which deals primarily with the properties of polygons and circles. The need to learn about ellipses, parabolas, and other curves produced the need for a new mathematical methodology, which Descartes provided. Analytic, or coordinate, geometry allows us to graph the equations of curves and to represent curves algebraically.

Analytic geometry is now part of standard high school mathematics courses. It has provided a foundation for applied mathematics of all types.

8 Linear Equations and Systems

Like many other planned cities, Chicago, Illinois, is laid out in a grid pattern. This pattern suggests a coordinate plane, which you will study in this chapter.

334

Using Two Variables

8-1 Equations in Two Variables

Objective To solve equations in two variables over given domains of the variables.

In previous chapters, the equations you have solved have contained only one variable. In this chapter, you will learn how to solve some equations containing two variables.

One-variable equations	**Two-variable equations**
$2x - 3 = 7$	$4x + 3y = 10$
$y = 9$	$xy = 6$

The solutions to equations in one variable are numbers; the solutions to equations in two variables are *pairs* of numbers. For example, the pair of numbers $x = 1$ and $y = 2$ is a **solution** of the equation

$$4x + 3y = 10 \quad \text{because} \quad 4 \cdot 1 + 3 \cdot 2 = 10.$$

The solution $x = 1$ and $y = 2$ is usually written as $(1, 2)$, with the x-value written first. A pair of numbers, such as (1, 2), for which the order of the numbers is important, is called an **ordered pair.**

The ordered pair (1, 2) is not the only solution of the equation $4x + 3y = 10$.

$(4, -2)$ is a solution because $4 \cdot 4 + 3 \cdot (-2) = 10.$

$(-2, 6)$ is a solution because $4 \cdot (-2) + 3 \cdot 6 = 10.$

$\left(\frac{3}{2}, \frac{4}{3}\right)$ is a solution because $4 \cdot \frac{3}{2} + 3 \cdot \frac{4}{3} = 10.$

$(3, -1)$ is *not* a solution because $4 \cdot 3 + 3 \cdot (-1) \neq 10.$

The equation $4x + 3y = 10$ has many solutions. However, if both x and y are required to be whole numbers, then (1, 2) is the only solution. When you find the set of all solutions of an equation, whether it is a one- or two-variable equation, you are said to have **solved** the equation.

Example 1 Solve $2x + y = 3$ if x and y are whole numbers.

Solution If $x = 0$, then $2(0) + y = 3$ and $y = 3$. (0, 3)

If $x = 1$, then $2(1) + y = 3$ and $y = 1$. (1, 1)

If $x \geq 2$, then $2x \geq 4$ and there are no more solutions.

$\therefore$ the solutions are (0, 3) and (1, 1). ***Answer***

Teaching References

Lesson Commentary, pp. T108–T112

Assignment Guide, pp. T63–T65

Supplementary Materials

- Practice Masters 46–52
- Tests 27–30
- Resource Book
  - Practice Exercises, pp. 102–106
  - Tests, pp. 40–43
  - Enrichment Activity, p. 155
  - Practice in Problem Solving/Word Problems, pp. 176–180
- Algebra Action

Extra Practice

- Skills, pp. 621–622
- Problems, pp. 643–644

Alternate Test, p. T17

Problem Solving Strategies

Drawing a Diagram
The coordinate plane is used in Section 8-2 to make clear the relationship between lines and linear equations. In Section 8-3 it is used to show how pairs of lines are related in the plane.

Word Problem Plan
The five-step plan is used in Section 8-5 in conjunction with charts and systems of equations to solve problems.

Types of Word Problems
Students learn to recognize and solve word problems such as wind, water, digit, age, and fraction problems in Sections 8-8 and 8-9.

(continued)

Problem Solving Strategies (continued)

Trial and Error
After setting up an appropriate equation students can use trial and error to solve the Challenges after Sections 8-2, 8-6, and 8-9.

Deduction
Students have the opportunity to make deductive arguments to prove divisibility tests in the Extra following Section 8-9.

Teaching Suggestions
p. T108

Suggested Extensions
p. T109

Chalkboard Examples

1. Is (3, 2) a solution of the equation $2x - y = 4$? Why or why not? Yes, because $2 \cdot 3 - 2 = 6 - 2 = 4$.
2. Is (5, −1) a solution of the equation $x - y = 4$? Why or why not? No, because $5 - (-1) = 5 + 1 = 6 \neq 4$.
3. Solve $3x - 4y = 7$ for y in terms of x.
$3x - 4y = 7$
$-4y = -3x + 7$
$y = \frac{3}{4}x - \frac{7}{4}$
4. Solve $3x + 2y = 8$ if x and y represent whole numbers.
First solve for y in terms of x. Then beginning with 0, substitute successive whole numbers for x and find corresponding values of y. If y is a whole number, the ordered pair is a solution. {(0, 4), (2, 1)}

Example 2 Solve $xy = 4 - x$ if x and y are whole numbers.

Solution

1. Solve the given equation for y in terms of x.

$$xy = 4 - x$$
$$y = \frac{4 - x}{x}$$

2. Replace x with successive whole numbers and calculate the corresponding values of y. If y is a whole number, you have found a solution pair.

∴ the solutions are (1, 3), (2, 1), and (4, 0). ***Answer***

x	$y = \frac{4 - x}{x}$	Solution
0	denominator = 0	No
1	$\frac{4 - 1}{1} = 3$	(1, 3)
2	$\frac{4 - 2}{2} = 1$	(2, 1)
3	$\frac{4 - 3}{3} = \frac{1}{3}$	No
4	$\frac{4 - 4}{4} = 0$	(4, 0)
Values of x greater than 4 give negative values of y.		

Example 3 Dana spent \$13 on posters and notebooks. The posters cost \$2 each and the notebooks cost \$3 each. How many of each did she buy?

Solution

Step 1 The problem asks for the number of posters and the number of notebooks Dana bought.

Step 2 Let p = number of posters, and n = number of notebooks.

	Number	× Price	= Cost
Posters	p	2	$2p$
Notebooks	n	3	$3n$

Step 3 Since the total cost is \$13, you have: $2p + 3n = 13$

Step 4 Solve for p: $2p = 13 - 3n$

$$p = \frac{13 - 3n}{2}$$

Both n and p must be whole numbers because Dana cannot buy a negative or fractional number of posters or notebooks.

Step 5 Check that (1, 5) and (3, 2) are solutions of the problem:

$$2(5) + 3(1) = 13$$
$$2(2) + 3(3) = 13$$

∴ Dana bought either 1 notebook and 5 posters or 3 notebooks and 2 posters. ***Answer***

n	$p = \frac{13 - 3n}{2}$	Solution
1	$\frac{13 - 3}{2} = 5$	(1, 5)
2	$\frac{13 - 6}{2} = \frac{7}{2}$	No
3	$\frac{13 - 9}{2} = 2$	(3, 2)
4	$\frac{13 - 12}{2} = \frac{1}{2}$	No
Values of n greater than 4 give negative values of p.		

When solving equations in two variables, it is customary to give the numbers in a solution pair in the alphabetical order of the variables. Therefore, in Example 3 the solutions were given as (n, p) instead of (p, n).

Oral Exercises

State whether each ordered pair of numbers is a solution of the given equation.

1. $x - y = 5$
   $(9, 4), (7, 3)$
   Yes; No
2. $x + 2y = 8$
   $(3, 3), (0, 4)$
   No; Yes
3. $3x + y = 6$
   $(2, 0), (3, -1)$
   Yes; No
4. $12 - y = 3x$
   $(5, -3), \left(\frac{1}{3}, 11\right)$
   Yes; Yes
5. $y = x^2$
   $(-3, 9), (4, 2)$
   Yes; No
6. $x^2 + y^2 = 10$
   $(1, 3), (-3, -1)$
   Yes; Yes
7. $st = 6$
   $(3, -2), \left(\frac{9}{2}, \frac{4}{3}\right)$
   No; Yes
8. $a^2 - 4b^2 = 0$
   $(-2, 1), (1, 2)$
   Yes; No

Solve each equation for y in terms of x.

9. $2x + y = 4$ $\quad y = 4 - 2x$
10. $3x - y = 7$ $\quad y = 3x - 7$
11. $x = 4 + 3y$ $\quad y = \frac{x - 4}{3}$
12. $2x + 5y = 9$ $\quad y = \frac{9 - 2x}{5}$

Solve each equation if x and y are whole numbers.

13. $x + y = 3$
    $(0, 3), (1, 2), (2, 1), (3, 0)$
14. $x + 2y = 7$
    $(1, 3), (3, 2), (5, 1), (7, 0)$
15. $2xy = 8$
    $(1, 4), (2, 2), (4, 1)$
16. $x^2 = -y^2$
    $(0, 0)$

Written Exercises

State whether each ordered pair is a solution of the given equation.

A

1. $2x + 3y = 13$
   $(5, 1), (11, -3)$
   Yes; Yes
2. $5x - 4y = 9$
   $(7, 6), (-3, -6)$
   No; Yes
3. $3a - 4b = 11$ Yes; Yes
   $\left(\frac{1}{3}, -\frac{5}{2}\right), \left(-\frac{5}{3}, -4\right)$
4. $3m - 2n = 6$
   $(0, 3), \left(\frac{5}{3}, -\frac{1}{2}\right)$
   No; Yes
5. $2x^2 - 4y^2 = 4$
   $(4, -3), (0, -1)$
   No; No
6. $x^2 + y^2 = 50$
   $(-7, -1), (5, -5)$
   Yes; Yes
7. $3st = t^2$
   $(-3, -9), \left(\frac{1}{6}, -\frac{1}{2}\right)$
   Yes; No
8. $ab = a^2 - a$
   $(4, 3), (0, 37.2)$
   Yes; Yes

Solve each equation for y in terms of x.

9. $3x - 2y = 7$ $\quad y = \frac{3x - 7}{2}$
10. $4y - 3x = 1$ $\quad y = \frac{3x + 1}{4}$
11. $7x^2 - 3y = 4$ $\quad y = \frac{7x^2 - 4}{3}$
12. $x^2y = 3$ $\quad y = \frac{3}{x^2}$
13. $\frac{8}{x + y} = 6$ $\quad y = \frac{4 - 3x}{3}$
14. $\frac{2}{x} = \frac{3}{y + 7}$ $\quad y = \frac{3x - 14}{2}$

Solve for the variable indicated in color.

15. $2a - 3b = 7$ $\quad a = \frac{7 + 3b}{2}$
16. $5n + 3m = 7$ $\quad m = \frac{7 - 5n}{3}$
17. $4p - 3q = 0$ $\quad q = \frac{4p}{3}$
18. $5s - 7t = 8$ $\quad t = \frac{5s - 8}{7}$
19. $\frac{a - 2b}{3} = \frac{a}{4}$ $\quad a = 8b$
20. $\frac{3n - 2}{5} - \frac{1 - m}{4} = \frac{1}{2}$

20. $m = \frac{23 - 12n}{5}$

5. The sum of 3 times one whole number and 4 times a second is 12. Find the numbers.

$3x + 4y = 12$; $4y = -3x + 12$; $y = -\frac{3}{4}x + 3$

Substitute 0, 1, 2, 3, 4 for x and check whether y is a whole number. (If $x > 4$, $3x + 4y > 12$.)

The numbers are 0 and 3 or 4 and 0.

Suggested Assignments

Minimum
337/1–21 odd, 29

Average
337/1–33 odd

Maximum
337/1–37 odd

Additional A Exercises

State whether each ordered pair is a solution of the given equation.

1. $7x - 2y = 0$;
   $(2, 7)$ Yes
   $(3, 4)$ No
2. $2a - 3b = 16$;
   $\left(-\frac{1}{2}, -5\right)$ No
   $\left(-\frac{5}{2}, -7\right)$ Yes
3. $x^2 + 3y^2 = 75$;
   $(5, 0)$ No
   $(0, 5)$ Yes

Solve each equation for y in terms of x.

4. $5x - 6y = 3$
   $y = \frac{5x - 3}{6}$
5. $12y - 3x^2 = 15$
   $y = \frac{x^2 + 5}{4}$
6. $x^2y = 9$ $\quad y = \frac{9}{x^2}$

Additional Answers
Written Exercises

21. (1, 4), (3, 3), (5, 2), (7, 1), (9, 0)
22. (0, 7), (1, 4), (2, 1)
23. (1, 11), (3, 6), (5, 1)
24. (0, 12), (2, 9), (4, 6), (6, 3), (8, 0)
25. (0, 5), (3, 4), (4, 3), (5, 0)
26. (0, 3), (2, 1)
27. (1, 6), (2, 3), (3, 2), (6, 1)
28. (1, 2), (4, 1)
29. 13 45's and 1 LP, 9 45's and 2 LP's, 5 45's and 3 LP's, or 1 45 and 4 LP's
30. 1 blue and 8 green, 2 blue and 6 green, 3 blue and 4 green, or 4 blue and 2 green

Mixed Review Exercises

1. Divide $x^4 - y^4$ by $x - y$. $x^3 + x^2y + xy^2 + y^3$

Solve.

2. $\frac{2}{x-1} = \frac{5}{2x+1}$ 7
3. $\frac{m}{22} = \frac{56}{112}$ 11
4. Simplify $\left(\frac{1}{m^{-2}}\right)^3$. Give your answer in terms of positive exponents. m^6

Solve the following equations if all the variables represent whole numbers.

B
21. $x + 2y = 9$
22. $3x + y = 7$
23. $5x + 2y = 27$
24. $3a + 2b = 24$
25. $x^2 + y^2 = 25$
26. $2s^2 + t^2 = 9$
27. $5nm = 30$
28. $y^2t = 4$

29. Mona bought several 45 rpm records costing \$2 each and several LP records costing \$8 each. If she spent \$34, how many of each kind of record did she buy? (There is more than one solution.)

30. Hank and Jill Arbor spent \$100 for some spruce trees. Some were blue spruce priced at \$20 each, and the rest were green spruce priced at \$10 each. How many of each kind of spruce did the Arbors buy? (There is more than one solution.)

31. Ed Haley spent \$280 for some baby pigs and some chickens. The pigs cost \$40 each and the chickens \$3 each. If Ed bought more than one pig, how many pigs and how many chickens did he buy? 4 pigs and 40 chicks

32. The perimeter of the figure at the right is 60. Find x and y if they represent positive integers. $x = 2$, $y = 3$

In Exercises 33–36, find an ordered pair that is a solution of both equations.

C
33. $y = 3x$; $2x + y = 15$ (3, 9)
34. $x = y - 2$; $x + 4y = 18$ (2, 4)
35. $a + b = 27$; $a - b = 11$ (19, 8)
36. $3r - s = 2$; $2r + s = 8$ (2, 4)
37. Solve for y: $\frac{1}{x} + \frac{1}{y} = \frac{1}{2}$ $y = \frac{2x}{x-2}$
38. If a and b are positive two-digit integers, how many solutions are there of the equation $2a + 3b = 100$? 9

Computer Exercises

For students with some programming experience

Write a BASIC program that checks whether an ordered pair entered with an INPUT statement is a solution to a given equation. RUN the program for the following equations with the given ordered pairs.

1. $3x - 2y = 1$; (3, 4) Sol.
2. $4x + y = 10$; $(-3, 2)$ Not sol.
3. $xy + y^2 = 6$; (1, 2) Sol.
4. $x^2 + y^2 = 25$; $(-4, -3)$ Sol.
5. $x^2y + xy^2 = 0$; $(-1, -1)$ Not sol.
6. $x^2 + (xy)^2 = 45$; $(3, -2)$ Sol.

8-2 Points, Lines, and Their Graphs

Objective To graph ordered pairs and linear equations in two variables.

You know how to graph a number as a point on a number line. Ordered pairs are graphed as points in a "number plane." You can construct a "number plane" as follows:

1. Draw a horizontal number line, called the **horizontal axis.**
2. Draw a second number line intersecting the first at right angles so that both number lines have the same zero point, or **origin** (O). The second number line is called the **vertical axis.**
3. Indicate the positive direction on each axis by an arrowhead. The positive direction is usually to the right on the horizontal axis and upward on the vertical axis, as shown in the first diagram.

The horizontal axis is usually labeled with an x and is referred to as the ***x*-axis.** The vertical axis is usually labeled with a y and is referred to as the ***y*-axis.**

The diagram at the right shows a point A that is the **graph of the ordered pair** (2, 3). Point A is located by moving 2 units to the right of the origin and 3 units up. The numbers 2 and 3 are called the **coordinates** of point A; 2 is the ***x*-coordinate,** or **abscissa,** of A and 3 is the ***y*-coordinate,** or **ordinate,** of A. Although there is a difference between the ordered pair of numbers (2, 3) and the point A, it is customary to stress the association between the two by referring to the point $A(2, 3)$.

The diagrams below illustrate how to locate, or **plot,** the points $B(-2, 4)$, $C(4, -2)$, and $D(-3, -1)$.

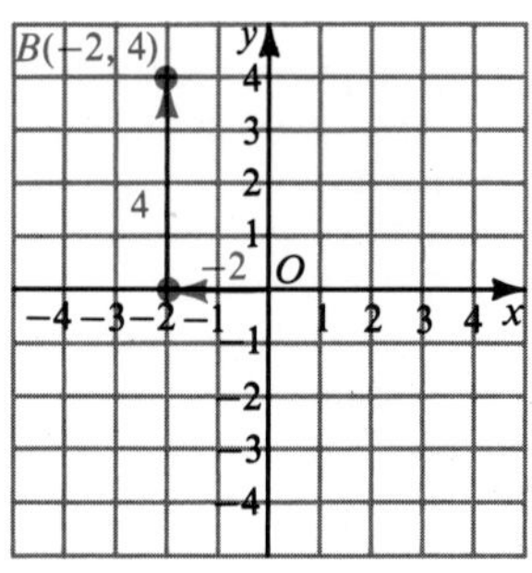

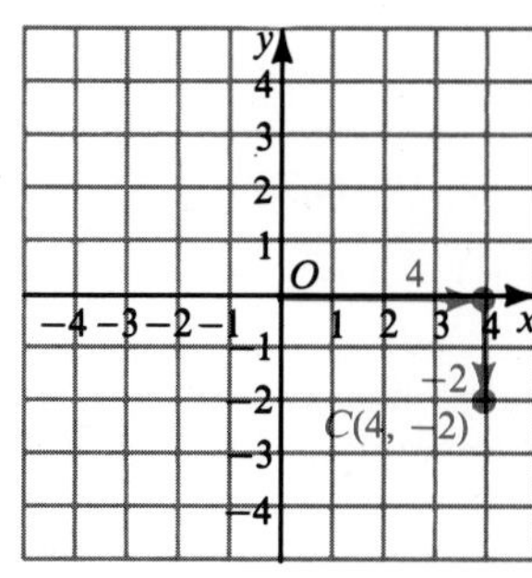

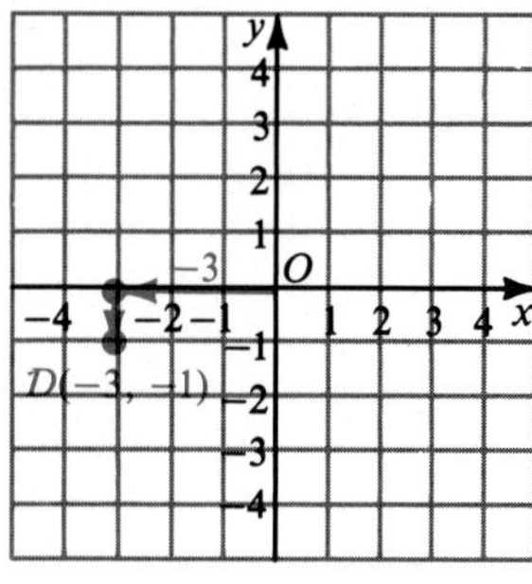

Teaching Suggestions
p. T109

Suggested Extensions
p. T109

Chalkboard Examples

1. Plot the points (−3, 11), (5, 3), (0, 8), (−1, 9), (2, 6), and (9, −1) in a coordinate plane. Tell what you observe about the points on the graph and the algebraic relationship between the abscissa and the ordinate of each ordered pair.
   All the points lie on a line. For each ordered pair, the sum of the abscissa and the ordinate is 8.

Name an ordered pair satisfying each condition.
Answers may vary. One example is given.

2. The abscissa is 3. (3, 5)
3. The ordinate is −2. (0, −2)
4. The graph is on the x-axis. (1, 0)
5. The ordinate is the opposite of the abscissa. (−2, 2)
6. $y = 1$ (0, 1)
7. $x + y = 3$ (2, 1)

Common Errors

Some students may need to be reminded that the quadrants of the coordinate plane are numbered in order in a counterclockwise rather than in a clockwise direction.

Students may also confuse the equations of vertical and horizontal lines with values of variables, thus assuming that such equations represent points rather than lines. For this reason, discuss Example 2 on page 341 with your class in detail.

Supplementary Materials

Practice Master 46
Resource Book, p. 102

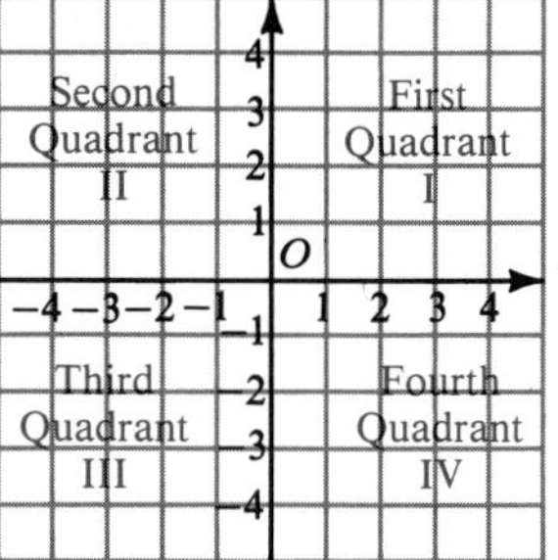

The x- and y-axes are sometimes referred to as **coordinate axes** and the number plane is then called a **coordinate plane.** The coordinate axes separate a coordinate plane into four **quadrants** as shown in the figure at the right. Points on the coordinate axes are not considered to be in any quadrant.

The **graph of an equation** in two variables consists of all the points that are associated with the solutions of the equation. For example, the equation $x + 2y = 6$ has as some of its solutions the ordered pairs (0, 3), (2, 2), (4, 1), (6, 0), and (−2, 4). These solutions are graphed at the left below. Of course, the equation $x + 2y = 6$ has many other solutions too; for example, $(1, 2\frac{1}{2})$ and (6.2, −0.1). The graphs of all solutions lie on the straight line shown at the right below. This line is the graph of the equation $x + 2y = 6$.

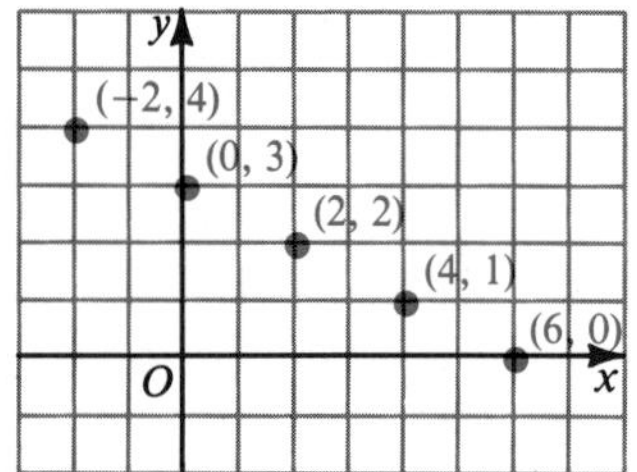

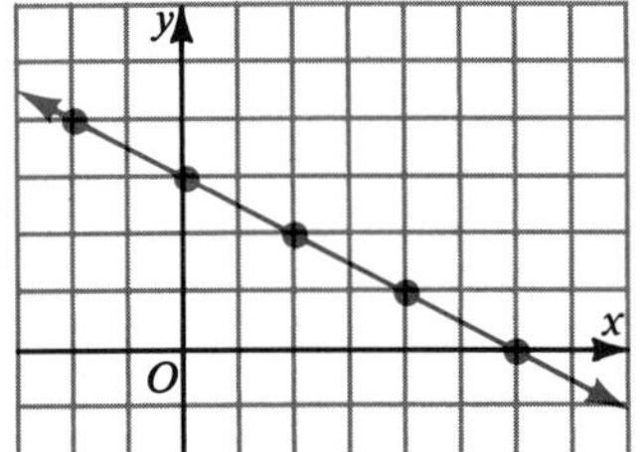

The equation $x + 2y = 6$ is an example of a **linear equation,** so named because its graph is a line. All linear equations in the variables x and y can be written in the form

$$ax + by = c$$

where a, b, and c are real numbers with a and b not both zero. If a, b, and c are integers, the equation is said to be in **standard form.**

Linear equations in standard form	**Linear equations not in standard form**	**Nonlinear equations**
$2x - 5y = 7$	$\frac{1}{2}x + 4y = 12$	$x^2y + 3y = 4$
$4x + 9y = 0$	$y = 3x - 2$	$xy = 6$
$y = 3$	$x + y - 1 = x - y + 1$	$\frac{1}{x} + 3y = 1$

Since two points determine a line, you need to find only two solutions of a linear equation in order to graph it. However, it is a good idea to find a third solution as a check. The most convenient solutions to use are those where the line crosses the x-axis ($y = 0$) and the y-axis ($x = 0$).

Example 1 Graph $2x - 3y = 6$ in a coordinate plane.

Solution

Let $y = 0$:
$2x - 3(0) = 6$
$2x = 6$
$x = 3$; *Solution* $(3, 0)$

Let $x = 0$:
$2(0) - 3y = 6$
$-3y = 6$
$y = -2$; *Solution* $(0, -2)$

Any third solution, such as $(6, 2)$, can be used as a check.

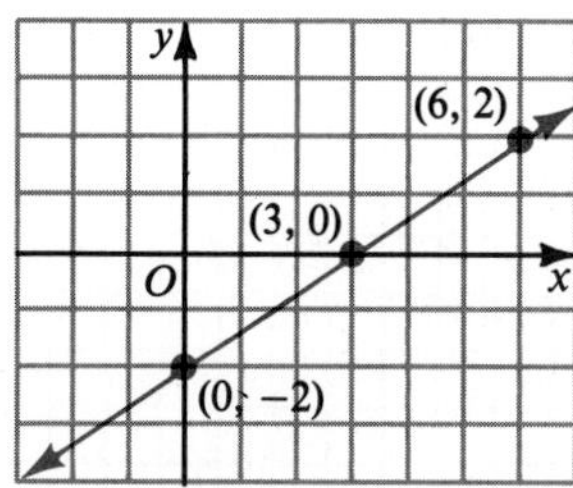

Example 2 **a.** Graph $x = 2$ in a coordinate plane.
b. Graph $y = -3$ in a coordinate plane.

Solution **a.** The equation places no restriction on y. All points with x-coordinate 2 are graphs of solutions. The graph of $x = 2$ is a vertical line.

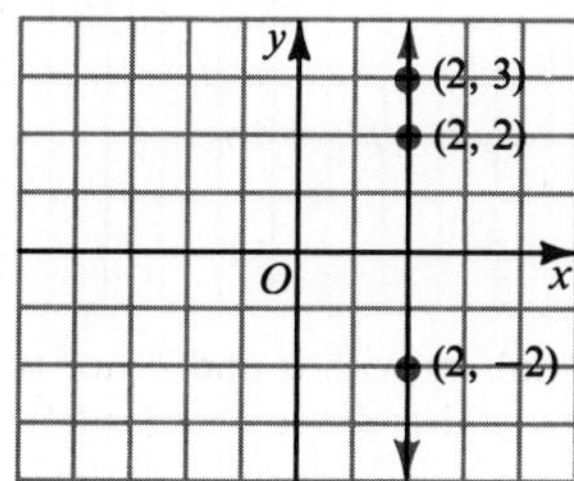

b. The equation places no restriction on x. All points with y-coordinate -3 are graphs of solutions. The graph of $y = -3$ is a horizontal line.

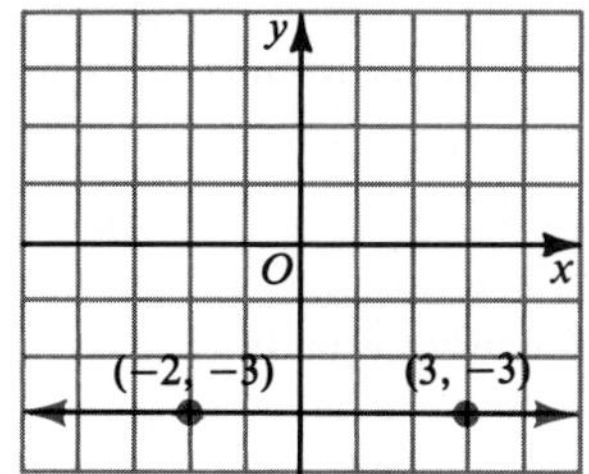

Suggested Assignments

Minimum
343/1–35 odd
S 337/10–20 even

Average
343/14–42 even, 43, 44
S 338/30, 32

Maximum
343/14–42 even, 43, 44
R 344/*Self-Test 1*

Additional A Exercises

Plot the graph of each of the given points.

1. $T(0, -7)$
2. $V(-4, 2)$
3. $Z\left(4\frac{1}{2}, -2\right)$

See graph below.

Graph each equation.

4. $x = -6$
5. $x + y = 0$
6. $2x - 5y = 5$

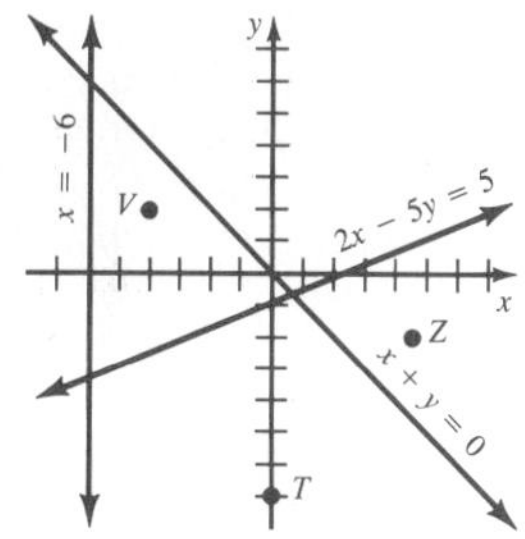

Mixed Review Exercises

1. Simplify:
$\dfrac{-90x^2y^2 - 30x^2y - 15}{15}$
$-6x^2y^2 - 2x^2y - 1$
2. Express $(3a + 5)(7a - 10)$ as a polynomial.
$21a^2 + 5a - 50$
3. The length of a rectangle is twice the width and the perimeter is equal numerically to the area. Find the dimensions. width, 3; length, 6
4. Express 0.0000197 in scientific notation.
1.97×10^{-5}

Additional Answers Oral Exercises

21. a. line parallel to y-axis through (2, 0)
    b. line parallel to y-axis through (−1, 0)
    c. y-axis
22. a. line parallel to x-axis through (0, −3)
    b. line parallel to x-axis through (0, 4)
    c. x-axis

Additional Answers Written Exercises

1–12.

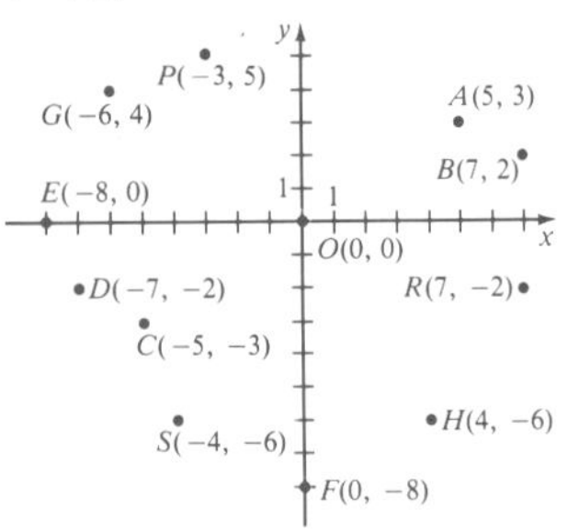

Oral Exercises

Exercises 1-20 refer to the diagram below.

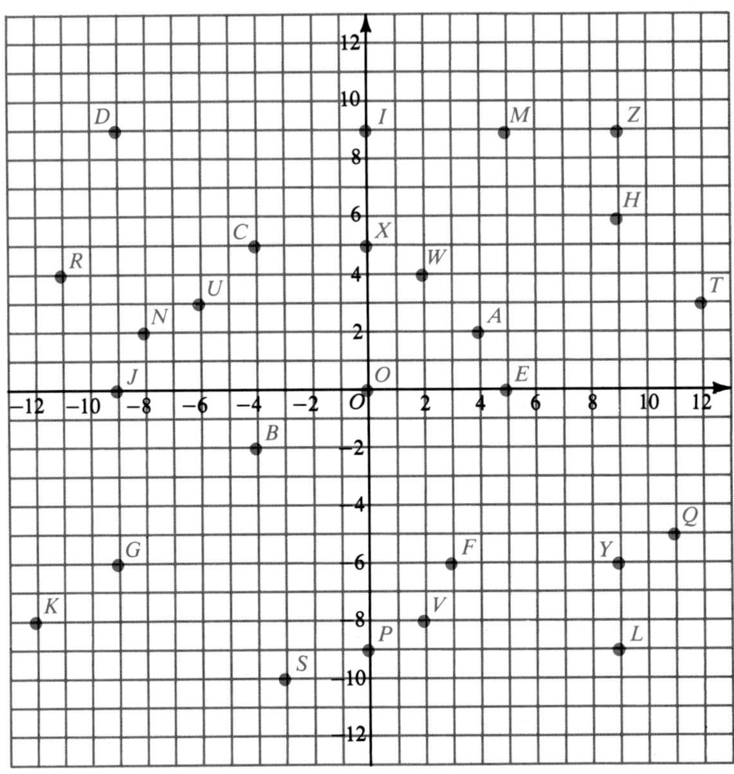

Name the point that is the graph of each ordered pair.

1. (2, 4) W
2. (4, 2) A
3. (−6, 3) U
4. (3, −6) F
5. (9, 6) H
6. (9, −6) Y
7. (0, −9) P
8. (−9, 0) J
9. (0, 9) I
10. (11, −5) Q
11. (−11, 4) R
12. (−3, −10) S

Give the coordinates and the quadrant (if any) of each point.

13. M (5, 9), I
14. L (9, −9), IV
15. D (−9, 9), II
16. B (−4, −2), III
17. E (5, 0), no quad.
18. V (2, −8), IV
19. G (−9, −6), III
20. X (0, 5), no quad.

Describe the graphs of the following equations.

21. a. $x = 2$ **b.** $x = -1$ **c.** $x = 0$

22. a. $y = -3$ **b.** $y = 4$ **c.** $y = 0$

Give the coordinates of the points where each graph crosses the x-axis and the y-axis.

23. $2x + y = 8$ (0, 8), (4, 0) **24.** $3x - y = 9$ (0, −9), (3, 0) **25.** $2x + 3y = 12$ (0, 4), (6, 0)

Classify each equation as a linear equation in standard form, a linear equation not in standard form, or a nonlinear equation.

26. $5x + 3y = 2$ linear eq., st. form

27. $\frac{5}{x} + \frac{3}{y} = 2$ nonlinear eq.

28. $\frac{x}{5} + \frac{y}{3} = 2$ linear eq., not st. form

29. $4x^2 + y^2 = 4$ nonlinear eq.

30. $x + y = x - y$ linear eq., not st. form

31. $xy = 4$ nonlinear eq.

Written Exercises

Plot the graph of each of the given points.

A **1.** $A(5, 3)$ **2.** $B(7, 2)$ **3.** $C(-5, -3)$ **4.** $D(-7, -2)$

5. $E(-8, 0)$ **6.** $F(0, -8)$ **7.** $G(-6, 4)$ **8.** $H(4, -6)$

9. $O(0, 0)$ **10.** $P(-3, 5)$ **11.** $R(7, -2)$ **12.** $S(-4, -6)$

Plot the points A, B, C, and D. Then connect A to B, B to C, C to D, and D to A. Is the resulting figure best described as a square, a rectangle, a parallelogram, or a trapezoid?

13. $A(-3, -4)$, $B(5, -2)$, $C(6, 4)$, $D(-2, 2)$ parallelogram

14. $A(-2, 0)$, $B(0, -4)$, $C(4, -2)$, $D(2, 2)$ square

15. $A(-4, -1)$, $B(-6, 5)$, $C(3, 8)$, $D(5, 2)$ rectangle

16. $A(-1, 4)$, $B(0, 1)$, $C(4, -1)$, $D(7, 0)$ trapezoid

Refer to the diagram on the previous page. Name the point(s) described.

17. The point is on the positive x-axis. *E*

18. The point is on the negative y-axis. *P*

19. The x-coordinate equals the y-coordinate. *Z, O*

20. The x-coordinate is the opposite of the y-coordinate. *D, L, O*

21. The x-coordinate is zero. *I, X, O, P*

22. The y-coordinate is zero. *J, O, E*

23. This point in Quadrant III is nearest the x-axis. *B*

24. This point in Quadrant IV is nearest the y-axis. *V*

Graph each equation.

25. $x = 3$ **26.** $y = 5$ **27.** $y = -2$ **28.** $x = -5$

29. $x - y = 6$ **30.** $x + y = 8$ **31.** $y = 2x + 3$ **32.** $y = -2x + 3$

33. $2x + y = 6$ **34.** $x - 3y = 9$ **35.** $4x - 3y = 12$ **36.** $2x + 5y = 10$

B **37.** $\frac{x}{2} = \frac{y}{3}$ **38.** $\frac{x}{4} + y = 0$ **39.** $\frac{x - y}{2} = \frac{x + y}{4}$ **40.** $\frac{y}{4} - \frac{x}{3} = \frac{1}{2}$

26.
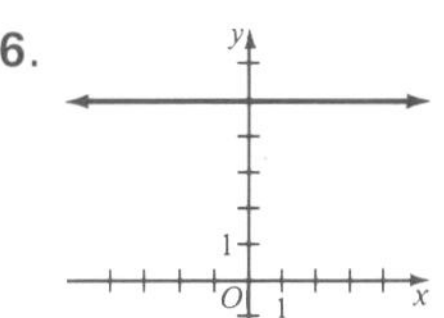

28.
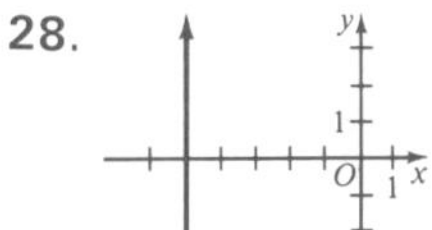

30.
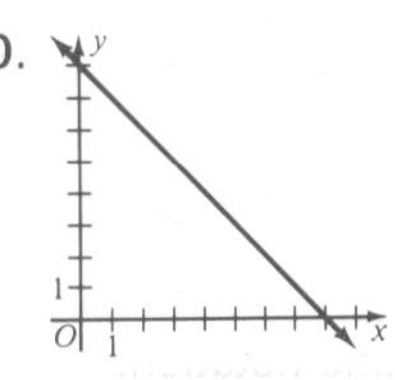

32.
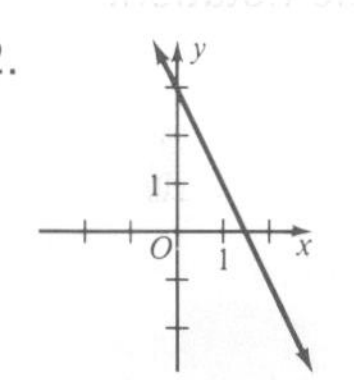

34.
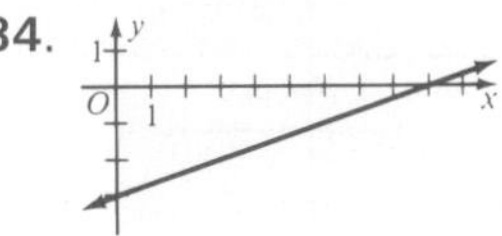

36.
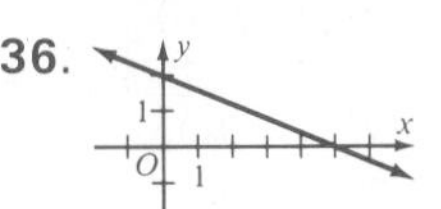

38.
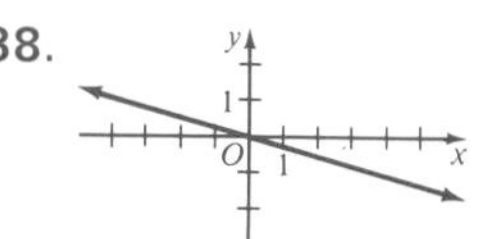

40.
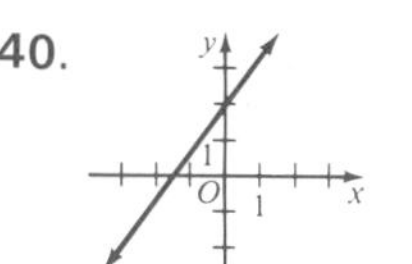

41. In one coordinate plane, graph the following six equations.
a. $y = x$ **b.** $y = 2x$ **c.** $y = 3x$ **d.** $y = -x$ **e.** $y = -2x$ **f.** $y = -3x$

42. In one coordinate plane, graph the following four equations.
a. $y = x + 1$ **b.** $y = x + 3$ **c.** $y = x - 1$ **d.** $y = x - 3$

In Exercises 43 and 44, (a) graph both equations in the same coordinate plane, (b) give the point that the graphs have in common, and (c) check that the coordinates of this point satisfy both equations.

43. $3x - y = 9$ and $3x - 5y = -15$

44. $2x - 3y = 12$ and $3x + 2y = 5$

Computer Exercises

For students with some programming experience

1. Modify the BASIC program you wrote for the Computer Exercises on page 338 so that it will check whether an ordered pair entered with an INPUT statement is a solution to a pair of linear equations $Ax + By = C$ and $Dx + Ey = F$. A, B, C, D, E, and F should also be entered with INPUT statements. RUN the program for the following pairs of linear equations.
   a. $x + 2y = 5$, $x + y = 1$ $(-3, 4)$ Sol.
   b. $5x - y = 7$, $3x + 2y = 1$ $(1, -2)$ Not sol.
   c. $x = -5$, $y = 3$ $(-5, 3)$ Sol.
2. Write a BASIC program that will find the points where a linear equation $Px + Qy = R$ will cross the x-axis and the y-axis, where P, Q, and R are entered with INPUT statements. The program should report if the graph does not cross either the x-axis or the y-axis. RUN the program for the following linear equations.
   a. $2x - 3y = 6$ (3, 0), (0, −2)
   b. $8x + y = 12$ (1.5, 0), (0, 12)
   c. $7x + 0y = -14$ (−2, 0), none
   d. $0 - 5y = 2$ none, (0, −0.4)
   e. $3x + 3y = 8$ $(2.\overline{6}, 0)$, $(0, 2.\overline{6})$
   f. $6x - 4y = 9$ (1.5, 0), (0, −2.25)

Self-Test 1

Vocabulary

solution (p. 335)	abscissa (p. 339)
ordered pair (p. 335)	y-coordinate (p. 339)
horizontal axis (p. 339)	ordinate (p. 339)
vertical axis (p. 339)	plot (p. 339)
origin (p. 339)	coordinate axes (p. 340)
x-axis (p. 339)	coordinate plane (p. 340)
y-axis (p. 339)	quadrants (p. 340)
graph of an ordered pair (p. 339)	graph of an equation (p. 340)
coordinates (p. 339)	linear equation (p. 340)
x-coordinate (p. 339)	standard form (p. 340)

Additional Answers
Written Exercises

42.
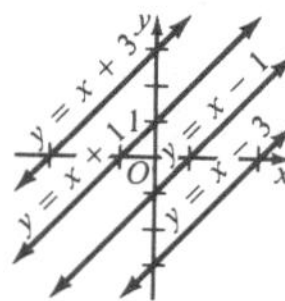

44.
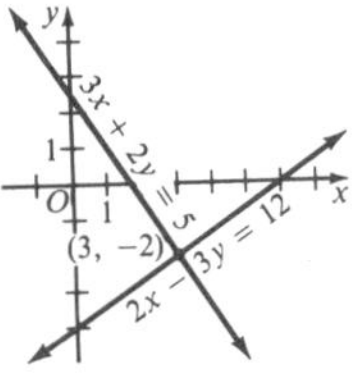

Additional Answers
Self-Test

5–7.
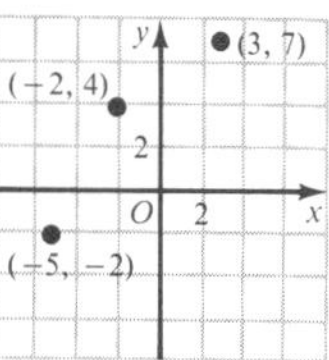

8.
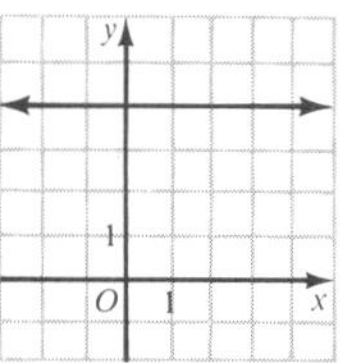

9.
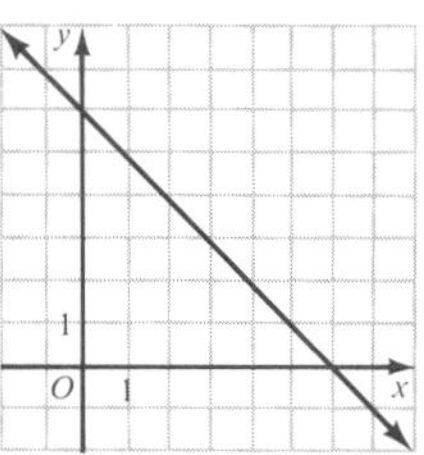

10.
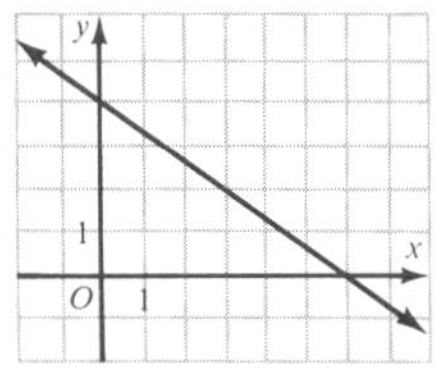

State whether or not each ordered pair of numbers is a solution of the given equation.

1. $2x + 4y = 12$
$(2, 2), \left(7, \frac{1}{2}\right)$
Yes; No

2. $3x + 5y = 30$
$(3, 5), (10, 0)$
No; Yes

Obj. 8-1, p. 335

Solve each equation for y in terms of x.

3. $2x - 3y = 6$ $y = \frac{2x - 6}{3}$

4. $5y + 2x = 10$ $y = \frac{10 - 2x}{5}$

Plot the graph of each of the given ordered pairs.

5. $(3, 7)$

6. $(-2, 4)$

7. $(-5, -2)$

Obj. 8-2, p. 339

Graph the equation.

8. $y = 4$

9. $x + y = 6$

10. $2x + 3y = 12$

Check your answers with those at the back of the book.

Computer Key-In

Exercises

1. a. Write a program that will print out ordered pairs of integers that can be used to graph $Ax + By = C$ when A and B are not zero. Let X vary from -5 to 5.

b. RUN the program for $2x + 3y = 6$ and $2x - 3y = 6$.

2. a. Change the program that you wrote for part (a) of Exercise 1 to print out pairs of whole numbers. Let x vary from 0 to 10.

b. RUN this program for $2x + 3y = 6$ and $2x - 3y = 6$.

3. a. Change the program that you wrote for part (a) of Exercise 1 to print out pairs of integers for $xy = k$. Avoid $x = 0$.

b. RUN the program for $xy = 12$ and $xy = -12$.

Note: The programs of Exercises 1 and 2 above can be used to do Exercises 29–36 on page 343.

Challenge

Find the smallest positive integer that when divided by 2, 3, and 7 leaves remainders of 1, 2, and 6, respectively. 41

Quick Quiz

1. Determine whether $(3, -2)$ is a solution of $4x + 3y = 6$. Yes

2. Find the solution set of $3x + 5y = 15$ if x and y represent whole numbers. $\{(0, 3), (5, 0)\}$

Plot the graph of each ordered pair.

3. $(-3, -2)$ **4.** $(2, 3)$

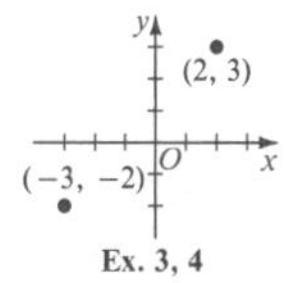

Ex. 3, 4

5. Graph the equation $2x - 3y = 6$.

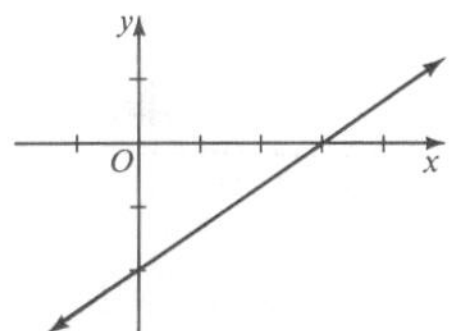

Additional Answers Computer Key-In

1. b. $(-3, 4)$, $(0, 2)$, $(3, 0)$; $(-3, -4)$, $(0, -2)$, $(3, 0)$

2. b. $(0, 2)$, $(3, 0)$; $(3, 0)$, $(6, 2)$, $(9, 4)$

3. b. $(-6, -2)$, $(-4, -3)$, $(-3, -4)$, $(-2, -6)$, $(-1, -12)$, $(1, 12)$, $(2, 6)$, $(3, 4)$, $(4, 3)$, $(6, 2)$; $(-6, 2)$, $(-4, 3)$, $(-3, 4)$, $(-2, 6)$, $(-1, 12)$, $(1, -12)$, $(2, -6)$, $(3, -4)$, $(4, -3)$, $(6, -2)$

Teaching Suggestions
p. T109

Suggested Extensions
p. T110

Chalkboard Examples

Solve each system of equations by the graphic method.

1. $y = x - 1$
   $x + y = 3$ (2, 1)
2. $2x + y = 2$
   $x - y = 4$ (2, −2)
3. $2x - y = 1$
   $3y + 3 = 6x$
   infinite number of sols.
4. $x + 2y = 3$
   $y = 2x - 1$ (1, 1)
5. $x - 3y = 2$
   $3y - 1 = x$ no solution

Solving Systems of Linear Equations

8-3 The Graphic Method

Objective To use graphs to solve systems of linear equations.

Two equations in the same variables form a **system of equations.** A **solution of a system** of two equations in two variables is an ordered pair of numbers that satisfies each of the equations. For example, consider the system

$$x - y = 4 \quad \text{and} \quad 2x + y = 5.$$

The ordered pair (3, −1) is a solution of this system because, when you substitute 3 for x and −1 for y, you obtain

$$3 - (-1) = 4 \quad \text{and} \quad 2 \cdot 3 + (-1) = 5.$$

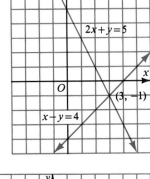

The graphs of $x - y = 4$ and $2x + y = 5$ are shown at the right. Notice that the point (3, −1) is the **intersection point** of the graphs. Since no other point lies on both of these lines, (3, −1) is the only solution.

Not all systems of equations have a solution, and some have more than one solution. The diagram at the right shows the graphs of the equations:

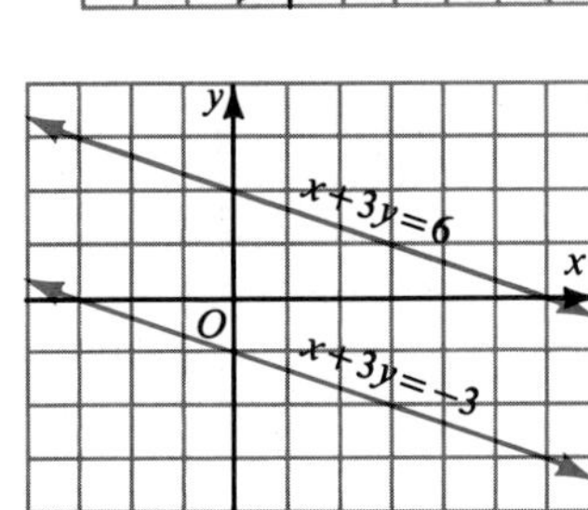

$$x + 3y = 6$$
$$x + 3y = -3$$

The graphs do not intersect. Lines in the same plane that do not intersect are **parallel lines.** This system has *no solution.*

The next diagram shows the graphs of:

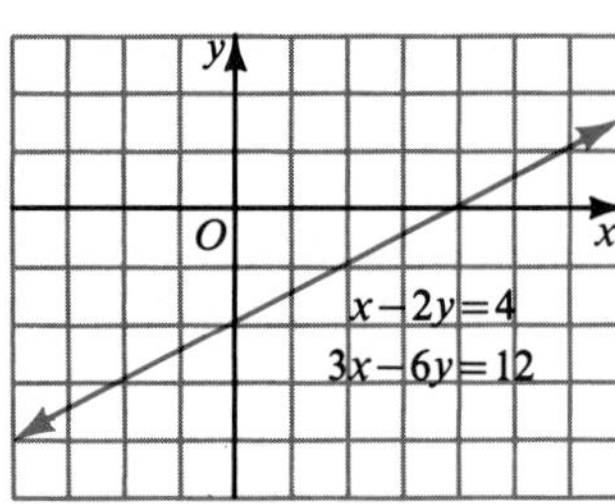

$$x - 2y = 4$$
$$3x - 6y = 12$$

The graphs *coincide.* Every solution of either equation is a solution of the other. The equations are equivalent (divide both sides of the second equation by 3). The coordinates of every point on the line shown form a solution. This system has an unlimited, or *infinite,* number of solutions.

Because a system of two equations imposes two conditions on the variables at the same time, the system is often called a **system of simultaneous equations.** When you find all the solutions of a system of simultaneous equations, you have **solved the system,** or **found the solution set.** The method of solving a system by using graphs is called the **graphic method.**

The Graphic Method

To solve a system of linear equations in two variables, draw the graph of each linear equation in the same coordinate plane.

1. If the lines intersect, the coordinates of the intersection point give the solution of the system.
2. If the lines are parallel, there is no solution.
3. If the lines coincide, there are an infinite number of solutions.

Oral Exercises

State whether the given ordered pair is a solution of the system.

1. (3, 1) Yes
$3x - y = 8$
$x + y = 4$

2. $(-1, 4)$ No
$4x + 3y = 8$
$3x + y = 0$

3. $(3, -3)$ Yes
$7x = 12 - 3y$
$y = 2x - 9$

State the solution of each system.

4. 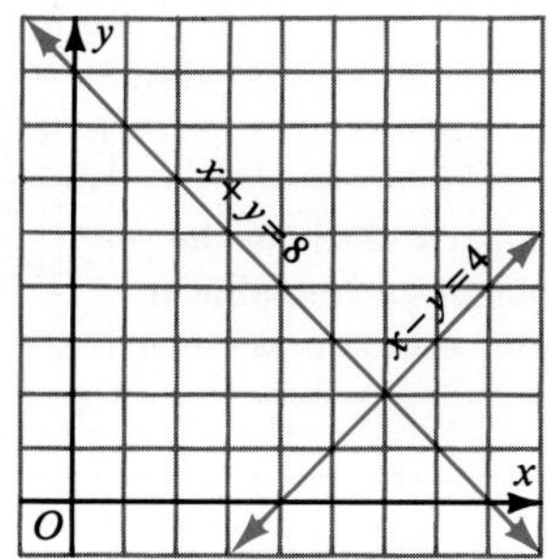

(6, 2)

5. 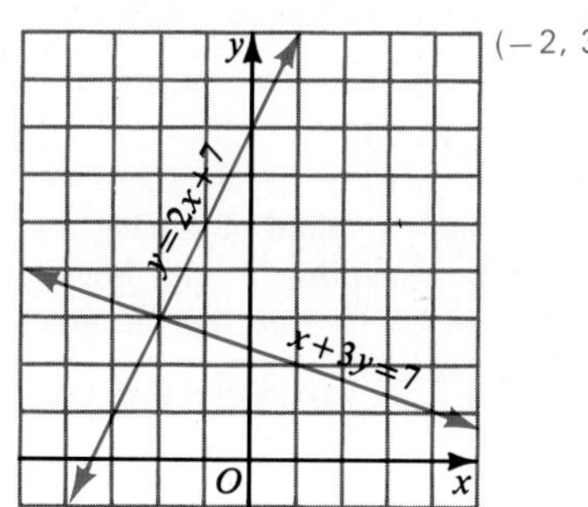

$(-2, 3)$

6. 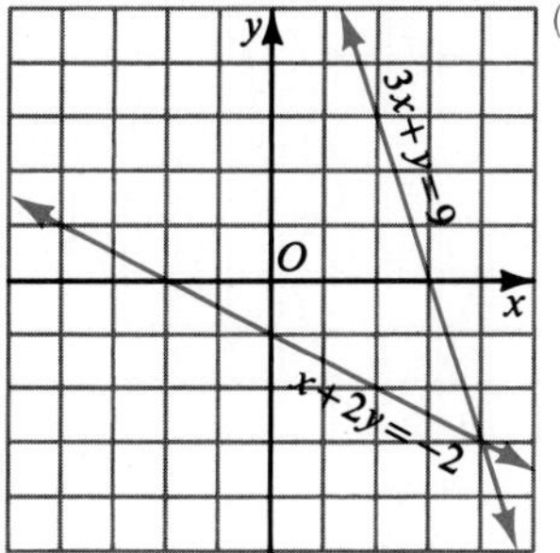

$(4, -3)$

7. 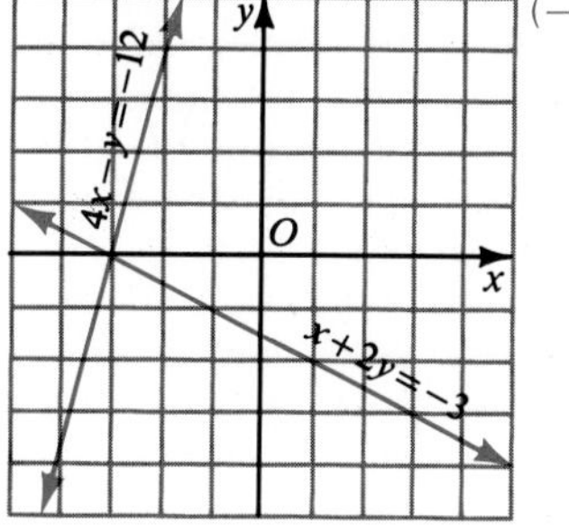

$(-3, 0)$

Additional Answer Oral Exercises

8. Substitute 3 for x and -2 for y in each of the equations. If both equations are true, then $(3, -2)$ is a solution.

Suggested Assignments

Minimum
348/1–14
R 344/*Self-Test 1*

Average
348/1–15 odd, 17–20
R 344/*Self-Test 1*

Maximum
348/1–11 odd, 13–20
S 338/38

Additional A Exercises

Solve each system of equations by the graphic method.

1. $x - y = 0$, $2x + 3y = 5$ $(1, 1)$
2. $2x - y = 7$, $x + 2y = 11$ $(5, 3)$
3. $-x + y = 3$, $3x = -9 - y$ $(-3, 0)$
4. $4x + y = -14$, $6x = 2y$ $(-2, -6)$
5. $\frac{-x + 6}{2} = 2y$, $y - 3x = 8$ $(-2, 2)$

8. Suppose the graphs of a pair of linear equations appear to intersect in the point $(3, -2)$. How can you check whether $(3, -2)$ really is a solution of the system?

9. If a system of linear equations has no solution, what do you know about the graphs of the equations? They are parallel.

10. Suppose $(1, 5)$ and $(3, 7)$ are known to be solutions of a system of two linear equations. Are there any other solutions? Yes, infinitely many.

Written Exercises

Solve each system by the graphic method.

A

1. $y = x$, $y = 9 - 2x$ $(3, 3)$

2. $y = -x$, $y = x + 4$ $(-2, 2)$

3. $x + y = 2$, $y = 2x + 5$ $(-1, 3)$

4. $3x + y = 1$, $y = x - 3$ $(1, -2)$

5. $x - y = 6$, $2x + y = 0$ $(2, -4)$

6. $2x - y = -1$, $3x + y = 6$ $(1, 3)$

7. $3x - 9y = 0$, $3y + 3 = x$ No sol.

8. $y = 3x$, $x + y = 8$ $(2, 6)$

9. $y = \frac{1}{2}x + 1$, $x + 2 = 2y$ Inf. many sols.

10. $2y - x = 2$, $x - 2y = 8$ No sol.

11. $y - 2x = -5$, $y - x = -3$ $(2, -1)$

12. $6x - 3y = 9$, $\frac{y + 3}{2} = x$ Inf. many sols.

Solve each system graphically. Estimate the coordinates of the intersection point to the nearest half unit.

B

13. $x + y = 3$, $x - y = 4$ $\left(3\frac{1}{2}, -\frac{1}{2}\right)$

14. $2x + y = -2$, $2x - 3y = 15$ $\left(1, -4\frac{1}{2}\right)$

15. $3x + 5y = 15$, $x - y = 4$ $\left(4\frac{1}{2}, \frac{1}{2}\right)$

16. $3y - 2x = 6$, $3y + 2x = 15$ $\left(2, 3\frac{1}{2}\right)$

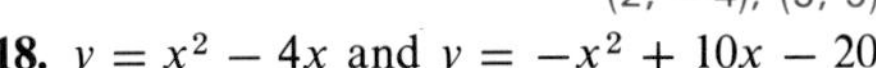

The graphic method of solving a system of equations is particularly useful when the equations are not linear. Estimate the solutions of each nonlinear system below by studying the graphs. Check whether your estimate satisfies both equations.

17. $y = x^2$ and $y = 8 - x^2$ $(2, 4), (-2, 4)$

18. $y = x^2 - 4x$ and $y = -x^2 + 10x - 20$ $(2, -4), (5, 5)$

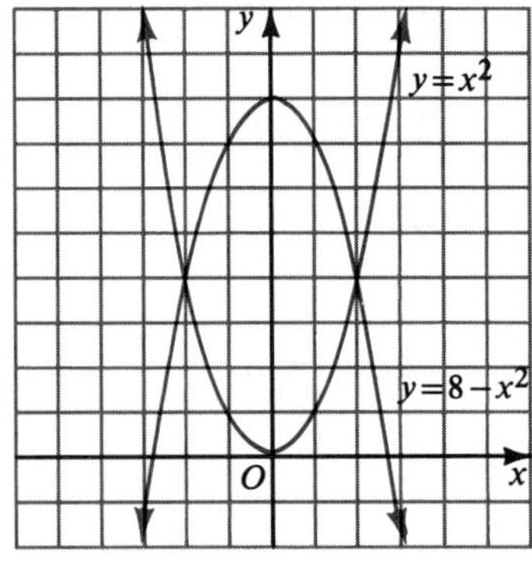

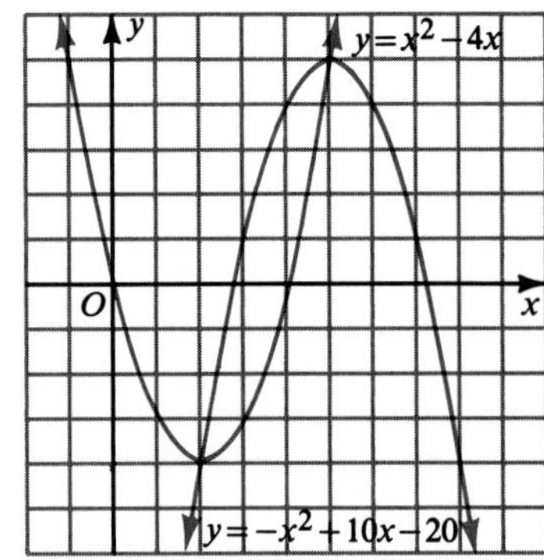

19. Where on the graph of $5x - 2y = 15$ is the x-coordinate equal to the y-coordinate? (5, 5)

20. Where on the graph of $3x - y = 12$ are the x- and y-coordinates opposites of each other? (3, −3)

21. Where on the graph of $4x + y + 12 = 0$ is the y-coordinate twice the x-coordinate? (−2, −4)

C 22. The triangular region is enclosed by the x-axis and by the graphs of $y = \frac{1}{2}x$ and $x + y = 9$. Find the area of this region. (*Hint:* Area of a triangle $= \frac{1}{2} \times$ base $\times$ height.) $\frac{27}{2}$

23. Find the area of the triangular region enclosed by the y-axis and the graphs of $x + 3y = 12$ and $x - 3y = 0$. 12

24. Find the area of the triangular region whose vertices are the points of intersection of the graphs of $2x + y = 5$, $y = x - 4$, and $y = 5$. 27

Career Note / Accountant

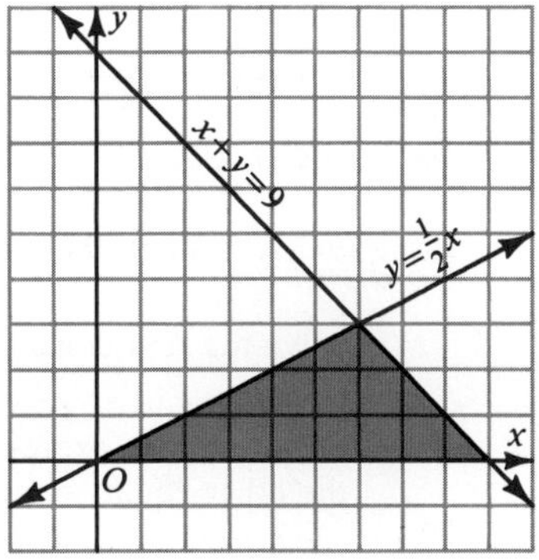

A company is considering opening a branch office. Before making a decision, the managers of the company will analyze financial reports prepared by an accountant. Accountants are responsible for recording and analyzing financial information. Some accountants specialize in a particular area of financial management, such as tax matters or budgeting. Accountants may serve as consultants to management or they may audit records, examining them for accuracy.

Accountants may work for the public, for government, or for industry. Certification is valuable in each of these fields, but it is a necessity for anyone considering work as a certified public accountant. To become certified, a candidate must pass an intensive four-part examination. Many states require an accountant to have a college degree and some states require additional college work beyond a bachelor's degree. Persons considering accounting as a career should be able to interpret facts and figures and to communicate clearly.

Additional Answers Written Exercises

1. (3, 3)
2. (−2, 2)
3. (−1, 3)
4. (1, −2)
5. (2, −4)
6. (1, 3)
7. no solution
8. (2, 6)
9. infinite number of sols.
10. no solution
11. (2, −1)
12. infinite number of sols.
13. $\left(3\frac{1}{2}, -\frac{1}{2}\right)$
14. $\left(1, -4\frac{1}{2}\right)$
15. $\left(4\frac{1}{2}, \frac{1}{2}\right)$
16. $\left(2, 3\frac{1}{2}\right)$

Mixed Review Exercises

Express in simplest form.

1. $\frac{8x - 24}{x^2 - 5x + 6}$ $\quad \frac{8}{x - 2}$ $(x \neq 2, x \neq 3)$

2. $\frac{yz^2}{6y^2 + 24y + 24} \div \frac{y^2z}{y^2 - 4}$ $\quad \frac{z(y - 2)}{6y(y + 2)}$ $(y \neq 0, y \neq \pm 2, z \neq 0)$

3. $\frac{a}{a - b} + \frac{6}{b - a} + \frac{3a}{a^2 - b^2}$ $\quad \frac{a^2 + ab - 3a - 6b}{(a + b)(a - b)}$ $(a \neq \pm b)$

4. Is (2, −3) a solution of the equation $2x - y = 7$? yes

Teaching Suggestions
p. T110

Suggested Extensions
p. T110

Chalkboard Examples

Solve each system by the substitution method.

1. $y = x + 7$
   $x + y = 1$
   $x + x + 7 = 1$
   $2x = -6$
   $x = -3$
   $y = -3 + 7 = 4$
   $(-3, 4)$
2. $x = 3y$
   $2x - 5y = 4$
   $2(3y) - 5y = 4$
   $6y - 5y = 4$
   $y = 4$
   $x = 3 \cdot 4 = 12$
   $(12, 4)$
3. $2x - y = 1$
   $3y + 3 = 6x$
   $2x - 1 = y$
   $3(2x - 1) + 3 = 6x$
   $6x - 3 + 3 = 6x$
   $6x = 6x$
   infinite number of sols.
4. $4s - 3t = 23$
   $s + 4t = 1$
   $s = 1 - 4t$
   $4(1 - 4t) - 3t = 23$
   $4 - 16t - 3t = 23$
   $-19t = 19$
   $t = -1$
   $s = 1 - 4(-1) = 5$
   $(5, -1)$

8-4 The Substitution Method

Objective To use the substitution method to solve systems of linear equations in two variables.

When the solution of a system of equations is an ordered pair that is not located near the origin or that does not contain whole numbers, the graphic method will not be useful. There are several algebraic methods of solving a system of equations without using their graphs. One of these is the **substitution method** illustrated in the examples below.

Example 1 Solve: $x + y = 14$
$3x + 2y = 48$

Solution

1. Solve the first equation for y.
   $$x + y = 14$$
   $$y = 14 - x$$
2. Substitute this expression for y in the other equation, and solve for x.
   $$3x + 2y = 48$$
   $$3x + 2(14 - x) = 48$$
   $$3x + 28 - 2x = 48$$
   $$x + 28 = 48$$
   $$x = 20$$
3. Substitute this value for x in the equation of Step 1, and find y.
   $$y = 14 - x$$
   $$y = 14 - 20$$
   $$y = -6$$
4. Check in *both* equations.
   $$x + y = 14 \qquad 3x + 2y = 48$$
   $$20 + (-6) \stackrel{?}{=} 14 \qquad 3(20) + 2(-6) \stackrel{?}{=} 48$$
   $$14 = 14 \checkmark \qquad 48 = 48 \checkmark$$

$\therefore$ the solution is $(20, -6)$. ***Answer***

In the first step of Example 1, it would have been just as easy to solve for x as it was for y. In the first step of Example 2 below, however, it is easier to solve the second equation for x than for y.

Example 2 Solve: $3x + 2y = 11$
$x + 4y = 2$

Solution

1. Solve the second equation for x (since its coefficient is 1).
   $$x + 4y = 2$$
   $$x = 2 - 4y$$
2. Substitute this expression for x in the other equation, and solve for y.
   $$3x + 2y = 11$$
   $$3(2 - 4y) + 2y = 11$$
   $$6 - 12y + 2y = 11$$
   $$-10y = 5$$
   $$y = -\frac{1}{2}$$

33. Without drawing the graphs, show that the graphs of $3x - y = 7$ and $6x - 2y = 5$ are parallel lines.

34. The graphs of the equations $ax + 4y = 6$ and $x + by = -8$ intersect at $(-2, 3)$. Find a and b. $a = 3,\ b = -2$

35. The graphs of $ax + by = 13$ and $ax - by = -3$ intersect at $(1, 4)$. Find a and b. $a = 5,\ b = 2$

C 36. The graphs of $x + 2y = 7$, $4x - y = 1$, and $6x + ay = 0$ intersect at the same point. Find a. $a = -2$

37. Determine whether the lines $3x - 5y = -1$, $x - y = 3$, and $2x - 3y = 1$ intersect at the same point. All three lines intersect at (8, 5).

Use the substitution method to solve each system.

38. $x + y + z = 180$
$y = 3x$ (20, 60, 100)
$z = 5x$

39. $a + b + c = 62$
$a = 2c - 5$ (19, 31, 12)
$b = 3c - 5$

40. $x + y + 2z = 1$ $\left(\frac{3}{2}, \frac{1}{2}, -\frac{1}{2}\right)$
$x - y = 1$
$x - z = 2$

41. $x - 2y + 3z = 13$
$x - 3z = -1$
$y + z = 1$
(5, −1, 2)

42. $c - a = b + 6$
$a + 5 = \frac{1}{2}c$
$a - 5 = \frac{1}{3}(b + 5)$
(12, 16, 34)

43. $a + b + c + d = 2$
$a - c = -2$
$b + c = 5$
$c - d = 7$
(1, 2, 3, −4)

Computer Exercises

For students with some programming experience

Write a BASIC program to print out a table of ordered pairs for each of two linear equations $Ax + By = C$ and $Dx + Ey = F$, where A, B, C, D, E, and F are entered with INPUT statements. The values of x should be a set of consecutive integers. If the two equations have an ordered pair in common, the program should report that the ordered pair is a solution of the system of equations. RUN the program for the given pairs of equations.

1. $2x - 7y = 9$, $x + y = 0$ $\quad x = \{0, 1, 2, 3, 4, 5\}$ (1, −1) is a solution.

2. $x + 3y = 1$, $\frac{1}{2}x - 4y = -5$ $\quad x = \{-3, -2, -1, 0, 1\}$ (−2, 1) is a solution.

3. $4x - 3y = 0$, $2x + y = 2$ $\quad x = \{0, 1, 2, 3, 4\}$ No pairs in common.

4. $3x - 4y = -6$, $3x - 2y = 0$ $\quad x = \{-2, -1, 0, 1, 2\}$ (2, 3) is a solution.

Additional Answer Written Exercises

33. $-y = 7 - 3x$; $y = 3x - 7$. Substituting, $6x - 2(3x - 7) = 5$; $6x - 6x + 14 = 5$; $14 = 5$. The equations have no common solution, so their graphs are parallel lines.

Mixed Review Exercises

1. Express $\frac{(ab)^3}{3} \cdot \left(\frac{ab}{2}\right)^2$ in simplest form. $\frac{a^5b^5}{12}$

2. Find the missing numerator: $\frac{4}{2x + 1} = \frac{?}{6x^2 + 13x + 5}$ $\quad 12x + 20$

3. Write $\frac{7}{a - 3} + 6$ as a single fraction in simplest form. $\frac{6a - 11}{a - 3}\ (a \neq 3)$

4. In which quadrant is $(-3, 2)$? II

Teaching Suggestions
p. T110

Suggested Extensions
p. T110

Chalkboard Examples

Solve, using two equations in two variables.

1. The sum of two numbers is 5. The larger number exceeds twice the smaller number by 14. Find the numbers.
   Let n = larger number
   k = smaller number
   $n + k = 5$
   $n - 2k = 14$
   $n = 2k + 14$
   $2k + 14 + k = 5$
   $3k = -9$
   $k = -3$
   $n = 2(-3) + 14 = 8$
   The numbers are 8 and -3.
2. The perimeter of a rectangle is 30 cm. The length is 1 cm more than the width. Find the dimensions.
   Let l = length
   w = width
   $2l + 2w = 30$
   $l = w + 1$
   $2(w + 1) + 2w = 30$
   $2w + 2 + 2w = 30$
   $4w = 28$
   $w = 7$
   $l = 7 + 1 = 8$
   The rectangle is 7 cm wide and 8 cm long.
3. A pet shop sold 23 puppies and kittens one week. They sold 9 more puppies than kittens. How many of each did they sell?
   Let p = number of puppies
   k = number of kittens

8-5 Solving Problems with Two Variables

Objective To use systems of linear equations in two variables to solve problems.

You have learned to solve problems using equations in one variable. Now you can solve problems with equations in two variables. Example 1 compares these two methods.

Example 1 June has 20 coins, all nickels and dimes, worth \$1.45. How many nickels and how many dimes does June have?

Solution 1 (one variable)

Step 1 The problem asks for the number of nickels and the number of dimes.

Step 2 Let x = the number of nickels. Then $20 - x$ = the number of dimes. Make a chart.

	Number ×	Value per coin =	Total Value
Nickels	x	5	$5x$
Dimes	$20 - x$	10	$10(20 - x)$

Step 3 The only fact not recorded in this chart is the total value of the coins, \$1.45. Use this fact to write an equation.

$$5x + 10(20 - x) = 145$$

Step 4
$$5x + 200 - 10x = 145$$
$$-5x = -55$$
$$x = 11$$
$$20 - x = 9$$

Step 5 The check is left to you.
∴ June has 11 nickels and 9 dimes. ***Answer***

Solution 2 (two variables)

Step 1 The problem asks for the number of nickels and the number of dimes.

Step 2 Let n = the number of nickels and d = the number of dimes. Make a chart.

	Number ×	Value per coin =	Total Value
Nickels	n	5	$5n$
Dimes	d	10	$10d$

Step 3 The two facts not recorded in the chart are the total number of coins, 20, and the total value, \$1.45. Use these facts to write a system of equations.

$$n + d = 20$$
$$5n + 10d = 145$$

Step 4 $d = 20 - n$ {Find d in terms of n.

$5n + 10(20 - n) = 145$ {Substitute.

$5n + 200 - 10n = 145$

$-5n = -55$

$n = 11$

$d = 20 - n = 20 - 11 = 9$

Step 5 The check is left to you.

∴ June has 11 nickels and 9 dimes. ***Answer***

It may appear that the two-variable solution involves more work than the one-variable solution. However, the two-variable solution has the advantage that the variables n and d remind you of nickels and dimes, so that you can write the equations $n + d = 20$ and $5n + 10d = 145$ more easily than the one-variable equation. Example 2 also shows that a wise choice of variables can make it easier to write equations that will solve the problem. Here A and B represent Al's money and Bob's money, respectively.

Example 2 Al and Bob together have \$80. Al has \$5 more than twice Bob's amount. How much money does each have?

Solution

Step 1 The problem asks for the amount of money each person has.

Step 2 Let A = the amount of Al's money and B = the amount of Bob's money.

Step 3 $A + B = 80$

$A = 5 + 2B$

Step 4 $(5 + 2B) + B = 80$ {Substitute $5 + 2B$ for A.

$5 + 3B = 80$

$3B = 75$

$B = 25$

$A = 5 + 2(25) = 55$

Step 5 *Check:* $A + B = 80$

$A = 5 + 2B$

$55 + 25 \stackrel{?}{=} 80; \quad 80 = 80 \checkmark$

$55 \stackrel{?}{=} 5 + 50; \quad 55 = 55 \checkmark$

∴ Bob has \$25 and Al has \$55. ***Answer***

$p + k = 23$

$p = k + 9$

$k + 9 + k = 23$

$2k = 14$

$k = 7$

$p = 7 + 9 = 16$

The shop sold 16 puppies and 7 kittens.

4. A developer bought 78 trees at a total cost of \$4050. The shade trees cost \$45 each and the evergreens cost \$60 each. How many of each type were bought?

Let s = number of shade trees

e = number of evergreens

$s + e = 78$

$45s + 60e = 4050$

$e = 78 - s$

$45s + 60(78 - s) = 4050$

$45s + 4680 - 60s = 4050$

$630 = 15s$

$s = 42$

$e = 78 - 42 = 36$

The developer bought 42 shade trees and 36 evergreens.

5. A bank teller has 112 \$5-bills and \$10-bills for a total of \$720. How many of each does the teller have?

Let f = number of \$5-bills

t = number of \$10-bills

$f + t = 112$

$5f + 10t = 720$

$t = 112 - f$

$5f + 10(112 - f) = 720$

$5f + 1120 - 10f = 720$

$400 = 5f$

$f = 80$

$t = 112 - 80 = 32$

The teller has 80 \$5-bills and 32 \$10-bills.

Supplementary Material

Test 27

Suggested Assignments

Minimum
357/*P*: 10–15
S 343/25–35 odd
Day 2 of Sec. 8-4 finishes Sec. 8-4 and starts Sec. 8-5.

Average
357/*P*: 16–20, 22
S 353/39, 40
Day 2 of Sec. 8-4 finishes Sec. 8-4 and starts Sec. 8-5.

Maximum
357/*P*: 1, 5, 9, 12, 15, 17, 20, 21
S 353/38, 40, 41

Additional Answers Oral Exercises

9. $P + M = 88$; $P = M + 17$
10. $S = 2F$; $S + F = 54$
11. $l = 2w - 1$; $2l + 2w = 40$

Additional A Exercises

1. Jeannette has 20 nickels and dimes worth $1.75. How many of each coin does she have? 5 nickels, 15 dimes
2. Dick has twice as much money as Connie. Together, they have $57. How much does each have? Dick, $38; Connie, $19
3. Tickets for the senior play cost $4 for adults, $2 for students. This year, there were 600 tickets sold and the class made $1900. How many of each type of ticket were sold? 350 adult, 250 student

Oral Exercises

Give a system of equations that can be used to solve each problem.

In Problems 1-4 use *n*, *d*, and *q* for the number of nickels, the number of dimes, and the number of quarters, respectively.

1. May has 30 nickels and dimes worth $2.40. How many nickels does May have? $n + d = 30$; $5n + 10d = 240$
2. Ed has 24 dimes and quarters worth $3.60. How many quarters does Ed have? $d + q = 24$; $10d + 25q = 360$
3. Peg has $5.50 in dimes and quarters. She has 8 more quarters than dimes. How many quarters does she have? $q = d + 8$; $10d + 25q = 550$
4. Luis and Julia have the same number of coins. Luis has only dimes and Julia has only quarters. If Julia has $1.80 more than Luis does, how much does each have? $d = q$; $10d + 180 = 25q$

In Problems 5-8, use *C*, *D*, *S*, and *T* for the amounts of money that Connie, Dick, Steve, and Tracy have, respectively.

5. Dick and Connie together have $36. Connie has $17 more than Dick. How much does each have? $D + C = 36$; $C - 17 = D$
6. Steve has three times as much money as Dick. Together they have $72. How much does each have? $S = 3D$; $S + D = 72$
7. Tracy has $12 more than Connie. If Tracy had $8 more, she would have twice as much as Connie. How much does each have? $T = C + 12$; $T + 8 = 2C$
8. Steve has $3 more than twice as much as Tracy. Together they have $57. How much does each have? $2T + 3 = S$; $S + T = 57$

In Exercises 9-14, use whatever variables seem appropriate.

9. Pat and Mike purchased a radio for $88. Pat paid $17 more than Mike. How much did each pay?
10. Sylvia sold twice as many tickets as Frank. They sold 54 tickets in all. How many did each sell?
11. The length of a rectangle is 1 cm less than twice its width. If the perimeter is 40 cm, find the dimensions.
12. Pea Porridge Pond was stocked with 2000 fish, all bass and trout. The ratio of bass to trout was 3 to 2. How many of each kind of fish were put in the pond?
$b + t = 2000$; $\frac{3}{2} = \frac{b}{t}$

13. A person invests $5000 in treasury notes and bonds. The notes pay 8% annual interest and the bonds pay 10% annual interest. If the annual income is $480, how much is invested in treasury notes? $n + b = 5000$; $0.08n + 0.1b = 480$

14. Adult tickets to a play cost $5 and student tickets cost $2. In all, 720 tickets were sold for a total of $2640. How many student tickets were sold? $a + s = 720$; $5a + 2s = 2640$

Problems

A 1–14. Solve the problems given in Oral Exercises 1–14.

Solve, using two equations in two variables.

B 15. The sum of two numbers is 38. Four times the smaller number exceeds three times the larger number by 12. Find the numbers. 18, 20

16. One number is 5 more than half of another number. The sum of the numbers is 47. Find the numbers. 28, 19

17. Alan Keme paid $2.94 for a liter of milk and two liters of fruit juice. He wanted to buy two liters of milk and one liter of fruit juice, but this would have cost $3.12 and Alan only had $3. How much does a liter of milk cost? $1.10

18. The length of a rectangle exceeds its width by 3 m. The perimeter is 58 m. Find the dimensions. 13 m by 16 m

19. Elma Lincoln invested $4000 more in bonds paying 12% annual interest than she did in stocks paying dividends of 5% per year. Her total annual income from these investments is $814.90. How much did she invest in bonds? $5970

20. A grocer wants to mix together some cashews costing $8 per kilogram with some Brazil nuts costing $10 per kilogram. The grocer wants to sell 12 kg of the mixture for $8.50 per kilogram. How many kilograms of cashews are needed? 9 kg

21. One number is 16 more than another. If the smaller number is subtracted from two thirds of the larger number, the result is one fourth of the sum of the two numbers. Find the numbers. 8, 24

Solve each problem by using a system of three equations in three variables.

C 22. I have 30 coins, all nickels, dimes, and quarters, worth $4.60. There are three times as many quarters as nickels and two more dimes than quarters. How many of each kind of coin do I have? 4 nickels, 14 dimes, 12 quarters

23. Carl, Diane, and Ed together have $46. Carl has half as much as Diane, and Diane has $2 more than Ed. How much does each have? Diane, $19.20; Carl, $9.60; Ed, $17.20

4. Jan and Jean are twins and each weighs half as much as their brother John. The three children's total weight is just 10 lb more than their father's weight. If the father weighs 150 pounds, find the weight of each child. 40, 40, 80

5. Kathleen invested $5000, some at 6% and the rest at 5%. Her annual income from the investments is $280. How much is invested at 5%? $2,000

Additional Answers Problems

1. 12 nickels
2. 8 quarters
3. 18 quarters
4. Julia, 12 quarters, or $3; Luis, 12 dimes, or $1.20
5. Connie, $26.50; Dick, $9.50
6. Dick, $18; Steve, $54
7. Connie, $20; Tracy, $32
8. Tracy, $18; Steve, $39
9. Mike, $35.50; Pat, $52.50
10. Frank, 18; Sylvia, 36
11. 7 cm by 13 cm
12. 1200 bass, 800 trout
13. $1000
14. 320 student tickets

Teaching Suggestions
p. T111

Suggested Extensions
p. T111

Chalkboard Examples

Solve by the addition-or-subtraction method.

1. $x + y = 14$
   $x - y = 4$

$$\begin{aligned} x + y &= 14 \\ x - y &= 4 \\ \hline 2x \quad &= 18 \\ x &= 9 \\ 9 + y &= 14 \\ y &= 5 \end{aligned}$$

(9, 5)

2. $3r + 2s = 2$
   $3r + s = 7$

$$\begin{aligned} 3r + 2s &= 2 \\ 3r + s &= 7 \\ \hline s &= -5 \\ 3r - 5 &= 7 \\ 3r &= 12 \\ r &= 4 \end{aligned}$$

(4, −5)

3. $x - 2y = 2$
   $3x = 2y + 10$

$$\begin{aligned} x - 2y &= 2 \\ 3x - 2y &= 10 \\ \hline -2x \quad &= -8 \\ x &= 4 \\ 4 - 2y &= 2 \\ -2y &= -2 \\ y &= 1 \end{aligned}$$

(4, 1)

4. $2p + q = 25$
   $2p = 5q + 7$

$$\begin{aligned} 2p + q &= 25 \\ 2p - 5q &= 7 \\ \hline 6q &= 18 \\ q &= 3 \\ 2p + 3 &= 25 \\ 2p &= 22 \\ p &= 11 \end{aligned}$$

(11, 3)

8-6 The Addition-or-Subtraction Method

Objective To use addition or subtraction to solve systems of linear equations in two variables.

When solving a system of two equations, you can sometimes add or subtract the equations to obtain a new equation with just one variable. This method is called the *addition-or-subtraction* method.

Example 1 (The Addition Method) Solve: $3x - y = 8$
$2x + y = 7$

Solution

1. Add similar terms of the two equations.

$$\begin{aligned} 3x - y &= 8 \\ 2x + y &= 7 \\ \hline 5x \quad &= 15 \end{aligned}$$

The y-terms are eliminated.

2. Solve the resulting equation. $x = 3$

3. Substitute $x = 3$ in either of the original equations to find y.

$$\begin{aligned} 2x + y &= 7 \\ 2 \cdot 3 + y &= 7 \\ y &= 1 \end{aligned}$$

4. Check in both original equations:

$$\begin{aligned} 2x + y &= 7 \\ 2 \cdot 3 + 1 &\stackrel{?}{=} 7 \\ 7 &= 7 \checkmark \end{aligned} \qquad \begin{aligned} 3x - y &= 8 \\ 3 \cdot 3 - 1 &\stackrel{?}{=} 8 \\ 8 &= 8 \checkmark \end{aligned}$$

∴ the solution is (3, 1). ***Answer***

Example 2 (The Subtraction Method) Solve: $4s + 5t = 6$
$4s - 2t = -8$

Solution

1. Subtract similar terms of the two equations.

$$\begin{aligned} 4s + 5t &= 6 \\ 4s - 2t &= -8 \\ \hline 7t &= 14 \end{aligned}$$

The s-terms are eliminated.

2. Solve the resulting equation. $t = 2$

3. Substitute $t = 2$ in either of the original equations to find s.

$$\begin{aligned} 4s + 5t &= 6 \\ 4s + 5 \cdot 2 &= 6 \\ 4s &= -4 \\ s &= -1 \end{aligned}$$

4. The check in both original equations is left to you.
   ∴ the solution is (−1, 2). ***Answer***

The addition-or-subtraction method is based on the addition property of equality. Note that in Example 2 the coefficients of s are the *same*, and in Example 1 the coefficients of y are *opposites*. Whenever two equations have the same or opposite coefficients for one of their terms, the addition-or-subtraction method can be used.

The Addition-or-Subtraction Method

To solve a system of linear equations in two variables:

1. Add or subtract the equations to eliminate one variable.
2. Solve the resulting equation for the other variable.
3. Substitute in either original equation to find the value of the first variable.
4. Check in both equations.

Oral Exercises

Use the addition method to solve for x.

1. $3x + 2y = 7$ $x = 1$
   $5x - 2y = 1$
2. $x - 5y = 1$ $x = 6$
   $2x + 5y = 17$
3. $4y + 3x = 9$
   $-4y - x = 7$
   $x = 8$

Use the subtraction method to solve for s.

4. $3t + 5s = 10$ $s = 2$
   $3t + s = 2$
5. $4s - 5t = 7$ $s = 2$
   $2s - 5t = 3$
6. $3s + 4t = 18$
   $-2s + 4t = 8$
   $s = 2$

Use the addition-or-subtraction method to solve for one of the variables.

7. $3a + 2b = 11$ $a = 3$
   $2a - 2b = 4$
8. $3p + 2q = 19$ $q = 2$
   $3p - 5q = 5$
9. $-4s + 7t = 10$
   $4s - 2t = 8$
   $t = \frac{18}{5}$

Written Exercises

6. (2, −3)
9. (3, −2)

Solve by the addition-or-subtraction method.

A

1. $x + y = 9$ (5, 4)
   $x - y = 1$
2. $a - b = 17$ (12, −5)
   $a + b = 7$
3. $2r - 3s = 17$ (4, −3)
   $2r + 3s = -1$
4. $2a - b = 3$ (2, 1)
   $4a + b = 9$
5. $2p - 5q = 30$ (10, −2)
   $2p + 7q = 6$
6. $7m + 8n = -10$
   $7m + 2n = 8$
7. $2r - 5s = 14$ $\left(\frac{23}{4}, -\frac{1}{2}\right)$
   $2r + 3s = 10$
8. $2k - 5p = 17$ (−4, −5)
   $6k - 5p = 1$
9. $3x - 2y = 13$
   $4x + 2y = 8$

5. $5k - 2n = 2$
   $3k + 2n = 30$

$$\begin{aligned} 5k - 2n &= 2 \\ 3k + 2n &= 30 \\ \hline 8k &= 32 \\ k &= 4 \\ 20 - 2n &= 2 \\ -2n &= -18 \\ n &= 9 \end{aligned}$$

(4, 9)

Supplementary Material

Practice Master 48

Suggested Assignments

Minimum
359/1–17
360/*P*: 1–4

Average
359/1–23 odd
360/*P*: 1, 3–7

Maximum
359/1–25 odd
360/*P*: 2–10 even

Additional A Exercises

Solve by the addition-or-subtraction method.

1. $x + y = 17$; $x - y = 1$
   (9, 8)
2. $a - 3b = -1$;
   $2a + 3b = 16$
   (5, 2)
3. $-3n + 9m = 6$;
   $3n + 4m = 7$
   (1, 1)
4. $8q + 12r = 20$;
   $5q + 12r = -1$
   (7, −3)
5. $9x - 10y = 2$·
   $9x + 2y = -22$
   (−2, −2)
6. $a - 2b = 0$;
   $a + 2b = 12$
   (6, 3)

Mixed Review Exercises

1. Find $16\frac{2}{3}\%$ of 90. 15
2. One liter of a type of salad dressing is 50% oil. How much oil should be added to make a solution which is 60% oil? 250 mL
3. Barbara and Steve work in a hotel. It takes Barbara 20 min to get a room ready for a new guest, but it takes Steve 30 min. How long would it take them if they worked together? 12 min
4. Solve by substitution: $9x - y = 11$, $2x + y = 11$ (2, 7)

Solve by the addition-or-subtraction method.

10. $4n - 7m = 13$, $2n - 7m = 3$ (1, 5)

11. $6a + 9b = 4$, $6a + 3b = 0$ $\left(-\frac{1}{3}, \frac{2}{3}\right)$

12. $-4x + y = 7$, $4x + 3y = 5$ (−1, 3)

13. Without drawing the graphs, state where the lines $2x + 4y = 2$ and $6x - 4y = 2$ intersect. $\left(\frac{1}{2}, \frac{1}{4}\right)$

14. State on which coordinate axis the two lines $5x - y = 3$ and $10x - y = 3$ intersect. y-axis

Express each equation in standard form. Then solve by either the substitution method or the addition-or-subtraction method.

B **15.** $a = 6b + 3$, $a + 2b = 5$ $\left(\frac{9}{2}, \frac{1}{4}\right)$

16. $x - 5y = 2$, $2x + y = 4$ (2, 0)

17. $c - 2d = 7$, $c + 3d = 2$ (5, −1)

18. $4(x - 2y) = 8$, $x + 6y = 2$ (2, 0)

19. $4(a - 2b) = 8$, $2(a + 4b) = -8$ (0, −1)

20. $n = 2 - 6m$, $\frac{1}{2}n - m = 1$ (0, 2)

21. $\frac{1}{2}(c + d) + 1 = 0$, $\frac{1}{2}(c - d) - 2 = 0$ (1, −3)

22. $\frac{1}{3}a - \frac{2}{3}b = 1$, $a + b + 7 = 0$ $\left(-\frac{11}{3}, -\frac{10}{3}\right)$

23. $y = \frac{2}{3}x$, $x + 6y = 30$ (6, 4)

24. $\frac{5a}{6} - \frac{b}{3} = 6$, $a + 2b = 0$ (6, −3)

25. $3n + 1 = \frac{k}{4}$, $n = \frac{k + 1}{15}$ $\left(24, \frac{5}{3}\right)$

26. $\frac{x + y}{3} - \frac{x - y}{2} = 42$, $\frac{x - y}{9} + \frac{x}{2} = 5$ (18, 54)

27. The graphs of $ax + by = 18$ and $ax - by = 6$ intersect at (3, −2). Find a and b. $a = 4$, $b = -3$

C **28.** The graphs of $5x - 3y = 35$, $7x - 3y = 43$, and $4x - ay = 61$ all intersect in the same point. Find a. $a = 9$

29. Show that the graphs of $\frac{x - 2y}{x + 2y} = \frac{1}{3}$ and $\frac{x - y}{x + y} = \frac{3}{5}$ coincide.
Both equations simplify to $x - 4y = 0$ with $(x, y) \neq (0, 0)$.

Problems

Solve using two equations in two variables. Use either the substitution method or the addition-or-subtraction method.

A **1.** The sum of two numbers is 21 and their difference is 5. What are the numbers? 13, 8

2. The sum of two numbers is 64. Twice the smaller number is 10 less than the larger number. Find the numbers. 18, 46

3. There are 812 students in a school. There are 36 more girls than boys. How many girls are there? 424

4. The ratio of the total number of animals in a zoo to the number of bears is 22:1. If the total number of animals minus the number of bears is 315, find the number of bears. 15

B 5. At an amusement park you get 5 points for each bull's eye you hit, but you lose 10 points for every miss. After 30 tries, Yolanda lost 90 points. How many bull's eyes did she have? 14

6. Since my uncle's farmyard appeared to be overrun with chickens and dogs, I asked him how many of each he had. Being a puzzler as well as a farmer, my uncle replied that his dogs and chickens had a total of 148 legs and 60 heads. How many dogs and how many chickens does my uncle have? 14 dogs, 46 chickens

7. If Linda Chu walks for 1 h and cycles for 2 h, she can travel 68 km. But if she walks for 2 h and cycles for 1 h, Linda travels 46 km. What are her walking and cycling speeds? walking, 8 km/h; cycling, 30 km/h

8. Daniel is ten years older than Gregory. Two years ago, he was twice as old as Gregory was then. How old is each now? Gregory, 12; Daniel, 22

C 9. If Tom gives Maria 30 cents, they will have equal amounts of money. But if Maria then gives Tom 50 cents, he will have twice as much money as she does. How much money does each have now? Tom, \$1.80; Maria, \$1.20

10. Five years ago, Megan's age was 5 years less than twice Tony's age. In three years, one third of Tony's age will be 12 years less than Megan's age. How old are they now? Tony, 12; Megan, 14

11. A shipment of 18 cars, some weighing 3,000 pounds apiece and the others 5,000 pounds each, has a total weight of 30 tons. Find the number of each kind of car. 15 3000-lb cars, 3 5000-lb cars

Challenge

The following "Problem of a Hundred Fowl" dates to sixth-century China:

If a rooster is worth 5 yuan, a hen is worth 3 yuan, and 3 chicks are worth 1 yuan, how many of each, 100 in all, would be worth 100 yuan? Assume that at least 5 roosters are required. 8 roosters, 11 hens, 81 chicks or 12 roosters, 4 hens, 84 chicks

Teaching Suggestions p. T111

Suggested Extensions p. T112

Chalkboard Examples

Solve.

1. $6x + y = 6$
   $3x + 2y = 9$

$$\begin{aligned} 6x + y &= 6 \\ 6x + 4y &= 18 \\ \hline -3y &= -12 \\ y &= 4 \\ 6x + 4 &= 6 \\ 6x &= 2 \\ x &= \frac{1}{3} \end{aligned}$$

$\left(\frac{1}{3}, 4\right)$

2. $x - 3y = 5$
   $2x - 8 = 6y$

$$\begin{aligned} 2x - 6y &= 10 \\ 2x - 6y &= 8 \\ \hline 0 &= 2 \end{aligned}$$

no solution

3. $5p + 12q = 13$
   $3p + 4q = 3$

$$\begin{aligned} 5p + 12q &= 13 \\ 9p + 12q &= 9 \\ \hline -4p &= 4 \\ p &= -1 \\ -3 + 4q &= 3 \\ 4q &= 6 \\ q &= \frac{3}{2} \end{aligned}$$

$\left(-1, \frac{3}{2}\right)$

4. $4s - 5t = 3$
   $3s + 2t = -15$

$$\begin{aligned} 8s - 10t &= 6 \\ 15s + 10t &= -75 \\ \hline 23s &= -69 \\ s &= -3 \\ -9 + 2t &= -15 \\ 2t &= -6 \\ t &= -3 \end{aligned}$$

$(-3, -3)$

8-7 Multiplication with the Addition-or-Subtraction Method

Objective To use multiplication with the addition-or-subtraction method to solve systems of linear equations.

To solve a system such as

$$\begin{aligned} 5x - 9y &= 17 \\ 4x + 3y &= 1, \end{aligned}$$

you cannot apply the addition-or-subtraction method immediately. Neither the terms in x nor the terms in y are the same or opposites. See what happens, however, when you multiply both sides of the second equation by 3:

$$\begin{aligned} 5x - 9y = 17 &\longrightarrow 5x - 9y = 17 \\ 3(4x + 3y) = 3(1) &\longrightarrow 12x + 9y = 3 \end{aligned}$$

You now have an equivalent system that can be solved by the addition-or-subtraction method, since the terms in y are opposites.

Sometimes you may need to transform both equations by multiplication before you can apply the addition-or-subtraction method, as shown in Example 1.

Example 1 Solve: $3a + 4b = -25$
$2a - 3b = 6$

Solution

1. Transform both equations by multiplication so that the terms in a are the same.

$$\begin{aligned} 2(3a + 4b) = 2(-25) &\longrightarrow 6a + 8b = -50 \\ 3(2a - 3b) = 3(6) &\longrightarrow 6a - 9b = 18 \end{aligned}$$

2. Subtract similar terms. $\qquad 17b = -68$

3. Solve the resulting equation. $\qquad b = -4$

4. Substitute in either of the *original* equations to find the corresponding value of the other variable.

$$\begin{aligned} 3a + 4b &= -25 \\ 3a + 4(-4) &= -25 \\ 3a - 16 &= -25 \\ 3a &= -9 \\ a &= -3 \end{aligned}$$

5. The check in both original equations is left to you.
   $\therefore$ the solution is $(-3, -4)$. ***Answer***

To solve a system of linear equations involving fractions, it is usually convenient to clear the equations of fractions first, as shown in Example 2.

Example 2 Solve: $\frac{5x}{4} + y = \frac{11}{2}$

$$x + \frac{y}{3} = 3$$

Solution

1. Transform each equation by multiplying by the LCD of its denominators.

$$4\left(\frac{5x}{4} + y\right) = 4\left(\frac{11}{2}\right) \longrightarrow 5x + 4y = 22$$

$$3\left(x + \frac{y}{3}\right) = 3(3) \longrightarrow 3x + y = 9$$

2. Multiply the second equation by 4 so that the terms in y are the same.

$$5x + 4y = 22 \longrightarrow 5x + 4y = 22$$

$$4(3x + y) = 4(9) \longrightarrow 12x + 4y = 36$$

3. Subtract similar terms. $\quad -7x = -14$

4. Solve the resulting equation. $\quad x = 2$

5. Substitute in either of the original equations to find the value of y.

$$x + \frac{y}{3} = 3$$

$$2 + \frac{y}{3} = 3$$

$$\frac{y}{3} = 1$$

$$y = 3$$

6. The check is left to you.
∴ the solution is (2, 3). ***Answer***

Oral Exercises

Explain how to use multiplication with the addition-or-subtraction method to solve each system by answering these questions:

a. Which equation(s) will you transform by multiplication?
b. By what number(s) will you multiply?
c. Will you then add or subtract similar terms?

1. $2x + y = 8$ First; 2;
$3x - 2y = 5$ add

2. $3a + 5b = 3$ Second; 3;
$a + 2b = 13$ subtract

3. $3x - 2t = 4$
$2x + t = 5$

4. $3c - 8d = 7$ Second; 3;
$c + 2d = -7$ subtract

5. $3a + b = 4$ First; 2;
$a - 2b = 6$ add

6. $x + y = 7$
$3x - 2y = 11$

7. $4x - 3y = 7$ Second; 3;
$5x - y = 6$ subtract

8. $4p - q = 6$ Second; 2;
$2p - 3q = 8$ subtract

9. $4x - 3y = 8$
$2x + y = 14$

5. $11j + 5k = 3$
$3j + 2k = 4$
$22j + 10k = 6$
$15j + 10k = 20$
$7j = -14$
$j = -2$
$-6 + 2k = 4$
$k = 5$
$(-2, 5)$

Common Errors

Some students become so involved with choosing appropriate multipliers for each equation that they forget to multiply *both* sides of an equation by the multiplier. Encourage such students to show their work.

Some students may make a similar error in solving the systems in Mixed Practice Exercises 16, 18, 25, and 26. Seeing $2(b + 6)$ on the right side of the second equation in Mixed Practice Exercise 16, for example, a student may multiply the left side by 2. Remind students who make this error that the 2 on the right side was already there and that by multiplying the left side by 2, they are multiplying only one side of the equation by 2.

Sometimes students check their solutions in their transformed equations instead of in the original equations. Point out that substituting a solution into an equation that has not been transformed correctly may not help them find an existing error.

Additional Answers Oral Exercises

3. Second; 2; add
6. First; 2; add
9. Second; 3; add

Additional Answers
Oral Exercises

10. First by 5; second by 2; add
11. First by 3; second by 2; subtract
12. First by 3; second by 2; subtract
13. First by 3; second by 2; subtract
14. First by 7, second by 2; add
15. First by 2; subtract
16. First by 3; subtract
17. First by 2; second by 7; add
18. First by 3; second by 4; add

Supplementary Materials

Practice Master 49
Resource Book, p. 105

Suggested Assignments

Minimum
Day 1: 364/1–19 odd
366/*P*: 1, 3, 5
S 360/18–22
Day 2: 365/1–12
366/*P*: 6–12

Average
Day 1: 364/1–25 odd
366/*P*: 3–11 odd
Day 2: 365/10–26 even
367/*P*: 16, 17, 19, 21–23

Maximum
Day 1: 364/1–27 odd
367/*P*: 12, 14, 15, 17–19
S 360/27–29
Day 2: 365/35, 36
365/10–30 even
367/*P*: 21, 23, 26–28

Explain how to use multiplication with the addition-or-subtraction method to solve each system by answering questions (a)-(c) on page 363.

10. $5p - 2q = 1$
$4p + 5q = 47$

11. $2c - 3d = -1$
$3c - 4d = -3$

12. $3r - 2s = 15$
$7r - 3s = 15$

13. $2a + 3b = 7$
$3a + 4b = 10$

14. $5a - 2b = 7$
$2a + 7b = -5$

15. $\frac{1}{2}x + 3y = 5$
$x - 2y = 2$

16. $\frac{1}{3}a + \frac{2}{3}b = 8$
$a - b = -3$

17. $3p + 7q + 18 = 0$
$5p - 2q + 30 = 0$

18. $3x + 4z + 2 = 0$
$2x - 3z - 10 = 0$

Written Exercises

A **1–18.** Solve each system in the Oral Exercises by using multiplication with the addition-or-subtraction method.

Express each equation in standard form. Then solve.

B **19.** $\frac{a}{4} + \frac{b}{3} = 2$ (4, 3)
$\frac{a}{2} - b = -1$

20. $\frac{x}{2} - y = 9$ (10, −4)
$x + \frac{y}{2} = 8$

21. $\frac{a}{6} + \frac{b}{4} = \frac{3}{2}$ (3, 4)
$\frac{2a}{3} = \frac{b}{2}$

22. $\frac{p}{8} + \frac{q}{6} = 1$ (−8, 12)
$\frac{p}{q} = \frac{-2}{3}$

23. $0.3x + 0.5y = 31$ (20, 50)
$0.2x - 0.1y = -1$

24. $0.05x + 0.06y = 215$
$x + y = 4000$
(2500, 1500)

25. $\frac{a + b}{3} - \frac{a - b}{5} = -4$ (6, −9)
$\frac{2a}{3} + \frac{b - 1}{5} = 2$

26. $c - 1 + \frac{d - 4}{2} = 14$ (13, 8)
$\frac{d + 2}{2} - \frac{c - 3}{5} = 3$

27. Determine whether the graphs of $3x - 4y = 3$, $6x + 6y = 13$, and $9x + 2y = 16$ intersect in a single point. $\left(\frac{5}{3}, \frac{1}{2}\right)$

28. The point (8, −3) is the intersection of the graphs of $ax + by = 25$ and $3ax - 5by = 3$. Find a and b. $a = 2$, $b = -3$

Solve for *x* and *y* by whatever method you prefer. (*Hint:* These equations are not linear in x and y. However, if you let $\frac{1}{x} = a$ and $\frac{1}{y} = b$, the equations become linear in a and b.)

C **29.** $\frac{1}{x} + \frac{1}{y} = 1$ $\left(\frac{1}{2}, -1\right)$
$\frac{3}{x} - \frac{2}{y} = 8$

30. $\frac{1}{x} + \frac{1}{y} = 5$ $\left(\frac{1}{2}, \frac{1}{3}\right)$
$\frac{3}{x} - \frac{5}{y} = -9$

31. $\frac{8}{x} + \frac{15}{y} = 33$ $\left(\frac{2}{3}, \frac{5}{7}\right)$
$\frac{4}{x} - \frac{35}{y} = -43$

Solve for x and y in terms of a and b.

32. $ax + y = 5$ $\left(\frac{2}{a}, 3\right)$
$3ax - 2y = 0$

33. $ax + by = 1$ $\left(\frac{6}{5a}, \frac{-1}{5b}\right)$
$3ax - 2by = 4$

34. $ax - by = 1$ $\left(\frac{a+b}{a^2+b^2}, \frac{a-b}{a^2+b^2}\right)$
$bx + ay = 1$

Solve for x, y, and z. (*Hint:* Eliminate one variable from the first two equations and then eliminate the same variable from the second two equations. This will give two new equations in two variables.)

35. $x + y + z = 7$
$2x - y + z = 4$
$3x + 2y + z = 11$ (1, 2, 4)

36. $x + y + z = 4$
$2x - y + z = 0$
$x - y + 2z = -3$ (2, 3, −1)

37. $x + 2y - z = 10$
$3x + y + 2z = 20$
$2x + y + z = 14$
$(x, 8 - x, 6 - x)$

Mixed Practice

Solve by the graphic method.

A **1.** $y - x = 5$
$y = 2x + 4$ (1, 6)

2. $x + y = 0$
$3x + y = -8$ (−4, 4)

3. $3x + 4y = 10$
$x - y = 1$ (2, 1)

Solve by the substitution method.

4. $a = 3b$ (−24, −8)
$a - 5b = 16$

5. $2c - d = 5$ (3, 1)
$4c + 5d = 17$

6. $4p = 3q$ (9, 12)
$3p - q = 15$

Solve by the addition-or-subtraction method.

7. $2a + 3b = -1$
$a - 3b = 4$ (1, −1)

8. $5x - 9y = -3$
$4x - 3y = 6$ (3, 2)

9. $2p + 3q + 1 = 0$ (1, −1)
$3p + 5q + 2 = 0$

Solve by whatever method you prefer.

B **10.** $y = x + 2$ (3, 5)
$2x + y = 11$

11. $x + y = 8$ (7, 1)
$x - 3y = 4$

12. $3x - 2y = 1$ (3, 4)
$4y = 7 + 3x$

13. $x - 5y = 2$ (2, 0)
$2x + y = 4$

14. $2a - 4b = 6$ (−1, −2)
$7 + a = -3b$

15. $r - s = 4$ (14, 10)
$r - 6 = 2(s - 6)$

16. $a - 2b = 10$ (14, 2)
$a + b = 2(b + 6)$

17. $t + u = 11$ (7, 4)
$(10t + u) - (10u + t) = 27$

18. $u - t = 5$ (2, 7)
$10t + u = 3(t + u)$

19. $3x + 2y = 21$ (5, 3)
$7x - 5y = 20$

20. $2a + 3b = 7$ (2, 1)
$3a + 4b = 10$

21. $5n - 2m = 1$ (7, 3)
$4n + 5m = 47$

22. $0.04x - 0.06y = 40$
$x + y = 6000$
(4000, 2000)

23. $2.4 = 0.3x + 0.4y$
$5x = 2 + 6y$ (4, 3)

24. $2x - \frac{5}{2}y = 13$
$\frac{x}{3} + \frac{y}{3} = \frac{14}{15}$ $\left(\frac{40}{9}, \frac{-74}{45}\right)$

25. $3a + 2b = 4$
$\frac{1}{3}(2a + b) = 1$ (2, −1)

26. $\frac{1}{3}(3a - 2b) = -3$
$3(a - b) = -9$ (−3, 0)

27. $\frac{x}{2} + \frac{y}{3} = -4$
$x + y = -10$
(−4, −6)

Additional Answers Written Exercises

1. (3, 2) 2. (−59, 36)
3. (1, 2) 4. (−3, −2)
5. (2, −2) 6. (5, 2)
7. (1, −1) 8. (1, −2)
9. (5, 4) 10. (3, 7)
11. (−5, −3) 12. (−3, −12)
13. (2, 1) 14. (1, −1)
15. (4, 1) 16. (6, 9)
17. (−6, 0) 18. (2, −2)

Additional Answers Mixed Practice

2.

Additional A Exercises

Solve by using multiplication with the addition-or-subtraction method.

1. $4x - 2y = 10;$
$3x - y = 12$
(7, 9)

2. $5a + 3b = 43;$
$-a + 7b = -1$
(8, 1)

3. $m + 2n = 6;$
$-2m + 4n = 28$
(−4, 5)

4. $2s + 3t = 35;$
$5s - 4t = 7$
(7, 7)

5. $4w - 4z = -8;$
$-3w + 5z = 0$
(−5, −3)

6. $\frac{1}{2}x + \frac{1}{3}y = 8;$
$x + 2y = 28$
(10, 9)

Mixed Review Exercises

1. Evaluate $\frac{a^2 - ab}{c}$ if $a = 5$, $b = 6$ and $c = 2$. $-\frac{5}{2}$
2. Solve $|x| = -2$ over the set of real numbers. No solution
3. Solve: $z + 8 = |23 - (-3)|$ 18
4. Solve, using 2 variables: The sum of 2 numbers is 32, but twice their difference is also 32. What are the numbers? 24 and 8

Solve. (*Hint:* See Exercises 35–37 on page 365.)

C

28. $x - y + z = 7$
$z = x - 3$
$y = -2z$ (4, −2, 1)

29. $r + s + t = 180$
$r = s + t$
$s = 4t$ (90, 72, 18)

30. $a + b + c = 8$
$b = \frac{a - c}{2}$
$b = \frac{a + c}{3}$ (5, 2, 1)

31. $\frac{3}{2x} + \frac{2}{y} = 16$
$\frac{2}{x} - \frac{1}{5y} = 7$ $\left(\frac{1}{4}, \frac{1}{5}\right)$

32. $\frac{3}{x} + \frac{4}{y} = 1$
$\frac{2}{x} - \frac{2}{y} = 10$ $\left(\frac{1}{3}, -\frac{1}{2}\right)$

33. $x + y + z = 0$
$x - 2y + 3z = 18$
$2x + 2y + 5z = 20$ $\left(-\frac{46}{9}, -\frac{14}{9}, \frac{20}{3}\right)$

Problems

Solve by whatever method you prefer.

A

1. The sum of two numbers is 50 and their difference is 18. Find the numbers. 16, 34
2. One number is 18 more than three times another number. The difference in the numbers is 54. Find the numbers. 18, 72
3. Al is 13 years older than Jack. Next year the ratio of their ages will be 3:2. How old is each now? Al, 38; Jack, 25
4. Last year Sue was three times as old as Pablo. Next year she will be twice as old as Pablo is. How old is each now? Sue, 7; Pablo, 3
5. The length of a rectangle is 20 cm greater than its width. The perimeter is 360 cm. What is the area? 8000 cm^2
6. A rectangle is four times as long as it is wide. If it were 6 m shorter and 6 m wider, it would be a square. What are the dimensions? 4 m by 16 m
7. Sally has \$21.40 in dimes and quarters, for a total of 100 coins. How many of each kind of coin does Sally have? 76 quarters, 24 dimes
8. Elizabeth Chin has twice as many dimes as quarters and four more quarters than nickels. If Elizabeth has \$7.80, how many coins does she have? 60 coins
9. The ratio of boys to girls at a school dance was 5:3. There would have been an equal number of boys and girls if there had been 3 more girls and 3 fewer boys. How many boys and how many girls were at the dance? 15 boys, 9 girls
10. Thomas takes 40 minutes to wash the family car and Joanna takes 60 minutes. How long will it take Thomas and Joanna to wash the car if they work together? 24 min
11. A movie theater charges \$4 for an adult ticket and \$2 for a child's ticket. One night 380 tickets were sold for a total of \$1320. How many children attended the movie that night? 100

12. A chemist has 500 g of a solution that is 40% acid. How many grams of water must be added to reduce the acidity to 25%? 300 g
13. A chemist has 800 g of a dye solution that is 20% of its original strength. How much dye must be added to increase the strength to 50%? 480 g
14. Five pens and four pencils cost \$2.55. But four pens and five pencils cost \$2.40. How much do the pens cost and how much do the pencils cost? pen, 35¢; pencil, 20¢
15. Becky's bill for 6 cans of grape juice and 4 cans of orange juice was \$13.20. When she got home, she found that she should have bought 4 cans of grape juice and 6 cans of orange juice. Although she mixed up the order, Becky did save 60 cents. How much does each can cost? orange juice, \$1.50; grape juice, \$1.20
16. Joe Tyson is the place kicker for his college football team. Last season he kicked 38 times and never missed. Each field goal scored 3 points and each point after touchdown scored 1 point for a total of 70 points. How many field goals did Joe kick? 16

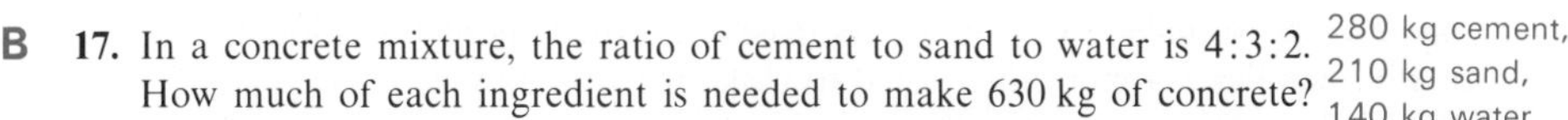

B 17. In a concrete mixture, the ratio of cement to sand to water is 4:3:2. How much of each ingredient is needed to make 630 kg of concrete? 280 kg cement, 210 kg sand, 140 kg water
18. The equation $2x + 6y = 35$ has no whole number solutions. Why not?
19. Find the area enclosed between the x-axis and the graphs of $x + y = 20$ and $3x - 2y = 0$. 120
20. A car traveled at a steady speed for 120 km. Due to a mechanical problem, it returned at half that speed. If the total time for the round trip was 4 h 30 min, find the two speeds. original, 80 km/h; return, 40 km/h
21. Edna Britten's income from two stocks each year totals \$280. Stock A pays dividends at the rate of 5% and stock B at the rate of 6%. If she has invested a total of \$5000, how much is invested in each stock? A: \$2000 B: \$3000
22. Luann Bailey usually takes 75 minutes to grade her students' algebra quizzes. After working for 30 minutes, another math teacher helps her finish the job in 15 minutes. How long would the second teacher take to grade the quizzes alone? $37\frac{1}{2}$ min
23. Before last weekend's hiking trip, Juanita mixed 3 kg of peanuts and raisins as an energy snack. The peanuts cost \$4.25 per kilogram and the raisins cost \$3.50 per kilogram. The whole mix cost \$12. How many kilograms of peanuts did Juanita have? 2 kg
24. Phil has 48 words to spell for a puzzle. As an incentive, his mother offers to pay him 10 cents for each word he spells correctly if Phil will pay her 6 cents for each word he spells incorrectly. If Phil makes \$1.92, how many words does he spell correctly? 30

Additional Answer Problems

18. If x and y are both whole numbers, $2x + 6y$ is even. But 35 is odd. Hence, $2x + 6y \neq 35$ if x and y are whole numbers.

25. Beatrice Robinson receives \$375 per year from a \$6000 investment in stocks and bonds. The bonds pay 10% interest and the stocks pay 5% in dividends. How much is invested in stocks? \$4500

26. Several ball bearings and cubes are balanced in a simple pan balance as shown. How many bearings does it take to balance one cube? 4 bearings

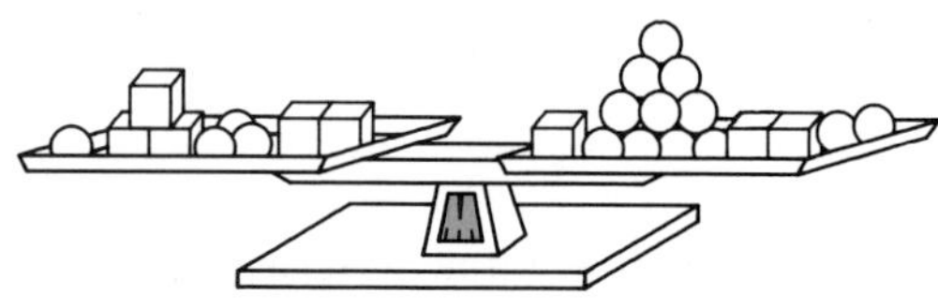

C 27. On a simple pan balance, 3 apples and 1 banana exactly balance 10 plums. Also, 1 apple and 6 plums balance 1 banana. How many plums will balance one banana? 7 plums

28. Roger, Sue, and Tim have \$155 between them. Roger has \$5 more than Sue and Tim together. If Sue gives Tim \$5, he will have twice as much as she does. How much does each have? Roger, \$80; Tim, \$45; Sue, \$30

29. If the length of a rectangle is increased by 12 and the width is decreased by 8, the area is unchanged. The area is also unchanged if the original length is increased by 5 and the original width is decreased by 4. Find the original dimensions of the rectangle. 30 by 28

30. If Alexandra increases her usual driving speed by 15 km/h, it will take her 2 h less to make a trip. If she decreases her usual speed by 15 km/h, it will take her 3 h more than usual to make the trip. How long is the trip? 900 km

Computer Key-In

Exercises

1. Use multiplication with the addition-or-subtraction method to verify that the solution of the system

$$\begin{aligned} Ax + By &= C \\ Dx + Ey &= F \end{aligned} \quad \text{is} \quad \left(\frac{CE - BF}{AE - BD}, \frac{AF - CD}{AE - BD}\right).$$

2. a. Using the result in Exercise 1, write a program to solve a system of linear equations in two variables. Provide for the case $AE - BD = 0$.

   b. RUN the program for each of the following.

$3x + 4y = -25$	$5x + 4y = 22$	$2x + 4y = 11$	$2x + y = 8$
$2x - 3y = 6$	$3x + y = 9$	$3x + 6y = 17$	$3x - 2y = 5$
$(-3, -4)$	$(2, 3)$	No sol.	$(3, 2)$

Note: The program of Exercise 2 above can be used to do Exercises 1–18 on pages 363–364.

Self-Test 2

Vocabulary system of equations (p. 346), solution of a system (p. 346), intersection point (p. 346), parallel lines (p. 346), system of simultaneous equations (p. 346), solution set (p. 346), equivalent system (p. 351)

Solve each system by the graphic method.

1. $x + y = 8$
   $x - y = 4$ (6, 2)

2. $x - 2y = 3$
   $2x - 3y = 4$ (−1, −2) **Obj. 8-3, p. 346**

Solve by the substitution method.

3. $3a - b = 14$
   $a = 2b - 2$ (6, 4)

4. $m - 2n = -8$
   $m + n = 4$ (0, 4) **Obj. 8-4, p. 350**

5. Solve by using two equations in two variables: The treasurer of the school play knows that 900 tickets were sold for a certain performance. If orchestra tickets sold for \$3 each and balcony tickets for \$2 each, and if the total receipts were \$2300, how many of each kind of ticket were sold? 500 orchestra, 400 balcony **Obj. 8-5, p. 354**

Solve by the addition-or-subtraction method.

6. $a - 2b = 0$
   $a + 2b = 12$ (6, 3)

7. $3c + 5d = 20$
   $-2c + 5d = 20$ (0, 4) **Obj. 8-6, p. 358**

Solve by using multiplication with the addition-or-subtraction method.

8. $3r - 8s = 7$
   $r + 2s = -7$ (−3, −2)

9. $2a + 3b = 12$
   $3a + 2b = 13$ (3, 2) **Obj. 8-7, p. 362**

Check your answers with those at the back of the book.

Calculator Key-In

If you used multiplication with the addition-or-subtraction method to solve

$$Ax + By = C$$
$$Dx + Ey = F,$$

you would obtain $x = \frac{CE - BF}{AE - BD}$ and $y = \frac{CD - AF}{BD - AE}$.

When the values of $A, B, \ldots, F$ are decimals, it is convenient to solve the system by using a calculator. Use a calculator and this method to solve the following systems.

1. $1.2x + 4.6y = 16.2$ (2, 3)
   $3.1x + 2.1y = 12.5$

2. $2.3x + 1.6y = 14.9$ (3, 5)
   $4.1x + 3.2y = 28.3$

Additional Answers
Self-Test 2

1.

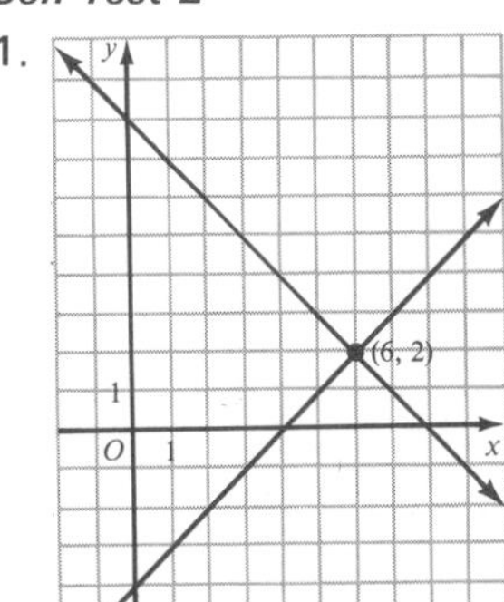

2.

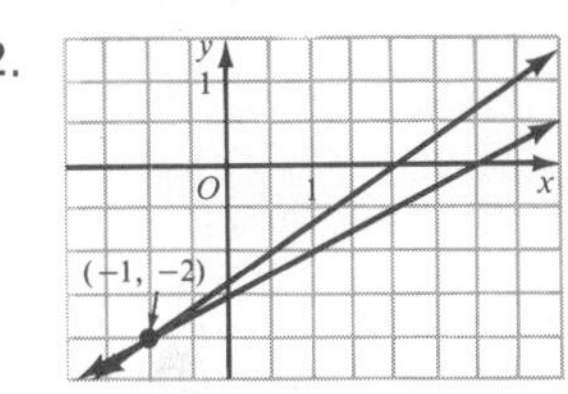

Quick Quiz

1. Solve by the graphic method.
   $y = \frac{3}{4}x + 1$ (4, 4)
   $2x - y = 4$
2. Solve by the substitution method.
   $x + 2y = 3$ (−7, 5)
   $y - x = 12$
3. Solve using two equations in two variables. A bank contains 75 dimes and quarters for a total of \$11.55. How many of each coin are in the bank?
   48 dimes, 27 quarters
4. Solve by the addition-or-subtraction method.
   $y - 2x = 15$ (−4, 7)
   $2x + 3y = 13$
5. Solve. $2x - 2y = 3$
   $4x + 11y = -4$
   $\left(\frac{5}{6}, -\frac{2}{3}\right)$

Reading Algebra / *Problem-Solving Strategies*

If you are to be a successful problem solver, you must first master the art of reading word problems. Before you begin solving a set of problems, be sure you have read the accompanying lesson in your textbook and have worked through all the text examples. Then, for each problem, read the problem slowly and carefully. Do not begin writing until you have determined what you are being asked to find and until you have chosen a strategy for finding it. Be sure the strategy that you have chosen is appropriate and that any formulas involved are correct. When you have found an answer, check it to be sure that it makes sense and that it is correct. The time you spend on planning and checking will be well worthwhile. Planning and checking will improve your chances of achieving success on the first try and will help you to develop a sound problem-solving strategy.

If you find that you are having trouble understanding a word problem or figuring out how to begin solving it, there are a number of things you can do. The first is rereading. Perhaps you overlooked something when you first read the problem. Then, attempt to break the problem down. You may be able to use the parts that you understand to make sense of the parts that you do not. It may also help to organize the information in a table or chart, or to draw a diagram.

Exercises

1. A coin box contains $26.50 in dimes and quarters. There are 157 coins altogether. How many of each type of coin are in the box? 85 dimes, 72 quarters

2. The length of a rectangle is 4 cm more than twice the width. The perimeter is 56 cm. Find the length and the width. 8 cm wide by 20 cm long

3. Two planes leave an airport at the same time flying in opposite directions. The first plane is traveling at a speed of 1100 km/h. After 4 h, the planes are 7600 km apart. Find the speed of the second plane. 800 km/h

4. The trip from Arquette to Carver takes 8 min longer during rush hour, when the average speed is 75 km/h, than in off-peak hours, when the average speed is 90 km/h. Find the distance between the two towns. 60 km

5. A rectangle is 5 cm longer than it is wide. If the length is doubled and the width is tripled, the area is increased by 420 cm^2. Find the original dimensions. 7 cm by 12 cm

6. The sum of two numbers is 11 and the sum of their squares is 65. Find the numbers. 4, 7

7. The edges of one cube are 2 cm longer than the edges of another. The volume of the smaller cube is 152 cm^3 less than the volume of the larger cube. Find the lengths of the edges of each cube. 4 cm; 6 cm

8. A soccer league signed up 440 players. The ratio of returning players to new players was 4:7. How many players were new? 280

Applications

8-8 Wind and Water Current Problems

Objective To use systems of equations to solve wind and water current problems.

Suppose that you can paddle a canoe at the rate, or speed, of 3 mph in still water. If you paddle downstream on a river with a current of 1 mph, your speed is increased to 3 + 1, or 4 mph. If you paddle upstream against the current, your speed is reduced to 3 − 1, or 2 mph. Since the current increases your speed downstream by as much as it decreases your speed upstream, you might think that the current has no effect on the total time for the round trip. However, the calculations below show that the current increases the total time.

Suppose that the trip is 12 miles downstream and 12 miles back upstream. The time for the trip downstream and the trip back upstream can be found in each case by using the relationship:

$$\text{Time} = \text{Distance} \div \text{Rate}$$

	No current			1 mph current		
	Rate ×	Time =	Distance	Rate ×	Time	= Distance
Downstream	3	4	12	3 + 1 = 4	12 ÷ 4 = 3	12
Upstream	3	4	12	3 − 1 = 2	12 ÷ 2 = 6	12

Total Time = 4 + 4 = 8 h

$$\text{Average Speed} = \frac{\text{Total distance}}{\text{Total time}} = \frac{24}{8} = 3 \text{ mph}$$

Total Time = 3 + 6 = 9 h

$$\text{Average Speed} = \frac{24}{9} = 2\frac{2}{3} \text{ mph}$$

The principles illustrated above apply with wind currents as well as water currents. Thus, if

r = the rate of a plane when there is no wind

and

w = the rate of wind,

then

$r + w$ = the rate of the plane flying with the wind

and

$r - w$ = the rate of the plane flying against the wind.

The basic formula for wind and water current problems is:

$$\text{Distance} = \text{Rate} \times \text{Time}$$

Teaching Suggestions
p. T112

Suggested Extensions
p. T112

Chalkboard Examples

1. A jet can travel at 950 km/h with the wind and 700 km/h against the wind. Find the rate of the plane in still air and the wind speed.

   Let r = rate of plane in still air in km/h
   w = wind speed in km/h

   $$\begin{aligned} r + w &= 950 \\ r - w &= 700 \\ \hline 2r &= 1650 \\ r &= 825 \\ 825 + w &= 950 \\ w &= 125 \end{aligned}$$

   The rate of the plane in still air is 825 km/h and the wind speed is 125 km/h.

2. Sam and Janet have rented a canoe. How far upstream can they paddle if their rate in still water is 5 km/h, the rate of the current is 3 km/h, and they must return to their starting point in 3 h?

   Let d = distance in kilometers they can travel upstream
   Their rate upstream is $5 - 3 = 2$ km/h.
   Their rate downstream is $5 + 3 = 8$ km/h.

   $$\begin{aligned} \frac{d}{8} + \frac{d}{2} &= 3 \\ d + 4d &= 24 \\ 5d &= 24 \\ d &= 4.8 \end{aligned}$$

   They can paddle 4.8 km upstream.

Chalkboard Examples

3. A boat can travel 45 km upstream in 3.6 h. The return trip takes 2 h. Find the rate of the boat in still water and the speed of the current.
Let r = rate of boat in still water in km/h
c = speed of current in km/h

$$\begin{aligned}(r-c)3.6 &= 45\\ r-c &= 12.5\\ (r+c)2 &= 45\\ r+c &= 22.5\\ r-c &= 12.5\\ \hline 2r &= 35\\ r &= 17.5\\ 17.5-c &= 12.5\\ c &= 5\end{aligned}$$

The rate of the boat in still water is 17.5 km/h and the rate of the current is 5 km/h.

4. A plane flies 3750 km in 3 h. On the return trip, the plane is flying against the wind and the trip takes 5 h. Find the rate of the plane in still air and the speed of the wind.
Let r = rate of plane in still air in km/h
w = speed of wind in km/h

$$\begin{aligned}(r+w)3 &= 3750\\ r+w &= 1250\\ (r-w)5 &= 3750\\ r-w &= 750\\ r+w &= 1250\\ \hline 2r &= 2000\\ r &= 1000\\ 1000+w &= 1250\\ w &= 250\end{aligned}$$

The rate of the plane in still air is 1000 km/h and the speed of the wind is 250 km/h.

Example A jet can travel the 6000 km distance between Washington, D.C. and London in 6 h with the wind. The return trip against the same wind takes 7.5 h. Find the rate of the jet in still air and the rate of the wind.

Solution

Step 1 The problem asks for the rate of the jet in still air and the rate of the wind.

Step 2 Let r = the rate of jet in km/h and let w = the rate of wind in km/h.

	Rate	× Time	= Distance
With the wind	$r + w$	6	6000
Against the wind	$r - w$	7.5	6000

Step 3 Use the information in the chart to write two equations:

$$6(r + w) = 6000, \quad \text{or} \quad r + w = 1000$$
$$7.5(r - w) = 6000, \quad \text{or} \quad r - w = 800$$

Step 4

$$\begin{aligned}r + w &= 1000\\ r - w &= 800\\ \hline 2r &= 1800\\ r &= 900\\ 900 + w &= 1000\\ w &= 100\end{aligned}$$

Step 5 The check is left to you.
∴ the rate of the jet is 900 km/h and the rate of the wind is 100 km/h. ***Answer***

Oral Exercises

Complete the table. All rates are in km/h.

	Rate of plane in still air	Rate of wind	Rate of plane with wind	Rate of plane against wind
1.	700	50	? 750	? 650
2.	825	100	? 925	? 725
3.	900	w	? $900 + w$	? $900 - w$
4.	p	w	? $p + w$	? $p - w$

The following rates are given in km/h.

r = rate of a rowboat in still water
s = rate of a swimmer in still water
c = rate of the current

What rate does each expression represent?

5. $r + c$ Rowboat with current
6. $r - c$ Rowboat against current
7. $s + c$ Swimmer with current
8. $s - c$ Swimmer against current

Using the variables *r*, *s*, and *c* above, write an equation that expresses the given fact.

9. The rate of the rowboat going downstream is 12 km/h. $r + c = 12$

10. The rate of the rowboat going upstream is 8 km/h. $r - c = 8$

11. The rate of the swimmer going downstream is 3 km/h. $s + c = 3$

12. The rate of the swimmer going upstream is 1 km/h. $s - c = 1$

13. Use the information in Exercises 11 and 12 to find the rate of the swimmer in still water and the rate of the current. Swimmer, 2 km/h; current, 1 km/h

14. Use the information in Exercises 9 and 10 to find the rate of the rowboat in still water and the rate of the current.
Rowboat in still water, 10 km/h; current, 2 km/h

Problems

Solve.

A **1.** Suppose a motorboat travels at 10 km/h in still water. The boat makes a trip 30 km downstream and back.
Complete each table.

No current

	Rate	× Time	= Distance
Downstream	? 10	? 3	30
Upstream	? 10	? 3	30

Total time = ? 6 h
Average speed = ? 10 km/h

5 km/h current

Rate	× Time	= Distance
? 15	? 2	30
? 5	? 6	30

Total time = ? 8 h
Average speed = ? 7.5 km/h

2. Suppose you can paddle a canoe in still water at 5 km/h and that you are going to travel 6 km up a river and 6 km back. If the river current is 1 km/h, find your total time and your average speed for the round trip. Total time, 2.5 h; average speed, 4.8 km/h

3. Sam can paddle in still water at 6 mph. The Saco River is flowing at 2 mph. How far downstream can Sam travel if he must return in two hours? $5.\overline{3}$ km downstream

Supplementary Material

Resource Book, pp. 105, 176–178

Suggested Assignments

Minimum
Day 1: 373/*P*: 1–5
R 369/*Self-Test 2*
Day 2: 373/*P*: 6–10
S 364/20, 21, 23, 24

Average
Day 1: 373/*P*: 1–11 odd
R 369/*Self-Test 2*
Day 2: 374/*P*: 8, 10, 12–14
378/*P*: 2–10 even
Day 2 finishes Sec. 8-8 and starts Sec. 8-9.

Maximum
Day 1: 373/*P*: 1–13 odd
R 369/*Self-Test 2*
Day 2: 374/*P*: 10, 12, 14, 15
378/*P*: 2–16 even
Day 2 finishes Sec. 8-8 and starts Sec. 8-9.

Additional A Exercises

Solve.

1. Suppose you can row a boat 6 km/h in still water and that you are going to travel 8 km up a river and then return. If the river current is 2 km/h, find your total time and average speed. 3 h, $5\frac{1}{3}$ km/h

2. The Farrells can row 10 km/h in still water. They are on a river whose current is 4 km/h. How far upstream can they travel if they want to be back at their starting point in one hour? 4.2 km

(*continued*)

Additional A Exercises *(continued)*

3. Jim can swim downstream at 4 m/s and upstream at 2 m/s. How fast can he swim in still water? 3 m/s

4. An airplane flies 3000 mi in 4 h, but takes 5 h to make the return trip. What is the plane's speed in still air? 675 mi/h
What is the wind speed? 75 mi/h

5. A small aircraft flies 400 km from Ardmore to Mackin and then returns. The plane travels 275 km/h in still air, and the wind speed is 25 km/h. Find the total time the trip took and the aircraft's average speed.
2 h 56 min, $272\frac{8}{11}$ km/h

Additional Answer Problems

15.	Rate ×	Time =	Dist.
With wind	$p + w$	$\frac{D}{p + w}$	D
Against wind	$p - w$	$\frac{D}{p - w}$	D

Total distance $= 2D$;

total time $= \frac{D}{p + w} + \frac{D}{p - w}$

$$\frac{2D}{\frac{D}{p + w} + \frac{D}{p - w}} = \frac{2D(p^2 - w^2)}{D(p - w) + D(p + w)} = \frac{2D(p^2 - w^2)}{Dp - wD + Dp + wD} = \frac{2D(p^2 - w^2)}{2Dp} = \frac{p^2 - w^2}{p}$$

4. A powerboat has a four-hour supply of gasoline. How far can this boat travel from the marina if the rate out against the current is 40 km/h and the rate back in with the current is 60 km/h? 96 km

5. A boat travels with the current at 22 km/h and travels against the current at 12 km/h. What is the rate of the boat in still water? What is the rate of the current? 17 km/h; 5 km/h

6. Hal can swim upstream at 1 m/s and downstream at 2.5 m/s. How fast can he swim in still water? How fast is the current? 1.75 m/s; 0.75 m/s

7. An airplane takes 3 h to fly 1200 km against the wind. The return trip takes 2 h. What would the speed of the plane be if there were no wind? What is the wind speed? 500 km/h; 100 km/h

8. A boat can go 20 km downstream in 2 h. The return trip takes 5 h. What would the speed of the boat be if there were no current? What is the speed of the current? 7 km/h; 3 km/h

9. The 4200 km trip from New York to San Francisco takes 6 h flying against the wind but only 5 h returning. Find the speed of the plane in still air and the wind speed. 770 km/h; 70 km/h

10. The 1080 km trip from Madrid to Paris takes 2 h flying against the wind and 1.5 h flying with the wind. Find the speed of the plane in still air and the wind speed. 630 km/h; 90 km/h

B **11.** A motorboat goes 36 km downstream in the same amount of time that it takes to go 24 km upstream. If the current is flowing at 3 km/h, what is the rate of the boat in still water? 15 km/h

12. The rate of the current in the Susquehanna River is 4 km/h. If a canoeist can paddle 5 km downstream in the same amount of time that she can paddle 1 km upstream, how fast can she paddle in still water? 6 km/h

13. The steamboat River Queen travels at the rate of 30 km/h in still water. If it can travel 45 km upstream in the same amount of time that it takes to go 63 km downstream, what is the rate of the current? 5 km/h

14. An airplane whose speed in still air is 760 km/h can travel 2000 km with the wind in the same amount of time that it takes to fly 1800 km against the wind. What is the wind speed? 40 km/h

C **15.** A plane has a speed of p km/h in still air. It makes a round trip flying with and against a wind of w km/h. Show that its average speed is $\frac{p^2 - w^2}{p}$ km/h.

8-9 Digit, Age, and Fraction Problems

Objective To use systems of equations to solve digit, age, and fraction problems.

Digit problems are based on our decimal system of numeration. Note the value of the number with digits h, t, and u shown below.

	Hundreds digit	Tens digit	Units digit	Value
$537 =$	5	3	7	$5 \cdot 100 + 3 \cdot 10 + 7 \cdot 1$
$604 =$	6	0	4	$6 \cdot 100 + 0 \cdot 10 + 4 \cdot 1$
$htu =$	h	t	u	$h \cdot 100 + t \cdot 10 + u \cdot 1$

Example 1 (Digit Problem)

The sum of the digits in a two-digit number is 15. The new number obtained when the digits are reversed is 27 more than the original number. Find the original number.

Solution

Step 1 The problem asks for the original number.

Step 2 Let $t =$ the tens digit of the original number.
Let $u =$ the units digit of the original number.

	Tens	Units	Value
Original number	t	u	$10t + u$
Number with digits reversed	u	t	$10u + t$

Step 3 Use the facts of the problem to write two equations.
Sum of digits of original number is 15: $t + u = 15$

Difference of the numbers is 27:

$$\begin{aligned}(10u + t) - (10t + u) &= 27\\ 10u + t - 10t - u &= 27\\ 9u - 9t &= 27\\ 9(u - t) &= 27\\ u - t &= 3\end{aligned}$$

Step 4

$$\begin{aligned}u + t &= 15\\ u - t &= 3\\ \hline 2u &= 18\\ u &= 9\end{aligned}$$

Substitute $u = 9$ in the second equation.

$$\begin{aligned}9 - t &= 3\\ t &= 6\end{aligned}$$

Step 5 The check is left to you.
∴ the solution is 69. ***Answer***

Teaching Suggestions
p. T112

Chalkboard Examples

Solve using a system of two equations in two variables.

1. The sum of the digits of a two-digit number is 15. If the digits are reversed, the number is increased by 9. Find the original number.

Let $t =$ tens digit of original number
$u =$ units digit of original number

$$\begin{aligned}t + u &= 15\\ 10t + u + 9 &= 10u + t\\ 9t - 9u &= -9\\ t - u &= -1\\ t + u &= 15\\ \hline 2t &= 14\\ t &= 7\\ 7 + u &= 15\\ u &= 8\end{aligned}$$

The number is 78.

2. Nine years ago, Frank was half as old as Marilyn. Now his age is two thirds her age. Find their ages now.

Let $f =$ Frank's age now
$m =$ Marilyn's age now

$$\begin{aligned}f &= \frac{2}{3}m\\ f - 9 &= \frac{1}{2}(m - 9)\\ \frac{2}{3}m - 9 &= \frac{1}{2}m - \frac{9}{2}\\ 4m - 54 &= 3m - 27\\ m &= 27\\ f &= \frac{2}{3} \cdot 27 = 18\end{aligned}$$

Frank is 18 and Marilyn is 27.

(*continued*)

Chalkboard Examples (*continued*)

3. The numerator of a fraction is 3 less than the denominator. If 1 is added to the numerator and the denominator, the resulting fraction is equivalent to $\frac{4}{5}$. Find the original fraction.

Let n = numerator of original fraction
d = denominator of original fraction

$$n = d - 3$$
$$\frac{n+1}{d+1} = \frac{4}{5}$$
$$5n + 5 = 4d + 4$$
$$5n - 4d = -1$$
$$5(d - 3) - 4d = -1$$
$$5d - 15 - 4d = -1$$
$$d = 14$$
$$n = 14 - 3$$
$$= 11$$

The original fraction is $\frac{11}{14}$.

4. In two years, Alice will be 3 times Bob's age now. Ten years ago she was 6 times his age then. Find their ages now.

Let a = Alice's age now
b = Bob's age now

$$a + 2 = 3b$$
$$a = 3b - 2$$
$$a - 10 = 6(b - 10)$$
$$a - 10 = 6b - 60$$
$$3b - 2 - 10 = 6b - 60$$
$$3b = 48$$
$$b = 16$$
$$a = 3 \cdot 16 - 2$$
$$a = 46$$

Alice is 46 and Bob is 16.

The technique of organizing the given facts of a problem in a chart is also useful when solving age problems involving two variables.

Example 2 (Age problem)

Five years ago, Janet was only $\frac{1}{5}$ of the age of her mother. Now she is $\frac{1}{3}$ of her mother's age. Find their ages now.

Solution

Step 1 The problem asks for Janet's age and her mother's age now.

Step 2 Let j = Janet's age now and let m = her mother's age now. Make a chart.

Age	Now	5 years ago
Janet	j	$j - 5$
Mother	m	$m - 5$

Step 3 Use the facts of the problem to write two equations.

Five years ago: $j - 5 = \frac{1}{5}(m - 5)$
Now: $j = \frac{1}{3}m$

Step 4 Simplify the equations.

$j - 5 = \frac{1}{5}(m - 5) \longrightarrow 5j - 25 = m - 5$
$j = \frac{1}{3}m \longrightarrow 3j = m$

Substitute $3j$ for m and solve.

$$5j - 25 = 3j - 5$$
$$2j - 25 = -5$$
$$2j = 20$$
$$j = 10$$
$$m = 3j = 30$$

Step 5 The check is left to you.

$\therefore$ Janet is 10 years old and her mother is 30. ***Answer***

Example 3 (Fraction problem)

The denominator of a fraction is 4 more than the numerator. If 2 is subtracted from each, the value of the resulting fraction is $\frac{1}{5}$. Find the original fraction.

Solution

Step 1 The problem asks for the original fraction.

Step 2 Let n = numerator of the original fraction and d = denominator of the original fraction. Then $\frac{n}{d}$ = the original fraction.

Step 3 Use the facts of the problem to write two equations.

$d = n + 4$

$\frac{n-2}{d-2} = \frac{1}{5}$, or $5(n-2) = d - 2$

Step 4 Simplify the equations and solve.

$$\begin{aligned} d = n + 4 &\longrightarrow -n + d = 4 \\ 5(n-2) = d - 2 &\longrightarrow 5n - d = 8 \\ &\quad 4n = 12 \\ &\quad n = 3 \end{aligned}$$

Substitute $n = 3$. $\quad -3 + d = 4$

$d = 7$

Step 5 The check is left to you.

$\therefore$ the original fraction is $\frac{3}{7}$. ***Answer***

5. If 4 is subtracted from the numerator and the denominator of a fraction, the value of the resulting fraction is $\frac{3}{8}$. However, if 8 is added to the numerator and the denominator of the original fraction, the value of the resulting fraction is $\frac{3}{4}$. Find the original fraction.

Let n = numerator of original fraction

d = denominator of original fraction

$$\frac{n-4}{d-4} = \frac{3}{8}$$

$$8n - 32 = 3d - 12$$

$$8n - 3d = 20$$

$$\frac{n+8}{d+8} = \frac{3}{4}$$

$$4n + 32 = 3d + 24$$

$$\begin{aligned} 4n - 3d &= -8 \\ 8n - 3d &= 20 \\ \hline -4n \quad &= -28 \\ n &= 7 \end{aligned}$$

$$\frac{3}{d-4} = \frac{3}{8}$$

$$3d - 12 = 24$$

$$3d = 36$$

$$d = 12$$

The fraction is $\frac{7}{12}$.

Supplementary Materials

Practice Master 50

Test 28

Resource Book, pp. 106, 179–180

Oral Exercises

A two-digit number has tens digit *t* and units digit *u*. Express the following in terms of *t* and *u*.

1. The value of the two-digit number. $10t + u$
2. The value of the two-digit number obtained by reversing the digits. $10u + t$
3. The tens digit exceeds the units digit by 5. $t = u + 5$
4. The units digit exceeds the tens digit by 8. $u = t + 8$
5. The tens digit is one half the units digit. $t = \frac{1}{2}u$

A three-digit number has hundreds digit *h*, tens digit *t*, and units digit *u*. Express the following as equations.

6. The sum of the digits is 12. $h + t + u = 12$
7. The tens digit is twice the sum of the other two digits. $t = 2(h + u)$
8. The units digit is the difference of the tens digit minus the hundreds digit. $u = t - h$
9. The number obtained by reversing the order of the digits exceeds the original number by 99. $100u + 10t + h = 100h + 10t + u + 99$

Let *b* = Bob's age now and *c* = Claire's age now. Express the following in terms of *b* and *c*.

10. Bob's age in 6 years. $b + 6$
11. Claire's age in 6 years. $c + 6$
12. Bob's age 2 years ago. $b - 2$
13. Claire's age 2 years ago. $c - 2$
14. The sum of their ages in 6 years. $b + c + 12$
15. The sum of their ages 2 years ago. $b + c - 4$

Suggested Assignments

Minimum

Day 1: 378/*P*: 1–4, 7–9
S 365/13–16

Day 2: 378/*P*: 5, 6, 9, 13, 14
R 382/*Self-Test 3*

Average

379/*P*: 16–21
R 382/*Self-Test 3*

Day 2 of Sec. 8-8 finishes Sec. 8-8 and starts Sec. 8-9.

Maximum

379/*P*: 19–24, 28
R 382/*Self-Test 3*

Day 2 of Sec. 8-8 finishes Sec. 8-8 and starts Sec. 8-9.

Additional A Exercises

Solve each of the following problems about two-digit numbers.

1. The sum of the digits of a two-digit number is 10. If the digits are reversed, the number is increased by 72. What is the original number? 19
2. A number is ten times the sum of its digits. The tens digit is two greater than the units digit. Find the number. 20

Solve by using a system of two equations in two variables.

3. Carole is twice Lorraine's age. In six years, the sum of their ages will be 30. How old are they now? Carole, 12; Lorraine, 6
4. Seven years ago, my father's age was five times mine. Right now, his age is the sum of our two ages 7 years ago. How old am I? 14

A fraction is represented by $\frac{n}{d}$. Express in terms of n and d the new fractions obtained by following the given directions.

16. Increase both the numerator and the denominator by 4. $\frac{n+4}{d+4}$

17. Decrease both the numerator and the denominator by 7. $\frac{n-7}{d-7}$

18. Interchange the numerator and the denominator. $\frac{d}{n}$

19. Increase the numerator by 5 and decrease the denominator by 3. $\frac{n+5}{d-3}$

Problems

Solve each of the following problems about two-digit numbers.

A **1.** The sum of the digits of a two-digit number is 11. If the digits are reversed, the number is increased by 45. What is the original number? 38

2. A two-digit number is four times the sum of its digits. If its digits are reversed, the new number is 36 more than the original number. What is the original number? 48

3. If 18 is added to a two-digit number, the digits are reversed. The sum of the digits is 16. Find the original number. 79

4. The sum of the digits of a two-digit number is 6. If the digits are reversed, the number is decreased by 36. What is the original number? 51

5. A number is 8 times the sum of its digits. The tens digit is 5 greater than the units digit. Find the number. 72

6. The sum of the digits is 13. If the number represented by reversing the digits is subtracted from the original number, the result is 27. Find the original number. 85

Solve by using a system of two equations in two variables.

7. Alicia is 7 years older than Bruce. Next year she will be twice as old as he will be. How old is she now? 13 years old

8. In 1943 the Brooklyn Bridge was 10 times as old as the Golden Gate Bridge. That same year, the difference in their ages was 54 years. Find the year of completion for each bridge. Brooklyn Bridge, 1883; Golden Gate, 1937

9. Karen's mother is twice as old as Karen is. Eleven years ago she was 3 times as old as Karen was. Find Karen's present age. 22 years old

10. Two years ago, Al's age was 1 year less than twice Ed's. Four years from now, Al's age will be 8 years more than half Ed's. How old is Al? 9 years old

11. In 1984, the Eiffel Tower was $\frac{19}{20}$ as old as the Washington Monument. If the Washington Monument was built 5 years earlier than the Eiffel Tower, find the age of each in 1984. Washington Monument, 100; Eiffel Tower, 95

12. Anita is $\frac{3}{4}$ as old as Judy. Four years ago Anita was $\frac{2}{3}$ as old as Judy. How old is each? Anita, 12; Judy, 16

13. The denominator of a fraction is 8 more than the numerator. If 3 is added to both the numerator and the denominator, the value of the resulting fraction is $\frac{1}{2}$. What is the original fraction? $\frac{5}{13}$

14. The denominator of a fraction is 9 more than the numerator. If the numerator is decreased by 3 and the denominator is increased by 3, the value of the resulting fraction is $\frac{1}{4}$. What is the original fraction? $\frac{8}{17}$

15. If 1 is subtracted from the numerator of a fraction, the value of the resulting fraction is $\frac{1}{2}$. However, if 7 is added to the denominator of the original fraction the value of the resulting fraction is $\frac{1}{3}$. Find the original fraction. $\frac{5}{8}$

16. If the numerator of a fraction is increased by 4, the value of the resulting fraction is $\frac{3}{4}$. If the denominator of the original fraction is increased by 2, the value of the resulting fraction is $\frac{1}{2}$. Find the original fraction. $\frac{11}{20}$

17. A fraction has value $\frac{2}{3}$. When 15 is added to its numerator, the resulting fraction equals the reciprocal of the value of the original fraction. Find the original fraction. $\frac{12}{18}$

18. A fraction's value is $\frac{4}{5}$. When its numerator is increased by 9, the new fraction equals the reciprocal of the value of the original fraction. Find the original fraction. $\frac{16}{20}$

Solve each of the following problems about three-digit numbers.

B 19. A number between 300 and 400 is forty times the sum of its digits. The tens digit is 6 more than the units digit. Find the number. 360

20. The sum of the three digits is 12. The tens digit exceeds the hundreds digit by the same amount that the units digit exceeds the tens digit. If the digits are reversed, the new number exceeds the original number by 198. Find the original number. 345

21. The sum of the three digits is 9, and the tens digit is 1 more than the hundreds digit. When the digits are reversed, the new number is 99 less than the original number. Find the original number. 342

Solve by using a system of two equations in two variables.

22. A father, being asked his age and that of his son, said, "If you add 4 to my age and divide the sum by 4, you will have my son's age. But 6 years ago I was $7\frac{1}{2}$ times as old as my son." Find their ages. son, 10; father, 36

5. If 3 is subtracted from the numerator of a fraction, the value of the resulting fraction is $\frac{1}{2}$. If 6 is added to the denominator of the original fraction, the value of the new fraction is also $\frac{1}{2}$. What is the original fraction? $\frac{7}{8}$

6. A fraction has value $\frac{3}{4}$. When 14 is added to the numerator, the resulting fraction has a value equal to the reciprocal of the original fraction. Find the original fraction. $\frac{18}{24}$

Mixed Review Exercises

1. Simplify $-(3m^2)^2$. $-9m^4$
2. Multiply: $(b - 3)(b^2 + 7b - 6)$ $b^3 + 4b^2 - 27b + 18$
3. Give the prime factorization of 96. $2^5 \cdot 3$
4. Solve by using the addition-or-subtraction method: $12x + 4y = 0$ $(-1, 3)$ $3x + 4y = 9$

Solve by using a system of two equations in two variables.

23. James said, "If I were $\frac{1}{2}$ as old as I am, and Noriko were $\frac{3}{4}$ as old as she is, the sum of our ages would be 3 years more than my age alone. But if I were $\frac{2}{3}$ as old as I am, and Noriko were $\frac{1}{4}$ as old as she is, together our ages would be 2 years younger than I am alone." How old is James? 18

24. Laura is 3 times as old as Maria was when Laura was as old as Maria is now. In 2 years, Laura will be twice as old as Maria was 2 years ago. Find their present ages. Maria, 12; Laura, 18

25. The two digits in the numerator of a fraction whose value is $\frac{2}{9}$ are reversed in its denominator. The reciprocal of the fraction is the value obtained when 27 is added to the original numerator and 71 is subtracted from the original denominator. Find the original fraction. $\frac{18}{81}$

26. The numerator equals the sum of the two digits in the denominator. The value of the fraction is $\frac{1}{4}$. When both numerator and denominator are increased by 3, the resulting fraction has the value $\frac{1}{3}$. Find the original fraction. $\frac{6}{24}$

27. The two digits in the numerator of a fraction are reversed in its denominator. If 1 is subtracted from both the numerator and the denominator, the value of the resulting fraction is $\frac{1}{2}$. The fraction whose numerator is the difference and whose denominator is the sum of the units and tens digits equals $\frac{2}{5}$. Find the original fraction. $\frac{37}{73}$

C **28.** Find a two-decimal-place number between 0 and 1 such that the sum of its digits is 9 and such that if the digits are reversed the number is increased by 0.27. 0.36

29. The numerator of a fraction is a two-digit number and the denominator is that number with the digits reversed. The value of the fraction is $\frac{7}{4}$. Find the fraction. (*Hint:* There are four possible answers.) $\frac{21}{12}$, $\frac{42}{24}$, $\frac{63}{36}$, or $\frac{84}{48}$

30. Cindy's age equals the sum of Paul's age and Sue's age. Two years ago, Cindy was 4 times as old as Sue was, and two years from now, Cindy will be 1.4 times as old as Paul will be. How old is each now? (*Hint:* Use a system of three equations in three variables.) Cindy, 26; Sue, 8; Paul, 18

31. A man is three times as old as his son was at the time when the father was twice as old as his son will be two years from now. Find the present age of each person if the sum of their ages is 55 years. father, 39; son, 16

Challenge

Solve if a, b, and c are positive integers:

$$4a - 11b + 12c = 22$$
$$a + 5b - 4c = 17$$

(7, 6, 5)

Biographical Note / *Emily Warren Roebling*

Emily Warren Roebling (1843–1903), who helped supervise the completion of the Brooklyn Bridge, was born in Cold Spring, New York. She was married to Washington Roebling, an engineer whose father, John Roebling, was commissioned to build the Brooklyn Bridge. In order to prepare for the construction, Emily and Washington Roebling went to Europe, where Washington studied the experimental method of using pneumatic caissons, or watertight chambers of compressed air, to sink underwater foundations. Within months of their return to the United States, John Roebling was injured at the bridge site and died three weeks later. Washington Roebling, who had assisted his father on several previous bridge-building projects, became chief engineer, but was incapacitated by caisson disease (the bends) ten years before the bridge was completed.

In order to continue the project, Emily Roebling studied calculus, the details of cable construction, and the procedures involved in bridge building. She learned how to read bridge specifications, how to determine the stress various materials could tolerate, and how to calculate catenary curves. As surrogate chief engineer, she negotiated with the representatives of various construction supply firms, made daily visits to the bridge to inspect the work, and delivered explicit instructions to the assistant engineers. She kept her husband informed of the progress made each day.

Nine months before the completion of the bridge the board of trustees tried to displace Washington Roebling as chief engineer. As a result of a presentation Emily Roebling made before the American Society of Civil Engineers, Roebling secured the backing of the engineering profession and retained his position. Throughout 1882 and 1883 articles that she wrote regarding the project appeared in Brooklyn newspapers.

As was stated at the opening-day ceremonies on May 24, 1883, the bridge is a tribute to Emily Roebling's intense and sustained involvement. A plaque in her honor was placed on the bridge in 1950 by The Brooklyn Engineers Club.

After the completion of the bridge, Emily Roebling involved herself in a number of social, political, and philanthropic works. She was involved with the management of the 1893 World's Fair and traveled extensively in Europe. Emily Roebling later planned and was the general contractor for the Roeblings' home in Trenton, New Jersey. Eventually she studied law at New York University, graduating in 1899 with an award-winning essay.

Quick Quiz

Solve using a system of two equations in two variables.

1. A canoeist takes $1\frac{1}{2}$ h to paddle 6 km against the current. The return trip takes only $\frac{3}{4}$ h. Find the rate of the canoe in still water and the rate of the current. rate in still water = 6 km/h; rate of current = 2 km/h
2. Two years ago, Amy's grandmother was 14 times as old as Amy. In six years, her grandmother will be 6 times as old as Amy. Find their ages now. 7 and 72
3. The denominator of a fraction is 20 greater than the numerator. If 6 is subtracted from the numerator and the denominator, the value of the resulting fraction is $\frac{5}{9}$. Find the original fraction. $\frac{31}{51}$
4. The sum of the digits of a two-digit number is 13. If the digits are reversed, the number is increased by 45. Find the original number. 49

Self-Test 3

Solve by using a system of two equations in two variables.

1. A boat travels upstream at 16 km/h. The same boat travels downstream at 30 km/h. What is the rate of the boat in still water? What is the rate of the current? 23 km/h; 7 km/h **Obj. 8-8, p. 371**
2. The sum of the digits in a two-digit number is 15. If the digits are reversed, the number is decreased by 27. What is the number? 96 **Obj. 8-9, p. 375**
3. Six years ago Ella was twice as old as her brother Sanford. Six years from now Sanford will be as old as Ella is now. Find their current ages. Ella, 18; Sanford, 12
4. The numerator of a fraction is 3 less than the denominator. If 5 is added to each, the value of the resulting fraction is $\frac{3}{4}$. Find the original fraction. $\frac{4}{7}$

Check your answers with those at the back of the book.

Extra / *Proving Divisibility Tests*

You may have learned the following divisibility tests in an earlier course.

Divisibility by	Test
2	Number must end in 0, 2, 4, 6, or 8
3	Sum of digits must be divisible by 3
4	Last two digits must be divisible by 4 (81,736 is divisible by 4 because 36 is.)
5	Number must end in 0 or 5
6	Number must pass tests for both 2 and 3
8	Last 3 digits must be divisible by 8 (145,320 is divisible by 8 because 320 is.)
9	Sum of digits must be divisible by 9

These tests rely on our decimal system of numeration. They can be proved by writing expressions for the values of the numbers involved.

Example Prove the divisibility test for 9 for a three-digit number.

Solution A three-digit number with digits h, t, and u has a value of $100h + 10t + u = (99h + 9t) + (h + t + u)$. Since $99h + 9t$ is divisible by 9, the entire right-hand side of the equation is divisible by 9 if and only if the sum of the digits, $h + t + u$, is divisible by 9.

Exercises

1. Prove the test for divisibility by 3 for a three-digit number.
2. The number 87,154,316 can be written as $(871{,}543) \cdot 100 + 16$. Explain why you need look only at the last two digits to see if the original number is divisible by 4.
3. Prove the test for divisibility by 4 for a six-digit number.
4. Prove the test for divisibility by 8 for a six-digit number. (*Hint:* See Exercise 3.)
5. Prove that a six-digit number is divisible by 11 if and only if the sum of the first, third, and fifth digits minus the sum of the second, fourth, and sixth digits is divisible by 11.
6. Devise a test to check whether eleven-digit numbers are divisible by 11.

Chapter Summary

1. The solution set of a linear equation in two variables is the set of all ordered pairs of numbers that make the equation into a true statement.
2. Ordered pairs of real numbers can be graphed as points in a coordinate plane. The graph of a linear equation in two variables is a line.
3. The solutions of pairs of linear equations in two variables can be estimated by graphing, and computed by the substitution method or the addition-or-subtraction method. Multiplication may have to be used with the addition-or-subtraction method.
4. Systems of linear equations in two variables may be used to solve word problems involving wind, water current, age, fractions, and digits, as well as other types.

Chapter Review

Give the letter of the correct answer.

1. Which ordered pair is a solution of $2x - 3y = -5$? 8-1
a. $(1, 1)$ **b.** $(4, 1)$ **(c.)** $(-1, 1)$ **d.** $(-4, 1)$

2. Solve $2x - 3y = 9$ for y in terms of x.
a. $y = \frac{2}{3}x - 9$ **(b.)** $y = \frac{2}{3}x - 3$
c. $x = \frac{3}{2}y + \frac{9}{2}$ **d.** $x = \frac{2}{3}y + \frac{2}{9}$

Additional Answers
Extra

1. A three-digit number with digits h, t, and u has value $100h + 10t + u = 99h + 9t + (h + t + u)$. Since $99h + 9t$ is divisible by 3, the whole expression is divisible by 3 if and only if the sum of the digits is divisible by 3.
2. $871{,}453 \cdot 100$ is divisible by 4 because 100 is divisible by 4. Thus, the number is divisible by 4 because 16 is divisible by 4.
3. Let a, b, c, h, t, u be the digits of a 6-digit number whose value is $a \cdot 10^5 + b \cdot 10^4 + c \cdot 10^3 + h \cdot 10^2 + t \cdot 10 + u = 100(a \cdot 10^3 + b \cdot 10^2 + c \cdot 10 + h) + 10t + u$. Since 4 divides 100, 4 divides the number if and only if 4 divides $10t + u$.
4. Let a, b, c, h, t, u be the digits of a 6-digit number whose value is $a \cdot 10^5 + b \cdot 10^4 + c \cdot 10^3 + h \cdot 10^2 + t \cdot 10 + u = 1000(a \cdot 10^2 + b \cdot 10 + c) + 100h + 10t + u$. Since 8 divides 1000, 8 divides the number if and only if 8 divides $(100h + 10t + u)$.

(*continued*)

Additional Answers Extra
(continued)

5. Let the 6-digit number be represented by $a \cdot 10^5 + b \cdot 10^4 + c \cdot 10^3 + h \cdot 10^2 + t \cdot 10 + u$. This can be rewritten as $11 \cdot 10^4 \cdot a + 11(b - a)10^3 + 11(c - b + a)10^2 + 11(h - c + b - a)10 + 11(t - h + c - b + a) + (u - t + h - c + b - a)$. The first 5 terms are divisible by 11. Thus, the number is divisible by 11 if and only if $u - t + h - c + b - a$ is divisible by 11.
6. The number is divisible by 11 if and only if the sum of the odd-place digits minus the sum of the even-place digits is divisible by 11.

3. In which quadrant is the graph of $(-3, 5)$? 8-2

a. I (**b.**) II **c.** III **d.** IV

4. Where is the graph of $(-3, 0)$ in the coordinate plane?

a. in Quadrant II **b.** in Quadrant III
(**c.**) on the x-axis **d.** on the y-axis

5. The solution of the system $\begin{aligned} x + 2y &= 11 \\ 5x - y &= 11 \end{aligned}$ is $(3, 4)$. 8-3

How are the graphs of the two equations related?

a. The graphs are parallel.
b. The graphs coincide.
(**c.**) The graphs intersect at $(3, 4)$.
d. The graphs intersect at $(3, 0)$ and $(0, 4)$.

6. Solve by the substitution method: 8-4

$$\begin{aligned} 2x + y &= 6 \\ 3x - 2y &= 2 \end{aligned}$$

(**a.**) $(2, 2)$ **b.** $(-2, -2)$ **c.** $(3, 0)$ **d.** $(0, -2)$

7. Solve by using two equations in two variables: One positive integer is 18 less than a second positive integer. If the sum of twice the greater and three times the smaller is 86, find each integer. 8-5

a. 18 and 68 **b.** 34 and 52 **c.** 18 and 104 (**d.**) 10 and 28

8. Solve by the addition-or-subtraction method: 8-6

$$\begin{aligned} p - 6q &= -3 \\ 3p + 6q &= 15 \end{aligned}$$

a. $(1, 3)$ (**b.**) $(3, 1)$ **c.** $(-3, -1)$ **d.** $(-1, -3)$

9. Solve by using multiplication with the addition-or-subtraction method: 8-7

$$\begin{aligned} 4a + 3b &= -24 \\ 5a - 2b &= -7 \end{aligned}$$

a. $(3, 4)$ **b.** $(4, 3)$ (**c.**) $(-3, -4)$ **d.** $(-4, -3)$

10. A small plane can fly 240 km in 3 h with the wind, but only 210 km in 3 h against the wind. Find the rate of the wind. 8-8

a. 75 km/h **b.** 80 km/h (**c.**) 5 km/h **d.** 10 km/h

11. The sum of the digits of a two-digit number is 8. If the digits are reversed, the number is increased by 54. Find the original number. 8-9

a. 71 (**b.**) 17 **c.** 26 **d.** 62

12. Hector will be twice as old as Will in 5 years. Five years ago Hector was three times as old as Will. How old is Will now?

a. 35 **b.** 20 (**c.**) 15 **d.** 5

13. The denominator of a fraction is 7 more than the numerator. If 5 is added to each, the value of the resulting fraction is $\frac{1}{2}$. Find the original fraction.

a. $\frac{7}{14}$ **b.** $\frac{9}{2}$ **c.** $\frac{5}{12}$ (**d.**) $\frac{2}{9}$

Chapter Test

State whether each ordered pair of numbers is a solution of the given equation.

1. $-3x + 2y = 12$
$(-2, 3), (4, 0)$ Yes; No

2. $7x - 5y = -3$
$(-1, -2), (-4, -5)$ No; Yes 8-1

Solve each equation for y in terms of x.

3. $2x + y = 12$ $y = 12 - 2x$

4. $2x - 3y = -5$ $y = \frac{2x + 5}{3}$

Draw a coordinate plane and plot the graph of each of the given points.

5. $(5, 3)$ **6.** $(0, -6)$ **7.** $(-3, -4)$ **8.** $(-2, 5)$ 8-2

Graph each equation.

9. $y = 2x - 1$ **10.** $2x + 6y = 12$

11. Solve by the graphic method: 8-3

$$2x + 5y = 9$$
$$3x - 2y = 4$$
(2, 1)

12. Solve by the substitution method: 8-4

$$8x + y = 3$$
$$5x + 2y = -27$$
(3, −21)

13. Solve, using two equations in two variables: This year, the total number of dogs and cats sold by the Animal Adoption Agency was 1216. Last year, 420 more cats and double the number of dogs were sold for a total of 2024. How many of each were sold this year? 388 dogs, 828 cats 8-5

14. Solve by the addition-or-subtraction method: 8-6

$$4x - 5y = 0$$
$$8x + 5y = -60$$
(−5, −4)

15. Solve by using multiplication with the addition-or-subtraction method: 8-7

$$-7x + y = -16$$
$$3x + 2y = 2$$
(2, −2)

Solve by using a system of two equations in two variables.

16. A small plane can fly 2400 km in 10 h flying into the wind. With the wind behind it, the plane can fly 3200 km in 10 h. What is the speed of the plane in still air and what is the speed of the wind? 280 km/h; 40 km/h 8-8

17. The numerator of a fraction is 3 less than the denominator. If 25 is added to each, the value of the resulting fraction is equal to $\frac{9}{10}$. Find the original fraction. $\frac{2}{5}$ 8-9

Alternate Test p. T17

Supplementary Materials

Practice Masters 51–52
Tests 29–30
Resource Book, pp. 40–43, 155

Extra Practice

Skills, pp. 621–622
Problems, pp. 643–644

Additional Answers
Chapter Test

5–8.

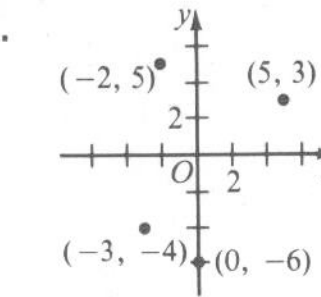

9.

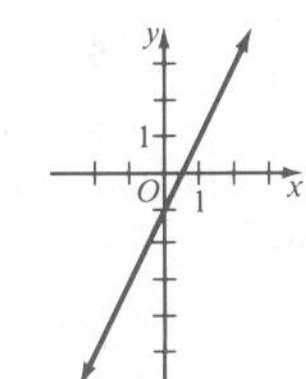

10.

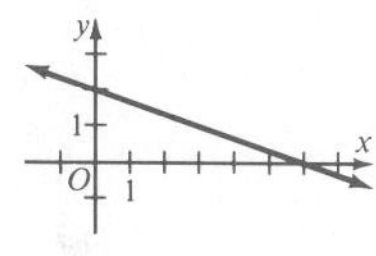

11.

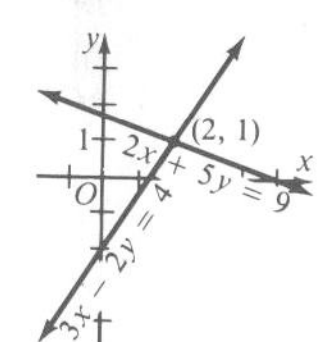

Additional Answers Cumulative Review

1. $7p^2q + 4p - 21q^3$
3. $-3j^4k^4 + 24j^4k^3 - 27j^3k^4$
4. $10c^3 + 14c^2 - 7c - 3$
6. $81z^4 - 36bz + 36z^3b - 16b^2$
8. $\frac{4b^3 - b^2 + 5b + 1}{(2b-1)(2b+1)}$
13. $(8z + 9y)^2$
14. $(8x^2 - 9y^2)(8x^2 + 9y^2)$
24. $\left\{\frac{5}{3}, -\frac{5}{2}\right\}$

28.

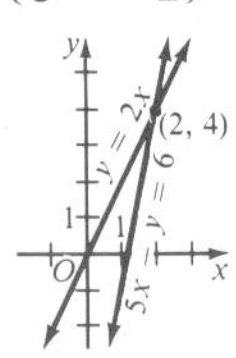

Cumulative Review (Chapters 1–8)

Perform the indicated operations. Express the answers in simplest form. Assume that no denominator is zero.

1. $(28p^4q^3 + 16p^3q^2 - 84p^2q^5) \div (2pq)^2$
2. $(-3xy^3z^2)^3(x^2yz)^5$ $-27x^{13}y^{14}z^{11}$
3. $-3j^3(jk^4 - 8jk^3 + 9k^4)$
4. $(5c - 3)(2c^2 + 4c + 1)$
5. $(21z - 3)(2z + 4)$ $42z^2 + 78z - 12$
6. $(9z^3 - 4b)(9z + 4b)$
7. $\frac{28t^2 + 27t + 5}{4t + 1}$ $7t + 5$
8. $\frac{3}{2b - 1} + \frac{b^2 + 2}{1 - 4b^2} + b$
9. $\frac{x^2 + x - 12}{x^2 - x - 6} \div \frac{5x^2 + 5x - 60}{x + 2}$ $\frac{1}{5(x-3)}$
10. $10y^2 + 27y - 15 \div (2y + 7)$ $10y^2 + 27y - \frac{15}{2y + 7}$
11. $(2.4 \times 10^5)(0.3 \times 10^7)$ 7.2×10^{11}
12. $\left(\frac{z^{-3}}{z^{-5}}\right)^4$ z^8

Factor completely. If the polynomial cannot be factored, write "prime."

13. $64z^2 + 144zy + 81y^2$
14. $64x^4 - 81y^4$
15. $40x^2 + 26x + 1$ prime
16. $28y^2 + 37y + 12$ $(7y + 4)(4y + 3)$
17. $6y^2 - 17y - 10$ $(2y + 1)(3y - 10)$
18. $16y^2 - 25x^2 + 10x - 1$ $(4y - 5x + 1)(4y + 5x - 1)$

Solve. Assume that no denominator is zero. If the equation is an identity or has no solution, state that fact.

19. $\frac{7}{8}t + 9 = 23$ 16
20. $16 - \frac{1}{2}|m| = 5$ $\{-22, 22\}$
21. $\frac{1}{5}(x - 6) = 34 - 3x$ 11
22. $169x^2 - 81 = 0$ $-\frac{9}{13}, \frac{9}{13}$
23. $25b^2 + 36 = 60b$ $\frac{6}{5}$
24. $-6z^2 - 5z + 25 = 0$
25. $15y^2 + 59y - 4 = 0$ $\left\{\frac{1}{15}, -4\right\}$
26. $\frac{2x + 1}{x - 3} + \frac{x + 3}{2x + 1} = \frac{2x}{3 - x}$ $\left\{\frac{2}{3}, \frac{-4}{3}\right\}$
27. $0.4(850 - z) + 0.65z = 300$ -160
28. Solve the system $\begin{array}{l} y = 2x \\ 5x - y = 6 \end{array}$ graphically. (2, 4)

Solve algebraically.

29. $\begin{array}{l} 4x + 3y = 12 \\ 3y - 8x = -12 \end{array}$ $\left(2, \frac{4}{3}\right)$
30. $\begin{array}{l} 3x = y + 1 \\ 4x + 3y = 10 \end{array}$ (1, 2)
31. $\begin{array}{l} 2x + 5y = 9 \\ 3x - 2y = 4 \end{array}$ (2, 1)
32. The sum of the digits of a two-digit number is 6. When the digits are reversed, the resulting number is 6 greater than 3 times the original number. Find the original number. 15
33. Flying with the wind, a jet was able to complete a 3360 km trip in 4 h. Flying against the wind, the jet made the return trip in 7 h. Find the speed of the jet in still air and the wind speed. 660 km/h; 180 km/h
34. How many kilograms of nuts worth \$5 per kilogram should be mixed with 6 kg of nuts worth \$9 per kilogram to produce a mix worth \$6.50 per kilogram? 10 kg
35. The square of the sum of two consecutive odd integers is 16 times the sum of the integers. Find the integers. 7 and 9 or −1 and 1

Maintaining Skills

Factor completely. If the polynomial cannot be factored, write "prime."

Example 1 $24x^2y - 60xy^4$ ***Solution*** $24x^2y - 60xy^4 = 12xy(2x - 5y^3)$

1. $25b^2c^3 + 15b^5c^4$ — $5b^2c^3(5 + 3b^3c)$
2. $12m^3 - 15mn^2 - 8n^2$ — prime
3. $9u^5v + 36u^4v^2 - 15u^4v^3$ — $3u^4v(3u + 12v - 5v^2)$
4. $-vt^3 + 40t^2v^3 - v^6$ — $v(-t^3 + 40t^2v^2 - v^5)$
5. $-24x^7y^5 + 32x^6y^3 - 8x^2y^4$ — $-8x^2y^3(3x^5y^2 - 4x^4 + y)$
6. $20m^6n^6 - 4m^6n^5 + 24m^5n^7$ — $4m^5n^5(5mn - m + 6n^2)$

Example 2 $81y^4 - 16$

Solution $81y^4 - 16 = (9y^2 + 4)(9y^2 - 4) = (9y^2 + 4)(3y + 2)(3y - 2)$

Example 3 $9y^2 + 30y + 25$

Solution $9y^2 + 30y + 25 = (3y)^2 + 2(3y \cdot 5) + 5^2 = (3y + 5)^2$

7. $z^3 - 121z$ — $z(z - 11)(z + 11)$
8. $27bc^2 - 12b$ — $3b(3c - 2)(3c + 2)$
9. $-x^6 + 49$ — $(7 - x^3)(7 + x^3)$
10. $9t^2 - 12t + 4$
11. $25m^4 + 9$ prime
12. $1 - 16z^8$
13. $16a^2 - 40a + 25$ — $(4a - 5)^2$
14. $4t^2 - 16t + 16$ — $4(t - 2)^2$
15. $25x^2 + 30x + 9$ — $(5x + 3)^2$

Example 4 $g^2 - 2g - 35$ ***Solution*** $g^2 - 2g - 35 = (g + 5)(g - 7)$

16. $z^2 + 8z - 16$ — prime
17. $b^2 + 11b + 18$ — $(b + 9)(b + 2)$
18. $y^2 - 9y + 18$ — $(y - 6)(y - 3)$
19. $-c^2 + 5cd + 14d^2$
20. $2d^2 + 18d - 72$
21. $x^2 + 10x + 21$
22. $4c^2 - 36c + 32$ — $4(c - 8)(c - 1)$
23. $n^2 - 5np + 6p^2$ — $(n - 2p)(n - 3p)$
24. $7f + f^2 - 30$ — $(f + 10)(f - 3)$

Example 5 $3cd + 21d - 2c - 14$

Solution $3cd + 21d - 2c - 14 = 3d(c + 7) - 2(c + 7) = (3d - 2)(c + 7)$

25. $rt - 2st + 3r - 6s$
26. $2xy - y^2 + 6x - 3y$
27. $s^2 - 4t^2 - 12t - 9$
28. $x^2 - 10x + 25 - y^2$ — $(x - 5 - y)(x - 5 + y)$
29. $16a^2 - 9b^2 + 30b - 25$ — $(4a - 3b + 5)(4a + 3b - 5)$
30. $s^2t - 5s^2 + 5t - 2$ — prime

Example 6 $10p^2 - 19p - 15$

Solution Test the possibilities for the first terms: $10p$ and p; $5p$ and $2p$.
Test the possibilities for the second terms: -15 and 1; 15 and -1; -5 and 3; 5 and -3.
$10p^2 - 19p - 15 = (5p + 3)(2p - 5)$

31. $3b^2 + 2b - 5$ — $(3b + 5)(b - 1)$
32. $10t^2 + 3t - 1$ — $(5t - 1)(2t + 1)$
33. $6m^2 - 8m - 8$ — $2(3m + 2)(m - 2)$
34. $6a^2 + 7a - 3$
35. $25z^3 + 15z^2 + 2z$
36. $14 + 15y - 9y^2$
37. $-7y^2 - 20y + 3$ — $(1 - 7y)(y + 3)$
38. $22n + 8n^2 - 6$ — $2(4n - 1)(n + 3)$
39. $12b^2 - 14b - 10$ — $2(2b + 1)(3b - 5)$

Additional Answers
Maintaining Skills

10. $(3t - 2)^2$
12. $(1 - 2z^2)(1 + 2z^2) \cdot (1 + 4z^4)$
19. $(7d - c)(2d + c)$
20. $2(d + 12)(d - 3)$
21. $(x + 7)(x + 3)$
25. $(t + 3)(r - 2s)$
26. $(y + 3)(2x - y)$
27. $(s - 2t - 3) \cdot (s + 2t + 3)$
34. $(3a - 1)(2a + 3)$
35. $z(5z + 1)(5z + 2)$
36. $(2 + 3y)(7 - 3y)$

Additional Answer
Mixed Review

1.

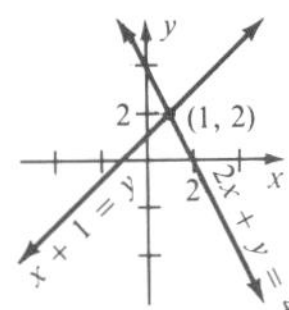

Mixed Review

Skills and Problem Solving

1. Solve the system $\begin{matrix} x + 1 = y \\ 2x + y = 4 \end{matrix}$ graphically. (1, 2)

Solve. Assume that no denominator is zero.

2. $20x^2 + 32x + 3 = 0$ $-\frac{1}{10}, -\frac{3}{2}$

3. $\frac{1}{3}(x + 4) = 6$ 14

4. $\frac{2}{x + 1} - \frac{1}{x} = \frac{1}{x - 1}$ $\frac{1}{3}$

5. $(4x - 1)(x + 3) = (2x + 1)^2 + 6x$ 4

6. The sum of the digits of a two-digit number is one eighth of the number with the digits reversed. The tens digit is 5 less than the ones digit. Find the number. 27

7. On a number line, point A has coordinate -8 and point B has coordinate 16. Find the coordinate of the point two thirds of the way from A to B. 8

8. How many kilograms of salt must be added to 12 kg of an 8% salt solution to make a solution that is 20% salt? 1.8 kg

Factor completely. If the polynomial cannot be factored, write "prime."

9. $9x^2 + 30x + 25$ $(3x + 5)^2$

10. $9x^2 + 34x + 25$ $(9x + 25)(x + 1)$

11. A rowboat traveled 3.6 km downstream in 24 min. The return trip took 1 h 12 min. Find, in kilometers per hour, the rate of the current and the rate of the boat in still water. current, 3 km/h; boat, 6 km/h

12. The perimeter of a triangle with sides that are in the ratio 3:4:5 is 216 cm. Find the lengths of the sides. 54 cm, 72 cm, 90 cm

13. The sum of the squares of two consecutive odd integers is 2 more than 8 times their sum. Write an equation in one variable describing this relationship. $n^2 + (n + 2)^2 = 2 + 8(n + n + 2)$

14. The Lamarques invested $8000 in accounts paying 6% annual simple interest and in bonds paying 8% annual simple interest. If they had reversed the amounts of their investments, they would have earned $80 less. How much money did they invest in each?
$6000 in bonds, $2000 in accounts

Express in scientific notation.

15. $1\frac{1}{4}$ million 1.25×10^6

16. $(6.02 \times 10^{23})(4.0 \times 10^{-12})$ 2.408×10^{12}

Solve.

17. $\begin{matrix} y = 7x - 16 \\ 3x + 2y = 2 \end{matrix}$ $(2, -2)$

18. $\begin{matrix} 4x - 5y = 0 \\ 8x + 5y = -60 \end{matrix}$ $(-5, -4)$

19. $\begin{matrix} 6x + 2y = 3 \\ -9x + 8y = 1 \end{matrix}$ $\left(\frac{1}{3}, \frac{1}{2}\right)$

Preparing for College Entrance Exams

Strategy for Success

Depending upon how a multiple-choice test is scored, it may not be good to guess. However, if you can eliminate several of the possible answers, it may be worthwhile to guess. For example, suppose you do not know the answer to a problem, but your knowledge of algebra tells you the answer must be a positive integer. This may help you eliminate some of the choices and improve your chances of guessing correctly.

Decide which is the best of the choices given and write the corresponding letter on your answer sheet.

1. The inlet pipe on a water tank can fill the tank in 8 hours. When the tank was full, both the inlet pipe and the drain pipe were accidentally opened. Twenty-four hours later, the tank was empty. How many hours would it take to empty a full tank if only the drain pipe were open? A
(A) 6 hours **(B)** 12 hours **(C)** 9 hours **(D)** 10 hours

2. A runner won a 5 km road race with a time of exactly 15 min. An observer, using a watch that was running fast, clocked the winning time at 15 min 24 s. To the nearest tenth of a minute, how many minutes does the observer's watch gain in a day? B
(A) 24.0 min **(B)** 38.4 min **(C)** 58.4 min **(D)** 61.0 min **(E)** 61.6 min

3. The length of a rectangle is 3 cm less than twice its width. A second rectangle is such that each of its dimensions is the reciprocal of the corresponding dimension of the first rectangle. The perimeter of the second rectangle is $\frac{1}{5}$ the perimeter of the first. Find the perimeter of the first rectangle. A
(A) 9 cm **(B)** 6 cm **(C)** 18 cm **(D)** 12 cm

4. A total of \$12,000 was invested in accounts earning 8% annual simple interest and in bonds earning 12% annual simple interest. If twice as much of the \$12,000 had been invested in bonds, the earnings would have been \$160 higher. How much was invested in bonds? C
(A) \$1000 **(B)** \$2000 **(C)** \$4000 **(D)** \$6000

5. A shopper paid \$7.70 for 2 containers of milk and 3 containers of apple juice. It would have cost 60 cents more for 2 containers of apple juice and 3 containers of milk. How much would it cost to buy one container of each? C
(A) \$2.60 **(B)** \$2.90 **(C)** \$3.20 **(D)** \$3.60 **(E)** \$3.80

6. Which method(s) could be used to solve: $\begin{matrix} xy = 9 \\ x + y = 6 \end{matrix}$? D

I. Graphing II. Multiplication with Addition-or-Subtraction III. Substitution
(A) I only **(B)** II only **(C)** III only **(D)** I, II, and III
(E) I and III only

About the Photo

The quality of sound produced by a violin is affected by the shape, type, and finish of the wood from which it is constructed. The pitch of a sound produced is affected by the frequency at which a string vibrates, which in turn is affected by the tension, length, and mass per unit length of the string.

When a violinist tightens a peg at the neck of the violin, the tension on the string increases and the frequency of vibration increases. This produces a higher pitch. When a violinist tunes the instrument, he or she finds the right tension and the right pitch for each string.

When a violinist presses the bow against a string and the string against the neck of the violin, the length of the string decreases. The frequency of vibration increases and the pitch of the sound is higher.

Lastly the heavier the string, the lower the frequency of vibration and the lower the pitch. Strings that produce bass sounds are wrapped in metal to give them a greater mass per unit length.

Since musical instruments, such as the violin, produce distinctive repeating wave patterns that can be represented mathematically, microcomputers can be programmed to produce a virtually limitless variety of musical sounds, including those produced by conventional instruments.

9 Introduction to Functions

The pitch of a musical tone is determined by its frequency. The frequency of a tone played on a violin is a function of the tension, the length, and the mass of a string. (See Exercises 9–10, page 428.)

390

Linear Equations

9-1 Slope of a Line

Objective To find the slope of a line.

To describe the steepness, or *slope,* of an airplane's flight path shortly after take-off, you estimate the vertical *rise* for every 100 m of horizontal *run* and calculate the ratio:

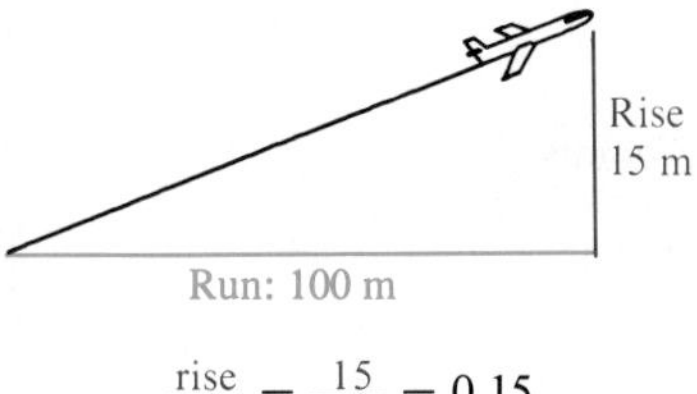

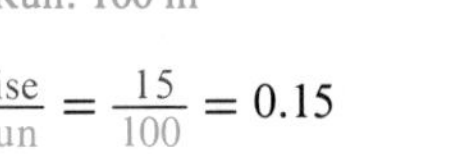

$$\frac{\text{rise}}{\text{run}} = \frac{15}{100} = 0.15$$

To describe the slope of a straight line, choose any two points on the line, count the units in the rise and the run from one point to the other, and calculate the ratio of the rise to the run.

Example 1

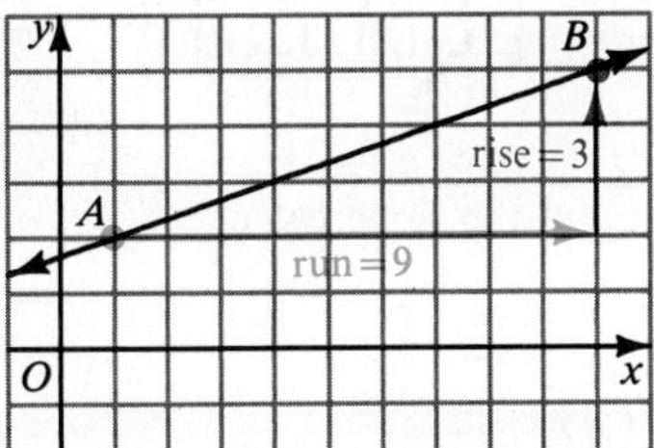

$$\text{slope} = \frac{\text{rise}}{\text{run}} = \frac{3}{9} = \frac{1}{3}$$

Example 2

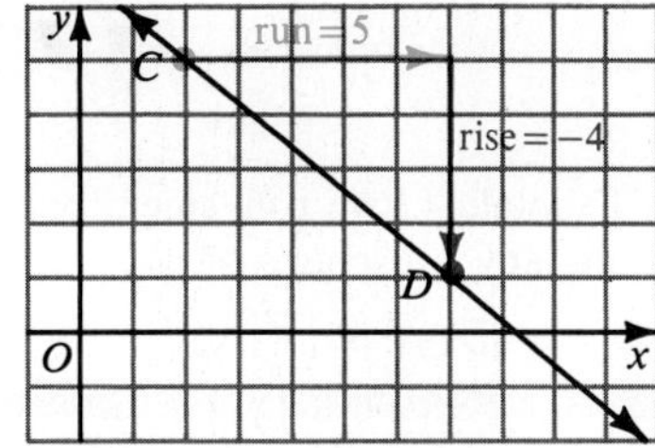

$$\text{slope} = \frac{\text{rise}}{\text{run}} = \frac{-4}{5} = -\frac{4}{5}$$

In Example 1, the line passes through the points $A(1, 2)$ and $B(10, 5)$. The rise, or vertical change, in moving from point A to point B is the difference between the y-coordinates: $5 - 2 = 3$. The run, or horizontal change, in moving from point A to point B is the difference between the x-coordinates: $10 - 1 = 9$.

Teaching References

Lesson Commentary, pp. T113–T117

Assignment Guide, pp. T64–T66

Supplementary Materials
- Practice Masters 53–60
- Tests 31–34
- Resource Book
  - Practice Exercises, pp. 107–113
  - Tests, pp. 44–49
  - Enrichment Activity, pp. 156–157
  - Mixed Review, pp. 138–141
- Algebra Action

Extra Practice
- Skills, pp. 622–626
- Problems, pp. 644–646

Alternate Test, p. T18

Cumulative Review, p. T26

Problem Solving Strategies

Generalizing from Specific
Numerical examples are used in Section 9-1 to develop the general notion of slope.

Looking for a Pattern
The Challenge following Section 9-4 asks students to obtain general formulas for sums by studying numerical examples.

Using a Chart
The notions of function and variation are introduced to students by use of tabular data, mapping diagrams, and graphs.

Trial and Error
Students might use trial and error along with the process of elimination to solve the Challenge following Section 9-7.

Teaching Suggestions
p. T113

Suggested Extensions
p. T113

Chalkboard Examples

1. Find the slope of the line through the points (1, 6) and (3, −2).
   $\text{slope} = \frac{-2 - 6}{3 - 1} = \frac{-8}{2} = -4$
2. Find the slope of the line whose equation is $2x - 3y = 18$.
   Find two points on the line, say (0, −6) and (9, 0). The slope is $\frac{0 - (-6)}{9 - 0} = \frac{6}{9} = \frac{2}{3}$.
3. Find the slope of the line whose equation is $y = 3x - 9$.
   Find two points on the line, say (0, −9) and (3, 0). The slope is $\frac{0 - (-9)}{3 - 0} = \frac{9}{3} = 3$.

   Determine whether the points in each exercise lie on the same line. If they do, find the slope of the line.
4. (0, −2), (1, 1), (2, 4), (3, 7)

x	y
0	−2
1	1
2	4
3	7

(Horizontal changes: 1, 1, 1; vertical changes: 3, 3, 3)

The ratio of vertical change to horizontal change is constant: $\frac{3}{1} = 3$. The points lie on a line whose slope is 3.

The coordinates of a pair of points on a line can be used to calculate the slope of the line:

$$\textbf{slope} = \frac{\text{rise}}{\text{run}} = \frac{\text{vertical change}}{\text{horizontal change}} = \frac{\text{difference between } y\text{-coordinates}}{\text{difference between } x\text{-coordinates}}$$

Thus, if

(x_1, y_1), read "x sub 1, y sub 1," and
(x_2, y_2), read "x sub 2, y sub 2,"

are any two different points on a line,

$$\textbf{slope} = \frac{y_2 - y_1}{x_2 - x_1} \qquad (x_1 \neq x_2).$$

Notice that the differences are taken in the same order.

Example 3 Find the slope of the line through the points (3, 8) and (5, 4).

Solution Let $x_1 = 3$, $y_1 = 8$, $x_2 = 5$, and $y_2 = 4$.

Then, $\text{slope} = \frac{y_2 - y_1}{x_2 - x_1} = \frac{4 - 8}{5 - 3} = \frac{-4}{2} = -2$ ***Answer***

Example 4 Find the slope of the line whose equation is $3x - 2y = 6$.

Solution

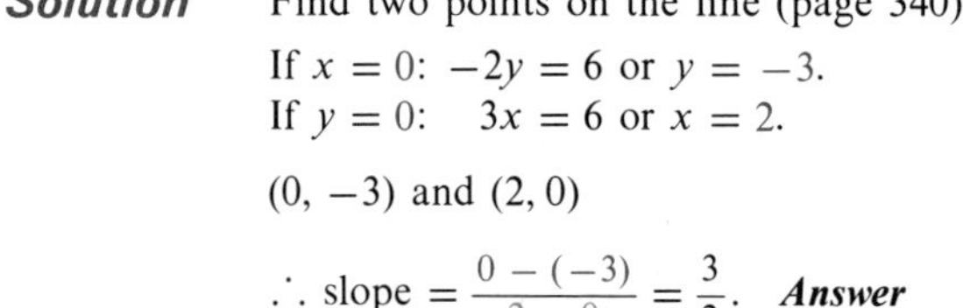

Find two points on the line (page 340):
If $x = 0$: $-2y = 6$ or $y = -3$.
If $y = 0$: $3x = 6$ or $x = 2$.

(0, −3) and (2, 0)

$\therefore \text{slope} = \frac{0 - (-3)}{2 - 0} = \frac{3}{2}$. ***Answer***

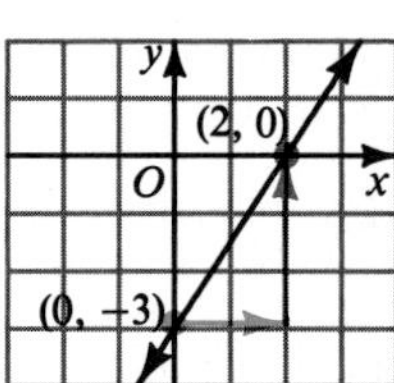

In Example 4, two convenient points were chosen, but the slope calculated using any two points on the line would be $\frac{3}{2}$.

A basic property of a line is that its slope is constant.

Example 5 Determine whether the points whose coordinates are given lie on the same line. If they do, find the slope of the line.

a. (−1, 9), (0, 5), (1, 1), (2, −3)
b. (0, 0), (2, 1), (4, 3), (6, 4)
c. (−2, 5), (0, 6), (6, 9), (2, 7)

Solution *Plan:* Arrange the coordinates of the points in a table in order of increasing x-coordinates. Then, compute the changes in the x-coordinates (blue) and the y-coordinates (red) and the ratio, as you move from one point to the next.

(a)

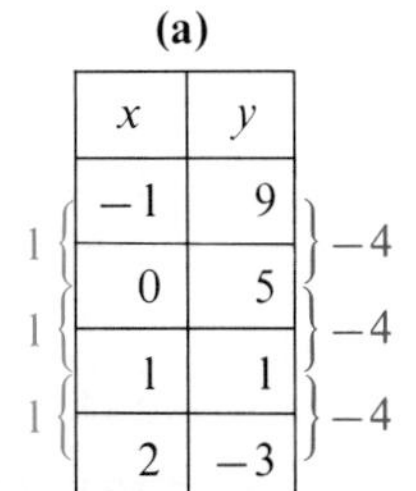

	x	y	
	-1	9	
1			-4
	0	5	
1			-4
	1	1	
1			-4
	2	-3	

The ratio of vertical change to horizontal change is constant:

$$\frac{-4}{1} = -4.$$

The points lie on a line whose slope is -4.

(b)

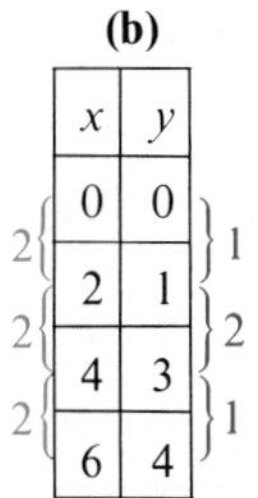

	x	y	
	0	0	
2			1
	2	1	
2			2
	4	3	
2			1
	6	4	

The ratio of vertical change to horizontal change is *not* constant. The points do *not* lie on a line.

(c)

	x	y	
	-2	5	
2			1
	0	6	
2			1
	2	7	
4			2
	6	9	

The ratio of vertical change to horizontal change is constant: $\frac{1}{2}$. The points lie on a line whose slope is $\frac{1}{2}$.

Points that lie on the same line are said to be **collinear.**

Whenever a line rises from left to right, its slope is a positive number (Examples 1 and 4). When it falls from left to right, its slope is a negative number (Examples 2 and 3). The slope of the horizontal line joining $(-3, 1)$ and $(2, 1)$ in the figure at the right is

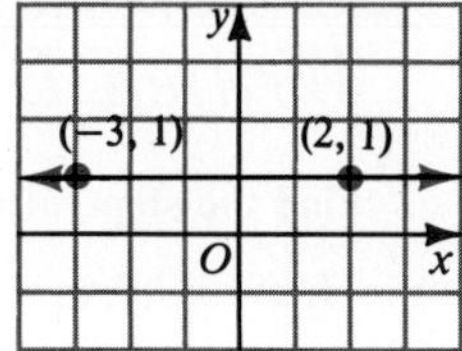

$$\frac{1 - 1}{2 - (-3)} = \frac{0}{5} = 0.$$

In fact,

the slope of every horizontal line is 0.

If you use the formula on page 392 to try to compute the slope of the vertical line shown at the right, you find that the denominator is 0. Since you cannot divide by zero, the formula does not apply.

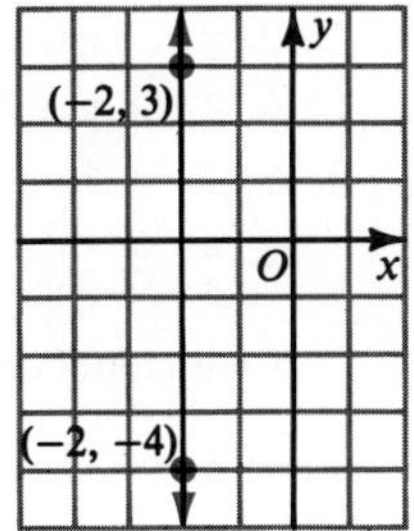

Vertical lines have no slope.

5. (1, 3), (2, 5), (3, 8), (4, 12)

	x	y	
	1	3	
1			2
	2	5	
1			3
	3	8	
1			4
	4	12	

The ratio of vertical change to horizontal change is not constant. The points do not lie on a line.

Common Errors

Perhaps because x-coordinates are usually written first and considered first in graphing points, some students may incorrectly think of the slope as $\frac{x_2 - x_1}{y_2 - y_1}$. You can point out that "rise" sounds like "y's" to help these students remember that the vertical change, or numerator of the slope ratio, is the difference of the y-coordinates.

Some students may also try to use expressions such as $\frac{y_2 - y_1}{x_1 - x_2}$ to find the slope of a line. Point out that although it doesn't matter which of two ordered pairs one considers first, the differences $y_2 - y_1$ and $x_2 - x_1$ or $y_1 - y_2$ and $x_1 - x_2$, must be taken in the same order.

Students may have trouble remembering whether it is the slope of a vertical or a horizontal line that is zero. Encourage students to think about whether the rise or run of a vertical or a horizontal line is zero rather than trying to memorize the slopes of such lines.

Supplementary Material

Resource Book, p. 107

Suggested Assignments

Minimum
394/1–35 odd
S 343/34, 36

Average
394/1–39 odd
S 343/25–35 odd

Maximum
394/1–41 odd
S 343/37, 39

Additional A Exercises

Find the slope of the line through the given points.

1. (1, 2), (−3, −4) $\frac{3}{2}$
2. (7, −6), (−5, 2) $-\frac{2}{3}$

Find the slope of each line whose equation is given.

3. $6x - 2y = 14$ 3
4. $3x + 4y = 7$ $\frac{-3}{4}$
5. $y + 5 = -3$ 0

Additional Answers Written Exercises

29.

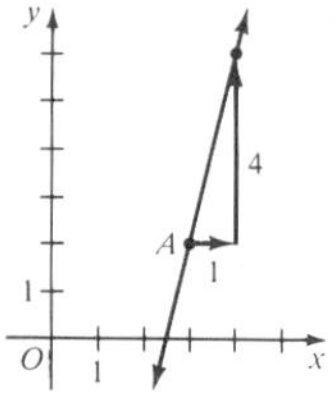

30.

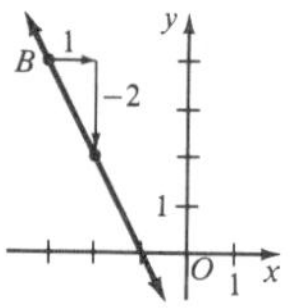

31.

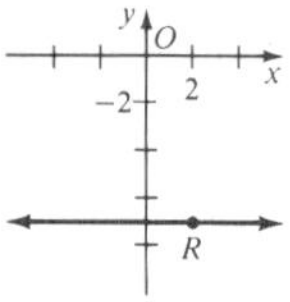

Oral Exercises

Find the slope of each line.

1. $\frac{3}{4}$

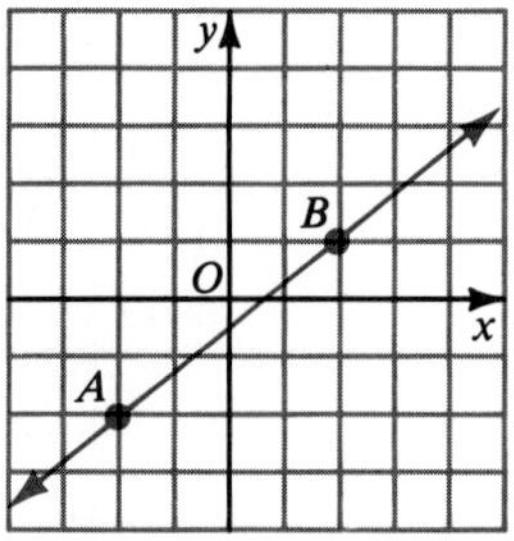

2. $-\frac{6}{5}$

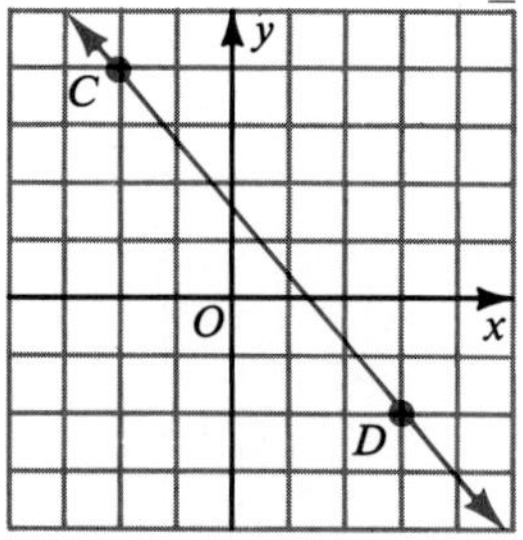

3. 0

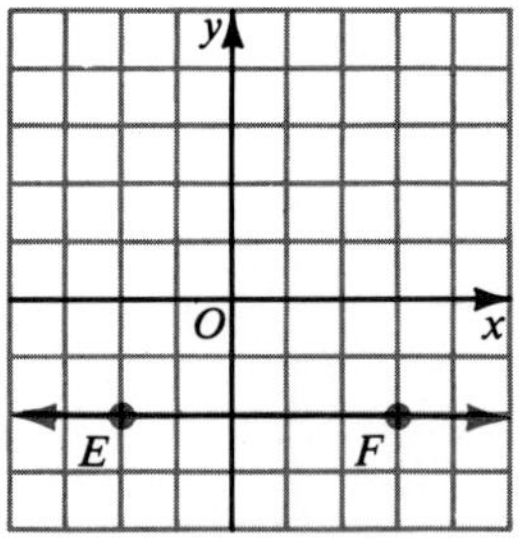

4. $\frac{1}{5}$

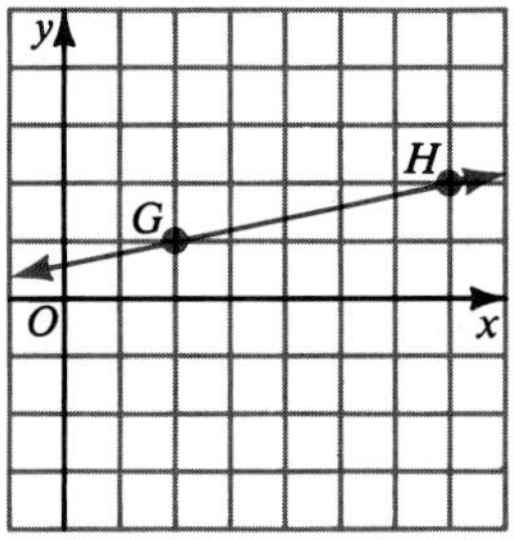

5. $-\frac{5}{2}$

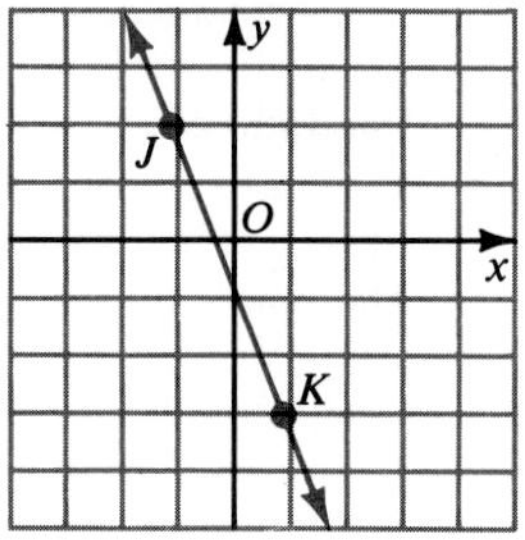

6. no slope

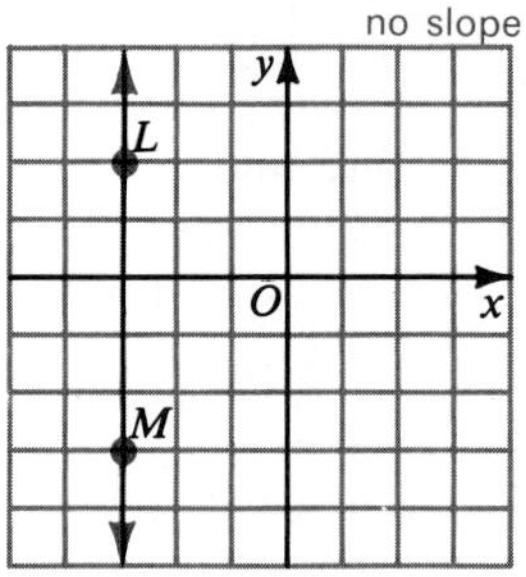

Written Exercises

Find the slope of the line through the given points.

A

1. (9, 5), (7, 6) $-\frac{1}{2}$
2. (2, −4), (5, −6) $-\frac{2}{3}$
3. (−8, 1), (−6, 3) 1
4. (2, 7), (4, 3) −2
5. (−5, 3), (6, 5) $\frac{2}{11}$
6. (3, −4), (9, 4) $\frac{4}{3}$
7. (−2, −2), (0, 0) 1
8. (7, 2), (−2, 2) 0
9. (1, 8), (1, −2) no slope
10. (−6, −7), (−4, −4) $\frac{3}{2}$
11. (0, −1), (5, −1) 0
12. (0, 0), (4, 10) $\frac{5}{2}$

Find the slope of each line whose equation is given.

13. $y = 5x - 2$ 5
14. $y = 3x - 2$ 3
15. $y = -3x + 8$ −3
16. $2x + y = 4$ −2
17. $x - y = 7$ 1
18. $5x - y = 16$ 5
19. $2x + 3y = 12$ $-\frac{2}{3}$
20. $4x + 3y = 36$ $-\frac{4}{3}$
21. $8x - 3y = 24$ $\frac{8}{3}$
22. $4x + 5y = 20$ $-\frac{4}{5}$
23. $y = -5$ 0
24. $y - 7 = 0$ 0

If the points are collinear, find the slope of the line through them.

25. (0, 4), (1, 2), (2, 0), (3, −2) −2
26. (4, 3), (5, 5), (6, 7), (7, 10) not collinear
27. (0, −1), (1, −2), (2, −4), (−1, 0) not collinear
28. (1, −1), (−1, 2), (−3, 5), (−5, 8) $-\frac{3}{2}$

Through the given point, draw a line with the given slope.

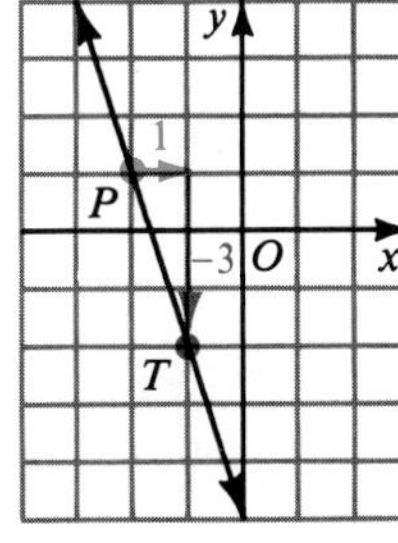

Example $P(-2, 1)$; slope -3

Solution 1. Plot point P.

2. Write the slope as the fraction $\frac{-3}{1}$. From P, measure 1 unit to the right and 3 units down to locate a second point, T. Draw the line through P and T.

29. $A(3, 2)$; slope 4

30. $B(-3, 4)$; slope -2

31. $R(2, -7)$; slope 0

32. $N(-2, -1)$; slope $\frac{2}{7}$

33. $K(-5, 1)$; slope $-\frac{1}{2}$

34. $H(4, -3)$; slope $-\frac{3}{5}$

B **35.** The vertices of a triangle are $A(-4, 6)$, $B(5, 6)$, and $C(-4, -2)$. Find the slope of each side of the triangle.

36. The vertices of a rectangle are $M(-2, -3)$, $N(3, 2)$, $P(10, -5)$, and $Q(5, -10)$. Find the slope of each side of the rectangle.

37. Determine the slope of the line through the points (4, 6) and (0, 4). Find the value of y if $(8, y)$ lies on this line. $\frac{1}{2}$; 8

38. The slope of a line through the point (1, 3) is 1.5. If the point $(-3, y)$ lies on the line, find the value of y. -3

39. A line with slope -4 passes through the points $(-7, c)$ and $(1, 3c)$. Find the value of c. -16

40. A line with slope -3 passes through the points $(-8, p)$ and $(2, 3p)$. Find the value of p. -15

C **41.** The vertices of a square are $A(3, 5)$, $B(11, 3)$, $C(9, -5)$, and $D(1, -3)$. Use the idea of slope to show that the point $M(6, 0)$ lies on the diagonal joining A and C, and on the diagonal joining B and D.

42. The vertices of a right triangle are $P(-4, 2)$, $Q(-4, -6)$, and $R(6, -6)$. Use the idea of slope to show that $S(1, -2)$ lies on one of the sides of the triangle.

Computer Exercises

For students with some programming experience

Write a BASIC program that prints the coordinates of points on a line when the slope and the coordinates of a given point on the line are entered with INPUT statements. RUN the program for the following data.

1. $m = 2$; $(-1, -3)$; 5 more points

2. $m = 0$; $(-4, -2)$; 3 more points

3. $m = -\frac{1}{2}$; $(0, 6)$; 10 more points

4. $m = \frac{4}{3}$; $(2, 5)$; 5 more points

32.

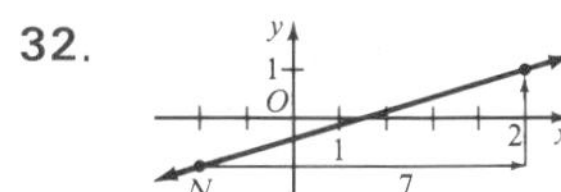

33.

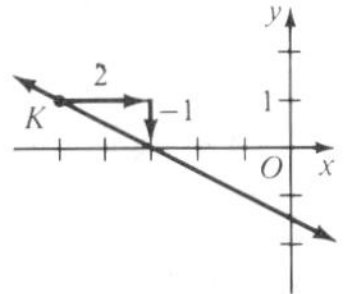

34.

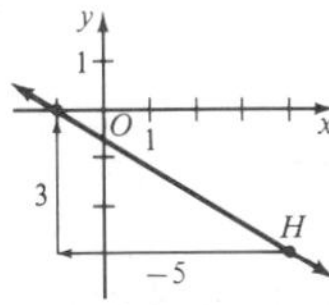

35. $\overline{AB}$, slope = 0; $\overline{BC}$, slope = $\frac{8}{9}$; $\overline{CA}$, no slope

36. $\overline{MN}$, slope = 1; $\overline{NP}$, slope = -1; $\overline{PQ}$, slope = 1; $\overline{QM}$, slope = -1

41. The slopes of $\overline{AC}$ and $\overline{AM}$ are both $-\frac{5}{3}$; thus M lies on $\overline{AC}$. The slopes of $\overline{DB}$ and $\overline{DM}$ are both $\frac{3}{5}$; thus M lies on $\overline{DB}$.

42. $\overline{PQ}$ has no slope; the slope of $\overline{QR}$ = 0; and the slope of $\overline{PR} = -\frac{4}{5}$. Since the slope of $\overline{SP} = -\frac{4}{5}$, S lies on $\overline{PR}$.

Additional Answers Computer Exercises

Answers may vary. Examples are given.

2. $(-3, -2)$, $(-2, -2)$, $(-1, -2)$

4. $(3, 6.\overline{3})$, $(4, 7.\overline{6})$, $(5, 9)$, $(6, 10.\overline{3})$, $(7, 11.\overline{6})$

Teaching Suggestions
p. T113

Chalkboard Examples

Write a linear equation in standard form whose graph has the given slope and *y*-intercept.

1. $m = -2, b = \frac{1}{2}$

   $y = -2x + \frac{1}{2};$

   $2y = -4x + 1;$

   $4x + 2y = 1$

2. $m = \frac{2}{5}, b = -1$

   $y = \frac{2}{5}x + (-1);$

   $5y = 2x - 5;$

   $2x - 5y = 5$

Change each equation to the slope-intercept form. Then draw the graph, using only the slope and *y*-intercept.

3. $x - y = 3$ $y = x - 3$

4. $x + 2y = 6$

   $y = -\frac{1}{2}x + 3$

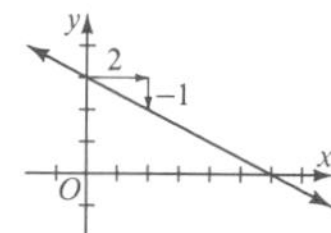

5. Show that the lines $2x - y = 0$ and $2x - y = 4$ are parallel.
   Write each equation in slope-intercept form:

   $y = 2x$ and $y = 2x - 4$

   Since the slope of each line is the same and the *y*-intercepts are different, the lines are parallel.

9-2 The Slope-Intercept Form of a Linear Equation

Objective To use the slope-intercept form of a linear equation.

The table shows the coordinates of a few of the points on the graph of the linear equation $y = 2x$. The graph is the straight line that has slope $\frac{2}{1}$, or 2, and that passes through the origin.

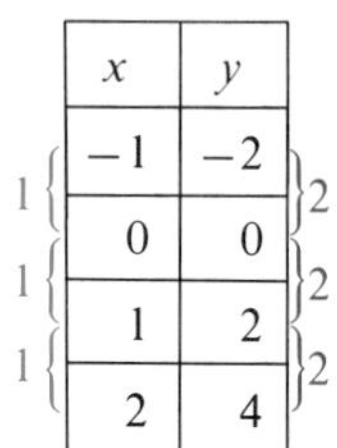

x	y
-1	-2
0	0
1	2
2	4

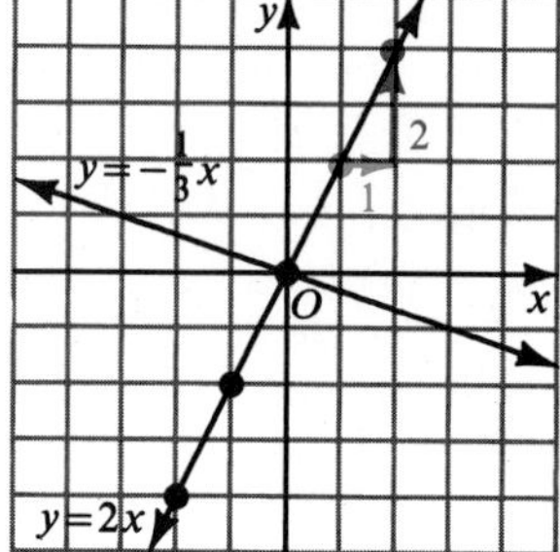

The graph of the equation $y = -\frac{1}{3}x$ is a line that has slope $-\frac{1}{3}$ and passes through the origin.

For every real number m, the graph in a coordinate plane of the equation

$$y = mx$$

is the line that has slope m and passes through the origin.

The graphs of the linear equations

$$y = 2x \quad \text{and} \quad y = 2x + 4$$

have been drawn on the same set of axes. The lines have equal slopes, but they cross the *y*-axis at different points. The *y*-coordinate of a point where a graph intersects the *y*-axis is called the ***y*-intercept** of the graph.

To determine the *y*-intercept of a line, replace x with 0 in the equation of the line:

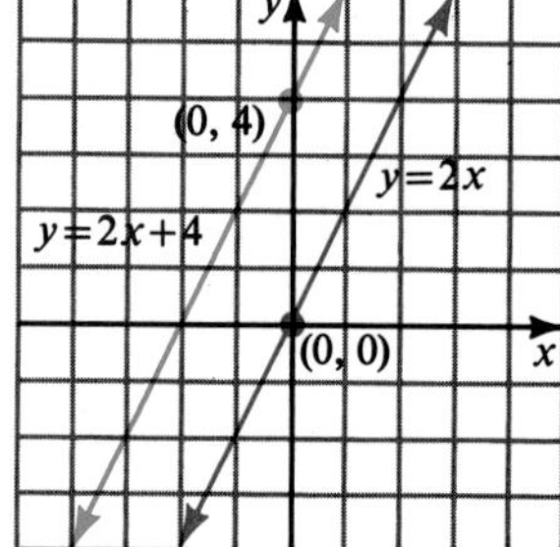

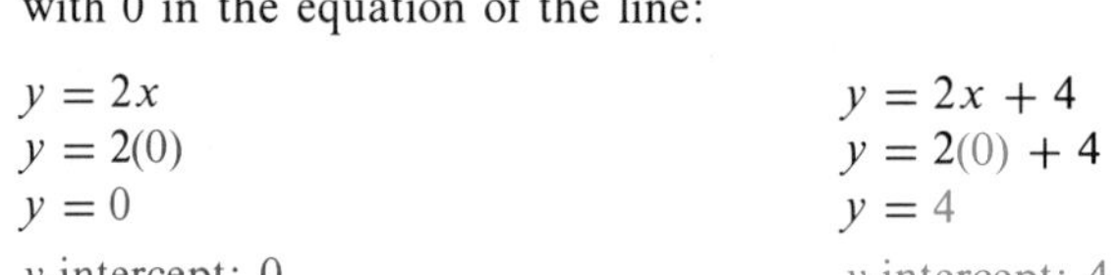

$y = 2x$	$y = 2x + 4$
$y = 2(0)$	$y = 2(0) + 4$
$y = 0$	$y = 4$
y-intercept: 0	*y*-intercept: 4

If you write $y = 2x$ as $y = 2x + 0$, you can see that the constant term in the following equations is the y-intercept of each graph:

$$y = 2x + 0 \qquad y = 2x + 4$$

For all real numbers m and b, the graph in a coordinate plane of the equation

$$y = mx + b$$

is the line whose slope is m and whose y-intercept is b. This is called the **slope-intercept form** of an equation of a line.

Example 1 Write a linear equation in standard form whose graph has the given slope and y-intercept.

a. $m = -4$, $b = -3$ **b.** $m = \frac{1}{5}$, $b = 2$

Solution First write an equation of the form $y = mx + b$. Then transform it into an equivalent equation in the form $Ax + By = C$, where A, B, and C are integers.

a. $y = -4x + (-3)$
$4x + y = -3$ ***Answer***

b. $y = \frac{1}{5}x + 2$
$5y = x + 10$
$-x + 5y = 10$ ***Answer***

If you solve linear equations for y, the coefficient of x is the slope of the graph of the linear equation.

Example 2 Use only the y-intercept and slope to graph the equation $2x - 3y = 6$.

Solution Solve for y to transform the equation into the form $y = mx + b$.

$$2x - 3y = 6$$
$$-3y = -2x + 6$$
$$y = \frac{2}{3}x - 2$$

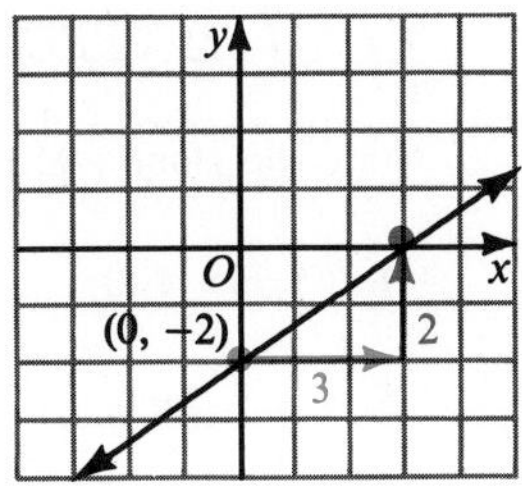

Since the y-intercept is -2, plot $(0, -2)$. Since the slope is $\frac{2}{3}$, measure 3 units to the right of $(0, -2)$ and 2 units up to locate a second point. Draw the line through the two points.

Common Errors

Some students may think that the coefficient of x is the slope of the graph of a linear equation when the equation is in standard form. Point out that this is true only when the equation of a line is expressed in slope-intercept form.

Some students may be confused when the slope-intercept form of a linear equation is written $y = b + mx$. Point out that according to the commutative axiom for addition $y = b + mx = mx + b$. Thus, for example, the slope of the line represented by the equation $y = 2 - 3x$ is -3, not 2.

Some students may think that linear equations such as $\frac{1}{2}x + 4y = -3$ and $5y + 1 = 0$ are expressed in standard form. Refer these students to the definition of a linear equation in standard form on page 340.

Supplementary Material

Practice Master 53

Suggested Assignments

Minimum
Day 1: 399/2–24 even
S 395/36–38
Day 2: 399/3, 5, 19–25 odd, 26, 27, 31

Average
Day 1: 399/2–32 even
S 395/38, 40
Day 2: 399/25–33 odd, 34, 38
402/2–16 even
Day 2 finishes Sec. 9-2 and starts Sec. 9-3.

Maximum
399/2–38 even
S 395/40, 42

Additional A Exercises

Write an equation in standard form of the line that has the given slope and y-intercept.

1. $m = 4; b = 1$
$4x - y = -1$

2. $m = -\frac{1}{2}; b = -3$
$x + 2y = -6$

3. $m = \frac{3}{2}; b = -4$
$3x - 2y = 8$

Change each equation to the slope-intercept form. Then draw the graph, using only the slope and y-intercept.

4. $3x - 2y = 8$
$y = \frac{3}{2}x - 4$

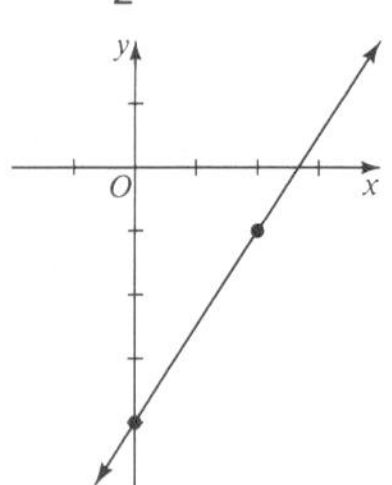

Example 3 Show that the lines whose equations are $2x + y = 8$ and $2x + y = 6$ are parallel.

Solution

1. Recall (page 346) that parallel lines do not intersect. Therefore, to show that the given lines are parallel, you can show that the *system* of equations

$$2x + y = 8$$
$$2x + y = 6$$

has *no solution.*

2. Write each equation in slope-intercept form:

$$y = -2x + 8$$
$$y = -2x + 6$$

3. Use the substitution method (page 351) to solve the system in Step 2. You find

$$-2x + 8 = -2x + 6$$
or
$$8 = 6$$

4. Since Step 3 produces a false statement, the system has no solution.

$\therefore$ the given lines are parallel. ***Answer***

Notice that the parallel lines in Example 3 have the same slope, -2. In general:

Different lines with the same slope are parallel. Also, parallel lines that are not vertical have the same slope.

With this information, you can tell whether or not two nonvertical lines are parallel by inspecting the slope-intercept form of their equations.

Oral Exercises

State the slope and y-intercept of each line whose equation is given.

1. $y = 4x$ 4; 0
2. $y = 5x - 3$ 5; -3
3. $y = \frac{1}{2}x + 2$ $\frac{1}{2}$; 2
4. $y = -3x$ -3; 0
5. $y = -2x - \frac{1}{3}$ -2; $-\frac{1}{3}$
6. $y = \frac{3}{4}x + \frac{1}{2}$ $\frac{3}{4}$; $\frac{1}{2}$
7. $y = -\frac{2}{5}x$ $-\frac{2}{5}$; 0
8. $y = 6x - 1.5$ 6; -1.5

State an equation of the line that has the given slope and y-intercept.

9. $m = 3, b = 2$ $y = 3x + 2$ **10.** $m = 3, b = 0$ $y = 3x$ **11.** $m = -2, b = -1$ $y = -2x - 1$ **12.** $m = -1, b = 7$ $y = -x + 7$

Written Exercises

Write an equation in standard form of the line that has the given slope and y-intercept.

A **1.** $m = 2, b = \frac{1}{3}$ $-6x + 3y = 1$ **2.** $m = -3, b = \frac{2}{3}$ $9x + 3y = 2$ **3.** $m = \frac{1}{5}, b = 4$ $x - 5y = -20$

4. $m = -\frac{3}{4}, b = 2$ $3x + 4y = 8$ **5.** $m = 6, b = -\frac{3}{5}$ $30x - 5y = 3$ **6.** $m = -\frac{2}{3}, b = -1$ $2x + 3y = -3$

7. $m = \frac{7}{3}, b = -\frac{1}{6}$ $14x - 6y = 1$ **8.** $m = -\frac{5}{4}, b = -\frac{7}{8}$ $10x + 8y = -7$ **9.** $m = 0, b = -6$ $y = -6$

10. $m = 0, b = 15$ $y = 15$ **11.** $m = -2.1, b = -0.4$ $21x + 10y = -4$ **12.** $m = 1.8, b = -2.5$ $18x - 10y = 25$

Change each equation to the slope-intercept form. Then draw the graph, using only the slope and y-intercept.

13. $x + y = 5$ **14.** $2x - y = -3$ **15.** $x - y = 4$

16. $-x + 3y = 9$ **17.** $x - 2y = 6$ **18.** $2y - 3x = -6$

19. $2x + 3y = 0$ **20.** $4x - 3y = 12$ **21.** $-4x + 5y = 15$

22. $5x = 2y$ **23.** $2x - 3y - 6 = 0$ **24.** $3y = 7$

Use the slope-intercept form of the equations to determine whether each system has a solution.

B **25.** $2x - 3y = 7$, $-2x + 3y = 4$ no solution **26.** $x - 2y = 1$, $2x + y = 4$ one solution **27.** $x - y = 4$, $y - x = -4$ infinitely many solutions

28. $4x - y = 1$, $-8x + 2y = -2$ infinitely many solutions **29.** $\frac{x}{2} + \frac{y}{2} = 5$, $2x + 2y = 3$ no solution **30.** $\frac{x}{3} - \frac{y}{3} = 2$, $3x - 3y = 1$ no solution

31. Write an equation of the line that has y-intercept -4 and is parallel to the graph of $y = 3x - 1$. $y = 3x - 4$

32. Write an equation of the line that is parallel to the graph of $y - 2x = 1$ and has the same y-intercept as the graph of $4y + 3x = 20$. $y = 2x + 5$

33. In the equation $3y + px = 5$, for what value of p is the graph of the equation parallel to the graph of $x - y = 4$? the graph of $x + y = 4$? -3; 3

34. In the equation $dy + 3x = 2$, for what value of d is the graph of the equation parallel to the graph of $x - 6y = 0$? the y-axis? -18; 0

5. $4y + 5x = 8$
$y = -\frac{5}{4}x + 2$

6. $4x - 2y = 6$
$y = 2x - 3$

Additional Answers Written Exercises

14. $y = 2x + 3$

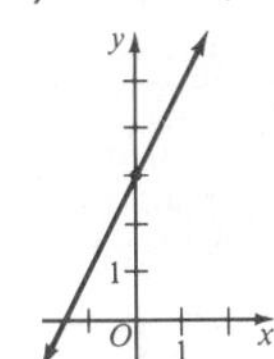

16. $y = \frac{1}{3}x + 3$

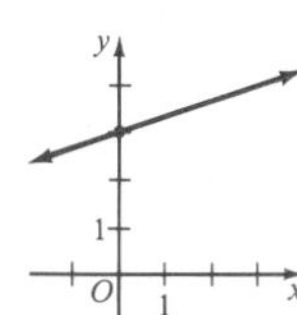

18. $y = \frac{3}{2}x - 3$

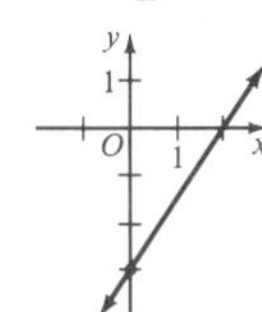

(continued)

Additional Answers Written Exercises

20. $y = \frac{4}{3}x - 4$

22. $y = \frac{5}{2}x$

24. $y = \frac{7}{3}$

Mixed Review Exercises

1. Express as a product: $27x^3y + 18x^2y^2 + 36xy^3$ $9xy(3x^2 + 2xy + 4y^2)$

Factor completely.

2. $625 - x^4$ $(25 + x^2)(5 - x)(5 + x)$
3. $x^2 - 16x + 63$ $(x - 7)(x - 9)$
4. The value of a fraction is $\frac{1}{2}$. If 7 is added to the denominator and 4 is subtracted from the numerator, the value of the fraction becomes $\frac{1}{5}$. What is the original fraction? $\frac{9}{18}$

In Exercises 35–37, use the points $A(5, 3)$, $B(2, 6)$, and $C(-2, 0)$.

35. Find r if the line joining A to $(r, 2r)$ is parallel to the line joining B and C. -9

36. Find s if the line joining B to $(s + 4, s)$ is parallel to the line joining A and C. 12

37. Find t if the line joining C to $(-3t, 2t + 1)$ is parallel to the line joining A and B. 3

C **38.** A radio beacon is located at $(-1, 0)$ and another at $(2, -1)$. A navigator's equipment tells her that the line joining her position to the first beacon has slope -5 and the line joining her position to the second has slope 3. What is the navigator's location? $\left(\frac{1}{4}, -\frac{25}{4}\right)$

39. Using the standard form of a linear equation, $Ax + By = C$, find a formula for the slope and a formula for the y-intercept in terms of the coefficients, assuming that $B \neq 0$. slope $= -\frac{A}{B}$; y-intercept $= \frac{C}{B}$

Historical Note / *The Seqt of a Pyramid*

To ensure the uniform slope of the faces of a pyramid, the ancient Egyptians determined the pyramid's *seqt*. "Seqt" was the ratio of the run to the rise. (Modern-day architects use the same ratio to describe the slope of a wall, terrace, bank, or pier.) The run was always measured in hands, while the rise was always measured in cubits. There were seven hands in a cubit.

Problems 56 and 57 of the Rhind mathematical papyrus, a collection of 85 practical problems copied from some earlier document by the scribe Ahmes about 1550 B.C., deal with the seqt of a pyramid. Problem 56 asks one to find the seqt of a pyramid 250 cubits high having a square base of 360 cubits on a side. The answer given is $5\frac{1}{25}$ hands per cubit. (Note that the measurements are not expressed in the same units.) Problem 57 asks one to find the height of a pyramid having a square base 140 cubits on a side and a seqt of 5 hands and 1 finger per cubit. (Not surprisingly, there were 4 fingers in a hand.) The answer given is $93\frac{1}{3}$ cubits.

The great pyramid of Cheops has a square base 440 cubits on a side and is 280 cubits high. Its seqt, then, is $5\frac{1}{2}$ hands per cubit.

9-3 Determining an Equation of a Line

Objective To find an equation of a line given the slope and one point on the line, or given two points on the line.

The line shown in the diagram has slope $\frac{3}{4}$ and passes through the point $(-3, -2)$. The slope-intercept form of the equation of this line is

$$y = \frac{3}{4}x + b.$$

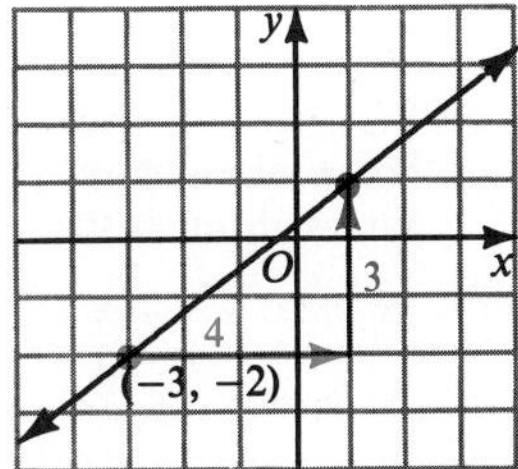

Since the point $(-3, -2)$ is on the line, its coordinates satisfy the equation. You can substitute to find the value of b.

$$-2 = \frac{3}{4}(-3) + b$$

$$-2 = -\frac{9}{4} + b$$

$$\frac{1}{4} = b$$

Therefore, an equation of the line with slope $\frac{3}{4}$ and passing through $(-3, -2)$ is $y = \frac{3}{4}x + \frac{1}{4}$, or in standard form, $-3x + 4y = 1$.

Example Write an equation of the line passing through the points $(-2, -1)$ and $(4, 8)$.

Solution

$$\text{slope} = \frac{\text{difference between } y\text{-coordinates}}{\text{difference between } x\text{-coordinates}}$$

$$= \frac{8 - (-1)}{4 - (-2)} = \frac{9}{6} = \frac{3}{2}$$

$\therefore$ the slope-intercept form of the equation is

$$y = \frac{3}{2}x + b.$$

Choose one of the points, say $(4, 8)$. Since it lies on the line, its coordinates satisfy the equation. Substitute to find the value of b:

$$8 = \frac{3}{2}(4) + b$$

$$8 = 6 + b$$

$$2 = b$$

$\therefore$ an equation of the line is $y = \frac{3}{2}x + 2$. ***Answer***

As shown in the text above the Example, you can find an equation of a line if you know the slope and one point on the line. To determine an equation of a line when two points on the line are given, you first find the slope and then find the y-intercept as shown in the Example.

Teaching Suggestions
p. T114

Chalkboard Examples

1. The point (3, 1) is on a line whose equation is $y = \frac{2}{3}x + b$. Find the value of b.
   $1 = \frac{2}{3}(3) + b$
   $1 = 2 + b$
   $b = -1$

Write an equation in standard form of the line described.

2. The line passes through the point (4, 2) and has slope -5.
   $y = -5x + b$
   $2 = -5(4) + b$
   $22 = b$
   $y = -5x + 22$
   $5x + y = 22$
3. The line passes through points (1, 1) and (2, 4).
   $\text{Slope} = \frac{4 - 1}{2 - 1} = 3$
   $y = 3x + b$
   $1 = 3(1) + b$
   $-2 = b$
   $y = 3x - 2$
   $3x - y = 2$
4. The line passes through points (3, 0) and (1, 6).
   $\text{Slope} = \frac{6 - 0}{1 - 3} = -3$
   $y = -3x + b$
   $0 = -3(3) + b$
   $9 = b$
   $y = -3x + 9$
   $3x + y = 9$

Supplementary Materials

Test 31
Resource Book, p. 108

Suggested Assignments

Minimum
402/1–4, 6–28 even
S 394/16–20 even

Average
402/18–28 even, 29–33
R 403/*Self-Test 1*
Day 2 of Sec. 9-2 finishes Sec. 9-2 and starts Sec. 9-3.

Maximum
402/2–28 even, 29–35
S 400/37, 39

Additional A Exercises

1. The point $(-3, 5)$ is on a line whose equation is $y = \frac{3}{4}x + b$. Find the value of b. $\frac{29}{4}$

Write an equation in standard form of the line that has the given slope and passes through the given point.

2. $m = 2$, $(-4, 7)$ $2x - y = -15$
3. $m = -\frac{1}{2}$, $(1, 1)$ $x + 2y = 3$
4. $m = -3$, $(2, -3)$ $3x + y = 3$

Write an equation in standard form of the line passing through the given points.

5. $(7, 7)$, $(2, -2)$ $9x - 5y = 28$
6. $(4, -3)$, $(3, -6)$ $3x - y = 15$
7. $(0, 0)$, $(2, 5)$ $5x - 2y = 0$

Written Exercises

Each given point is on a line whose equation is $y = \frac{3}{4}x + b$. Find each value of b.

A
1. $(8, 1)$ -5
2. $(-8, 3)$ 9
3. $(0, -7)$ -7
4. $(-2, -5)$ $-\frac{7}{2}$

Write an equation in standard form of the line that has the given slope and passes through the given point.

5. $m = 2$; $(-3, 1)$ $-2x + y = 7$
6. $m = 4$; $(-2, 3)$ $-4x + y = 11$
7. $m = -3$; $(4, 6)$ $3x + y = 18$
8. $m = -2$; $(3, -1)$ $2x + y = 5$
9. $m = \frac{3}{2}$; $(0, 3)$ $-3x + 2y = 6$
10. $m = \frac{4}{3}$; $(1, 0)$ $-4x + 3y = -4$
11. $m = -\frac{4}{5}$; $(-1, -6)$ $4x + 5y = -34$
12. $m = -1$; $(5, 1)$ $x + y = 6$
13. $m = -\frac{1}{2}$; $(0, 0)$ $x + 2y = 0$
14. $m = \frac{9}{7}$; $(-14, 3)$ $9x - 7y = -147$
15. $m = 0$; $\left(\frac{1}{2}, -4\right)$ $y = -4$
16. $m = 0$; $\left(-3, \frac{5}{8}\right)$ $8y = 5$

Write an equation in standard form of the line passing through the given points.

17. $(1, -1)$, $(5, 6)$ $-7x + 4y = -11$
18. $(4, 0)$, $(-1, 2)$ $2x + 5y = 8$
19. $(4, 1)$, $(-3, 1)$
20. $(-1, 2)$, $(4, 7)$ $x - y = -3$
21. $(3, 4)$, $(2, 6)$ $2x + y = 10$
22. $(7, 1)$, $(3, 2)$
23. $(3, -1)$, $(6, 7)$ $-8x + 3y = -27$
24. $(-3, -1)$, $(1, -4)$
25. $(0, -1)$, $(1, 4)$
26. $(-1, -2)$, $(0, 3)$ $-5x + y = 3$
27. $(-2, 0)$, $(2, -3)$ $3x + 4y = -6$
28. $(3, 0)$, $(-2, 5)$

Write an equation in standard form for each line described.

B
29. The line that passes through the point $(-1, 3)$ and is parallel to the graph of $3x - y = 4$. $3x - y = -6$
30. The line that is parallel to the graph of $x - 2y + 7 = 0$ and contains the point $(-4, 0)$. $-x + 2y = 4$
31. The line that passes through the point $(-4, -5)$ and has the same y-intercept as the graph of $x + 3y + 9 = 0$. $-x + 2y = -6$
32. The line that contains the points $(7, 1)$, $(p, 0)$, and $(0, p)$ for $p \neq 0$. $x + y = 8$

C
33. The line that has slope $\frac{1}{3}$ and passes through the point of intersection of the graphs of $2x - 7y = 15$ and $x - y = 5$. $-x + 3y = -7$
34. The line that has slope $\frac{1}{2}$ and passes through the point of intersection of the graphs of $x - 6y = 10$ and $x - y = 5$. $x - 2y = 6$
35. The line whose x-intercept is -6 and whose y-intercept is 2. (The *x-intercept* of a line is the x-coordinate of the point where the line crosses the x-axis.) $x - 3y = -6$

Self-Test 1

Vocabulary slope (p. 392) collinear (p. 393) y-intercept (p. 396) slope-intercept form of an equation (p. 397)

1. Find the slope of the line that passes through the points (2, 3) and (4, 6). $\frac{3}{2}$ **Obj. 9-1, p. 391**
2. Find the slope of the line $y = 7$. 0
3. Find the slope and y-intercept of the line whose equation is $3x - 7y = 28$. slope $= \frac{3}{7}$; y-intercept $= -4$ **Obj. 9-2, p. 396**
4. Write an equation in standard form of the line with slope 3 that passes through the point $(-2, -1)$. $-3x + y = 5$ **Obj. 9-3, p. 401**
5. Write an equation in standard form of the line through the points (5, 0) and (0, −5). $x - y = 5$

Check your answers with those at the back of the book.

Computer Key-In

Exercises

1. **a.** Write a formula and then write a program to find the slope of the line between the points ($X1$, $Y1$) and ($X2$, $Y2$). When is there no slope? $m = \frac{Y2 - Y1}{X2 - X1}$; when $X2 = X1$
   b. RUN the program for each of the following.

   (2, 3) and (1, 5) −2
   (−3, 2) and (1, 5) 0.75
   (2, 3) and (2, 5) no slope
   (2, 5) and (−2, 5) 0

2. **a.** Using the standard form of the equation of a line, $Ax + By = C$, write formulas for the x-intercept, the y-intercept, and the slope. $x = \frac{C}{A}$; $y = \frac{C}{B}$; $m = -\frac{A}{B}$
   b. Write a program to find the items in part (a). RUN your program for $3x - 2y = 6$, $3x = 6$, and $2y = 6$.
3. **a.** Write a program to transform an equation of a line in standard form to an equation in slope-intercept form.
   b. RUN the program for $3x - 2y = 6$, $3x = 6$, and $2y = 6$.

Note: The program of Exercise 1 above can be used to do Exercises 1–12 on page 394. The program of Exercise 3 above can be used to do Exercises 13–24 on page 399.

Additional Answers Written Exercises

19. $y = 1$
22. $x + 4y = 11$
24. $3x + 4y = -13$
25. $-5x + y = -1$
28. $x + y = 3$

Quick Quiz

1. Find the slope of the line that passes through (1, 4) and (−3, 0). slope $= \frac{0 - 4}{-3 - 1} = 1$
2. Find the slope of the line whose equation is $y = -4$. slope $= 0$
3. Find the slope and the y-intercept of the line whose equation is $3x - 2y = 5$. slope $= \frac{3}{2}$ y-intercept $= -\frac{5}{2}$
4. Write an equation in standard form of the line with slope −2 that passes through the point (1, 5). $2x + y = 7$
5. Write an equation in standard form of the line that passes through the points (−3, 2) and (1, −2). $x + y = -1$

Additional Answers Computer Key-In

2. b. 2; −3; 1.5
   2; no y-intercept; no slope
   no x-intercept; 3; 0
3. b. $y = 1.5x - 3$; $x = 2$; $y = 3$

Teaching Suggestions
p. T114

Chalkboard Examples

1. List the members of the range of $f: t \rightarrow 4t - 3$ if the domain $D = \{0, 1, 2, 3\}$.
   $\{-3, 1, 5, 9\}$

Given $g: x \rightarrow 4x - x^2$, find the following values of g.

2. $g(1)$ $4(1) - 1^2 = 3$
3. $g(-1)$
   $4(-1) - (-1)^2 = -5$
4. $g(2)$ $4(2) - 2^2 = 4$

Given $F(s) = s^2 + 4s - 5$, find the following values of F.

5. $F(0)$
   $0^2 + 4(0) - 5 = -5$
6. $F(-2)$ $(-2)^2 + 4(-2) - 5 = -9$
7. $F(1)$ $1^2 + 4(1) - 5 = 0$

9-4 Functions Defined by Equations

Objective To understand what a function is and how to find its values.

An equation such as $y = 7x + 1$ assigns to each number in the domain of the variable x another number, the value of y. For example, if the domain of x is $\{2, 4, 6\}$, the equation $y = 7x + 1$ assigns the following values to y:

$$y = 7 \cdot 2 + 1 = 15$$
$$y = 7 \cdot 4 + 1 = 29$$
$$y = 7 \cdot 6 + 1 = 43$$

D		R
2	→	15
4	→	29
6	→	43

Thus, the given equation pairs each member of $\{2, 4, 6\}$ with a single member of $\{15, 29, 43\}$, as shown by the diagram. This example illustrates the mathematical idea of a *function.*

A **function** consists of two sets, the **domain** and the **range,** and a *rule* that assigns to each member of the domain *exactly one* member of the range. Each member of the range must be assigned to *at least one* member of the domain.

In the preceding example, the rule that defines the function is the equation $y = 7x + 1$, the domain D is $\{2, 4, 6\}$, and the range R is $\{15, 29, 43\}$.

The rule that defines a function may also be written using an arrow notation and a single letter, such as f, g, F, or H, to name the function. The **arrow notation**

$$f: x \longrightarrow 7x + 1$$

is read "the function f that assigns $7x + 1$ to x" or "the function f that pairs x with $7x + 1$." To specify a function completely, you must also describe the domain of the function. The numbers assigned by the rule then form the range.

Example 1 List the members of the range of

$$g: x \longrightarrow 4 + 3x - x^2$$

if the domain $D = \{-1, 0, 1, 2\}$.

Solution In $4 + 3x - x^2$ replace x with each member of D to find the members of the range R.

x	$4 + 3x - x^2$
-1	$4 + 3(-1) - (-1)^2 = 0$
0	$4 + 3(0) - 0^2 = 4$
1	$4 + 3(1) - 1^2 = 6$
2	$4 + 3(2) - 2^2 = 6$

$\therefore R = \{0, 4, 6\}$ ***Answer***

Notice that the function g in Example 1 assigns the number 6 to both 1 and 2. In specifying the range of g, however, you name 6 only once.

Members of the range of a function are called **values of the function.** Thus, in Example 1, the values of the function g are 0, 4, and 6. To indicate that the function g assigns to 2 the value 6, you write

$$g(2) = 6$$

which may be read "g of 2 equals 6" or "the value of g at 2 is 6." Notice that $g(2)$ is *not* the product of g and 2. It names the number that g assigns to 2.

Example 2 Given $F: z \rightarrow z^4 - 1$ with the set of real numbers as the domain, find **a.** $F(1)$ **b.** $F(-1)$ **c.** $F(2)$.

Solution First write the equation: $F(z) = z^4 - 1$
Then: **a.** $F(1) = 1^4 - 1 = 0$
b. $F(-1) = (-1)^4 - 1 = 0$
c. $F(2) = 2^4 - 1 = 15$

You may use whatever variable you choose to define a function. For example, $G: t \rightarrow t^4 - 1$ with the set of real numbers as the domain is the same function as F in Example 2. Both F and G assign to each real number its fourth power decreased by 1.

Oral Exercises

Given the function g: $x \longrightarrow 5 - 2x$, find the following values of g.

1. $g(0)$ 5 **2.** $g(-1)$ 7 **3.** $g(1)$ 3 **4.** $g(2)$ 1

5. $g(-2)$ 9 **6.** $g(5)$ -5 **7.** $g(8)$ -11 **8.** $g(-8)$ 21

State the range of each function.

9. $f: w \rightarrow w + 3$, $D = \{0, 1, 2\}$ $\{3, 4, 5\}$

10. $g: n \rightarrow 4 - n$, $D = \{-1, 0, 1\}$ $\{5, 4, 3\}$

11. $F: p \rightarrow p^3$, $D = \left\{-\frac{1}{3}, 0, \frac{1}{3}\right\}$ $\left\{-\frac{1}{27}, 0, \frac{1}{27}\right\}$

12. $G: x \rightarrow x^2 - 1$, $D = \{-1, 0, 1\}$ $\{0, -1\}$

13. $h: x \rightarrow 5x^2$, $D = \{0, 1, 2\}$ $\{0, 5, 20\}$

14. $H: a \rightarrow a^3 + 2$, $D = \left\{0, \frac{1}{2}, 1\right\}$ $\left\{2, \frac{17}{8}, 3\right\}$

Complete the following statements about the function f: $x \longrightarrow x^2 - 4$.

15. The value of f at -2 is _?_. 0

16. The value of f at 2 is _?_. 0

17. The value of f at _?_ is -4. 0

18. The value of f at both _?_ and _?_ is 0. 2, -2

Common Errors

Students sometimes make errors in finding the value of a function such as $f(x) = -x^2$ because they think that $-x^2 = (-x)^2$. Be sure to point out why these two expressions are not equal.

Some students may not understand the difference between the notation $f(0)$ and the equation $f(x) = 0$ (see Written Exercises 35–40). Be sure students realize the meaning of each (see also Exercises 33–36 on page 417 and the Extra on page 567).

Occasionally students think that fractional expressions such as Written Exercises 21, 22, 27, and 28 are meaningless when the value of the variable is 0. Show them that this is not the case. Remind them that such expressions are meaningless only if the denominator equals 0.

Supplementary Material

Practice Master 54

Suggested Assignments

Minimum
Day 1: 406/2–30 even
R 403/*Self-Test* 1
Day 2: 406/32–44 even
410/1, 5
Day 2 finishes Sec. 9-4 and covers Sec. 9-5.

Average
Day 1: 406/2–34 even
S 400/35–37
Day 2: 406/35–45
410/1, 5, 7
Day 2 finishes Sec. 9-4 and covers Sec. 9-5.

Maximum
Day 1: 406/2–34 even
R 403/*Self-Test 1*
Day 2: 406/35–46
410/1–7 odd
Day 2 finishes Sec. 9-4 and covers Sec. 9-5.

Additional A Exercises

1. Given $f: x \to 7 - 2x$, find the value of $f(-3)$. 13
2. Given $H(s) = s^2 + 3s$, find the value of $H\left(\frac{1}{2}\right)$. $\frac{7}{4}$

Find all the values of each function.

3. $f(x) = x^2 + 1$, $D = \left\{-1, 0, 1, \frac{1}{2}, 2\right\}$ 2, 1, $\frac{5}{4}$, 5
4. $g(x) = \frac{12}{2x + 1}$, $D = \{-1, 0, 3\}$ $-12, 12, \frac{12}{7}$

Written Exercises

Given $f: x \longrightarrow 7 - 2x$, find the following values of f.

A 1. $f(0)$ 7 2. $f(1)$ 5 3. $f(-1)$ 9 4. $f(-2)$ 11

5. $f(-4)$ 15 6. $f(5)$ -3 7. $f\left(\frac{1}{2}\right)$ 6 8. $f\left(-\frac{1}{2}\right)$ 8

Given $H(s) = s^2 + 3s$, find the following values of H.

9. $H(-3)$ 0 10. $H(0)$ 0 11. $H(1)$ 4 12. $H(-1)$ -2

13. $H(-2)$ -2 14. $H(3)$ 18 15. $H\left(-\frac{2}{3}\right)$ $-\frac{14}{9}$ 16. $H\left(\frac{1}{3}\right)$ $\frac{10}{9}$

Find all the values of each function.

17. $g(x) = 5x + 1$, $D = \{-1, 0, 1\}$ $\{-4, 1, 6\}$
18. $f(x) = 3x - 4$, $D = \{1, 2, 3\}$ $\{-1, 2, 5\}$
19. $f(x) = 4 - 3x - x^2$, $D = \{1, 2, 4\}$ $\{0, -6, -24\}$
20. $m(x) = x^2 + 3x - 4$, $D = \{-1, -2, -4\}$ $\{-6, -6, 0\}$
21. $G(n) = 6 + \frac{1}{n + 2}$, $D = \{-3, -1, 0\}$ $\left\{5, 7, \frac{13}{2}\right\}$
22. $F(t) = \frac{8}{3t + 1}$, $D = \{-1, 0, 1\}$ $\{-4, 8, 2\}$

Find the range of each function.

23. $s: z \to 5 - 4z$, $D = \{-2, 0, 2\}$ $\{13, 5, -3\}$
24. $h: y \to -1 - 2y$, $D = \{-3, 0, 1\}$ $\{5, -1, -3\}$
25. $r: x \to \frac{10}{x}$, $D = \{1, 2, -5\}$ $\{10, 5, -2\}$
26. $n: t \to \frac{12}{t - 1}$, $D = \{2, 3, 4\}$ $\{12, 6, 4\}$
27. $K: p \to \frac{p^2 + 1}{3p - 1}$, $D = \{-1, 0, 1\}$ $\left\{-\frac{1}{2}, -1, 1\right\}$
28. $M: v \to \frac{v^2 - v}{v + 1}$, $D = \{-2, 0, 2\}$ $\left\{-6, 0, \frac{2}{3}\right\}$

B 29. $g: a \to 4a^2 - 1$, $D = \{-1, 0, 1\}$ $\{3, -1\}$
30. $h: b \to (b - 3)^2$, $D = \{0, 2, 4\}$ $\{9, 1\}$
31. $f: z \to z^2 - 5z + 6$, $D = \{2, 3, 4\}$ $\{0, 2\}$
32. $k: x \to x^3 - 5x^2 + 6x$, $D = \{0, 2, 3\}$ $\{0\}$
33. $G: t \to (t^2 + 2t)^2$, $D = \{-2, 0, 1, 2\}$ $\{0, 9, 64\}$
34. $F: p \to p(1 - p^2)^3$, $D = \{-2, -1, 0, 1\}$ $\{54, 0\}$

In each of Exercises 35–40, (a) find $f(0)$; (b) solve $f(x) = 0$.

35. $f(x) = 2x - 12$ -12; 6
36. $f(x) = -\frac{1}{2}x + 5$ 5; 10
37. $f(x) = x^4 - x^2$ 0; $\{0, 1, -1\}$
38. $f(x) = x - x^3$ 0; $\{0, 1, -1\}$
39. $f(x) = \frac{x + 1}{x - 2}$ $-\frac{1}{2}$; -1
40. $f(x) = \frac{x^2 - 3x + 2}{x + 1}$ 2; $\{1, 2\}$

Given that $f(x) = 3x + 4$ and $g(x) = -x^2$, find each of the following.

41. $\frac{1}{2}g(6)$ -18 42. $2f(5)$ 38 43. $f(1) + g(1)$ 6 44. $f(2) \cdot g(2)$ -40

In Exercises 45–47, let $f(x) = x^2$ and $g(x) = 2x$. Find each of the following. (*Hint:* To find $g[f(2)]$, first find $f(2)$.)

C 45. a. $g(1)$ 2 b. $f(1)$ 1 c. $g[f(1)]$ 2 d. $f[g(1)]$ 4

46. a. $g(-2)$ -4 b. $f(-2)$ 4 c. $g[f(-2)]$ 8 d. $f[g(-2)]$ 16

47. Is there any real number x for which $f[g(x)] = g[f(x)]$? If there is such a number, find it. If there is no such number, explain why not. yes; 0

48. If $f(x) = x + 1$, and $g[f(x)] = x$, what is $g(x)$? $g(x) = x - 1$

Computer Exercises

For students with some programming experience

Write a BASIC program to calculate the value of a given function for values of x entered with READ . . . DATA statements. Recall that the BASIC statement that corresponds to $f(x) = x^2$ is DEF FNA(X) = X↑2. RUN the program for the functions given below.

1. $f(x) = 3x - 7$; $x = -2, 0, 1, 10$ $-13, -7, -4, 23$
2. $f(x) = x^2 + 3x + 2$; $x = -1, -2, 0, 1$ $0, 0, 2, 6$
3. $f(x) = 2^x$; $x = -4, -1, 0, 1, 2, 4$ $0.0625, 0.5, 1, 2, 4, 16$
4. $f(x) = 9 - x^2$; $x = -3, -1, 0, 2, 3, 4$ $0, 8, 9, 5, 0, -7$

Challenge

1. a. Find each sum.

$$\frac{1}{1\cdot 2} + \frac{1}{2\cdot 3} = \underline{\ ?\ } \quad \frac{2}{3}$$

$$\frac{1}{1\cdot 2} + \frac{1}{2\cdot 3} + \frac{1}{3\cdot 4} = \underline{\ ?\ } \quad \frac{3}{4}$$

$$\frac{1}{1\cdot 2} + \frac{1}{2\cdot 3} + \frac{1}{3\cdot 4} + \frac{1}{4\cdot 5} = \underline{\ ?\ } \quad \frac{4}{5}$$

b. If this addition pattern were continued for 100 fractions, what would the sum be? $\frac{100}{101}$

c. If this addition pattern were continued for n fractions, what would the sum be? $\frac{n}{n+1}$

2. a. Find each sum.

$$\frac{1}{1\cdot 3} + \frac{1}{3\cdot 5} = \underline{\ ?\ } \quad \frac{2}{5}$$

$$\frac{1}{1\cdot 3} + \frac{1}{3\cdot 5} + \frac{1}{5\cdot 7} = \underline{\ ?\ } \quad \frac{3}{7}$$

$$\frac{1}{1\cdot 3} + \frac{1}{3\cdot 5} + \frac{1}{5\cdot 7} + \frac{1}{7\cdot 9} = \underline{\ ?\ } \quad \frac{4}{9}$$

b. If this addition pattern were continued for 50 fractions, what would the sum be? $\frac{50}{101}$

c. If this addition pattern were continued for n fractions, what would the sum be? $\frac{n}{2n+1}$

Find the range of each function.

5. $f: x \to 3x - 2$, $D = \{-7, 0, 5\}$ $R = \{-23, -2, 13\}$

6. $g: x \to \frac{x^2 + 2}{x - 3}$, $D = \{2, 4, 5\}$ $R = \left\{-6, 18, \frac{27}{2}\right\}$

Mixed Review Exercises

Express as a polynomial.

1. $(2x - 7)(5x + 3)$ $10x^2 - 29x - 21$
2. $(2m + 3)^2$ $4m^2 + 12m + 9$
3. Factor: $x^2 - 4x - 77$ $(x - 11)(x + 7)$
4. Write an equation in standard form of the line that has slope $\frac{1}{4}$ and y-intercept -7. $x - 4y = 28$

Teaching Suggestions
p. T114

Suggested Extensions
p. T115

Chalkboard Examples

1. The table below shows the amount of rainfall in Center City during the first 6 months of the year.

Month	Rainfall (in mm)
January	12
February	15
March	21
April	47
May	52
June	39

a. Make a bar graph for the function.

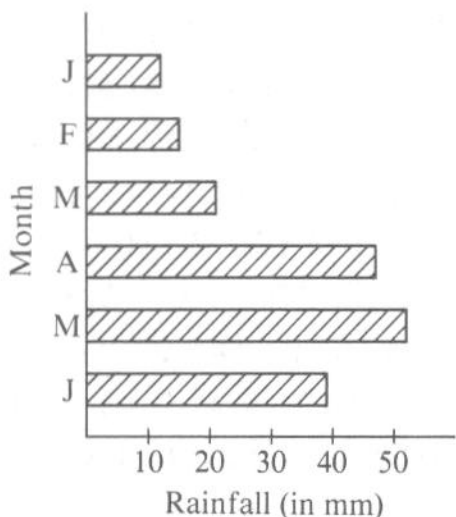

b. List the domain and range of the function.
$D = \{$January, February, March, April, May, June$\}$
$R = \{12, 15, 21, 47, 52, 39\}$

c. Why does the table describe a function?
Each member of the domain is paired with exactly one member of the range.

9-5 Functions Described by Tables and Graphs

Objective To define functions without using equations.

Species	Number of Chromosomes
Corn	40
Domestic fowl	78
Fruit fly	8
Horse	64
Human	46
Mouse	40
Tomato	24

The table at the right shows the number of chromosomes associated with each of several biological species. This association is a function. But, unlike the functions in Section 9-4, the chromosome function does not have a rule that can be given by an equation. Instead, the rule is incorporated in the table of ordered pairs. The domain of the function is the set of first coordinates:

{corn, domestic fowl, fruit fly, horse, human, mouse, tomato}.

The range of the function is the set of second coordinates:

$$\{8, 24, 40, 46, 64, 78\}.$$

It is easier to compare the chromosome numbers if the facts are displayed in a *bar graph.* In the following graph, the members of the domain are listed on the left along the vertical axis. For each member of the domain a horizontal bar is drawn to represent the corresponding value in the range of the function. Notice that the scale of the bars starts at zero, so that their relative lengths are correct.

Chromosomes in Various Species

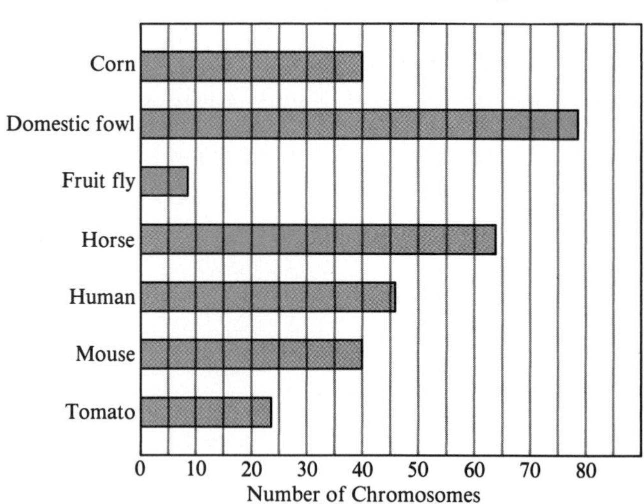

When the members of the domain of a function are in a numerical succession, it may be better to use a *broken-line graph* such as the one shown below.

Receipts at Chuck's Chicken Restaurants

Fiscal Year	Receipts (in millions)
1975	$250
1977	265
1979	246
1981	280
1983	300
1985	370

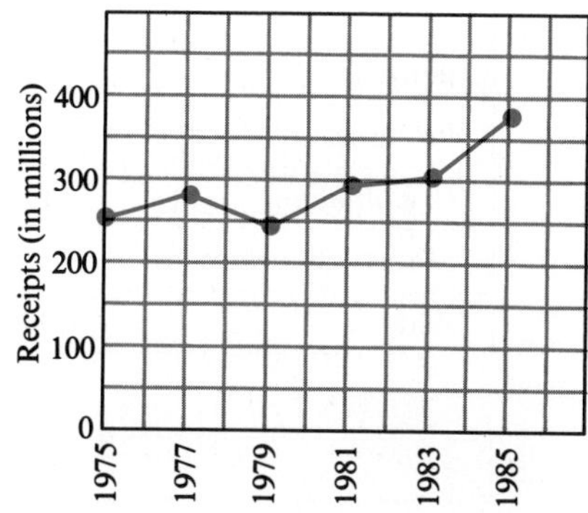

Note that in this graph the members of the domain are listed along the horizontal axis.

The line segments of the graph do *not* necessarily show the actual receipts for even-numbered years. They do, however, help you to see the trends over time.

Oral Exercises

State the domain and range of the function shown by each table.

1.

Tree	Height in feet
Douglas fir	40
Juniper	10
Oak	25
Poplar	30
Weeping willow	30
Yew	12

2.

Appliance	Percent of total electrical energy used in the home
Air-conditioner	8
Clothes dryer	5
Electric range	15
Refrigerator	20
T.V.	9
Water heater	38
All others	5

2. Make a broken-line graph for the data given below.

Month	Hours of Overtime
July	12
August	27
September	10
October	31
November	22
December	45

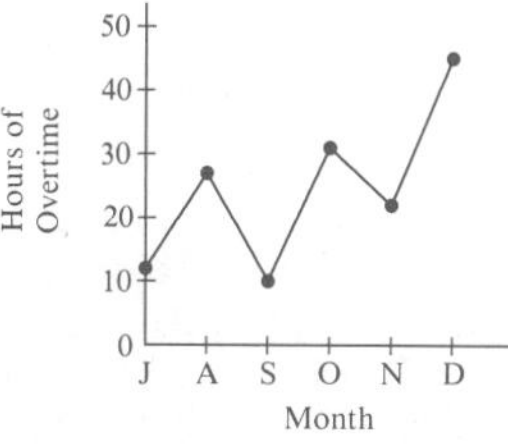

Common Error

Students may have trouble graphing functions such as those in Written Exercises 3, 4, 6, and 7, where elements of the range are negative. Point out that it is reasonable for the bars of bar graphs to be drawn from zero in one direction to represent positive values of the range and from zero in the opposite direction to represent negative values.

Additional Answers
Oral Exercises

1. $D = \{$Douglas fir, juniper, oak, poplar, weeping willow, yew$\}$;
   $R = \{10, 12, 25, 30, 40\}$
2. $D = \{$air-conditioner, clothes dryer, electric range, refrigerator, t.v., water heater, all others$\}$;
   $R = \{5, 8, 9, 15, 20, 38\}$

Additional Answers
Oral Exercises

3. $D = \{$acetic acid, benzene, bromine, cyclobutane, methyl chloride, water$\}$;
$R = \{-24, 13, 59, 80, 100, 118\}$
4. $D = \{$clothing, food, housing, medical care, utilities$\}$;
$R = \{-2, -1, 1.5, 3.5, 4\}$
5. $D = \{1970, 1971, 1972, 1973, 1974, 1975, 1976, 1977, 1978, 1979, 1980\}$;
$R = \{1.30, 1.68, 1.80, 3.44, 10.17, 10.37, 11.23, 12.27, 12.37, 19.49, 31.50\}$
6. $D = \{1980, 1981, 1982, 1983, 1984, 1985, 1986\}$;
$R = \{-0.30, 0.75, 0.90, 1.12, 1.43, 1.65, 2.05\}$

Supplementary Material

Resource Book, p. 109

Suggested Assignments

Minimum
Day 2 of Sec. 9-4 finishes Sec. 9-4 and covers Sec. 9-5.

Average
Day 2 of Sec. 9-4 finishes Sec. 9-4 and covers Sec. 9-5.

Maximum
Day 2 of Sec. 9-4 finishes Sec. 9-4 and covers Sec. 9-5.

State the domain and range of the function shown by each table.

3.

Substance	Boiling point (°C)
Acetic acid	118
Benzene	80
Bromine	59
Cyclobutane	13
Methyl chloride	−24
Water	100

4.

Item	Percent change in cost over one year
Clothing	−2
Food	−1
Housing	3.5
Medical care	4
Utilities	1.5

5.

Cost of a Barrel of Crude Oil											
Year	1970	1971	1972	1973	1974	1975	1976	1977	1978	1979	1980
Cost	\$1.30	\$1.68	\$1.80	\$3.44	\$10.17	\$10.37	\$11.23	\$12.37	\$12.27	\$19.49	\$31.50

6.

Earnings Per Share of Common Foods Corp.							
Year	1980	1981	1982	1983	1984	1985	1986
Earnings per Share (\$)	−0.30	0.75	0.90	1.12	1.43	1.65	2.05

Written Exercises

A **1-4.** Make a bar graph for the function shown in each table in Oral Exercises 1–4.

5-6. Make a broken-line graph for each function shown in Oral Exercises 5 and 6.

7. Show on a broken-line graph beginning with January the average monthly temperature (°C) in Greenough:

−2, −0.5, 4, 12, 18, 23, 26, 25.5, 21, 16, 7, 1.5

8. Make a broken-line graph of the number of students with colds recorded for the months September through June:

10, 21, 25, 34, 32, 40, 42, 30, 24, 15

Exercises 9 and 10 require you to find data. Sources that you may use are results of experiments in your science classes, surveys that you conduct in your class or neighborhood, or reference materials in your library.

Answers may vary.

B **9.** Find data suitable for presentation as a bar graph, and then draw the graph.

10. Find data suitable for presentation on a broken-line graph, and then draw the graph.

Application / *Line of Best Fit*

Is your future income related to the number of years you attend school? Is there a correlation between achievers in mathematics and achievers in physics? Scatter graphs or diagrams often are used to show researchers whether a relationship exists between two measurements. Researchers can then base predictions on the patterns they observe in these relationships.

In the chart below are shown physics marks and mathematics marks for the same eight people. Each pair of measurements is plotted as a point (x, y) on a graph. If the plotted points tend to cluster around a line (shown in color), called the *line of best fit,* since it fits closer to the points than any other line, then a clear relationship exists.

Mathematics Marks	Physics Marks
28	20
52	44
80	72
48	52
50	60
96	84
98	95
35	28

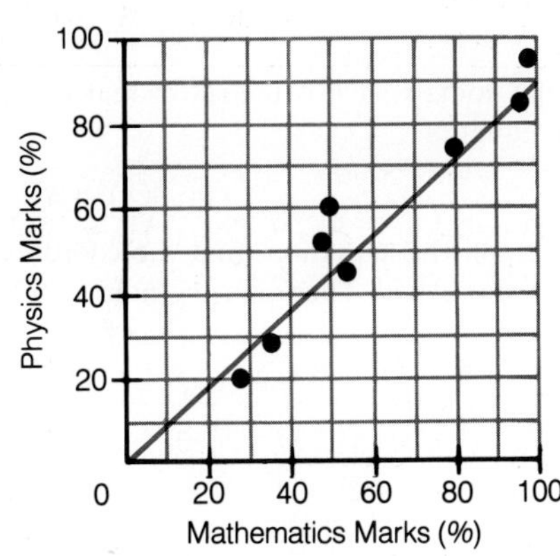

With sufficient data, mathematicians can then make predictions based on this correlation. Although you can fit a line "by eye," mathematicians have derived exact formulas for determining the line of best fit. Determining patterns in relationships is an important aspect of a mathematician's or statistician's work.

Additional Answers
Written Exercises

2.

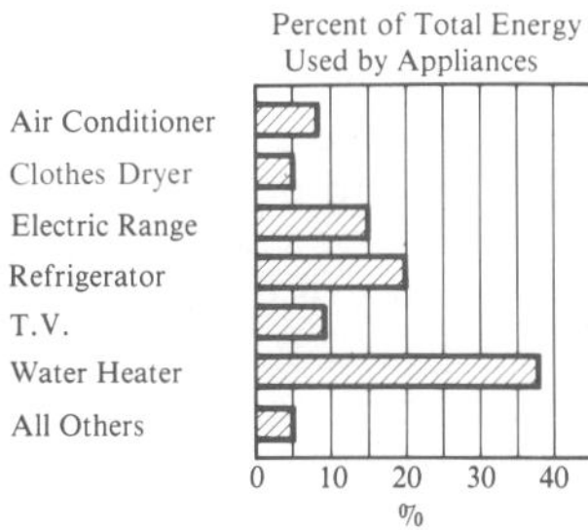

4.

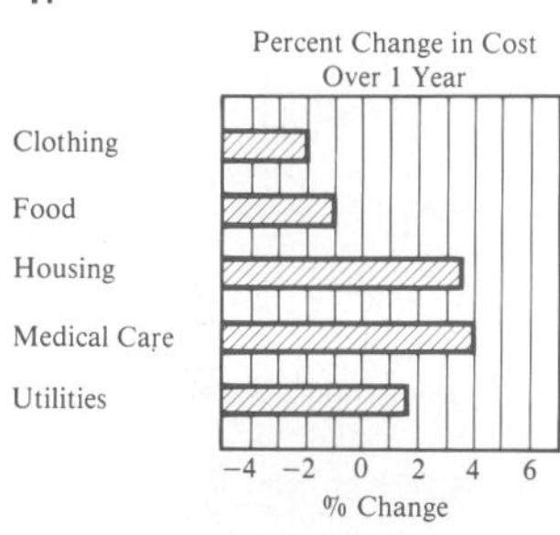

6.

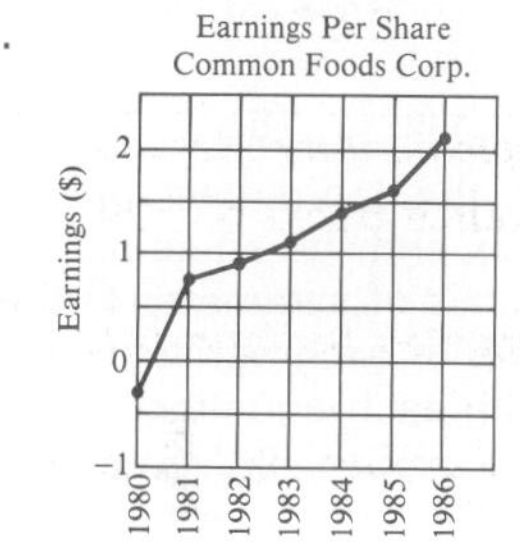

8.

Number of Students with Colds

Teaching Suggestions
p. T115

Chalkboard Examples

State whether the graph of each quadratic equation opens upward or downward. Find the coordinates of the vertex of the graph.

1. $y = 2x^2 - 2x + 1$
   upward;
   x-coordinate of vertex:
   $-\frac{b}{2a} = -\frac{(-2)}{2(2)} = \frac{1}{2}$
   y-coordinate of vertex:
   $2\left(\frac{1}{2}\right)^2 - 2\left(\frac{1}{2}\right) + 1 = \frac{1}{2}$
   vertex: $\left(\frac{1}{2}, \frac{1}{2}\right)$
2. $y = -x^2 + 8x - 1$
   downward;
   x-coordinate of vertex:
   $-\frac{b}{2a} = -\frac{8}{2(-1)} = 4$
   y-coordinate of vertex:
   $-(4)^2 + 8(4) - 1 = 15$
   vertex: (4, 15)

Find the coordinates of the vertex and the equation of the axis of symmetry of the graph of each equation. Graph each equation.

3. $y = 2x^2 - 4x + 1$
   $-\frac{b}{2a} = -\frac{(-4)}{2(2)} = 1$

   $y = 2(1)^2 - 4(1) + 1 = -1$
   vertex: $(1, -1)$
   axis of symmetry: $x = 1$

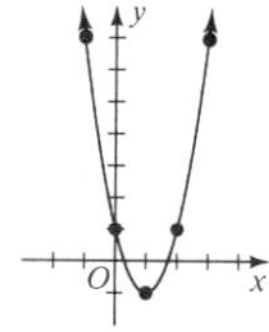

9-6 Linear and Quadratic Functions

Objective To graph linear and quadratic functions.

The function g defined by the formula

$$g(x) = 3x - 2$$

is called a *linear function.* If its domain is the set of all real numbers, then we call the straight line that is the graph of the equation

$$y = g(x) = 3x - 2$$

the **graph** of g. The slope of the graph is 3; the y-intercept is -2.

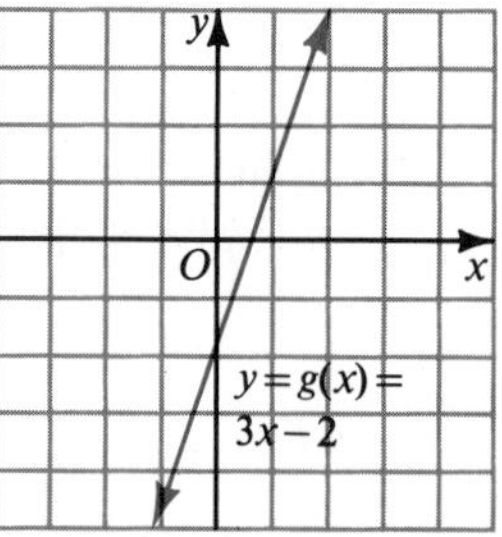

In general,

> A function f given by
>
> $$f(x) = mx + b$$
>
> is a **linear function.**
>
> If its domain is the set of real numbers, then its graph is the straight line with slope m and y-intercept b.

Now, consider the function h defined by the formula

$$h(x) = x^2 - 2x - 2.$$

If the domain of h is the set of real numbers, then its graph is the graph of the equation

$$y = h(x) = x^2 - 2x - 2.$$

To graph this equation, find the coordinates of selected points, as shown in the table below. Then plot the points and connect them with a smooth curve.

x	$x^2 - 2x - 2 = y$
-2	$(-2)^2 - 2(-2) - 2 = 6$
-1	$(-1)^2 - 2(-1) - 2 = 1$
0	$0^2 - 2(0) - 2 = -2$
1	$1^2 - 2(1) - 2 = -3$
2	$2^2 - 2(2) - 2 = -2$
3	$3^2 - 2(3) - 2 = 1$
4	$4^2 - 2(4) - 2 = 6$

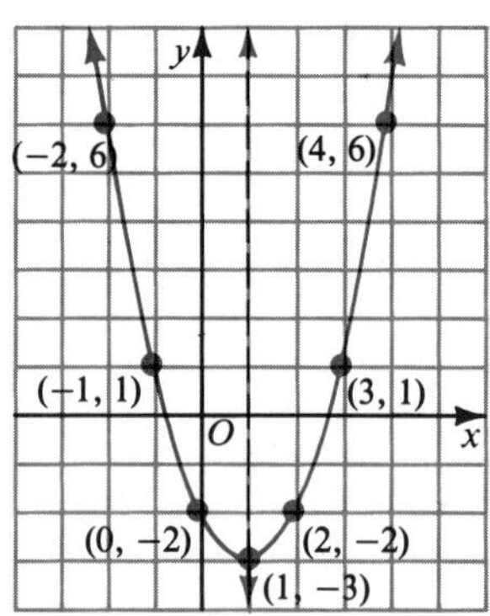

The curve shown beside the table is a **parabola.** This parabola opens upward and has a **minimum point** (lowest point): $(1, -3)$. The y-coordinate of this point is the least value of the function.

The vertical line $x = 1$, containing the minimum point, is called the **axis of symmetry** of the parabola. If you fold the graph along the axis of symmetry, the two halves of the parabola coincide.

Compare the parabola just seen with the graph of the function k defined by the equation

$$y = k(x) = -x^2 + 2x + 2.$$

x	$-x^2 + 2x + 2 = y$
-2	$-(-2)^2 + 2(-2) + 2 = -6$
-1	$-(-1)^2 + 2(-1) + 2 = -1$
0	$-0^2 + 2(0) + 2 = 2$
1	$-1^2 + 2(1) + 2 = 3$
2	$-2^2 + 2(2) + 2 = 2$
3	$-3^2 + 2(3) + 2 = -1$
4	$-4^2 + 2(4) + 2 = -6$

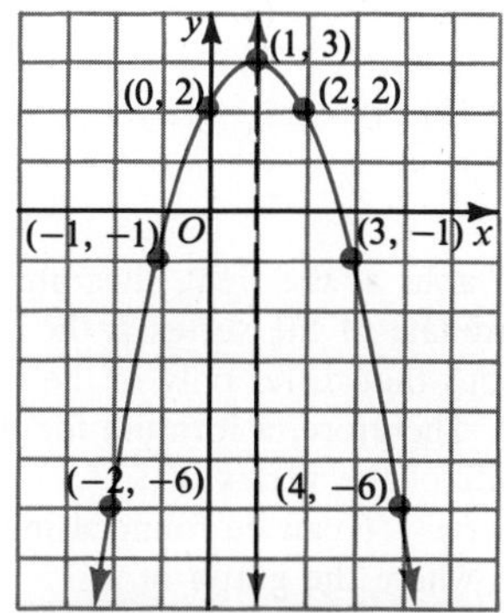

This graph is a parabola that opens downward and has a **maximum point** (highest point): $(1, 3)$. The y-coordinate of the maximum point is the greatest value of the function. Note that the maximum point $(1, 3)$ lies on the axis of symmetry, the line $x = 1$.

Parabolas occur in a variety of everyday settings. You can see them in bridges, arches, fountains, fireworks, and the spouts of water from a fireboat.

In general:

A function f given by

$$f(x) = ax^2 + bx + c \quad (a \neq 0)$$

is a **quadratic function.**
If its domain is the set of real numbers, then its graph is a parabola.
If a is positive, the parabola opens upward.
If a is negative, the parabola opens downward.

4. $y = -x^2 + 6x - 5$

$$-\frac{b}{2a} = -\frac{6}{2(-1)} = 3$$

$y = -(3)^2 + 6(3) - 5 = 4$

vertex: $(3, 4)$

axis of symmetry: $x = 3$

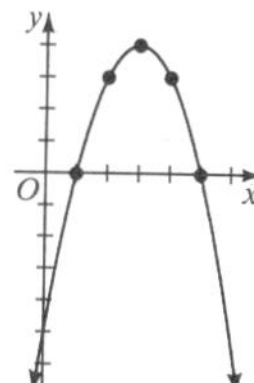

Common Errors

Sometimes students think that when a in the equation $f(x) = ax^2 + bx + c$ is positive a parabola has a maximum point and that when a is negative a parabola has a minimum point. Refer them to the last two statements on page 413, and show them that when a parabola *opens upward* it has a *minimum* point and that when a parabola *opens downward* it has a *maximum* point.

Some students may confuse maximum or minimum value with maximum or minimum point. Point out that the maximum (or minimum) value of a quadratic function is the y-coordinate of the maximum (or minimum) point of the graph of the quadratic function.

Supplementary Materials

Practice Master 55
Test 32
Resource Book, p. 110

Suggested Assignments

Minimum
416/1–17 odd, 19, 25
S 410/2, 7

Average
416/1–27 odd
S 402/34, 35

Maximum
416/1–31 odd, 32
S 407/47, 48

Additional A Exercises

1. Draw the graph of $f(x) = 2x + 1$.

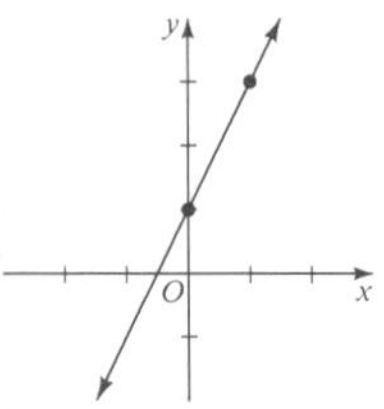

Find the coordinates of the vertex and the equation of the axis of symmetry of the graph of each equation. Use the vertex and at least six other points to graph the equation.

2. $y = -\frac{1}{2}x^2$

Graph shows $\left(1, -\frac{1}{2}\right)$, $\left(-1, -\frac{1}{2}\right)$, $(2, -2)$, $(-2, -2)$, $\left(3, -4\frac{1}{2}\right)$, $\left(-3, -4\frac{1}{2}\right)$

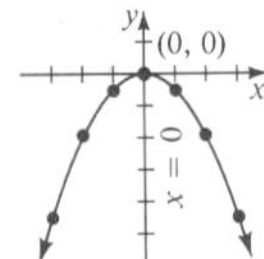

The minimum or maximum point of a parabola is called the **vertex.** Notice that in the examples shown on the previous pages, the points, except the vertex, occur in *pairs that have the same y-coordinate.* Also, the average of the x-coordinates of any such pair is the x-coordinate of the vertex. For the parabola on page 413:

Pairs of Points	
$(-2, -6)$	$(4, -6)$
$(-1, -1)$	$(3, -1)$
$(0, 2)$	$(2, 2)$

Average of x-coordinates

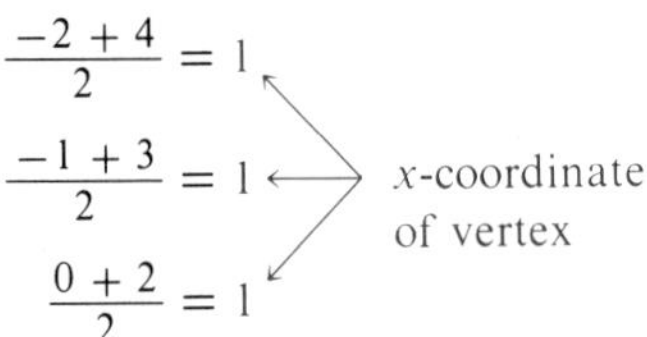

The graphs at the right illustrate that the x-coordinate of the vertex is the same for equations that differ only in the constant term. Therefore, a formula for the x-coordinate of the vertex of $y = ax^2 + bx + c$ can be found using the two points where the graph of $y = ax^2 + bx$ crosses the x-axis; that is, the points where $y = 0$.

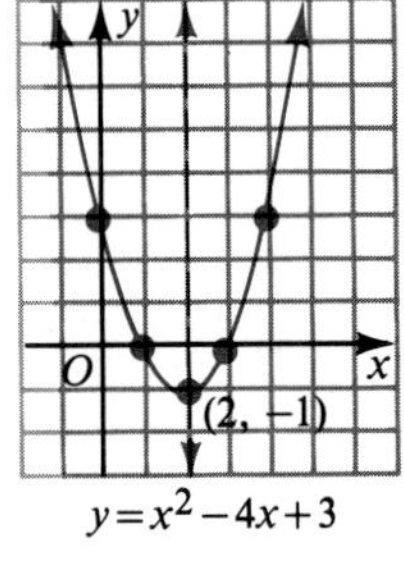

$y = x^2 - 4x + 3$

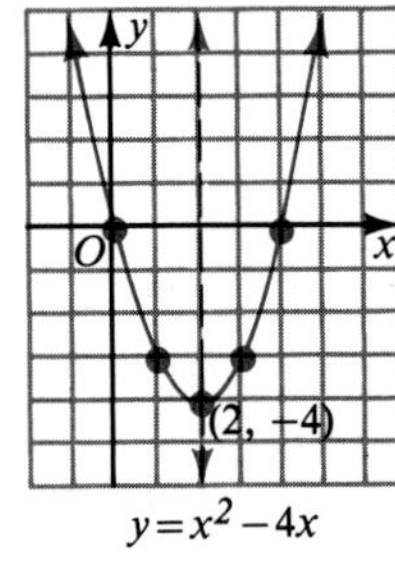

$y = x^2 - 4x$

Let $y = 0$:

$$0 = ax^2 + bx$$
$$0 = x(ax + b)$$
$$x = 0 \quad \text{or} \quad ax + b = 0$$
$$\therefore x = 0 \quad \text{or} \quad x = -\frac{b}{a}$$

The average of these x-coordinates is $\dfrac{0 + \left(-\frac{b}{a}\right)}{2}$, or $-\dfrac{b}{2a}$.

Therefore:

The x-coordinate of the vertex of the parabola

$$y = ax^2 + bx + c \quad (a \neq 0)$$

is $-\dfrac{b}{2a}$.

The axis of symmetry is the line $x = -\dfrac{b}{2a}$.

Unless otherwise stated, you may assume that the domain of each linear or quadratic function is the set of real numbers.

Example Find the coordinates of the vertex of the graph of

$$H: x \longrightarrow 2x^2 + 4x - 3.$$

Use the vertex and six other points to graph H. Identify and draw the axis of symmetry.

Solution 1. x-coordinate of vertex $= -\frac{b}{2a} = -\frac{4}{4} = -1$

2. To find the y-coordinate of the vertex, substitute -1 for x.

$$\begin{aligned} y &= 2x^2 + 4x - 3 \\ y &= 2(-1)^2 + 4(-1) - 3 \\ &= 2 - 4 - 3 = -5 \end{aligned}$$

$\therefore$ the vertex is $(-1, -5)$.

3. Construct a table. For values of x, choose three numbers greater than -1 and three less than -1 to obtain paired points with the same y-coordinate.

	x	$2x^2 + 4x - 3 = y$
	-4	$2(-4)^2 + 4(-4) - 3 = 13$
	-3	$2(-3)^2 + 4(-3) - 3 = 3$
	-2	$2(-2)^2 + 4(-2) - 3 = -3$
Vertex	-1	$2(-1)^2 + 4(-1) - 3 = -5$
	0	$2(0)^2 + 4(0) - 3 = -3$
	1	$2(1)^2 + 4(1) - 3 = 3$
	2	$2(2)^2 + 4(2) - 3 = 13$

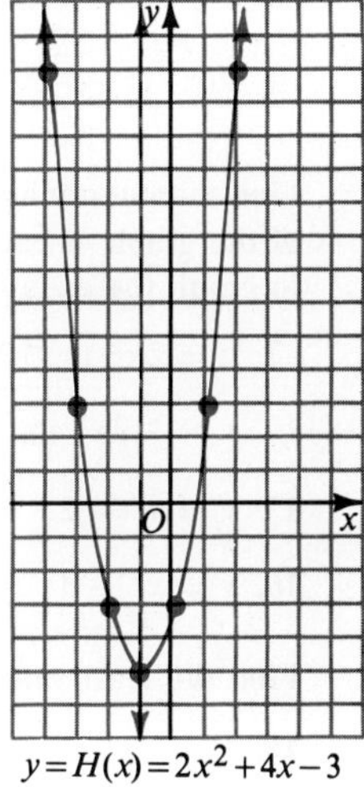

$y = H(x) = 2x^2 + 4x - 3$

4. Plot the points, and through them draw a smooth curve.

5. The axis of symmetry is the line $x = -1$ (shown as a dashed line on the graph).

Oral Exercises

State the slope and y-intercept of the graph of each linear function.

1. $f: x \rightarrow -2x + 7$ -2; 7
2. $g: x \rightarrow 4x - 8$ 4; -8
3. $p(x) = 4 - \frac{5x}{2}$ $-\frac{5}{2}$; 4
4. $t(x) = -\frac{x}{2}$ $-\frac{1}{2}$; 0
5. $t(x) = 0$ 0; 0
6. $h(x) = 9$ 0; 9

3. $y = 3x^2$

$(-3, 27)$, $(3, 27)$, $x = 0$, $(-2, 12)$, $(2, 12)$, $(-1, 3)$, $(1, 3)$, O, x, y

4. $y = x^2 + x - 12$

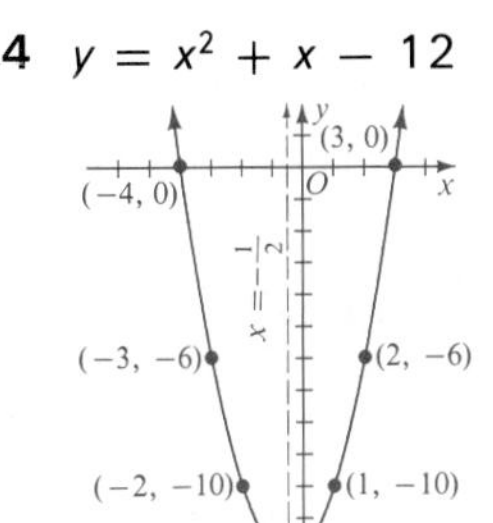

5. Find the least value of $f(x) = x^2 + 6x + 8$. -1

6. Find the greatest value of $f(x) = 3x - x^2$. $\frac{9}{4}$

Mixed Review Exercises

1. Factor: $3a + 6b - a^2 - 2ab$
$(3 - a)(a + 2b)$

2. Solve: $15x^2 + 16 = 34x$
$x = \frac{2}{3}, \frac{8}{5}$

3. Express $\frac{m^3 + 5m^2 + m + 5}{m^2 + 10m + 25}$ in simplest form, noting any restrictions on the variable.
$\frac{m^2 + 1}{m + 5}$, $m \neq -5$

4. Find $f(-3)$ given $f(x) = x^2 + 4x + 1$. -2

Additional Answers Written Exercises

2.

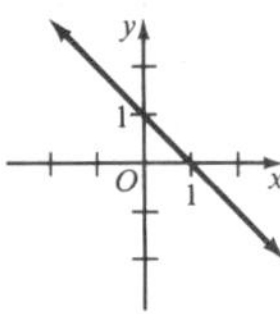

4.

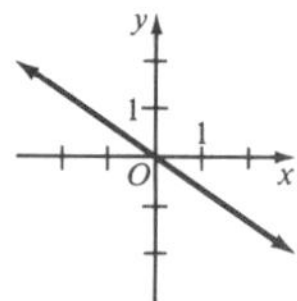

8.

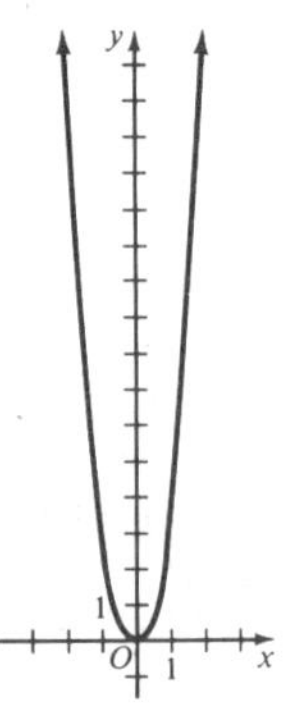

12.

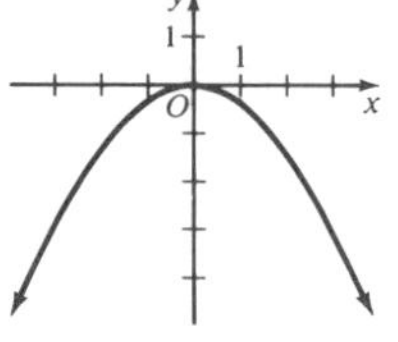

16.

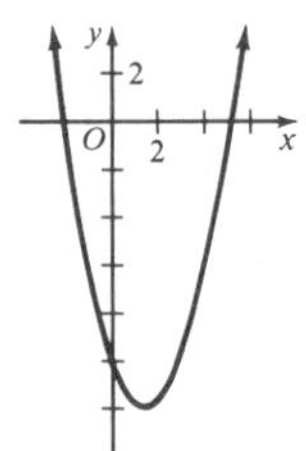

18.

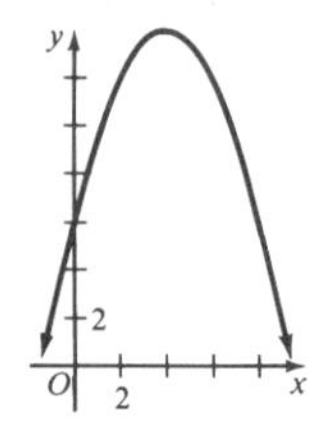

State whether the graph of each quadratic equation opens upward or downward.

7. $y = x^2 - 6x + 3$ upward
8. $y = -2x^2 + 3x + 1$ downward
9. $y = 4 - x^2$ downward
10. $x^2 - 4 = y$ upward
11. $3x^2 - 3x = y$ upward
12. $y = \frac{-x^2}{3}$ downward

State whether the graph of each quadratic function has a minimum or a maximum point.

13. $f\colon x \to x^2 - 4x + 1$ min.
14. $g\colon x \to -3 - 2x - x^2$ max.
15. $h\colon x \to 7x^2 - x$ min.
16. $P\colon x \to 1 - x^2$ max.
17. $T\colon x \to -8x^2 + x - 6$ max.
18. $f\colon x \to \frac{3x^2}{7}$ min.

Written Exercises

Draw the graph of each function.

A

1. $g\colon x \to x - 3$
2. $f\colon x \to -x + 1$
3. $q(x) = 2 - \frac{x}{3}$
4. $d(x) = -\frac{3}{4}x$
5. $r(x) = -7$
6. $n(x) = 0$

Find the coordinates of the vertex and the equation of the axis of symmetry of the graph of each equation. Use the vertex and at least six other points to graph the equation.

7. $y = 2x^2$ $(0, 0)$; $x = 0$
8. $y = 4x^2$ $(0, 0)$; $x = 0$
9. $y = -x^2$ $(0, 0)$; $x = 0$
10. $y = -3x^2$ $(0, 0)$; $x = 0$
11. $y = \frac{1}{3}x^2$ $(0, 0)$; $x = 0$
12. $y = -\frac{1}{3}x^2$ $(0, 0)$; $x = 0$
13. $y = x^2 - 2x$ $(1, -1)$; $x = 1$
14. $y = -x^2 + 4x$ $(2, 4)$; $x = 2$
15. $y = -x^2 - 5x + 6$ $\left(-\frac{5}{2}, \frac{49}{4}\right)$; $x = -\frac{5}{2}$
16. $y = x^2 - 3x - 10$ $\left(\frac{3}{2}, -\frac{49}{4}\right)$; $x = \frac{3}{2}$
17. $y = 2 - \frac{1}{2}x^2$ $(0, 2)$; $x = 0$
18. $y = 6 + 4x - \frac{1}{2}x^2$ $(4, 14)$; $x = 4$

Find the least value of each function.

19. $f\colon x \to x^2 + 5x$ $-\frac{25}{4}$
20. $g\colon x \to x^2 + 9$ 9
21. $h\colon x \to x^2 - x - 12$ $-\frac{49}{4}$
22. $t\colon x \to 4 - 10x + 5x^2$ -1
23. $G\colon x \to 9x^2 - 4$ -4
24. $F\colon x \to \frac{1}{4}x^2$ 0

Find the greatest value of each function.

25. $g\colon x \to -x^2 - 7x$ $\frac{49}{4}$
26. $f\colon x \to 4x - 2x^2$ 2
27. $H\colon x \to -x^2 - 8x - 15$ 1
28. $K\colon x \to 1 - 3x - 6x^2$ $\frac{11}{8}$
29. $f(x) = x - 2x^2$ $\frac{1}{8}$
30. $h(x) = 1 - \frac{1}{3}x^2$ 1

B

31. a. On the same set of axes draw the graphs of $y = x^2$, $y = x^2 + 1$, and $y = x^2 - 2$.
    b. Use your results in part (a) to describe the changes in the graph of $y = x^2 + c$ as the value of c increases; as c decreases.

32. **a.** On the same set of axes draw the graphs of $y = \frac{1}{2}x^2$, $y = x^2$, and $y = 2x^2$.
b. On the same set of axes draw the graphs of $y = -\frac{1}{2}x^2$, $y = -x^2$, and $y = -2x^2$.
c. Use your results in parts (a) and (b) to describe the change in the graph of $y = ax^2$ as $|a|$ increases. As $|a|$ increases, the graph becomes steeper.

The *zeros* of a function f are the values of x for which $f(x) = 0$. In Exercises 33 and 34, find (a) $f(0)$; (b) the zeros of f.

33. $f(x) = x^2 + 3x - 4$ -4; -4, 1

34. $f(x) = x^2 - 8x + 12$ 12; 6, 2

35. Interpret the zeros of the function f in terms of the graph of f. They are the x-intercepts.

36. Interpret $f(0)$ in terms of the graph of f. It is the y-intercept, the point where the graph crosses the y-axis.

Self-Test 2

Vocabulary

function (p. 404)
domain of a function (p. 404)
range of a function (p. 404)
arrow notation (p. 404)
value of a function (p. 405)
linear function (p. 412)
graph (p. 412)
parabola (p. 413)
minimum point (p. 413)
axis of symmetry (p. 413)
maximum point (p. 413)
quadratic function (p. 413)
vertex (p. 414)

1. Given $f(x) = 5x - 1$, find $f(2)$. 9 **Obj. 9-4, p. 404**
2. Find the range of g if $g\colon n \to n^2 + 2n + 3$ and $D = \{-1, 0, 1, 2, 3\}$. $R = \{2, 3, 6, 11, 18\}$
3. The table below shows a function. **Obj. 9-5, p. 408**
   a. State the domain and range of the function.
   b. Graph the function by means of a bar graph or a broken-line graph, whichever is more suitable.

Amount dissolved in 100 g of water at 20°C				
Substance	Boric Acid	Salt	Sodium Nitrate	Sugar
Amount	4.8 g	36.0 g	88.0 g	203.9 g

4. Find the coordinates of the vertex and the equation of the axis of symmetry of the graph of $y = 2x^2 - 4x + 1$. $(1, -1)$; $x = 1$ **Obj. 9-6, p. 412**
5. Find the least value of the function $f\colon x \to 1 + \frac{1}{5}x^2$. 1

Check your answers with those at the back of the book.

Quick Quiz

1. Given $g(x) = 3x + 5$, find $g(3)$. 14
2. Find the range of h if $h\colon t \to t^2 - t + 2$ and $D = \{-2, -1, 0, 1, 2\}$. $\{2, 4, 8\}$
3. The table below shows a function.

Item	Number Sold
Birds	7
Fish	41
Gerbils	15
Hamsters	25

   a. State the domain and range of the function. $D = \{$Birds, Fish, Gerbils, Hamsters$\}$ $R = \{7, 41, 15, 25\}$
   b. Graph the function by means of a bar graph or a broken-line graph, whichever is more suitable.

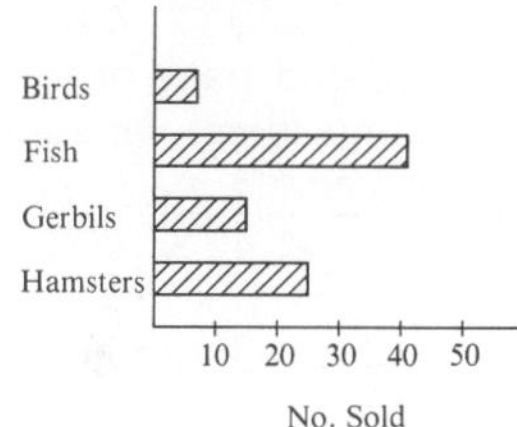

4. Find the coordinates of the vertex and the equation of the axis of symmetry of the graph of the equation $y = x^2 + 4x - 5$. vertex: $(-2, -9)$ axis of symmetry: $x = -2$
5. Find the least value of the function $g\colon x \to 2x^2 - 8x$. -8

Teaching Suggestions
p. T115

Chalkboard Examples

Find the constant of variation.

1. y varies directly as x, and $y = 12$ when $x = 48$.
$y = kx$
$k = \frac{y}{x} = \frac{12}{48} = \frac{1}{4}$

2. a varies directly as b, and $a = -14$ when $b = -2$.
$a = kb$
$k = \frac{a}{b} = \frac{-14}{-2} = 7$

3. If t varies directly as s, and $t = 75$ when $s = 25$, find t when $s = 5$.
$t = ks$; $75 = k(25)$;
$k = 3$
$t = 3s$; $t = 3(5) = 15$

4. Find the value of y if $(3, y)$ and $(7, 49)$ are ordered pairs of the same direct variation.
Method 1
$y = kx$; $49 = k(7)$;
$k = 7$
$y = 7x$; $y = 7(3) = 21$
Method 2
$\frac{y_1}{x_1} = \frac{y_2}{x_2}$; $\frac{y}{3} = \frac{49}{7}$;
$7y = 3(49)$
$y = 21$

5. The amount a babysitter earns is directly proportional to the number of hours worked. If \$7 is earned for 4 hours of work, how much is earned for 10 hours of work?
$\frac{7}{4} = \frac{x}{10}$; $x = 17.5$
\$17.50 is earned.

Variation

9-7 Direct Variation

Objective To use the concept of direct variation to solve problems.

The table below shows the weight w at sea level of a gold ingot whose volume is v cubic centimeters.

Volume in cubic centimeters: v	Weight in grams: w
1	19.1
2	38.2
3	57.3
4	76.4
5	95.5

You can see that

$$w = 19.1\,v$$

and that this equation defines a linear function. Notice that if the volume of the ingot is doubled, the weight is doubled; if the volume is tripled, the weight is tripled, and so on. You say that the weight *varies directly as* the volume. This function is an example of a *direct variation.*

A **linear direct variation** (or simply, a **direct variation**) is a function defined by an equation of the form

$$y = kx, \text{ where } k \text{ is a nonzero constant.}$$

You can say that *y varies directly as x*, or *y varies with x*. The constant k is called the **constant of variation.**

When the domain is the set of real numbers, the graph of a direct variation is a straight line with slope k that passes through the origin.

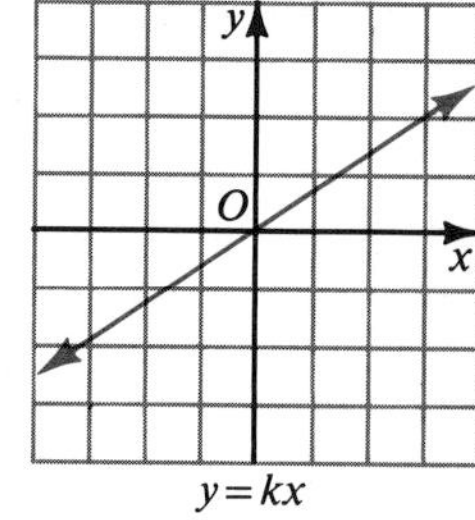

$y = kx$

Example 1 Given that d varies directly as t, and that $d = 86$ when $t = 2$, find the following.
a. the constant of variation **b.** the value of d when $t = 3$

Solution Let $d = kt$.
a. Substitute $d = 86$ and $t = 2$; $86 = k \cdot 2$
$43 = k$ ***Answer***
b. Substitute $k = 43$ and $t = 3$: $d = 43 \cdot 3 = 129$ ***Answer***

Suppose that two ordered pairs of a direct variation defined by $y = kx$ are

$$(x_1, y_1) \text{ and } (x_2, y_2),$$

and that neither x_1 nor x_2 equals zero. The coordinates of these ordered pairs satisfy $y = kx$:

$$y_1 = kx_1 \text{ and } y_2 = kx_2.$$

From these equations you can write the ratios

$$\frac{y_1}{x_1} = k \text{ and } \frac{y_2}{x_2} = k.$$

Since each ratio equals k, the ratios are equal.

$$\frac{y_1}{x_1} = \frac{y_2}{x_2}, \text{ read "}y_1 \text{ is to } x_1 \text{ as } y_2 \text{ is to } x_2\text{."}$$

This equation, which states that two ratios are equal, is a proportion (page 282). For this reason, k is sometimes called the **constant of proportionality,** and y is said to be *directly proportional to x.*

When you use a proportion to solve a problem, you will find it helpful to recall that the product of the extremes equals the product of the means.

6. The distance indicated on a map varies directly with the actual distance. If a distance of 20 km is represented by 5 cm, how would an actual distance of 64 km be represented?

$\frac{20}{5} = \frac{64}{x}$; $x = 16$

The distance on the map is 16 cm.

Example 2 The amount of interest earned on savings is directly proportional to the amount of money saved. If \$26 interest is earned on \$325, how much interest will be earned on \$900 in the same period of time?

Solution

Step 1 The problem asks for the interest on \$900, given that the interest on \$325 is \$26.

Step 2 Let i, in dollars, be the interest on d dollars.

$$i_1 = 26 \qquad i_2 = \underline{\ ?\ }$$
$$d_1 = 325 \qquad d_2 = 900$$

Step 3 An equation can be written in the form $\frac{i_1}{d_1} = \frac{i_2}{d_2}$:

$$\frac{26}{325} = \frac{i_2}{900}$$

Step 4

$$26(900) = 325i_2$$
$$23{,}400 = 325i_2$$
$$72 = i_2$$

Step 5 The check is left to you.

∴ the interest earned on \$900 will be \$72. ***Answer***

Suggested Assignments

Minimum

Day 1: 421/2–20 even
422/*P*: 1, 3
R 417/*Self-Test 2*

Day 2: 422/*P*: 2, 4–11
S 416/20, 26

Average

Day 1: 421/2–22 even
422/*P*: 1, 3, 5
R 417/*Self-Test 2*

Day 2: 422/*P*: 6–11
426/1–7 odd, 10–13

Day 2 finishes Sec. 9-7 and starts Sec. 9-8.

Maximum

Day 1: 421/1, 2, 5, 7, 10–13, 18–22 even
422/*P*: 3, 5, 8
R 417/*Self-Test 2*

Day 2: 423/*P*: 7, 9–14
426/1–7 odd, 10–14

Day 2 finishes Sec. 9-7 and starts Sec. 9-8.

Examples 1 and 2 illustrate two methods of solving problems involving direct variation. To solve Example 2 by the method shown in Example 1, first write the equation $i = kd$ and solve for the constant of variation, k, by using the fact that $i = 26$ when $d = 325$. Then use the resulting value of k to find the value of i when $d = 900$. Complete the problem this way for yourself. You will find the exercises and problems of this section easier if you understand *both* methods.

Oral Exercises

State whether or not the equation defines a direct variation. For each direct variation, state the constant of variation.

1. $y = 5x$ yes; 5 **2.** $p = 7s$ yes; 7 **3.** $xy = 2$ no **4.** $d = 2.8t$ yes; 2.8

5. $\frac{1}{3}x = 7$ no **6.** $\frac{y}{x} = -2$ yes; -2 **7.** $p = \frac{7}{q}$ no **8.** $C = \pi d$ yes; π

9. $A = \pi r^2$ no **10.** $\frac{c}{d} = 1$ yes; 1 **11.** $y = 2x^3$ no **12.** $\frac{x}{y} = \frac{3}{2}$ yes; $\frac{2}{3}$

State whether or not the given ordered pairs are in a direct variation.

Example (6, 8), (9, 12), (18, 24)

Solution $\frac{8}{6} = \frac{4}{3}, \frac{12}{9} = \frac{4}{3}, \frac{24}{18} = \frac{4}{3}$. Since the ratios are equal, the ordered pairs are in the direct variation $y = \frac{4}{3}x$.

13. (2, 4), (6, 12), (10, 20) yes
14. (1, 3), $(-6, -18)$, (5, 15) yes
15. (1, 1), (2, 1), (3, 3) no
16. $(-1, 2)$, $(2, -4)$, $(4, -8)$ yes
17. $(-1, 9)$, $(2, -18)$, $(-3, 27)$ yes
18. (0, 0), $(5, -10)$, $(-3, -6)$ no

State whether or not each statement is true. If it is not true, give a reason why it is not true.

19. Every linear function is a direct variation. false. Linear functions of the form $f(x) = ax + b$, where $b \neq 0$, are not direct variations.

20. All direct variations are linear functions. true

21. Some linear functions are direct variations. true

22. No function is both a linear function and a direct variation. false. All functions of the form $f(x) = ax$ are both linear functions and direct variations.

State whether or not each formula expresses direct variation.

23. $\frac{x_1}{y_1} = \frac{x_2}{y_2}$ yes **24.** $\frac{x_1}{x_2} = \frac{y_1}{y_2}$ yes **25.** $\frac{y_1}{x_2} = \frac{y_2}{x_1}$ no **26.** $\frac{y_2}{x_2} = \frac{y_1}{x_1}$ yes

Written Exercises

In Exercises 1-6, find the constant of variation.

A 1. y varies directly as x, and $y = 13$ when $x = 52$. $\frac{1}{4}$

2. y varies directly as x, and $y = 8$ when $x = 72$. $\frac{1}{9}$

3. t varies directly as s, and $t = -28$ when $s = -4$. 7

4. h varies directly as m, and $h = 368$ when $m = -16$. -23

5. W is directly proportional to m, and $W = 300$ when $m = 12$. 25

6. P is directly proportional to t, and $P = 490$ when $t = 35$. 14

7. If y varies directly as x, and $y = 900$ when $x = 6$, find y when $x = 10$. 1500

8. If d varies directly as z, and $d = 12$ when $z = 48$, find d when $z = 30$. $7\frac{1}{2}$

9. If h is directly proportional to a, and $h = 425$ when $a = 8.5$, find h when $a = 12$. 600

10. If r is directly proportional to A, and $r = 14$ when $A = 87.5$, find r when $A = 25$. 4

In each exercise find the missing value if (x_1, y_1) and (x_2, y_2) are ordered pairs of the same direct variation.

11. $x_1 = 15, y_1 = 9$
$x_2 = 40, y_2 = \underline{\ ?\ }$ 24

12. $x_1 = 45, y_1 = \underline{\ ?\ }$ 75
$x_2 = 60, y_2 = 100$

13. $x_1 = 3.6, y_1 = 3$
$x_2 = \underline{\ ?\ }, y_2 = 1$ 1.2

14. $x_1 = \underline{\ ?\ }, y_1 = 7$ 5.95
$x_2 = 7.65, y_2 = 9$

15. $x_1 = \frac{1}{10}, y_1 = \frac{1}{6}$
$x_2 = \frac{2}{5}, y_2 = \underline{\ ?\ }$ $\frac{2}{3}$

16. $x_1 = \frac{6}{5}, y_1 = \underline{\ ?\ }$ $\frac{1}{5}$
$x_2 = \frac{2}{3}, y_2 = \frac{1}{9}$

For the direct variation described, state (a) a formula and (b) a proportion.

Example The speed, v, of a skydiver in free fall is directly proportional to the number, t, of seconds of fall. After 3 s, the speed is 29.4 m/s.

Solution

a. $v = kt$; $v = 29.4$ when $t = 3$.

$29.4 = k(3)$, $k = \frac{29.4}{3} = 9.8$

$v = 9.8t$

b. Let $v_1 = 29.4$ and $t_1 = 3$. $\frac{29.4}{3} = \frac{v_2}{t_2}$

B 17. The heat, H, required to melt a substance varies directly with its mass, m. Forty-nine calories of heat are needed to melt one gram of copper. $H = 49m$; $\frac{49}{1} = \frac{H_2}{m_2}$

18. The length, L, of the shadow of a tree at any moment varies directly with the height, h, of the tree. At a certain moment, a tree 40 m tall casts a shadow 28 m long. $L = \frac{7}{10}h$; $\frac{L_1}{h_1} = \frac{28}{40}$

Additional A Exercises

Find the constant of variation.

1. y varies directly as x and $y = 18$ when $x = 6$. 3

2. y varies directly as x and $y = \frac{1}{3}$ when $x = \frac{1}{2}$. $\frac{2}{3}$

3. s is directly proportional to p and $s = 60$ when $p = 5$. 12

4. s is directly proportional to p and $s = 256$ when $p = 16$. 16

In each exercise find the missing value if (x_1, y_1) and (x_2, y_2) are ordered pairs of the same direct variation.

5. $x_1 = 6, y_1 = 5$
$x_2 = 3, y_2 = \underline{\ ?\ }$ $2\frac{1}{2}$

6. $x_1 = 27, y_1 = 72$
$x_2 = 24, y_2 = \underline{\ ?\ }$ 64

For the direct variation described, state (a) a formula and (b) a proportion.

19. The weight, M, of an astronaut on the moon is directly proportional to the weight, E, on Earth. An astronaut weighing 84 kg on Earth weighs 14 kg on the moon. $M = \frac{1}{6}E$; $\frac{M_1}{E_1} = \frac{14}{84}$

20. Distance, m, on a map varies directly with the actual distance, d. On a certain map, 1 cm represents 2 km. $m = \frac{1}{200{,}000}d$; $\frac{1}{200{,}000} = \frac{m_2}{d_2}$

21. At any given temperature, the electric resistance of wire is directly proportional to its length. At 20°C, 500 m of No. 18 gauge copper wire has a resistance of 10.295 ohms. $r = 0.02059l$; $\frac{10.295}{500} = \frac{r_2}{l_2}$

22. Under constant pressure, the volume, V, of a dry gas is directly proportional to its temperature, T, in degrees Kelvin. A sample of oxygen occupies a volume of 5 L at 300°K. $V = \frac{1}{60}T$; $\frac{V_1}{T_1} = \frac{5}{300}$

In Exercises 23 and 24, suppose that (x_1, y_1) and (x_2, y_2) are ordered pairs of a direct variation and that no coordinate is 0. Show that the given statement is true.

C 23. $\frac{y_1}{x_1} = \frac{y_2}{x_2}$

24. $\frac{y_1}{y_2} = \frac{x_1}{x_2}$

Problems

Solve.

A 1. The area covered by a painter is directly proportional to the number of hours worked. A painter covered 54 m^2 in the first eight hours on the job. How large an area will the painter cover in 36 h? 243 m^2

2. The amount of sand used in mixing mortar is directly proportional to the amount of lime used. If 2 bags of lime are mixed with 5 bags of sand, how much sand is mixed with 15 bags of lime in a shipment of this mortar? $37\frac{1}{2}$ bags

3. Nine grams of hydrochloric acid neutralize 10 g of lye. At this rate, how many grams of lye are neutralized by 72 g of hydrochloric acid? 80 g

4. A school lunchroom buys 10 kg of ground beef to prepare 110 servings of chili. At this rate, how many servings can the lunchroom make with 25 kg of ground beef? 275 servings

5. A mass of 25 g stretches a spring 10 cm. If the distance a spring is stretched is directly proportional to the mass, what mass will stretch the spring 16 cm? 40 g

6. A mass of 27 kg causes a diving board to bend 1.8 cm. If the amount of bending varies directly as the mass, what mass will cause the board to bend 1.2 cm? 18 kg

7. A formula for dishwashing detergent calls for mixing 100 g of sodium metaphosphate with 300 g of trisodium phosphate. If you use this formula, how much sodium metaphosphate do you mix with 681 g of trisodium phosphate? 227 g

8. When an electric current is 32 A (amperes), the electromotive force is 288 V (volts). Find the force when the current is 45 A if the force varies directly as the current. 405 V

9. In making a monster movie, model figures were used to create the illusion of great size. What was the scale of the models if an ape that appeared to be 54 ft in height was actually a model 20 in. tall? 5:162

10. In a scale model of a sailboat, an object that is 6 feet tall is represented by a figure 8 inches high. How tall should the mast of the sailboat be in the model if the actual mast of the sailboat is 38 feet tall? $4\frac{2}{9}$ ft

B 11. Two thermometers are exactly the same except that thermometer F is marked off into 180 equal units and thermometer C is marked off into 100 equal units. A length equal to 66.6 units on thermometer F is equal to a length of how many units on thermometer C? 37 units

12. The odometer on the Bristers' car was not measuring distance correctly. For the 220 km trip from home to the grandparents' home, the odometer registered only 216.7 km. On the return trip, the Bristers had to detour for road repairs. If the odometer registered 453.1 km for the round trip, how many actual kilometers was the detour? 20 km

13. On a map, 1 cm represents an actual distance of 75 m. Find the area of a piece of land that is represented on the map by a rectangle measuring 12.5 cm by 16 cm. 1,125,000 m^2

14. If the circumference of a circle varies directly as the diameter, and the diameter varies directly as the radius, show that the circumference varies directly as the radius. $C = k_1d$; $d = k_2r$. Substituting for d: $C = k_1(k_2r) = k_1k_2r$. But k_1k_2 is a constant, so C varies directly as r.

Challenge

If at least one coin of each kind is used, how can you change a dollar into 15 coins, each less than a quarter in value? 9 dimes, 1 nickel, and 5 pennies

Mixed Review Exercises

1. Express $\frac{m^2 - n^2}{6m^2n} \div \frac{m + n}{3m}$ in simplest form. $\frac{m - n}{2mn}$ $(m \neq 0, n \neq 0, m \neq -n)$

2. Simplify: $\frac{3c}{c - 2d} + \frac{4d}{2d - c}$ $\frac{3c - 4d}{c - 2d} (c \neq 2d)$

3. Divide: $\frac{7x^3 + 22x^2 + 38x + 5}{7x + 1}$ $x^2 + 3x + 5$

4. Find the constant of variation if y varies directly as x and $y = 35$ when $x = 25$. $\frac{7}{5}$

Teaching Suggestions
p. T116

Chalkboard Examples

1. a. Complete the ordered pairs so that they belong to the inverse variation $xy = 36$.
$(2, \underline{?})$, $(6, \underline{?})$, $(9, \underline{?})$
18 6 4

b. Graph the equation $xy = 36$ for positive values of x and y.

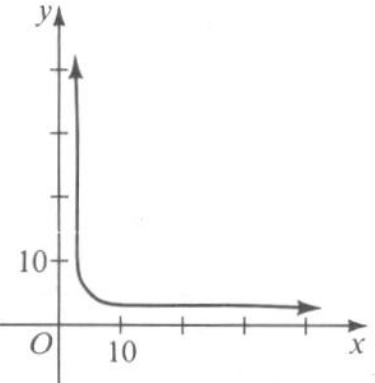

2. If x varies inversely as y and $x = 3$ when $y = 10$, find the constant of variation.
$xy = k$
$3(10) = k$
$k = 30$

3. If x varies inversely as y, find y_2 if $x_1 = 4$, $y_1 = 16$, and $x_2 = 32$.
$x_1 y_1 = x_2 y_2$
$4(16) = 32y_2$
$y_2 = 2$

4. A child with a mass of 25 kg is sitting 2 m from the fulcrum of a seesaw. How far from the fulcrum should a 100-kg adult sit in order to balance the seesaw?
$m_1 d_1 = m_2 d_2$
$25(2) = 100\, d_2$
$d_2 = 0.5$
The adult should sit 0.5 m from the fulcrum.

9-8 Inverse Variation

Objective To use the concept of inverse variation to solve problems.

The table shows the time, t, that it takes a car to cover a distance of 60 km traveling at the rate of r km/h. You can see that

Rate in km/h: r	Time in hours: t
20	3
40	$\frac{3}{2}$
60	1
80	$\frac{3}{4}$

$$rt = 60.$$

Notice that if the rate of travel is increased, the time required is decreased, so that the product is always 60. You can say that the time *varies inversely as* the rate. This example illustrates an *inverse variation.*

An **inverse variation** is a function defined by an equation of the form

$$xy = k, \text{ where } k \text{ is a nonzero constant.}$$

$$y = \frac{k}{x}, \text{ where } x \neq 0.$$

You can say that *y varies inversely as x* or *y is inversely proportional to x.* The constant k is the **constant of variation.**

The graph of an inverse function is not a straight line, since the defining equation

$$xy = k$$

is not linear; the term xy is of degree 2. The graph of $xy = 1$ is shown below. This graph is called a **hyperbola.**

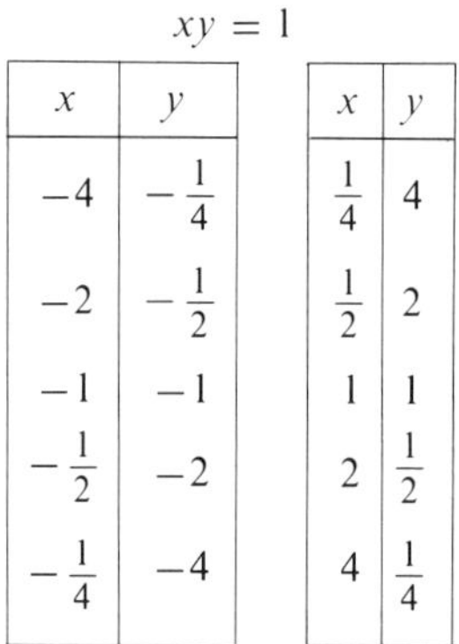

$xy = 1$

x	y
-4	$-\frac{1}{4}$
-2	$-\frac{1}{2}$
-1	-1
$-\frac{1}{2}$	-2
$-\frac{1}{4}$	-4

x	y
$\frac{1}{4}$	4
$\frac{1}{2}$	2
1	1
2	$\frac{1}{2}$
4	$\frac{1}{4}$

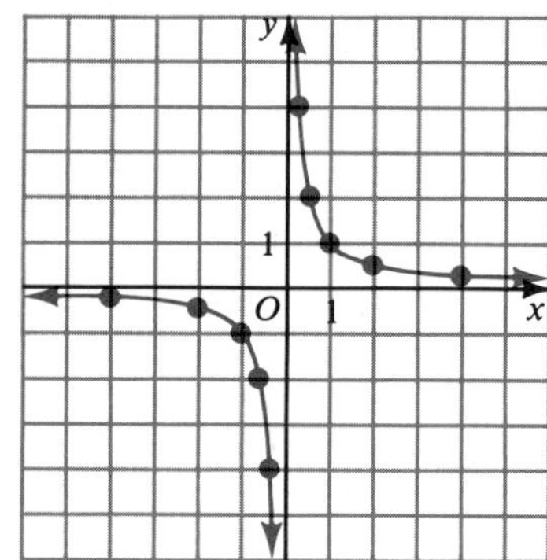

Since neither x nor y can have the value 0, neither of the two branches of the hyperbola intersects an axis.

For every nonzero value of k, the graph of $xy = k$ is a hyperbola. When k is positive, the branches of the graph are in Quadrants I and III. When k is negative, the graph is in Quadrants II and IV.

In some practical problems involving inverse variation, negative answers are meaningless, and the domain and the range are limited to positive numbers. The graph of such an inverse variation has only the branch in Quadrant I.

If (x_1, y_1) and (x_2, y_2) are ordered pairs of the same inverse variation, then the coordinates satisfy the equation $xy = k$:

$$x_1y_1 = k \quad \text{and} \quad x_2y_2 = k.$$

Therefore,

$$x_1y_1 = x_2y_2.$$

Compare:

Direct Variation	***Inverse Variation***
$y = kx$	$xy = k, \text{ or } y = \frac{k}{x}$
$\frac{y_1}{x_1} = \frac{y_2}{x_2}$	$x_1y_1 = x_2y_2$

These equations can be written in other equivalent forms, but the forms shown are the easiest to remember. *For direct variation the quotients of coordinates are constant, and for inverse variation the products are constant.*

One example of inverse variation is the law of the lever. A lever is a bar pivoted at a point called the fulcrum. If masses m_1 and m_2 are placed at distances d_1 and d_2 from the fulcrum, and the lever is at balance, then

$$m_1d_1 = m_2d_2.$$

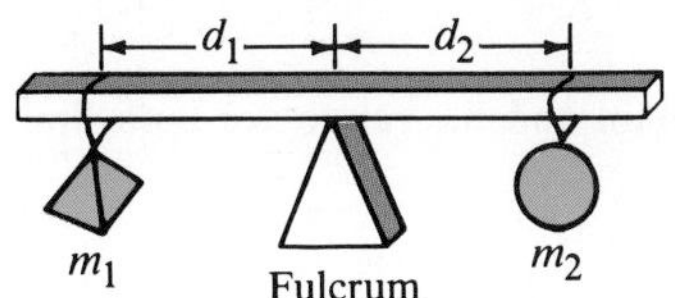

Example If a 12 g mass is 60 cm from the fulcrum of a lever, how far from the fulcrum is a 45 g mass that balances it?

Solution Let $m_1 = 12$, $d_1 = 60$, and $m_2 = 45$. $d_2 = \underline{\ ?\ }$

Use $m_1d_1 = m_2d_2$.

$$12(60) = 45d_2$$
$$16 = d_2$$

$\therefore$ the distance of the 45 g mass from the fulcrum is 16 cm. ***Answer***

5. A triangle has an altitude of 3 cm and a base of 10 cm. Find the base of another triangle of equal area whose altitude is 5 cm.

$\frac{1}{2}b_1h_1 = \frac{1}{2}b_2h_2$, or

$b_1h_1 = b_2h_2$

$10(3) = b_2(5)$

$b_2 = 6$

The base is 6 cm.

6. Paula walks to school in 30 min at an average rate of 6 km/h. The time it takes her to walk varies inversely as her rate of walking. How fast must she walk in order to get there in 20 min?

$r_1t_1 = r_2t_2$

$6\left(\frac{1}{2}\right) = r_2\left(\frac{1}{3}\right)$

$r_2 = 9$

She must walk at a rate of 9 km/h.

Common Error

Students may have difficulty remembering that the equation $y = kx$, or $\frac{y}{x} = k$, represents a direct variation whereas the equation $xy = k$, or $y = \frac{k}{x}$, represents an inverse variation. Emphasize that a direct variation is called a *linear* direct variation because $y = kx$ $(y = kx + 0)$ is the equation of a *line* and that the equation $xy = k$, whose graph is a hyperbola, is quadratic.

Supplementary Material

Practice Master 56

Suggested Assignments

Minimum

Day 1: 426/1–15 odd
428/*P*: 2, 8

Day 2: 427/*P*: 1–11 odd
S 423/*P*: 12, 13

Average
427/*P*: 1–13 odd
S 416/31, 32

Day 2 of Sec. 9-7 finishes Sec. 9-7 and starts Sec. 9-8.

Maximum
428/*P*: 3–17 odd
S 417/33–36

Day 2 of Sec. 9-7 finishes Sec. 9-7 and starts Sec. 9-8.

Additional Answers Written Exercises

1. 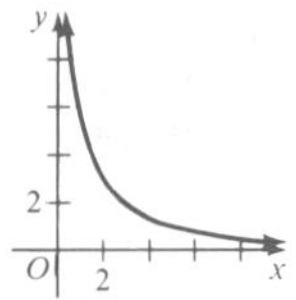

2. 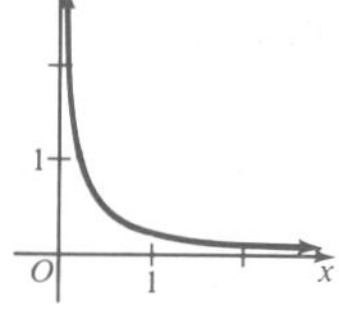

3. 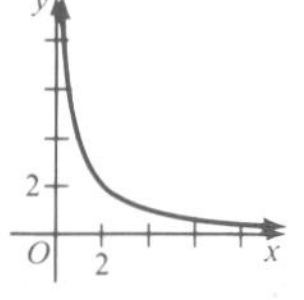

4. 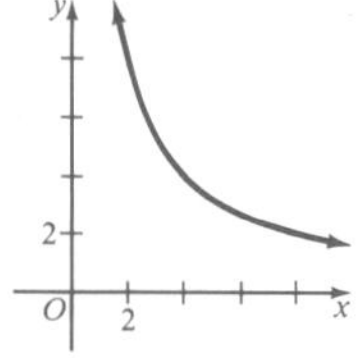

Oral Exercises

State whether each equation defines an inverse variation or a direct variation (k is a constant).

1. $\frac{y}{x} = k$ direct
2. $y = \frac{k}{x}$ inverse
3. $p = \frac{k}{z}$ inverse
4. $xy = 45$ inverse
5. $d = 2.5t$ direct
6. $m = \frac{1}{d}$ inverse
7. $\frac{n_1}{b_1} = \frac{n_2}{b_2}$ direct
8. $a_1b_1 = a_2b_2$ inverse
9. $\frac{1}{3} = rt$ inverse
10. $\frac{3}{4} = \frac{h}{s}$ direct
11. $\frac{x}{y} = \frac{1}{k}$ direct
12. $kxy = 2$ inverse

Complete the ordered pairs so that they belong to the given inverse variation.

13. $xy = 24$ and $(x, y) = (2, \underline{\ ?\ })$ $(\underline{\ ?\ }, 8)$ $(-6, \underline{\ ?\ })$ 12; 3; −4
14. $v = \frac{100}{m}$ and $(m, v) = (25, \underline{\ ?\ })$ $(\underline{\ ?\ }, 5)$ $(-2, \underline{\ ?\ })$ 4; 20; −50
15. $288 = pq$ and $(p, q) = (8, \underline{\ ?\ })$ $(-3, \underline{\ ?\ })$ $(\underline{\ ?\ }, 9)$ 36; −96; 32
16. $xy = -1$ and $(x, y) = (-1, \underline{\ ?\ })$ $\left(\frac{1}{4}, \underline{\ ?\ }\right)$ $(\underline{\ ?\ }, 2)$ 1; −4; $-\frac{1}{2}$
17. If $rs = k$, and r is tripled while k remains the same, how does s change? s is divided by 3.
18. If $d = rt$, and t is halved while d remains constant, how does r change? r is doubled.

Written Exercises

Graph each equation if the domain and the range are both limited to the set of positive numbers.

A

1. $xy = 6$
2. $4xy = 1$
3. $x = \frac{4}{y}$
4. $\frac{x}{2} = \frac{8}{y}$

Find the missing value if (x_1, y_1) and (x_2, y_2) are ordered pairs of the same inverse variation.

5. $x_1 = 3, y_1 = 54, x_2 = 2, y_2 = \underline{\ ?\ }$ 81
6. $x_1 = 30, y_1 = 10, x_2 = \underline{\ ?\ }, y_2 = 12$ 25
7. $x_1 = \underline{\ ?\ }, y_1 = 19.5, x_2 = 11.7, y_2 = 10.5$ 6.3
8. $x_1 = 32, y_1 = \underline{\ ?\ }, x_2 = 8, y_2 = \frac{1}{4}$ $\frac{1}{16}$

Exercises 9 and 10 refer to the lever at balance shown on page 425. Find the missing value.

9. $m_1 = 24, m_2 = 8, d_1 = 6, d_2 = \underline{\ ?\ }$ 18
10. $m_1 = \underline{\ ?\ }, m_2 = 40, d_1 = 5, d_2 = 7$ 56

For the inverse variation described, state (a) a formula and (b) a proportion.

Example The height h of a right circular cylinder of fixed volume varies inversely as the area A of the base. A cylinder 4 units high has a base of 10 square units.

Solution **a.** $Ah = k$; $h = 4$, when $A = 10$.

$\therefore\ 10(4) = k,\ k = 40$

$$Ah = 40, \quad \text{or} \quad h = \frac{40}{A}$$

b. $A_1h_1 = A_2h_2$

Dividing by h_1h_2, you obtain the proportion:

$$\frac{A_1}{h_2} = \frac{A_2}{h_1}$$

Let $A_1 = 10$ and $h_1 = 4$. $\quad \dfrac{10}{h_2} = \dfrac{A_2}{4}$

B **11.** The length l and width w of a rectangle of given area vary inversely as each other. When the length is 15, the width is 4. $lw = 60$; $\frac{15}{w_2} = \frac{l_2}{4}$

12. The force, f, needed to shift a heavy log varies inversely as the length, l, of the crowbar used. When the length is 2 m, the force needed is 1.5 N (newtons). $fl = 3$; $\frac{1.5}{l_2} = \frac{f_2}{2}$

13. The frequency f of a periodic wave is inversely proportional to the length l of the wave. The frequency is 2.5 Hz (hertz) when the wavelength is 0.60 m. $fl = 1.5$; $\frac{2.5}{l_2} = \frac{f_2}{0.6}$

14. The time, t, required to drive between two cities is inversely proportional to the average speed, r, of the truck. It took 3 h at an average speed of 78 km/h. $rt = 234$; $\frac{78}{t_2} = \frac{r_2}{3}$

15. At a fixed temperature, the volume, V, of a gas varies inversely as the pressure, P. A volume of 465 cm^3 of a gas is at a pressure of 725 mm. $VP = 337{,}125$; $\frac{465}{P_2} = \frac{V_2}{725}$

16. The amount of current, I, flowing through a circuit is inversely proportional to the amount of resistance, R, of the circuit. In a circuit with a resistance of 18 ohms there is a current of 0.25 A. $IR = 4.5$; $\frac{0.25}{R_2} = \frac{I_2}{18}$

Problems

Solve.

A **1.** The number of days needed to pave a section of highway varies inversely as the number of people working on the job. It takes 18 days for 2 people to complete the project. If the job has to be finished in 4 days, how many people are needed? 9 people

Additional A Exercises

Graph each equation if the domain and the range are both limited to the set of positive numbers.

1. $xy = 2$

Ex. 1

2. $x = \frac{5}{y}$

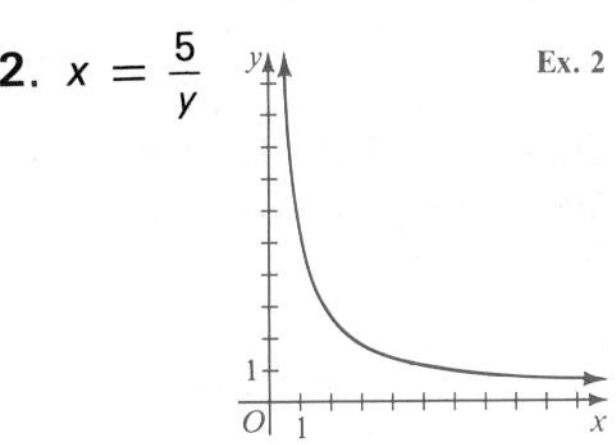

Find the missing value if (x_1, y_1) and (x_2, y_2) are ordered pairs of the same inverse variation.

3. $x_1 = 20$, $y_1 = 7$
$x_2 = 4$, $y_2 =$ _?_ 35

4. $x_1 = 64$, $y_1 = \frac{3}{8}$
$x_2 =$ _?_, $y_2 = 6$ 4

Refer to the lever shown at balance on p. 425. Find the missing value.

5. $m_1 =$ _?_, $d_1 = \frac{1}{7}$ 49
$m_2 = 21$, $d_2 = \frac{1}{3}$

Mixed Review Exercises

1. Express 45 m : 25 cm in simplest form. 180 : 1

2. Solve: $\frac{x}{2} + \frac{x+4}{6} = 4$ 5

3. What percent of 200 is 70? 35%

4. Find the least value of the function: $f: x \to x^2 + 4x - 5$ -9

2. The interest rate required to yield a given income is inversely proportional to the amount of money invested. Jane Kidd has $75,000 invested at 6%. How much money must she have invested to receive the same income if the rate of return is 7.5%? $60,000

3. A rectangle has length 48 cm and width 35 cm. Find the length of another rectangle of equal area whose width is 21 cm. 80 cm

4. The winner of a race ran the distance in 45 s at an average speed of 9.6 m/s. The runner who came in last finished in 48 s. What was the last runner's average speed? 9 m/s

5. A fifteen-centimeter pulley runs at 300 rpm (revolutions per minute). How fast does the five-centimeter pulley it drives revolve, if the number of revolutions per minute varies inversely as the diameter? 900 rpm

6. A gear with 42 teeth revolves at 1200 rpm and meshes with a gear having 72 teeth. What is the speed of the second gear if the rotational speed of a gear wheel varies inversely with the number of teeth? 700 rpm

7. In buying shares of stock each month, James Halloran uses the dollar-cost averaging system. With this system the number of shares purchased varies inversely with the price per share. If Mr. Halloran bought 150 shares at $8 per share on January 2, how many shares did he purchase on February 2 when the price was $20 per share? 60 shares

8. The number of floors in a building of given height varies inversely as the distance between the floors. If a building can contain 52 floors when the floors are 3.3 m apart, how many floors can be contained in the building if the floors are 3.9 m apart? 44 floors

9. A string on a violin is 25.8 cm long and produces a tone whose frequency is 440 Hz. By how much should the string be shortened to produce a tone of frequency 516 Hz, if the frequency of a vibrating string is inversely proportional to its length? 3.8 cm

10. The frequency of a vibrating string is inversely proportional to its diameter. A violin string with diameter 0.50 mm produces a tone of frequency 440 Hz. What is the frequency of the tone produced by a similar string whose diameter is 0.05 mm larger? 400 Hz

In Exercises 11–14, apply the law of the lever.

11. If Tim weighs 126 lb and Joel weighs 168 lb, how far from the seesaw support must Tim sit to balance Joel who is 2 yd from it? $2\frac{2}{3}$ yd

12. One end of a pry bar is under a 700 kg boulder. The fulcrum of the bar is 15 cm from the boulder and 1.75 m from the other end of the bar. What mass at that end of the bar will balance the boulder? 60 kg

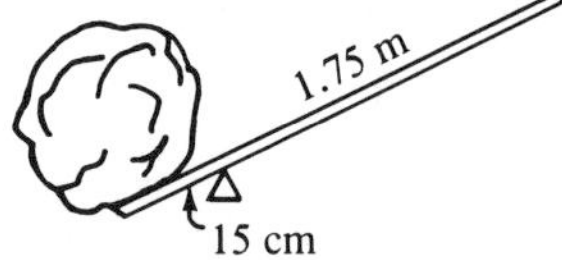

B **13.** A 12 g mass is placed at one end of a meter stick. A 28 g mass is placed at the other end. Where should the fulcrum be placed to have the meter stick balanced? 70 cm from the 12 g mass

14. A lever has a 500 kg steel ball on one end and a 300 kg log on the other end. The lever is balanced, and the steel ball is 1 m closer to the fulcrum than the log. How far from the fulcrum is the log? 2.5 m

For the wave motion of sound, the following formula holds:

$$fl = v,$$

where f is the frequency (number of cycles per second), l is the wavelength (in meters), and v is the speed of sound (about 335 m/s in air). Use this information in the following problems.

15. The frequency of a note an octave above a given note is twice that of the given note. How does the wavelength of the higher note compare with that of the lower note? It is $\frac{1}{2}$ that of the lower note.

16. If the wavelength of a note is $\frac{3}{2}$ that of a given note, how do the frequencies compare? The new frequency is $\frac{2}{3}$ that of the given note.

17. An open organ pipe produces a sound wave that has a length that is twice the length of the pipe. Find the length of an open pipe that will produce the note A with the frequency 440. Give the answer to the nearest tenth of a meter. 0.4 m

18. A stopped organ pipe produces a sound wave that has a length that is four times the length of the pipe. What is the frequency of the sound produced by a stopped organ pipe 2 m long? 41.9 Hz

Computer Exercises

For students with some programming experience

Write a BASIC program in which at least three ordered pairs are entered with INPUT statements. The program should then report whether the data represents a direct variation, an inverse variation, or neither. RUN the program for the following sets of ordered pairs.

1. (2, 3), (8, 12), (10, 15), (−24, −36) direct

2. (12, −4), (−16, 3), (−15, 3.2) inverse

3. (0, 0), (3, 4), (9, 8), (−2, −3) neither

Teaching Suggestions
p. T116

Suggested Extensions
p. T116

Chalkboard Examples

1. If y varies directly as x^2 and $x = 3$ when $y = 18$, find y when $x = 2$.

   Method 1

   $y = kx^2$
   $18 = k(3)^2$
   $k = 2$
   $y = 2(2)^2 = 8$

   Method 2

   $\frac{y_1}{{x_1}^2} = \frac{y_2}{{x_2}^2}$
   $\frac{18}{3^2} = \frac{y_2}{2^2}$
   $\frac{18}{9} = \frac{y_2}{4}$
   $y_2 = 8$

2. If y varies inversely as x^2, and $x = 3$ when $y = 18$, find y when $x = 2$.

   Method 1

   $y = \frac{k}{x^2}$
   $18 = \frac{k}{3^2}$; $k = 162$
   $y = \frac{162}{2^2} = 40\frac{1}{2}$

   Method 2

   ${x_1}^2 y_1 = {x_2}^2 y_2$
   $(3)^2(18) = (2)^2 y_2$
   $40\frac{1}{2} = y_2$

9-9 Direct and Inverse Variation Involving Squares

Objective To use quadratic direct variation and variation inversely as a square in problem solving.

In the world around you, there are many examples in which a quantity varies either directly or inversely *as the square* of another quantity. For example, the area of a circle varies directly as the square of the radius: $A = \pi r^2$. This is an example of a *quadratic direct variation.*

A **quadratic direct variation** is a function defined by an equation of the form

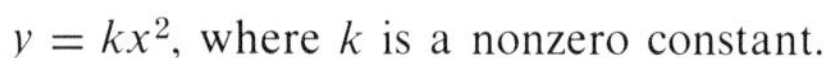

$y = kx^2$, where k is a nonzero constant.

If (x_1, y_1) and (x_2, y_2) are ordered pairs of the same quadratic direct variation, and neither x_1 nor x_2 is zero, then:

$$\frac{y_1}{{x_1}^2} = \frac{y_2}{{x_2}^2}$$

You say that *y varies directly as x^2* or *y is directly proportional to x^2.*

Example 1 Given that A varies directly as the square of d, and $A = 48$ when $d = 4$, find the value of A when $d = 20$.

Solution

Method 1

Use $A = kd^2$.
$48 = k(4)^2$
$48 = 16k$
$3 = k$
$\therefore A = 3d^2$

For $d = 20$:
$A = 3(20)^2$
$A = 1200$ ***Answer***

Method 2

Use $\frac{A_1}{{d_1}^2} = \frac{A_2}{{d_2}^2}$.
$\frac{48}{4^2} = \frac{A_2}{(20)^2}$
$\frac{48}{16} = \frac{A_2}{400}$
$16A_2 = 19{,}200$
$A_2 = 1200$ ***Answer***

The intensity of sound *varies inversely as the square* of the distance of a listener from the source of sound. Thus, if you halve the distance between yourself and a drummer, the intensity of the sound that reaches your ears will be quadrupled.

An **inverse variation as the square** is a function defined by an equation of the form

$x^2y = k$, where k is a nonzero constant.

This function may also be written as $y = \frac{k}{x^2}$, where $x \neq 0$.

You say that *y varies inversely as* x^2 or *y is inversely proportional to* x^2.

If (x_1, y_1) and (x_2, y_2) are ordered pairs of the function defined by $x^2y = k$, then

$$x_1^2y_1 = x_2^2y_2.$$

Example 2 Given that h varies inversely as the square of r, and that $h = 5$ when $r = 2$, find the value of h when $r = 8$.

Solution

Method 1

Use $h = \frac{k}{r^2}$.

$$5 = \frac{k}{2^2}$$

$$20 = k$$

$$\therefore h = \frac{20}{r^2}$$

For $r = 8$:

$$h = \frac{20}{8^2}$$

$$h = \frac{20}{64} = \frac{5}{16} \quad \textit{Answer}$$

Method 2

Use $r_1^2h_1 = r_2^2h_2$.

$$2^2(5) = 8^2h_2$$

$$20 = 64h_2$$

$$h_2 = \frac{5}{16} \quad \textit{Answer}$$

Oral Exercises

Translate each statement into a formula. Use *k* as the constant of variation where needed.

1. The distance, d, that an object falls from rest is directly proportional to the square of the time, t. $d = kt^2$
2. The force between two point charges of static electricity is inversely proportional to the square of the distance, d, between them. $fd^2 = k$
3. The illumination, E, of a surface is inversely proportional to the square of the distance, r, from the surface to the source of light. $Er^2 = k$
4. The area, A, of the surface of a steel ball varies directly as the square of the radius, r, of the ball. $A = kr^2$
5. The quantity, Q, of heat energy in an electric circuit is directly proportional to the square of the current, I. $Q = kI^2$
6. The time, t, required to fill a fuel tank varies inversely as the square of the diameter, d, of the hose. $td^2 = k$

3. The area of a square varies directly as the square of a side. If a square with a side 3 cm long has an area of 9 cm², what is the area of a square with a side 6 cm long?

$$\frac{A_1}{s_1^2} = \frac{A_2}{s_2^2}$$

$$\frac{9}{3^2} = \frac{A_2}{6^2}$$

$$A_2 = 36$$

The area is 36 cm^2.

4. The height of a cylinder of a given volume varies inversely as the square of the radius. If a cylinder of radius 3 cm has a height of 4 cm, what is the height of a cylinder of equal volume with radius 2 cm?

$$h_1r_1^2 = h_2r_2^2$$

$$(4)(3)^2 = h_2(2)^2$$

$$h_2 = 9$$

The height is 9 cm.

Suggested Assignments

Minimum
432/*P*: 1–6
R 438/*Self-Test 3*, 1–3

Average
432/*P*: 3–9
S 429/*P*: 14–16

Maximum
432/*P*: 3, 5, 7–11
S 422/23, 24

Additional A Exercises

Solve.

1. The area of a circular garden varies directly as the square of its radius. If a garden has a 10-ft radius and an area of 314 ft^2, what is the area of a garden with radius 12 ft? 452.16 ft^2
2. The distance an object falls in a vacuum is directly proportional to the square of the time it's been falling. After 3 s, a ball has fallen 144 ft. How far will it have fallen after 6 s? 576 ft
3. The volume of a glass sphere is directly proportional to the cube of the radius of the sphere. If a sphere has a 2-in. radius and a volume of 33.5 in^3, what is the volume of a sphere with radius 3? 113.0625 in.^{3}

Mixed Review Exercises

1. How much salt must be added to 50 cm^3 of a 10% saline solution to produce a 25% saline solution? 10 cm^3
2. Express 18 million in scientific notation. 1.8×10^7
3. Is $(-2, 5)$ a solution of the equation $3x + y = 11$? no
4. Find x_2 if (x_1, y_1) and (x_2, y_2) are ordered pairs of the same direct variation and $x_1 = 51$, $y_1 = 34$, and $y_2 = 14$. 21

Problems

Solve.

A

1. The amount of material required to cover a ball is directly proportional to the square of its diameter. A ball with a diameter of 14 cm requires 616 cm^2 of material to cover it. How much material is needed to cover a ball with a diameter of 35 cm? 3,850 cm^2
2. The price of a diamond varies directly as the square of its mass. If a 1.5-carat diamond costs \$2025, find the price of a similar diamond 2 carats in mass. \$3600
3. The distance required for an automobile to come to a stop varies directly as the square of its speed. If the stopping distance for a car traveling at 80 km/h is 175 m, what is the distance required for a car traveling 48 km/h to stop? 63 m
4. Wind pressure on a flat surface varies directly as the square of the velocity of the wind. If the pressure from a 35 km/h wind was measured at 0.024 g/cm^2, find the pressure when the wind's velocity was 42 km/h. 0.03456 g/cm^2
5. The brightness of the illumination of an object varies inversely as the square of the distance from the object to the source of light. At a distance of 1.2 m directly in front of a light source, illumination on a page of a book was measured to be 250 lm/m^2 (lumens per square meter). If the page were moved 0.4 m closer to the light source, what would the illumination measure? 562.5 lm/m^2
6. The time needed to fill a tank varies inversely as the square of the radius of the hose. If a hose of radius 3 cm takes 4.5 min to fill the tank, how long will it take to fill the same tank with a hose that is 2 cm greater in radius? 1.62 min

B

7. The strength of a radio signal is inversely proportional to the square of the distance from the source of the signal. If an observer moves from a position 50 m from the source of the signal to a position 200 m from the source, how does the strength of the signal at the second position compare with the strength at the first position? It is $\frac{1}{16}$ as strong.
8. At or above the surface of Earth, the acceleration due to gravity, g, is inversely proportional to the square of the distance from the center of Earth. Compare the value of g at a point 1.6×10^7 m from the center of Earth with that of g at a point 0.8×10^7 m from the center of Earth. It is $\frac{1}{4}$ as large.
9. The height of a circular cylinder of given volume varies inversely as the square of the radius of the base. How much greater is the radius of a cylinder 3 m high than the radius of a cylinder 6 m high with the same volume? It is $\sqrt{2}$ times as great.

10. The surface area of a human body is approximately directly proportional to the square of the person's height. How many times as much skin does a man 6 ft tall have compared to a child 2 ft tall?
approx. 9 times as much

C 11. The volume of a sphere varies directly as the cube of the radius. If the ratio of the radii of two spheres is 4:3, what is the ratio of the volumes of the spheres? 64:27

12. The heat radiated from a star is directly proportional to the fourth power of the surface temperature of the star. If the surface temperature of one star is $1\frac{1}{2}$ times as great as the surface temperature of a second star of the same size, what is the ratio of the amounts of heat radiated by the stars? 81:16

Computer Key-In

To find ordered pairs to be used in graphing the related parabola of a quadratic function, it is convenient to compute these ordered pairs on either side of the vertex. The following program first finds the vertex and then gives a set of ordered pairs to be used in graphing.

```
10 PRINT "TO FIND COORDINATES"
20 PRINT "OF POINTS ON A GRAPH"
30 PRINT "OF Y = AX↑2 + BX + C:"
40 PRINT "INPUT A (<> 0), B, C";
50 INPUT A,B,C
60 IF A=0 THEN 40
70 LET X1=-B/(2*A)
80 LET Y1=A*X1*X1+B*X1+C
90 PRINT "VERTEX AT (";X1;",";Y1;")"
100 PRINT "X","Y"
110 LET X1=INT(X1)
120 FOR X=X1-5 TO X1+5
130 PRINT X,A*X*X+B*X+C
140 NEXT X
150 END
```

Exercises

RUN the program for the following. Draw each graph.

1. $y = x^2 - 2x - 2$
2. $y = -x^2 + 2x + 2$
3. $y = x^2 - 4x + 3$
4. $y = x^2 - 4x$
5. $y = 2x^2 + 4x - 3$
6. $y = -x^2 - 5x + 6$

Note: The program above can be used to do Exercises 7–18 on page 416.

Additional Answers
Computer Key-In

1.
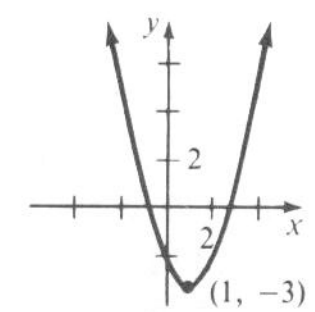

2.
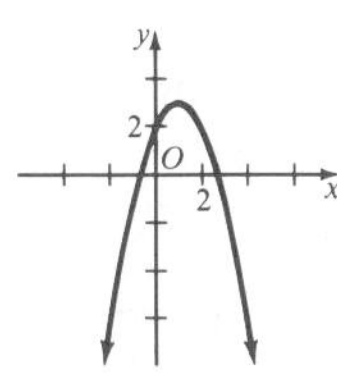

3.
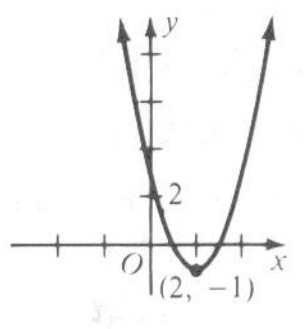

4.
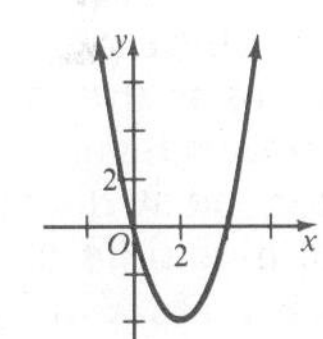

5.
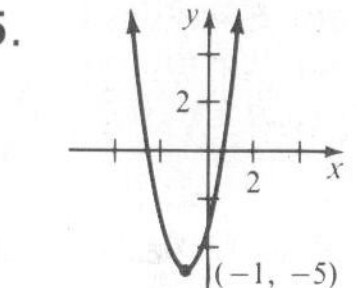

6.
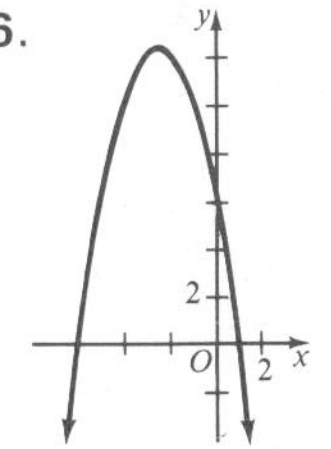

Teaching Suggestions
p. T117

Chalkboard Examples

1. The area of a trapezoid varies jointly as the height and the sum of the bases. A trapezoid with area 30 m^2 has height 6 m and the sum of its bases is 10 m. Find the area of a trapezoid with height 4 m if the sum of its bases is 12 m.

$$\frac{A_1}{h_1 b_1} = \frac{A_2}{h_2 b_2}$$
$$\frac{30}{6 \cdot 10} = \frac{A_2}{4 \cdot 12}$$
$$A_2 = 24$$
The area is 24 m^2.

2. The volume of a gas varies directly as the temperature and inversely as the pressure. A given gas has a volume of 3 L at a temperature of 360°K (Kelvin) and a pressure of 1.5 atm (atmospheres). What will its volume be at 300°K and pressure of 2.5 atm?

$$\frac{V_1 P_1}{T_1} = \frac{V_2 P_2}{T_2}$$
$$\frac{3(1.5)}{360} = \frac{V_2(2.5)}{300}$$
$$V_2 = 1.5$$
The volume is 1.5 L.

9-10 Joint and Combined Variation

Objective To solve problems involving joint variation and combined variation.

If Wanda earns \$400 next summer and puts her earnings into a savings account, the amount of simple interest she will receive depends on her bank's interest rate and on the length of time that she leaves the money in the account:

$$I = 400rt$$

The interest is directly proportional to the product of the rate and the time. You say that the interest *varies jointly as* the rate and the time.

In general, if a variable varies directly as the product of two or more other variables, the resulting relationship is called a **joint variation.** If z varies jointly as x and y, you can express the relationship in the following equations. For a nonzero constant k:

$$z = kxy \quad \text{and} \quad \frac{z_1}{x_1 y_1} = \frac{z_2}{x_2 y_2}$$

Example 1 The volume of a right circular cone varies jointly as the height, h, and the square of the radius, r. If $V = 616$ when $h = 12$ and $r = 7$, find V when $h = 9$ and $r = 14$.

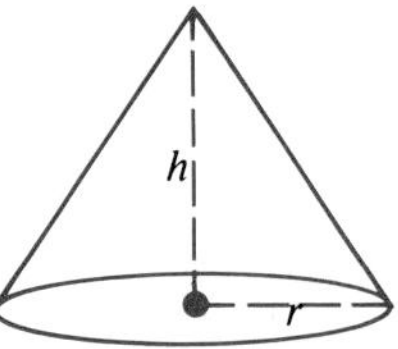

Solution Let $V_1 = 616$, $h_1 = 12$, $r_1 = 7$, $h_2 = 9$, and $r_2 = 14$. $V_2 = \underline{\ ?\ }$

$$\frac{V_1}{h_1 r_1^2} = \frac{V_2}{h_2 r_2^2}$$
$$\frac{616}{12(7)^2} = \frac{V_2}{9(14)^2}$$
$$12(49)V_2 = 9(196)(616)$$
$$V_2 = 1848 \quad \textit{Answer}$$

If a variable varies *directly* as one variable and *inversely* as another, the resulting relationship is called a **combined variation.** For example, if z varies directly as x and inversely as y, you can express the relationship in the following equations. For a nonzero constant k:

$$zy = kx \quad \left(\text{or } z = \frac{kx}{y}\right) \quad \text{and} \quad \frac{z_1 y_1}{x_1} = \frac{z_2 y_2}{x_2}$$

Example 2 The power, P, of an electric current varies directly as the square of the voltage, V, and inversely as the resistance, R. If 6 volts applied across a resistance of 3 ohms produces 12 watts of power, how much power will 9 volts applied across a resistance of 6 ohms produce?

Solution Let $P_1 = 12$, $V_1 = 6$, $R_1 = 3$, $V_2 = 9$, and $R_2 = 6$. $P_2 = \underline{\ ?\ }$

$$\frac{P_1R_1}{V_1^2} = \frac{P_2R_2}{V_2^2}$$

$$\frac{12(3)}{6^2} = \frac{P_2(6)}{9^2}$$

$$36(6)P_2 = 36(81)$$

$$P_2 = \frac{81}{6} = \frac{27}{2}$$

$\therefore$ the amount of power produced is 13.5 watts. ***Answer***

Oral Exercises

Translate each statement into a formula. Use k as the constant of variation where needed.

1. T varies jointly as n and p. $T = knp$
2. R varies directly as d and inversely as t. $Rt = kd$
3. y varies directly as the square of x and inversely as z. $yz = x^2k$
4. I varies directly as r and inversely as the square of t. $It^2 = kr$
5. p varies directly as the square of m and inversely as the square of s. $ps^2 = km^2$
6. I varies jointly as P, r, and t. $I = kPrt$
7. The mass, m, of a rectangular block varies jointly as the length, l, width, w, and depth, d, of the block. $m = klwd$
8. The area, A, of a triangle varies jointly as the base, b, and the altitude, h. $A = kbh$
9. The volume, V, of a gas varies directly as the temperature, T, and inversely as the pressure, P. $VP = kT$
10. The power, P, of an electric current varies directly as the square of the voltage, V, and inversely as the resistance, R. $PR = kV^2$
11. The centrifugal force, F, of an object moving in a circular path is directly proportional to the square of its velocity, v, and inversely proportional to the radius, r, of its path. $Fr = kv^2$
12. The intensity, I, of illumination at any point is directly proportional to the strength, s, of the light source and inversely proportional to the square of the distance, d, from the source. $Id^2 = ks$
13. The lateral surface, S, of a cylinder varies jointly as the radius, r, and the height, h, of the cylinder. $S = krh$
14. The heat, H, generated by an electric stove element varies jointly as the resistance, R, and the square of the current, C. $H = kRC^2$

3. The number of hours required to type mailing labels varies directly as the number of labels to be typed and inversely as the number of typists working. If 4 typists can type 2160 labels in 3 h, how long will it take 6 typists to type 4320 labels?

$$\frac{h_1t_1}{l_1} = \frac{h_2t_2}{l_2}$$

$$\frac{3 \cdot 4}{2160} = \frac{h_2 \cdot 6}{4320}$$

$$h_2 = 4$$

It will take 4 hours.

Common Error

It may be difficult for students to remember that a joint variation is represented by the equation $z = kxy$, whereas $z = \frac{kx}{y}$ represents a combined variation, because in everyday language people make little distinction between the words *joint* and *combined.* It may help to point out that a *combined* variation *combines* a direct variation and an indirect variation, whereas a *joint* variation is a direct variation involving a *product of variables.*

Supplementary Materials

Practice Master 57
Test 33
Resource Book, p. 111

Suggested Assignments

Average
436/1–4, 7;
P: 2, 3, 5, 8, 9, 11
R 438/*Self-Test 3*

Maximum
436/1, 4, 6–10;
P: 2–12 even
R 438/*Self-Test 3*

Additional A Exercises

Solve.

1. If x varies directly as y and inversely as z, and $x = 50$ when $y = 75$ and $z = 9$, find x when $y = 2$ and $z = 72$. $\frac{1}{6}$
2. If m varies jointly as n and the square of p, and $m = 40$ when $n = 20$ and $p = 2$, find m when $n = 30$ and $p = 3$. 135
3. P varies directly as the square of s and inversely as q. If $P = 50$ when $s = 5$ and $q = 3$, find P when $s = 4$ and $q = 4$. 24
4. The number of persons needed to do a job varies directly as the amount of work to be done and inversely as the time in which the job must be done. If 4 people can wash 5 cars in 1 h, how many people will be needed to wash 200 cars in 8 h? 20

Written Exercises

A

1. If y varies directly as a and inversely as b, and $y = 20$ when $a = 60$ and $b = 8$, find y when $a = 96$ and $b = 16$. 16
2. If d varies jointly as r and t, and $d = 27$ when $r = 18$ and $t = 6$, find d when $r = 30$ and $t = 10$. 75
3. If M varies jointly as v and the square of u, and $M = 9$ when $v = 15$ and $u = 6$, find M when $v = 25$ and $u = 12$. 60
4. If C varies inversely as the square of h and directly as n, and $C = 1$ when $h = 11$ and $n = 50$, find C when $h = 2$ and $n = 6$. 3.63
5. If y varies jointly as the square of x and the cube of z, and $y = 135$ when $x = 2$ and $z = 3$, find y when $x = \frac{1}{2}$ and $z = 2$. $\frac{5}{2}$
6. If Q varies directly as the square of t and inversely as the cube of r, and $Q = 129.6$ when $t = 12$ and $r = 2$, find Q when $t = 15$ and $r = 3$. 60

B

7. If x varies jointly as u and v, how does x change when both u and v are doubled? when u is doubled and v is halved? quadrupled; remains the same
8. If N varies directly as r and inversely as s, how does N change when both r and s are tripled? when r is tripled and s is halved? remains the same; 6 times as large
9. In the formula $h = \frac{y^2xw}{5}$, x remains constant. If y is doubled and w is tripled, how is h changed? It is 12 times as large.
10. In the formula $F = \frac{\pi rt^2}{s}$, r remains constant, t is halved, and s is doubled. How does F change? F is $\frac{1}{8}$ as large.

Problems

Solve.

A

1. The volume of a pyramid varies jointly as the height and the area of the base. A pyramid 15 cm high whose base has an area of 36 cm^2 has a volume of 180 cm^3. What is the volume if the height is 21 cm and the area of the base is 25 cm^2? 175 cm^3
2. The lateral surface area of a cylindrical column varies jointly as the radius and the height of the column. For a radius of 0.5 yd and a height of 4 yd, the surface area is 12.4 yd^2. What is the radius, if the surface area is 471 yd^2 and the height is 50 yd? approx. 1.5 yd
3. When a wire carries an electric current for a given time, the heat developed varies jointly as the resistance and the square of the current. If a 6 ampere current produces 130 J (joules) of heat in a wire with a resistance of 15 ohms, find the resistance in a wire carrying a current of 9 amperes, if the heat developed is 195 J. 10 ohms

4. The volume of a right circular cylinder varies jointly as its height and the square of its radius. If a right circular cylinder of height 10 cm and radius 4 cm has a volume of 160π cm^3, find the volume of one with a height of 8 cm and a radius of 3 cm. 72π cm^3

In Exercises 5 and 6, apply the statement: The number of persons needed to do a job varies directly as the amount of work to be done and inversely as the time in which the job must be done.

5. If 2 students in the typing pool can type 210 pages in 3 days, how many students will be needed to type 700 pages in 2 days? 10 students

6. If 2 workers can erect 400 m of fence in 10 h, how long will it take 5 workers to erect 600 m of fence? 6 h

7. The load that can be borne by a square horizontal beam supported at its ends varies directly as the square of its depth and inversely as the length between its supports. A beam 4 m long and 0.2 m deep bears 620 kg. What load can a beam 10 m long and 0.3 m deep bear? 558 kg

8. The cost of operating an appliance varies jointly as the number of watts drawn, the hours of operation, and the cost per kilowatt-hour. A 6000-watt convection oven operates for 10 minutes for 15¢ at 7.5¢ per kilowatt-hour. What is the cost of cooking two meals if each meal takes 70 minutes to cook? \$2.10

B 9. Using the mass of the sun as the unit of mass, and measuring distance in astronomical units (AU) and time in years, the total mass of a double star is directly proportional to the cube of the maximum distance between the stars and inversely proportional to the square of the period (the time it takes each star to revolve about the other). The double star Sirius has a period of 50.0 years, a maximum distance of 41.0 AU, and a total mass of 3.45. What is the total mass of Capella if its period is 0.285 years and the maximum distance is 1.51 AU? 5.30

10. The area of a trapezoid varies jointly as the sum of the lengths of the two parallel sides and the distance between the parallel sides. When the lengths of the parallel sides are 7 cm and 9 cm and the distance between them is 4 cm, the area is 32 cm^2. If the area is to remain constant and the height is reduced to 0.5 cm, what is the sum of the lengths of the parallel sides? 128 cm

11. The heat lost through a windowpane varies jointly as the difference of the inside and outside temperatures and the window area, and inversely as the thickness of the pane. If 49.5 joules of heat are lost through a pane 40 cm by 28 cm that is 0.8 cm thick, in one hour when the temperature difference is 44°C, how many joules are lost in one hour through a pane 0.5 cm thick having an area that is 0.25 the area of the other pane, when the temperature difference is 40°C? 18 joules

Mixed Review Exercises

1. Express $\left(\frac{-y^2}{2}\right)^3 \cdot \frac{y}{2}$ in simplest form. $-\frac{y^7}{16}$

2. Find the LCD for $\frac{3}{x^2y}$, $\frac{4}{3xy^2}$, and $\frac{18}{12xy^4}$. $12x^2y^4$

3. Write $\frac{z}{z-5} - \frac{z}{z+5} + 3$ as a fraction in simplest form. $\frac{3z^2 + 10z - 75}{(z+5)(z-5)}$ $(z \neq \pm 5)$

4. Graph $\frac{x}{2} = \frac{1}{y}$ if the domain and range are both limited to the set of positive numbers.

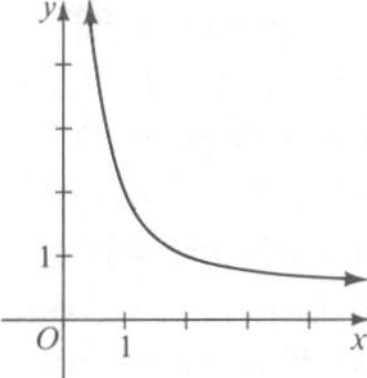

C 12. The heat generated by a stove element varies jointly as the resistance and the square of the current. What is the effect on the heat generated in the following cases?

a. The current is unchanged but the resistance is doubled. doubles

b. The resistance is unchanged but the current is doubled. increases 4 times

c. The current is tripled and the resistance is doubled. increases 18 times

13. The power in an electric circuit varies directly as the square of the voltage and inversely as the resistance. What is the effect on the power in the following cases?

a. The resistance is constant and the voltage is doubled. increases 4 times

b. The voltage is constant and the resistance is doubled. is halved

c. The voltage is doubled and the resistance is quadrupled. remains the same

Quick Quiz

1. The total cost of a given quantity of peaches varies directly as the number purchased. If 8 peaches cost \$1.40, how many peaches can be purchased for \$2.45? 14 peaches
2. The time it takes Jessica to walk home from school varies inversely as the rate at which she walks. If it takes her 20 min to walk home at 7.5 km/h, how long will it take her at 5 km/h? 30 min
3. If y varies inversely as the square of x, and $y = 40$ when $x = 5$, find the value of y when $x = 2$. 250
4. If a varies directly as the square of b and inversely as c, and $a = 12$ when $b = 6$ and $c = 9$, find a when $b = 4$ and $c = 6$. 8

Self-Test 3

Vocabulary

linear direct variation (p. 418)
constant of variation (p. 418, 424)
constant of proportionality (p. 419)
inverse variation (p. 424)
hyperbola (p. 424)
quadratic direct variation (p. 430)
inverse variation as the square (p. 430)
joint variation (p. 434)
combined variation (p. 434)

Solve.

1. A worker's earnings are directly proportional to the number of hours worked. If \$59.20 is earned for 8 hours of work, how much is earned for 35 hours of work? \$259 **Obj. 9-7, p. 418**
2. Four friends on a ski trip pay \$140 each to share the rent of a cabin. The cost per person varies inversely as the number of persons sharing the rent. How many people sharing the rent would make the cost \$80 per person? 7 people **Obj. 9-8, p. 424**
3. The distance that the signal from a radio station travels varies directly as the square of the number of kilowatts (kW) it produces. A 40 kW station can broadcast a distance of 64 km. How far could the station broadcast if it produced 70 kW? 196 km **Obj. 9-9, p. 430**
4. The mass of a circular coin varies jointly as the thickness and the square of the radius of the coin. A silver coin 2 cm in radius and 0.2 cm thick has a mass of 26.4 g. What is the mass of a silver coin 4 cm in radius and 0.3 cm thick? 158.4 g **Obj. 9-10, p. 434**

Check your answers with those at the back of the book.

Application / *Illumination*

Suppose you had to use a flashlight to help you see an object at a very close range. You would need to hold the light close to the object to make it clearer and brighter. To see a larger area, you would put more distance between the light and the object.

Scientists have measured how illumination is related to distance and brightness. The brightness, or intensity (I), of a light source is measured in units called candelas (cd). A 100-watt bulb gives about 130 cd. Illumination is the amount of light energy per second that falls on a unit area. Illumination is measured in luxes (lx).

Illumination is directly proportional to the intensity of the source. If the intensity is doubled, the illumination is doubled. Illumination on a surface is also dependent on its distance from the source. The farther the light source is from the surface, the lower the illumination.

Specifically, illumination (E) on a surface perpendicular to a light source varies inversely as the square of the distance (r) from the light source:

$$E = \frac{I}{r^2}$$

Thus, if the distance from the light source is doubled, the illumination is one fourth of what it was originally. If the distance is tripled, the illumination is one ninth. This equation is called the *law of illumination*.

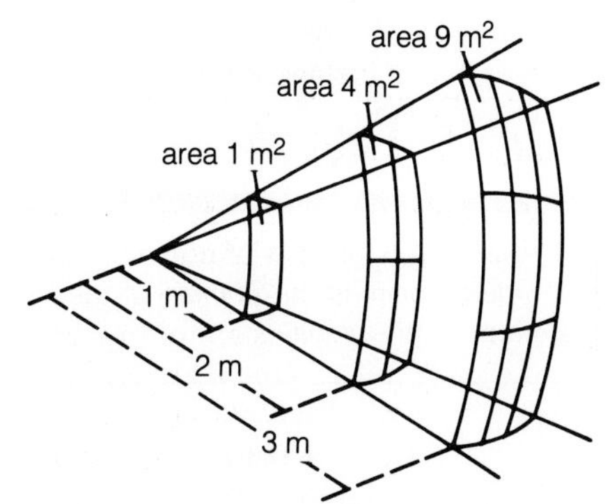

Example What illumination is provided on the surface of a table 3 m directly below a 99 cd lamp?

Solution Use the formula to solve for E.

$$E = \frac{99}{3^2} = 11$$

$\therefore$ the illumination is 11 lx.

Exercises

1. What illumination is provided on a surface 4 m from a 160 cd lamp? 10 lx
2. If a light is giving 315 cd from 3 m above a desk top, what illumination is provided? 35 lx
3. If a lamp gives 216 cd, how far must it be placed from a table surface to provide 24 lx of illumination? 3 m
4. What is the illumination of a 120 cd lamp at a distance of 2 m? 30 lx
5. What illumination is provided on the surface of a desk 2.5 m directly below a 125 cd lamp? 20 lx

Additional Answers
Extra

1. $D = \{2, 3\}$; $R = \{0, 3, 4, 6\}$; no
2. $D = \{1, 2, 3, 4\}$; $R = \{-1, 3, 5, 8\}$; yes
3. $D = \{1, 2, 3, 4\}$; $R = \{-3, -1, 0, 6\}$; yes
4. $D = \{0, 5\}$; $R = \{0, 1, 2, 4\}$; no
5. $D = \{-2, -1, 1, 2\}$; $R = \{1, 4\}$; yes
6. $D = \{4, 9\}$; $R = \{-3, -2, 2, 3\}$; no
7. $D = \{-1, 1, 2, 4\}$; $R = \{1, 2\}$; yes
8. $D = \{0\}$; $R = \{-3, -1, 1, 2\}$; no
9. $D = \{-2, 2, 4\}$; $R = \{-3, -1, 0, 1\}$; no
10. $D = \{-3, -2, -1, 1, 2, 3\}$; $R = \{-3, -2, -1, 1, 2, 3\}$; yes
11. $D = \{-3, -2, -1, 0, 1, 2, 3\}$; $R = \{-2, -1, 0, 1\}$; yes
12. $D = \{-3, -2, -1, 1\}$; $R = \{-3, -1, 1, 2, 3\}$; no
13. 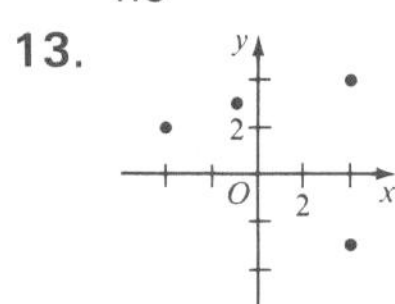

not a function; 2 points plotted for $x = 4$
14. 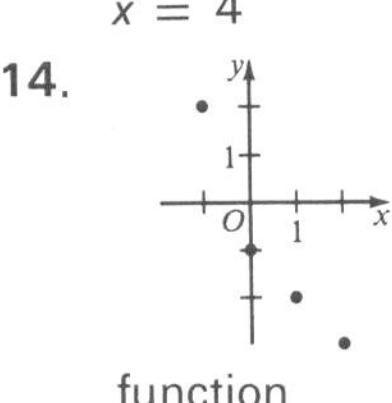

function

Extra / Relations

The diagram at the right shows how each number in the set

$$D = \{0, 1, 2, 3\}$$

is paired with one or more numbers in the set

$$R = \{-1, 1, 2, 3\}.$$

The same pairing is shown in the adjoining table, and in the listing of the ordered pairs of numbers.

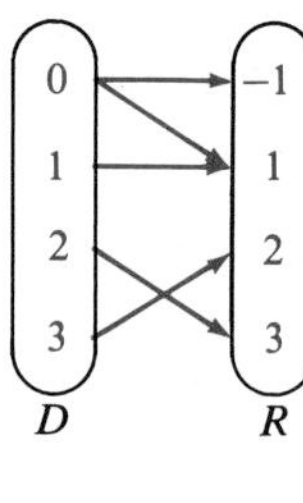

D	R
0	-1
0	1
1	1
2	3
3	2

$$\{(0, -1), (0, 1), (1, 1), (2, 3), (3, 2)\}$$

Notice that this pairing assigns to the number 0 in D two different numbers, -1 and 1 in R. Therefore, the pairing is *not* a function with domain D and range R. For, in a function, each member of the domain is assigned *exactly one* partner in the range. The pairing described above is an example of a *relation*.

A *relation* is any set of ordered pairs. The set of first coordinates in the ordered pairs is the *domain* of the relation, and the set of second coordinates is the *range*.

The figure at the right shows the graphs of all the ordered pairs that form the relation described above. We call this set the *graph of the relation*.

Of course, a function is a special kind of relation.

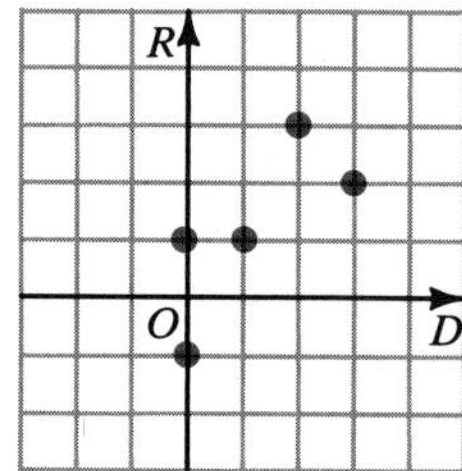

A function is a relation in which different ordered pairs have different first coordinates.

Thus, in the graph of a function, there is only one point plotted for each value in the domain.

Exercises

State the domain and range of each relation. Is the relation a function?

1. $\{(3, 4), (2, 3), (3, 6), (2, 0)\}$
2. $\{(1, -1), (2, 3), (3, 5), (4, 8)\}$
3. $\{(2, -1), (3, 0), (4, 6), (1, -3)\}$
4. $\{(5, 0), (5, 1), (5, 2), (0, 4)\}$
5. $\{(-1, 1), (1, 1), (2, 4), (-2, 4)\}$
6. $\{(4, 2), (4, -2), (9, 3), (9, -3)\}$

Give the domain and range of the relation graphed in each diagram. Is the relation a function?

7. 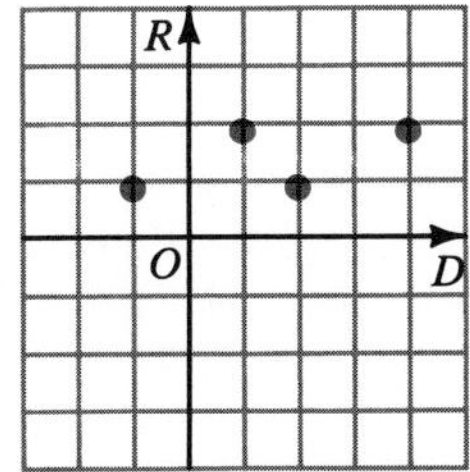

8. 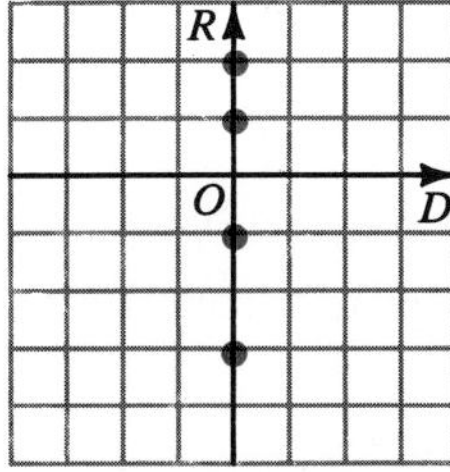

9. 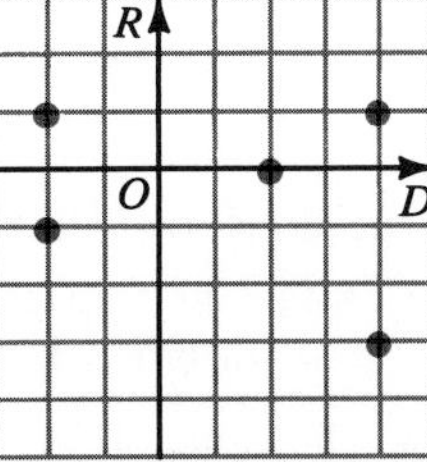

10 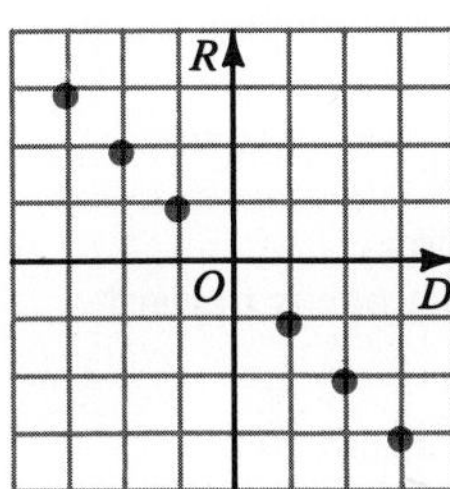

11. 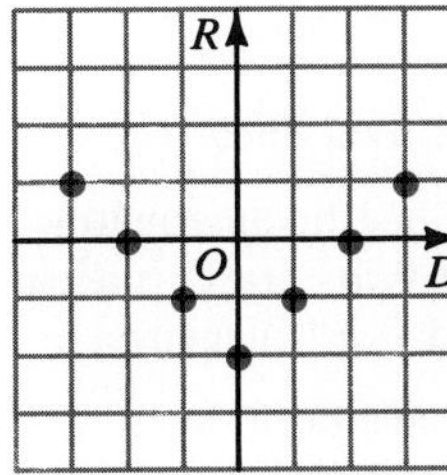

12. 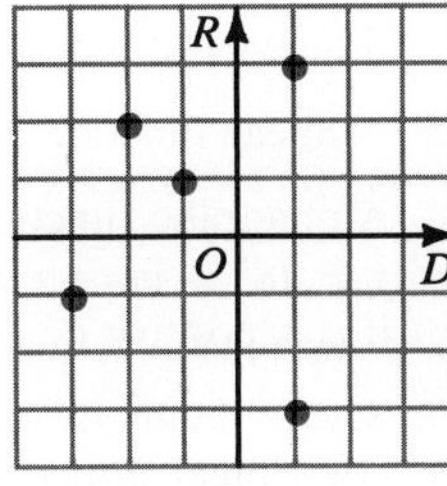

In Exercises 13–18, graph each relation and determine whether it is a function. If it is not a function, explain how that fact shows up on the graph.

13. $\{(-4, 2), (-1, 3), (4, 4), (4, -3)\}$

14. $\{(0, -1), (1, -2), (2, -3), (-1, 2)\}$

15. $\{(-3, 2), (0, 1), (3, -2), (-3, 0)\}$

16. $\{(-1, 1), (0, 0), (1, 1), (2, 4)\}$

17. $\{(0, 0), (1, 2), (2, 9), (-2, -7)\}$

18. $\{(1, 0), (2, 3), (3, -1), (1, 5)\}$

19. Consider the set of all ordered pairs of real numbers (x, y) that satisfy the equation $|y| = |x|$. Is this set of ordered pairs a relation? a function? Justify your answers.

20. The circle shown at the right is the graph of the equation $x^2 + y^2 = 4$. Do the coordinates of the points of the circle form a relation? a function? Why or why not? If the points form a relation (or function), what are the domain and range?

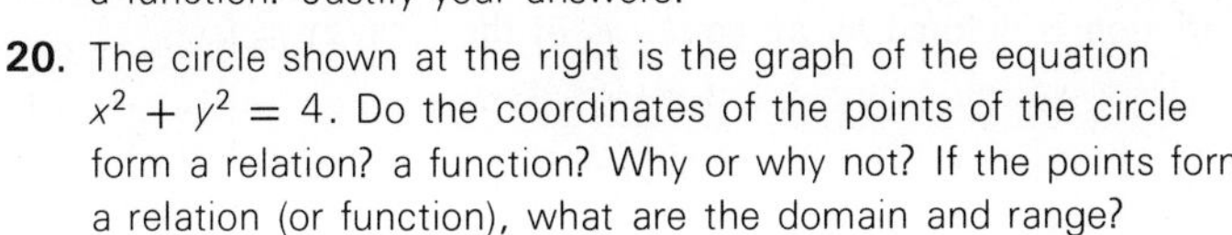

In Exercises 21–24, consider the set of all ordered pairs (x, y) as described. Is the set a relation? Is it a function?

21. (x, y), where x is the name of a telephone subscriber in your town and y is the subscriber's telephone number. yes; no

22. (x, y), where x is the name of each mother in your town and y is the name of her child. yes; no

23. (x, y), where x is the name of each man in London, England, and y is his right thumbprint. yes; yes

24. (x, y), where x is any nonvertical line in the coordinate plane and y is its slope. yes; yes

15. 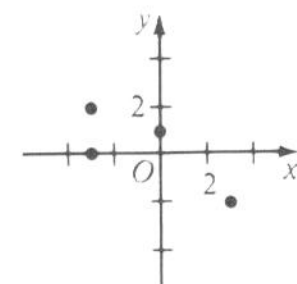

not a function; 2 points plotted for $x = -3$

16. 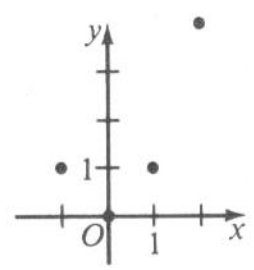

function

17. 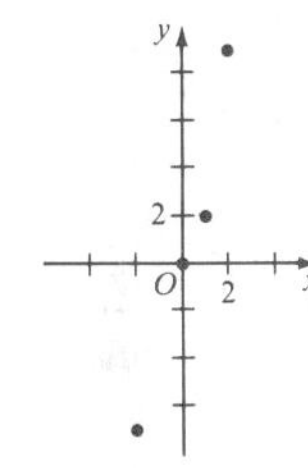

function

18. 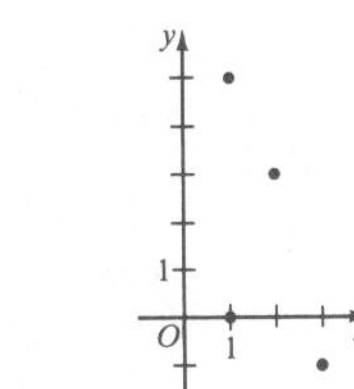

not a function; 2 points plotted for $x = 1$

19. yes, because a relation is a set of ordered pairs; no, because different ordered pairs of the set, for example, (1, 1) and (1, −1), have the same first coordinates

20. yes, because they form a set of ordered pairs; no, because 2 points are plotted for every value of the domain between −2 and 2; $D = R = \{-2, 2$, and the real numbers between -2 and $2\}$

Supplementary Materials

Practice Masters 58–60
Test 34
Resource Book,
pp. 44–49, 112–113, 138–141, 156–157

Extra Practice

Skills, pp. 622–626
Problems, pp. 644–646

Chapter Summary

1. The slope of a line can be found by using any two points on the line. Different lines with the same slope are parallel.
2. An equation of a line can be found from: (a) the slope and the y-intercept; (b) the slope and any point on the line; (c) two points on the line.
3. A function can be defined by an equation, a table, a correspondence, or a set of ordered pairs.
4. The value of a function F at 2 is denoted by $F(2)$. Any value of a function can be found by replacing the variable in the function equation by the given number.
5. A linear function is defined by a linear equation. Its graph is a line.
6. A quadratic function is defined by an equation of the form $y = ax^2 + bx + c = 0,\ a \neq 0$. Its graph is a parabola that opens upward if a is positive or downward if a is negative.
7. Several kinds of variation have been described (k is a nonzero constant):
   a. A linear direct variation is a linear function defined by an equation of the form $y = kx$.
   b. An inverse variation is a function defined by an equation of the form $xy = k\left(\text{or } y = \frac{k}{x}\right)$.
   c. A quadratic direct variation is a quadratic function defined by an equation of the form $y = kx^2$.
   d. An inverse variation as the square is a function defined by an equation of the form $x^2y = k\left(\text{or } y = \frac{k}{x^2}\right)$.
   e. A joint variation is defined by an equation of the form $z = kxy$.
   f. A combined variation is defined by an equation of the form $zy = kx$ or $z = \frac{kx}{y}$.

Chapter Review

Give the letter of the correct answer.

1. Find the slope of the line that passes through the points $(4, 4)$ and $(-4, 6)$. 9-1

a. -4 **b.** 0 **(c.)** $-\frac{1}{4}$ **d.** no slope

2. Find the slope of the line whose equation is $y - 8 = 0$.

a. 8 **(b.)** 0 **c.** -8 **d.** no slope

3. Write an equation in standard form of the line that has slope $-\frac{1}{3}$ and y-intercept 5. 9-2

a. $y = -\frac{1}{3}x + 5$
b. $-x + 3y = 15$
c. $-5x + y = -\frac{1}{3}$
(d.) $x + 3y = 15$

4. Find the slope and y-intercept of the line whose equation is $3x = 2y$.

a. $m = \frac{2}{3}, b = 0$
b. $m = -\frac{3}{2}, b = 0$
c. $m = 3, b = -2$
(d.) $m = \frac{3}{2}, b = 0$

5. Find b given that the point $(12, -3)$ lies on the line whose equation is $y = -\frac{4}{3}x + b$. 9-3

(a.) 13
b. -19
c. 8
d. 16

6. Write an equation in standard form of the line that passes through the points $(0, -7)$ and $(-7, 0)$.

a. $-x + y = 7$
b. $-x + y = -7$
(c.) $x + y = -7$
d. $y = -7$

7. Find $G(0)$ given $G(x) = 8 - 4x$. 9-4

a. 0
b. 2
(c.) 8
d. 4

8. Find $F(-1)$ given $F(x) = 6 - x^2$.

a. 49
b. 7
c. 4
(d.) 5

9. State the range of the function $\{(-1, 1), (0, 0), (1, 1), (2, 6)\}$. 9-5

a. $\{0, 1, 2, 3, 4, 5, 6\}$
b. $\{-1, 0, 1, 2\}$
c. $\{(-1, 1), (1, 1)\}$
(d.) $\{0, 1, 6\}$

10. Find the least value of the function $f: x \to x^2 + 8x + 3$. 9-6

(a.) -13
b. 3
c. -4
d. 8

11. Find the greatest value of the function $t: x \to x - x^2$.

a. $\frac{1}{2}$
(b.) $\frac{1}{4}$
c. 0
d. $-\frac{1}{4}$

12. Find the constant of variation if y varies directly as x, and $y = 19$ when $x = 95$. 9-7

a. 5
(b.) $\frac{1}{5}$
c. 19
d. 95

13. Find the missing value if (75, 30) and (__?__, 18) are ordered pairs of the same inverse variation. 9-8

(a.) 125
b. 75
c. 45
d. 7.2

14. If y varies inversely as x^2, and x is halved, then y is __?__. 9-9

a. doubled
(b.) quadrupled
c. divided by 4
d. halved

15. If r varies directly as the cube of t and inversely as the square of s, and $r = \frac{1}{2}$ when $s = 6$ and $t = 2$, find r when $s = 12$ and $t = 4$. 9-10

a. $\frac{1}{4}$
b. 0
c. $\frac{1}{2}$
(d.) 1

Alternate Test p. T18

Additional Answers Chapter Test

13. $y = 3x - 1$

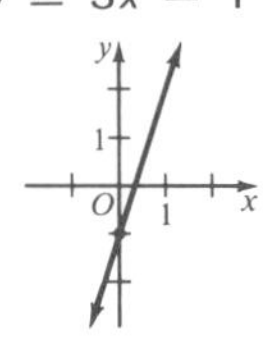

14. $y = \frac{1}{3}x - 2$

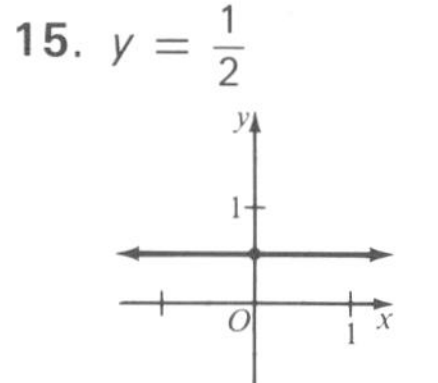

15. $y = \frac{1}{2}$

16. $y = -\frac{1}{2}x + 3$

Chapter Test

Find the slope of the line passing through the two given points.

1. $(-6, 0), (8, -7)$ $-\frac{1}{2}$
2. $(-5, 7), (8, 7)$ 0 — 9-1
3. $(9, 5), (9, -5)$ no slope
4. $(-2, 4), (3, -1)$ -1

Find the slope of each line whose equation is given.

5. $y = -3x + 2$ -3
6. $x + y = 0$ -1
7. $3x - 5y = 15$ $\frac{3}{5}$
8. $2x + 4y = 1$ $-\frac{1}{2}$

Write an equation in standard form of the line that has the given slope and y-intercept.

9. $m = 1;\ b = 0$ $x - y = 0$
10. $m = -\frac{5}{8};\ b = 6$ $5x + 8y = 48$ — 9-2
11. $m = 0;\ b = -\frac{1}{3}$ $3y = -1$
12. $m = \frac{7}{4};\ b = 8$ $7x - 4y = -32$

Change each equation to the slope-intercept form. Then draw the graph using only the slope and y-intercept.

13. $3x - y = 1$
14. $-x + 3y + 6 = 0$
15. $2y = 1$
16. $x + 2y - 6 = 0$

Write an equation in standard form of the line that has the given slope and passes through the given point.

17. $m = -3;\ (0, -1)$ $3x + y = -1$
18. $m = \frac{5}{2};\ (-6, 7)$ $5x - 2y = -44$ — 9-3
19. $m = 0;\ \left(2, -\frac{1}{4}\right)$ $4y = -1$
20. $m = \frac{3}{4};\ (-3, -4)$ $3x - 4y = 7$

21. Write an equation in standard form of the line passing through the points $(-4, -6)$ and $(4, 10)$. $2x - y = -2$

Find the range of each function.

22. $F(t) = \frac{1}{1 + 3t},\ D = \{-1, 0, 2\}$ $R = \left\{-\frac{1}{2}, 1, \frac{1}{7}\right\}$ — 9-4
23. $g: x \rightarrow x^2 - 1,\ D = \left\{-1, -\frac{1}{2}, 6\right\}$ $R = \left\{0, -\frac{3}{4}, 35\right\}$
24. $f: x \rightarrow \frac{2x}{3} - 1,\ D = \{-6, -3, 0, 3\}$ $R = \{-5, -3, -1, 1\}$
25. $f(x) = \frac{2x - 1}{3},\ D = \{-6, -3, 0, 3\}$ $R = \left\{-\frac{13}{3}, -\frac{7}{3}, -\frac{1}{3}, \frac{5}{3}\right\}$

26. The table below shows a function. 9-5
  a. State the domain and range of the function.
  b. Graph the function by means of a bar or a broken-line graph, whichever is more suitable.

Region	% of Forested Land
Central	18
Lake States	25
Middle Atlantic	58
New England	81
Pacific Coast	38
Rocky Mountain	25
South	39

Draw the graph of each function.

27. $g: x \rightarrow 1 - \frac{x}{2}$

28. $t(x) = -1$ 9-6

29. Find the coordinates of the vertex and the equation of the axis of symmetry of the graph of the equation $y = 2x - x^2$. Use the vertex and at least six other points to graph the equation.

Find the missing value if (x_1, y_1) and (x_2, y_2) are ordered pairs of the same direct variation.

30. $x_1 = 7.2$, $y_1 = 3$
$x_2 = \underline{\ ?\ }$ 4.8, $y_2 = 2$

31. $x_1 = \frac{1}{5}$, $y_1 = \underline{\ ?\ }$ $\frac{1}{9}$ 9-7
$x_2 = \frac{3}{10}$, $y_2 = \frac{1}{6}$

32. The number of bolts a machine can make varies directly as the running time of the machine. If a machine can make 1000 bolts in six hours, in how many hours can it make 300 bolts? $1\frac{4}{5}$ h

33. Graph $\frac{x}{3} = \frac{4}{y}$ if the domain and the range are both limited to the set of positive numbers. 9-8

34. The area of a square is directly proportional to the square of its diagonal. If the area of a square having a diagonal 16 cm long is 128 cm^2, what is the area of a square having a diagonal 24 cm long? 288 cm^2 9-9

35. If V varies jointly as B and h, and $V = 50$ when $B = 25$ and $h = 6$, find h when $B = 36$ and $V = 108$. 9 9-10

26. a. D = {Central, Lake States, Middle Atlantic, New England, Pacific Coast, Rocky Mountain, South};
R = {18, 25, 38, 39, 58, 81}

b.

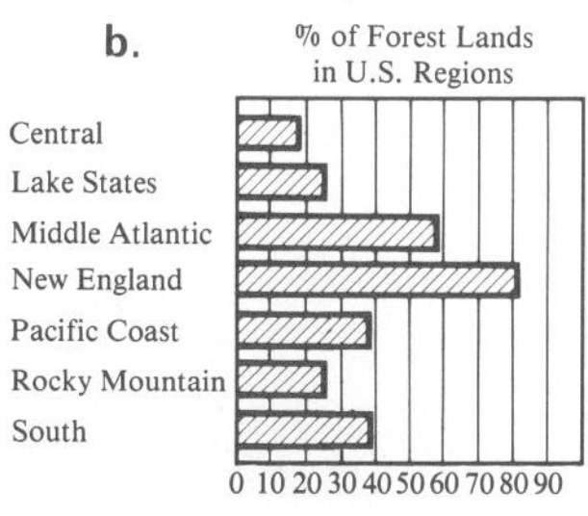

27.

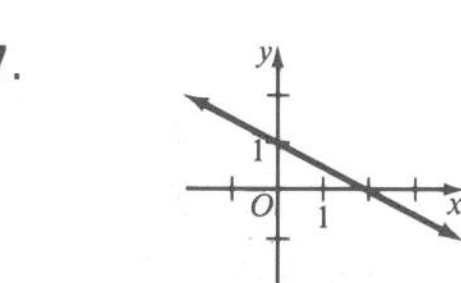

28.

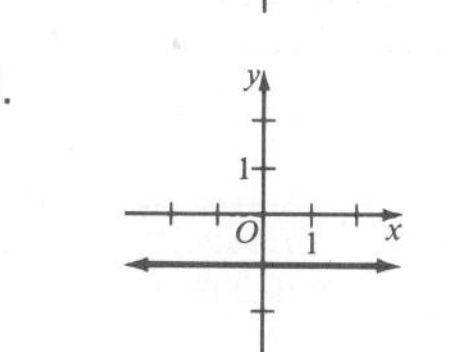

29. (1, 1); $x = 1$

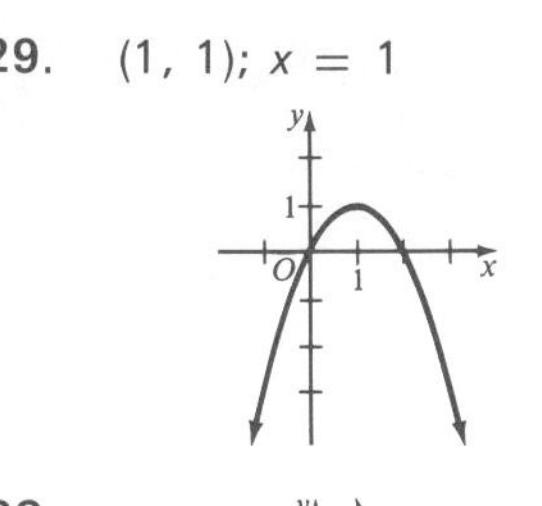

33.

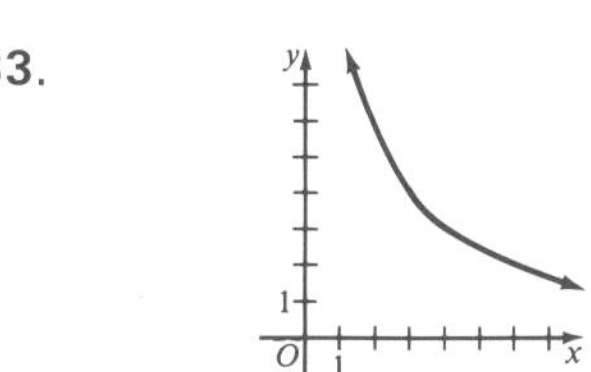

Cumulative Review p. T26

Cumulative Review (Chapters 1–9)

Simplify.

1. $(3y - 2z) - (-8z + 2y)$ $6z + y$
2. $(8x - 4z)(2x + 3z)$ $16x^2 + 16xz - 12z^2$
3. $2m^2n(10m^2 + 3mn + 5n^2)$ $20m^4n + 6m^3n^2 + 10m^2n^3$
4. $(2x^3y^2z^4)^4 \div (4x^2yz^3)^2$ $x^8y^6z^{10}$
5. $(5b - 8c)^2$ $25b^2 - 80bc + 64c^2$
6. $(3.2 \times 10^{-8})(1.5 \times 10^{12})$ 4.8×10^4

Factor completely.

7. $12x^2 + 17x - 7$ $(4x + 7)(3x - 1)$
8. $4y^2 - 12y + 9$ $(2y - 3)^2$
9. $3z^2 - 21z - 24$ $3(z - 8)(z + 1)$

Express in simplest form. Assume that no denominator is zero.

10. $\dfrac{a^2 - a - 2}{a^2 + 2a + 1}$ $\dfrac{a - 2}{a + 1}$
11. $\dfrac{x^2 + 4x + 3}{x + 1} \cdot \dfrac{(x^2 - 1)}{2x^2 + x - 1}$ $\dfrac{(x + 3)(x - 1)}{2x - 1}$
12. $\dfrac{3z^2 + 8z - 3}{3z^2 + 5z - 2} \div \dfrac{z^2 + 6z + 9}{z^3 - 4z}$ $\dfrac{z(z - 2)}{z + 3}$
13. $\dfrac{t}{t - 2} - \dfrac{t}{t + 2} - 3$ $\dfrac{-3t^2 + 4t + 12}{(t - 2)(t + 2)}$

Write an equation in standard form for each line described.

14. The line with slope 4 that passes through $(-1, -2)$. $4x - y = -2$
15. The line through $(5, 2)$ and $(2, 5)$. $x + y = 7$
16. The line that contains $(1, 3)$ and is parallel to $2x + y = 4$. $2x + y = 5$
17. Find the range of the function $f\colon x \rightarrow x^2 - x + 1$ with domain $\{-3, -2, -1, 0, 1, 2, 3\}$. $R = \{13, 7, 3, 1\}$

Graph each equation.

18. $2x + 4y = 7$
19. $y = x^2 + x + 1$
20. Find the coordinates of the vertex and the equation of the axis of symmetry of the graph of $y = 2x^2 + 3x + 4$. $\left(-\frac{3}{4}, 2\frac{7}{8}\right)$; $x = -\frac{3}{4}$

Solve each equation or system. Assume that no denominator is zero.

21. $3(x + 5) = 2(2x - 3)$ 21
22. $2|x| + 1 = 5$ $\{-2, 2\}$
23. $y\%$ of $50 = 27$ 54
24. $9a^2 - 12a + 4 = 0$ $\frac{2}{3}$
25. $36b^2 - 25 = 0$ $\left\{\frac{5}{6}, -\frac{5}{6}\right\}$
26. $10t^2 + t = 3$ $\left\{\frac{1}{2}, -\frac{3}{5}\right\}$
27. $\dfrac{1}{x + 1} + 1 = x + 2$ $\{0, -2\}$
28. $\dfrac{y + 1}{y + 2} = \dfrac{y + 4}{y - 1}$ $-\frac{3}{2}$
29. $\dfrac{2z}{z - 3} - \dfrac{1}{z + 1} = -1$ $\left\{0, \frac{1}{3}\right\}$
30. $y = x - 1$; $2x + 3y = 7$ $(2, 1)$
31. $3x + 4y = 8$; $5x - 4y = 4$ $\left(\frac{3}{2}, \frac{7}{8}\right)$
32. $2x + 7y = 29$; $3x - 4y = -29$ $(-3, 5)$

33. If x varies directly as the square of y and inversely as the cube of z, and $x = 3.6$ when $y = 3$ and $z = 2$, find x when $y = 2$ and $z = \frac{1}{2}$. 102.4

34. For a given distance, the speed at which a car travels varies inversely as the time it travels. If it takes 1.5 h to travel a distance at 84 km/h, how long would it take to travel the same distance at 90 km/h? 1.4 h

Additional Answers Cumulative Review

18.

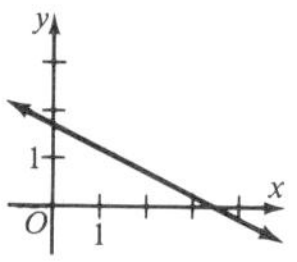

19. $\left(-\frac{1}{2}, \frac{3}{4}\right)$

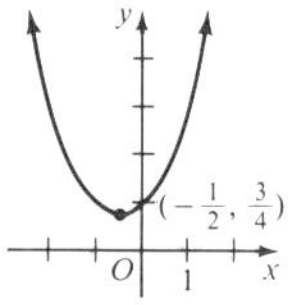

Maintaining Skills

Simplify. Assume that no denominator is zero.

Example 1 $\frac{5x + 15}{2x} \cdot \frac{4x^3}{x^2 + 6x + 9} = \frac{5(x + 3)}{2x} \cdot \frac{4x^3}{(x + 3)^2} = \frac{20x^3(x + 3)}{2x(x + 3)^2} = \frac{10x^2}{x + 3}$

1. $\frac{ab}{4a - 4b} \cdot \frac{a^2 - ab}{ab}$ $\frac{a}{4}$
2. $\frac{2x - 14}{-5x} \cdot \frac{5x^3}{3x - 21}$ $-\frac{2x^2}{3}$
3. $\frac{8f + 24g}{2f - 4g} \cdot \frac{4f - 8g}{2f + 6g}$ 8
4. $\frac{m + 2}{2m - 6} \cdot \frac{m^2 - 5m + 6}{2m + 4}$ $\frac{m - 2}{4}$
5. $\frac{3z - 6}{5z} \cdot \frac{z^2 - z - 6}{z^2 - 4}$ $\frac{3(z - 3)}{5z}$
6. $\frac{x^2 - 4}{x^2 - 9} \cdot \frac{2x^2 + 6x}{x - 2}$ $\frac{2x(x + 2)}{x - 3}$
7. $\frac{3t^2 + 2t - 1}{5t^2 - 9t - 2} \cdot \frac{10t^2 - 13t - 3}{2t^2 - t - 3}$ $\frac{3t - 1}{t - 2}$
8. $\frac{b^2 + 12b + 36}{36 - b^2} \cdot \frac{b^2 - 5b - 6}{2b^2 - 2b - 84}$ $\frac{b + 1}{2(7 - b)}$

Example 2 $\frac{2m^2 + 5m + 2}{m^2 + 4m + 3} \div \frac{m + 2}{2m^2 + 7m + 3}$

Solution $\frac{(2m + 1)(m + 2)}{(m + 3)(m + 1)} \cdot \frac{(2m + 1)(m + 3)}{m + 2} = \frac{(2m + 1)^2}{m + 1}$

9. $\frac{10a - 10b}{ab} \div \frac{2a - 2b}{a^2b^2}$ $5ab$
10. $\frac{16m^2 - n^2}{6m + 3n} \div \frac{4mn - n^2}{2mn + n^2}$ $\frac{4m + n}{3}$
11. $\frac{2b^2 + 17b + 21}{b + 1} \div (b + 7)$ $\frac{2b + 3}{b + 1}$
12. $\frac{z^2 + z}{-z^2 - 2z - 1} \div \frac{z^2 - 3z}{2z^2 - 2}$ $\frac{2(z - 1)}{3 - z}$
13. $\frac{c^2 - c - 6}{c^2 + 2c - 15} \div \frac{c^2 - 4c - 5}{c^2 - 25}$ $\frac{c + 2}{c + 1}$
14. $\frac{6t^2 - t - 2}{12t^2 + 5t - 2} \div \frac{8t^2 - 6t + 1}{4t^2 - 1}$ $\frac{(3t - 2)(2t + 1)^2}{(4t - 1)^2(3t + 2)}$
15. $\frac{r^2 - r - 20}{r^2 - 6r + 5} \cdot \frac{r^2 - 36}{r^2 - 9} \div \frac{r^2 + 7r + 12}{r^2 + 5r - 6}$ $\frac{(r - 6)(r + 6)^2}{(r - 3)(r + 3)^2}$

Example 3 $\frac{b}{b - 2} - \frac{2}{b^2 - 4} + 1$

Solution $\frac{b(b + 2) - 2 + (b + 2)(b - 2)}{(b + 2)(b - 2)} = \frac{b^2 + 2b - 2 + b^2 - 4}{(b + 2)(b - 2)} = \frac{2(b^2 + b - 3)}{(b + 2)(b - 2)}$

16. $\frac{2t - 3}{r^2t} + \frac{r - t}{r^2t}$ $\frac{t + r - 3}{r^2t}$
17. $\frac{x + 2y}{x - y} + \frac{x + y}{x - y}$ $\frac{2x + 3y}{x - y}$
18. $\frac{3b + 2}{b^3} - \frac{2b + 2}{b^3}$ $\frac{1}{b^2}$
19. $\frac{w - 2}{w - 3} - \frac{w^2 + w}{w - 3}$ $\frac{-2 - w^2}{w - 3}$
20. $z + \frac{z - 1}{z + 1} + 1$ $\frac{z(z + 3)}{z + 1}$
21. $\frac{8}{v^2 - 1} + \frac{v}{v + 1}$
22. $\frac{s}{s - t} - \frac{s}{s + t}$ $\frac{2st}{(s - t)(s + t)}$
23. $\frac{3b}{2b - 1} - b$ $\frac{2b(2 - b)}{2b - 1}$
24. $\frac{z + 3}{z - 1} + \frac{z}{z + 2}$
25. $\frac{d - 3}{2d + 1} + \frac{1}{d + 1}$ $\frac{d^2 - 2}{(2d + 1)(d + 1)}$
26. $\frac{v + 4}{v + 2} - \frac{v + 2}{v + 4}$ $\frac{4(v + 3)}{(v + 2)(v + 4)}$
27. $\frac{t}{t^2 - 4} - \frac{5t}{4 - t^2}$
28. $\frac{2b}{b + 2} + \frac{b + 1}{b} - 1$ $\frac{2b^2 + b + 2}{b(b + 2)}$
29. $\frac{x + 4}{x - 4} - \frac{x - 4}{x + 3} + 2$
30. $\frac{3a + b}{a^2 - b^2} - \frac{1}{a + b}$

Additional Answers Maintaining Skills

21. $\frac{v^2 - v + 8}{(v - 1)(v + 1)}$
24. $\frac{2(z^2 + 2z + 3)}{(z - 1)(z + 2)}$
27. $\frac{6t}{(t + 2)(t - 2)}$
29. $\frac{2x^2 + 13x - 28}{(x - 4)(x + 3)}$
30. $\frac{2}{a - b}$

About the Photo

Management decisions, whether in the manufacture of computer chips, as shown in the photograph, of automobiles, or of any other product, require the balancing of many cost, production, and availability factors. Managers seek to minimize production costs and delays while maximizing profits. Linear programming, a branch of applied mathematics, is designed to handle such optimization problems. Limited resources and their allocation requirements are represented by linear inequalities. It is not unusual for the number of variables involved in management considerations to be very large. Because solving linear programming problems can be complex, time consuming, and laborious, computers are generally used to perform the numerous calculations involved in obtaining optimum solutions.

10 Inequalities

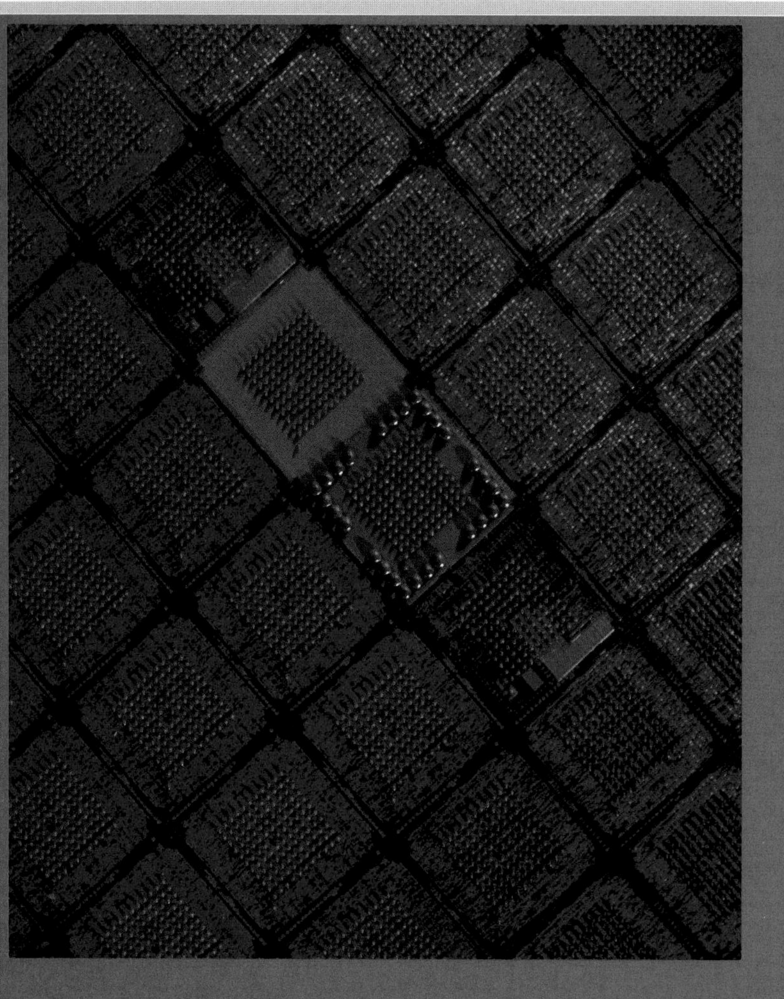

Linear programming (see pages 487–490) can be used to help large-scale manufacturers of computer chips and other items make decisions related to inventory, manufacturing, and profits.

448

Inequalities in One Variable

10-1 Order of Real Numbers

Objective To review the concept of order and to graph certain inequalities.

A number line pictures order relations among real numbers.

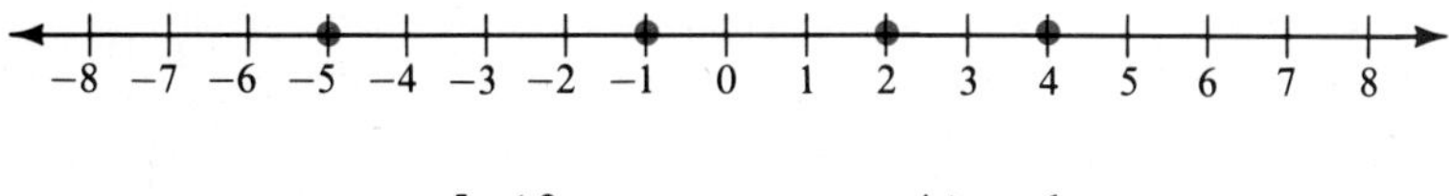

$-5 < 2$ — -5 is less than 2

$4 > -1$ — 4 is greater than -1

Recall (page 37) that on a horizontal number line any number x is:

1. less than every number whose graph is to the right of the graph of x;
2. greater than every number whose graph is to the left of the graph of x.

The sentence

$-3 < x < 2$, read "-3 is less than x and x is less than 2,"

means that x denotes a number *between* -3 and 2. You can also read the sentence as "x is greater than -3 and less than 2." The same comparisons are stated in the sentence

$$2 > x > -3.$$

Are the following statements true?

$\underbrace{-4 < 1 < 5}_{\text{True}}$ $\qquad$ $\underbrace{-4 < 8 < 5}_{\text{False}}$

The one on the right is false because 8 is *not* less than 5 (although -4 is less than 8).

For a statement like $-4 < 8 < 5$ to be true *both* "less than" statements of order must be true.

Sometimes it is convenient to indicate that one number is greater than or equal to another number. This can be written

$x \geq 5$, read "x is greater than or equal to 5."

Similarly, you can write $x \leq 5$ for "x is less than or equal to 5." The statements

$$6 \geq 5 \quad \text{and} \quad 5 \geq 5$$

are both true since such statements are true *either* if the first number is greater than the second *or* if the first number equals the second.

Teaching References

Lesson Commentary, pp. T117–T120

Assignment Guide, pp. T65–T67

Supplementary Materials
- Practice Masters 61–65
- Tests 35–37
- Resource Book
  - Practice Exercises, pp. 114–118
  - Tests, pp. 50–53
  - Enrichment Activity, p. 158
- Algebra Action

Extra Practice
- Skills, pp. 626–628
- Problems, p. 646

Alternate Test, p. T19

Problem Solving Strategies

Generalizing from Specific
Students see the general properties of order by looking at relevant numerical cases in Section 10-2.

Word Problem Plan
In Section 10-3 students use the five-step plan in conjunction with diagrams and inequalities to solve problems.

Solve a Simpler Problem
Students can graph linear inequalities and systems of linear inequalities by first graphing the related equations, which are simpler.

Deduction
The Challenge following Section 10-8 provides the opportunity to deduce the answer since methods such as simulation will not work.

Teaching Suggestions
p. T117

Suggested Extensions
p. T118

Chalkboard Examples

1. If $n \in \{0, 1, 2, 3, 4\}$, what is the solution set of $2n + 2 > 5$?
   Replace n with each of its values in turn:
   $2(0) + 2 > 5$ False
   $2(1) + 2 > 5$ False
   $2(2) + 2 > 5$ True
   $2(3) + 2 > 5$ True
   $2(4) + 2 > 5$ True
   $\therefore$ The solution set is $\{2, 3, 4\}$.
2. Translate into symbols: "-1 is less than 2 and 2 is less than 5."
   $-1 < 2 < 5$
3. Translate into words: $-5 < 0 < 1$ Negative five is less than zero and zero is less than one.
4. Describe the numbers whose graph is given below.
   The real numbers greater than 2.
5. Draw the graph of $-2 < m \leq 3$, given that the domain of m is the set of real numbers.
6. Classify each statement as true or false.
   a. $\left(\frac{2}{3}\right)^2 \geq \frac{2}{3}$ False
   b. $|-2| + |-5| \geq |-2 - 5|$ True
   c. $|-1| \leq |-9|$ True

Here are three *inequalities:*

$$-2 < 0 \qquad 4x - 3 > 2 \qquad y + 7 \leq 9$$

the sides

An **inequality** is formed by placing an inequality symbol ($>$, $<$, $\geq$, $\leq$) between numerical or variable expressions, called the **sides** of the inequality.

As in the case of equations, an inequality containing a variable is called an *open sentence* (page 10). You solve such an inequality by finding the values of the variable for which the inequality is a true statement. Such values are called **solutions of the inequality;** they make up the **solution set of the inequality.**

Example 1 If $y \in \{-1, 0, 1, 2, 3, 4\}$, what is the solution set of $y + 7 \leq 9$?

Solution Replace y with each of its values in turn:

$$y + 7 \leq 9$$

$-1 + 7 \leq 9$	True	$2 + 7 \leq 9$	True
$0 + 7 \leq 9$	True	$3 + 7 \leq 9$	False
$1 + 7 \leq 9$	True	$4 + 7 \leq 9$	False

$\therefore$ the solution set is $\{-1, 0, 1, 2\}$. ***Answer***

When you graph the numbers in the solution set of an open sentence on a number line, you say that you have drawn the **graph of the open sentence.** The graph of the inequality $y + 7 \leq 9$ in Example 1 is shown below.

Example 2 Solve $-3 \leq x < 2$ and draw its graph if the domain of x is the set of real numbers.

Solution For the inequality to be a true statement, x must denote any number between -3 and 2, including -3, but not 2.

$\therefore$ the solution set is {the real numbers greater than or equal to -3 and less than 2}. ***Answer***

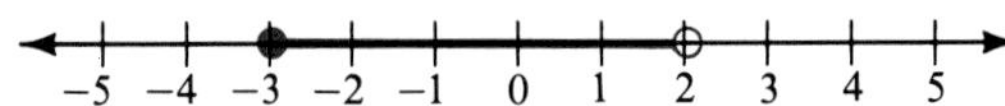

Notice that the graph includes all the points on the number line from the graph of -3 up to, but not including, the graph of 2. The open circle shows that 2 is not a solution.

Oral Exercises

Classify each statement as true or false.

1. $9 \geq -4$ true **2.** $17 \leq 23$ true **3.** $-14 \leq -23$ false **4.** $-1 \geq -2$ true

5. $-7 < 6 < 14$ true **6.** $4 > -4 > -1$ false **7.** $2 > 0 > -6$ true **8.** $-1.5 < 0.5 < 2.5$ true

9. $|-5| \geq 0$ true **10.** $|-2| > |-8|$ false **11.** $2^4 < 4^2$ false **12.** $\left(\frac{1}{3}\right)^2 \geq \frac{1}{3}$ false

Describe the numbers whose graphs appear in color. There may be more than one correct description.

Example 1

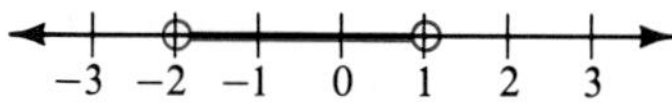

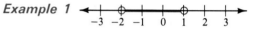

Solution The real numbers between -2 and 1, or the real numbers greater than -2 and less than 1

Example 2

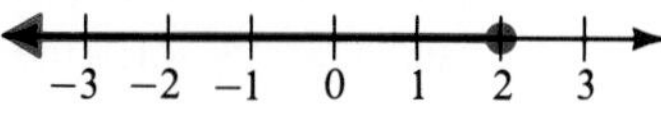

Solution The real numbers less than or equal to 2

13. $\{-3, -1, 0, 2\}$

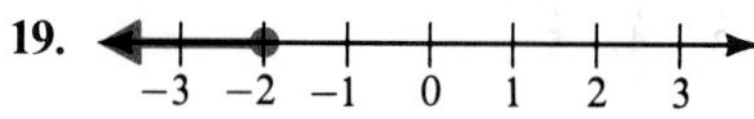

14. $\{-2, 0, 2\}$ −3 −2 −1 0 1 2 3

15. −3 −2 −1 0 1 2 3

16. −3 −2 −1 0 1 2 3

17. −3 −2 −1 0 1 2 3

18. −3 −2 −1 0 1 2 3

19. −3 −2 −1 0 1 2 3

20. −3 −2 −1 0 1 2 3

Written Exercises

Translate the statements into symbols.

A **1.** 6 is greater than -7. $6 > -7$

2. -8 is less than -4. $-8 < -4$

3. -12 is less than or equal to -9. $-12 \leq -9$

4. 4 is greater than or equal to 1. $4 \geq 1$

5. 3 is greater than 2 and less than 3.5.

6. 0 is greater than $-\frac{1}{2}$ and less than 1.

7. -15 is between -10 and -20.

8. 3 is between 4 and -4. $-4 < 3 < 4$

9. 2.8 is greater than 2 and 2 is greater than 0. $2.8 > 2 > 0$

10. -1.5 is less than -1 and -1 is less than -0.5. $-1.5 < -1 < -0.5$

Suggested Assignments

Minimum
451/1–28

Average
451/1–34

Maximum
451/1–25 odd, 27–38

Additional A Exercises

Translate the statements into symbols.

1. 3 is greater than or equal to -4. $3 \geq -4$

2. -7 is between -15 and -1. $-15 < -7 < -1$

3. Classify as true or false: $|-15| \leq |-14|$ False

Solve each inequality if $x \in \{-2, -1, 0, 1, 2, 3\}$.

4. $2x < 1$ $\{-2, -1, 0\}$

5. $7 - x \leq 7$ $\{0, 1, 2, 3\}$

Additional Answers Oral Exercises

15. the real numbers greater than or equal to -2

16. the real numbers greater than or equal to -2 and less than or equal to 3

17. the real numbers greater than -1 and less than or equal to 3

18. the real numbers greater than or equal to 0

19. the real numbers less than or equal to -2

20. the real numbers less than 1

Additional Answers Written Exercises

5. $2 < 3 < 3.5$

6. $-\frac{1}{2} < 0 < 1$

7. $-20 < -15 < -10$

Additional Answers
Written Exercises

19. $\{-4, -3, -2, -1, 0, 1\}$
20. $\{2, 3, 4\}$
21. $\{-2, -1, 0, 1, 2, 3, 4\}$
22. $\{-4, -3, -2, -1, 0, 1\}$
23. $\{-4, -3, -2, -1, 0, 1, 2, 3, 4\}$
24. $\{-4, -3, -2, -1, 0, 1, 2\}$
25. $\{-4, 4\}$
26. $\{-2, -1, 0, 1, 2\}$
27. {the real numbers greater than 3}
28. {the real numbers between 0 and 4}
29. $\{-5, -4, -3, -2, -1, 0\}$
30. $\{-1, 0, 1, 2, 3, 4\}$
31. {the real numbers between 0 and 6}
32. {the real numbers between -3 and 3}
33. $\{-5, -4, -3, -2, -1\}$
34. $\{-5, -4, -3, -2, -1\}$

35–38. Answers may vary. An example is given.

35. a. $x = -2, y = -3$
b. $x = 3, y = 2$
36. a. $x = 0, y = -1$
b. $x = 1, y = -1$
37. a. $x = 3, y = 2$
b. $x = 3, y = -2$
38. a. $x = 1, y = 5$
b. $x = 5, y = 1$

Translate the statements into symbols.

11. The absolute value of n is greater than or equal to n. $|n| \geq n$
12. The absolute value of n is greater than or equal to the opposite of n. $|n| \geq -n$

Classify each statement as true or false.

13. $|-0.7| < -0.5$ false
14. $\left|-\frac{1}{4}\right| \geq 0$ true
15. $|-10| < |-25|$ true
16. $|4 - 1| \leq |1 - 4|$ true
17. $-6 < 1 < 7$ true
18. $8 > 0 > 3$ false

Solve each inequality if $x \in \{-4, -3, -2, -1, 0, 1, 2, 3, 4\}$.

19. $4x < 8$
20. $3x \geq 6$
21. $-2x < 6$
22. $x + 1 < 3$
23. $-5 - x \leq 1$
24. $2 - x \geq 0$
25. $x^2 \geq 10$
26. $x^2 \leq 5$

Solve each inequality over the given domain and draw its graph.

B

27. $21 < 7x$; {the positive numbers}
28. $3y < 12$; {the positive numbers}
29. $-5 \leq x < 1$; {the integers}
30. $4 \geq t \geq -1$; {the integers}
31. $6 > v > 0$; {the real numbers}
32. $-3 < m < 3$; {the real numbers}
33. $-5 \leq h < 1$; {the negative integers}
34. $5 \geq s > -6$; {the negative integers}

For each statement in Exercises 35-38:
a. Find a pair of values of x and y for which the statement is true.
b. Find a pair of values of x and y for which the statement is false.

C

35. If $x \geq y$, then $|x| \leq |y|$.
36. If $x \geq 0$ and $y < 0$, then $xy \geq 0$.
37. If $x > y$, then $xy > y^2$.
38. $|x - y| > x - y$

Computer Exercises

For students with some programming experience

Write a BASIC program to find the solution set of an inequality in one variable for a specified domain of the variable. RUN the program to find the solution set for each of the following inequalities with the given domains.

1. $2x - 5 < 7$; $x \in \{0, 1, 2, \ldots, 10\}$ $\{0, 1, 2, 3, 4, 5\}$
2. $x^2 - x < 6$; $x \in \{-4, -3, -2, \ldots, 1, 2, 3, 4\}$ $\{-1, 0, 1, 2\}$
3. $|4 - 5x| > 13$; $x \in \{0, 1, 2, 3, 4, 5\}$ $\{4, 5\}$
4. $|x^2 + 3x| < -1$; $x \in \{0, 1, 2, 3, 4, 5\}$ $\emptyset$
5. $x^2 + 3x + 4 < 10$; $x \in \{-3, -2, -1, 0, 1, 2, 3\}$ $\{-3, -2, -1, 0, 1\}$
6. $x^2 - 4x + 1 > 6$; $x \in \{0, 1, 2, 3, \ldots, 8, 9, 10\}$ $\{6, 7, 8, 9, 10\}$

10-2 Solving Inequalities

Objective To transform inequalities in order to solve them.

Only the first of the following statements is true:

$$-6 < 5 \qquad -6 = 5 \qquad -6 > 5$$

True False False

In comparing real numbers, you make the following basic assumption:

Axiom of Comparison

For all real numbers a and b, one and only one of the following statements is true:

$$a < b, \quad a = b, \quad \text{or} \quad a > b.$$

Now suppose you know two facts about the graphs of three numbers a, b, and c.

1. The graph of a is to the left of the graph of b: $a < b$
2. The graph of b is to the left of the graph of c: $b < c$

a b c

Where is the graph of a relative to the graph of c? You can see that it is to the left of c: $a < c$

In general, the following assumption is made:

Transitive Axiom of Order

For all real numbers a, b, and c:

1. If $a < b$ and $b < c$, then $a < c$;
2. If $c > b$ and $b > a$, then $c > a$.

What happens when the same number is added to each side of an inequality?

$$2 < 7 \qquad\qquad 2 < 7$$

$$\underbrace{2+3}_{5} < \underbrace{7+3}_{10} \qquad\qquad \underbrace{2-3}_{-1} < \underbrace{7-3}_{4}$$

These numerical examples suggest the axiom of order stated on the following page. (Recall that subtracting a number is the same as adding the opposite of that number.)

Teaching Suggestions
p. T118

Chalkboard Examples

In each exercise, assume that the domain of the variable is the set of real numbers.

Solve and graph.

1. $4s - 1 > 11$
$4s > 12$
$s > 3$
{the real numbers greater than 3}

−1 0 1 2 3 4 5

2. $2 - 3u \geq 8$
$-3u \geq 6$
$u \leq -2$
{the real numbers less than or equal to −2}

−5 −4 −3 −2 −1 0 1

3. $2t - 4 + 5(5 + t) \geq 0$
$2t - 4 + 25 + 5t \geq 0$
$7t + 21 \geq 0$
$7t \geq -21$
$t \geq -3$
{the real numbers greater than or equal to −3}

−4 −3 −2 −1 0 1 2

Solve each inequality.

4. $4(1 - x) + 9 < 2x - 5$
$4 - 4x + 9 < 2x - 5$
$13 - 4x < 2x - 5$
$18 < 6x$
$3 < x$
{the real numbers greater than 3}

5. $\frac{2}{5}m - 2 < \frac{1}{10}(m + 1)$
$10\left(\frac{2}{5}m\right) - 20 < m + 1$
$4m - 20 < m + 1$
$3m < 21$
$m < 7$
{the real numbers less than 7}

Common Errors

Some students may graph inequalities that have the variable on the right side incorrectly. Encourage them to transform inequalities so that the variable is always on the left side. Point out, for example, that if $2 > x$, then $x < 2$.

Students may forget to reverse the direction of the inequality when they should or reverse it when they shouldn't. Some students reverse the direction of the inequality when they use subtraction to transform an inequality. Some incorrectly reverse the direction of the inequality when they multiply or divide both sides by the same positive number if the side of the inequality without the variable is negative. Refer these students to page 454.

Supplementary Materials

Practice Master 61
Resource Book, p. 114

Suggested Assignments

Minimum
456/1–8, 9–41 odd

Average
457/9–55 odd
S 452/35–38

Maximum
457/9–47 odd, 49–56

Addition Axiom of Order

For all real numbers a, b, and c:

1. If $a < b$, then $a + c < b + c$;
2. If $a > b$, then $a + c > b + c$.

What happens when each side of the inequality $-3 < 2$ is multiplied by a nonzero real number?

Multiply by 5: Is it true that $5(-3) < 5(2)$?
Yes, $-15 < 10$.

Multiply by -5: Is it true that $-5(-3) < -5(2)$?
No, $15 > -10$.

This example suggests that multiplying each side of an inequality by a negative number *reverses the direction,* or order, of the inequality.

In general, the following assumption is made:

Multiplication Axiom of Order

For all real numbers a, b, and c such that

$c > 0$:	$c < 0$:
1. If $a < b$, then $ac < bc$;	1. If $a < b$, then $ac > bc$;
2. If $a > b$, then $ac > bc$.	2. If $a > b$, then $ac < bc$.

Multiplying both sides of an inequality by zero does not produce an inequality; the result is the identity $0 = 0$.

The axioms that have been stated guarantee that the following transformations of a given inequality always produce an **equivalent inequality,** that is, one with the same solution set.

Transformations That Produce an Equivalent Inequality

1. Substituting for either side of the inequality an expression equivalent to that side.
2. Adding to (or subtracting from) each side the same real number.
3. Multiplying (or dividing) each side by the same positive number.
4. Multiplying (or dividing) each side by the same negative number and reversing the direction of the inequality.

To solve an inequality, you usually try to transform it into a simple equivalent inequality whose solution set can be seen at once.

You may assume that the domain of all variables is the set of real numbers unless otherwise stated.

Example 1 Solve $5x - 1 < 11 + 3x$ and draw its graph.

Solution

$5x - 1 < 11 + 3x$

$5x - 1 + 1 < 11 + 3x + 1$ Add 1 to each side.

$5x < 12 + 3x$

$5x - 3x < 12 + 3x - 3x$ Subtract $3x$ from each side.

$2x < 12$

$\frac{2x}{2} < \frac{12}{2}$ Divide each side by 2.

$x < 6$

∴ the solution set is {the real numbers less than 6}.
The graph is:

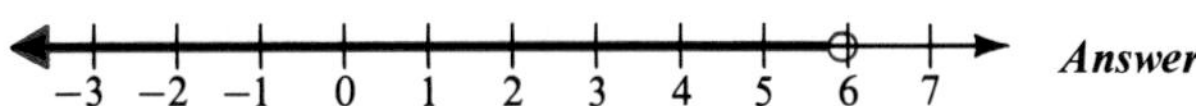

Answer

To solve an inequality, you take the same steps used to solve equations:

1. Simplify each side of the inequality.
2. Use the inverse operations to undo any indicated additions or subtractions.
3. Use the inverse operations to undo any indicated multiplications or divisions.

Example 2 Solve and graph $2(z - 8) + 9 \geq 3(4 - z) - 4$.

Solution

$2(z - 8) + 9 \geq 3(4 - z) - 4$

$2z - 16 + 9 \geq 12 - 3z - 4$

$2z - 7 \geq 8 - 3z$

$5z \geq 15$

$z \geq 3$

∴ the solution set is {the real numbers greater than or equal to 3}.
The graph is:

Answer

Additional A Exercises

Solve each inequality.

1. $x - 7 \leq 16$ $x \leq 23$
2. $\frac{p}{-13} < -3$ $p > 39$
3. $8 < 7 + \frac{1}{3}n$ $n > 3$
4. $7j \geq 16j - 18$ $j \leq 2$
5. $6(2 - x) < 3(x - 2)$ $x > 2$
6. $\frac{3}{8}y + 1 \geq \frac{9}{8}$ $y \geq \frac{1}{3}$

Mixed Review Exercises

1. Simplify $(2^{-2} + 3^0)^{-1}$. $\frac{4}{5}$
2. Solve, using two equations in two variables: Last week, Jane's and Joe's highest bowling scores totaled 514, but Jane's was 50 points less than Joe's. What were their scores? 232 and 282
3. Solve by the graphic method:
   $2x + y = 14$ (5, 4)
   $x - y = 1$
4. Solve by using multiplication with the addition-or-subtraction method:
   $2x + 3y = 1$ (5, −3)
   $5x + 4y = 13$

Additional Answers
Oral Exercises

1. Subtr. 3 from both sides.
2. Add 2 to both sides.
3. Add 2 to both sides.
4. Subtr. 5 from both sides.
5. Div. both sides by 4.
6. Div. both sides by 2.
7. Div. both sides by -6 and reverse the direction of the inequality.
8. Mult. both sides by 2.
9. Mult. both sides by 7.
10. Mult. both sides by -2 and reverse the direction of the inequality.
11. Div. both sides by 3.
12. Mult. both sides by -3 and reverse the direction of the inequality.
13. Add 5 to both sides; $y < 13$
14. Subtr. 2 from both sides; $5 < x$
15. Div. both sides by 10; $p > 10$
16. Div. both sides by -4 and reverse the direction of the inequality; $2 > c$
17. Mult. both sides by 2; $w \geq 24$
18. Mult. both sides by -4 and reverse the direction of the inequality; $4 \geq r$

Oral Exercises

Tell how to transform the first inequality to obtain the second one.

1. $t + 3 < 7$; $t < 4$

2. $s - 2 > 7$; $s > 9$

3. $-1 < x - 2$; $1 < x$

4. $y + 5 < 0$; $y < -5$

5. $4p < 20$; $p < 5$

6. $2m < -16$; $m < -8$

7. $-6a < 18$; $a > -3$

8. $\frac{z}{2} > 3$; $z > 6$

9. $2 > \frac{v}{7}$; $14 > v$

10. $\frac{r}{-2} < -10$; $r > 20$

11. $3y < \frac{1}{2}$; $y < \frac{1}{6}$

12. $-\frac{t}{3} > 0$; $t < 0$

Explain how to transform each inequality in order to solve it. Then state the transformed inequality.

13. $y - 5 < 8$

14. $7 < x + 2$

15. $10p > 100$

16. $-8 < -4c$

17. $\frac{w}{2} \geq 12$

18. $-1 \leq -\frac{r}{4}$

Written Exercises

Match each inequality in Exercises 1-8 with its solution set in a-h.

A

1. $y - 2 \geq 7$ d

2. $10 > z + 10$ h

3. $6p \neq 24$ c

4. $16 < 8v$ f

5. $-28 > -7m$ b

6. $\frac{d}{4} < -5$ g

7. $2 - g > 0$ e

8. $2 \leq \frac{w}{-3}$ a

a.
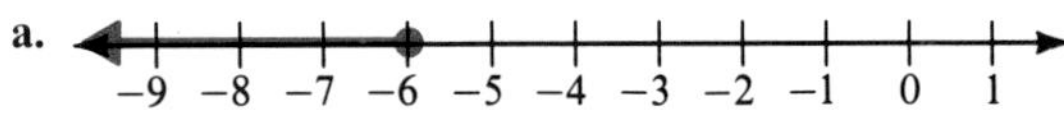

b.
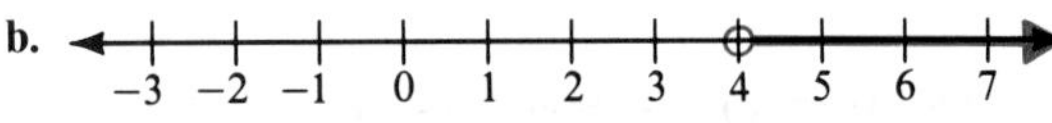

c.
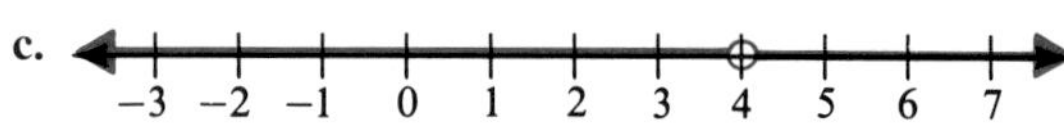

d.
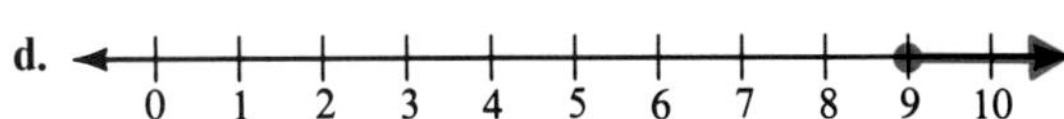

e.
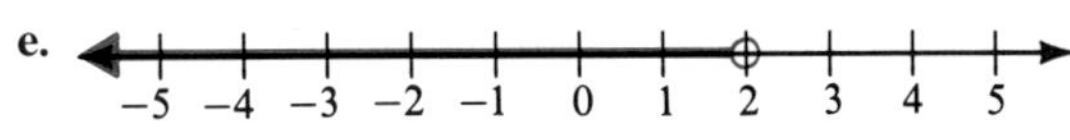

f.

g.
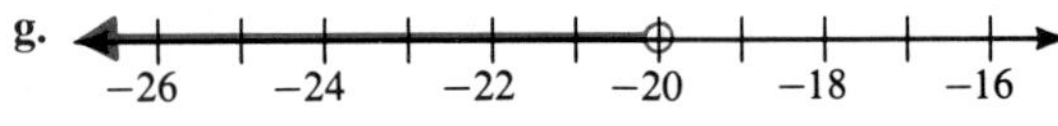

h.
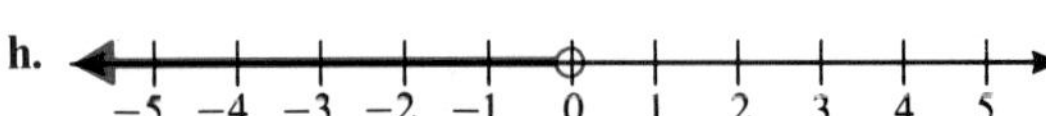

Solve each inequality and draw its graph.

9. $n - 4 > 11$

10. $a + 5 < 14$

11. $-\frac{y}{2} > 4$

12. $3q < 15$

13. $36 < \frac{x}{-9}$

14. $-9 < \frac{s}{3}$

15. $-6m \geq 6$

16. $-5w \leq 25$

17. $\frac{x}{2} - 4 > -6$

18. $3v + 2 > 8$

19. $-\frac{z}{3} \geq 0$

20. $7 \geq 2k - 5$

21. $\frac{3}{2}t - 7 < 2$

22. $-3 \leq 3 - \frac{u}{2}$

23. $-1 < 9 + \frac{2}{3}g$

24. $5 + \frac{x}{4} \leq 8$

25. $12 - \frac{3}{2}c > 0$

26. $0 > 8 - \frac{4}{3}b$

Solve each inequality.

27. $5y < 4y + 6$

28. $7f - 6 > 6f + 12$

29. $4r - 5 < 5r + 7$

30. $1 + 2r > 7 - r$

31. $8 - 2b \geq 4 - b$

32. $3(x - 4) \leq 9$

33. $8 < 2(4 - m)$

34. $4(n - 6) < 2(n - 2)$

35. $5(1 - t) \geq 4(3 - t)$

36. $7(2 - v) \geq -(v - 8)$

37. $\frac{5}{6}r + 1 \geq \frac{4}{3}$

38. $\frac{1}{8} < 5 - \frac{3}{4}a$

Solve each inequality and draw its graph.

B **39.** $5(x - 1) \geq \frac{5}{4}x$

40. $\frac{4}{3}y \leq 8(y - 5)$

41. $n - \frac{5}{2} > \frac{3}{4}(n - 6)$

42. $4w - \frac{1}{2}(3w + 10) \geq 0$

43. $5(5 - k) - 7(7 + k) < 0$

44. $4(v - 3) > 3(v + 4) - 9$

45. $4\left(r - \frac{1}{2}\right) - 3 \leq 5(r - 1) + 4$

46. $3(t - 1) - 2(t + 2) \leq 3 - 5t$

47. $5 - a + 2(a - 3) \geq 5(a + 1)$

48. $2(2b - 1) - 3(b + 1) > 3b + 7$

Given that a and b are real numbers such that $a > b$, describe the real numbers c for which each statement is true.

C **49.** $ac > bc$ positive

50. $ac < bc$ negative

51. $ac = bc$ 0

52. $\frac{a}{c} > \frac{b}{c}$ positive

53. $\frac{a}{c} < \frac{b}{c}$ negative

54. $ac^2 > bc^2$ all real numbers except 0

55. $\frac{a}{c^2} < \frac{b}{c^2}$ none

56. $ac^2 = bc^2$ 0

Classify each statement as true for all real numbers a and b such that $a > b > 0$ or false for some a and b such that $a > b > 0$. If you classify a statement as false, give an example of values for which it is false.

57. $a > 0$ true

58. $a^2 > a$ false; $a = \frac{1}{2}$

59. $ab > 0$ true

60. $a + b > a$ true

61. $a^2 > b$ false; $a = \frac{1}{2}$, $b = \frac{1}{3}$

62. $a^2 > ab$ true

63. $ab > b^2$ true

64. $a^2 > b^2$ true

Additional Answers
Written Exercises

9. {the real numbers greater than 15}
10. {the real numbers less than 9}
11. {the real numbers less than −8}
12. {the real numbers less than 5}
13. {the real numbers less than −324}
14. {the real numbers greater than −27}
15. {−1 and the real numbers less than −1}
16. {−5 and the real numbers greater than −5}
17. {the real numbers greater than −4}
18. {the real numbers greater than 2}
19. {0 and the real numbers less than 0}
20. {6 and the real numbers less than 6}
21. {the real numbers less than 6}
22. {12 and the real numbers less than 12}
23. {the real numbers greater than −15}
24. {12 and the real numbers less than 12}
25. {the real numbers less than 8}
26. {the real numbers greater than 6}
27. {the real numbers less than 6}
28. {the real numbers greater than 18}
29. {the real numbers greater than −12}
30. {the real numbers greater than 2}

(continued p. 463)

Additional Answers Reading Algebra

2. **a.** greater than **b.** open; right **c.** {the real numbers greater than 2}

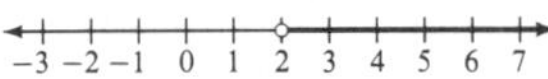

4. **a.** less than or equal to **b.** closed; left **c.** {the real numbers less than or equal to 12}

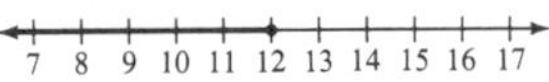

6. **a.** less than or equal to **b.** closed; left **c.** {the real numbers less than or equal to 12}

8. **a.** greater than or equal to **b.** closed; right **c.** {the real numbers greater than or equal to 1}

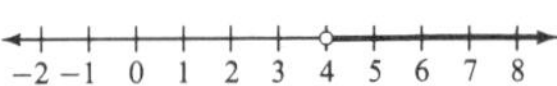

10. **a.** less than **b.** open; right **c.** {the real numbers greater than 4}

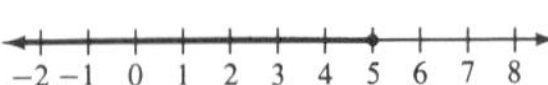

12. **a.** less than or equal to **b.** closed; left **c.** {the real numbers less than or equal to 5}

Reading Algebra / *Inequalities*

When working with inequalities, it is extremely important to read both the symbols and the words slowly and carefully. Unlike equations that involve only the equals sign, $=$, inequalities can contain any of the four inequality symbols, $<$, $>$, $\leq$, $\geq$, and which of these symbols is used determines what your answer will be. For example, the equation $2x + 6 = 14$ is equivalent to $x = 4$ and the solution set is simply $\{4\}$. The inequalities $2x + 6 < 14$, $2x + 6 > 14$, $2x + 6 \leq 14$, and $2x + 6 \geq 14$, however, all have different solution sets.

$2x + 6 < 14$ is equivalent to $x < 4$. The solution set is {the real numbers less than 4}.

$2x + 6 > 14$ is equivalent to $x > 4$. The solution set is {the real numbers greater than 4}.

$2x + 6 \leq 14$ is equivalent to $x \leq 4$. The solution set is {4, and the real numbers less than 4}.

$2x + 6 \geq 14$ is equivalent to $x \geq 4$. The solution set is {4, and the real numbers greater than 4}.

Word problems involving inequalities also require very careful reading. An important step in solving this type of problem is determining which symbol to use when you write your inequality. Is the problem asking for a solution that is less than, greater than, less than or equal to, or greater than or equal to a particular number or expression? Before you write your inequality you should be certain that you are going to use the correct symbol.

Combined inequalities involve the words "and" and "or." These types of inequalities must be read extremely carefully, as they can involve the same numbers and symbols, but have different solutions, depending on whether they are joined by "and" or "or."

Exercises

For each of the following:

a. Determine whether the inequality symbol means less than, greater than, less than or equal to, or greater than or equal to.

b. Determine whether the graph has a closed circle or an open circle and whether the graph goes to the right or the left of that circle.

c. Solve and graph the solution.

1. $x - 3 > 12$

2. $3y + 1 > 7$

3. $5 \geq 2y - 3$

4. $12 + y \leq 24$

5. $-9 < 21 + 2m$

6. $-6 \leq 6 - k$

7. $18 - 3y > 0$

8. $1 + 3r \geq 5 - r$

9. $2x - 3 < 4x + 5$

10. $21 - 15x < -8x - 7$

11. $4(t - 2) > 5(t - 3)$

12. $6(z - 5) \leq 15 + 5(7 - 2z)$

10-3 Solving Problems Involving Inequalities

Objective To solve problems that involve inequalities.

Example 1 The width of a rectangular computer screen is 20 cm less than twice the length. The perimeter is more than 56 cm. Find the minimum dimensions of the screen, if each dimension, in centimeters, is an integer.

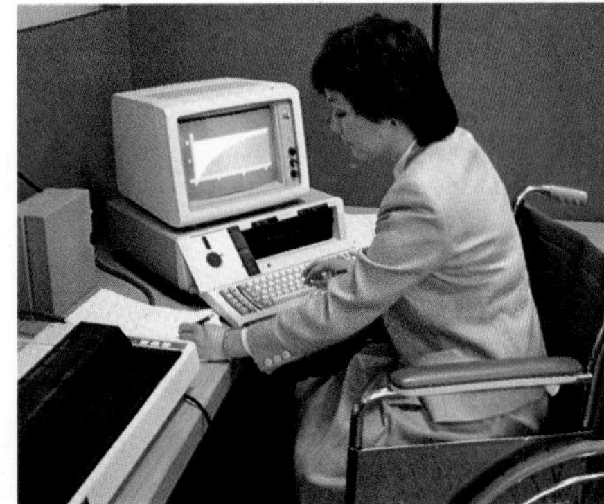

Solution

Step 1 The problem asks for the minimum length, l, and width, w, in centimeters. We are told that:
a. l and w are integers;
b. w is 20 cm less than twice l;
c. the perimeter $(2l + 2w)$ is more than 56 cm.

Step 2 Let l = length in centimeters.
Then $2l - 20$ = width in centimeters.

Step 3 The perimeter is more than 56 cm.

Step 4
$$\begin{aligned} 2l + 2(2l - 20) &> 56 \\ 2l + 4l - 40 &> 56 \\ 6l - 40 &> 56 \\ 6l &> 96 \\ l &> 16 \end{aligned}$$

∴ the minimum length is 17 cm.
The minimum width is 2(17) − 20, or 14 cm.

Step 5 *Check:* (1) Is the width 20 cm less than twice the length?

$$14 \stackrel{?}{=} 2(17) - 20$$
$$14 = 14 \checkmark$$

(2) Is the perimeter more than 56 cm?

$$2(17) + 2(14) = 34 + 28 = 62;\ 62 > 56 \checkmark$$

(3) Are the dimensions the least possible? Suppose the length were the next smaller integer, 16. Then, the width would be 2(16) − 20, or 12 cm. The perimeter would be 2(16) + 2(12), or 56 cm, which is *not* greater than 56 cm.

∴ the dimensions are 17 cm and 14 cm. ***Answer***

Teaching Suggestions
p. T118

Chalkboard Examples

Using the variable indicated in parentheses, translate each of the following statements into symbols.

1. The sale price of the coat (c) is no more than \$49. $c \le 49$
2. On their trip, the Jacksons' mileage (m) was at least 125 mi each day. $m \ge 125$
3. Lee's earnings (e) were between \$600 and \$750 this year. $600 < e < 750$
4. The temperature (t) last night was at most 15°C. $t \le 15$
5. Find all sets of three positive consecutive odd integers such that their sum is less than the sum of the smallest integer and ten.

Step 2 Let n = the smallest positive odd integer. Then $n + 2$ and $n + 4$ represent the next two consecutive odd integers.

Step 3 $n + (n + 2) + (n + 4) < n + 10$

Step 4 $3n + 6 < n + 10$
$2n < 4$
$n < 2$
Since n is positive, $0 < n < 2$, so $n = 1$.

∴ the set is {1, 3, 5}.

Example 2 Find all sets of three positive consecutive odd integers such that twice the sum of the first two is less than three times the third.

Solution

Step 1 The problem asks for three consecutive odd integers that are positive.

Step 2 Let the first of these integers be n. Then, in natural order, the other two are $n + 2$ and $n + 4$.

Step 3 $\underbrace{\text{Twice the sum of the first two}}\ \underbrace{\text{is less than}}\ \underbrace{\text{three times the third.}}$

$$2[n + (n + 2)] < 3(n + 4)$$

Step 4

$$\begin{aligned} 2(2n + 2) &< 3n + 12 \\ 4n + 4 &< 3n + 12 \\ 4n &< 3n + 8 \\ n &< 8 \end{aligned}$$

Since the least number in the set must be positive, odd, and less than 8, there are only four choices: 1, 3, 5, and 7.

$\therefore$ the four sets are $\{1, 3, 5\}$, $\{3, 5, 7\}$, $\{5, 7, 9\}$, and $\{7, 9, 11\}$.

Step 5 *Check:* Is twice the sum of the first two consecutive odd integers less than three times the greatest?

Check for $\{1, 3, 5\}$: $2(1 + 3) \stackrel{?}{<} 3(5)$
$8 < 15$ ✓

Check for $\{3, 5, 7\}$: $2(3 + 5) \stackrel{?}{<} 3(7)$
$16 < 21$ ✓

Check for $\{5, 7, 9\}$: $2(5 + 7) \stackrel{?}{<} 3(9)$
$24 < 27$ ✓

Check for $\{7, 9, 11\}$: $2(7 + 9) \stackrel{?}{<} 3(11)$
$32 < 33$ ✓

To show that these four sets of integers are *all* the solutions, check the next possible set of three consecutive odd integers, $\{9, 11, 13\}$, to see whether the condition is satisfied.

$$2(9 + 11) \stackrel{?}{<} 3(13)$$
$$40 < 39 \quad \text{False}$$

$\therefore$ the required sets are $\{1, 3, 5\}$, $\{3, 5, 7\}$, $\{5, 7, 9\}$, and $\{7, 9, 11\}$.

Answer

To translate phrases such as "is at least" and "is no less than" or "is at most" and "is no more than" into mathematical terms, you use the symbols $\geq$ or $\leq$. For example:

The age of the tree is at least 70 years:	$a \geq 70$
The rent is no less than \$400 per month:	$r \geq 400$
The price of the paperback book is at most \$5.95:	$p \leq 5.95$
Her time in the 10 km race was no more than 40 min:	$t \leq 40$

Common Errors

Some students confuse *is at least* with *is less than* (see Written Exercises 4 and 10) and *is at most* with *is more than* (see Written Exercises 5 and 8). Point out that *is at least* means *is greater than or equal to* and that *is at most* means *is less than or equal to*.

Some students make errors because they forget to check their answers with the words of the problems. Again, be sure to stress the importance of this step.

Supplementary Materials

Test 35
Resource Book, p. 115

Suggested Assignments

Minimum
461/2–14 even
462/*P*: 1–3, 7, 9, 10

Average
461/2–18 even
462/*P*: 2, 4, 7, 10, 14

Maximum
461/1–17 odd
462/*P*: 2, 4, 10, 13, 17
S 457/57–64

Additional A Exercises

For each of the following, choose a variable to represent the number indicated in parentheses, and use it to write an inequality based on the given information. (Do not solve.)

1. Maria, who is older than her 12-year-old brother, is 4 years younger than Sue. (Sue's age)
$s - 4 > 12$

Written Exercises

9. $n;\ 5n + 10(2n) + 25\left(\frac{1}{2}n\right) \le 1140$

For each of the following:

a. Choose a variable to represent the number indicated in color.

b. Use the variable to write an inequality based on the given information. (Do not solve.)

A 1. Isabel, who is not yet 21 years old, is two years older than Ida. (Ida's age) $i;\ i + 2 < 21$

2. After typing 15 pages of manuscript, a typist had fewer than 36 pages left to type. (the number of pages of manuscript the typist had originally) $p;\ p - 15 < 36$

3. A sales executive traveled a certain number of kilometers by airplane and then one tenth as far by automobile. Her total trip was more than 3000 km. $a;\ a + \frac{a}{10} > 3000$

4. The number of County Community College students enrolled in liberal arts is one half the number enrolled in applied arts and sciences. The total number of students in these programs is at least 8000. $l;\ l + \frac{1}{2}l \ge 8000$

5. In a marathon, Fred ran 15 more kilometers than half the number Jim ran. Fred ran at most 36 km. $k;\ \frac{1}{2}k + 15 \le 36$

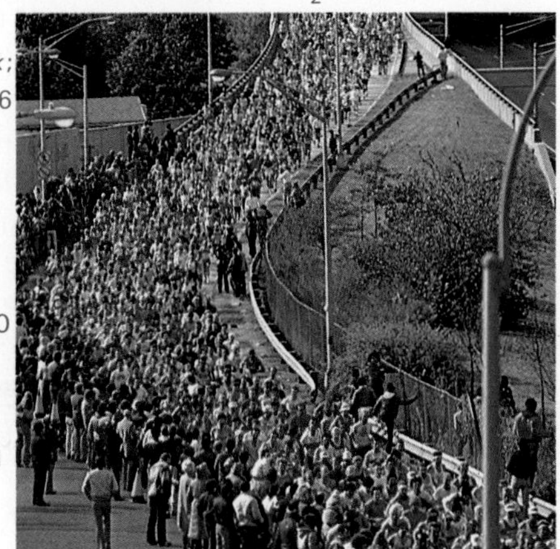

6. A homeowner figures that the total of the monthly mortgage payment and the home's operating expenses is no more than $900. The mortgage payment is $100 more than twice the operating expenses. $e;\ e + 2e + 100 \le 900$

7. The sum of three consecutive odd integers is no less than 51. (the middle integer) $m;\ (m - 2) + m + (m + 2) \ge 51$

8. The product of two consecutive even integers is at most 360. (the greater integer) $g;\ g(g - 2) \le 360$

9. A coin bank containing only quarters, dimes, and nickels has twice as many dimes as nickels and half as many quarters as nickels. In all the bank contains no more than $11.40. (the number of nickels)

10. Two trucks start from the same point at the same time, but travel in opposite directions. One truck travels at 86 km/h, the other at 78 km/h. After some hours of traveling, the trucks are at least 650 km apart. $t;\ 86t + 78t \ge 650$

B 11. If a motorist drove 10 km/h faster, then in 3 h he would travel farther than he does in 4 h at his present speed. $r;\ 3(r + 10) > 4r$

12. Eight years from now, Violette will be more than twice as old as she is now. (her age now) $a;\ a + 8 > 2a$

2. The sum of four consecutive integers is greater than 100. (smallest integer) $n + (n + 1) + (n + 2) + (n + 3) > 100$

3. John, Rick, and Matt all read books for their research papers. John read the most, Matt read 3 fewer than John, and Rick read 5 fewer than John. All together, they read more than 20 books. (number of books John read) $j + (j - 3) + (j - 5) > 20$

4. On a certain test, a student's score is determined by giving 1 point for each correct answer, 0 points for each unanswered question, and $-\frac{1}{4}$ point for each incorrect answer. Jan answered 10 more questions right than wrong and her score was less than 50. (number right) $r - \frac{1}{4}(r - 10) < 50$

5. Fred has 3 times as many $20 bills as $10 bills. He has at least $300. (number of $10 bills) $10t + 20 \cdot 3t \ge 300$

6. Two friends start from school and walk toward the mountains, one at 5 km/h and the other at 8 km/h. After a few hours they are at least 6 km apart. (number of hours) $8h - 5h \ge 6$

17. n; $5(n + 2) - (n + 1) \geq 9 + 2n$

Mixed Review Exercises

1. Find the slope of the line whose equation is $2x - 3y = 15$. $\frac{2}{3}$
2. Change $-2x + 4y + 7 = 0$ to slope-intercept form. $y = \frac{1}{2}x - \frac{7}{4}$
3. Write an equation in standard form of the line that has slope -2 and passes through the point $(2, -2)$. $2x + y = 2$
4. If A varies jointly as b and a and $A = 40$ when $a = 8$ and $b = 10$, find a when $A = 50$ and $b = 10$. 10

For each of the following:

a. Choose a variable to represent the number indicated in color.

b. Use the variable to write an inequality based on the given information. (Do not solve.)

13. A dowel 25 cm long is cut into two pieces. One piece is at least 1 cm longer than twice as long as the other piece. (the length of the shorter piece) s; $2s + 1 \leq 25 - s$
14. At a school cafeteria, a student paid 90 cents for a whole-wheat muffin and a glass of milk. The milk cost less than two thirds of the cost of the muffin. m; $90 - m < \frac{2}{3}m$
15. The smaller of two consecutive odd integers is no less than 15 more than one fourth of the greater. n; $n - 2 \geq \frac{1}{4}n + 15$
16. The greater of two consecutive even integers is no more than 50 less than five times the smaller. s; $s + 2 \leq 5s - 50$
17. There are three consecutive integers such that five times the greatest diminished by the second is at least nine more than twice the least.
18. Three consecutive odd integers are such that their sum is more than 57 decreased by twice the greatest of the three integers. n; $n + (n - 2) + (n - 4) > 57 - 2n$

In Exercises 19-20, express in symbols the property that is stated in words.

C 19. The absolute value of the sum of two real numbers is no greater than the sum of the absolute values of the numbers. $|a + b| \leq |a| + |b|$

20. The square of the sum of two nonnegative real numbers is at least as great as 4 times the product of the numbers. For $a \geq 0$ and $b \geq 0$, $(a + b)^2 \geq 4ab$.

Problems

Solve.

A 1. A bakery makes bread in which the ratio of whole-wheat flour to white flour is 5:2. How much white flour is used in making a batch of bread containing at least 35 kg of flour? at least 10 kg of white flour

2. Dimes minted before 1965 contained copper and silver in the ratio 1:9. At least how much silver was in a sack of those coins, weighing no less than 100 kg? at least 90 kg of silver
3. The sum of two consecutive integers is less than 75. Find the pair of integers with the greatest sum. 36, 37
4. The sum of two consecutive even integers is less than 500. Find the pair with the greatest sum. 248, 250
5. Of all pairs of consecutive odd integers whose sum is greater than 80, find the pair whose sum is least. 41, 43

6. Of all pairs of consecutive integers whose sum is no more than 100, find the pair whose sum is greatest. 49, 50

7. Between them, Terry and Jane have 50 cassettes. If Jane has more than two thirds as many cassettes as Terry, at least how many cassettes does Jane have? At most how many does Terry have? 21 cassettes; 29 cassettes

8. A bag contains 100 marbles, some red, the rest blue. If there are no more than $1\frac{1}{2}$ times as many red marbles as blue ones in the bag, at most how many red marbles are in the bag? At least how many blue ones are in the bag? 60 red marbles; 40 blue marbles

9. Two sides of a triangle have the same length. The third side is 20 cm longer than each of the other sides. The perimeter is no less than 95 cm. At least how long are the sides of the triangle? 25 cm, 25 cm, 45 cm

10. There are 3 exams in a marking period. A student received grades of 74 and 83 on the first two exams. What grade must the student get on the last exam to obtain an average for the marking period of no less than 80? at least an 83

11. Peter is 3 years older than Diane. Twenty years ago Peter was at least twice as old as Diane was. At most how old is Diane? 23 years old

12. Cheryl's father is 7 times as old as Cheryl. Two years ago he was at most 9 times as old as Cheryl was. At least how old is Cheryl? 8 years old

B

13. At 1 P.M. two trains, traveling toward each other, leave from towns that are 312 km apart. One train averages at most 82 km/h, and the other at most 74 km/h. What is the earliest possible time for them to meet? 3 P.M.

14. If Marva were able to increase her average cycling speed by 3.5 km/h, she would be able to cover in 2 h a distance at least as great as that which now takes her 3 h. What is the best average speed she achieves at present? 7 km/h

15. A brine solution contains 90 kg of water and 6 kg of salt. At least how much salt must be added to obtain a solution that is no less than 10% salt? 4 kg of salt

16. At least how many grams of copper must be alloyed with 380 g of pure silver to produce an alloy that is no more than 89.1% pure silver? 46.49 g of copper

17. A pair of consecutive integers has the property that 6 times the smaller is less than 5 times the greater. Find the greatest such integers. 4, 5

18. The sum of four consecutive integers decreased by 18 is greater than twice the smallest of the four. What are the four smallest such integers? 7, 8, 9, 10

19. The units digit of a certain two-digit number is 5 more than the tens digit. Thirty-six times the tens digit is greater than the number with the digits reversed. Find the least possible value of the original number. 38

20. If the digits of a certain two-digit number are reversed, the resulting number is 9 less than the original number. The sum of the digits is at most 7. Find the greatest possible value of the original number. 43

Additional Answers
Written Exercises
(p. 457)

31. {4 and the real numbers less than 4}
32. {7 and the real numbers less than 7}
33. {the real numbers less than 0}
34. {the real numbers less than 10}
35. {−7 and the real numbers less than −7}
36. {1 and the real numbers less than 1}
37. $\left\{\frac{2}{5}\right.$ and the real numbers greater than $\left.\frac{2}{5}\right\}$
38. $\left\{\right.$the real numbers less than $\left.\frac{13}{2}\right\}$
39. $\left\{\frac{4}{3}\right.$ and the real numbers greater than $\left.\frac{4}{3}\right\}$
40. {6 and the real numbers greater than 6}
41. {the real numbers greater than −8}
42. {2 and the real numbers greater than 2}
43. {the real numbers greater than −2}
44. {the real numbers greater than 15}
45. {−4 and the real numbers greater than −4}
46. $\left\{\frac{5}{3}\right.$ and the real numbers less than $\left.\frac{5}{3}\right\}$
47. $\left\{-\frac{3}{2}\right.$ and the real numbers less than $\left.-\frac{3}{2}\right\}$
48. {the real numbers less than −6}

21. Mike walked at the rate of 5.2 km/h in a straight path from his campsite to a ranch. He returned immediately on horseback at the rate of 7.8 km/h. Upon his return, he found that he had been gone no more than 3.5 h. At most how far is it from his campsite to the ranch? 10.92 km

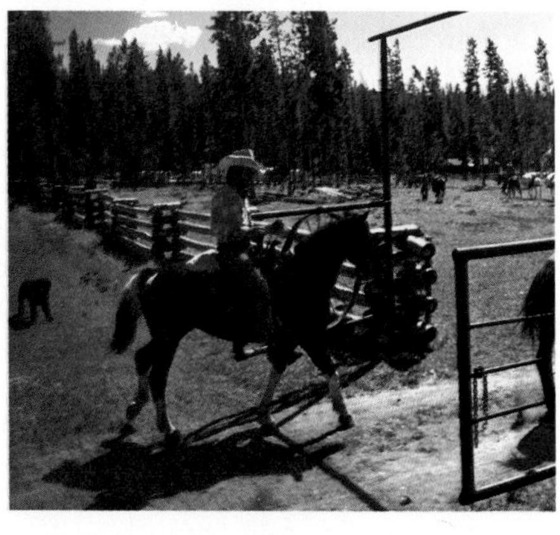

22. The length of a rectangle exceeds the width by 8 cm. If each dimension were 4 cm greater, the area would be no less than 128 cm² more. Find the least possible dimensions of the rectangle. width, 10 cm; length, 18 cm

C 23. During the first week of their vacation trip, the Gomez family spent \$200 more than three fifths of their vacation money and had more than \$400 less than half of it left. If they started their trip with a whole number of dollars, what was the greatest amount of vacation money they could have had? \$1999

24. Two consecutive odd integers have the property that three times their product is at least 11 more than the sum of their squares. Find the greatest such negative integers. -5, -3

25. Three consecutive integers have the property that the difference of the squares of the greatest and least integers exceeds the middle integer by more than 126. Find the smallest three consecutive integers having this property. 42, 43, 44

26. Verna decided to sell her collection of paperback books. To Fred, she sold 2 books, and one fifth of what was left. Later, to Joan she sold 6 books, and one fifth of what then remained. If she sold more books to Fred than to Joan, what was the least possible number of books in her original collection? 97

Self-Test 1

Vocabulary

inequality (p. 450)
sides of an inequality (p. 450)
solutions of an inequality (p. 450)
solution set of an inequality (p. 450)
graph of an open sentence (p. 450)
equivalent inequalities (p. 454)

1. Translate the statement "-2 is between -5 and -1" into symbols. $-5 < -2 < -1$ **Obj. 10-1, p. 449**

2. Solve $4x + 7 \leq 15$ if the domain of x is $\{-3, -2, -1, 0, 1, 2, 3\}$. $\{-3, -2, -1, 0, 1, 2\}$

Solve and graph.

3. $r - 9 < -1$

4. $5 - 3t \leq 20$ **Obj. 10-2, p. 453**

Solve.

5. A purse contains 20 coins, some of which are dimes and the rest nickels. Altogether, the coins are worth more than \$1.40. At least how many dimes are in the purse? 9 dimes **Obj. 10-3, p. 459**

Check your answers with those at the back of the book.

Extra / *Intersection and Union of Sets*

The diagrams below show how shading can be used to represent the relationships among the sets:

$$A = \{1, 2, 3, 4, 5\}$$
$$B = \{2, 4, 6\}$$
$$C = \{7, 8\}$$

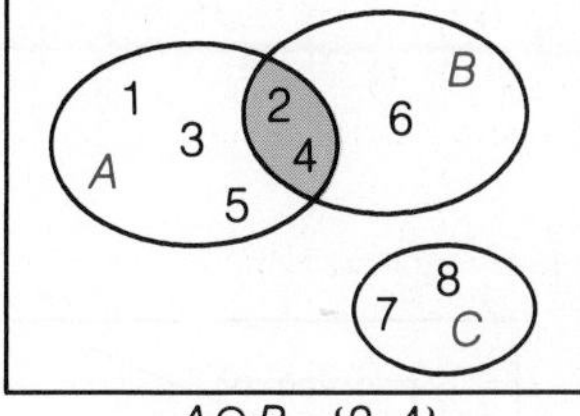

$A \cap B = \{2, 4\}$

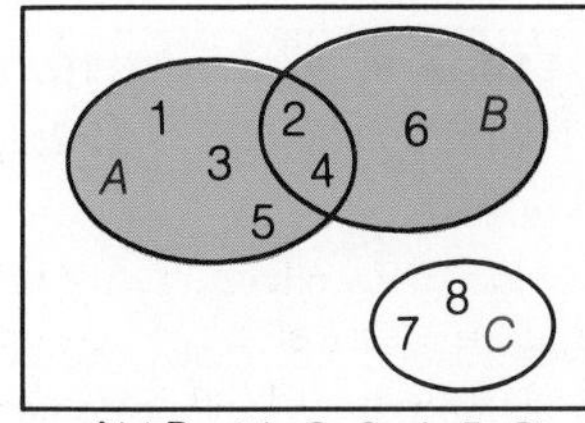

$A \cup B = \{1, 2, 3, 4, 5, 6\}$

To find the *intersection* of A and B, we shade the region consisting of those members and only those members *common to both* set A and set B. From the diagram at the left above, you can see that the intersection of $\{1, 2, 3, 4, 5\}$ and $\{2, 4, 6\}$ is $\{2, 4\}$. This is written

$$\{1, 2, 3, 4, 5\} \cap \{2, 4, 6\} = \{2, 4\}.$$

Notice in the diagrams that the regions A and C do not overlap. Two sets, such as A and C, that have no members in common are called *disjoint sets*. Their intersection is the empty set: $A \cap C = \emptyset$.

In the diagram at the right above, we shade the region consisting of the members that belong to *at least one* of the sets A and B, in order to find the *union* of A and B. This diagram shows that the union of $\{1, 2, 3, 4, 5\}$ and $\{2, 4, 6\}$ is $\{1, 2, 3, 4, 5, 6\}$. This is written

$$\{1, 2, 3, 4, 5\} \cup \{2, 4, 6\} = \{1, 2, 3, 4, 5, 6\}.$$

Additional Answers Self-Test 1

3. {the real numbers less than 8}

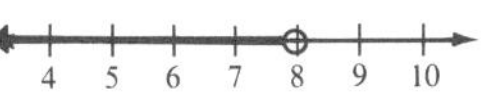

4. {-5 and the real numbers greater than -5}

Quick Quiz

1. Translate the statement "4 is between -1 and 7" into symbols. $-1 < 4 < 7$
2. Solve $3x - 4 \geq 11$ if the domain of x is $\{1, 2, 3, 4, 5, 6, 7, 8\}$. $\{5, 6, 7, 8\}$

Solve and graph.

3. $b - 2 < -4$ {the real numbers less than -2}
4. $3 - 2n \leq 9$ {the real numbers greater than or equal to -3}
5. A bank contains 22 coins, some of which are dimes and the rest quarters. In all, the coins are worth more than \$3.40. At least, how many quarters are in the bank? at least 9 quarters

Exercises

Refer to the diagram and list the members of each of the following sets.

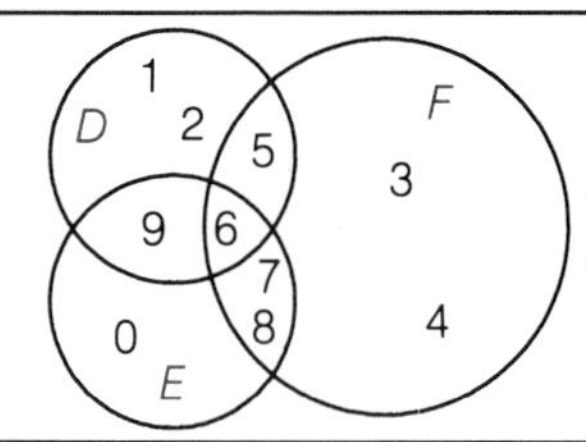

1. $D \cap E$
2. $D \cup E$
3. $E \cup F$
4. $E \cap F$
5. $(D \cap E) \cap F$
6. $D \cup (E \cap F)$
7. $D \cap (E \cup F)$
8. $(D \cup E) \cup F$
9. $(D \cap F) \cup (E \cap F)$
10. Express {6, 7, 8, 9} in terms of D, E, and F.

Specify the union and the intersection of the given sets. If the sets are disjoint, say so.

11. {−2, −3, −4}, {−3, −2, −1, 0}
12. {−1, 0, 1}, {0, 1, 2, 3}
13. {3, 5, 7}, {4, 6, 8}
14. {6, 8}, {5, 6, 7, 8, 9}
15. {3, 4, 6, 8, 12}, {2, 4, 6, 8, 10}
16. {−5, −4, −3}, {−2, −1, 0}

In Exercises 17–24, refer to the number lines shown and describe each set.

P = {the real numbers greater than −1}
Q = {the real numbers between −3 and 3}
R = {the real numbers less than 2}

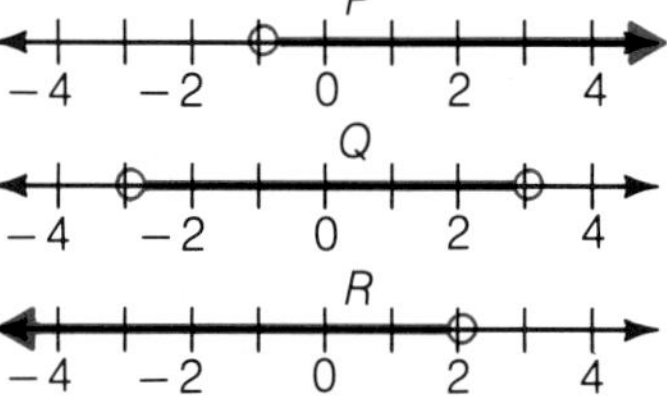

17. $P \cap R$
18. $P \cap Q$
19. $P \cup Q$
20. $P \cup R$
21. $Q \cap R$
22. $Q \cup R$
23. $P \cap (Q \cap R)$
24. $P \cup (Q \cap R)$

For each of Exercises 25 and 26, make two copies of the diagram shown at the right. On your copies shade the regions representing the sets named.

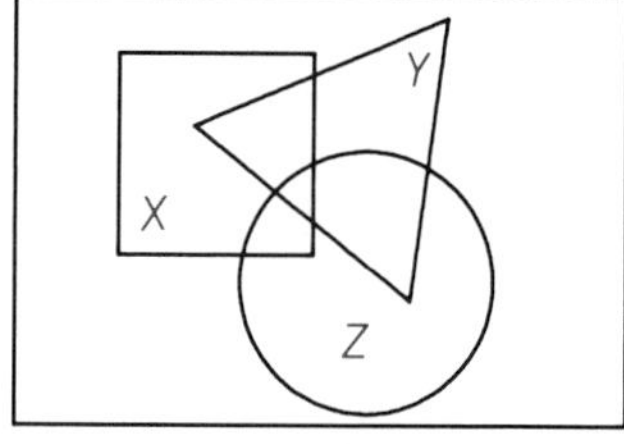

25. $X \cap (Y \cup Z)$; $(X \cap Y) \cup (X \cap Z)$
26. $X \cup (Y \cap Z)$; $(X \cup Y) \cap (X \cup Z)$
27. State a "distributive axiom" that appears to be true on the basis of Exercise 25.
28. State a "distributive axiom" that appears to be true on the basis of Exercise 26.
29. Copy the diagram at the right and write in the remaining members of these sets:

J = {1, 3, 5, 7, 9}
K = {−3, −1, 1, 3, 4}
L = {1, 2, 3, 4, 5, 6, 7}
M = {3, 4, 5, 6, 7}

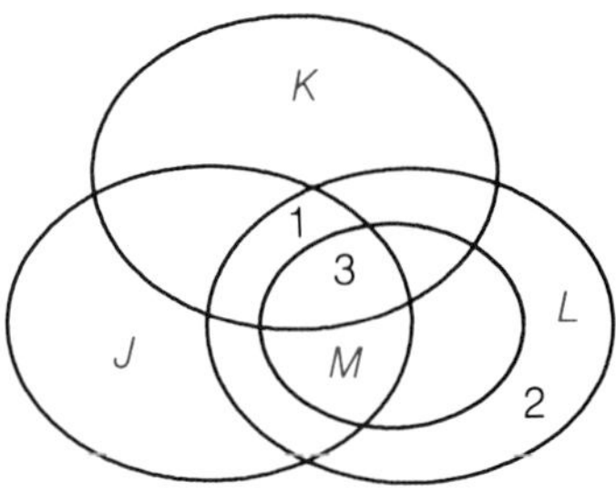

Additional Answers
Extra

1. {9, 6}
2. {0, 1, 2, 5, 6, 7, 8, 9}
3. {0, 3, 4, 5, 6, 7, 8, 9}
4. {6, 7, 8}
5. {6}
6. {1, 2, 5, 6, 7, 8, 9}
7. {5, 6, 9}
8. {0, 1, 2, 3, 4, 5, 6, 7, 8, 9}
9. {5, 6, 7, 8}
10. $(E \cap D) \cup (E \cap F)$ or $E \cap (D \cup F)$
11. {−4, −3, −2, −1, 0}; {−3, −2}
12. {−1, 0, 1, 2, 3}; {0, 1}
13. {3, 4, 5, 6, 7, 8}; ∅; disjoint sets
14. {5, 6, 7, 8, 9}; {6, 8}
15. {2, 3, 4, 6, 8, 10, 12}; {4, 6, 8}
16. {−5, −4, −3, −2, −1, 0}; ∅; disjoint sets
17. {the real numbers between −1 and 2}
18. {the real numbers between −1 and 3}
19. {the real numbers greater than −3}
20. {the real numbers}
21. {the real numbers between −3 and 2}
22. {the real numbers less than 3}
23. {the real numbers between −1 and 2}
24. {the real numbers greater than −3}

25–26. The two diagrams for each exercise are identical.

Biographical Note / *Daniel Hale Williams*

Daniel Hale Williams (1856–1931) was a pioneer in heart surgery. After serving as a surgeon's apprentice for almost two years, Williams attended Chicago Medical College and received his diploma in 1883. Dr. Williams opened a medical practice in Chicago's South Side, where he often performed successful surgery in his office or in patients' homes. Realizing a need for a hospital that would admit and give quality care to all and provide training for nurses, Williams was instrumental in founding Provident Hospital, the first interracial hospital established in the United States. Because the hospital contained only twelve beds, only the seriously ill or those in need of surgery could be admitted. Still, the percentage of recoveries at the hospital was far higher than average. Williams' colleagues, impressed by his extraordinary techniques and skill, often observed him as he performed surgery.

Dr. Williams' most famous case occurred on July 9, 1893. A young man who had been stabbed in the chest was admitted to the hospital. Risking his career and reputation, Williams opened the chest cavity, something no one had done before, cleansed the wound, rejoined an artery, and stitched the membrane surrounding the heart. The successful operation saved the life of the patient and won Williams the praise of the medical world. The following year he was appointed chief surgeon of Freedmen's Hospital in Washington, D.C. Williams completely reorganized and modernized the hospital, adding departments in bacteriology and pathology and instituting training programs for nurses and interns. In addition to the many honors he received, he was elected vice president of the National Medical Association, which he had actively helped to organize.

Challenge

What is wrong with the following "proof" that $0 > 3$?

$$a > 3$$
$$3a > 3(3)$$
$$3a - a^2 > 9 - a^2$$
$$a(3 - a) > (3 - a)(3 + a)$$
$$a > 3 + a$$
$$\therefore 0 > 3$$

The direction of the inequality should be reversed because it was divided by $3 - a$, which is negative.

25. 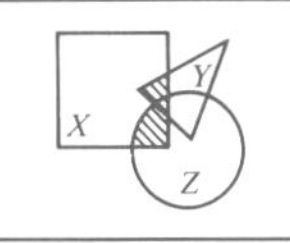

26. 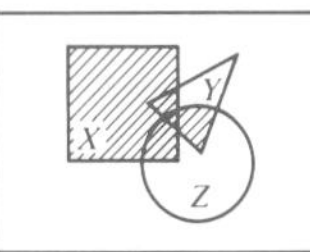

27. $X \cap (Y \cup Z) = (X \cap Y) \cup (X \cap Z)$

28. $X \cup (Y \cap Z) = (X \cup Y) \cap (X \cup Z)$

29. 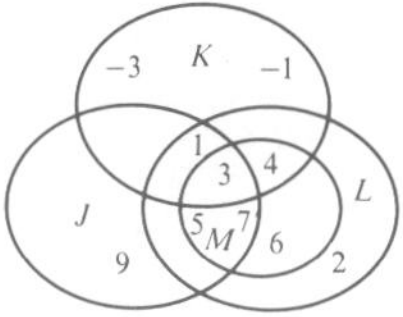

Teaching Suggestions p. T119

Suggested Extensions p. T119

Chalkboard Examples

Solve each open sentence and graph each solution set.

1. $-2 < m + 1 \leq 4$
   $-3 < m \leq 3$
   {3, and the real numbers between -3 and 3}

2. $3 - 4n < -5$ or $2n + 1 \leq 9$
   $-4n < -8$ or $2n \leq 8$
   $n > 2$ or $n \leq 4$
   {all real numbers}

3. $1 + 5y < -4$ or $4y > y + 9$
   $5y < -5$ or $3y > 9$
   $y < -1$ or $y > 3$
   {the real numbers less than -1 or greater than 3}

Solve.

4. $-1 \leq 4x + 3 < x - 6$
   $-4 \leq 4x < x - 9$
   $-4 \leq 4x$ and $4x < x - 9$
   $-1 \leq x$ and $3x < -9$
   $-1 \leq x$ and $x < -3$
   $\emptyset$

5. $-4 < 1 - m \leq 5$
   $-5 < -m \leq 4$
   $5 > m \geq -4$
   {-4, and the real numbers between -4 and 5}

468

Combining Open Sentences

10-4 Solving Combined Inequalities

Objective To find the solution sets of combined inequalities.

Each of the four sentences below involves one or two inequalities.

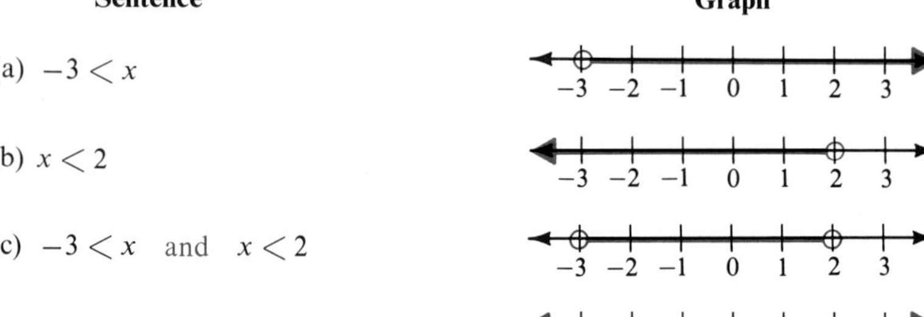

The sentence in (c) is formed by joining the sentences in (a) and (b) by the word and. Such a sentence is called a **conjunction.** To **solve a conjunction** of two open sentences in a given variable, you find the values of the variable for which *both* sentences are true. Note that the conjunction in (c) can be written in the compact form

$$-3 < x < 2.$$

The graph consists of the points that belong to *both* the graph of $-3 < x$ and the graph of $x < 2$.

In (d) above, the inequalities in (a) and (b) have been joined by the word or. A sentence formed by joining two sentences by the word *or* is called a **disjunction.** To **solve a disjunction** of two open sentences, you find the values of the variable for which *at least one* of the sentences is true (that is, one or the other or both are true). Notice that *every* real number is a solution of the disjunction in (d).

Recall (page 449) that the disjunction

$$y > 2 \quad \text{or} \quad y = 2$$

is usually written "$y \geq 2$." Similarly, when you write "$y \leq 2$," you mean

$$y < 2 \quad \text{or} \quad y = 2.$$

Example 1 What is the solution set of the
a. conjunction: $t < 5$ and $t \geq 5$?
b. disjunction: $t < 5$ or $t \geq 5$?

Solution a. The empty set.
b. The set of all real numbers. ***Answer***

To solve conjunctions and disjunctions of inequalities, you use the transformations listed on page 454.

Example 2 Find the solution set of $-4 \leq x - 2 < 3$, and draw its graph.

Solution To solve the inequality $-4 \leq x - 2 < 3$, you solve the conjunction

$$\begin{array}{rcr} -4 \leq x - 2 & \text{and} & x - 2 < 3 \\ -4 + 2 \leq x - 2 + 2 & | & x - 2 + 2 < 3 + 2 \\ -2 \leq x & \text{and} & x < 5 \end{array}$$

$$-2 \leq x < 5$$

$\therefore$ the solution set is $\{-2$, and the real numbers between -2 and $5\}$.
The graph is:

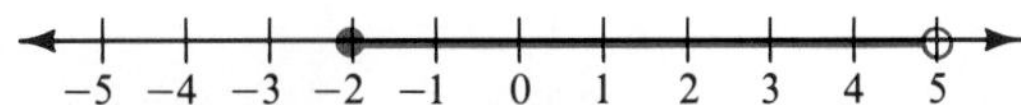

Below is a more compact way of transforming the conjunction in Example 2:

$$-4 \leq x - 2 < 3$$
$$-4 + 2 \leq x - 2 + 2 < 3 + 2$$
$$-2 \leq x < 5$$

Example 3 Solve the following disjunction and draw its graph:

$$4w - 1 < 3 \quad \text{or} \quad 3w \geq w + 8$$

Solution

$$\begin{array}{rcr} 4w - 1 < 3 & \text{or} & 3w \geq w + 8 \\ 4w - 1 + 1 < 3 + 1 & | & 3w - w \geq w - w + 8 \\ 4w < 4 & | & 2w \geq 8 \\ \frac{4w}{4} < \frac{4}{4} & | & \frac{2w}{2} \geq \frac{8}{2} \\ w < 1 & \text{or} & w \geq 4 \end{array}$$

$\therefore$ the solution set is {4, and the real numbers greater than 4 or less than 1}.
The graph is:

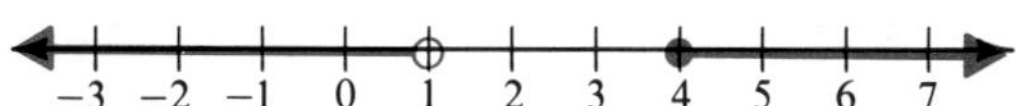

Common Error

Some students may think that the solution set of a conjunction such as $x < 4$ and $x \geq 4$ is {all the real numbers}. Because *and* means *both* in everyday language, students may feel that the solution sets of both inequalities should be included in the solution set of the conjunction. Point out that in mathematics, only values of the variable that are common to the solution sets of *both* inequalities should be included in the solution set of the conjunction.

Supplementary Materials

Practice Master 62
Resource Book, p. 116

Suggested Assignments

Minimum
Day 1: 470/1–12
S 462/*P*: 4, 5, 11, 12
R 464/*Self-Test 1*
Day 2: 471/13–22
475/1–6
Day 2 finishes Sec. 10-4 and starts Sec. 10-5.

Average
471/1-31 odd
S 462/*P*: 3, 5, 11
R 464/*Self-Test 1*

Maximum
471/1-37 odd
S 463/*P*: 16, 20, 22
R 464/*Self-Test 1*

Additional A Exercises

Draw the graph of each open sentence.

1. $s \leq 4$ or $s > 7$

0 1 2 3 4 5 6 7 8

2. $-4 \leq m \leq 4$

−4 −3 −2 −1 0 1 2 3 4

Solve each open sentence and graph the solution set.

3. $-5 < m + 3 \leq 1$
   $-8 < m \leq -2$

−8 −7 −6 −5 −4 −3 −2 −1 0

4. $-31 \leq 5x + 1 \leq 41$
   $\frac{-32}{5} \leq x \leq 8$

−8 −6 −4 −2 0 2 4 6 8

5. $2x + 3 \leq -2$ or $2x + 3 \geq 5$
   $x \leq \frac{-5}{2}$ or $x \geq 1$

−4 −3 −2 −1 0 1 2 3 4

6. $5x - 3 < 7$ or $5x - 3 > 12$
   $x < 2$ or $x > 3$

0 1 2 3 4 5 6 7 8

Additional Answers Written Exercises

1.

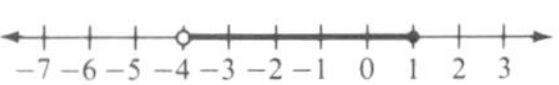

2.

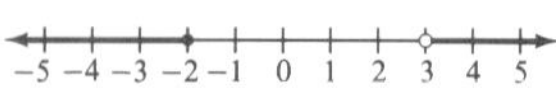

3.

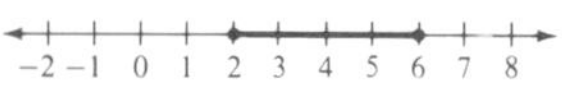

4.

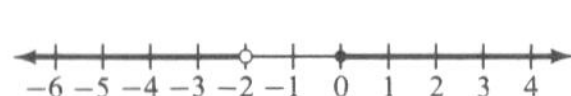

Oral Exercises

In Exercises 1-7, match each graph with one of the open sentences in a-g.

1. 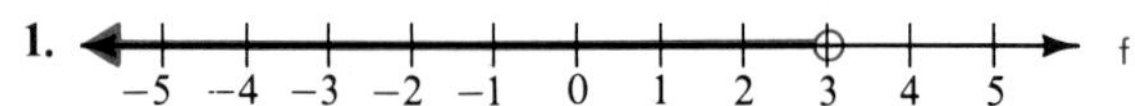 f

2. −5 −4 −3 −2 −1 0 1 2 3 4 5 b

3. −5 −4 −3 −2 −1 0 1 2 3 4 5 a

4. −5 −4 −3 −2 −1 0 1 2 3 4 5 g

5. 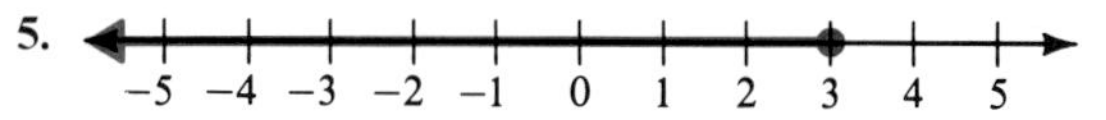 d

6. −5 −4 −3 −2 −1 0 1 2 3 4 5 c

7. 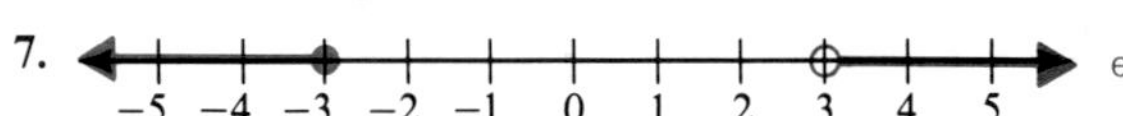 e

a. $t > 3$
b. $t \geq 3$ or $t < -3$
c. $-3 < t < 3$
d. $t \leq 3$
e. $t \leq -3$ or $t > 3$
f. $t < 3$
g. $-3 \leq t \leq 3$

In Exercises 8-12, match each open sentence with an equivalent inequality in a-e.

8. $x < 4$ and $x > -1$ e
9. $x = 4$ or $x < 4$ c
10. $x \leq 4$ and $x > -1$ d
11. $x = 4$ or $x > 4$ a
12. $x \leq 4$ and $x \geq -1$ b

a. $x \geq 4$
b. $-1 \leq x \leq 4$
c. $x \leq 4$
d. $-1 < x \leq 4$
e. $-1 < x < 4$

Written Exercises

Draw the graph of each open sentence.

A

1. $-4 < t \leq 1$
2. $r > 3$ or $r \leq -2$
3. $2 \leq n \leq 6$
4. $s < -2$ or $s \geq 0$

Solve each open sentence and graph each solution set that is not empty.

5. $-1 < a + 2 < 4$
6. $-2 < y - 2 \leq 1$
7. $-5 < -5 + z < 3$
8. $-6 \leq 3 + r < 4$

9. $-3 \leq 2a + 1 < 7$

10. $-2 < 2b - 1 \leq 5$

11. $-7 \leq 3m - 1 < 2$

12. $-8 < 3n + 7 \leq 1$

13. $y - 1 < -3$ or $y - 1 \geq 3$

14. $h + 5 \leq -2$ or $h + 5 \geq 2$

15. $3x + 2 \leq -4$ or $3x + 2 \geq 4$

16. $1 + 2y < -9$ or $1 + 2y > 9$

17. $2n - 1 \leq -5$ or $5 \leq 2n - 1$

18. $2d - 5 < -7$ or $7 < 2d - 5$

B

19. $-5 \leq -x \leq 3$

20. $-8 \leq -2x \leq 6$

21. $-3 \leq 1 - t < 4$

22. $-2 < 3 - y \leq 1$

23. $-9 < 1 - 2x \leq 7$

24. $-7 < -1 - 3x \leq 8$

25. $-3m < 12$ and $8 + 2m < 0$

26. $-6r < 18$ or $12 + 4r > 0$

27. $-8 \leq -3 - s < -1$

28. $-9 < -10 - p \leq -4$

29. $7 - v > 8$ or $v - 7 > 8$

30. $t - 5 \geq 2$ or $5 - t \geq 2$

31. $9 - 2p > 11$ or $9 - 2p < -1$

32. $7 - 3g \geq 10$ or $-2 \geq 7 - 3g$

33. $2d - 7 \geq -10$ and $2d - 7 \leq d - 5$

34. $9 - y \leq 3 - 2y$ and $-1 - 2y \geq -5$

C

35. $8 - c < 2c + 5 \leq 9 + c$

36. $5 - d \leq 3 - 2d$ or $d + 2 > 3d - 2$

37. $3(1 - w) \geq 6$ or $3w - 7 \leq 2w - 1$

38. $1 - 4m \leq 3 - 5m \leq m - 3$

39. Find all sets of four consecutive even integers whose sum is between -6 and 14. {−4, −2, 0, 2}, {−2, 0, 2, 4}, {0, 2, 4, 6}

40. Aaron is three years older than Ben and Ben is three years older than Chris. The sum of their ages in years is between 12 and 21. How old are Aaron, Ben, and Chris if the product of their ages is 80? 8, 5, and 2

41. Find an example of real values of a, b, c, and d for which the following statement is **(a)** true; **(b)** false.

If $a > b$ and $c > d$, then $ac > bd$.

42. Find a value of k so that the solution set of

$$k - 5 \leq x - 6 \leq 3$$

will be the same as the solution set of

$$3x - 7 \leq 2(1 + x) \quad \text{and} \quad 5x - 7 \geq 23.$$ 5

Computer Exercises

For students with some programming experience

The sum of two numbers must be no more than 10, but their product must be at least 9. Write a BASIC program to list all the ordered pairs (x, y) that satisfy these requirements if it is known that x and y are both positive integers.

5. {the real numbers between −3 and 2}
6. {3 and the real numbers between 0 and 3}
7. {8 and the real numbers between 0 and 8}
8. {−9, 1, and the real numbers between −9 and 1}
9. {−2 and the real numbers between −2 and 3}
10. {3 and the real numbers between $-\frac{1}{2}$ and 3}
11. {−2 and the real numbers between −2 and 1}
12. {−2 and the real numbers between −5 and −2}
13. {4 and the real numbers greater than 4 or less than −2}
14. {−7, −3, and the real numbers greater than −3 or less than −7}
15. {−2, $\frac{2}{3}$, and the real numbers greater than $\frac{2}{3}$ or less than −2}
16. {the real numbers less than −5 or greater than 4}
17. {−2, 3, and the real numbers less than −2 or greater than 3}
18. {the real numbers less than −1 or greater than 6}
19. {−3, 5, and the real numbers between −3 and 5}
20. {−3, 4, and the real numbers between −3 and 4}

(continued p. 495)

Teaching Suggestions
p. T119

Suggested Extensions
p. T119

Chalkboard Examples

1. Find the distance between -5 and 6.
$|-5 - 6| = |-11| = 11$

Solve and graph.

2. $|r + 4| = 1$
$r + 4 = -1$ or $r + 4 = 1$
$r = -5$ or $r = -3$
$\{-5, -3\}$

−8 −7 −6 −5 −4 −3 −2 −1 0

3. $|w + 2| < 3$
$-3 < w + 2 < 3$
$-5 < w < 1$
{the real numbers between -5 and 1}

−6 −5 −4 −3 −2 −1 0 1 2

4. $|x - 3| > 1$
$x - 3 < -1$ or $x - 3 > 1$
$x < 2$ or $x > 4$
{the real numbers less than 2 or greater than 4}

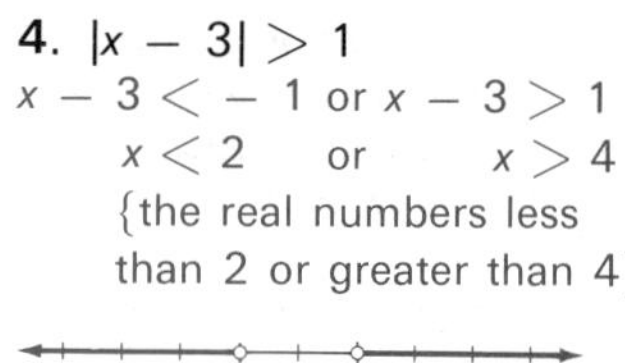

Suggested Assignments

Minimum
475/7–20
477/1–12
S 471/23–26
Day 2 of Sec. 10-4 finishes Sec. 10-4 and starts Sec. 10-5. This assignment finishes Sec. 10-5 and covers Sec. 10-6.

Average
475/1–25
S 471/28–34 even

Maximum
475/1–34
S 464/*P*: 26

10-5 Absolute Value in Open Sentences

Objective To solve equations and inequalities involving absolute value.

The figure below suggests a useful way to think about absolute value (page 35).

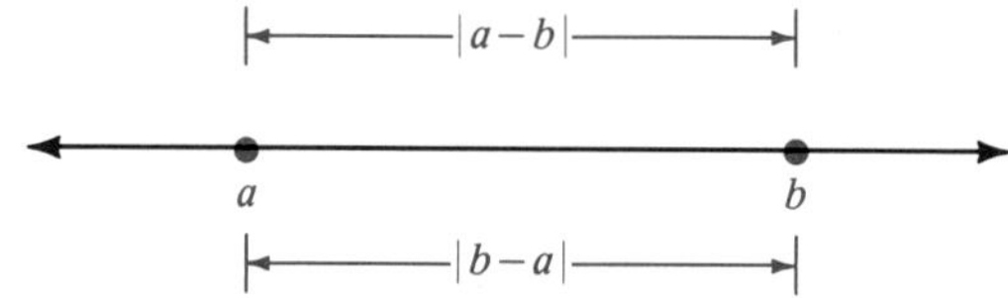

On a number line, the distance between the graphs of the numbers a and b is the absolute value of the difference of a and b. For simplicity, we usually speak of "the distance between a and b" instead of "the distance between the graphs of a and b."

Example 1 Find the distance between:

a. 5 and 11 **b.** -7 and 2 **c.** -8 and -13

Solution

a. $|5 - 11| = |-6| = 6$
b. $|-7 - 2| = |-9| = 9$
c. $|-8 - (-13)| = |-8 + 13| = |5| = 5$

Example 2 Solve $|y - 2| = 3$.

Solution 1 To satisfy the equation $|y - 2| = 3$, y must be a number whose distance from 2 is 3. Thus, to arrive at y, start at 2 and move 3 units in either direction on the number line.

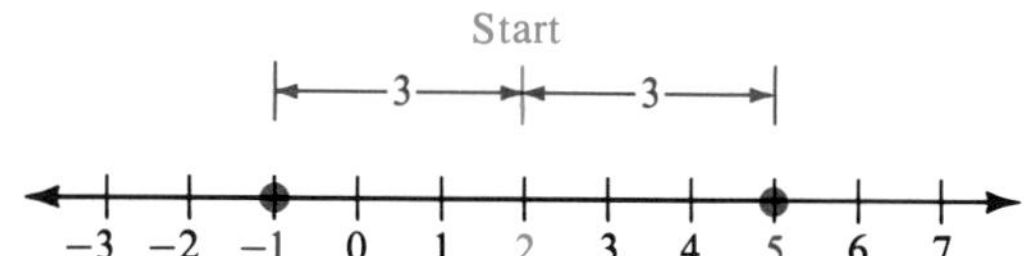

You arrive at 5 and -1 as the values of y.

$\therefore$ the solution set is $\{-1, 5\}$. ***Answer***

Solution 2 Another way to solve Example 2 is to note that

$$|y - 2| = 3$$

is equivalent to the disjunction

$$y - 2 = -3 \quad \text{or} \quad y - 2 = 3$$
$$y = -1 \quad \text{or} \quad y = 5$$

$\therefore$ the solution set is $\{-1, 5\}$. ***Answer***

Example 3 Solve and graph $|x + 1| \leq 4$.

Solution 1 Because $x + 1 = x - (-1)$, $|x + 1| \leq 4$ is equivalent to

$$|x - (-1)| \leq 4.$$

Hence, the distance between x and -1 must be no more than 4.

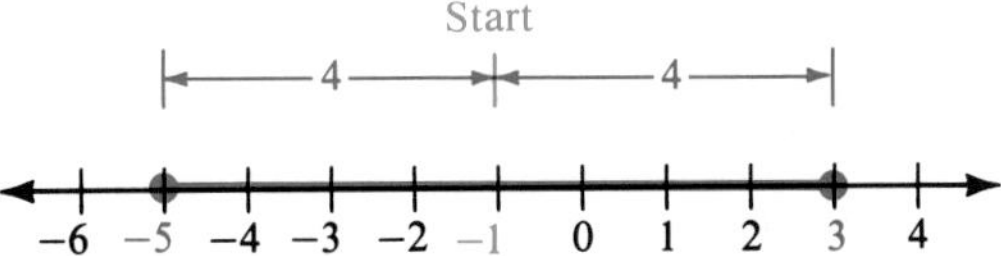

So, starting at -1, the numbers up to and including 3 will satisfy the given inequality, along with the numbers down to and including -5. Thus, the given inequality is equivalent to

$$-5 \leq x \leq 3.$$

∴ the solution set is {−5, 3, and the real numbers between −5 and 3}. The graph is shown above. ***Answer***

Solution 2 Use the fact that $|x + 1| \leq 4$ is equivalent to the conjunction:

$$-4 \leq x + 1 \leq 4$$
$$-4 - 1 \leq x + 1 - 1 \leq 4 - 1$$
$$-5 \leq x \leq 3$$

∴ the solution set and graph are as given above. ***Answer***

Example 4 Solve and graph $|t - 3| > 2$.

Solution 1 The distance between t and 3 must be greater than 2, as shown in the graph below.

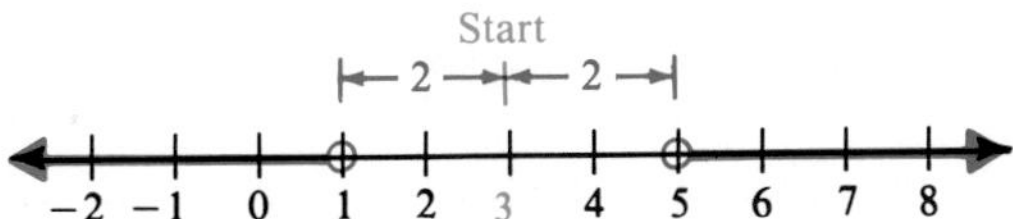

Therefore, the given inequality is equivalent to the disjunction

$$t < 1 \quad \text{or} \quad t > 5.$$

∴ the solution set is {the real numbers less than 1 or greater than 5}, and the graph is shown above. ***Answer***

(Solution 2 is on the next page.)

Common Error

Students may make mistakes in solving equations and inequalities involving absolute value because they do not know when such an open sentence is equivalent to a conjunction and when it is equivalent to a disjunction of two open sentences that do not involve absolute value. You may help students by pointing out that when $b \geq 0$ inequalities of the form $|x| < b$ (or $|x| \leq b$) are equivalent to the conjunction $x < b$ and $x > -b$ (or $x \leq b$ and $x \geq -b$), whereas inequalities of the form $|x| > b$ (or $|x| \geq b$) are equivalent to the disjunction $x > b$ or $x < -b$ (or $x \geq b$ or $x \leq -b$).

Additional A Exercises

Write an equation or inequality involving absolute value to describe each graph. Use x as the variable.

1. −3 −2 −1 0 1 2 3
   $|x| \leq 3$

2. −6 −5 −4 −3 −2 −1 0
   $|x + 3| > 2$

Solve each open sentence and draw its graph.

3. $|t - 6| = 3$ $t = 3, 9$
   1 2 3 4 5 6 7 8 9

4. $|m| < 9$ $-9 < m < 9$
   −12 −9 −6 −3 0 3 6 9 12

5. $|x - 1| \geq 3.5$
   $x \geq 4.5$ or $x \leq -2.5$
   −3 −2 −1 0 1 2 3 4 5

Solution 2 $|t - 3| > 2$ is equivalent to the disjunction:

$$t - 3 < -2 \quad \text{or} \quad t - 3 > 2$$
$$t < 1 \quad \text{or} \quad t > 5$$

$\therefore$ the solution set and graph are as in Solution 1. ***Answer***

Oral Exercises

In Exercises 1-6, express the distance between the given numbers in terms of absolute value. Then, find the distance.

1. 8 and 3 $|8 - 3|$; 5
2. 4 and 9 $|9 - 4|$; 5
3. 6 and -2 $|6 - (-2)|$; 8
4. -1 and 10 $|10 - (-1)|$; 11
5. -2 and -3 $|-3 - (-2)|$; 1
6. -7 and -5 $|-7 - (-5)|$; 2

In Exercises 7-18:
a. Translate the sentence into a statement involving the distance between numbers.
b. State a conjunction or disjunction equivalent to the given sentence.

Example 1 $|r + 2| > 7$

Solution **a.** The distance between r and -2 is greater than 7.
b. $r + 2 > 7$ or $r + 2 < -7$

7. $|x - 1| = 4$
8. $|y - 6| = 8$
9. $|r| = 5$
10. $|p| < 8$
11. $|n - 4| \le 3$
12. $|n - 4| > 3$
13. $|v + 5| \ge 2$
14. $|v + 5| \le 2$
15. $4 \le |1 - s|$
16. $5 \ge |3 - q|$
17. $1 \ge |2 + m|$
18. $6 \le |3 + w|$

In Exercises 19-24, match each open sentence with its graph in a-f.

19. $|x| \le 2$ f
20. $|x| \ge 2$ a
21. $|x - 3| = 2$ e
22. $|x + 2| > 2$ d
23. $|x - 1| = 2$ b
24. $|3 - x| < 2$ c

a. −5 −4 −3 −2 −1 0 1 2 3 4 5
b. −5 −4 −3 −2 −1 0 1 2 3 4 5
c. −5 −4 −3 −2 −1 0 1 2 3 4 5
d. −5 −4 −3 −2 −1 0 1 2 3 4 5
e. −5 −4 −3 −2 −1 0 1 2 3 4 5
f. −5 −4 −3 −2 −1 0 1 2 3 4 5

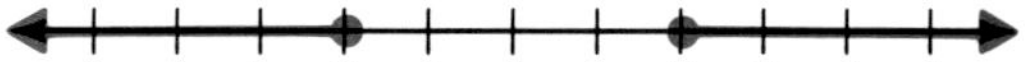

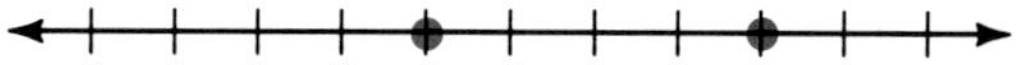

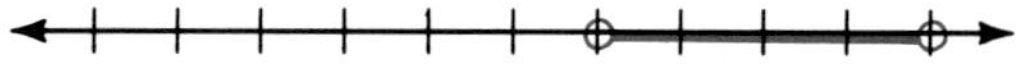

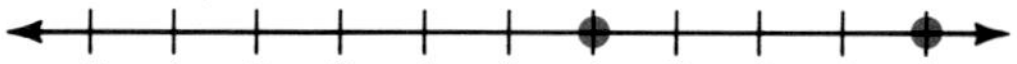

Additional Answers
Oral Exercises

7. a. The distance between x and 1 is 4.
b. $x - 1 = 4$ or $x - 1 = -4$

8. a. The distance between y and 6 is 8.
b. $y - 6 = 8$ or $y - 6 = -8$

9. a. The distance between r and 0 is 5.
b. $r = 5$ or $r = -5$

10. a. The distance between p and 0 is less than 8.
b. $-8 < p < 8$

11. a. The distance between n and 4 is less than or equal to 3.
b. $-3 \le n - 4 \le 3$

12. a. The distance between n and 4 is greater than 3.
b. $n - 4 > 3$ or $n - 4 < -3$

13. a. The distance between v and -5 is greater than or equal to 2.
b. $v + 5 \ge 2$ or $v + 5 \le -2$

14. a. The distance between v and -5 is less than or equal to 2.
b. $-2 \le v + 5 \le 2$

15. a. The distance between 1 and s is greater than or equal to 4.
b. $1 - s \ge 4$ or $1 - s \le -4$

16. a. The distance between 3 and q is less than or equal to 5.
b. $-5 \le 3 - q \le 5$

Use absolute value to state an inequality equivalent to each conjunction or disjunction.

Example 2 $-8 \le k - 10 \le 8$

Solution $|k - 10| \le 8$

25. $-3 < z + 7 < 3$ $|z + 7| < 3$
26. $-1 \le 9 - h \le 1$ $|9 - h| \le 1$
27. $a + 10 > 4$ or $a + 10 < -4$ $|a + 10| > 4$
28. $7 + b \ge 5$ or $7 + b \le -5$ $|7 + b| \ge 5$
29. $-2 \le -3 - p \le 2$ $|-3 - p| \le 2$
30. $-1 + q \le -9$ or $-1 + q \ge 9$ $|q - 1| \ge 9$

Written Exercises

Write an equation or an inequality involving absolute value to describe each graph. Use x as the variable.

A

1. 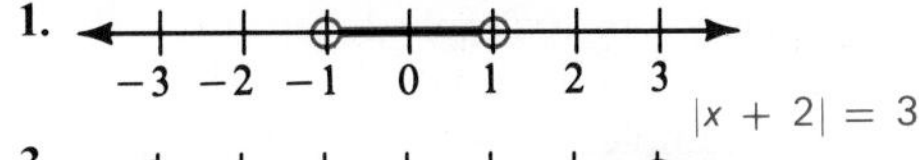
$-3\ \ -2\ \ -1\ \ 0\ \ 1\ \ 2\ \ 3$ $|x| < 1$

2. $-3\ \ -2\ \ -1\ \ 0\ \ 1\ \ 2\ \ 3$ $|x| \ge 1$

3. $-5\ \ -4\ \ -3\ \ -2\ \ -1\ \ 0\ \ 1$ $|x + 2| = 3$

4. $-2\ \ -1\ \ 0\ \ 1\ \ 2\ \ 3\ \ 4$ $|x - 2| = 1$

5. $-2\ \ -1\ \ 0\ \ 1\ \ 2\ \ 3\ \ 4$ $|x - 1| \ge 3$

6. $-6\ \ -5\ \ -4\ \ -3\ \ -2\ \ -1\ \ 0$ $|x + 3| < 3$

Solve each open sentence and draw its graph.

7. $|m - 8| = 1$
8. $|k + 9| = 4$
9. $|6 + x| = 7$
10. $|7 - y| = 4$
11. $|r| < 2.5$
12. $|s| \ge 1.5$
13. $|y + 6| > 2$
14. $|t + 3| < 4$
15. $|6 - p| \le 4$
16. $|4 - v| \ge 5$
17. $|-2 - a| \ge 4$
18. $|-1 - b| \le 6$

B

19. $3|s| - 2 \ge 7$
20. $4|p| - 1 < 15$
21. $|3 - z| + 8 > 12$
22. $|2 - q| - 3 < 1$
23. $1 - 2|r| \ge -7$
24. $4 - 3|y| < 1$
25. $7 - |2 - p| \le 5$
26. $8 - |1 - x| > 7$
27. $2(3|a| - 1) \le 10$
28. $\dfrac{8 - 3|b|}{2} \ge 1$

C

29. $|x - 1| = \dfrac{x}{2}$
30. $|y + 1| = \dfrac{y}{3}$
31. $|y - 3| = y - 3$
32. $|t - 3| > t - 3$
33. $|n + 5| < n + 5$
34. $|n + 5| \ge n + 5$

17. a. The distance between m and -2 is less than or equal to 1.
b. $-1 \le m + 2 \le 1$
18. a. The distance between w and -3 is greater than or equal to 6.
b. $3 + w \ge 6$ or $3 + w \le -6$

Additional Answers Written Exercises

7. $\{7, 9\}$
8. $\{-13, -5\}$
9. $\{-13, 1\}$
10. $\{3, 11\}$
11. {the real numbers between -2.5 and 2.5}
12. {-1.5, 1.5, and the real numbers greater than 1.5 or less than -1.5}
13. {the real numbers greater than -4 or less than -8}
14. {the real numbers between -7 and 1}
15. {2, 10, and the real numbers between 2 and 10}
16. {-1, 9, and the real numbers less than -1 or greater than 9}
17. {-6, 2, and the real numbers less than -6 or greater than 2}
18. {-7, 5, and the real numbers between -7 and 5}
19. {-3, 3, and the real numbers less than -3 or greater than 3}
20. {the real numbers between -4 and 4}

(continued p. 497)

Teaching Suggestions
p. T120

Chalkboard Examples

Solve and graph.

1. $|2x + 1| = 5$
   $2x + 1 = -5$ or
   $2x + 1 = 5$
   $2x = -6$ or $2x = 4$
   $x = -3$ or $x = 2$
   $\{-3, 2\}$

2. $\left|\frac{n}{2}\right| > 1$
   $\frac{n}{2} < -1$ or $\frac{n}{2} > 1$
   $n < -2$ or $n > 2$
   {the real numbers less than -2 or greater than 2}

3. $|3k - 2| \leq 7$
   $-7 \leq 3k - 2 \leq 7$
   $-5 \leq 3k \leq 9$
   $\frac{-5}{3} \leq k \leq 3$
   $\left\{-\frac{5}{3}\right.$, 3, and the real numbers between $-\frac{5}{3}$ and $\left.3\right\}$

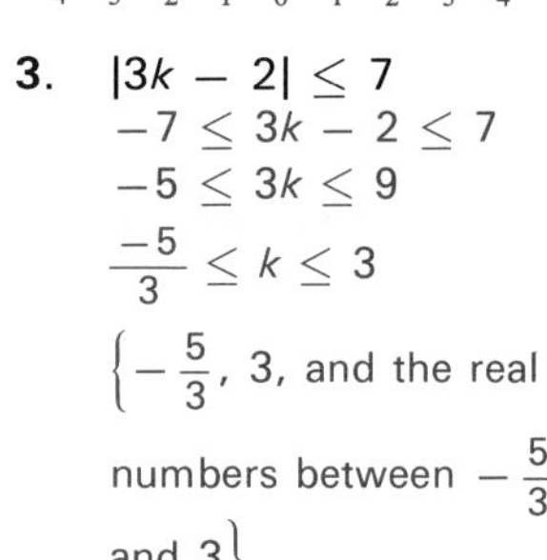

4. $|2m - 1| > 7$
   $2m - 1 < -7$ or
   $2m - 1 > 7$
   $2m < -6$ or $2m > 8$
   $m < -3$ or $m > 4$
   {the real numbers less than -3 or greater than 4}

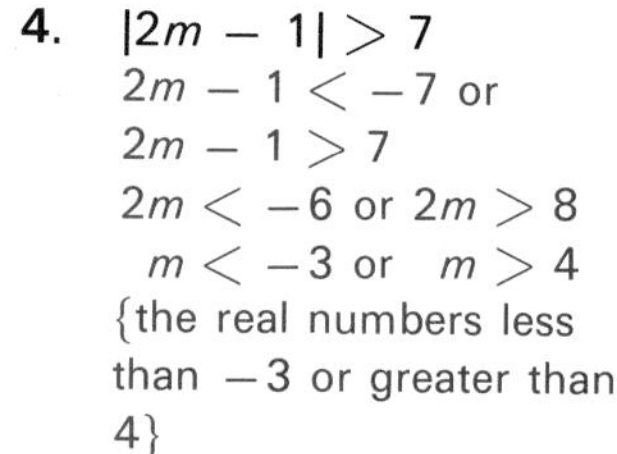

Supplementary Materials

Practice Master 63
Resource Book, p. 117

10-6 Absolute Values of Products in Open Sentences

Objective To extend your skill in solving open sentences that involve absolute value.

Example 1 Solve $|2p - 5| = 7$.

$|2p - 5| = 7$ is equivalent to the disjunction:

$$\begin{array}{rcl} 2p - 5 = -7 & \text{or} & 2p - 5 = 7 \\ 2p - 5 + 5 = -7 + 5 & & 2p - 5 + 5 = 7 + 5 \\ 2p = -2 & & 2p = 12 \\ \frac{2p}{2} = \frac{-2}{2} & & \frac{2p}{2} = \frac{12}{2} \\ p = -1 & \text{or} & p = 6 \end{array}$$

$\therefore$ the solution set is $\{-1, 6\}$. ***Answer***

To use a number line to solve the open sentence in Example 1, recall (page 69) that the absolute value of a product of numbers equals the product of the absolute values of the numbers. For example:

1. $|-8 \times 5| = |-40| = 40 = 8 \times 5 = |-8| \times |5|$
2. $|(-3)(-2)| = |6| = 3 \times 2 = |-3| \times |-2|$

Using this property of absolute value, you see that

$$|2p - 5| = \left|2\left(p - \frac{5}{2}\right)\right| = 2\left|p - \frac{5}{2}\right|.$$

Therefore, the open sentence in Example 1,

$$|2p - 5| = 7,$$

is equivalent to

$$2\left|p - \frac{5}{2}\right| = 7.$$

$$\therefore \left|p - \frac{5}{2}\right| = \frac{7}{2}$$

Start
$\frac{7}{2}$ $\frac{7}{2}$
-3 -2 -1 0 1 $2\frac{1}{2}$ 4 5 6 7

Since the distance between p and $\frac{5}{2}$ on the number line must be $\frac{7}{2}$, the solutions of $|p - \frac{5}{2}| = \frac{7}{2}$ and, therefore, of $|2p - 5| = 7$ are -1 and 6, as shown on the diagram above.

Example 2 Solve and graph $|12 - 3k| \geq 6$.

Solution 1 Since $|12 - 3k| = |(-3)(k - 4)| = 3|k - 4|$,

$$|12 - 3k| \geq 6$$

is equivalent to

$$3|k - 4| \geq 6.$$

$$\therefore |k - 4| \geq 2$$

Start

$|\leftarrow 2 \rightarrow|\leftarrow 2 \rightarrow|$

−2 −1 0 1 2 3 4 5 6 7 8

The distance between k and 4 must be 2 or more, as pictured above. Therefore, the given inequality is equivalent to the disjunction

$$k \leq 2 \quad \text{or} \quad k \geq 6.$$

$\therefore$ the solution set is {2, 6, and the real numbers less than 2 or greater than 6}. The graph is shown above. ***Answer***

Solution 2 Because $|12 - 3k| = |3k - 12|$, the given inequality is equivalent to

$$|3k - 12| \geq 6.$$

This is a compact form of the disjunction:

$$\begin{array}{rcr} 3k - 12 \leq -6 & \text{or} & 3k - 12 \geq 6 \\ 3k \leq 6 & | & 3k \geq 18 \\ k \leq 2 & \text{or} & k \geq 6 \end{array}$$

$\therefore$ the solution set and graph are as given in Solution 1. ***Answer***

Written Exercises

Solve each open sentence and draw its graph.

A

1. $|2x| = 10$
2. $|5y| = 35$
3. $\left|\frac{y}{3}\right| \geq 1$
4. $\left|\frac{t}{3}\right| \leq 2$
5. $|2a - 1| = 7$
6. $|3b - 2| = 7$
7. $|4d - 9| \leq 3$
8. $|5h - 2| \geq 8$
9. $|4 + 5n| \leq 16$
10. $|1 + 8c| > 23$
11. $\left|\frac{y}{3} - 2\right| \geq 3$
12. $\left|\frac{x}{2} - 3\right| \leq 2$

Suggested Assignments

Minimum
The assignment for Sec. 10-5 finishes Sec. 10-5 and covers Sec. 10-6.

Average
477/1–12, 13–17 odd
S 463/*P*: 6, 12, 16

Maximum
477/1–18, 19–23 odd
S 462/19, 20

Additional Answers Written Exercises

1. {−5, 5}
2. {−7, 7}
3. {3, −3, and the real numbers greater than 3 or less than −3}
4. {−6, 6, and the real numbers between −6 and 6}
5. {−3, 4}
6. $\left\{\frac{-5}{3}, 3\right\}$
7. $\left\{\frac{3}{2}\right.$, 3, and the real numbers between $\frac{3}{2}$ and $\left.3\right\}$
8. $\left\{2, -\frac{6}{5}\right.$, and the real numbers greater than 2 or less than $\left.-\frac{6}{5}\right\}$
9. $\left\{-4, \frac{12}{5}\right.$, and the real numbers between −4 and $\left.\frac{12}{5}\right\}$
10. {the real numbers less than −3 or greater than $\left.\frac{11}{4}\right\}$
11. {−3, 15, and the real numbers greater than 15 or less than −3}
12. {2, 10, and the real numbers between 2 and 10}

Additional Answers Written Exercises

13. {the real numbers between $-\frac{19}{3}$ and 7}

14. {0, 9, and the real numbers between 0 and 9}

15. $\left\{\frac{1}{2}, -1\right\}$

16. $\left\{\frac{11}{3}, 1\right\}$

17. ∅

18. {the real numbers between 0 and $\frac{4}{5}$}

Quick Quiz

Solve each open sentence and graph its solution set.

1. $5x - 1 \le -6$ or $3 - x \le 1$
{−1, 2, and the real numbers less than −1 or greater than 2}
−4 −3 −2 −1 0 1 2 3 4

2. $-3 < 2x - 1 < 5$
{the real numbers between −1 and 3}
−4 −3 −2 −1 0 1 2 3 4

3. $|2 - x| = 3$ {−1, 5}
−2 −1 0 1 2 3 4 5 6

4. $|x - 2| < 5$
{the real numbers greater than −3 and less than 7}
−5 −3 −1 1 3 5 7 9 11

5. $|3x + 2| = 7$ $\left\{-3, \frac{5}{3}\right\}$
−4 −3 −2 −1 0 1 2 3 4

6. $|2x + 1| \ge 1$
{−1, 0, and the real numbers less than −1 or greater than 0}
−4 −3 −2 −1 0 1 2 3 4

Solve each open sentence and draw its graph.

B

13. $|1 - (2 - 3x)| < 20$

14. $|6 - (2y - 3)| \le 9$

15. $5 + 3|4g + 1| = 14$

16. $2|3k - 7| + 11 = 19$

17. $8 - 5|3 - 2t| > 23$

18. $21 - 4|2 - 5w| > 13$

Classify each of the following sentences as true for all real values of the variable or false for some real value. If you classify a sentence as false, give at least one value of the variable for which it is false.

C

19. $|a^2| = a^2$ true

20. $|-a^2| = a^2$ true

21. $\left|\frac{a}{2}\right| = \frac{a}{2}$ false; −2

22. $|a - 2| < |a + 2|$ false; −7

23. $|a + 1| \le |a| + 1$ true

24. $|a| - 1 \le |a - 1|$ true

25. During January in Colton the absolute value of the temperature in degrees Celsius never exceeded 10°. In degrees Fahrenheit, what were the greatest and least possible temperatures in Colton that month? (*Hint:* $C = \frac{5}{9}(F - 32)$, where C and F are the temperatures in degrees Celsius and Fahrenheit, respectively.)
50°F, 14°F

Self-Test 2

Vocabulary conjunction (p. 468) · disjunction (p. 468) · solve a conjunction (p. 468) · solve a disjunction (p. 468)

Solve each open sentence and graph its solution set.

1. $3x - 1 > 8$ or $2 - x > 0$

2. $-2 \le y + 4 < 5$ — **Obj. 10-4, p. 468**

3. $3m + 1 \le -5$ or $3m - 1 \ge 5$

4. $-5 \le 3x + 1 < 4$

5. $|x - 4| = 4$

6. $|3 - n| \ge 2$ — **Obj. 10-5, p. 472**

7. $|1 - y| = 1$

8. $|x + 1| < 2$

9. $|4s - 13| \le 7$

10. $|2p - 4| = 10$ — **Obj. 10-6, p. 476**

11. $|2m - 1| = 5$

12. $|1 - 2a| < 3$

Check your answers with those at the back of the book.

Computer Key-In

The following program will print the graph of an open sentence in one variable. Notice that the open sentence is written into the program in line 80.

```
10  PRINT "TO GRAPH AN OPEN SENTENCE,"
20  PRINT "INPUT EXTENT OF GRAPH--"
30  PRINT "M, N, INTEGERS, M<N";
40  INPUT M,N
50  IF M >= N THEN 20
60  REM---SENTENCE INSIDE LOOP
70  FOR X=M TO N
80  IF (5*X-1)<(3+3*X) THEN 110
90  PRINT "-";
100  GOTO 120
110  PRINT "*";
120  NEXT X
130  PRINT "X"
140  REM---PRINT "0"
150  FOR I=M TO N
160  IF I <> 0 THEN 190
170  PRINT "0"
180  GOTO 210
190  PRINT " ";   <- Single space between quotation marks
200  NEXT I
210  END
```

(If possible, save this program for use in later computer sections.)

Exercises

Use $M = -10$ and $N = 10$.

1. RUN the program as it is written.
2. Change line 80 to include the inequality $2(x - 8) + 9 \geq 3(4 - x) - 4$ and RUN the program again.

Change line 80 and RUN the program for each of the following.

3. a. $-3 \leq x$ b. $x < 2$ c. $-3 \leq x$ and $x < 2$
4. a. $-5 < x$ b. $x \leq 1$ c. $-5 < x$ and $x \leq 1$
5. $-3 \geq x$ or $x > 2$
6. $-5 > x$ or $x \geq 1$
7. $|x - 3| > 2$
8. $|x + 1| \leq 4$
9. $|2x - 5| = 7$
10. $|12 - 3x| \geq 6$

Note: The program above can be used to do Exercises 1–38 on pages 470–471, Exercises 7–34 on page 475, and Exercises 1–18 on pages 477–478.

Additional Answers
Computer Key-In

1.
```
************---------X
           0
```

2. 80 IF 2*(X − 8) + 9 > = 3*(4 − X) − 4 THEN 110
3. a. 80 IF X > = −3 THEN 110
   b. 80 IF X < 2 THEN 110
   c. 80 IF X > = −3 AND X < 2 THEN 110
4. a. 80 IF X > − 5 THEN 110
   b. 80 IF X < = 1 THEN 110
   c. 80 IF X > −5 AND X < = 1 THEN 110
5. 80 IF X < = −3 OR X > 2 THEN 110
6. 80 IF X < −5 OR X > = 1 THEN 110
7. 80 IF ABS(X − 3) > 2 THEN 110
8. 80 IF ABS(X + 1) < = 4 THEN 110
9. 80 IF ABS(2*X − 5) = 7 THEN 110
10. 80 IF ABS(12 − 3*X) > = 6 THEN 110

Teaching Suggestions
p. T120

Chalkboard Examples

Graph each inequality in a coordinate plane.

1. $x \geq -2$

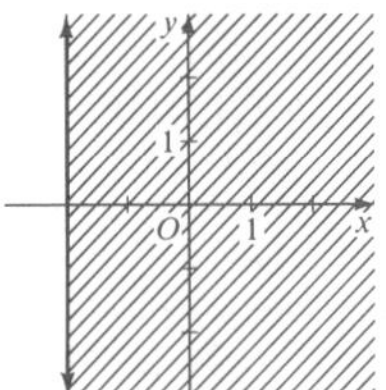

2. $y < 1$

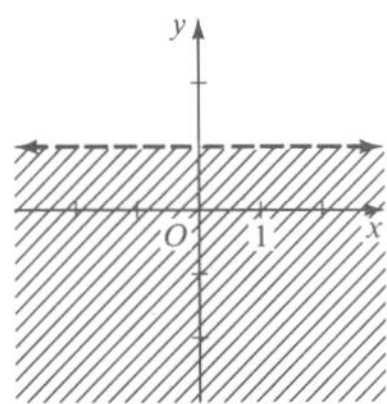

3. $y > 2x + 1$

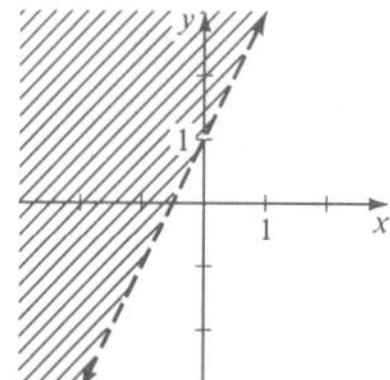

4. $3x + y \leq 3$

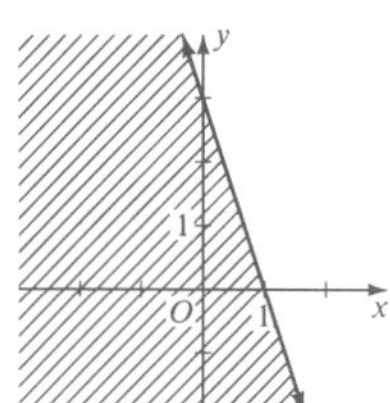

Inequalities in Two Variables

10-7 Graphing Linear Inequalities

Objective To graph linear inequalities in two variables.

The graph of the linear equation

$$y = x + 2$$

separates the coordinate plane into three sets of points:

the points *on* the line,
the points *above* the line,
the points *below* the line.

The regions above and below the line are called **open half-planes,** and the line is the **boundary** of each half-plane.

If you start at any point on the line, say $P(2, 4)$, and move upward from P, the y-coordinate increases. If you move downward from P, the y-coordinate decreases.

Thus, the upper open half-plane is the graph of the inequality

$$y > x + 2$$

and the lower open half-plane is the graph of the inequality

$$y < x + 2.$$

The graphs of

$$y > x + 2, \qquad y = x + 2, \qquad \text{and} \qquad y < x + 2$$

completely cover the coordinate plane. The upper half-plane and the boundary line together form the graph of

$$y \geq x + 2.$$

The lower half-plane and the boundary line together form the graph of

$$y \leq x + 2.$$

The graph of an open half-plane and its boundary is called a **closed half-plane.**

The graphs of inequalities are shown by shading. If the boundary line is part of a graph, it is drawn as a solid line. If the boundary line is *not* part of the graph, it is drawn as a dashed line. This is shown by the figures at the top of the following page.

(a) $y > x + 2$ (b) $y \geq x + 2$ (c) $y < x + 2$ (d) $y \leq x + 2$

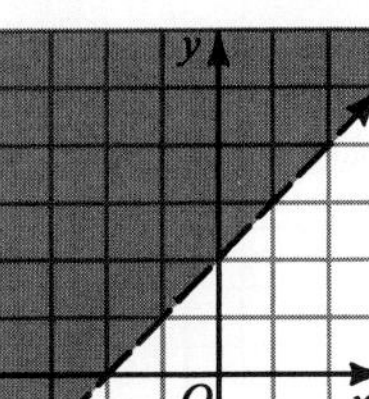

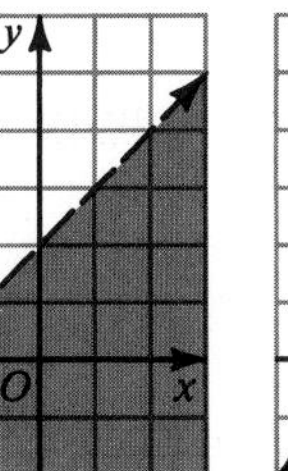

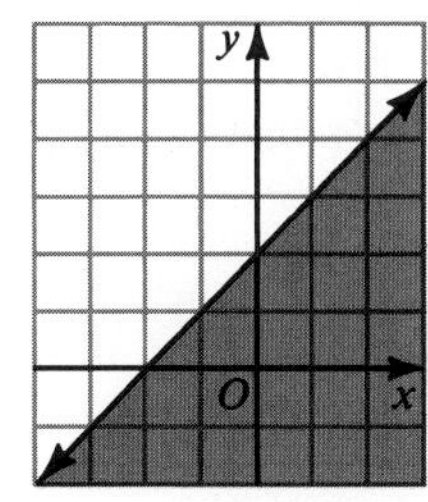

In general, you follow these steps.

To graph a linear inequality in the variables x and y, when the coefficient of y is not zero:

1. Transform the given inequality into an equivalent inequality that has y alone as one side.
2. Graph the equation of the boundary. Use a solid line if the symbol $\geq$ or $\leq$ is used; use a dashed line if $>$ or $<$ is used.
3. Shade the appropriate region.

Example 1 Graph $2x - 3y \geq -6$.

Solution 1. Transform the inequality:

$$2x - 3y \geq -6$$
$$-3y \geq -6 - 2x$$
$$y \leq 2 + \frac{2}{3}x$$

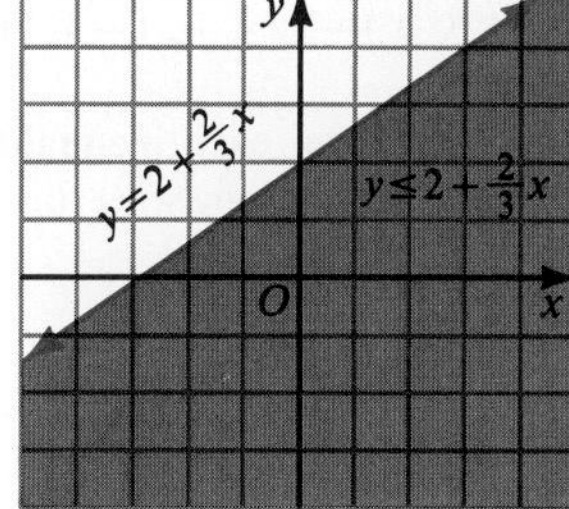

2. Draw the boundary line $y = 2 + \frac{2}{3}x$ as a *solid* line, since the symbol $\leq$ includes the equals sign.
3. Shade the region *below* the line since the symbol $\leq$ includes the less than sign.

Check: Choose a point of the graph not on the boundary, say (0, 0). See whether its coordinates satisfy the given inequality:

$$2x - 3y \geq -6$$
$$2(0) - 3(0) \overset{?}{\geq} -6$$
$$0 \geq -6 \ \checkmark$$

Thus, (0, 0) is in the solution set, and the correct region has been shaded.

Common Error

Some students may have trouble deciding which open half-plane to shade when graphing linear inequalities in a coordinate plane. Discuss the method shown in the examples in detail, and emphasize the method of checking shown in Example 1. You can point out that the coordinates of any point on the boundary line must satisfy the inequality given in Example 1 and that the coordinates of any point chosen from the unshaded region must not satisfy it.

Supplementary Material

Test 36

Suggested Assignments

Minimum

Day 1: 482/1–4, 9–18, 25–29
R 478/*Self-Test 2*

Day 2: 483/19–21, 30–33
485/1–11 odd

Day 2 finishes Sec. 10-7 and covers Sec. 10-8.

Average

482/1–4, 9–18, 25–29
R 478/*Self-Test 2*

Maximum

482/1–4, 9–18, 25–29, 34, 35
S 478/25
R 478/*Self-Test 2*

Additional Answers
Oral Exercises

1. yes; no; no
2. no; yes; no
3. yes; no; yes
4. yes; yes; no
5. yes; no; no
6. yes; no; yes
7. $y < 3 - x$; $y = 3 - x$
8. $y > 1 + x$; $y = 1 + x$
9. $y \geq 9 - 3x$; $y = 9 - 3x$
10. $y \leq -2 - 2x$; $y = -2 - 2x$
11. $y > -\frac{3}{2}x$; $y = -\frac{3}{2}x$
12. $y < -3x$; $y = -3x$
13. $y < \frac{1}{6}x$; $y = \frac{1}{6}x$
14. $y > -\frac{2}{3}x$; $y = -\frac{2}{3}x$
15. $y \leq x - 1$; $y = x - 1$
16. $y \geq 2x$; $y = 2x$
17. $y < \frac{1}{8}x - 3$; $y = \frac{1}{8}x - 3$
18. $y > x - 6$; $y = x - 6$

Additional Answers
Written Exercises

2. 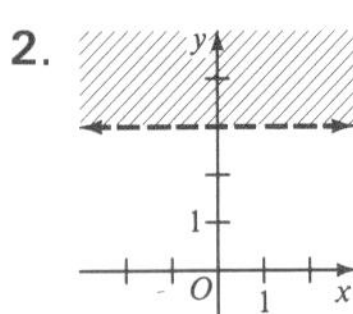

4. 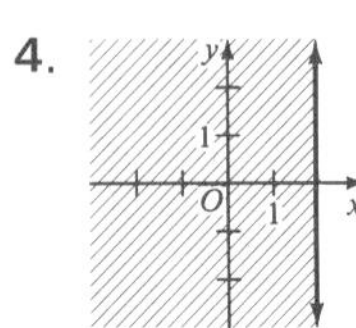

Example 2 Graph $y > 1$.

Solution Graph $y = 1$ as a dashed horizontal line. Shade the open half-plane above the line, since $y > 1$.

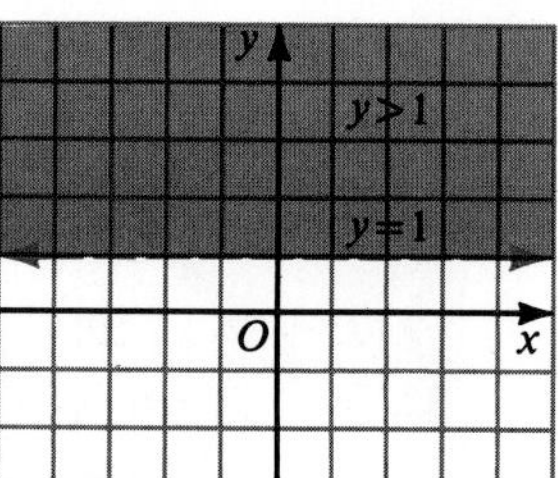

The next example shows how to graph a linear inequality in x and y when the coefficient of y is 0.

Example 3 Graph $x < -3$.

Solution Show the graph of $x = -3$ as a dashed vertical line. The coordinates of any point to the left of that vertical line satisfy $x < -3$. Therefore, the graph of $x < -3$ is the open half-plane to the left of the graph of $x = -3$.

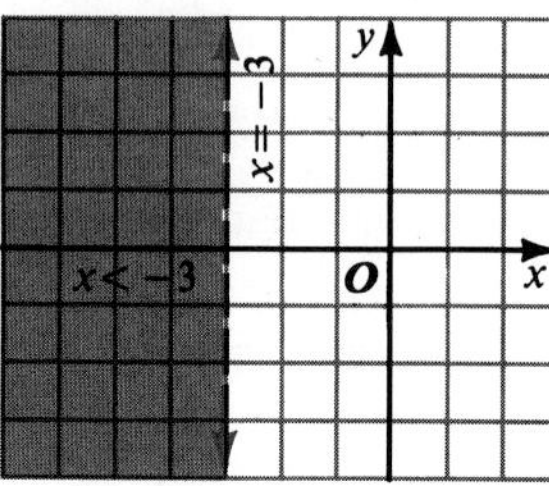

Oral Exercises

State whether the given points belong to the graph of the given inequality.

1. $x \geq 4$; (4, 2), (−4, 5), (0, 0)
2. $y < -3$; (2, −3), (4, −4), (0, 0)
3. $y < x + 3$; (2, 4), (−2, 1), (0, 0)
4. $y \leq 2x - 1$; (2, 0), (1, 1), (0, 0)
5. $x + 2y < 0$; (−3, 1), (3, −1), (0, 0)
6. $x - 3y \geq -2$; (1, −1), (−1, 1), (0, 0)

Transform each inequality into an equivalent inequality having y alone as one side. Then state the equation of the boundary of the graph.

7. $x + y < 3$
8. $-x + y > 1$
9. $3x + y \geq 9$
10. $2x + y \leq -2$
11. $3x + 2y > 0$
12. $15x + 5y < 0$
13. $6y < x$
14. $2x > -3y$
15. $x - y \geq 1$
16. $14x - 7y \leq 0$
17. $x - 8y > 24$
18. $6 > x - y$

Written Exercises

Graph each inequality.

A

1. $y \geq 3$
2. $y > 3$
3. $x < 2$
4. $x \leq 2$
5. $x > 0$
6. $y < 0$
7. $y \geq -1$
8. $x \leq -4$
9. $y < x + 2$
10. $y > -x + 1$
11. $y \leq 3 - 2x$
12. $y \geq 1 - 3x$

Transform each inequality into an equivalent inequality with y as one side. Then graph the inequality.

13. $x + y < 2$ **14.** $x - y \geq 3$ **15.** $x - 2y \leq -7$

16. $2x + y > -4$ **17.** $3x - y > 6$ **18.** $y - 2x \leq -3$

19. $3x - 2y \geq 10$ **20.** $3y - 2x < 0$ **21.** $7x + 4y \leq x - 8$

22. $3y - 5 > 2x - 6$ **23.** $3(x - y) \geq 4x + 7$ **24.** $5y - 8 < 2(x + 2y)$

In each of Exercises 25–33, write an inequality whose graph is shown.

$y > -2$

B 25.

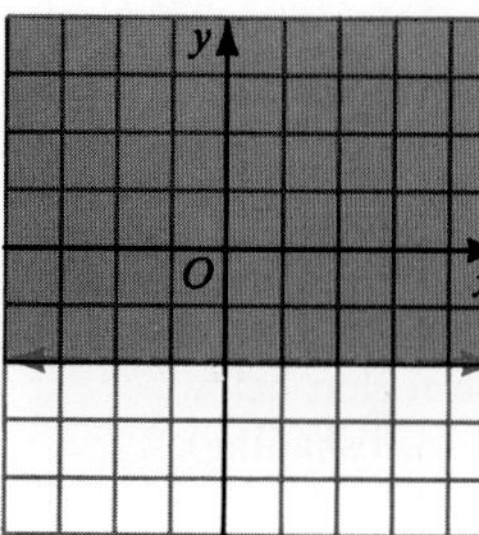

$x \leq 2$

26.

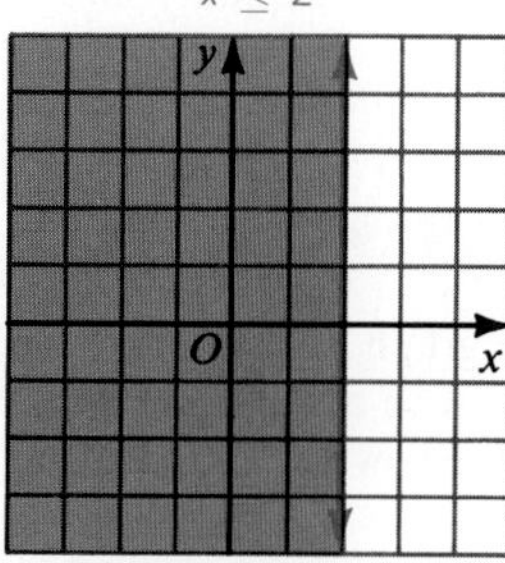

$y \leq -\frac{2}{3}x + 2$

27.

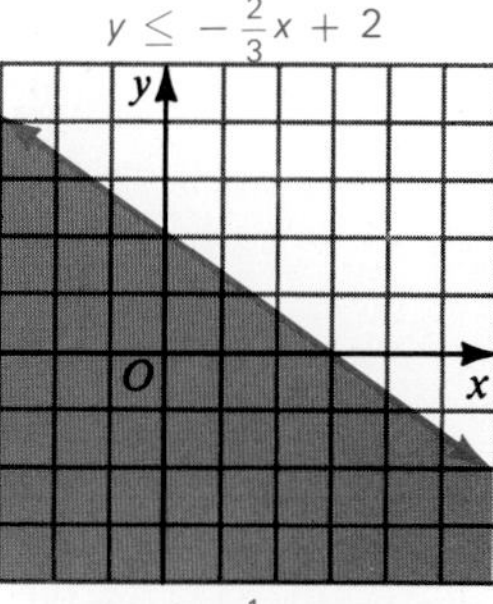

$y < -\frac{3}{2}x$

28.

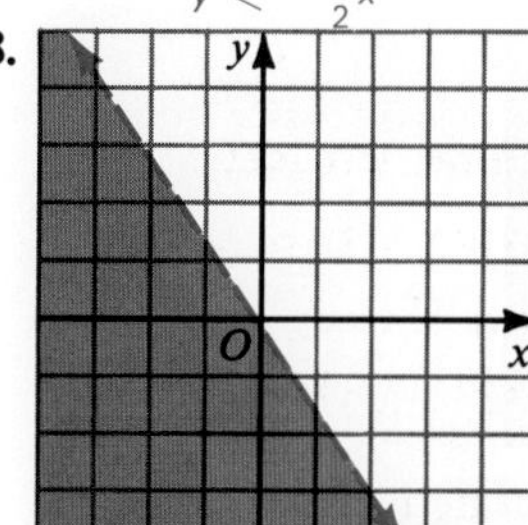

$y \geq \frac{5}{3}x + 5$

29.

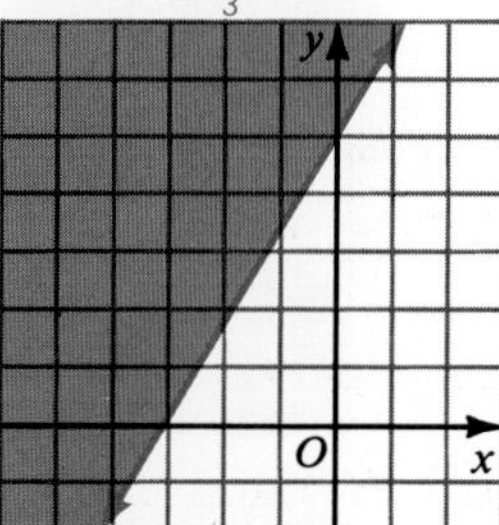

$y < -\frac{1}{2}x - 2$

30.

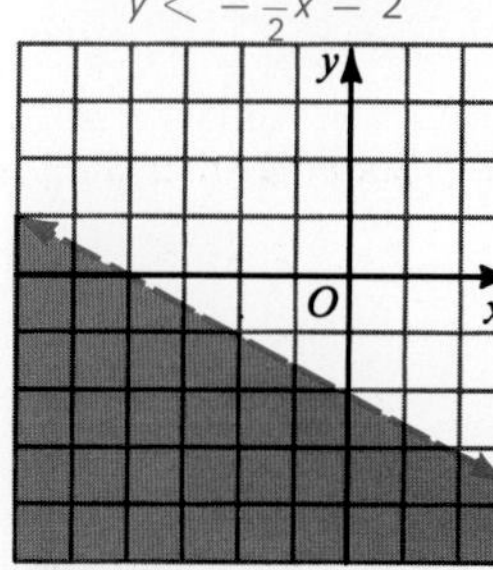

31.

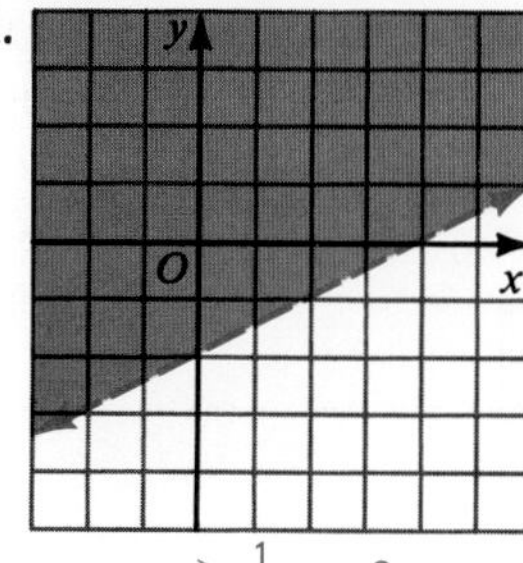

$y > \frac{1}{2}x - 2$

32.

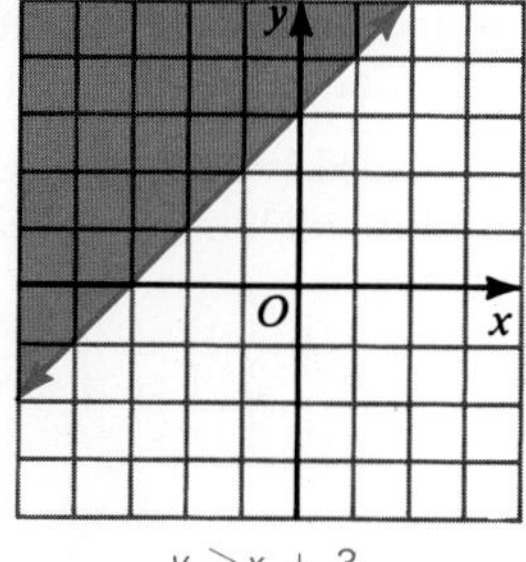

$y \geq x + 3$

33.

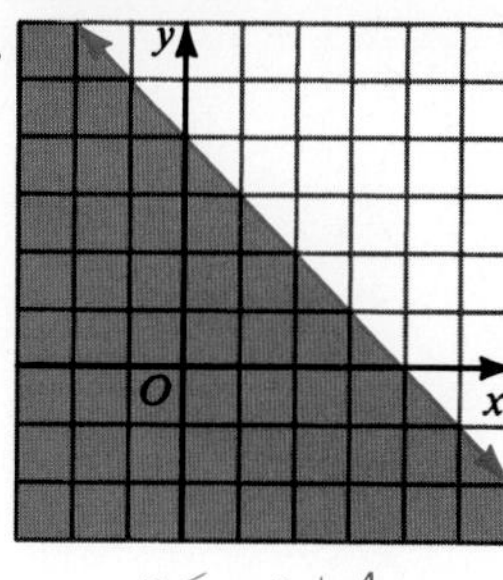

$y \leq -x + 4$

Graph each of the following in a coordinate plane.

C 34. $|y| > 2$ **35.** $|y| < 2$ **36.** $y = |x|$

37. $y = -|x|$ **38.** $y > |x|$ **39.** $y \leq |x|$

6.

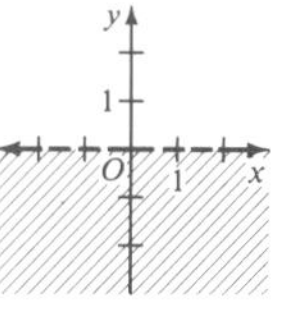

8.

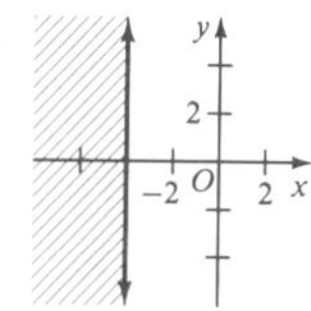

10.

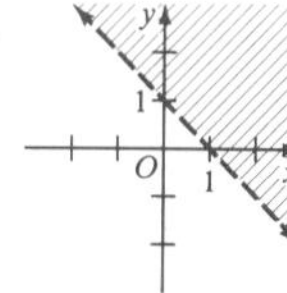

12.

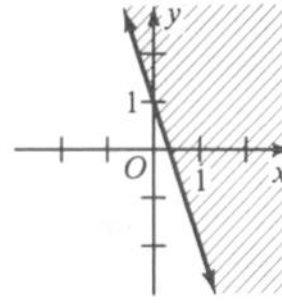

14. $y \leq x - 3$

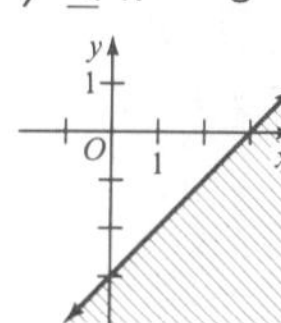

16. $y > -2x - 4$

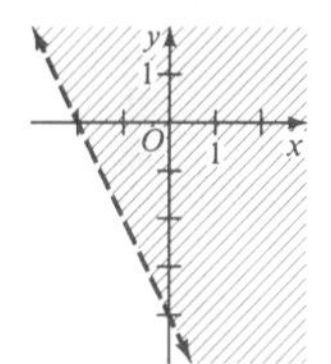

18. $y \leq 2x - 3$

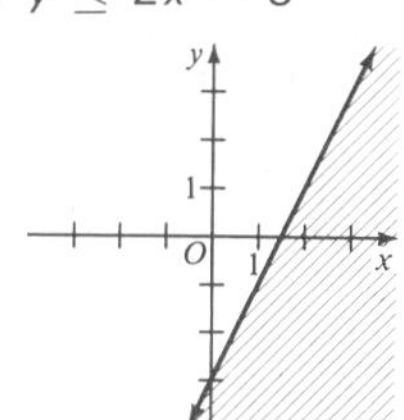

(continued p. 488)

Teaching Suggestions
p. T120

Suggested Extensions
p. T120

Chalkboard Examples

Graph the solution of each of the following systems.

1. $y > 1$
   $x < 3$

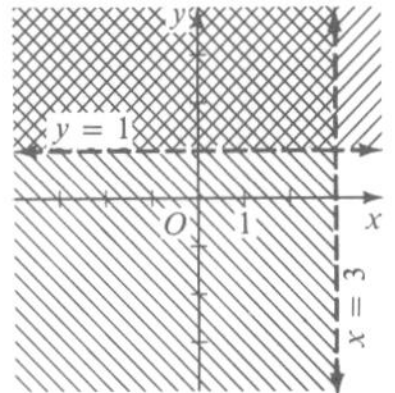

2. $y \geq x$
   $x < 1$

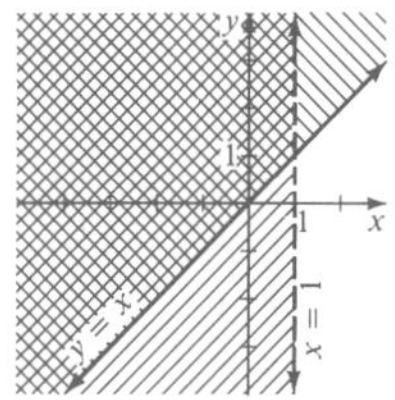

Supplementary Materials

Practice Master 64
Resource Book, p. 118

Suggested Assignments

Minimum
Day 2 of Sec. 10-7 finishes Sec. 10-7 and covers Sec. 10-8.

Average
Day 1: 485/1–12
S 478/14–18 even
Day 2: 485/13–22
R 487/*Self-Test 3*

Maximum
485/1–21 odd, 23–26
R 487/*Self-Test 3*

10-8 Systems of Linear Inequalities

Objective To graph the solution set of a system of two linear inequalities in two variables.

You can use graphs to find the solution set of a system of linear inequalities.

Example Graph the solution set of the system:

$$y - x - 3 \leq 0$$
$$2x + 3y \geq -6$$

Solution

1. Transform each inequality into an equivalent one with y as one side.

$$y - x - 3 \leq 0 \longrightarrow y \leq x + 3$$
$$2x + 3y \geq -6 \longrightarrow y \geq -\frac{2}{3}x - 2$$

2. Draw the graph of $y = x - 3$, the boundary for the first inequality. Use a solid line and shade the region below this line to show the graph of $y \leq x - 3$ (red shading).

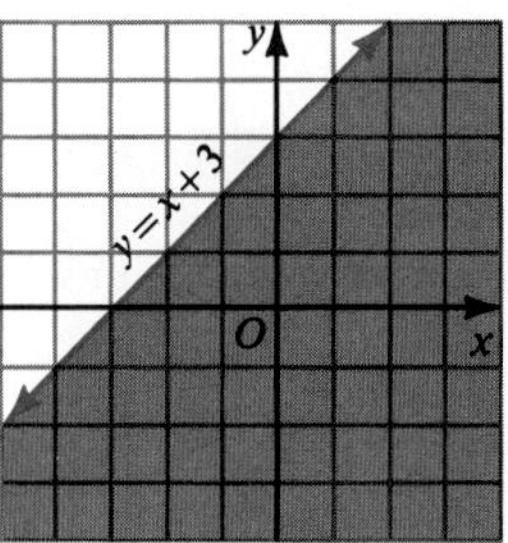

3. In the same coordinate system, draw the graph of $y = -\frac{2}{3}x - 2$, the boundary for the second inequality. Use a solid line, and shade the region above this line to show the graph of $y \geq -\frac{2}{3}x - 2$ (blue shading).

4. The doubly shaded region resulting from Steps 2 and 3 is the graph of the solution set of the given system.

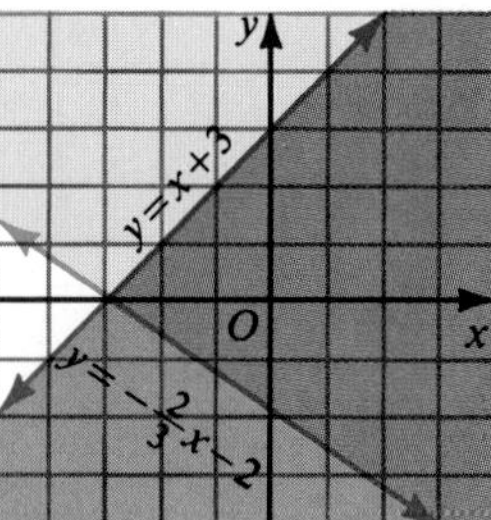

Oral Exercises

Give a system of two linear inequalities whose solution set is shown by the shaded region in each graph.

$x > -4;\ y \geq 2$

1. 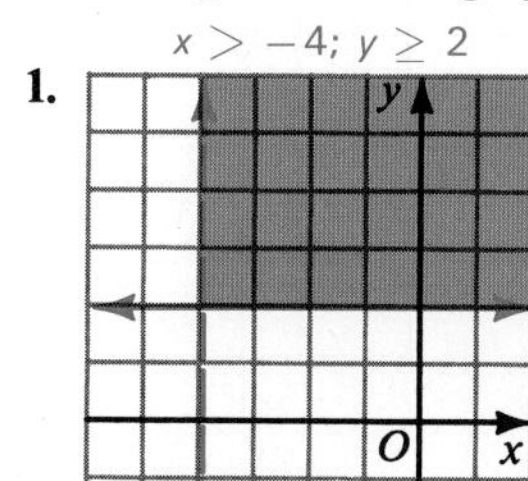

$x \geq -1;\ y \leq 3$

2. 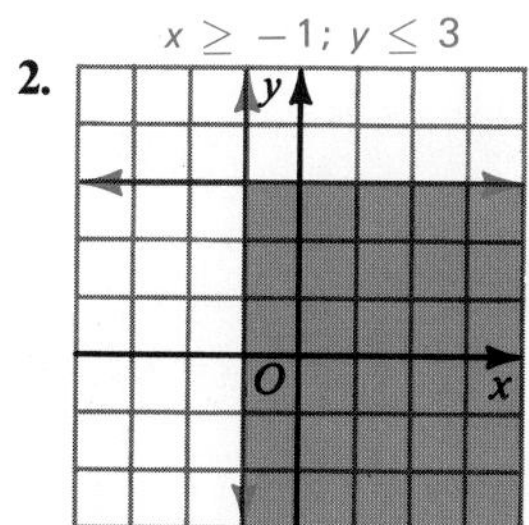

$x < 3;\ y > -5$

3. 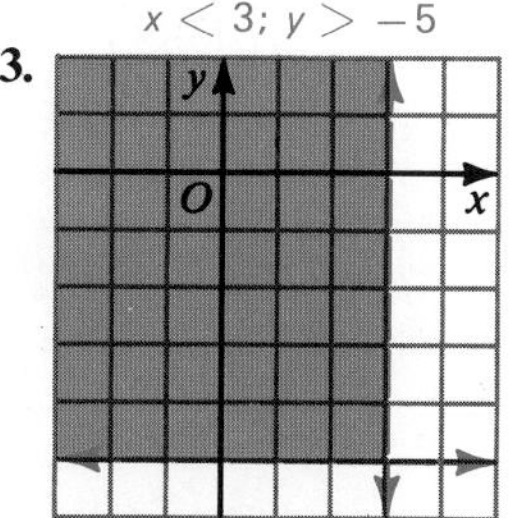

State whether or not each ordered pair is a solution of the system: $y \geq 6$ and $x < 4$.

4. $(0, 0)$ no **5.** $(4, 6)$ no **6.** $(3, 6)$ yes **7.** $(-2, 6)$ yes **8.** $(-2, -6)$ no
9. $(6, 4)$ no **10.** $(5, 9)$ no **11.** $(4, 3)$ no **12.** $(0, 8)$ yes **13.** $(0, 6)$ yes

State whether each point belongs to the graph of the solution set of the system: $y \leq 3$ and $x - y \leq 5$.

14. $(0, -5)$ yes **15.** $(9, 3)$ no **16.** $(10, 3)$ no **17.** $(-10, 3)$ yes **18.** $(-10, 4)$ no
19. $(0, 0)$ yes **20.** $(8, 3)$ yes **21.** $(0, -6)$ no **22.** $(-4, -6)$ yes **23.** $(-9, 2)$ yes

Written Exercises

Graph each pair of inequalities and indicate the solution set of the system with crosshatching or shading.

A

1. $y > 0$, $x \geq 0$
2. $y \leq 5$, $x \geq 1$
3. $y > 2$, $x < -3$
4. $y < -4$, $x > 4$
5. $y < x$, $x > 2$
6. $y > 3x$, $x < 1$
7. $x \leq 4$, $y > 6 - x$
8. $x > -2$, $y \leq 2x + 7$
9. $y \leq x + 1$, $y \geq 1 - x$
10. $y < 4x + 4$, $y > -4x + 4$
11. $y > 3x - 2$, $y < 3x + 6$
12. $y < 5x + 5$, $y > 5 - 5x$

B

13. $x + y \leq 7$, $x - y \geq 3$
14. $x + y \geq 5$, $x - 2y > 8$
15. $3x - y > -1$, $x - y > -5$
16. $x - y < 7$, $x - 3y > 15$
17. $3x - 4y < -12$, $3x + 4y > 0$
18. $2x - 5y > 0$, $x - 4y \leq -6$

Additional Answers
Written Exercises

2. 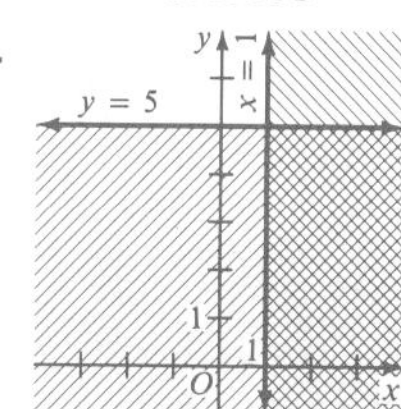

4. 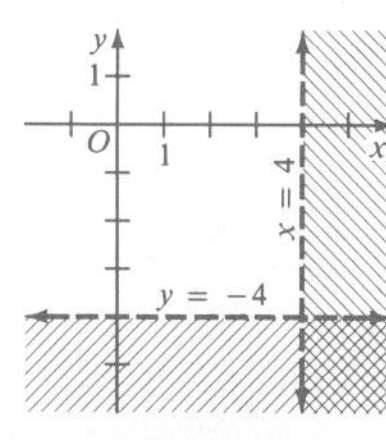

6. 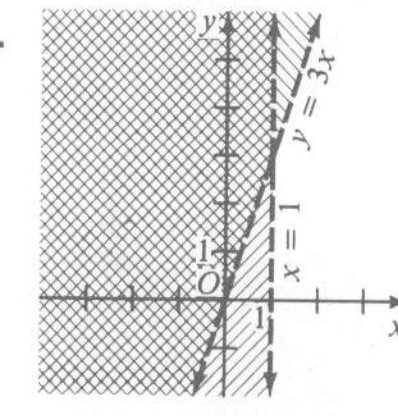

8. 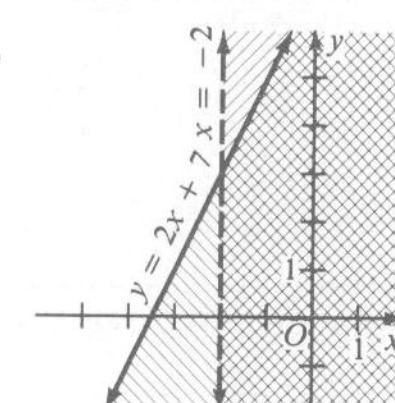

10. 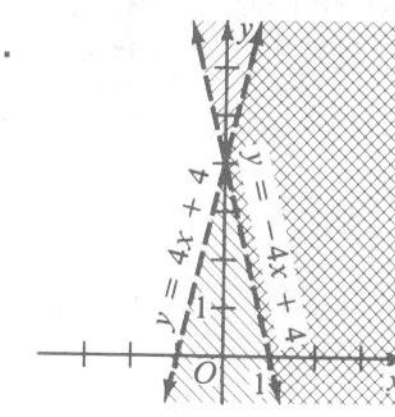

12. 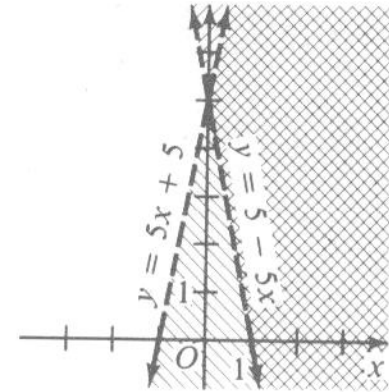

Additional Answers
Written Exercises

14.

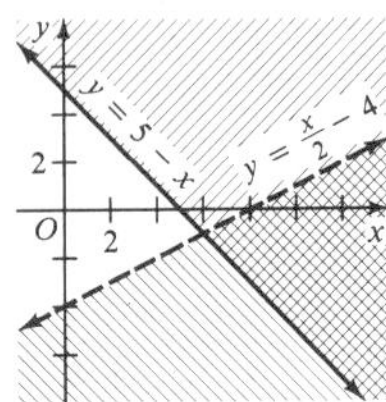

16.

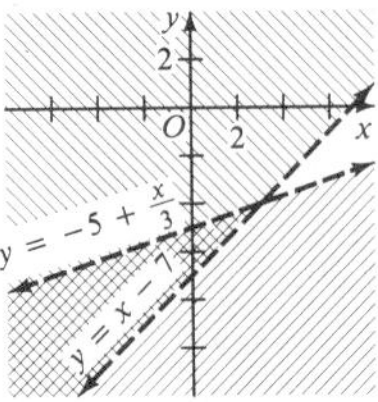

18.

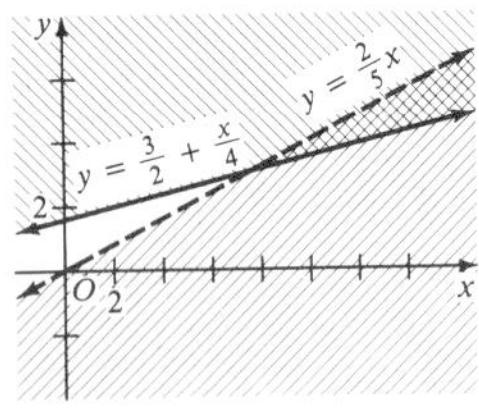

26. $(-3, -1)$, $(-3, -6)$, $(0, 0)$

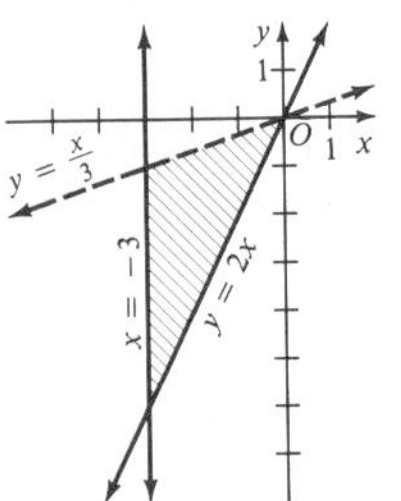

28. $(-3, -1)$, $(-3, 3)$, $(3, -1)$, $(3, 1)$

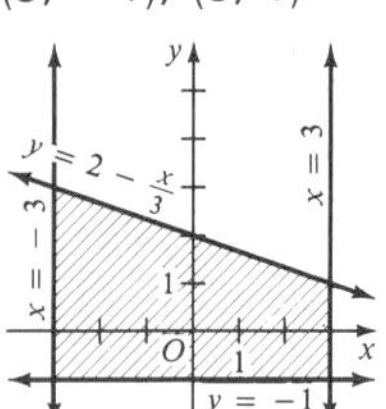

Write a system of linear inequalities whose solution set is shown by the shaded region in each graph.

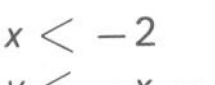

19.

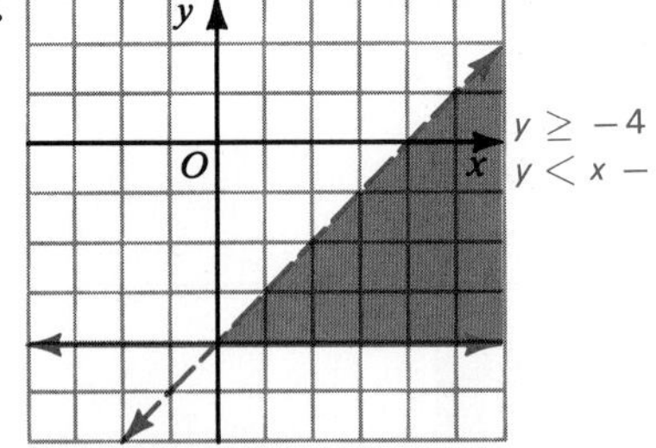

20.

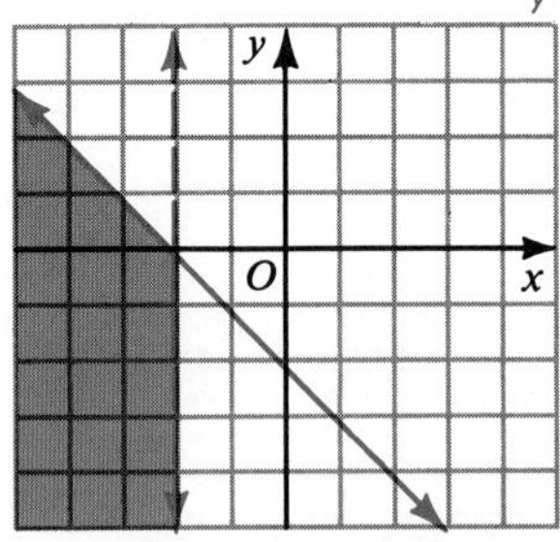

21.

$y < -2x + 2$

$y < \frac{2}{3}x - \frac{10}{3}$

22.

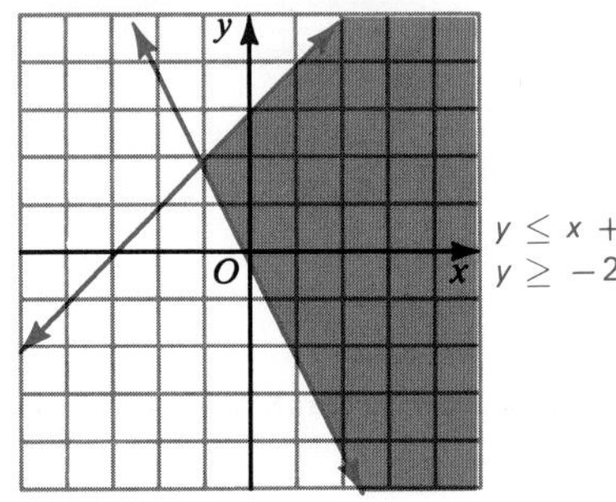

Example

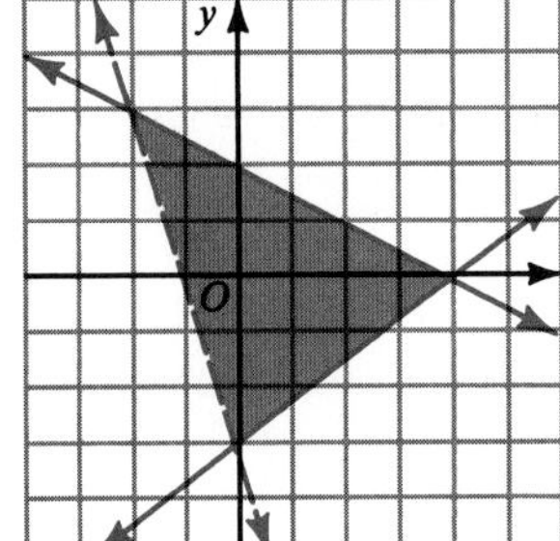

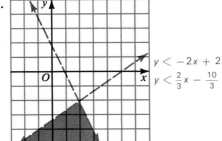

Solution $y \geq \frac{3}{4}x - 3$

$y > -3x - 3$

$y \leq -\frac{1}{2}x + 2$

C 23.

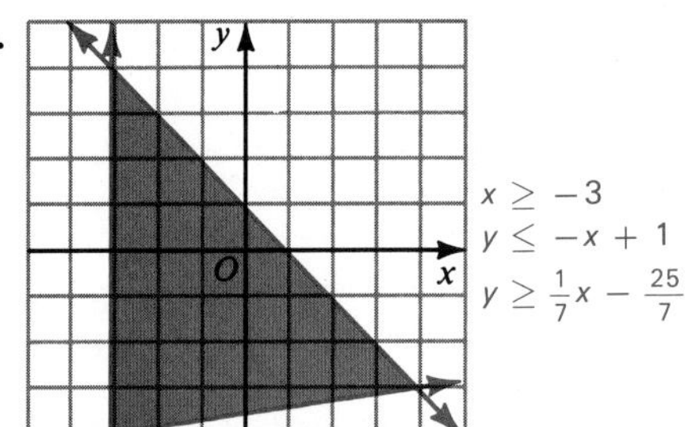

$x \geq -2$, $x \leq 4$,

$y \leq \frac{1}{3}x + \frac{8}{3}$, $y \geq -\frac{1}{3}x - \frac{8}{3}$

24.

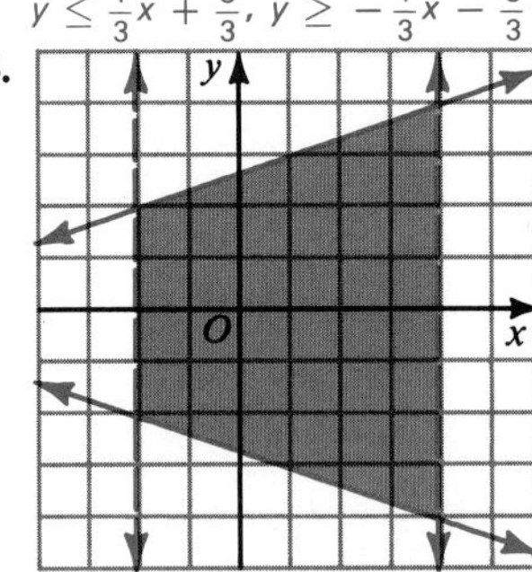

Graph each system of inequalities. Determine exactly the *corner points* of the graph of the solution set of the system, that is, the points where boundary lines intersect.

25. $y \geq x$
$y \geq -x$
$y < 2$

26. $y \geq 2x$
$3y < x$
$x \geq -3$

27. $2x - y \geq 4$
$x \leq -1$
$|y| \leq 2$

28. $x + 3y \leq 6$
$y \geq -1$
$|x| \leq 3$

Self-Test 3

Vocabulary open half-plane (p. 480) closed half-plane (p. 480)
boundary (p. 480)

Graph each inequality in a coordinate plane.

1. $x > 5$ **2.** $x + 2y \leq 6$ **Obj. 10-7, p. 480**

3. Graph the solution set of the system: **Obj. 10-8, p. 484**

$$x - y > 5$$
$$3x + y \geq -1$$

Check your answers with those at the back of the book.

Calculator Key-In

You can compare two fractions with the aid of a calculator. First change each fraction to a decimal by dividing numerator by denominator. Then compare the decimals.

True or false?

1. $\frac{5}{8} > \frac{9}{20} > \frac{6}{13}$
false, $\frac{9}{20} < \frac{6}{13}$

2. $\frac{17}{23} < \frac{18}{24} < \frac{19}{25}$
true

3. $\frac{90}{101} > \frac{91}{102} > \frac{92}{103}$
false, $\frac{90}{101} < \frac{91}{102} < \frac{92}{103}$

Extra / *Linear Programming*

Decisions in business and industry often aim at making certain quantities, such as profit, as large as possible, or other quantities, such as cost, as small as possible. Of course, a decision to maximize or to minimize a given quantity is usually subject to some conditions (*constraints*). When the quantity can be represented by a linear equation and the constraints can be represented by a system of linear inequalities, the decision problem can be solved by using techniques developed in a branch of mathematics called *linear programming*.

Quick Quiz

Graph each inequality in a coordinate plane.

1. $y < 2$

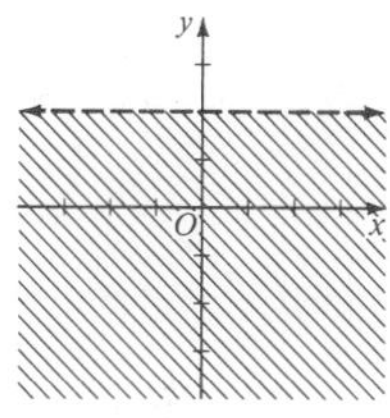

2. $2x - y \geq 4$

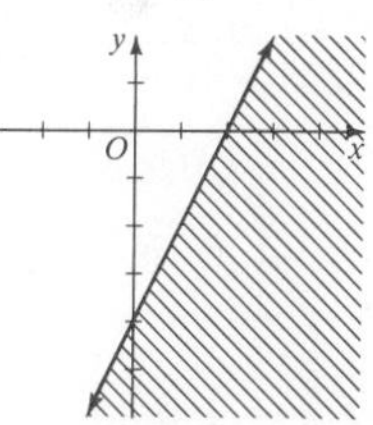

3. Graph the solution set of the system:
$x + y < 2$
$x - 2y \leq 4$

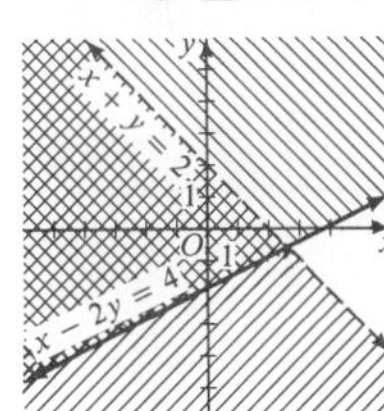

Additional Answers
Written Exercises
(continued from p. 483)

20. $y < \frac{2}{3}x$

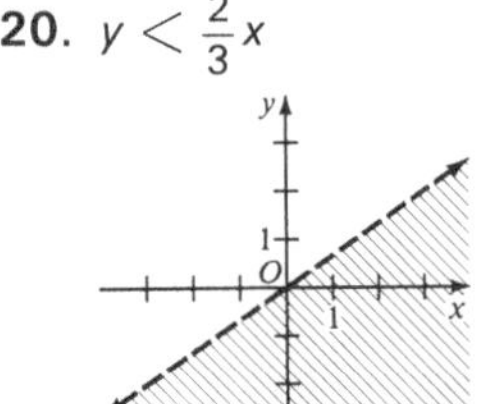

22. $y > \frac{2}{3}x - \frac{1}{3}$

24. $y < 2x + 8$

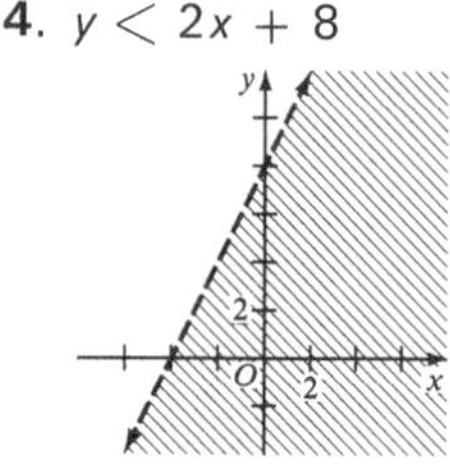

34.

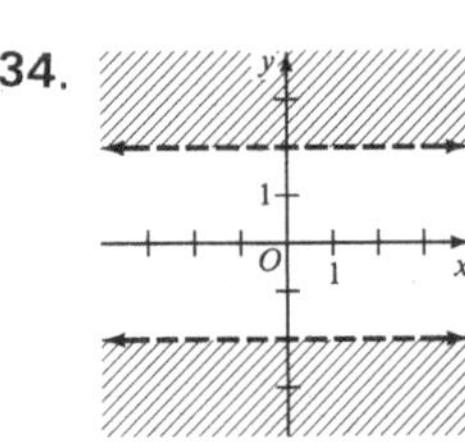

36.

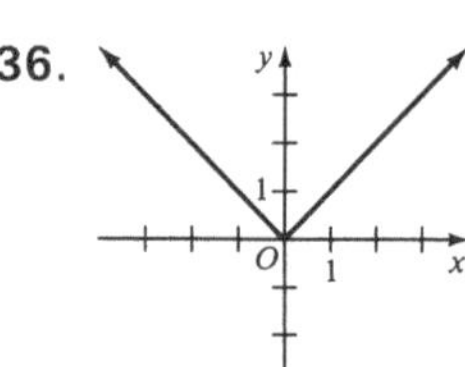

38.

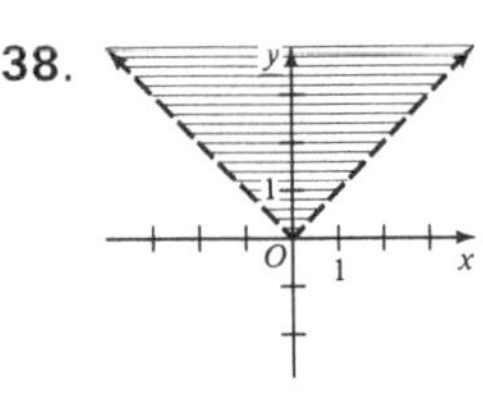

Example

A machine shop makes two automotive parts, I and II, each requiring the use of three machines, A, B, and C. Each Part I requires 4 minutes on machine A, 4 minutes on machine B, and 5 minutes on machine C. Each Part II requires 5 minutes on machine A, 1 minute on machine B, and 6 minutes on machine C. The shop makes a profit of \$8 on each Part I and \$5 on each Part II. However, the number of units of Part II produced must not be less than half the number of Part I. Also, each day, the shop has available only 120 minutes of machine A, 72 minutes of machine B, and 180 minutes of machine C for the production of Parts I and II. What should the daily production of these parts be to maximize the shop's profit?

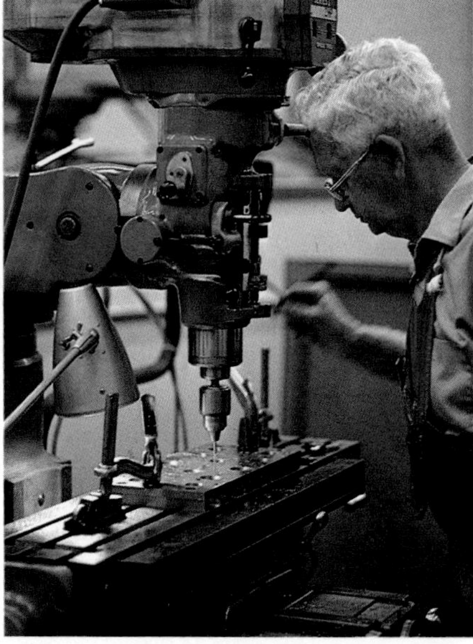

Solution

Let x = number of units of Part I
y = number of units of Part II
P = total profit on Parts I and II

The data in the problem are summarized in the following chart and the inequalities below.

		Minutes on Machine			Profit per Unit
Part	Number	A	B	C	
I	x	4	4	5	\$8
II	y	5	1	6	\$5
Available Time		120	72	180	

$4x + 5y \le 120$ (Total time on machine A must not exceed 120 min)
$4x + y \le 72$ (Total time on machine B must not exceed 72 min)
$5x + 6y \le 180$ (Total time on machine C must not exceed 180 min)

$y \ge \frac{1}{2}x$ (Number of units of Part II must not be less than half the number of Part I)

$\left.\begin{array}{l} x \ge 0 \\ y \ge 0 \end{array}\right\}$ (A negative number of parts cannot be produced.)

We want to find values of x and y that maximize P subject to these inequalities (constraints) where

$$P = 8x + 5y.$$

Step 1
Graph the solution set of this system of inequalities. The solution set is shaded and is called the *feasible region*.

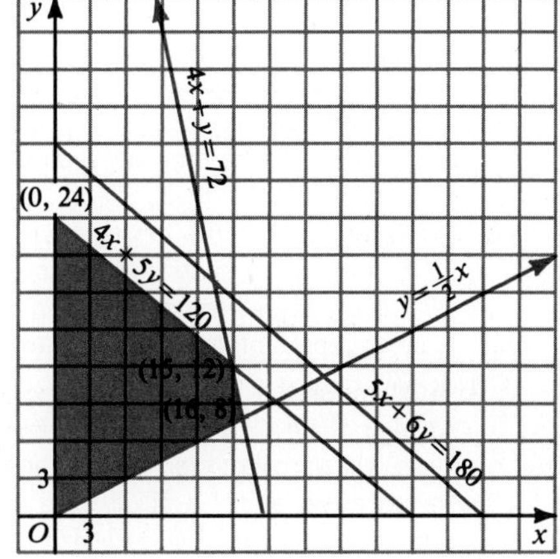

Step 2
Find the points of the feasible region where the boundary lines intersect. These points are called *corner points*. The corner points are (0, 0), (16, 8), (15, 12), and (0, 24).

A remarkable fact, proved in more advanced mathematics courses, is that if a maximum or minimum value of a *linear expression* $ax + by$ exists, it must occur at a corner point of the feasible region. We use this fact in the next step.

Step 3
Evaluate $P = 8x + 5y$ at each corner point.

(0, 0): $P = 8(0) + 5(0) = 0$
(16, 8): $P = 8(16) + 5(8) = 168$
(15, 12): $P = 8(15) + 5(12) = 180$
(0, 24): $P = 8(0) + 5(24) = 120$

The maximum value of P is \$180, which occurs at (15, 12). Therefore, to maximize its profit, the machine shop should produce 15 units of Part I and 12 units of Part II each day.

Exercises

1. **a.** Draw the graph of the solution set of the system of inequalities

$$x \geq 2y + 4$$
$$x + y \geq -2$$
$$4x + y \leq 4$$

b. Find the corner points of the solution set. $\left(\frac{4}{3}, -\frac{4}{3}\right)$, (2, −4), (0, −2)

c. Find the maximum and minimum values of $4x + 7y$ subject to the inequalities in part (a). max., −4; min., −20

2. Find x and y to maximize $R = x + 3y$ subject to the constraints $x \geq 2$, $y \geq 1$, $x + 2y \leq 8$, $x + y \leq 6$. (2, 3)

Additional Answers
Extra

1. a.

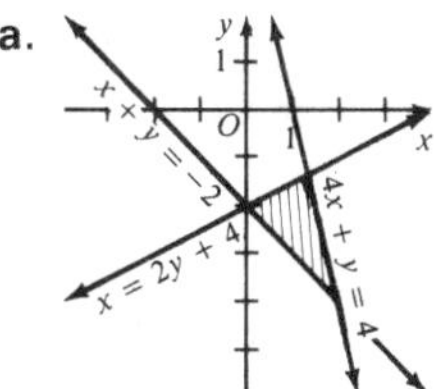

Additional Answers
Extra

3. b.

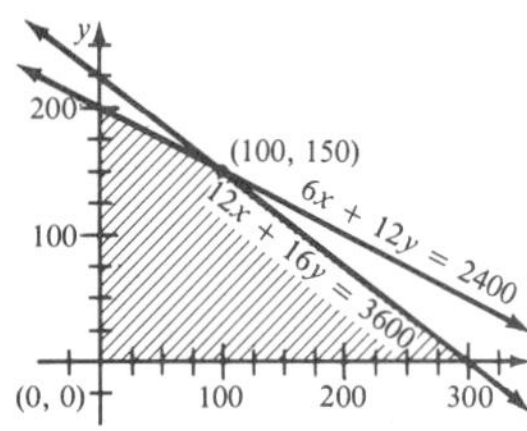

c. The farmer can plant 200 acres of soybeans and no corn or 150 acres of soybeans and 100 acres of corn.

3. a. A farmer plants two crops, corn and soybeans. The expenses are \$6 for each acre of corn planted and \$12 for each acre of soybeans planted. Each acre of corn requires 12 bushels of storage, and each acre of soybeans requires 16 bushels of storage. The farmer has at most 3600 bushels of storage available and \$2400 to spend on these expenses. Choose variables for the number of acres of corn and soybeans planted. Write four inequalities that express the conditions of the problem. $6c + 12s \leq 2400;\ 12c + 16s \leq 3600;\ c \geq 0;\ s \geq 0$

b. Graph the solution set of the system of inequalities described in part (a). State the coordinates of the corner points for this feasible region.

c. Suppose that the farmer earns a profit of \$24 for each acre of corn and \$48 for each acre of soybeans. Find two ways the farmer can satisfy the conditions while maximizing the profits. (Notice that a linear programming problem can have more than one solution.)

4. Each week the School Bus Service needs at least 650 L of diesel fuel, 324 L of gasoline, and 48 L of oil to keep the school buses in operation. Western Petroleum Company can deliver 130 L of diesel fuel, 36 L of gasoline, and 4 L of oil for a bulk wholesale rate of \$50. A similar plan, costing \$62.50, is available from Carib Oil Company for 65 L of diesel fuel, 54 L of gasoline, and 12 L of oil. How many standing orders should the School Bus Service place with each oil company to meet its weekly petroleum needs at the least cost?

3 orders with Western and 4 orders with Carib

Challenge

The diagrams illustrate some equalities of mass among spheres, cubes, cylinders, and cones. What is the least number of objects that will balance the final scale? 1 sphere and 1 cube

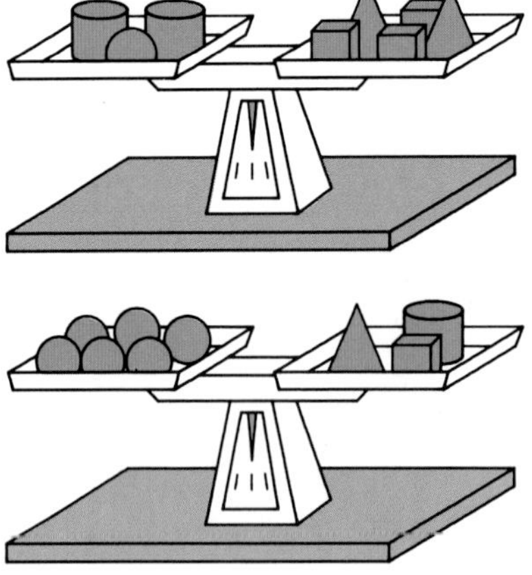

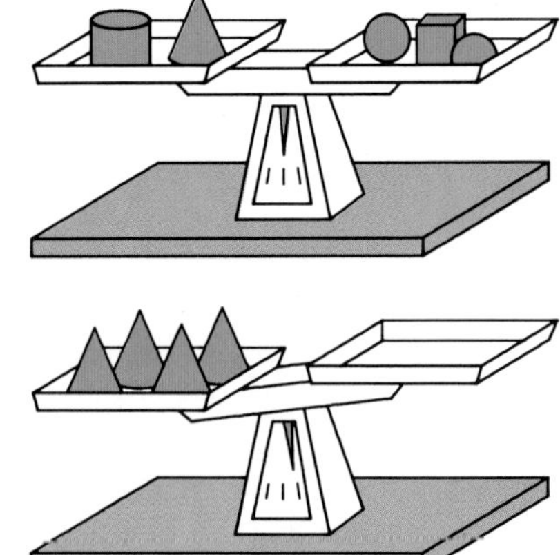

Computer Key-In

The program on page 479 can be expanded to graph equations and inequalities in two variables. First insert this line:

```
15 PRINT "IN TWO VARIABLES,"
```

Study the diagram shown at the right as you insert or change the lines listed below.

The graph will be printed from the top down. First print "Y" above the y-axis:

```
51 REM---PRINT "Y"
52 FOR I=M TO N
53 IF I <> 0 THEN 56
54 PRINT "Y"
55 GOTO 65
56 PRINT " ";
57 NEXT I
```

```
51 ?  —  57 ?    PRINT "Y"
65 ?    FOR Y=N TO M STEP −1
    70 ?    FOR X=M TO N
            IF X=0 PRINT Y-AXIS
            IF Y=0 PRINT X-AXIS
    120
     ?      NEXT X
180     PRINT "X"
 ?      NEXT Y
```

(Compare lines 51–57 with lines 140–200 on page 479.)

In order for the values of y to decrease, you must reverse M and N and use STEP −1:

```
65 FOR Y=N TO M STEP -1
```

Change line 80 for each open sentence. Use these lines to print the axes:

```
81 IF X=0 THEN 87
82 IF Y=0 THEN 90
84 PRINT " ";
85 GOTO 120
87 PRINT "!";
88 GOTO 120
```

```
130 REM---PRINT "X"
140 IF Y=0 THEN 170
150 PRINT
160 GOTO 180
170 PRINT "X"
180 NEXT Y
```

Delete lines 190 and 200.

(If possible, save this program for later use.)

Exercises

1. Revise and LIST the program as shown above. Copy the diagram, replacing the question marks with the program line numbers. See above.

Change line 80 in the program to graph the following.

2. $y > x + 2$
3. $y \geq x + 2$
4. $y = x + 2$
5. $y < x + 2$
6. $y - x \leq 3$ and $2x + 3y \geq -6$
7. $x + y \leq 7$ and $x - y \geq 3$

Note: The program of Exercise 1 above can be used to do Exercises 13–24 on page 483 and Exercises 9–18 on page 485.

Additional Answers
Computer Key-In

2. 80 IF Y > X + 2 THEN 110

3. 80 IF Y > = X + 2 THEN 110

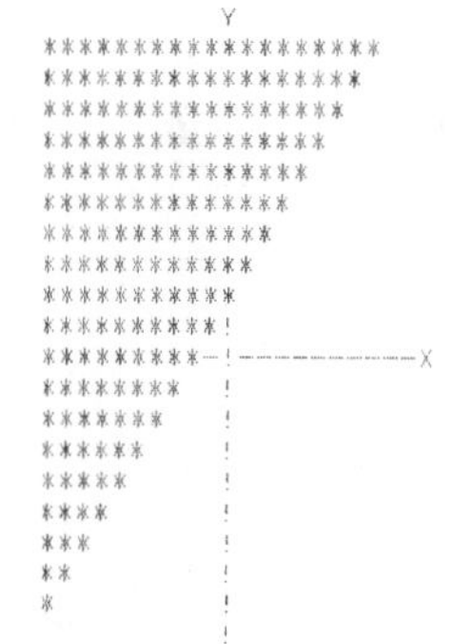

4. 80 IF Y = X + 2 THEN 110

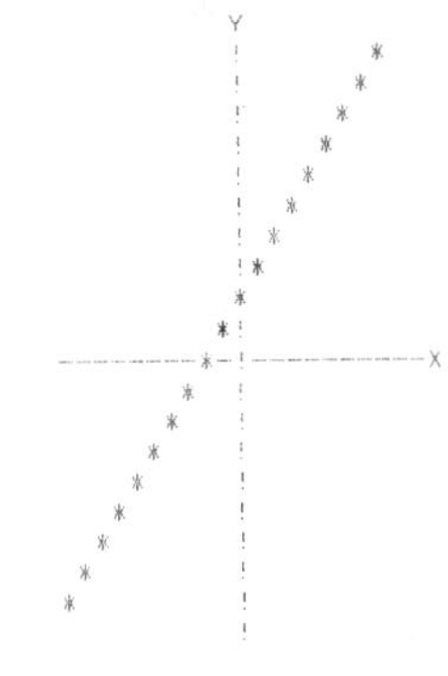

(continued)

Additional Answers
Computer Key-In

5. 80 IF Y < X + 2 THEN 110

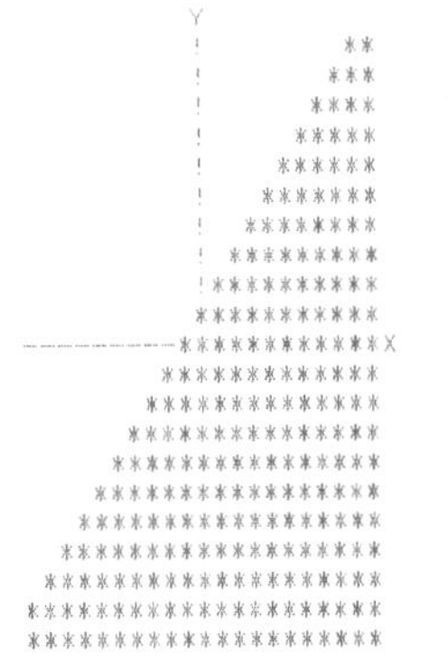

6. 80 IF (Y − X) < = 3 AND (2*X + 3*Y) > = −6 THEN 110

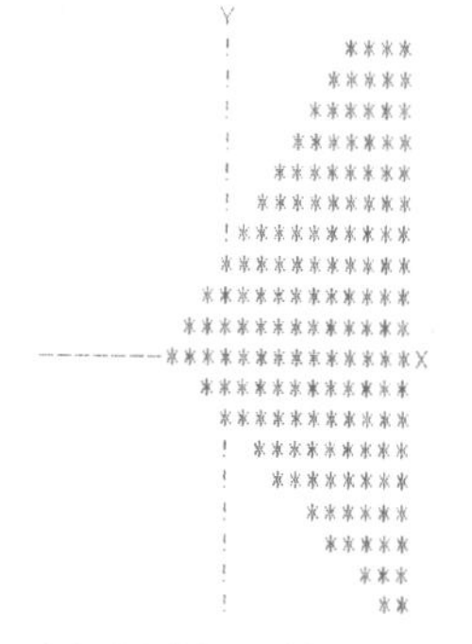

7. 80 IF (X + Y) < = 7 AND (X − Y) > = 3 THEN 110

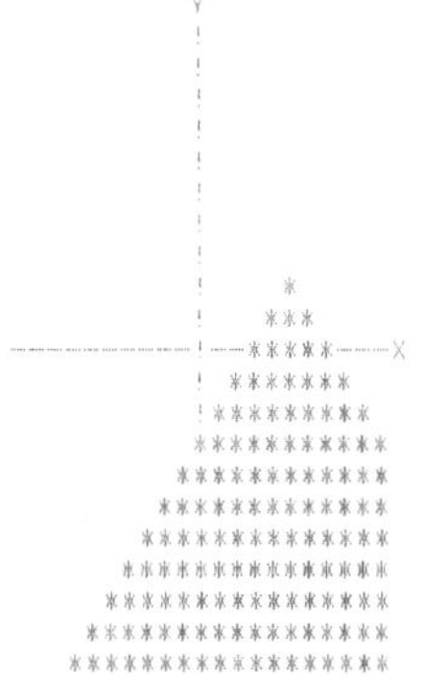

Chapter Summary

1. The symbols $>$, $<$, $\geq$, and $\leq$ are used to express inequalities. $-2 < 4 < 9$ (or $9 > 4 > -2$) means that 4 is between -2 and 9.
2. Open inequalities can be solved by transformations to obtain simple equivalent inequalities whose solution sets can be seen at a glance. The graph of the solution set of an inequality in one variable can be shown on a number line.
3. Sentences joined by "and" are conjunctions. A conjunction is true if and only if it is formed of true statements. Sentences joined by "or" are disjunctions. A disjunction of statements is true if at least one of the statements is true.
4. The distance between the graphs of two numbers a and b on a number line is the absolute value of the difference between a and b. This concept can be used to solve open sentences involving the absolute value of a variable. These open sentences also may be written as equivalent conjunctions or disjunctions.
5. The solution set of a linear inequality in two variables is an open or closed half-plane.
6. The graph of the solution set of a system of inequalities consists of the points common to the graphs of all the inequalities in the system.

Chapter Review

Give the letter of the correct answer.

1. Which statement is true? **10-1**
a. $-7 < -10 < -12$ **b.** $8 > -6 > 4$
(c.) $-9 < -4 < 2$ **d.** $-5 > 3 > 0$

2. Find the solution set of $1 - x \leq 0$ if $x \in \{-4, -2, 0, 2, 4\}$.
a. $\{-4, -2, 0, 2, 4\}$ **b.** $\{-4, -2\}$ **(c.)** $\{2, 4\}$ **d.** $\{0\}$

3. Find an inequality equivalent to $-3x < 12$. **10-2**
a. $x > -36$ **b.** $x < -36$ **(c.)** $x > -4$ **d.** $x < -4$

4. Find an inequality equivalent to $3(3 + y) < 5(5 + y)$.
a. $y < -8$ **(b.)** $y > -8$ **c.** $y < 8$ **d.** $y > 8$

5. Represent the statement "The product of two consecutive even integers is at most 80" as an inequality. **10-3**
a. $n(n + 1) \geq 80$ **b.** $n(n + 1) \leq 80$
c. $n(n + 2) \geq 80$ **(d.)** $n(n + 2) \leq 80$

6. Which is the graph of the solution set of $x < 4$ or $x > 4$? **10-4**

(a.) 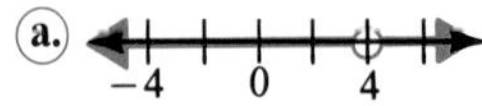

b. 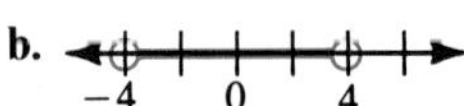

c. 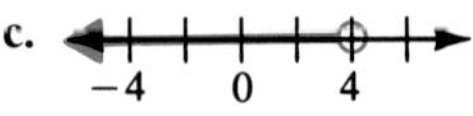

7. Which is the graph of the conjunction $-6 \le x$ and $x < 4$?

a. 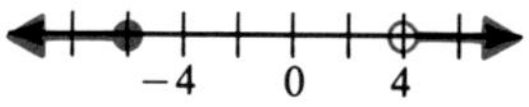

(b.) 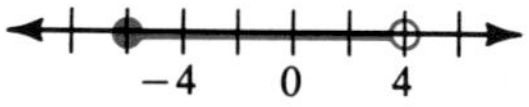

c. 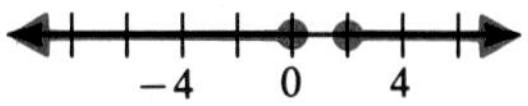

d. 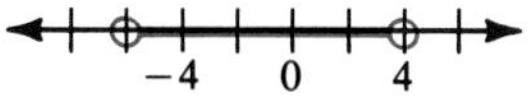

8. Which open sentence states that the distance from a to 2 is greater than 4? 10-5

a. $a - 2 > 4$ b. $a - 2 \ge 4$ (c.) $|a - 2| > 4$ d. $|a - 2| \ge 4$

9. Which inequality is equivalent to $|6n - 3| < 9$? 10-6

a. $|2n - 1| < 9$ (b.) $|2n - 1| < 3$

c. $|n - 3| < 9$ d. $|2n - 1| > -3$

10. What is the equation of the boundary of the graph of the inequality $x - 2y > 4$? 10-7

a. $y = 2x - 4$ (b.) $y = \frac{1}{2}x - 2$ c. $y \le \frac{1}{2}x - 2$ d. $y \ge 2x - 4$

11. Which point belongs to the graph of the solution set of the system: 10-8

$$x > -3$$
$$y \le 2x + 5$$

a. (0, 7) (b.) (0, −7) c. (−7, 0) d. (−2, 7)

Chapter Test

1. Classify the statement as true or false: $5 > -\frac{1}{2} > -3$ true 10-1
2. Find the solution set of $y + 2 < 3$ if $y \in \{-2, -1, 0, 1, 2\}$. $\{-2, -1, 0\}$
3. Solve the inequality $5 \ge 2x - 3$ and graph the solution set on a number line. 10-2
4. Of all pairs of consecutive odd integers whose sum is greater than 75, find the pair whose sum is the least. 37, 39 10-3

Solve each open sentence and graph its solution set.

5. $-1 \le 2c + 1 < 5$ 6. $k + 5 \le -3$ or $k + 5 \ge 3$ 10-4
7. $|3 - y| = 4$ 8. $|y + 1| < 2$ 10-5
9. $|6 - 2x| = 4$ 10. $|2m - 1| \le 5$ 10-6

Graph each inequality in a coordinate plane.

11. $y \le 3$ 12. $y \ge 3 - x$ 10-7
13. Graph the solution set of the system: $y < 2x + 2$, $y > 2 - 2x$ 10-8

Additional Answers Chapter Test

3. {4 and the real numbers less than 4}

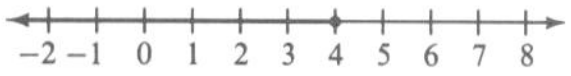

5. {−1 and the real numbers between −1 and 2}

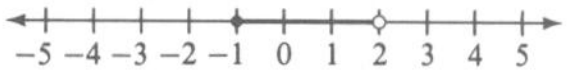

6. {−8, −2, and the real numbers less than −8 or greater than −2}

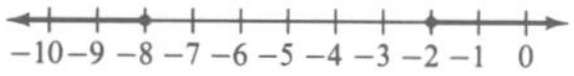

7. {−1, 7}

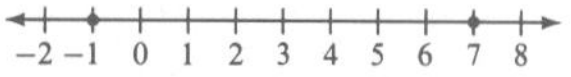

8. {the real numbers between −3 and 1}

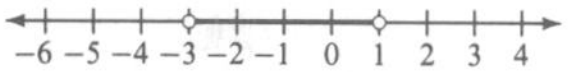

9. {1, 5}

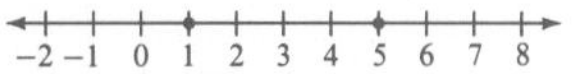

10. {−2, 3, and the real numbers between −2 and 3}

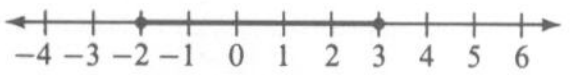

11. 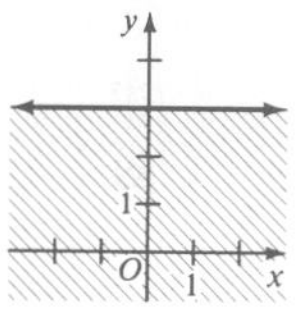

12. 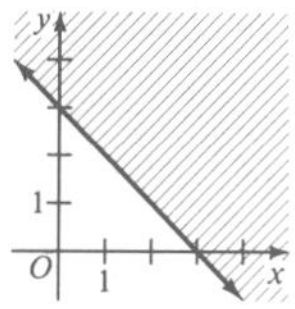

13. 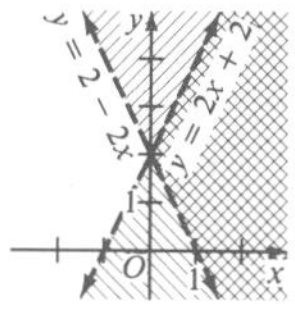

Alternate Test p. T19

Supplementary Materials

Practice Master 65
Test 37
Resource Book, pp. 50–53, 158

Extra Practice

Skills, pp. 626–628
Problems, p. 646

Additional Answers Cumulative Review

18.

−3 −2 −1 0 1 2 3 4 5 6 7

19.

−5 −4 −3 −2 −1 0 1 2 3 4 5

20.

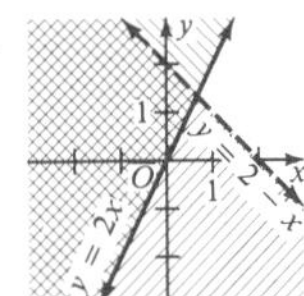

29. $\left\{-1, \frac{5}{3}\right\}$

32. $\left\{-\frac{1}{2}, 0\right\}$

36. {−2 and the real numbers less than −2}

37. $\left\{\text{the real numbers less than } -\frac{6}{5}\right\}$

38. $\left\{\text{the real numbers between } -\frac{1}{3} \text{ and } 1\right\}$

Cumulative Review (Chapters 1–10)

Simplify. Assume that no denominator is zero.

1. $(-7b + 4) + (3b - 8)$ $-4b - 4$
2. $2x^2(8x^3 - 6x^2 + 9x)$ $16x^5 - 12x^4 + 18x^3$
3. $(3x^3y^4)^5 \div (9xy^8)$ $27x^{14}y^{12}$
4. $(3x + 5y)(7x - 4y)$ $21x^2 + 23xy - 20y^2$
5. $(5c - d)(3c^2 - 4cd + 8d^2)$ $15c^3 - 23c^2d + 44cd^2 - 8d^3$
6. $(11t - 7v)^2$ $121t^2 - 154tv + 49v^2$
7. $\dfrac{3x^2 - 8x - 3}{9x^2 + 9x + 2}$ $\dfrac{x - 3}{3x + 2}$
8. $(12m^3n^2 - 11r^3)(12m^3n^2 + 11r^3)$ $144m^6n^4 - 121r^6$
9. $\dfrac{4.8 \times 10^{21}}{2.0 \times 10^{15}}$ 2.4×10^6
10. $\dfrac{z^2 + 8z + 16}{z^2 + 7z + 12} \cdot \dfrac{z^2 - 9}{z^2 + z - 12}$ 1
11. $\dfrac{y^3 + 4y^2 + 3y}{y^2 + 5y + 6} \div \dfrac{y^2 + y}{y^3 + 2y^2}$ y^2
12. $\dfrac{z + 2}{3z + 9} + \dfrac{1}{z - 3} - 1$ $\dfrac{-2(z^2 - z - 15)}{3(z + 3)(z - 3)}$

Factor completely.

13. $30z^2 + 240z + 96$ $6(5z^2 + 40z + 16)$
14. $52t^2 + 31t - 6$ $(13t - 2)(4t + 3)$
15. $16z^2 - y^2 - 10y - 25$ $(4z - y - 5)(4z + y + 5)$

Write an equation in standard form for each line described.

16. The line that contains $(-4, 3)$ and $(6, 1)$. $x + 5y = 11$
17. The line that has slope $\frac{1}{2}$ and contains $(5, 6)$. $x - 2y = -7$

Graph each inequality.

18. $|x - 2| \leq 4$
19. $2y + 1 < -5$ or $3y - 5 > 1$
20. Graph the solution set of the system: $x + y < 2$, $2x - y \leq 0$

Solve each equation, inequality, or system. Assume that no denominator is zero.

21. $|z| - 3 = 4$ $\{-7, 7\}$
22. $5q - 3 = 12$ 3
23. 24% of $m = 18$ 75
24. $b^2 - 8 = 1$ $\{-3, 3\}$
25. $5(d - 3) = 3(2d - 5)$ 0
26. $12y^2 + 5y = 2$ $\left\{-\frac{2}{3}, \frac{1}{4}\right\}$
27. $x^2 + 4x + 3 = 0$ $\{-3, -1\}$
28. $2b^2 + 9b - 5 = 0$ $\left\{\frac{1}{2}, -5\right\}$
29. $3z^2 - 2z - 5 = 0$
30. $\dfrac{n - 1}{n} - \dfrac{1}{n + 1} = 1$ $-\frac{1}{2}$
31. $\dfrac{b + 1}{b + 2} - \dfrac{b + 2}{b + 1} = \dfrac{1}{b + 2}$ $-\frac{4}{3}$
32. $\dfrac{t}{3t + 1} + \dfrac{1}{t - 1} = \dfrac{3t + 1}{t - 1}$
33. $y = 5x - 1$, $2x + 3y = 14$ $(1, 4)$
34. $3r + 2s = -4$, $4r + 2s = -8$ $(-4, 4)$
35. $6m + 5n = 4$, $4m + 3n = 2$ $(-1, 2)$
36. $5 + 4t \leq -3$
37. $3 - 5b > 9$
38. $2|3x - 1| + 1 < 5$
39. Marcy can do a job alone in 5 hours. If Mark helps her, they can do the job together in 3 hours. How long would Mark take working alone? $7\frac{1}{2}$ h
40. The units digit of a two-digit number is 1 less than the tens digit. Nine times the tens digit is less than the number with the digits reversed. Find the least such number. 65

Maintaining Skills

Solve. If the equation is an identity or has no solution, state that fact. Assume that no denominator is zero.

Example 1 $12t^2 - 3 = 5t$

Solution

$$12t^2 - 5t - 3 = 0$$
$$(4t - 3)(3t + 1) = 0$$
$$4t - 3 = 0 \quad \text{or} \quad 3t + 1 = 0$$
$$4t = 3 \qquad 3t = -1$$
$$t = \frac{3}{4} \qquad t = -\frac{1}{3}$$

The check is left to you. The solution set is $\left\{\frac{3}{4}, -\frac{1}{3}\right\}$.

1. $t^2 - 6t - 40 = 0$ $\{10, -4\}$
2. $x^2 = 15x - 56$ $\{8, 7\}$
3. $y^2 + 12y + 36 = 0$ $\{-6\}$
4. $n^2 + 400 = 40n$ $\{20\}$
5. $5z^2 + 4z = 1$ $\left\{\frac{1}{5}, -1\right\}$
6. $10m^2 + 29m + 10 = 0$ 6. $\left\{-\frac{2}{5}, -\frac{5}{2}\right\}$
7. $8 + 14z = 15z^2$ $\left\{-\frac{2}{5}, \frac{4}{3}\right\}$
8. $21b^2 + 25b + 6 = 0$ $\left\{-\frac{1}{3}, -\frac{6}{7}\right\}$
9. $9d^2 + 7d = 16$ $\left\{-\frac{16}{9}, 1\right\}$

Example 2 $\dfrac{z+3}{z+1} + \dfrac{z}{z-2} = \dfrac{2}{z-2}$

Solution Note that $z \neq -1$ or $z \neq 2$.

$$(z+1)(z-2)\left[\frac{z+3}{z+1} + \frac{z}{z-2}\right] = (z+1)(z-2)\left(\frac{2}{z-2}\right)$$
$$(z-2)(z+3) + z(z+1) = 2(z+1)$$
$$z^2 + z - 6 + z^2 + z = 2z + 2$$
$$2z^2 = 8$$
$$z^2 = 4$$
$$z = 2 \text{ or } z = -2$$

The check is left to you. The solution set is $\{-2\}$.

10. $\dfrac{1}{x} + \dfrac{3}{x} = 4$ $\{1\}$
11. $\dfrac{2}{3} + \dfrac{2}{t} = \dfrac{10}{3t}$ $\{2\}$
12. $\dfrac{5}{y} - \dfrac{4}{y} = \dfrac{1}{y}$ identity
13. $\dfrac{a+5}{a} + \dfrac{2}{a^2} = 1$ $\left\{-\frac{2}{5}\right\}$
14. $y - \dfrac{y}{y+1} = \dfrac{1}{y+1}$ $\{1\}$
15. $\dfrac{3}{4b-6} - \dfrac{1}{2b-3} = 0$
16. $\dfrac{3x}{x+1} - \dfrac{1}{x} = \dfrac{x+1}{x}$ $\left\{2, -\frac{1}{2}\right\}$
17. $\dfrac{b-2}{b+2} + \dfrac{b}{b-2} = 2$ $\{6\}$
18. $\dfrac{1}{t} - \dfrac{1}{t+1} = \dfrac{t+2}{t^2+t}$
19. $\dfrac{x^2+12}{x^2-4} - \dfrac{1}{x-2} = \dfrac{3}{x-2}$
20. $\dfrac{5}{d-1} - \dfrac{10}{d^2-1} = 3$ $\left\{\frac{2}{3}\right\}$
21. $\dfrac{b^2+1}{b^2-1} = \dfrac{b}{b-1} + \dfrac{2}{b+1}$
22. $\dfrac{x}{x+1} - \dfrac{5}{x^2-3x-4} = \dfrac{x+1}{x-4}$ no sol.
23. $\dfrac{y^2-2y+2}{y^2-2y-3} - \dfrac{y}{y-3} = \dfrac{4}{y+1}$ $\{2\}$

Additional Answers Maintaining Skills

15. no solution
18. no solution
19. no solution
21. no solution

Additional Answers Written Exercises (p. 471)

21. {4 and the real numbers between −3 and 4}
22. {2 and the real numbers between 2 and 5}
23. {−3 and the real numbers between −3 and 5}
24. {−3 and the real numbers between −3 and 2}
25. ∅
26. {the real numbers greater than −3}
27. {5 and the real numbers between −2 and 5}
28. {−6 and the real numbers between −6 and −1}
29. {the real numbers greater than 15 or less than −1}
30. {7, 3, and the real numbers greater than 7 or less than 3}
31. {the real numbers less than −1 or greater than 5}
32. {−1, 3, and the real numbers greater than 3 or less than −1}

(continued)

Mixed Review

Skills and Problem Solving

Factor completely. If the polynomial cannot be factored, write "prime."

1. $20b^2 - 13b - 15$ $(4b - 5)(5b + 3)$

2. $16t^2 - 8t - 9v^2 + 1$ $(4t - 1 - 3v)(4t - 1 + 3v)$

3. $3z^2 + 5z + 4$ prime

4. How many groups of three consecutive integers are there such that their sum is equal to twice the second integer? one

5. If x varies directly as the square of y and inversely as the cube of z, and $x = 5$ when $y = \frac{1}{4}$ and $z = \frac{1}{2}$, find the constant of variation. 10

6. 21 is what percent of 25? 84

7. 35% of what number is 49? 140

8. Write an equation in standard form of the line that contains $(-5, 6)$ and has y-intercept -3. $9x + 5y = -15$

Solve each equation, inequality, or system. Assume that no denominator is zero.

9. $|3x - 4| > 2$

10. $\frac{2a - 5}{a + 1} - \frac{a - 3}{2a + 1} = \frac{5a + 2}{2a^2 + 3a + 1}$ $\left\{-\frac{1}{3}, 4\right\}$

11. $2x^2 - 4x = 30$ $\{5, -3\}$

12. $\frac{t}{t + 1} + \frac{3}{t} = 1$ $-\frac{3}{2}$

13. $x^2 + 5 = x^2 + 10x + 25$ -2

14. $4x + 5y = 9$
$3x + 4y = 8$ $(-4, 5)$

15. How many liters of water must be evaporated from 84 L of a 5% acid solution to obtain a solution that is 20% acid? 63 L

16. The width of a rectangle is 4 cm less than half the length. The perimeter is less than 36 cm. Find the greatest possible width the rectangle could have, given that the width must be an integer. 3 cm

17. On a boat ride, the trip upstream took 2.5 h longer than the return trip. If the whole trip took 5.8 h and covered 132 km, find the rate of the current and the speed of the boat in still water. rate of current, 12.05 km/h; speed of boat, 27.95 km/h

Simplify. Assume that no denominator is zero. (Give the answer to Exercise 18 in scientific notation.)

18. $\frac{7{,}000{,}000}{0.0035}$ 2×10^9

19. $(2^{-3} - 3^{-2})^{-1}$ 72

20. $\frac{n + 1}{n - 1} \div (n^2 - 1) + \frac{1}{n + 1}$ $\frac{n^2 - n + 2}{(n + 1)(n - 1)^2}$

21. The sides of a triangle are in the ratio 5:8:11. The perimeter is 72 m. Find the lengths of the sides. 15 m, 24 m, 33 m

Graph the solution set.

22. $2x - y \geq -1$
$6x + 3y \leq 3$

23. $\frac{1}{2}|x - 3| \geq 2$

24. $2x - 4y = 3$

Additional Answers Written Exercises
(p. 471)

33. $\left\{-\frac{3}{2}, 2, \text{and the real numbers between } -\frac{3}{2} \text{ and } 2\right\}$

34. $\{-6$ and the real numbers less than $-6\}$

35. $\{4$ and the real numbers between 1 and $4\}$

36. {the real numbers less than 2}

37. {6 and the real numbers less than 6}

38. {1, 2, and the real numbers between 1 and 2}

41. Answers may vary. Example: **a.** $a = 20$, $b = 3$, $c = 40$, $d = 5$ **b.** $a = 4$, $b = -3$, $c = 0$, $d = -2$

Additional Answers Mixed Review

9. $\left\{\text{the real numbers greater than 2 or less than } \frac{2}{3}\right\}$

22.

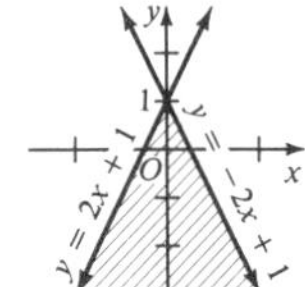

23.

−2 −1 0 1 2 3 4 5 6 7 8

24.

$\left(\frac{7}{2}, 1\right)$ $\left(-\frac{1}{2}, -1\right)$ $\left(\frac{3}{2}, 0\right)$

Preparing for College Entrance Exams

Strategy for Success

Remember that you are asked to determine the *best* answer. More than one answer may be "right" to some degree. Do not choose the first answer that seems reasonable. Be sure to check all possible choices before determining which is the best answer.

Decide which is the best of the choices given and write the corresponding letter on your answer sheet.

1. Identify the point(s) on the line that contains $(-4, 3)$ and has slope $-\frac{1}{4}$. A

I. $(8, 0)$ II. $(-1, -3)$ III. $(-12, -13)$

(A) I only **(B)** II only **(C)** III only
(D) I, II, and III **(E)** None of the above

2. Find an equation of the line that intersects the y-axis at the same point as the line containing $(2, 2)$ and $(-4, -1)$ and that is parallel to the line containing $(6, 6)$ and $(-3, 3)$. A

(A) $x - 3y = -3$ **(B)** $x - 2y = -8$ **(C)** $x + 2y = 8$ **(D)** $2x + y = 4$

3. For the function $f\colon x \rightarrow \frac{1}{x^2}$ the domain is the set of all real numbers except 0. Identify the true statement. D

(A) $f(x)$ varies inversely as x.
(B) The function has exactly one zero.
(C) The range of f is the set of all nonnegative numbers.
(D) $f(x)$ varies inversely as x^2.
(E) The graph of f is a parabola.

4. A given rectangle has area 24. The graph of the length as a function of the width: D

(A) is a parabola that opens upward. **(B)** is a parabola that opens downward.
(C) is a hyperbola. **(D)** is one branch of a hyperbola.
(E) cannot be determined from the given information.

5. How many sets of three consecutive positive even integers are there such that three times the sum of the first two integers is less than five times the third integer? D

(A) none **(B)** two **(C)** four **(D)** six **(E)** eight

6. Identify the inequality whose graph is shown at the right. B

(A) $x + 3y \leq 9$ **(B)** $x + 3y \geq 9$
(C) $3x - y \leq 3$ **(D)** $3x - y \geq 3$

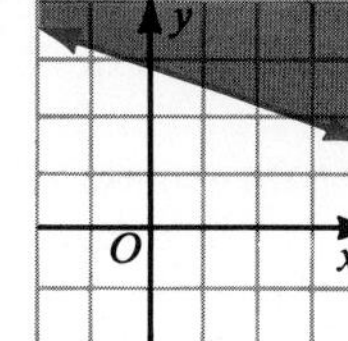

Additional Answers
Written Exercises
(p. 475)

21. {the real numbers greater than 7 or less than -1}
22. {the real numbers between -2 and 6}
23. {-4, 4, and the real numbers between -4 and 4}
24. {the real numbers greater than 1 or less than -1}
25. {0, 4, and the real numbers less than 0 or greater than 4}
26. {the real numbers between 0 and 2}
27. {-2, 2, and the real numbers between -2 and 2}
28. {-2, 2, and the real numbers between -2 and 2}
29. $\left\{2, \frac{2}{3}\right\}$
30. $\emptyset$
31. {3 and the real numbers greater than 3}
32. {the real numbers less than 3}
33. $\emptyset$
34. {all the real numbers}

About the Photo

The photograph shows the use of triangles in the construction of a tower. Unlike rectangular forms, which can be made into parallelograms by pushing on one vertex, triangular forms remain rigid. Therefore such forms are suitable and appropriate for construction.

The Pythagorean theorem mentioned in the caption was known long before the time of Pythagoras. While he did not actually discover the theorem, Pythagoras and the members of the Pythagorean school devised a rule for finding some of the integer triples that could be the lengths of the sides of a right triangle. Thus the Pythagoreans were most likely the first to study the relationship among the sides of a right triangle aside from any practical use in surveying or construction.

11 Rational and Irrational Numbers

Triangles are often used in construction. As you will learn in this chapter, the lengths of the sides of right triangles can be found by using the Pythagorean theorem if the lengths of two of the three sides are known.

498

Rational Numbers

11-1 Properties of Rational Numbers

Objective To learn and apply some properties of real numbers.

A real number that can be written as the quotient of two integers is called a **rational number.** Thus, the following numbers are rational numbers:

$$0 = \frac{0}{1} \qquad 5 = \frac{5}{1} \qquad 7\frac{2}{3} = \frac{23}{3} \qquad 0.48 = \frac{48}{100} \qquad -\frac{5}{9} = \frac{-5}{9}$$

Using the properties of fractions, a rational number can be expressed as a quotient of integers in an unlimited number of ways:

$$2 = \frac{4}{2} = \frac{8}{4} = \frac{-12}{-6} = \cdots \qquad -3\frac{1}{3} = \frac{-10}{3} = \frac{20}{-6} = \cdots \qquad 36\% = \frac{36}{100} = \frac{18}{50} = \cdots$$

To determine which of two rational numbers is greater, you can write the numbers with the same positive denominator and compare their numerators.

Example 1 Compare $\frac{11}{3}$ and $\frac{17}{5}$.

Solution The LCD is 15.

$$\frac{11}{3} = \frac{55}{15} \qquad \frac{17}{5} = \frac{51}{15}$$

Because $55 > 51$, $\frac{55}{15} > \frac{51}{15}$.

Thus, $\frac{11}{3} > \frac{17}{5}$. ***Answer***

The procedure used in Example 1 may be generalized as follows:

For all integers a and b and all positive integers c and d:

$$\frac{a}{c} > \frac{b}{d} \quad \text{if and only if} \quad ad > bc.$$

Similarly, $\frac{a}{c} < \frac{b}{d}$ if and only if $ad < bc$.

(See Exercise 36 on page 503 for a proof of this last statement.)

Teaching References

Lesson Commentary, pp. T120–T126

Assignment Guide, pp. T65–T67

Supplementary Materials
- Practice Masters 66–72
- Tests 38–41
- Resource Book
  - Practice Exercises, pp. 119–123
  - Tests, pp. 54–57
  - Enrichment Activity, p. 159
- Algebra Action

Extra Practice
- Skills, pp. 628–631
- Problems, pp. 647–648

Alternate Test, p. T20

Problem Solving Strategies

Generalizing from Specific
In Sections 11-1 through 11-3 numerical examples suggest the general rules governing operations with rational numbers and radicals.

Deduction
In Sections 11-4 and 11-6 students see how deduction is used to prove that $\sqrt{2}$ is irrational and to derive a formula for distance in the coordinate plane.

Teaching Suggestions
p. T121

Chalkboard Examples

Replace the _?_ with $<$, $=$, or $>$ to make a true statement.

1. $\frac{7}{10}$ _?_ $\frac{11}{15}$
   The LCD is 30.
   $\frac{7}{10} = \frac{21}{30}, \frac{11}{15} = \frac{22}{30}$
   $\frac{21}{30} < \frac{22}{30}$
   $\therefore \frac{7}{10} < \frac{11}{15}$
2. $\frac{116}{25}$ _?_ $\frac{128}{32}$
   Compare the products of the means and extremes.
   $116 \times 32 = 3712$
   $128 \times 25 = 3200$
   $116 \times 32 > 128 \times 25$
   $\frac{116}{25} > \frac{128}{32}$
3. $-\frac{4}{5}$ _?_ $-\frac{23}{33}$
   Write with positive denominators:
   $\frac{-4}{5}$ _?_ $\frac{-23}{33}$
   $-4 \times 33 = -132$
   $5 \times (-23) = -115$
   $\therefore -\frac{4}{5} < -\frac{23}{33}$
4. Arrange in order from least to greatest:
   $\frac{3}{4}, \frac{5}{8}, \frac{7}{10}$
   The LCD is 40.
   $\frac{30}{40}, \frac{25}{40}, \frac{28}{40}$
   $\therefore$ The solution is $\frac{5}{8}, \frac{7}{10}, \frac{3}{4}$.

Thus, $\frac{4}{9} > \frac{3}{8}$ because $(4)(8) > (3)(9)$;

$-\frac{5}{6} > -\frac{7}{8}$ because $(-5)(8) > (-7)(6)$.

Example 2 Compare $-\frac{13}{7}$ and $-\frac{9}{5}$.

Solution Write $-\frac{13}{7}$ as $\frac{-13}{7}$ and $-\frac{9}{5}$ as $\frac{-9}{5}$. Then use the technique shown above to compare $\frac{-13}{7}$ and $\frac{-9}{5}$.

$(-13)(5) < (-9)(7)$ because $-65 < -63$.

Thus, $-\frac{13}{7} < -\frac{9}{5}$. ***Answer***

Rational numbers are different from integers in several ways. For example, given any integer, there is a next larger integer: -5 follows -6, 1 follows 0, 15 follows 14, and so on. There is, however, no "next larger" rational number after a given rational number. This property of rational numbers is called the *density* property.

The Density Property for Rational Numbers

Between every pair of different rational numbers there is another rational number.

If a and b are rational numbers, and $a < b$, then: The number halfway from a to b is $a + \frac{1}{2}(b - a)$; the number one third of the way from a to b is $a + \frac{1}{3}(b - a)$; and so on.

Thus, the density property implies that it is possible to find an infinite number of rational numbers between two given rational numbers.

Example 3 Find a rational number between $\frac{9}{4}$ and $\frac{17}{6}$.

Solution Choose, for example, the number halfway between $\frac{9}{4}$ and $\frac{17}{6}$. This number can be expressed as

$$\frac{9}{4} + \frac{1}{2}\left(\frac{17}{6} - \frac{9}{4}\right).$$

$$\frac{17}{6} - \frac{9}{4} = \frac{34}{12} - \frac{27}{12} = \frac{7}{12}$$

$$\frac{9}{4} + \frac{1}{2}\left(\frac{7}{12}\right) = \frac{9}{4} + \frac{7}{24} = \frac{54}{24} + \frac{7}{24} = \frac{61}{24}$$

Check: Is $\frac{9}{4} < \frac{61}{24} < \frac{17}{6}$?

$$9(24) \stackrel{?}{<} (61)(4) \qquad (61)(6) \stackrel{?}{<} (17)(24)$$
$$216 < 244 \checkmark \qquad 366 < 408 \checkmark$$

$\therefore$ a rational number between $\frac{9}{4}$ and $\frac{17}{6}$ is $\frac{61}{24}$. ***Answer***

In Example 3, the number chosen to be found was halfway between the two given numbers. The number halfway between two numbers is also the average of the two numbers since

$$a + \frac{1}{2}(b - a) = \frac{2a}{2} + \frac{b - a}{2} = \frac{a + b}{2}.$$

Oral Exercises

Express each number as a ratio of integers.

Example 4.35 ***Solution*** $\frac{435}{100}$

Answers to Exs. **1–8** may vary.

1. 3.5 $\frac{35}{10}$ **2.** -2.8 $\frac{-28}{10}$ **3.** $-3\frac{1}{4}$ $\frac{-13}{4}$ **4.** 52% $\frac{52}{100}$

5. -9 $\frac{-9}{1}$ **6.** 25 $\frac{25}{1}$ **7.** 0 $\frac{0}{a}$, $a \neq 0$ **8.** $\frac{5}{9} + \left(-\frac{7}{9}\right)$ $\frac{-2}{9}$

Which rational number in each pair is greater?

9. $\frac{9}{13}, \frac{11}{13}$ $\frac{11}{13}$ **10.** $-\frac{3}{8}, -\frac{5}{8}$ $-\frac{3}{8}$ **11.** $-3, \frac{1}{2}$ $\frac{1}{2}$

12. $-3, -\frac{1}{2}$ $-\frac{1}{2}$ **13.** $\frac{7}{12}, \frac{2}{3}$ $\frac{2}{3}$ **14.** $-\frac{10}{3}, -\frac{14}{4}$ $-\frac{10}{3}$

Written Exercises

Replace the _?_ with <, =, or > to make a true statement.

A **1.** $\frac{1}{6}$ _?_ $\frac{6}{42}$ > **2.** $\frac{2}{3}$ _?_ $\frac{11}{15}$ < **3.** $\frac{28}{43}$ _?_ $\frac{31}{37}$ <

4. $-\frac{12}{19}$ _?_ $-\frac{17}{24}$ > **5.** $\frac{35}{72}$ _?_ $\frac{53}{107}$ < **6.** $\frac{138}{55}$ _?_ $\frac{243}{78}$ <

7. $26\frac{4}{7}$ _?_ $\frac{194}{8}$ > **8.** $-\frac{214}{14}$ _?_ $-15\frac{2}{3}$ > **9.** $\frac{392}{9}$ _?_ $44\frac{5}{8}$ <

5. Find the number halfway between $\frac{7}{2}$ and $\frac{13}{3}$.

$$a + \frac{1}{2}(b - a)$$
$$= \frac{7}{2} + \frac{1}{2}\left(\frac{13}{3} - \frac{7}{2}\right)$$
$$= \frac{7}{2} + \frac{1}{2}\left(\frac{5}{6}\right)$$
$$= \frac{42}{12} + \frac{5}{12} = \frac{47}{12}$$

6. Find the number one third of the way from $\frac{7}{2}$ to $\frac{13}{3}$.

$$a + \frac{1}{3}(b - a)$$
$$= \frac{7}{2} + \frac{1}{3}\left(\frac{13}{3} - \frac{7}{2}\right)$$
$$= \frac{7}{2} + \frac{1}{3}\left(\frac{5}{6}\right)$$
$$= \frac{63}{18} + \frac{5}{18}$$
$$= \frac{68}{18} = \frac{34}{9}$$

Suggested Assignments

Minimum
501/1–29 odd

Average
501/1–33 odd

Maximum
501/1–35 odd, 36

Additional A Exercises

Replace the ? with <, =, or > to make a true statement.

1. $\frac{11}{17} \;?\; \frac{21}{36}$ >

2. $\frac{198}{50} \;?\; \frac{211}{52}$ <

Arrange each group of numbers in order from least to greatest.

3. $-6.8, \frac{-37}{5}, \frac{-19}{3}$ $\frac{-37}{5}, -6.8, \frac{-19}{3}$

4. $\frac{12}{47}, \frac{4}{15}, \frac{1}{4}, \frac{9}{35}$ $\frac{1}{4}, \frac{12}{47}, \frac{9}{35}, \frac{4}{15}$

Find the number halfway between the given numbers.

5. $\frac{7}{12}, \frac{5}{6}$ $\frac{17}{24}$

6. $\frac{-26}{5}, \frac{-2}{15}$ $\frac{-8}{3}$

Mixed Review Exercises

Simplify.

1. $\frac{3^3 - 2 \times 3}{2^4 - 1}$ $\frac{7}{5}$

2. $8 \cdot 8^m$ 8^{m+1}

3. Multiply: $-6bc(-3bc + c^2 + b^2)$ $18b^2c^2 - 6bc^3 - 6b^3c$

4. Graph $x < y + 4$ in a coordinate plane.

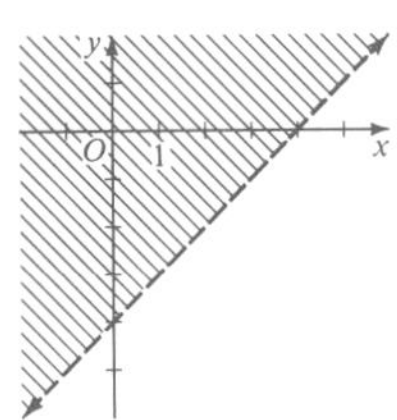

Arrange each group of numbers in order from least to greatest.

10. $\frac{2}{3}, \frac{3}{4}, \frac{4}{7}$ $\frac{4}{7}, \frac{2}{3}, \frac{3}{4}$

11. $\frac{3}{8}, -\frac{4}{9}, \frac{5}{6}$ $-\frac{4}{9}, \frac{3}{8}, \frac{5}{6}$

12. $-3.8, -\frac{35}{8}, -3$ $-\frac{35}{8}, -3.8, -3$

13. $5.6, \frac{107}{18}, \frac{303}{56}$ $\frac{303}{56}, 5.6, \frac{107}{18}$

14. $\frac{9}{35}, \frac{7}{15}, \frac{1}{3}, \frac{8}{37}$ $\frac{8}{37}, \frac{9}{35}, \frac{1}{3}, \frac{7}{15}$

15. $-\frac{3}{7}, -\frac{3}{5}, -\frac{6}{7}, -\frac{5}{9}$ $-\frac{6}{7}, -\frac{3}{5}, -\frac{5}{9}, -\frac{3}{7}$

Find the number halfway between the given numbers.

16. $\frac{3}{8}, \frac{4}{9}$ $\frac{59}{144}$

17. $\frac{7}{11}, \frac{3}{4}$ $\frac{61}{88}$

18. $-\frac{11}{19}, -\frac{13}{25}$ $-\frac{261}{475}$

19. $-\frac{37}{160}, -\frac{9}{42}$ $-\frac{1497}{6720}$

20. $-4\frac{3}{5}, -5\frac{5}{6}$ $-\frac{313}{60}$

21. $-4\frac{3}{7}, 8\frac{1}{3}$ $\frac{41}{21}$

If $x \in \{0, 1, 2, 3\}$, state whether each fraction increases or decreases in value as x takes on its values in increasing order.

22. $\frac{x}{6}$ increases

23. $\frac{x+2}{5}$ increases

24. $\frac{9}{x+3}$ decreases

25. $\frac{8-3x}{5}$ decreases

26. $\frac{12}{8+3x}$ decreases

B

27. Find the number one third of the way from $\frac{4}{7}$ to $1\frac{3}{4}$. $\frac{27}{28}$

28. Find the number one fourth of the way from $-\frac{1}{9}$ to $-\frac{7}{8}$. $-\frac{87}{288}$

29. Find the number one fifth of the way from $-\frac{2}{3}$ to $\frac{3}{5}$. $-\frac{31}{75}$

30. Find the number two thirds of the way from $\frac{1}{4}$ to $\frac{5}{3}$. $\frac{43}{36}$

31. Find a rational number between $\frac{1}{3}$ and $\frac{3}{4}$. example: $\frac{13}{24}$

32. Find a rational number between $-\frac{1}{5}$ and $-\frac{1}{9}$. example: $-\frac{1}{6}$

33. Write an expression for the number halfway between $\frac{4a}{7}$ and $-\frac{a}{9}$. $\frac{29a}{126}$

34. Write an expression for the number one sixth of the way from $-\frac{9b}{7}$ to $-\frac{4b}{5}$. $-\frac{253b}{210}$

35. a. Sue and Diane agree to share evenly the expenses of a vacation trip to the seashore. For convenience, instead of each paying half of each individual expense, they agree to take turns paying and then settle accounts at the end of the trip. During the trip, Sue paid \$60 and Diane paid \$80. Sue said to Diane, "I owe you half the difference, which is \$10." Was Sue right? yes

b. In general, suppose Sue paid a dollars and Diane paid b dollars, where $b > a$. Show that if Sue gives Diane $\frac{1}{2}(b - a)$ dollars, then each will have paid exactly half the total expense. The money Sue paid plus what she owes Diane is $a + \frac{1}{2}(b - a) = a + \frac{1}{2}b - \frac{1}{2}a = \frac{1}{2}a + \frac{1}{2}b = \frac{1}{2}(a + b)$, or half the total.

C **36.** Give the reason for each statement in the proof of the following theorem: For all integers a and b and all positive integers c and d, $\frac{a}{c} < \frac{b}{d}$ if and only if $ad < bc$.

Proof: If $\frac{a}{c} < \frac{b}{d}$, then $ad < bc$.

1. $\frac{a}{c} < \frac{b}{d}$	1. Given
2. $\frac{ad}{cd} < \frac{bc}{cd}$	2. ___?___ Multiplication rule for fractions
3. $ad < bc$	3. ___?___ Multiplication axiom of order

$\therefore$ if $\frac{a}{c} < \frac{b}{d}$, then $ad < bc$.

Proof: If $ad < bc$, then $\frac{a}{c} < \frac{b}{d}$.

1. $ad < bc$	1. Given
2. $\frac{ad}{cd} < \frac{bc}{cd}$ (since $cd > 0$)	2. ___?___ Multiplication axiom of order
3. $\frac{a}{c} < \frac{b}{d}$	3. ___?___ Cancellation rule for fractions

$\therefore$ if $ad < bc$, then $\frac{a}{c} < \frac{b}{d}$.

$\therefore \frac{a}{c} < \frac{b}{d}$ if and only if $ad < bc$.

State conditions for w and z that make the following true.

37. $\frac{x}{w} > \frac{x}{z}$; $x > 0$ $w < z$; $wz > 0$

38. $\frac{x}{w} < \frac{x}{z}$; $x < 0$ $w < z$; $wz > 0$

39. $\frac{x}{w - z} < \frac{x}{z - w}$; $x > 0$ $w < z$

40. $\frac{x}{w - z} > \frac{x}{z - w}$; $x < 0$ $w < z$

Challenge

A parallelogram is a figure in geometry. Geometry is a branch of mathematics. Therefore, a parallelogram is a figure in mathematics.

No canaries are in my house. My house is in the Canary Islands. Therefore, no canaries are in the Canary Islands.

Is this reasoning logical? The reasoning in the first paragraph is logical, but the reasoning in the second paragraph is not.

Teaching Suggestions
p. T121

Suggested Extensions
p. T121

Chalkboard Examples

Round to the nearest tenth.

1. 5.12 5.1
2. 26.763 26.8
3. $2.\overline{4}$ 2.4

Round to the nearest thousandth.

4. 6.42184 6.422
5. $-2.\overline{1}$ -2.111
6. $5.\overline{6}$ 5.667

Express each rational number as a terminating or repeating decimal.

7. $\frac{11}{40}$ 0.275
8. $\frac{16}{37}$ $0.\overline{432}$

Express each rational number as a fraction in simplest form.

9. 0.265 $\frac{265}{1000} = \frac{53}{200}$
10. $0.\overline{54}$

$$\begin{aligned} 100N &= 54.\overline{54} \\ N &= 0.\overline{54} \\ \hline 99N &= 54 \end{aligned}$$

$$N = \frac{54}{99} = \frac{6}{11}$$

$$\therefore 0.\overline{54} = \frac{6}{11}$$

11. $2.3\overline{1}$

$$\begin{aligned} 10N &= 23.1\overline{1} \\ N &= 2.3\overline{1} \\ \hline 9N &= 20.8 \end{aligned}$$

$$N = \frac{20.8}{9} = \frac{208}{90} = \frac{104}{45}$$

$$\therefore 2.3\overline{1} = \frac{104}{45}$$

11-2 Decimal Forms of Rational Numbers

Objective To express rational numbers as decimals or fractions.

To write a common fraction as a decimal, you divide the numerator by the denominator. If the remainder is zero, the decimal is called a **terminating, ending,** or **finite decimal.** The division at the right shows that $\frac{7}{16}$ can be expressed as the terminating decimal 0.4375.

$$\begin{array}{r} 0.4375 \\ 16\overline{)7.0000} \\ \underline{6\,4} \\ 60 \\ \underline{48} \\ 120 \\ \underline{112} \\ 80 \\ \underline{80} \\ 0 \end{array}$$

$$\frac{7}{16} = 7 \div 16 = 0.4375$$

If the remainder is not zero, you continue dividing until the remainders start to repeat.

$$\frac{16}{30} \longrightarrow \begin{array}{r} 0.533 \\ 30\overline{)16.000} \\ \underline{15\,0} \\ 1\,00 \\ \underline{90} \\ 100 \\ \underline{90} \\ 10 \end{array} \qquad \frac{5}{11} \longrightarrow \begin{array}{r} 0.4545 \\ 11\overline{)5.0000} \\ \underline{4\,4} \\ 60 \\ \underline{55} \\ 50 \\ \underline{44} \\ 60 \\ \underline{55} \\ 5 \end{array} \qquad \frac{4}{7} \longrightarrow \begin{array}{r} 0.5714285 \\ 7\overline{)4.0000000} \\ \underline{3\,5} \\ 50 \\ \underline{49} \\ 10 \\ \underline{7} \\ 30 \\ \underline{28} \\ 20 \\ \underline{14} \\ 60 \\ \underline{56} \\ 40 \\ \underline{35} \\ 5 \end{array}$$

The decimal quotients shown above are **nonterminating, unending,** or **infinite.** They are also called **repeating** or **periodic** because the same digit or block of digits repeats unendingly.

$$\frac{16}{30} = 0.533\ldots \qquad \frac{5}{11} = 0.4545\ldots \qquad \frac{4}{7} = 0.5714285\ldots$$

The dots indicate that the decimals continue unendingly. A bar is used to indicate the block of digits that repeat, as shown below.

$$\frac{16}{30} = 0.5\overline{3} \qquad \frac{5}{11} = 0.\overline{45} \qquad \frac{4}{7} = 0.\overline{571428}$$

When you divide a positive integer n by a positive integer d, the remainder r at each step must be zero or a positive integer less than d. For example, if the divisor is 8, the remainders will be 0, 1, 2, 3, 4, 5, 6, or 7, and the division will terminate or begin repeating within 7 steps after only zeros remain to be brought down. In general:

For every integer n and every positive integer d, the decimal numeral of the rational number $\frac{n}{d}$ either terminates or eventually repeats in a block of fewer than d digits.

To express a terminating decimal as a common fraction, express the decimal as a common fraction with a power of ten as the denominator. This fraction is often expressed in simplest form.

$$0.34 = \frac{34}{100} = \frac{17}{50} \qquad 0.425 = \frac{425}{1000} = \frac{17}{40}$$

The following examples show how to express a repeating decimal as a common fraction.

Example 1 Express $0.5\overline{81}$ as a common fraction.

Solution Let $N =$ the number. $\quad N = 0.5\overline{81}$

Multiply N by 10^n, where n is the number of digits in the block of repeating digits.

Since $0.5\overline{81}$ has 2 digits in the repeating block, $n = 2$. Thus, you multiply by 10^2, or 100. $\quad 100N = 100(0.5\overline{81})$

Note that since $0.5\overline{81}$ means $0.5818181\ldots$, $0.5\overline{81}$ can be written as $0.581\overline{81}$. Thus:

$$100(0.5\overline{81}) = 100(0.581\overline{81}) = 58.1\overline{81}$$

Subtract N from $100N$ and solve for N.

$$\begin{aligned} 100N &= 58.1\overline{81} \\ N &= 0.5\overline{81} \\ \hline 99N &= 57.600 \end{aligned}$$

$$N = \frac{57.6}{99} = \frac{576}{990} = \frac{64}{110} = \frac{32}{55}$$

$\therefore 0.5\overline{81} = \frac{32}{55}$ ***Answer***

Common Errors

Some students make errors in rounding because they consider more digits than they should. For example, students may round 1.349 to the nearest tenth incorrectly because they first round the 4 in hundredths' place to a 5 and then round the 3 in tenths' place to 4. Point out that they should focus on the place to which they are rounding and look only at the digit immediately to the right.

Students may make errors in changing repeating decimals to fractions in exercises such as Written Exercise 37. Remind students, for example, that $0.\overline{5} \neq 0.5$.

Supplementary Materials

Practice Master 66
Resource Book, p. 119

Suggested Assignments

Minimum
507/2–40 even
S 502/28, 30

Average
507/2–40 even
S 502/34, 35

Maximum
507/2–40 even, 41, 42

Additional A Exercises

Express each rational number as a terminating or repeating decimal.

1. $\frac{5}{6}$ $0.8\overline{3}$

2. $-\frac{7}{8}$ -0.875

3. $2\frac{2}{15}$ $2.1\overline{3}$

Express each rational number as a fraction in simplest form.

4. 0.725 $\frac{29}{40}$

5. $-0.41\overline{5}$ $-\frac{187}{450}$

6. $0.\overline{09}$ $\frac{1}{11}$

Example 2 Express $0.\overline{285}$ as a common fraction.

Solution Let $N =$ the number.

$$1000N = 285.\overline{285}$$

Subtract

$$N = 0.\overline{285}$$

$$999N = 285.000$$

$$N = \frac{285}{999} = \frac{95}{333}$$

$$\therefore\ 0.\overline{285} = \frac{95}{333}$$ ***Answer***

All terminating decimals and all repeating decimals represent rational numbers that can be written in the form $\frac{n}{d}$ where n is an integer and d is a positive integer.

It is often convenient to use an approximation of a lengthy decimal. For example, you may approximate $\frac{12}{17}$ as

$$0.70588 \quad \text{or} \quad 0.706 \quad \text{or} \quad 0.71.$$

To round a decimal:
1. If the first digit dropped is 5 or more, add 1 to the last digit retained.
2. If the first digit dropped is less than 5, leave the retained digits unchanged.

The following examples show approximations of nonterminating decimals. The symbol $\approx$ means "is approximately equal to."

$$\frac{11}{12} = 0.91\overline{6} \approx 0.917 \text{ to the nearest thousandth}$$
$$\approx 0.92 \text{ to the nearest hundredth}$$

$$\frac{5}{6} = 0.8\overline{3} \approx 0.83 \text{ to the nearest hundredth}$$
$$\approx 0.8 \text{ to the nearest tenth}$$

$$\frac{95}{37} = 2.\overline{567} \approx 2.6 \text{ to the nearest tenth}$$
$$\approx 3 \text{ to the nearest unit}$$

$$\frac{176}{333} = 0.\overline{528} \approx 0.5 \text{ to the nearest tenth}$$
$$\approx 1 \text{ to the nearest unit}$$

$x = 2.1\overline{3}$

$10x = 21.\overline{3}$

$100x = 213.\overline{3}$

$$\begin{array}{r} 213 \\ -21 \\ \hline 192 \end{array}$$

$90x = 192$

$\frac{192}{90} = 2\frac{12}{90} = \frac{6}{45} = \frac{2}{15}$

Oral Exercises

Round each number to the nearest tenth.

1. 3.752 3.8 **2.** −0.837 −0.8 **3.** $3.\overline{5}$ 3.6 **4.** $2.3\overline{73}$ 2.4 **5.** $-0.\overline{78}$ −0.8

6–10. Round the numbers in Exercises 1–5 to the nearest hundredth.
6. 3.75 7. −0.84 8. 3.56 9. 2.37 10. −0.79

Written Exercises

Express each rational number as a terminating or repeating decimal.

A **1.** $\frac{3}{8}$ 0.375 **2.** $\frac{9}{2}$ 4.5 **3.** $\frac{5}{9}$ $0.\overline{5}$ **4.** $-\frac{2}{5}$ −0.4

5. $\frac{31}{25}$ 1.24 **6.** $\frac{11}{12}$ $0.91\overline{6}$ **7.** $\frac{11}{3}$ $3.\overline{6}$ **8.** $\frac{3}{7}$ $0.\overline{428571}$

9. $-\frac{5}{18}$ $-0.2\overline{7}$ **10.** $\frac{15}{32}$ 0.46875 **11.** $-2\frac{7}{20}$ −2.35 **12.** $3\frac{5}{11}$ $3.\overline{45}$

13. $\frac{82}{99}$ $0.\overline{82}$ **14.** $-5\frac{3}{4}$ −5.75 **15.** $-\frac{16}{33}$ $-0.\overline{48}$ **16.** $\frac{22}{37}$ $0.\overline{594}$

Express each rational number as a fraction in simplest form.

17. 0.66 $\frac{33}{50}$ **18.** 0.3 $\frac{3}{10}$ **19.** $0.\overline{5}$ $\frac{5}{9}$ **20.** $1.\overline{25}$ $\frac{124}{99}$

21. 0.325 $\frac{13}{40}$ **22.** $-0.31\overline{6}$ $-\frac{19}{60}$ **23.** 4.8 $\frac{24}{5}$ **24.** $2.3\overline{9}$ $\frac{12}{5}$

25. $0.\overline{07}$ $\frac{7}{99}$ **26.** $-1.\overline{18}$ $-\frac{13}{11}$ **27.** $-2.4\overline{6}$ $-\frac{37}{15}$ **28.** $0.\overline{714285}$ $\frac{5}{7}$

Find the difference of the given numbers. Then find the number halfway between them.

B **29.** $\frac{3}{4}$ and 0.756 0.006; 0.753 **30.** $\frac{1}{8}$ and 0.121 0.004; 0.123 **31.** 0.77 and $0.7\overline{7}$ $0.00\overline{7}$; $0.773\overline{8}$

32. 0.59 and $0.\overline{59}$ $0.00\overline{59}$; $0.59\overline{297}$ **33.** $\frac{8}{55}$ and 0.1452 $0.000\overline{2}$; $0.1\overline{453}$ **34.** 0.83 and $\frac{5}{6}$ $0.00\overline{3}$; $0.831\overline{6}$

Express both numbers as fractions and find their product.

35. $\frac{3}{4}$ and 0.5 **36.** 0.875 and $\frac{4}{7}$ **37.** $0.\overline{5}$ and $\frac{3}{5}$

38. $-3.\overline{3}$ and $0.\overline{6}$ **39.** $0.\overline{407}$ and $0.2\overline{7}$ **40.** $0.5\overline{6}$ and $1.4\overline{27}$

C **41. a.** Express $\frac{1}{7}$ and $\frac{5}{7}$ as repeating decimals. $\frac{1}{7} = 0.\overline{142857}$; $\frac{5}{7} = 0.\overline{714285}$

b. In the decimals that you found in part (a), what is the relationship between the blocks of digits that repeat?

c. Express $\frac{2}{7}$, $\frac{3}{7}$, and $\frac{6}{7}$ as decimals. $\frac{2}{7} = 0.\overline{285714}$; $\frac{3}{7} = 0.\overline{428571}$; $\frac{6}{7} = 0.\overline{857142}$

Additional Answers Written Exercises

35. $\frac{3}{4}, \frac{1}{2}; \frac{3}{8}$

36. $\frac{7}{8}, \frac{4}{7}; \frac{1}{2}$

37. $\frac{5}{9}, \frac{3}{5}; \frac{1}{3}$

38. $-\frac{10}{3}, \frac{2}{3}; -\frac{20}{9}$

39. $\frac{11}{27}, \frac{5}{18}; \frac{55}{486}$

40. $\frac{17}{30}, \frac{157}{110}; \frac{2669}{3300}$

41. b. Each repeating block contains the same digits in the same order, but each one starts with a different digit.

Mixed Review Exercises

1. Solve $D = \frac{1}{2}st^2$ for s. $s = \frac{2D}{t^2}$

2. The Mulligans' rectangular pool is surrounded by a walk 5 ft wide and enclosed by a fence. The pool is 30 ft longer than it is wide and the fenced area is 1375 ft². Find the width of the pool. 15 ft

3. Subtract: $\begin{array}{r} x^2 + 2x - 15 \\ x^2 - x - 16 \\ \hline 3x + 1 \end{array}$

4. Arrange $\frac{11}{17}$, $\frac{22}{32}$, and $\frac{5}{9}$ from least to greatest. $\frac{5}{9}, \frac{11}{17}, \frac{22}{32}$

42. **a.** Express $\frac{1}{9}$, $\frac{5}{9}$, and $\frac{7}{9}$ as repeating decimals. $\frac{1}{9} = 0.\overline{1}$; $\frac{5}{9} = 0.\overline{5}$; $\frac{7}{9} = 0.\overline{7}$

b. Express $\frac{1}{18}$, $\frac{5}{18}$, and $\frac{7}{18}$ as repeating decimals. $\frac{1}{18} = 0.0\overline{5}$; $\frac{5}{18} = 0.2\overline{7}$; $\frac{7}{18} = 0.3\overline{8}$

c. What is the relationship between the decimals in part (a) and part (b)? Each decimal in **(b)** is half the corresponding decimal in **(a)**.

43. Since $\frac{1}{99} = 0.\overline{01}$, $\frac{n}{99} = n(0.\overline{01})$ for $n < 100$.

a. Confirm the fact above by expressing $\frac{5}{99}$, $\frac{25}{99}$, and $\frac{74}{99}$ as decimals. $\frac{5}{99} = 0.\overline{05}$; $\frac{25}{99} = 0.\overline{25}$; $\frac{74}{99} = 0.\overline{74}$

b. Express 1 as $\frac{99}{99}$ to show that $0.\overline{9} = 1$.
$1 = \frac{99}{99} = 99(0.\overline{01}) = 0.\overline{99} = 0.\overline{9}$

Computer Key-In

A computer will express a rational number, such as $\frac{4}{7}$, as a decimal by having it PRINT 4/7. The result will display the fixed number of decimal places for which the computer is programmed.

However, a program can be written that will compute one digit at a time just as you do when you do long division. Then the computer can find as many digits as you wish. The computation for $\frac{4}{7}$ is given below.

As written:

```
   0.571428
7)4.000000
  3 5
    50
    49
     10
      7
      30
      28
       20
       14
        60
        56
         4
```

As calculated:

$4 \times 10 = 40$
$40 \div 7 = 5$, Remainder 5
$5 \times 10 = 50$
$50 \div 7 = 7$, Remainder 1
$1 \times 10 = 10$
$10 \div 7 = 1$, Remainder 3
$3 \times 10 = 30$
$30 \div 7 = 4$, Remainder 2
$2 \times 10 = 20$
$20 \div 7 = 2$, Remainder 6
$6 \times 10 = 60$
$60 \div 7 = 8$, Remainder 4

(Notice that when you "bring down a zero," you multiply the remainder by 10.)

The last remainder above, 4, is the same as the numerator. If the division is continued, the digits in the quotient will repeat in blocks. The calculation shown at the right above is the basis for the following computer program. See lines 130–170.

Additional Answers
Computer Key-In

1. $\frac{1}{7} = 0.\overline{142857}$
$\frac{2}{7} = 0.\overline{285714}$
$\frac{3}{7} = 0.\overline{428571}$
$\frac{4}{7} = 0.\overline{571428}$
$\frac{5}{7} = 0.\overline{714285}$
$\frac{6}{7} = 0.\overline{857142}$

2. $\frac{1}{2} = 0.5$
$\frac{1}{20} = 0.05$
$\frac{1}{3} = 0.\overline{3}$
$\frac{1}{30} = 0.0\overline{3}$
$\frac{1}{4} = 0.25$
$\frac{1}{40} = 0.025$

3. $\frac{1}{14} = 0.0\overline{714285}$
$\frac{3}{14} = 0.2\overline{142857}$
$\frac{5}{14} = 0.3\overline{571428}$
$\frac{9}{14} = 0.6\overline{428571}$
$\frac{11}{14} = 0.7\overline{857142}$
$\frac{13}{14} = 0.9\overline{285714}$

4. 1 and 2, respectively

```
10  PRINT "TO FIND A DECIMAL FOR N/D:"
20  PRINT "INPUT N, D (0 < N < D)";
30  INPUT N,D
40  PRINT N;" /";D;" = 0 .";
50  REM---THE NUMERATOR IS
60  REM---THE FIRST "REMAINDER"
70  REM---IN THE LOOP BELOW.
80  LET R=N
90  REM---THIS LOOP COMPUTES AND
100  REM---PRINTS ONE DIGIT, Q1,
110  REM---AT A TIME.
120  FOR I=1 TO D+3
130  LET A=R*10
140  LET Q=A/D
150  LET Q1=INT(Q)
160  PRINT Q1;
170  LET R=A-Q1*D
180  IF R=0 THEN 220
190  NEXT I
200  PRINT " ..."
210  GOTO 230
220  PRINT " TERMINATES"
230  END
```

Exercises

RUN the program given above to change each fraction to a decimal. If the decimal repeats, give the block of digits that repeats. Compare the results in each list.

1. $\frac{1}{7}, \frac{2}{7}, \frac{3}{7}, \frac{4}{7}, \frac{5}{7}, \frac{6}{7}$
2. $\frac{1}{2}, \frac{1}{20}, \frac{1}{3}, \frac{1}{30}, \frac{1}{4}, \frac{1}{40}$
3. $\frac{1}{14}, \frac{3}{14}, \frac{5}{14}, \frac{9}{14}, \frac{11}{14}, \frac{13}{14}$
4. What are the smallest whole numbers that can be used for N and D according to line 20 of the program?
5. Change line 20 to: `20 LET N = 1`

   Change line 30 to: `30 FOR D = 2 TO 20`

   Change the end of the program to complete the loop. RUN the revised program and compare the results.

Note: The program given above can be used to do Exercises 1–16 on page 507.

5. 230 NEXT D
240 END

$\frac{1}{2} = 0.5$

$\frac{1}{3} = 0.\overline{3}$

$\frac{1}{4} = 0.25$

$\frac{1}{5} = 0.2$

$\frac{1}{6} = 0.1\overline{6}$

$\frac{1}{7} = 0.\overline{142857}$

$\frac{1}{8} = 0.125$

$\frac{1}{9} = 0.\overline{1}$

$\frac{1}{10} = 0.1$

$\frac{1}{11} = 0.\overline{09}$

$\frac{1}{12} = 0.08\overline{3}$

$\frac{1}{13} = 0.\overline{076923}$

$\frac{1}{14} = 0.0\overline{714285}$

$\frac{1}{15} = 0.0\overline{6}$

$\frac{1}{16} = 0.0625$

$\frac{1}{17} = 0.\overline{0588235294117647}$

$\frac{1}{18} = 0.0\overline{5}$

$\frac{1}{19} = 0.\overline{052631578947368421}$

$\frac{1}{20} = 0.05$

Teaching Suggestions
p. T122

Suggested Extensions
p. T122

11-3 Rational Square Roots

Objective To find the square roots of numbers that have rational square roots.

You have learned that subtracting a number is the inverse of adding that number, and that dividing by a nonzero number is the inverse of multiplying by that number. The inverse of squaring a number is finding a *square root*. If $a^2 = b$, then a is called a **square root** of b. Because $8^2 = 64$ and $(-8)^2 = 64$, both 8 and -8 are square roots of 64.

The symbol $\sqrt{\ }$ is used to denote the **principal,** or nonnegative, square root of a positive number. Thus,

$$\sqrt{64} = 8 \quad \text{and} \quad -\sqrt{64} = -8.$$

The symbol $\sqrt{\ }$ is called the **radical sign,** and $\sqrt{64}$ is an example of a **radical.** An expression written beneath the radical sign, such as 64, is called the **radicand.** Often it is convenient to use *plus-or-minus* notation with radicals. For example:

$\pm\sqrt{64}$ means the positive or negative square root of 64.

In general, we have the following definition:

For all positive real numbers a, the symbol $\sqrt{a}$ denotes the principal square root of a.

It follows from the definition of square root that $(\sqrt{a})^2 = a$.

Zero has only one square root, namely zero itself; that is, $\sqrt{0} = 0$.

Because the square of every real number is either positive or zero, *negative numbers do not have square roots in the set of real numbers.*

The values of certain square roots can be seen at a glance; for example, $\sqrt{49} = 7$. You may be able to find other square roots by expressing them as a product of square roots that are familiar to you.

Notice that

$$\sqrt{9 \cdot 16} = \sqrt{144} = 12$$

and

$$\sqrt{9} \cdot \sqrt{16} = 3 \cdot 4 = 12.$$

This relationship suggests the following fact about square roots.

Product Property of Square Roots

For any nonnegative real numbers a and b:

$$\sqrt{ab} = \sqrt{a} \cdot \sqrt{b}$$

Example 1 Find $\sqrt{400}$.

Solution $\sqrt{400} = \sqrt{4} \cdot \sqrt{100} = 2 \cdot 10 = 20$

If you cannot see any squares that divide the radicand, begin by factoring the radicand. (See the material on factoring integers on page 183.)

Example 2 Find $\sqrt{2304}$.

Solution
$$\begin{aligned}\sqrt{2304} &= \sqrt{2^2 \cdot 3^2 \cdot 8^2}\\ &= \sqrt{2^2} \cdot \sqrt{3^2} \cdot \sqrt{8^2}\\ &= 2 \cdot 3 \cdot 8 = 48\end{aligned}$$

The examples $\sqrt{\frac{64}{16}} = \sqrt{4} = 2$ and $\frac{\sqrt{64}}{\sqrt{16}} = \frac{8}{4} = 2$ suggest another property of square roots.

Quotient Property of Square Roots

For any nonnegative real number a and any positive real number b:

$$\sqrt{\frac{a}{b}} = \frac{\sqrt{a}}{\sqrt{b}}$$

Example 3 Find $\sqrt{\frac{121}{1156}}$.

Solution $\sqrt{\frac{121}{1156}} = \frac{\sqrt{121}}{\sqrt{1156}} = \frac{11}{\sqrt{2^2 \cdot 17^2}} = \frac{11}{2 \cdot 17} = \frac{11}{34}$

Oral Exercises

Find the indicated square roots.

1. $\sqrt{9}$ 3
2. $\sqrt{36}$ 6
3. $\sqrt{64}$ 8
4. $\sqrt{121}$ 11
5. $\sqrt{169}$ 13
6. $\sqrt{12^2}$ 12
7. $\sqrt{61^2}$ 61
8. $\sqrt{47^2}$ 47
9. $(\sqrt{5})^2$ 5
10. $(\sqrt{21})^2$ 21
11. $\sqrt{\frac{1}{16}}$ $\frac{1}{4}$
12. $\sqrt{\frac{1}{81}}$ $\frac{1}{9}$
13. $\sqrt{\frac{100}{36}}$ $\frac{5}{3}$
14. $\sqrt{\frac{81}{25}}$ $\frac{9}{5}$
15. $\sqrt{\frac{144}{49}}$ $\frac{12}{7}$
16. $\sqrt{\left(\frac{4}{7}\right)^2}$ $\frac{4}{7}$
17. $\sqrt{\left(\frac{12}{23}\right)^2}$ $\frac{12}{23}$
18. $\left(\sqrt{\frac{5}{19}}\right)^2$ $\frac{5}{19}$
19. $\sqrt{5^2 - 4^2}$ 3
20. $\sqrt{8^2} - \sqrt{5^2}$ 3

Chalkboard Examples

Find the indicated square roots.

1. $\sqrt{49}$ $\sqrt{7^2} = 7$
2. $-\sqrt{900}$ $-\sqrt{2^2 \cdot 3^2 \cdot 5^2} = -(2 \cdot 3 \cdot 5) = -30$
3. $\sqrt{\frac{18}{98}}$ $\sqrt{\frac{9}{49}} = \frac{\sqrt{9}}{\sqrt{49}} = \frac{3}{7}$
4. $-\sqrt{0.36}$ $-\sqrt{\frac{36}{100}} = -\frac{\sqrt{36}}{\sqrt{100}} = -\frac{6}{10} = -\frac{3}{5}$
5. $\pm\sqrt{0.0196}$ $\pm\sqrt{\frac{196}{10{,}000}} = \pm\frac{14}{100} = \pm\frac{7}{50}$
6. Evaluate the expression $(\sqrt{x})^2 - \sqrt{x^2 + y^2}$ if $x = 3$ and $y = 4$. $(\sqrt{3})^2 - \sqrt{3^2 + 4^2} = 3 - \sqrt{9 + 16} = 3 - \sqrt{25} = 3 - 5 = -2$

Common Errors

In simplifying expressions such as those in Oral Exercise 19 and Written Exercises 36–39, students may incorrectly assume that $\sqrt{a^2 - b^2} = \sqrt{a^2} - \sqrt{b^2}$. Point out, for example, that $\sqrt{5^2 - 3^2} = \sqrt{25 - 9} = \sqrt{16} = 4$.

Some students may think, for example, that $\sqrt{0.09} = 0.03$. Remind them that $0.03(0.03) = 0.0009$ rather than 0.09, and encourage students to follow the method shown in the first example on page 512.

Supplementary Material

Test 38

Suggested Assignments

Minimum
512/1–39 odd, 40–43
S 507/19, 21, 27, 29

Average
512/1–49 odd
S 507/41

Maximum
512/1–49 odd
S 508/43
R 513/*Self-Test 1*

Additional A Exercises

Find the indicated square roots.

1. $\sqrt{676}$ 26
2. $\pm\sqrt{400}$ ± 20
3. $-\sqrt{\frac{9}{64}}$ $-\frac{3}{8}$
4. $\sqrt{\frac{1225}{81}}$ $\frac{35}{9}$
5. $\sqrt{0.25}$ 0.5
6. $\sqrt{0.0064}$ 0.08

Mixed Review Exercises

1. Simplify: $(-3x^4)^4$ $81x^{16}$
2. Multiply: $(c - d) \cdot (c^2 + 3cd - d^2 + 1)$ $c^3 + 2c^2d - 4cd^2 + d^3 + c - d$
3. Give the prime factorization of 120. $2^3 \cdot 3 \cdot 5$
4. Express $\frac{2}{45}$ as a decimal. $0.0\overline{4}$

Written Exercises

Find the indicated square roots.

A

1. $\sqrt{25}$ 5 **2.** $\sqrt{81}$ 9 **3.** $\sqrt{100}$ 10 **4.** $\sqrt{225}$ 15 **5.** $-\sqrt{441}$ -21

6. $\sqrt{324}$ 18 **7.** $-\sqrt{196}$ -14 **8.** $\sqrt{625}$ 25 **9.** $\pm\sqrt{289}$ ± 17 **10.** $\sqrt{576}$ 24

11. $\sqrt{1600}$ 40 **12.** $\sqrt{2025}$ 45 **13.** $\sqrt{1764}$ 42 **14.** $\sqrt{3136}$ 56 **15.** $\sqrt{8100}$ 90

16. $\sqrt{\frac{49}{900}}$ $\frac{7}{30}$ **17.** $\pm\sqrt{\frac{400}{81}}$ $\pm\frac{20}{9}$ **18.** $-\sqrt{\frac{225}{36}}$ $-\frac{5}{2}$ **19.** $\sqrt{\frac{1}{256}}$ $\frac{1}{16}$ **20.** $\sqrt{\frac{121}{441}}$ $\frac{11}{21}$

21. $-\sqrt{\frac{729}{100}}$ $-\frac{27}{10}$ **22.** $\sqrt{\frac{361}{2704}}$ $\frac{19}{52}$ **23.** $\sqrt{\frac{1024}{1849}}$ $\frac{32}{43}$ **24.** $\sqrt{\frac{676}{169}}$ 2 **25.** $\pm\sqrt{\frac{484}{529}}$ $\pm\frac{22}{23}$

Example $\sqrt{0.81} = \sqrt{\frac{81}{100}} = \frac{\sqrt{81}}{\sqrt{100}} = \frac{9}{10} = 0.9$

26. $\sqrt{0.09}$ 0.3 **27.** $-\sqrt{0.49}$ -0.7 **28.** $\sqrt{1.44}$ 1.2 **29.** $\pm\sqrt{2.25}$ ± 1.5 **30.** $-\sqrt{7.84}$ -2.8

31. $\sqrt{0.0169}$ 0.13 **32.** $\sqrt{0.0324}$ 0.18 **33.** $-\sqrt{0.2304}$ -0.48 **34.** $\sqrt{0.0004}$ 0.02 **35.** $\sqrt{0.0025}$ 0.05

Evaluate the expression $\sqrt{x^2 - y^2} - (\sqrt{x})^2$ for the given values of x and y.

36. $x = 5, y = 3$ -1 **37.** $x = 13, y = 12$ -8 **38.** $x = 15, y = 12$ -6 **39.** $x = 20, y = 16$ -8

Find the indicated square roots.

Example $\sqrt{\frac{12}{75}} = \sqrt{\frac{3 \cdot 4}{3 \cdot 25}} = \sqrt{\frac{4}{25}} = \frac{2}{5}$

B

40. $\sqrt{\frac{18}{32}}$ $\frac{3}{4}$ **41.** $-\sqrt{\frac{12}{75}}$ $-\frac{2}{5}$ **42.** $\sqrt{\frac{99}{44}}$ $\frac{3}{2}$ **43.** $\pm\sqrt{\frac{175}{28}}$ $\pm\frac{5}{2}$ **44.** $\sqrt{\frac{5}{180}}$ $\frac{1}{6}$

45. $\pm\sqrt{\frac{147}{192}}$ $\pm\frac{7}{8}$ **46.** $\sqrt{\frac{33}{132}}$ $\frac{1}{2}$ **47.** $\sqrt{\frac{200}{1152}}$ $\frac{5}{12}$ **48.** $-\sqrt{\frac{3200}{648}}$ $-\frac{20}{9}$ **49.** $\sqrt{\frac{882}{20{,}000}}$ $\frac{21}{100}$

Calculator Key-In

Many calculators have a square root key. It is possible to use this key to find the fourth root, eighth root, sixteenth root, and so on, of a number. For example, to find the eighth root of 32, press the square root key three times ($2^3 = 8$). The answer is 1.5422108.

Find the indicated roots of each number. Answers may vary slightly.

1. Fourth root of 48 2.632148
2. Fourth root of 196 3.7416573
3. Eighth root of 150 1.8707313
4. Eighth root of 38 1.5756978
5. Sixteenth root of 164 1.3753959
6. Thirty-second root of 200 1.1800683

Self-Test 1

Vocabulary rational number (p. 499), terminating decimal (p. 504), repeating decimal (p. 504), square root (p. 510), principal square root (p. 510), radicand (p. 510)

Find a rational number halfway between the given numbers.

1. $\frac{4}{7}$ and $\frac{5}{9}$ $\frac{71}{126}$ **2.** $\frac{5}{4}$ and $\frac{4}{3}$ $\frac{31}{24}$ **3.** $4\frac{1}{6}$ and $5\frac{1}{8}$ $\frac{223}{48}$ **Obj. 11-1, p. 499**

Which rational number is greater?

4. $\frac{4}{7}$ or $\frac{3}{5}$ $\frac{3}{5}$ **5.** $-\frac{33}{20}$ or $-\frac{37}{22}$ $-\frac{33}{20}$ **6.** $\frac{19}{18}$ or $\frac{13}{12}$ $\frac{13}{12}$

7. Express $\frac{6}{25}$ as a decimal. 0.24 **Obj. 11-2, p. 504**

8. Express $\frac{11}{8}$ as a decimal. 1.375

9. Express $\frac{7}{30}$ as a decimal. $0.2\overline{3}$

10. Express $\frac{24}{35}$ as a decimal. $0.6\overline{857142}$

11. Express $0.2\overline{02}$ as a fraction in simplest form. $\frac{20}{99}$

Find the indicated square roots.

12. $\sqrt{1024}$ 32 **13.** $\sqrt{\frac{64}{2025}}$ $\frac{8}{45}$ **14.** $\sqrt{2.56}$ 1.6 **Obj. 11-3, p. 510**

Check your answers with those at the back of the book.

Challenge

1. On the same set of axes, graph the following line segments to draw a picture.

$x = 0,\ 2 \le y \le 7$

$x = 18,\ 4 \le y \le 9$

$x + 3y = 21,\ 0 \le x \le 6$

$x - 3y = 6,\ 6 \le x \le 18$

$x - 3y = -27,\ 3 \le x \le 15$

$5x + 3y = 117,\ 15 \le x \le 18$

$x = 6,\ 0 \le y \le 5$

$x + 3y = 6,\ 0 \le x \le 6$

$x - y = -7,\ 0 \le x \le 3$

$x - 3y = -9,\ 6 \le x \le 18$

$5x + 3y = 45,\ 3 \le x \le 6$

2. Draw a picture on graph paper using line segments. Write a set of equations and inequalities to describe your picture as in Exercise 1.

Quick Quiz

Find a rational number halfway between the given numbers.

1. $\frac{1}{3}$ and $\frac{5}{6}$ $\frac{7}{12}$

2. $\frac{9}{7}$ and $\frac{7}{5}$ $\frac{47}{35}$

3. $3\frac{7}{8}$ and $4\frac{1}{4}$ $4\frac{1}{16}$

Which rational number is greater?

4. $\frac{5}{7}$ or $\frac{4}{5}$ $\frac{4}{5}$

5. $-\frac{16}{15}$ or $-\frac{28}{25}$ $-\frac{16}{15}$

6. $\frac{21}{16}$ or $\frac{27}{20}$ $\frac{27}{20}$

7. Express $\frac{21}{50}$ as a decimal. 0.42

8. Express $\frac{19}{16}$ as a decimal. 1.1875

9. Express $\frac{11}{60}$ as a decimal. $0.18\overline{3}$

10. Express $0.1\overline{06}$ as a fraction in simplest form. $\frac{7}{66}$

Find the indicated square roots.

11. $\sqrt{676}$ 26

12. $\sqrt{\frac{256}{1225}}$ $\frac{16}{35}$

13. $\sqrt{10.24}$ 3.2

Additional Answers Challenge

1.

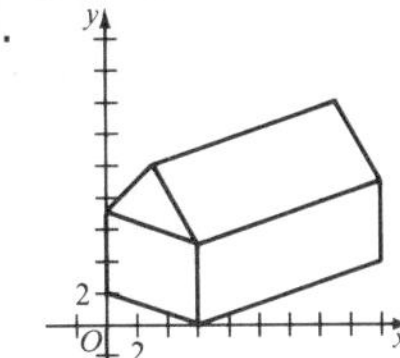

2. Answers may vary.

Teaching Suggestions
p. T122

Suggested Extensions
p. T123

Chalkboard Examples

Simplify.

1. $\sqrt{45}$ $\sqrt{9}\cdot\sqrt{5} = 3\sqrt{5}$
2. $\sqrt{784}$
   $\sqrt{16}\cdot\sqrt{49} = 4\cdot 7 = 28$
3. $4\sqrt{245}$
   $4\sqrt{49\cdot 5} = 4\cdot 7\sqrt{5} = 28\sqrt{5}$

Approximate each square root to the nearest hundredth. Use the table on page 650.

4. $\sqrt{175}$
   $\sqrt{5^2\cdot 7} = 5\sqrt{7} \approx 5(2.646) \approx 13.23$
5. $\sqrt{43}$
   $\sqrt{43} \approx 6.557 \approx 6.56$
6. $\sqrt{0.23}$
   $\frac{\sqrt{23}}{\sqrt{100}} \approx \frac{4.796}{10} = 0.4796 \approx 0.48$
7. $\sqrt{1.62}$
   $\frac{\sqrt{162}}{\sqrt{100}} = \frac{\sqrt{9^2\cdot 2}}{\sqrt{100}} = \frac{9\sqrt{2}}{10} \approx \frac{9(1.414)}{10} = 1.2726 \approx 1.27$

Supplementary Materials

Practice Master 67
Resource Book, p. 120

Irrational Numbers

11-4 Irrational Square Roots

Objective To simplify radicals and to find decimal approximations to irrational square roots.

You can use the Product Property of Square Roots to simplify radicals when the radicand has a factor that is the square of an integer other than 1.

Example 1 Simplify: **a.** $\sqrt{196}$ **b.** $\sqrt{50}$ **c.** $3\sqrt{96}$

Solution **a.** $\sqrt{196} = \sqrt{4}\cdot\sqrt{49} = 2\cdot 7 = 14$
b. $\sqrt{50} = \sqrt{25\cdot 2} = 5\sqrt{2}$
c. $3\sqrt{96} = 3\sqrt{16\cdot 6} = 3\cdot 4\sqrt{6} = 12\sqrt{6}$

Parts (b) and (c) of the example above suggest that some integers, such as 2 and 6, are not squares of integers. Integers that are not squares of integers do not have rational square roots. The following proof shows that 2 does not have a rational square root.

In this proof we begin by assuming that 2 has a rational square root and then show that this assumption leads to a contradiction. Hence, the original assumption that 2 has a rational square root must be false.

1. Assume that 2 has a rational square root.
2. Then, $\sqrt{2} = \frac{a}{b}$, where a and b are positive integers that have no common prime factor, that is, $\frac{a}{b}$ is in simplest form. Hence, a and b cannot both be even integers.
3. If $\sqrt{2} = \frac{a}{b}$, then $2 = \frac{a^2}{b^2}$. Since a^2 has the same prime factors as a, and b^2 has the same prime factors as b, a^2 and b^2 have no common prime factors. Thus, $\frac{a^2}{b^2}$ is in simplest form.
4. Multiplying $\frac{a^2}{b^2} = 2$ by b^2, we have $a^2 = 2b^2$. Thus, a must be even because its square is even. (Recall that the square of an even integer is even and that the square of an odd integer is odd.)
5. Since a is even, we may write $a = 2n$ for some integer n. Then, substituting $2n$ for a in $a^2 = 2b^2$, we have $(2n)^2 = 2b^2$, $4n^2 = 2b^2$, or $2n^2 = b^2$.

6. Since $2n^2 = b^2$, b must be even because its square is even. Therefore, we may write $b = 2m$ for some integer m.
7. This contradicts the fact that a and b are not both even. Therefore, 2 does not have a rational square root.

Since integers such as 2, 6, and 11 are not squares of integers, numbers such as $\sqrt{2}$, $\sqrt{6}$, and $\sqrt{11}$ are not in the set of rational numbers. These numbers are in another major subset of the real numbers called the set of *irrational numbers.*

TABLE ON PAGE 650

Irrational numbers are real numbers that cannot be expressed in the form $\frac{a}{b}$, where a and b are integers.

Irrational square roots are not the only irrational numbers, however. For example, π is an irrational number.

The set of real numbers is made up of the rational numbers and the irrational numbers. The real numbers have all the properties that you have studied thus far in this course. In addition, the set of real numbers has the *property of completeness.*

Property of Completeness

Every decimal represents a real number, and every real number can be represented as a decimal.

Terminating and repeating decimals represent rational numbers. Therefore, the decimals for irrational numbers neither terminate nor repeat. You can use a calculator or a table of square roots to find a decimal approximation of an irrational square root. For example, the Table of Square Roots on page 650 indicates that $\sqrt{87} \approx 9.327$. The product and quotient properties of square roots can be used with the table to approximate irrational square roots.

Example 2 Approximate $\sqrt{756}$ to the nearest hundredth.

Solution $\sqrt{756} = \sqrt{2^2 \cdot 3^2 \cdot 21} = \sqrt{2^2} \cdot \sqrt{3^2} \cdot \sqrt{21} = 6\sqrt{21}$

From the table: $\sqrt{21} \approx 4.583$

$6\sqrt{21} \approx 6(4.583) = 27.498$

$\therefore \sqrt{756} \approx 27.50$ ***Answer***

Suggested Assignments

Minimum
516/1–22
R 513/*Self-Test 1*

Average
516/1–28
R 513/*Self-Test 1*

Maximum
516/1–31
S 503/37–40

Additional A Exercises

Simplify.

1. $\sqrt{320}$ $8\sqrt{5}$
2. $\sqrt{1350}$ $5\sqrt{54}$
3. $4\sqrt{63}$ $12\sqrt{7}$
4. $\sqrt{990}$ $3\sqrt{110}$
5. $\sqrt{200}$ $10\sqrt{2}$
6. $15\sqrt{1280}$ $240\sqrt{5}$

Additional Answers Written Exercises

31. Assume that 3 has a rational square root. Then $\sqrt{3} = \frac{p}{q}$, where p and q are positive integers that have no common prime factor. If $\sqrt{3} = \frac{p}{q}$, then $3 = \frac{p^2}{q^2}$, and p^2 and q^2 have no common prime factor. Then $3q^2 = p^2$. Thus, p^2 and p are divisible by 3. Therefore, let $p = 3m$. Then $3q^2 = (3m)^2 = 9m^2$, and $q^2 = 3m^2$. Thus, both q^2 and q are divisible by 3. This contradicts the assumption that p and q have no common prime factor.

516

Example 3 Approximate $\sqrt{0.6}$ to the nearest ten-thousandth.

Solution $\sqrt{0.6} = \sqrt{\frac{60}{100}} = \frac{\sqrt{60}}{\sqrt{100}} \approx \frac{7.746}{10} = 0.7746$

$\therefore \sqrt{0.6} \approx 0.7746$ ***Answer***

Oral Exercises

State whether the following represent rational or irrational numbers.

1. $\sqrt{13}$ irrational **2.** $\sqrt{15}$ irrational **3.** $\sqrt{36}$ rational **4.** $\sqrt{43.8}$ irrational **5.** $\sqrt{0.64}$ rational

Simplify.

6. $\sqrt{75}$ $5\sqrt{3}$ **7.** $\sqrt{125}$ $5\sqrt{5}$ **8.** $\sqrt{108}$ $6\sqrt{3}$ **9.** $\sqrt{180}$ $6\sqrt{5}$ **10.** $\sqrt{220}$ $2\sqrt{55}$

Approximate each square root to the nearest tenth. Use the table on page 650 as necessary.

11. $\sqrt{600}$ 24.5 **12.** $\sqrt{1100}$ 33.2 **13.** $\sqrt{2800}$ 52.9 **14.** $\sqrt{3700}$ 60.8 **15.** $\sqrt{6300}$ 79.4

Written Exercises

Simplify.

A **1.** $\sqrt{225}$ 15 **2.** $\sqrt{40}$ $2\sqrt{10}$ **3.** $\sqrt{120}$ $2\sqrt{30}$ **4.** $2\sqrt{32}$ $8\sqrt{2}$ **5.** $5\sqrt{72}$ $30\sqrt{2}$

6. $\sqrt{676}$ 26 **7.** $9\sqrt{90}$ $27\sqrt{10}$ **8.** $\sqrt{324}$ 18 **9.** $12\sqrt{50}$ $60\sqrt{2}$ **10.** $6\sqrt{45}$ $18\sqrt{5}$

11. $10\sqrt{75}$ $50\sqrt{3}$ **12.** $4\sqrt{108}$ $24\sqrt{3}$ **13.** $\sqrt{128}$ $8\sqrt{2}$ **14.** $\sqrt{864}$ $12\sqrt{6}$ **15.** $\sqrt{7225}$ 85

In Exercises 16-30, use the table on page 650 as necessary. Approximate each square root to the nearest tenth.

B **16.** $\sqrt{800}$ 28.3 **17.** $-\sqrt{4800}$ -69.3 **18.** $-\sqrt{700}$ -26.5 **19.** $\sqrt{9200}$ 95.9 **20.** $\sqrt{5900}$ 76.8

Approximate each square root to the nearest hundredth.

21. $\sqrt{86}$ 9.27 **22.** $\sqrt{31}$ 5.57 **23.** $-\sqrt{0.3}$ -0.55 **24.** $\sqrt{0.73}$ 0.85 **25.** $-\sqrt{0.08}$ -0.28

Approximate each square root to the nearest unit.

26. $\sqrt{250{,}000}$ 500 **27.** $\sqrt{120{,}000}$ 346 **28.** $\sqrt{420{,}000}$ 648 **29.** $\sqrt{520{,}000}$ 721 **30.** $\sqrt{820{,}000}$ 906

C **31.** Prove that $\sqrt{3}$ is irrational. (*Hint:* Consider the proof for $\sqrt{2}$ being irrational.)

11-5 Square Roots of Variable Expressions

Objective To find square roots of variable expressions and to use them to solve equations and problems.

Is it always true that $\sqrt{a^2} = a$? Recall that the symbol $\sqrt{\ }$ stands for the principal, or nonnegative, square root of a number. Thus, when $a = -5$ you have

$$\sqrt{(-5)^2} = \sqrt{25} = 5.$$

Therefore, it is not necessarily true that $\sqrt{a^2} = a$. If a is nonnegative, $\sqrt{a^2} = a$; but if a is negative, then $\sqrt{a^2} = -a$. In either case, it is true that

$$\sqrt{a^2} = |a|.$$

When you are finding square roots of variable expressions, you must be careful to use absolute value signs, when needed, to ensure that your answer is nonnegative.

Example 1 Simplify: **a.** $\sqrt{121y^2}$ **b.** $\sqrt{49x^8}$ **c.** $\sqrt{y^2 - 8y + 16}$

Solution

a. $\sqrt{121y^2} = 11|y|$

b. $\sqrt{49x^8} = 7x^4$ (x^4 is always nonnegative.)

c. $\sqrt{y^2 - 8y + 16} = \sqrt{(y-4)^2} = |y - 4|$

Example 2 Solve $x^2 = 81$.

Solution 1

$$x^2 = 81$$
$$x^2 - 81 = 0$$
$$(x - 9)(x + 9) = 0$$
$$x = 9 \text{ or } x = -9$$

Solution 2

$$x^2 = 81$$
$$x = \pm\sqrt{81} = \pm 9$$

Check: $9^2 = 81$ and $(-9)^2 = 81$ ✓

$\therefore$ the solution set is $\{9, -9\}$. ***Answer***

Solution 2 is based upon the following property:

Property of Square Roots of Equal Numbers

If r and s are any real numbers, $r^2 = s^2$ if and only if $r = s$ or $r = -s$.

Teaching Suggestions
p. T123

Suggested Extensions
p. T123

Chalkboard Examples

Simplify.

1. $\sqrt{49x^2}$ $\sqrt{7^2 \cdot x^2} = 7|x|$

2. $\sqrt{225y^4}$
$\sqrt{15^2 \cdot (y^2)^2} = 15y^2$, since y^2 is nonnegative.

3. $\sqrt{n^2 - 16n + 64}$
$\sqrt{(n-8)^2} = |n - 8|$

Solve.

4. $m^2 - 121 = 0$
$m^2 = 121$
$m = \pm\sqrt{121} = \pm 11$
$\{-11, 11\}$

5. $25y^2 = 9$
$y^2 = \frac{9}{25}$
$y = \pm\sqrt{\frac{9}{25}} = \pm\frac{3}{5}$
$\left\{-\frac{3}{5}, \frac{3}{5}\right\}$

6. $20b^2 - 125 = 0$
$20b^2 = 125$
$b^2 = \frac{125}{20} = \frac{25}{4}$
$b = \sqrt{\frac{25}{4}} = \pm\frac{5}{2}$
$\left\{-\frac{5}{2}, \frac{5}{2}\right\}$

Common Error

Students often omit necessary absolute value signs when simplifying square roots of variable expressions (see the discussion at the top of page 517). Point out that it is not necessary to use absolute value signs when a quantity is known to be nonnegative.

Suggested Assignments

Minimum
518/2–36 even; *P*: 1, 3, 5
S 516/26–28

Average
518/2–42 even; *P*: 1, 3, 5

Maximum
518/2–46 even; *P*: 1, 5, 8, 9

Additional A Exercises

Simplify.

1. $\sqrt{125a^2b^2}$ $5|ab|\sqrt{5}$
2. $\sqrt{81m^{12}}$ $9m^6$
3. $-\sqrt{1.44x^5y^3}$ $-1.2x^2|y|\sqrt{xy}$
4. $\sqrt{\frac{441e^6}{16}}$ $\frac{21}{4}|e^3|$
5. Solve: $m^2 - 64 = 0$ $\{\pm 8\}$

Additional Answers Written Exercises

8. $-4|ab|$
9. $-3c^2$
10. $5|d^3|$
11. $9|x|y\sqrt{7y}$
12. $24|n^3|\sqrt{10}$
13. $2|r^3|s^2\sqrt{14}$
14. $\frac{x^2}{2}\left|\frac{y^3}{r}\right|$
15. $3\left|\frac{m}{n}\right|$
16. $-12|y|z^2$
17. $21|a^3|b^2$
18. $1.5\ m^4|n^3|$
19. $-1.8x^2$
20. $1.4|k^3|$
21. $\frac{2|e|}{25}$
22. $\frac{10|f^5|}{11}$
23. $\frac{13}{20s^6}$

$1.8 = \frac{9}{5}$ $1.4 = \frac{7}{5}$

Oral Exercises

Simplify.

1. $\sqrt{36y^2}$ $6|y|$ 2. $\sqrt{169x^2}$ $13|x|$ 3. $\sqrt{81a^4}$ $9a^2$ 4. $\sqrt{121x^2y^2}$ $11|xy|$ 5. $\sqrt{0.04b^6}$ $0.2|b^3|$

6. $\sqrt{\frac{x^2}{49}}$ $\frac{|x|}{7}$ 7. $\pm\sqrt{\frac{16}{a^4}}$ $\pm\frac{4}{a^2}$ 8. $\sqrt{\frac{x^4y^4}{25}}$ $\frac{x^2y^2}{5}$ 9. $\sqrt{\frac{r^6s^6}{64}}$ $\frac{|r^3s^3|}{8}$ 10. $\sqrt{\frac{m^{14}}{16n^8}}$ $\frac{|m^7|}{4n^4}$

Written Exercises

Simplify.

A 1. $\sqrt{144a^2}$ $12|a|$ 2. $\sqrt{32x^2}$ $4|x|\sqrt{2}$ 3. $\sqrt{75b^4}$ $5b^2\sqrt{3}$ 4. $\sqrt{45r^3}$ $3r\sqrt{5r}$ 5. $\sqrt{80a^2b^2}$ $4|ab|\sqrt{5}$

6. $-\sqrt{36x^2}$ $-6|x|$ 7. $\sqrt{81z^2}$ $9|z|$ 8. $-\sqrt{16a^2b^2}$ 9. $-\sqrt{9c^4}$ 10. $\sqrt{25d^6}$

11. $3\sqrt{63x^2y^3}$ 12. $8\sqrt{90n^6}$ 13. $\sqrt{56r^6s^4}$ 14. $\sqrt{\frac{x^4y^6}{4r^2}}$ 15. $\sqrt{\frac{27m^3n^2}{3mn^4}}$

16. $-\sqrt{144y^2z^4}$ 17. $\sqrt{441a^6b^4}$ 18. $\sqrt{2.25m^8n^6}$ 19. $-\sqrt{3.24x^4}$ 20. $\sqrt{1.96k^6}$

21. $\sqrt{\frac{4e^2}{625}}$ 22. $\sqrt{\frac{100f^{10}}{121}}$ 23. $\sqrt{\frac{169}{400s^{12}}}$ 24. $\sqrt{\frac{49g^{18}}{6400h^{20}}}$ 25. $\sqrt{\frac{169r^{50}}{25}}$

26. $\sqrt{y^2 + 6y + 9}$ $|y + 3|$ 27. $\sqrt{m^2 - 10m + 25}$ $|m - 5|$ 28. $\sqrt{49 + 14r + r^2}$ $|7 + r|$

Solve.

29. $a^2 = 16$ $\{-4, 4\}$ 30. $x^2 - 36 = 0$ $\{-6, 6\}$ 31. $d^2 - 1 = 0$ $\{-1, 1\}$

32. $64y^2 = 9$ $\left\{-\frac{3}{8}, \frac{3}{8}\right\}$ 33. $4c^2 - 25 = 0$ $\left\{-\frac{5}{2}, \frac{5}{2}\right\}$ 34. $81z^2 - 49 = 0$ 34. $\left\{-\frac{7}{9}, \frac{7}{9}\right\}$

35. $2m^2 - 32 = 0$ $\{-4, 4\}$ 36. $50b^2 - 200 = 0$ $\{-2, 2\}$ 37. $27p^2 - 75 = 0$ $\left\{-\frac{5}{3}, \frac{5}{3}\right\}$

Find both roots of each equation to the nearest tenth.

B 38. $x^2 = 657$ $\{-25.6, 25.6\}$ 39. $a^2 = 164$ $\{-12.8, 12.8\}$ 40. $r^2 = 0.29$ $\{-0.5, 0.5\}$

41. $c^2 - 204 = 0$ $\{-14.3, 14.3\}$ 42. $y^2 - 4.75 = 0$ $\{-2.2, 2.2\}$ 43. $n^2 - 11.16 = 0$

44. $7z^2 = 399$ $\{-7.5, 7.5\}$ 45. $8s^2 - 154 = 0$ $\{-4.4, 4.4\}$ 46. $6b^2 - 0.42 = 0$ $\{-0.3, 0.3\}$

C 47. $0.11m^2 = 6.38$ $\{-7.6, 7.6\}$ 48. $7k^2 = 130$ $\{-4.3, 4.3\}$

49. $(x - 1)^2 + (x + 1)^2 = 150$ $\{-8.6, 8.6\}$ 50. $(a + 3)^2 + (a - 3)^2 = 196$ $\{-9.4, 9.4\}$

Problems

Solve. Find each answer to the nearest tenth. Use $\pi \approx 3.14$.

A 1. Find the length of a side of a square whose area is 200 cm². 14.1 cm

2. Find the length of a side of a square whose area is the same as that of a rectangle whose dimensions are 18 cm by 24 cm. 20.8 cm

3. The length of the base of a triangle is 3 times the length of its altitude. Find the length of the base if the area of the triangle is 54 m^2. 18.0 m

4. Find the length of a side of a square if its area is the same as the area of a triangle with an altitude of 14 cm and a base of 9 cm. 7.9 cm

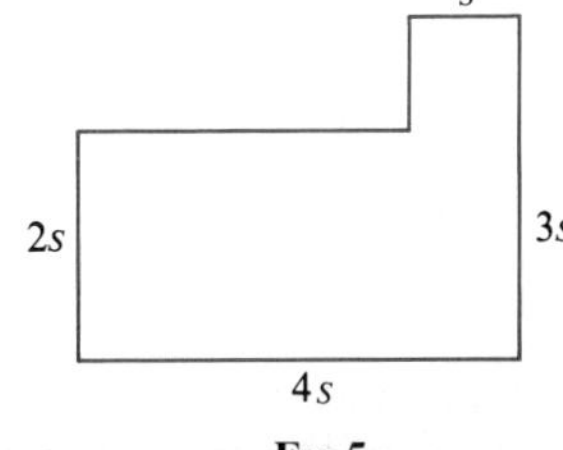

Ex. 5

5. If the area of the figure at the right is 400 mm^2, find s. 6.7 mm

6. A circle inside a square just touches its sides. If the area of the circle is 266.9 cm^2, what is the length of a side of the square? 18.4 cm

B 7. An old water pipe is to be replaced by a new one so that twice as much water can flow through the pipe. What is the ratio of the radius of the new pipe to that of the old pipe? $\frac{\sqrt{2}}{1} \approx 1.4$

8. A square quilt is to be made of 150 rectangular pieces 10 cm by 15 cm. How many meters of trim are required to edge the quilt? 6.0 m

9. The formula $s = 4.9t^2$ gives the approximate distance traveled in t seconds by an object falling from rest. How long does it take a rock falling from rest to travel 1587.6 m? 18.0 s

Let a, b, and c represent the lengths of the sides of a triangle, and let $s = \frac{1}{2}(a + b + c)$. Then the area, A, of the triangle is given by the formula $A = \sqrt{s(s - a)(s - b)(s - c)}$. Use the formula to answer the following questions. Find each answer to the nearest tenth.

C 10. What is the area of a triangle whose sides are 7 cm, 9 cm, and 12 cm long? 31.3 cm^2

11. What is the area of a triangle whose sides are 11 m, 16 m, and 21 m long? 86.5 m^2

Computer Exercises

For students with some programming experience

Write a BASIC program that will print out the square root of a nonnegative rational number entered with an INPUT statement. If the number that is INPUT is negative, the program should ask the user for another number. If the number that is INPUT is not a perfect square, the program should print out a decimal approximation of the square root to the degree of accuracy specified by the user.

24. $\frac{7|g^9|}{80h^{10}}$

25. $\frac{13|r^{25}|}{5}$

43. $\{-3.3, 3.3\}$

Mixed Review Exercises

1. Simplify $\frac{(-2x)^2}{-(4x^2)^3}$. $-\frac{1}{16x^4}$

2. Multiply: $(6a + 3)(4a - 2)$ $24a^2 - 6$

3. Factor $6x^2 - 20x + 14$ completely. $2(3x - 7)(x - 1)$

4. Approximate $\sqrt{3993}$ to the nearest hundredth, using the table on p. 650. 63.20

Teaching Suggestions
p. T123

Suggested Extensions
p. T124

11-6 The Pythagorean Theorem

Objective To use the Pythagorean theorem and its converse to construct lengths corresponding to irrational numbers and to solve geometric problems.

In this section you will see how the Pythagorean theorem can be used to find the lengths of sides of triangles that correspond to irrational numbers.

The Pythagorean Theorem

In any right triangle, the square of the length of the hypotenuse equals the sum of the squares of the lengths of the other two sides. For the triangle shown,

$$a^2 + b^2 = c^2.$$

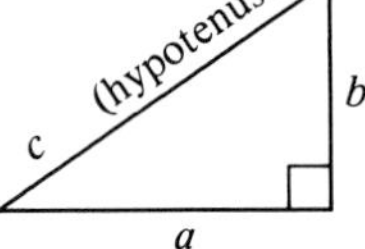

The following two diagrams suggest a proof of the theorem. Each diagram shows a square, $(a + b)$ units on a side, divided into other figures. The diagrams suggest different expressions for the area of a square $(a + b)$ units on a side. Equating these expressions leads to the equation $a^2 + b^2 = c^2$, as shown below.

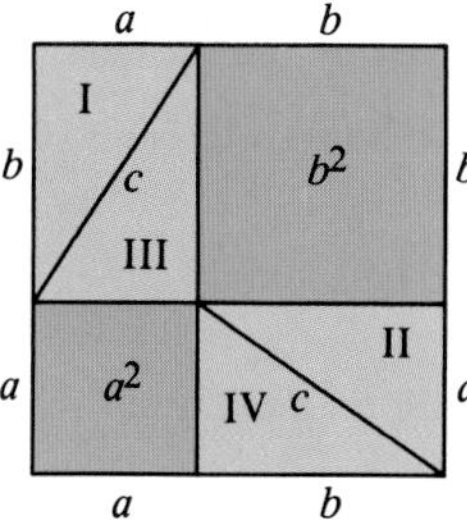

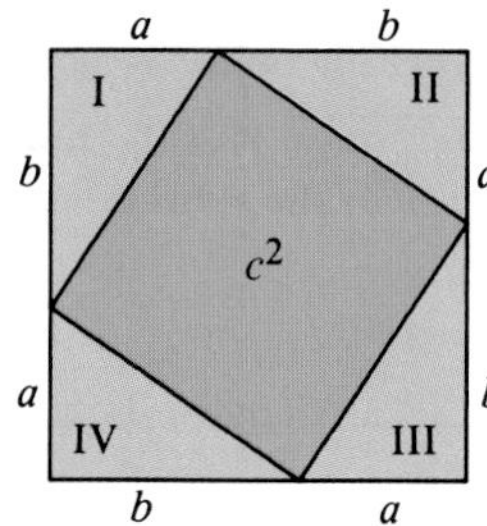

$$(a + b)^2 = a^2 + b^2 + 4\left(\frac{1}{2}ab\right) \qquad (a + b)^2 = c^2 + 4\left(\frac{1}{2}ab\right)$$

$$a^2 + b^2 + 4\left(\frac{1}{2}ab\right) = c^2 + 4\left(\frac{1}{2}ab\right)$$

$$\therefore\ a^2 + b^2 = c^2$$

To draw a line segment with a length of $\sqrt{2}$ units, draw a right triangle whose two shorter sides are 1 unit long, as shown in the following diagram.

Then:

$$a^2 + b^2 = c^2$$
$$1^2 + 1^2 = c^2$$
$$1 + 1 = c^2$$
$$2 = c^2$$
$$\pm\sqrt{2} = c$$

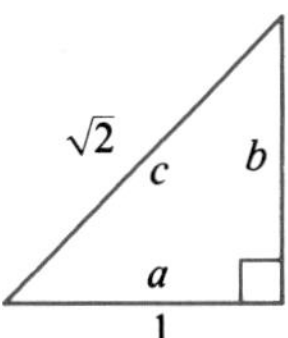

$\therefore$ the length of the hypotenuse is $\sqrt{2}$ units.

The following diagrams show that a segment $\sqrt{2}$ units long can be used to construct a segment $\sqrt{3}$ units long, that a segment $\sqrt{3}$ units long can be used to construct a segment $\sqrt{4}$ units long, and so on.

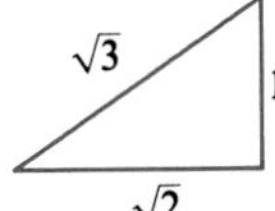

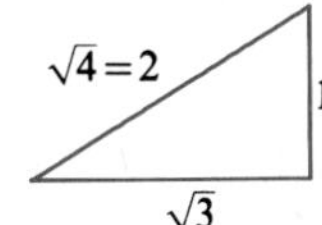

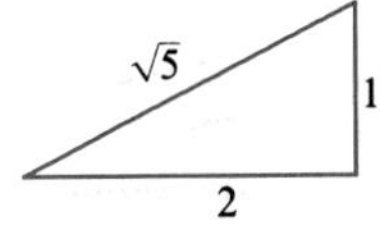

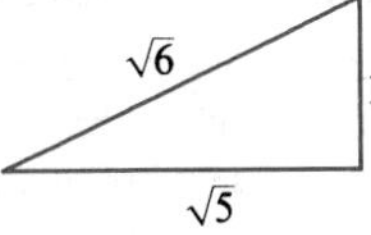

A series of such triangles can be used to locate irrational square roots such as $\sqrt{2}$, $\sqrt{3}$, and $\sqrt{5}$ on the number line. The arcs are drawn to transfer the length of the hypotenuse of each triangle to the x-axis. Note that $-\sqrt{2}$ is located $\sqrt{2}$ units to the left of 0.

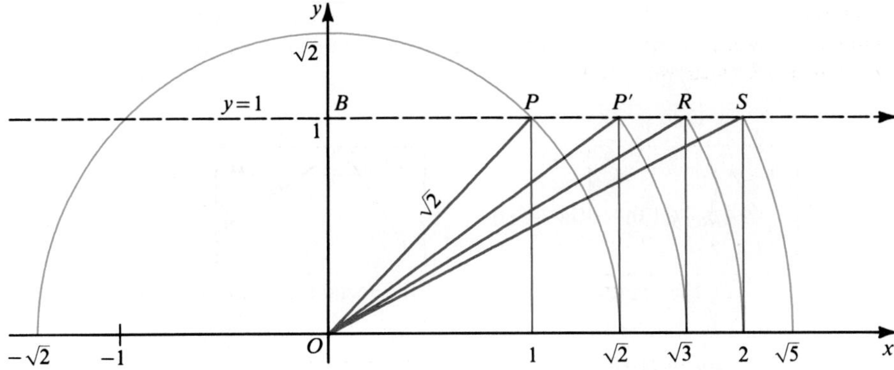

The converse of the Pythagorean theorem is also true. It can be used to see if a given triangle is a right triangle.

Converse of the Pythagorean Theorem

If the sum of the squares of the lengths of the two shorter sides of a triangle is equal to the square of the length of the longest side, then the triangle is a right triangle. The right angle will be opposite the longest side.

Chalkboard Examples

In the table below, a, b, and c represent the sides of a right triangle; c is the hypotenuse. Complete the table.

	a	b	c	
1.	6	8	?	10
2.	8	?	17	15
3.	?	$\sqrt{7}$	$\sqrt{27}$	$2\sqrt{5}$

4. Is a triangle with sides 8, 13, and 20 a right triangle?
   $8^2 = 64$, $13^2 = 169$, $20^2 = 400$
   $64 + 169 \neq 400$
   $\therefore$ the triangle is not a right triangle.
5. The length of one side of a triangle is 10 cm and the length of the hypotenuse is 26 cm. What is the length of the third side?
   $$a^2 + b^2 = c^2$$
   $$a^2 = c^2 - b^2$$
   $$a = \sqrt{c^2 - b^2}$$
   $$= \sqrt{26^2 - 10^2}$$
   $$= \sqrt{676 - 100}$$
   $$= \sqrt{576} = 24$$
   $\therefore$ the length of the third side is 24 cm.
6. Find the length of a side of a square whose diagonal is $11\sqrt{2}$ cm.
   $a^2 + b^2 = c^2$; $a = b$, so
   $$2a^2 = c^2$$
   $$2a^2 = (11\sqrt{2})^2$$
   $$2a^2 = 242$$
   $$a^2 = 121$$
   $$a = \sqrt{121} = 11$$
   $\therefore$ the length of a side is 11 cm.

Example 1 Is a triangle with sides 9, 40, and 41 a right triangle?

Solution

$$a^2 + b^2 = c^2$$
$$9^2 + 40^2 \stackrel{?}{=} 41^2$$
$$1681 = 1681 \checkmark$$

$\therefore$ a triangle with sides 9, 40, and 41 is a right triangle. ***Answer***

Example 2 The length of one side of a right triangle is 24 cm and the length of the hypotenuse is 25 cm. What is the length of the third side?

Solution

$$a^2 + b^2 = c^2$$
$$a^2 = c^2 - b^2$$
$$a = \sqrt{c^2 - b^2}$$
$$a = \sqrt{25^2 - 24^2}$$
$$a = \sqrt{625 - 576}$$
$$a = \sqrt{49} = 7$$

Check: $7^2 + 24^2 \stackrel{?}{=} 25^2$
$625 = 625 \checkmark$

$\therefore$ the length of the third side of the right triangle is 7 cm. ***Answer***

Example 3 What is the length of a diagonal of a rectangle whose width is 36 cm and whose length is 48 cm?

Solution

$$a^2 + b^2 = c^2$$
$$\sqrt{a^2 + b^2} = c$$
$$\sqrt{36^2 + 48^2} = c$$
$$\sqrt{1296 + 2304} = c$$
$$\sqrt{3600} = c$$
$$60 = c$$

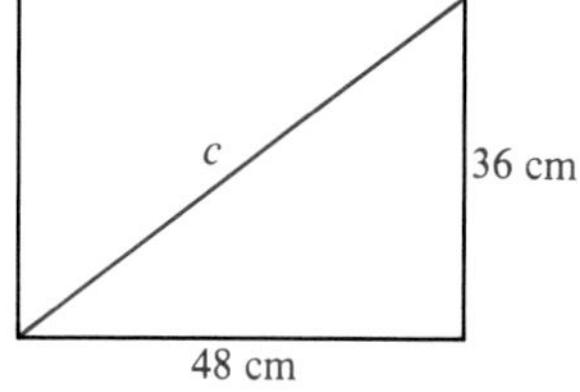

Check: $36^2 + 48^2 \stackrel{?}{=} 60^2$
$3600 = 3600 \checkmark$

$\therefore$ the length of a diagonal of the rectangle is 60 cm. ***Answer***

Oral Exercises

Evaluate.

1. $\sqrt{3^2 + 4^2}$ 5 **2.** $\sqrt{10^2 - 8^2}$ 6 **3.** $\sqrt{13^2 - 12^2}$ 5

State and solve an equation for the length of the unknown side.

4. $3^2 + b^2 = 5^2$; 4

5 3 b

5. $5^2 + 12^2 = c^2$; 13

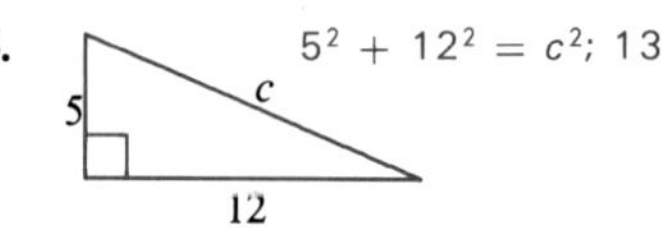

Written Exercises

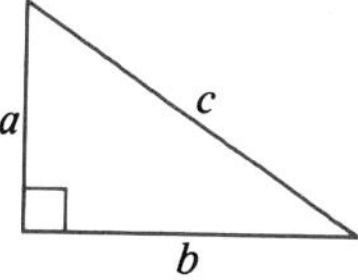

In Exercises 1-10, refer to the right triangle shown at the right. Find the missing length correct to the nearest hundredth.

A

1. $a = 9$, $b = 12$, $c =$ __?__ 15.00
2. $a = 5$, $b = 12$, $c =$ __?__ 13.00
3. $a = 7$, $b = 4$, $c =$ __?__ 8.06
4. $a = 11$, $b = 8$, $c =$ __?__ 13.60
5. $a = 7$, $b = 7$, $c =$ __?__ 9.90
6. $a = 16$, $b = 8$, $c =$ __?__ 17.89
7. $a =$ __?__, $b = 15$, $c = 17$ 8.00
8. $a =$ __?__, $b = 12$, $c = 19$ 14.73
9. $a = 6$, $b =$ __?__, $c = 40$ 39.55
10. $a = 3$, $b =$ __?__, $c = 6$ 5.20

State whether or not the three numbers given could represent the lengths of the sides of a right triangle.

11. 5, 10, 15 no
12. 14, 48, 50 yes
13. 9, 40, 41 yes
14. 15, 30, 34 no
15. 15, 20, 24 no
16. 17, 35, 39 no
17. a, $2a$, $3a$ no
18. $3a$, $4a$, $5a$ yes
19. $5a$, $12a$, $13a$ yes

In Exercises 20-25, refer to the diagram for Exercises 1-10. Find the missing length correct to the nearest hundredth.

B

20. $a = b = 10$, $c =$ __?__ 14.14
21. $a = 9$, $b = \frac{1}{3}a$, $c =$ __?__ 9.49
22. $a = 16$, $b = \frac{1}{4}a$, $c =$ __?__ 16.49
23. $a = \frac{1}{2}b$, $b = 12$, $c =$ __?__ 13.42
24. $a = \frac{3}{5}b$, $b = 15$, $c =$ __?__ 17.49
25. $a = \frac{5}{6}b$, $b = 18$, $c =$ __?__ 23.43

In Exercises 26-29, refer to the diagram for Exercises 1-10. Find *a* and *b* correct to the nearest hundredth.

C

26. $a = b$, $c = 80$ $a = b = 56.57$
27. $a = 3b$, $c = 20$ $a = 18.96$, $b = 6.32$
28. $a = \frac{1}{2}b$, $c = 25$ $a = 11.18$, $b = 22.36$
29. $a = \frac{2}{3}b$, $c = 52$ $a = 28.85$, $b = 43.27$

Computer Exercises

For students with some programming experience

Write a BASIC program that will report whether three numbers entered with INPUT statements could represent the lengths of the sides of a right triangle.

Common Error

Students sometimes substitute the length of a leg of a right triangle for c in the equation $a^2 + b^2 = c^2$. Emphasize that in this equation c represents the hypotenuse, which is the longest side of a right triangle.

Supplementary Materials

Practice Master 68
Test 39
Resource Book, p. 121

Suggested Assignments

Minimum
523/1-21 odd
524/*P*: 1, 3, 4

Average
523/1-23 odd
524/*P*: 1, 4, 5
S 519/*P*: 4, 6, 9

Maximum
523/1-27 odd
524/*P*: 1-7 odd
R 524/*Self-Test 2*

Additional A Exercises

Refer to the right triangle shown on p. 523. Find the missing length correct to the nearest hundredth.

1. $a = 7$, $b = 7$, $c =$ __?__ 9.90
2. $a =$ __?__, $b = 20$, $c = 40$ 34.64
3. $a = 7$, $b =$ __?__, $c = 15$ 13.27

State whether or not the three numbers given could represent the lengths of the sides of a right triangle.

4. 18, 24, 30 Yes
5. 50, 120, 130 Yes
6. 17, 18, 34 No

Mixed Review Exercises

Factor.

1. $m^2 + 3m - 88$
   $(m + 11)(m - 8)$
2. $s^2t + st^2 - 2s - 2t$
   $(st - 2)(s + t)$
3. Solve: $8x^2 + 14x = 15$
   $\frac{3}{4}, -\frac{5}{2}$
4. Simplify: $\sqrt{6.25x^4y^2b^6}$
   $2.5x^2|yb^3|$

Quick Quiz

Approximate each square root to the nearest hundredth using the Table of Square Roots on p. 650.

1. $\sqrt{79}$ 8.89
2. $\sqrt{2100}$ 45.83
3. $-\sqrt{0.55}$ -0.74

Simplify.

4. $\sqrt{25a^4b^4}$ $5a^2b^2$
5. $-\sqrt{81x^3y^6}$ $-9x|y^3|\sqrt{x}$
6. $\sqrt{0.49b^8}$ $0.7b^4$

Solve.

7. $y^2 = 400$ $\{-20, 20\}$
8. $m^2 - 100 = 0$
   $\{-10, 10\}$
9. $4c^2 - 25 = 0$
   $\left\{-\frac{5}{2}, \frac{5}{2}\right\}$
10. Find the hypotenuse of a right triangle whose legs are 5 cm and 8 cm. State your answer correct to the nearest hundredth.
    9.43 cm
11. Is a triangle with sides 6, 9, and 14 units long a right triangle?
    No, $6^2 + 9^2 \neq 14^2$

Problems

Make a sketch for each problem. Approximate each square root to the nearest hundredth.

A

1. Find the length of a diagonal of a rectangle whose dimensions are 7 cm by 24 cm. 25 cm
2. A rope 17 m long is attached to the top of a flagpole. The rope is just able to reach a point on the ground 8 m from the base of the pole. Find the height of the flagpole. 15 m
3. The diagonal of a square measures $9\sqrt{2}$ m. Find the length of a side of the square. 9 m
4. The base of an isosceles triangle is 16 cm long. The equal sides are each 22 cm long. Find the altitude (a) of the triangle. 20.49 cm

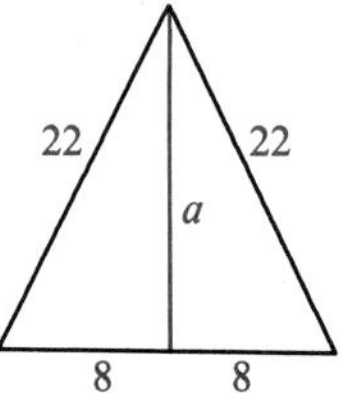

B

5. A right triangle has sides whose lengths can be expressed by consecutive even integers. Determine the length of each side. 6, 8, 10
6. The dimensions of a rectangular doorway are 200 cm by 80 cm. Can a circular mirror with a diameter of 220 cm be carried through the doorway? no

C

7. What is the length of the diagonal of a cube that is 30 cm on each side? 51.96 cm
8. What is the length of the diagonal of a rectangular box having length 40 cm, width 30 cm, and height 80 cm? Would a meter stick fit in the box? 94.34 cm; no
9. Ellen is standing on a dock 1.5 m above the water. She is pulling in a boat that is attached to the end of a 3.9 m rope. If she pulls in 1.4 m of rope, how far did she move the boat? 1.60 m

Self-Test 2

Vocabulary irrational numbers (p. 515) Pythagorean theorem (p. 520)

Approximate each square root to the nearest hundredth using the Table of Square Roots.

1. $\sqrt{97}$ 9.85 2. $\sqrt{1700}$ 41.23 3. $-\sqrt{0.88}$ -0.94 **Obj. 11-4, p. 514**

Simplify.

4. $\sqrt{81x^2y^2}$ $9|xy|$ 5. $-\sqrt{144a^6b^8}$ $-12|a^3|b^4$ 6. $\sqrt{0.25c^4}$ $0.5c^2$ **Obj. 11-5, p. 517**

Solve.

7. $s^2 = 49\{-7, 7\}$ **8.** $w^2 - 64 = 0\{-8, 8\}$ **9.** $36y^2 - 25 = 0\left\{-\frac{5}{6}, \frac{5}{6}\right\}$

Obj. 11-6, p. 520

10. Find c correct to the nearest hundredth if $a = 14$ and $b = 17$. 22.02

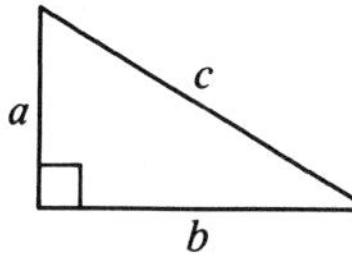

11. Is a triangle with sides 9, 12, and 14 units long a right triangle? no

Check your answers with those at the back of the book.

Extra / The Distance Formula

The distance between two points on the x-axis or on a line parallel to that axis is the absolute value of the difference between their abscissas. Using the notation $A'B'$ to denote the distance from A' to B', you can write the following:

$$A'B' = |2 - 8| = |8 - 2| = 6$$
$$AB = |2 - 8| = |8 - 2| = 6$$

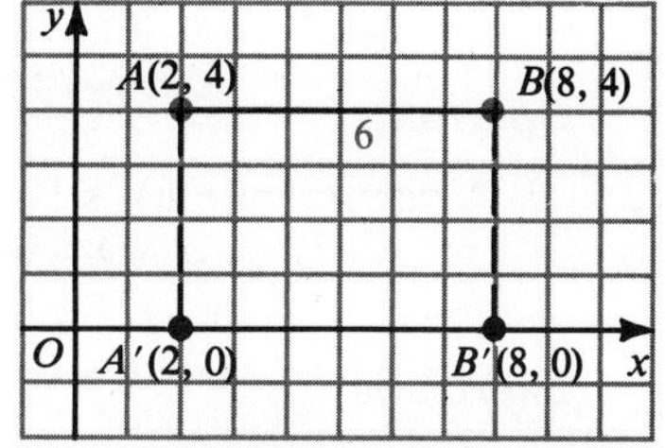

The distance between two points on the y-axis or on a line parallel to that axis is the absolute value of the difference between their ordinates.

$$A'C' = |3 - 7| = |7 - 3| = 4$$
$$AC = |3 - 7| = |7 - 3| = 4$$

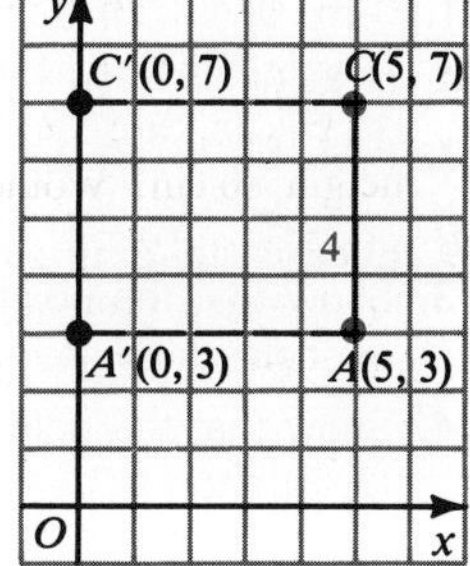

To find the distance between two points not on an axis or a line parallel to an axis, use the Pythagorean theorem:

$$AD = \sqrt{(AB)^2 + (BD)^2} = \sqrt{(8 - 2)^2 + (5 - 3)^2}$$
$$= \sqrt{6^2 + 2^2} = \sqrt{36 + 4}$$
$$= \sqrt{40} = 2\sqrt{10}$$

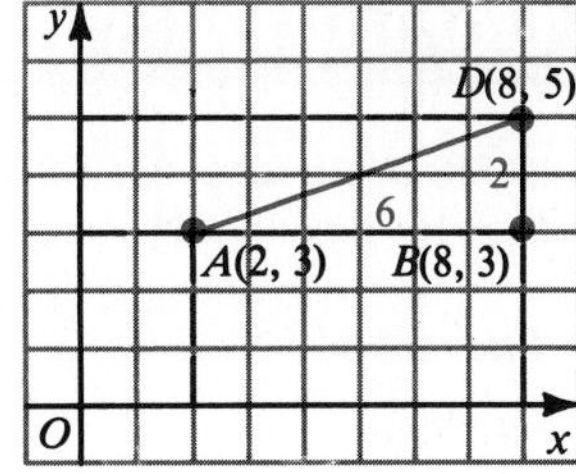

This method for finding the distance between any two points can be generalized as shown on the following page.

The Distance Formula

For any points $P_1(x_1, y_1)$ and $P_2(x_2, y_2)$

$$P_1P_2 = \sqrt{(x_2 - x_1)^2 + (y_2 - y_1)^2}$$

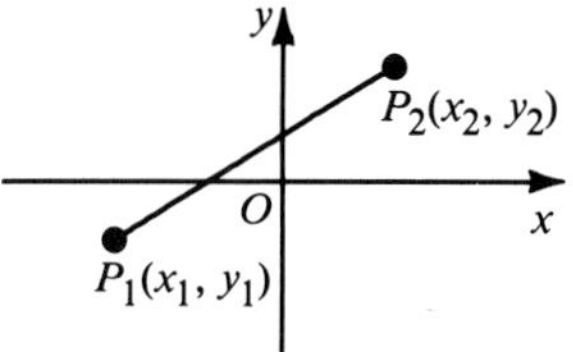

Example Find the distance between points $P(-3, 2)$ and $Q(5, 8)$.

Solution 1 $PQ = \sqrt{(-3 - 5)^2 + (2 - 8)^2}$
$= \sqrt{(-8)^2 + (-6)^2}$
$= \sqrt{64 + 36} = \sqrt{100} = 10$

Solution 2 $PQ = \sqrt{(5 - (-3))^2 + (8 - 2)^2}$
$= \sqrt{8^2 + 6^2}$
$= \sqrt{64 + 36} = \sqrt{100} = 10$

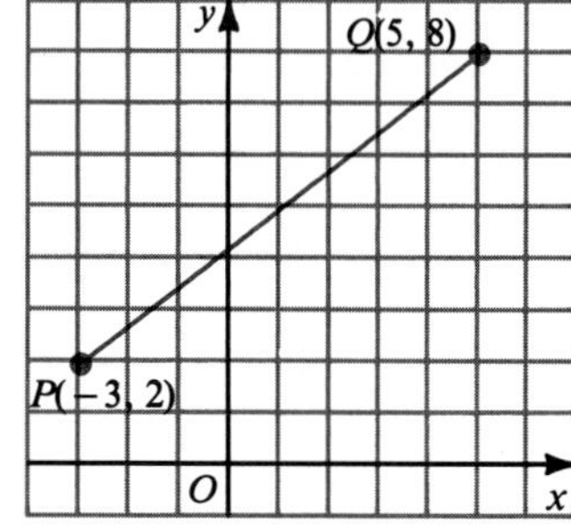

Exercises

Use the distance formula to find the distance between the points to the nearest tenth.

1. $(-5, 0), (3, 0)$ 8.0
2. $(0, 9), (0, -12)$ 21.0
3. $(2, 3), (8, 5)$ 6.3
4. $(10, 3), (-4, 9)$ 15.2
5. $(-4, -2), (-9, -6)$ 6.4
6. $(8, -1), (3, -5)$
7. $(-4, 6), (5, 2)$ 9.8
8. $(-3, 7), (-9, -6)$ 14.3
9. $(3, -3), (-8, -5)$
10. $(2, -5), (9, -7)$ 7.3
11. $(-2, 1), (-8, -5)$ 8.5
12. $(10, -1), (-9, 3)$
13. Show that the points $(1, 1)$, $(5, 2)$, and $(4, -2)$ are the vertices of an isosceles triangle.
14. Show that the point $(-2, -2)$ is the midpoint of the segment joining $(3, 8)$ and $(-7, -12)$.

Computer Key-In

BASIC has a function, SQR(N), for finding the square root of a number. Use this function to find SQR(16), SQR(25), SQR(2), and SQR(625).

Exercises

1. Write a program to find the distance between $(X1, Y1)$ and $(X2, Y2)$.
2. Use your program to check your answers to Exercises 1–12 above.

Additional Answers Extra

6. 6.4
9. 11.2
12. 19.4
13. The distance between (1, 1) and (5, 2) and the distance between (5, 2) and (4, −2) is $\sqrt{17}$.
14. The slopes of the lines passing through any 2 pairs of these 3 points is 2; thus, the points are collinear. The distance between (−2, −2) and each of the other points is $5\sqrt{5}$ (students may instead show that this distance is $\frac{1}{2}$ of the distance between (3, 8) and (−7, −12)).

Computer Key-In Commentary

Because of round-off errors, SQR (N) may not yield accurate results. SQR (25), for instance, may yield a number not exactly equal to 5.

Radical Expressions

11-7 Multiplication, Division, and Simplification of Radicals

Objective To simplify products and quotients of radicals.

You can use the product and quotient properties of square roots together with the commutative, associative, and distributive axioms to multiply, divide, and simplify square-root radicals.

An expression having a square-root radical is in **simplest form** when

1. no integral radicand has a square factor other than 1,
2. no fractions are under a radical sign, and
3. no radicals are in a denominator.

Example 1 Simplify the following expressions.

a. $3\sqrt{2} \cdot 5\sqrt{8}$ **b.** $\sqrt{3}(2 + \sqrt{3})$

Solution

a. $3\sqrt{2} \cdot 5\sqrt{8} = 3 \cdot 5 \cdot \sqrt{2} \cdot \sqrt{8} = 15\sqrt{16} = 15 \cdot 4 = 60$

b. $\sqrt{3}(2 + \sqrt{3}) = 2\sqrt{3} + \sqrt{3 \cdot 3} = 2\sqrt{3} + 3$

Example 2 Simplify the following expressions.

a. $\frac{3}{\sqrt{7}}$ **b.** $\sqrt{\frac{5}{8}}$ **c.** $\frac{5\sqrt{3}}{4\sqrt{5}}$

Solution

a. $\frac{3}{\sqrt{7}} = \frac{3 \cdot \sqrt{7}}{\sqrt{7} \cdot \sqrt{7}} = \frac{3\sqrt{7}}{(\sqrt{7})^2} = \frac{3\sqrt{7}}{7}$

b. $\sqrt{\frac{5}{8}} = \frac{\sqrt{5}}{\sqrt{8}} = \frac{\sqrt{5} \cdot \sqrt{2}}{\sqrt{8} \cdot \sqrt{2}} = \frac{\sqrt{10}}{\sqrt{16}} = \frac{\sqrt{10}}{4}$

c. $\frac{5\sqrt{3}}{4\sqrt{5}} = \frac{5\sqrt{3} \cdot \sqrt{5}}{4\sqrt{5} \cdot \sqrt{5}} = \frac{5\sqrt{3 \cdot 5}}{4(\sqrt{5})^2} = \frac{5\sqrt{15}}{4 \cdot 5} = \frac{\sqrt{15}}{4}$

The process of expressing a fraction with an irrational denominator, such as $\frac{3}{\sqrt{7}}$, as a fraction with a rational denominator, such as $\frac{3\sqrt{7}}{7}$, is called **rationalizing the denominator.**

Teaching Suggestions
p. T124

Suggested Extensions
p. T124

Chalkboard Examples

Simplify.

1. $3\sqrt{5} \cdot 7\sqrt{5}$
   $3 \cdot 7 \cdot \sqrt{5} \cdot \sqrt{5} =$
   $21\sqrt{25} = 21 \cdot 5 = 105$
2. $\sqrt{7}(2 + 2\sqrt{7})$
   $2\sqrt{7} + 2\sqrt{7 \cdot 7} =$
   $2\sqrt{7} + 2 \cdot 7 =$
   $2\sqrt{7} + 14$
3. $\sqrt{\frac{3}{7}}$
   $\frac{\sqrt{3}}{\sqrt{7}} = \frac{\sqrt{3}}{\sqrt{7}} \cdot \frac{\sqrt{7}}{\sqrt{7}} = \frac{\sqrt{21}}{7}$
4. $\frac{6\sqrt{5}}{7\sqrt{3}}$
   $\frac{6\sqrt{5}}{7\sqrt{3}} \cdot \frac{\sqrt{3}}{\sqrt{3}} = \frac{6\sqrt{5} \cdot \sqrt{3}}{7\sqrt{3} \cdot \sqrt{3}} =$
   $\frac{6\sqrt{15}}{7 \cdot 3} = \frac{2\sqrt{15}}{7}$

Additional A Exercises

Express in simplest form.

1. $7\sqrt{6} \cdot 4\sqrt{6}$ 168
2. $\sqrt{8} \cdot \sqrt{6} \cdot \sqrt{3}$ 12
3. $4\sqrt{507}$ $52\sqrt{3}$
4. $\sqrt{\frac{125}{3} \cdot \frac{3}{5}}$ 5
5. $\sqrt{\frac{8}{5}} \cdot \sqrt{\frac{60}{32}}$ $\sqrt{3}$
6. $\frac{9\sqrt{7}}{\sqrt{35}}$ $\frac{9\sqrt{5}}{5}$

Suggested Assignments

Minimum
Day 1: 528/1–20
 R 524/*Self-Test 2*
Day 2: 528/21–31
 S 518/*P*: 2, 4, 6

Average
Day 1: 528/1–24
 S 524/*P*: 2, 3
 R 524/*Self-Test 2*
Day 2: 528/25–35 odd
 530/1–10
Day 2 finishes Sec. 11-7 and starts Sec. 11-8.

Maximum
Day 1: 528/2–36 even
 S 519/*P*: 10, 11
 R 524/*Self-Test 2*
Day 2: 528/25–43 odd
 530/1–18
Day 2 finishes Sec. 11-7 and starts Sec. 11-8.

Additional Answers
Oral Exercises p. 529

1. $4\sqrt{7}$, $2\sqrt{7}$; $6\sqrt{7}$
2. $8\sqrt{5}$, $-2\sqrt{5}$; $6\sqrt{5}$
3. $2\sqrt{13}$, $-6\sqrt{13}$; $-4\sqrt{13}$
4. $2\sqrt{11}$, $5\sqrt{11}$; $8\sqrt{3} + 7\sqrt{11}$
5. $6\sqrt{14}$, $-3\sqrt{14}$; $3\sqrt{14} + \sqrt{3}$
6. none; $2\sqrt{21} - 4\sqrt{7} + 5\sqrt{3}$
7. $8\sqrt{3}$, $-7\sqrt{3}$; $\sqrt{3}$
8. $8\sqrt{15}$, $-5\sqrt{15}$, $7\sqrt{15}$; $10\sqrt{15}$
9. $6\sqrt{17}$, $-2\sqrt{17}$, $3\sqrt{17}$; $7\sqrt{17}$
10. $\sqrt{12}$, $\sqrt{3}$; $3\sqrt{3}$
11. $\sqrt{75}$, $\sqrt{3}$; $6\sqrt{3}$
12. $\sqrt{18}$, $\sqrt{2}$; $4\sqrt{2}$

Oral Exercises

Express in simplest form.

1. $\sqrt{2} \cdot \sqrt{3}$ $\sqrt{6}$
2. $\dfrac{\sqrt{27}}{\sqrt{3}}$ 3
3. $\dfrac{\sqrt{32}}{\sqrt{2}}$ 4
4. $\sqrt{5} \cdot 4\sqrt{2}$ $4\sqrt{10}$
5. $\sqrt{3} \cdot \sqrt{6}$ $3\sqrt{2}$
6. $\sqrt{2} \cdot \sqrt{12}$ $2\sqrt{6}$
7. $\dfrac{\sqrt{18}}{\sqrt{3}}$ $\sqrt{6}$
8. $\dfrac{\sqrt{54}}{\sqrt{2}}$ $3\sqrt{3}$
9. $\sqrt{5} \cdot \sqrt{15}$ $5\sqrt{3}$
10. $\sqrt{\dfrac{4}{7}}$ $\dfrac{\sqrt{28}}{7}$

Written Exercises

Express in simplest form.

A

1. $\sqrt{2} \cdot 3\sqrt{2}$ 6
2. $3\sqrt{7} \cdot 2\sqrt{7}$ 42
3. $\sqrt{3} \cdot \sqrt{5} \cdot \sqrt{6}$ $3\sqrt{10}$
4. $\sqrt{5} \cdot \sqrt{5} \cdot \sqrt{9}$ 15
5. $2\sqrt{5} \cdot \sqrt{7}$ $2\sqrt{35}$
6. $5\sqrt{2} \cdot \sqrt{5} \cdot \sqrt{8}$ $20\sqrt{5}$
7. $\sqrt{3} \cdot \sqrt{12}$ 6
8. $\sqrt{2} \cdot \sqrt{50}$ 10
9. $6\sqrt{288}$ $72\sqrt{2}$
10. $\sqrt{\dfrac{4}{7}} \cdot \sqrt{\dfrac{7}{4}}$ 1
11. $\sqrt{\dfrac{4}{9} \cdot \dfrac{18}{4}}$ $\sqrt{2}$
12. $\sqrt{\dfrac{9}{7} \cdot \dfrac{14}{36}}$ $\dfrac{\sqrt{2}}{2}$
13. $\sqrt{\dfrac{3}{4}} \cdot \sqrt{\dfrac{5}{6}}$ $\dfrac{\sqrt{10}}{4}$
14. $\sqrt{\dfrac{7}{3}} \cdot \sqrt{\dfrac{3}{28}}$ $\dfrac{1}{2}$
15. $\sqrt{\dfrac{4}{5}} \cdot \sqrt{\dfrac{10}{36}}$ $\dfrac{\sqrt{2}}{3}$
16. $\sqrt{2\dfrac{2}{5}} \cdot \sqrt{1\dfrac{2}{3}}$ 2
17. $\dfrac{1}{5}\sqrt{\dfrac{9}{2}} \cdot \dfrac{1}{2}\sqrt{\dfrac{2}{3}}$ $\dfrac{\sqrt{3}}{10}$
18. $\dfrac{15\sqrt{18}}{5\sqrt{2}}$ 9
19. $\sqrt{\dfrac{10}{13}} \cdot \sqrt{\dfrac{1}{2}}$ $\dfrac{\sqrt{65}}{13}$
20. $\dfrac{9\sqrt{3}}{\sqrt{24}}$ $\dfrac{9\sqrt{2}}{4}$
21. $3\sqrt{\dfrac{48}{9}}$ $4\sqrt{3}$
22. $\dfrac{7\sqrt{45}}{\sqrt{35}}$ $3\sqrt{7}$
23. $\dfrac{14\sqrt{320}}{2\sqrt{5}}$ 56
24. $\dfrac{13\sqrt{8}}{\sqrt{104}}$ $\sqrt{13}$

Simplify. Assume that all variables represent positive real numbers.

B

25. $(5\sqrt{ab^2})(-2\sqrt{a})$ $-10ab$
26. $(-x\sqrt{x^2y})(y\sqrt{xy^2})$ $-x^2y^2\sqrt{xy}$
27. $\sqrt{r}(4 - \sqrt{r})$ $4\sqrt{r} - r$
28. $\sqrt{m}(\sqrt{m^3} + 5)$ $m^2 + 5\sqrt{m}$
29. $(5\sqrt{2})(-2\sqrt{8})(3\sqrt{32})$ $-480\sqrt{2}$
30. $(4\sqrt{5})(-\sqrt{10})(2\sqrt{2})$ -80
31. $(\sqrt{2x})(\sqrt{3x})(2\sqrt{6x^2})$ $12x^2$
32. $\sqrt{27}\sqrt{3x}\sqrt{5x}$ $9x\sqrt{5}$
33. $(4\sqrt{7y})^2$ $112y$
34. $2n(\sqrt{5n})^2$ $10n^2$
35. $3x\sqrt{\dfrac{x}{y}} \cdot \sqrt{\dfrac{4x}{y}}$ $\dfrac{6x^2}{y}$
36. $2q\sqrt{\dfrac{3q}{2r}} \cdot \sqrt{\dfrac{q}{r}}$ $\dfrac{q^2\sqrt{6}}{r}$

C

37. $\sqrt{2a}(\sqrt{8a} - 3\sqrt{12a^2})$ $4a - 6a\sqrt{6a}$
38. $\sqrt{6m}(\sqrt{2m} - 3\sqrt{8m^2})$ $2m\sqrt{3} - 12m\sqrt{3m}$
39. $3\sqrt{8x^3}(2\sqrt{2x} - 5\sqrt{8x^4})$ $24x^2 - 120x^3\sqrt{x}$
40. $2\sqrt{10x^3}(3\sqrt{2x} - 5\sqrt{8x^4})$ $12x^2\sqrt{5} - 40x^3\sqrt{5x}$
41. $(3\sqrt{5y^3})^3$ $135y^4\sqrt{5y}$
42. $(2\sqrt{3y^3})^3$ $24y^4\sqrt{3y}$
43. $(\sqrt{10xy})^3(x\sqrt{5x^3y} - y\sqrt{10xy^3})$ $50x^4y^2\sqrt{2} - 100x^2y^4$
44. $(\sqrt{12xy})^3(x\sqrt{5x^2y} + y\sqrt{6xy^2})$ $24x^3y^2\sqrt{15x} + 72x^2y^3\sqrt{2y}$

11-8 Addition and Subtraction of Radicals

Objective To simplify sums and differences of radicals.

You can use the distributive axiom to simplify the sum of $3\sqrt{6}$ and $5\sqrt{6}$ because they have $\sqrt{6}$ as a common factor.

$$3\sqrt{6} + 5\sqrt{6} = (3 + 5)\sqrt{6} = 8\sqrt{6}$$

On the other hand, terms that have unlike radicands cannot be combined.

$$3\sqrt{5} - 5\sqrt{17} + 6\sqrt{5} = 9\sqrt{5} - 5\sqrt{17}$$

By expressing each radical in simplest form, you can sometimes combine terms in sums and differences of radicals.

Example Simplify $7\sqrt{3} - 6\sqrt{5} + 2\sqrt{75} - 3\sqrt{45}$.

Solution
$$\begin{aligned} 7\sqrt{3} - 6\sqrt{5} + 2\sqrt{75} - 3\sqrt{45} &= 7\sqrt{3} - 6\sqrt{5} + 2\sqrt{25 \cdot 3} - 3\sqrt{9 \cdot 5} \\ &= 7\sqrt{3} - 6\sqrt{5} + 2(5\sqrt{3}) - 3(3\sqrt{5}) \\ &= 7\sqrt{3} - 6\sqrt{5} + 10\sqrt{3} - 9\sqrt{5} \\ &= 17\sqrt{3} - 15\sqrt{5} \end{aligned}$$

To simplify sums or differences of square-root radicals:

1. Express each radical in simplest form.
2. Use the distributive axiom to add or subtract radicals with like radicands.

Oral Exercises

(See p. 528 for answers.)

Indicate the terms in each expression that can be expressed with the same radicand. Then state the expression in simplest form.

1. $4\sqrt{7} + 2\sqrt{7}$
2. $8\sqrt{5} - 2\sqrt{5}$
3. $2\sqrt{13} - 6\sqrt{13}$
4. $2\sqrt{11} + 8\sqrt{3} + 5\sqrt{11}$
5. $6\sqrt{14} - 3\sqrt{14} + \sqrt{3}$
6. $2\sqrt{21} - 4\sqrt{7} + 5\sqrt{3}$
7. $8\sqrt{3} - 7\sqrt{3}$
8. $8\sqrt{15} - 5\sqrt{15} + 7\sqrt{15}$
9. $6\sqrt{17} - 2\sqrt{17} + 3\sqrt{17}$
10. $\sqrt{12} + \sqrt{3}$
11. $\sqrt{75} + \sqrt{3}$
12. $\sqrt{18} + \sqrt{2}$

Teaching Suggestions
p. T125

Suggested Extensions
p. T125

Chalkboard Examples

Simplify.

1. $9\sqrt{11} - 5\sqrt{11}$
   $(9 - 5)\sqrt{11} = 4\sqrt{11}$
2. $4\sqrt{27} + 3\sqrt{3}$
   $4 \cdot 3\sqrt{3} + 3\sqrt{3} = (12 + 3)\sqrt{3} = 15\sqrt{3}$
3. $2\sqrt{50} + \sqrt{72}$
   $2\sqrt{5^2 \cdot 2} + \sqrt{6^2 \cdot 2} = 10\sqrt{2} + 6\sqrt{2} = 16\sqrt{2}$
4. $\sqrt{75} - \sqrt{24} + \sqrt{48} + \sqrt{54}$
   $\sqrt{5^2 \cdot 3} - \sqrt{2^2 \cdot 6} + \sqrt{4^2 \cdot 3} + \sqrt{3^2 \cdot 6} = 5\sqrt{3} - 2\sqrt{6} + 4\sqrt{3} + 3\sqrt{6} = 9\sqrt{3} + \sqrt{6}$
5. $3\sqrt{27} - \frac{1}{2}\sqrt{48} + 10\sqrt{\frac{3}{100}}$
   $3\sqrt{3^2 \cdot 3} - \frac{1}{2}\sqrt{4^2 \cdot 3} + 10\sqrt{\frac{3}{100}} = 9\sqrt{3} - 2\sqrt{3} + \sqrt{3} = 8\sqrt{3}$

Common Error

When adding or subtracting radicals, students may occasionally confuse operations, writing, for example, $4\sqrt{7} + 2\sqrt{7} = 6 \cdot 7 = 42$. This error can often be avoided by using the distributive property as shown in the example in the lesson. You may help students check the reasonableness of their answers by pointing out that just as 4 apples + 2 apples = 6 apples, $4\sqrt{7} + 2\sqrt{7} = 6\sqrt{7}$.

Supplementary Materials

Practice Master 69
Resource Book, p. 122

Suggested Assignments

Minimum
Day 1: 530/1–14
S 524/*P*: 2, 5, 6
Day 2: 530/15–27
S 512/22–28 even

Average
530/12–30 even
S 528/26–36 even
Day 2 of Sec. 11-7 finishes Sec. 11-7 and starts Sec. 11-8.

Maximum
530/19–36
S 524/*P*: 9
Day 2 of Sec. 11-7 finishes Sec. 11-7 and starts Sec. 11-8.

Additional A Exercises

Simplify.

1. $15\sqrt{2} - 8\sqrt{2}$ $7\sqrt{2}$
2. $5\sqrt{192} - 7\sqrt{3}$ $33\sqrt{3}$
3. $3\sqrt{24} + 4\sqrt{150}$ $26\sqrt{6}$
4. $-9\sqrt{75} + 10\sqrt{32}$ $-45\sqrt{3} + 40\sqrt{2}$
5. $\sqrt{432} - \sqrt{300} + \sqrt{192}$ $10\sqrt{3}$
6. $\sqrt{7} - \sqrt{\frac{4}{5}}$ $\frac{5\sqrt{7} - 2\sqrt{5}}{5}$

Mixed Review Exercises

Simplify.

1. $\frac{5}{m^2 - 4} - \frac{3}{2 - m}$ $\frac{3m + 11}{(m + 2)(m - 2)}$ $(m \neq \pm 2)$
2. $18\sqrt{847}$ $198\sqrt{7}$
3. Divide: $\frac{k^5 - k^4 + k^3 - k^2 + k - 1}{k - 1}$ $k^4 + k^2 + 1$
4. Solve: $\frac{135}{95} = \frac{27}{x}$ 19

Written Exercises

Simplify.

A

1. $7\sqrt{2} - 3\sqrt{2}$ $4\sqrt{2}$
2. $9\sqrt{3} + 8\sqrt{3}$ $17\sqrt{3}$
3. $-11\sqrt{23} - 5\sqrt{23}$ $-16\sqrt{23}$
4. $4\sqrt{45} - 3\sqrt{5}$ $9\sqrt{5}$
5. $2\sqrt{2} + 5\sqrt{50}$ $27\sqrt{2}$
6. $-2\sqrt{24} - 3\sqrt{6}$ $-7\sqrt{6}$
7. $2\sqrt{28} - 5\sqrt{63}$ $-11\sqrt{7}$
8. $5\sqrt{18} + 7\sqrt{25}$ $15\sqrt{2} + 35$
9. $4\sqrt{32} - 3\sqrt{27}$ $16\sqrt{2} - 9\sqrt{3}$
10. $-4\sqrt{75} + 3\sqrt{147}$ $\sqrt{3}$
11. $-11\sqrt{8} - 7\sqrt{12}$ $-22\sqrt{2} - 14\sqrt{3}$
12. $\sqrt{175} - 4\sqrt{112}$ $-11\sqrt{7}$
13. $11\sqrt{19} - 7\sqrt{11} + \sqrt{19}$ $12\sqrt{19} - 7\sqrt{11}$
14. $-4\sqrt{2} + 6\sqrt{72} - 8\sqrt{32}$ 0
15. $5\sqrt{28} + 2\sqrt{7} - \sqrt{14}$ $12\sqrt{7} - \sqrt{14}$
16. $-3\sqrt{54} + 5\sqrt{40} - 6\sqrt{96}$
17. $-\sqrt{338} - \sqrt{200} + \sqrt{162}$ $-14\sqrt{2}$
18. $2\sqrt{80} + 7\sqrt{44} - 8\sqrt{99}$ $8\sqrt{5} - 10\sqrt{11}$

16. $-33\sqrt{6} + 10\sqrt{10}$

Simplify.

Example
$$\sqrt{21} - \sqrt{\frac{3}{7}} = \sqrt{21} - \frac{\sqrt{3}}{\sqrt{7}}$$
$$= \sqrt{21} - \frac{\sqrt{3} \cdot \sqrt{7}}{\sqrt{7} \cdot \sqrt{7}}$$
$$= \sqrt{21} - \frac{\sqrt{21}}{7}$$
$$= \frac{7\sqrt{21} - \sqrt{21}}{7} = \frac{6\sqrt{21}}{7}$$

24. $\frac{21\sqrt{5}}{5} - \frac{3\sqrt{2}}{4}$
28. $\frac{2\sqrt{6}}{3} + \frac{\sqrt{30}}{6} - \frac{2\sqrt{10}}{3}$

19. $\sqrt{6} - \sqrt{\frac{2}{3}}$ $\frac{2\sqrt{6}}{3}$
20. $\sqrt{15} - \sqrt{\frac{5}{2}}$ $\sqrt{15} - \frac{\sqrt{10}}{2}$
21. $3\sqrt{18} + \sqrt{\frac{2}{25}}$ $\frac{46\sqrt{2}}{5}$
22. $\sqrt{\frac{5}{7}} - \sqrt{\frac{7}{5}}$ $-\frac{2\sqrt{35}}{35}$
23. $\sqrt{\frac{5}{6}} - \sqrt{\frac{3}{10}}$ $\frac{\sqrt{30}}{15}$
24. $7\sqrt{\frac{9}{5}} - \sqrt{\frac{9}{8}}$

B

25. $5\sqrt{5} + 2\sqrt{20} - 6\sqrt{\frac{9}{10}}$ $9\sqrt{5} - \frac{9\sqrt{10}}{5}$
26. $4\sqrt{\frac{5}{6}} - 3\sqrt{\frac{6}{5}} - \sqrt{30}$ $-\frac{14\sqrt{30}}{15}$
27. $2\sqrt{\frac{7}{2}} + 4\sqrt{\frac{7}{8}} - \frac{1}{2}\sqrt{98}$ $2\sqrt{14} - \frac{7\sqrt{2}}{2}$
28. $2\sqrt{\frac{2}{3}} + \sqrt{\frac{5}{6}} - \frac{1}{3}\sqrt{40}$
29. $2\sqrt{3}(\sqrt{27} - 3\sqrt{6})$ $18 - 18\sqrt{2}$
30. $5\sqrt{2}(4\sqrt{8} - 2\sqrt{12})$ $80 - 20\sqrt{6}$

Simplify. Assume that all variables represent positive real numbers.

C

31. $3\sqrt{36x^3} - 5\sqrt{9x^5}$ $18x\sqrt{x} - 15x^2\sqrt{x}$
32. $5\sqrt{90y^4} - 3y\sqrt{160y^2}$ $3y^2\sqrt{10}$
33. $\sqrt{\frac{x^2}{9} + \frac{x^2}{16}}$ $\frac{5x}{12}$
34. $\sqrt{\frac{x^2}{36} - \frac{x^2}{100}}$ $\frac{2x}{15}$
35. $\sqrt{\frac{x^2}{a^2} + \frac{x^2}{b^2}}$ $\frac{x\sqrt{a^2 + b^2}}{ab}$
36. $\sqrt{\frac{x}{a}} + \sqrt{\frac{a}{x}}$ $\frac{\sqrt{ax}(x + a)}{ax}$

11-9 Multiplication of Binomials Containing Radicals

Objective To multiply binomials containing square-root radicals.

When working with radicals, you sometimes need to use the special methods of multiplying binomials you learned in Chapter 5.

Example 1 Simplify $(5 + \sqrt{3})(5 - \sqrt{3})$.

Solution The pattern is $(a + b)(a - b) = a^2 - b^2$.

$$(5 + \sqrt{3})(5 - \sqrt{3}) = 5^2 - (\sqrt{3})^2$$
$$= 25 - 3 = 22$$

Example 2 Simplify $(5 + \sqrt{7})^2$.

Solution The pattern is $(a + b)^2 = a^2 + 2ab + b^2$.

$$(5 + \sqrt{7})^2 = (5)^2 + 2(5)(\sqrt{7}) + (\sqrt{7})^2$$
$$= 25 + 10\sqrt{7} + 7 = 32 + 10\sqrt{7}$$

Example 3 Simplify $(3\sqrt{2} - 5\sqrt{6})^2$.

Solution The pattern is $(a - b)^2 = a^2 - 2ab + b^2$.

$$(3\sqrt{2} - 5\sqrt{6})^2 = (3\sqrt{2})^2 - 2(3)(5)(\sqrt{2})(\sqrt{6}) + (5\sqrt{6})^2$$
$$= 9(2) - 30\sqrt{12} + 25(6)$$
$$= 18 - 30\sqrt{4(3)} + 150 = 168 - 60\sqrt{3}$$

If b and d are both nonnegative, then the binomials

$$a\sqrt{b} + c\sqrt{d} \quad \text{and} \quad a\sqrt{b} - c\sqrt{d}$$

are called **conjugates** of one another. Conjugates differ only in the sign of one term. If a, b, c, and d are all integers, then the product

$$(a\sqrt{b} + c\sqrt{d})(a\sqrt{b} - c\sqrt{d})$$

will be an integer (see Example 1). Conjugates can be used to rationalize binomial denominators that contain radicals.

Example 4 Rationalize the denominator of the fraction $\frac{2}{4 - 2\sqrt{7}}$.

Solution

$$\frac{2}{4 - 2\sqrt{7}} = \left(\frac{2}{4 - 2\sqrt{7}}\right)\left(\frac{4 + 2\sqrt{7}}{4 + 2\sqrt{7}}\right) = \frac{8 + 4\sqrt{7}}{16 - (2\sqrt{7})^2}$$
$$= \frac{8 + 4\sqrt{7}}{16 - 28} = \frac{8 + 4\sqrt{7}}{-12} = \frac{-2 - \sqrt{7}}{3}$$

Teaching Suggestions
p. T125

Suggested Extensions
p. T125

Chalkboard Examples

Simplify.

1. $(7 + \sqrt{2})(7 - \sqrt{2})$
   $7^2 - (\sqrt{2})^2 =$
   $49 - 2 = 47$
2. $(2\sqrt{3} - 3)^2$
   $(2\sqrt{3})^2 - 2(2\sqrt{3})(3) + 3^2 = 12 - 12\sqrt{3} + 9 = 21 - 12\sqrt{3}$
3. $(5 - 2\sqrt{5})(3 + 4\sqrt{5})$
   $15 + 14\sqrt{5} - 40 = -25 + 14\sqrt{5}$
4. Rationalize the denominator of the fraction $\frac{2}{3 + \sqrt{3}}$.
   $\frac{2}{3 + \sqrt{3}} \cdot \frac{3 - \sqrt{3}}{3 - \sqrt{3}} = \frac{6 - 2\sqrt{3}}{9 - 3} = \frac{6 - 2\sqrt{3}}{6} = \frac{3 - \sqrt{3}}{3}$

Common Errors

Sometimes students think that the conjugate of $4 + \sqrt{11}$, for example, is $-4 + \sqrt{11}$. Point out that the first terms of conjugate radicals are identical and that the second terms differ only in sign.

To rationalize the denominators of Written Exercises 26–28 and 30, some students may multiply each numerator by its conjugate and each denominator by its conjugate. Point out that to get an expression that is equivalent to the given fraction, the only expression that they can multiply by must equal 1.

Suggested Assignments

Minimum
532/1–29 odd

Average
532/1–31 odd
S 530/11–29 odd

Maximum
532/1–35 odd
S 530/31, 33, 35

Additional A Exercises

Express in simplest form.

1. $(5 - \sqrt{2})(5 + \sqrt{2})$ 23
2. $(\sqrt{13} + \sqrt{21}) \cdot (\sqrt{13} - \sqrt{21})$ -8
3. $(6 + \sqrt{5})^2$ $41 + 12\sqrt{5}$
4. $(3\sqrt{5} - \sqrt{6})^2$ $51 - 6\sqrt{30}$
5. $4\sqrt{3}(7\sqrt{12} - 5\sqrt{27})$ -12
6. $-8\sqrt{5}(8\sqrt{5} - 4\sqrt{125})$ 480

Mixed Review Exercises

1. Solve: $x + \frac{x}{6} = 2x - \frac{x+8}{2}$ 12
2. 90 is 30% of what number? 300
3. Penn County's Helping Hand project reported a 12% increase in the number of volunteers it has this year. If it had 150 volunteers last year, how many does it have this year? 168
4. Simplify: $\sqrt{27} + 2\sqrt{48} - 4\sqrt{75}$ $-9\sqrt{3}$

Oral Exercises

Complete. Express in simplest form.

1. $(\sqrt{3} + 2)(\sqrt{3} - 2) = 3 - \underline{?} = \underline{?}$ 4; -1
2. $(7 - \sqrt{5})(7 + \sqrt{5}) = 49 - \underline{?} = \underline{?}$ 5; 44
3. $(\sqrt{2} + 5)^2 = 2 + \underline{?} + 25 = 27 + \underline{?}$ $10\sqrt{2}$; $10\sqrt{2}$
4. $(4 - \sqrt{7})^2 = 16 - \underline{?} + \underline{?} = \underline{?}$ $8\sqrt{7}$; 7; $23 - 8\sqrt{7}$

State the conjugate of each binomial.

5. $9 + 3\sqrt{5}$ $9 - 3\sqrt{5}$
6. $-8 - 5\sqrt{11}$ $-8 + 5\sqrt{11}$
7. $-6 + 5\sqrt{7}$ $-6 - 5\sqrt{7}$
8. $3 - 7\sqrt{11}$ $3 + 7\sqrt{11}$

Written Exercises

Express in simplest form.

A

1. $(2 - \sqrt{5})(2 + \sqrt{5})$ -1
2. $(4 + \sqrt{11})(4 - \sqrt{11})$ 5
3. $(\sqrt{17} + 4)(\sqrt{17} - 4)$ 1
4. $(\sqrt{13} - 9)(\sqrt{13} + 9)$ -68
5. $(\sqrt{15} - \sqrt{3})(\sqrt{15} + \sqrt{3})$ 12
6. $(\sqrt{19} + \sqrt{21})(\sqrt{19} - \sqrt{21})$ -2
7. $(5 + \sqrt{3})^2$ $28 + 10\sqrt{3}$
8. $(7 - \sqrt{7})^2$ $56 - 14\sqrt{7}$
9. $(2\sqrt{2} - 3)^2$ $17 - 12\sqrt{2}$
10. $(\sqrt{11} + \sqrt{3})^2$ $14 + 2\sqrt{33}$
11. $(\sqrt{13} + 2\sqrt{5})^2$ $33 + 4\sqrt{65}$
12. $(2\sqrt{7} - \sqrt{2})^2$ $30 - 4\sqrt{14}$
13. $2\sqrt{5}(3\sqrt{10} - 4\sqrt{5})$ $30\sqrt{2} - 40$
14. $5\sqrt{3}(2\sqrt{6} - 4\sqrt{15})$ $30\sqrt{2} - 60\sqrt{5}$
15. $-2\sqrt{7}(3\sqrt{14} - 5\sqrt{7})$ $-42\sqrt{2} + 70$
16. $4\sqrt{6}(5\sqrt{3} - \sqrt{12})$ $36\sqrt{2}$

B

17. $(4\sqrt{3} - 5)(2\sqrt{3} + 3)$ $9 + 2\sqrt{3}$
18. $(\sqrt{2} + 5\sqrt{11})(4\sqrt{2} - 3\sqrt{11})$ $-157 + 17\sqrt{22}$
19. $(3\sqrt{7} - 6\sqrt{5})(4\sqrt{7} + \sqrt{5})$ $54 - 21\sqrt{35}$
20. $(7\sqrt{13} + 2\sqrt{6})(2\sqrt{13} + 3\sqrt{6})$ 20. $218 + 25\sqrt{78}$
21. $(5\sqrt{10} - 2\sqrt{3})(5\sqrt{10} + 7\sqrt{3})$ $208 + 25\sqrt{30}$
22. $(8\sqrt{6} - 2\sqrt{3})(2\sqrt{6} - 3\sqrt{3})$ $114 - 84\sqrt{2}$

Rationalize the denominator of each fraction.

23. $\frac{4}{1 + \sqrt{2}}$ $4\sqrt{2} - 4$
24. $\frac{3}{\sqrt{5} - 2}$ $3\sqrt{5} + 6$
25. $\frac{1}{3 - \sqrt{3}}$ $\frac{3 + \sqrt{3}}{6}$
26. $\frac{1 - \sqrt{2}}{2 + \sqrt{2}}$ $\frac{4 - 3\sqrt{2}}{2}$
27. $\frac{2 + \sqrt{5}}{1 - \sqrt{3}}$ $\frac{2 + \sqrt{5} + 2\sqrt{3} + \sqrt{15}}{-2}$
28. $\frac{\sqrt{3} - 4}{\sqrt{7} + 2}$ $\frac{\sqrt{21} - 4\sqrt{7} - 2\sqrt{3} + 8}{3}$
29. $\frac{7}{3\sqrt{3} + 4}$ $\frac{21\sqrt{3} - 28}{11}$
30. $\frac{4 + 2\sqrt{2}}{2\sqrt{5} - 3}$ $\frac{8\sqrt{5} + 4\sqrt{10} + 12 + 6\sqrt{2}}{11}$

If $f(x) = x^2 - 4x + 1$, find these function values.

31. $f(\sqrt{7})$ $8 - 4\sqrt{7}$
32. $f(\sqrt{2} + 1)$ $-2\sqrt{2}$
33. $f(\sqrt{3} + 2)$ 0
34. $f(\sqrt{5} - 1)$ $11 - 6\sqrt{5}$

35. Show that $(1 + \sqrt{3})$ and $(1 - \sqrt{3})$ are roots of the equation $x^2 - 2x - 2 = 0$.

36. Show that $5 + \sqrt{3}$ and $5 - \sqrt{3}$ are roots of the equation $x^2 - 10x + 22 = 0$.

37. Show that $\frac{1}{3} + \frac{\sqrt{7}}{3}$ and $\frac{1}{3} - \frac{\sqrt{7}}{3}$ are roots of the equation $3x^2 - 2x - 2 = 0$.

C 38. Write an expression in simplest form for the area of a rectangle whose base is $\frac{5\sqrt{2} + 3}{5}$ units and whose height is $\frac{3\sqrt{2} - 2}{3}$ units. $\frac{24 - \sqrt{2}}{15}$

Simplify each expression, assuming that the value of each variable is nonnegative.

39. $(\sqrt{x} + y)(\sqrt{x} - y)$ $x - y^2$

40. $(x + 2\sqrt{3})^2$ $x^2 + 4x\sqrt{3} + 12$

41. $(3r\sqrt{s} - 2q)(5r\sqrt{s} + 3q)$ $15r^2s - qr\sqrt{s} - 6q^2$

42. $\sqrt{\frac{x}{y}} - 2\sqrt{\frac{y}{x}} + \sqrt{xy}$ $\frac{\sqrt{xy}(x - 2y + xy)}{xy}$

Historical Note / π

The number π occurs naturally as the ratio of the circumference of a circle to its diameter. Since π is irrational, it is not possible to get an exact value for it. Throughout history, however, mathematicians have tried to obtain better approximations for it.

The first known approximation (other than just using 3) was given in the Rhind mathematical papyrus as $(\frac{4}{3})^4$, or 3.1604 . . . . This was used until 240 B.C. when Archimedes calculated π to be between $\frac{223}{71}$ and $\frac{22}{7}$, or 3.14, to two decimal places. Four hundred years later this approximation was improved slightly to $\frac{377}{120}$, or 3.1416.

In China, Tsu Ch'ung-chih gave a value for π of $\frac{355}{113}$, or 3.1415929 . . . , which is correct to six decimal places. Indian mathematicians used $\frac{62,832}{20,000}$, although this was later refined to $\frac{754}{240}$.

Following the Middle Ages, European mathematicians once again tried to get better approximations for π. François Viète found π to nine decimal places in 1579 and Adrianus Romanus calculated it to fifteen places fourteen years later. In 1706, the calculation had reached 100 decimal places and William Jones became the first person to use the symbol π to represent the number. By 1737 π was in general use.

In 1767 π was shown to be an irrational number, although this did not stop people from calculating more decimal places. By the mid-nineteenth century π had been calculated to over 400 places. In 1948 the last calculation by hand was done to 808 places.

Since 1949 computers have been used to calculate approximations for π. The first attempt in 1949 produced 2037 decimal places (after 70 hours). By 1967 the value had been calculated to over 500,000 places.

Additional Answers
Written Exercises

35. $(1 + \sqrt{3})^2 - 2(1 + \sqrt{3}) - 2 = 1 + 2\sqrt{3} + 3 - 2 - 2\sqrt{3} - 2 = 0$; $(1 - \sqrt{3})^2 - 2(1 - \sqrt{3}) - 2 = 1 - 2\sqrt{3} + 3 - 2 + 2\sqrt{3} - 2 = 0$

36. $(5 + \sqrt{3})^2 - 10(5 + \sqrt{3}) + 22 = 25 + 10\sqrt{3} + 3 - 50 - 10\sqrt{3} + 22 = 0$; $(5 - \sqrt{3})^2 - 10(5 - \sqrt{3}) + 22 = 25 - 10\sqrt{3} + 3 - 50 + 10\sqrt{3} + 22 = 0$

37. $3\left(\frac{1}{3} + \frac{\sqrt{7}}{3}\right)^2 - 2\left(\frac{1}{3} + \frac{\sqrt{7}}{3}\right) - 2 = 3\left(\frac{1}{9} + \frac{2\sqrt{7}}{9} + \frac{7}{9}\right) - \frac{2}{3} - \frac{2\sqrt{7}}{3} - 2 = \frac{1}{3} + \frac{2\sqrt{7}}{3} + \frac{7}{3} - \frac{2}{3} - \frac{2\sqrt{7}}{3} - 2 = 0$; $3\left(\frac{1}{3} - \frac{\sqrt{7}}{3}\right)^2 - 2\left(\frac{1}{3} - \frac{\sqrt{7}}{3}\right) - 2 = 3\left(\frac{1}{9} - \frac{2\sqrt{7}}{9} + \frac{7}{9}\right) - \frac{2}{3} + \frac{2\sqrt{7}}{3} - 2 = \frac{1}{3} - \frac{2\sqrt{7}}{3} + \frac{7}{3} - \frac{2}{3} + \frac{2\sqrt{7}}{3} - 2 = 0$

Teaching Suggestions
p. T126

Chalkboard Examples

Solve.

1. $\sqrt{x} = 10$
   Squaring, $x = 100$
   Check: $\sqrt{100} = 10$ ✓
   $\therefore$ the solution is 100.
2. $\sqrt{3x + 1} = 5$
   Squaring, $3x + 1 = 25$
   $3x = 24$
   $x = 8$
   Check: $\sqrt{3 \cdot 8 + 1} \stackrel{?}{=} 5$
   $\sqrt{25} = 5$ ✓
   $\therefore$ the solution is 8.
3. $\sqrt{3n^2 + 1} = 7$
   Squaring, $3n^2 + 1 = 49$
   $3n^2 = 48$
   $n^2 = 16$
   $n = \pm 4$
   Since both roots check, the solutions are 4 and -4.
4. $\sqrt{2m^2 - 25} = m$
   Squaring,
   $2m^2 - 25 = m^2$
   $m^2 = 25$
   $m = \pm 5$
   Since 5 checks but -5 does not, the solution is 5.

Suggested Assignments

Minimum
535/1–23 odd
536/*P*: 1–4
R 537/*Self-Test 3*

Average
535/2–32 even
536/*P*: 1–6, 9
R 537/*Self-Test 3*

Maximum
Day 1: 535/2–30 even
536/*P*: 3–6, 9, 10
S 533/38, 39, 42
Day 2: 535/31–47 odd
536/*P*: 11, 12
R 537/*Self-Test 3*

11-10 Simple Radical Equations

Objective To solve simple radical equations.

An equation that has a variable in the radicand is called a **radical equation.** Simple radical equations are solved by isolating the radical on one side of the equals sign and then squaring both sides of the equation.

Example 1 Solve $\sqrt{x} = 12$.

Solution

$$\sqrt{x} = 12$$
$$(\sqrt{x})^2 = 144 \quad \{\text{Square both sides.}$$
$$x = 144$$

Check: $\sqrt{144} \stackrel{?}{=} 12$
$12 = 12$ ✓

$\therefore$ the solution is 144. ***Answer***

Example 2 Solve $\sqrt{4x + 1} + 5 = 8$.

Solution

$$\sqrt{4x + 1} + 5 = 8$$
$$\sqrt{4x + 1} = 3$$
$$4x + 1 = 9$$
$$4x = 8$$
$$x = 2$$

Check: $\sqrt{4(2) + 1} + 5 \stackrel{?}{=} 8$
$\sqrt{8 + 1} + 5 \stackrel{?}{=} 8$
$\sqrt{9} + 5 \stackrel{?}{=} 8$
$8 = 8$ ✓

$\therefore$ the solution is 2. ***Answer***

When you square both sides of an equation, the new equation is not necessarily equivalent to the original equation. Therefore, you must *check every apparent root in the original equation* to see whether it is a root. By the multiplication property of equality, any root of the original equation is also a root of the squared equation. Thus, you are sure to find all the roots of the original equation among the roots of the squared equation.

Example 3 Solve $\sqrt{10x^2 - 96} - 2x = 0$.

Solution

$$\sqrt{10x^2 - 96} - 2x = 0$$
$$\sqrt{10x^2 - 96} = 2x \quad \{\text{Isolate the radical.}$$
$$10x^2 - 96 = 4x^2 \quad \{\text{Square both sides.}$$
$$6x^2 = 96$$
$$x^2 = 16$$
$$x = 4 \text{ or } x = -4$$

Check: $\sqrt{10(4)^2 - 96} - 2(4) \stackrel{?}{=} 0$
$\sqrt{160 - 96} - 8 \stackrel{?}{=} 0$
$\sqrt{64} - 8 \stackrel{?}{=} 0$
$8 - 8 = 0$ ✓

$\sqrt{10(-4)^2 - 96} - 2(-4) \stackrel{?}{=} 0$
$\sqrt{160 - 96} + 8 \stackrel{?}{=} 0$
$8 + 8 \neq 0$
-4 is not a solution.

$\therefore$ the solution is 4. ***Answer***

Oral Exercises

Solve.

1. $\sqrt{x} = 5$ 25
2. $\sqrt{y} = 6$ 36
3. $\sqrt{d} = 11$ 121
4. $\sqrt{y} = 20$ 400
5. $\sqrt{4a} = 10$ 25
6. $\sqrt{3m} = 9$ 27

State the first step in the solution of each equation.

7. $\sqrt{3x} = 6$ $3x = 36$
8. $\sqrt{5a + 4} = 12$ $5a + 4 = 144$
9. $\sqrt{27z - 12} = 5z$ $27z - 12 = 25z^2$
10. $\sqrt{z - 7} = 8$ $z - 7 = 64$
11. $2\sqrt{3b} = 4$ $4(3b) = 16$
12. $\sqrt{5x} - 3 = 12$ $\sqrt{5x} = 15$

Written Exercises

31. $\{-3\sqrt{7}, 3\sqrt{7}\}$ 33. $\{-\sqrt{19}, \sqrt{19}\}$
32. $\left\{-\frac{\sqrt{69}}{3}, \frac{\sqrt{69}}{3}\right\}$ 36. $\sqrt{15}$

Solve.

A

1. $\sqrt{x} = 10$ 100
2. $\sqrt{y} = 14$ 196
3. $\sqrt{2m} = 8$ 32
4. $\sqrt{3a} = 9$ 27
5. $\sqrt{4m} = \frac{1}{3}$ $\frac{1}{36}$
6. $\sqrt{8x} = \frac{2}{5}$ $\frac{1}{50}$
7. $\sqrt{n} + 2 = 7$ 25
8. $\sqrt{z} - 3 = 8$ 121
9. $\frac{1}{3} + \sqrt{x} = 2$ $\frac{25}{9}$
10. $\sqrt{\frac{x}{2}} = 3$ 18
11. $\sqrt{\frac{a}{5}} = 6$ 180
12. $\sqrt{y - 3} = 2$ 7
13. $\sqrt{m + 5} = 1$ -4
14. $3\sqrt{2b} = 6$ 2
15. $5\sqrt{3z} = 3$ $\frac{3}{25}$
16. $\sqrt{4x} + 2 = 6$ 4
17. $\sqrt{3x} - 5 = 4$ 27
18. $\sqrt{8a} + 3 = 4$ $\frac{1}{8}$
19. $\sqrt{2z + 3} + 1 = 4$ 3
20. $\sqrt{5y - 2} + 3 = 9$ $\frac{38}{5}$
21. $\sqrt{6x - 1} - 4 = -1$ $\frac{5}{3}$
22. $\sqrt{\frac{4y}{3}} + 2 = 10$ 48
23. $\sqrt{\frac{8b}{5}} - 3 = 4$ $\frac{245}{8}$
24. $\sqrt{\frac{7m}{6}} - 1 = 8$ $\frac{486}{7}$

B

25. $\sqrt{\frac{2x + 3}{5}} = 3$ 21
26. $\sqrt{\frac{4n - 5}{7}} = 3$ 17
27. $\sqrt{\frac{7k - 10}{9}} = 4$ 22
28. $\sqrt{r} = 4\sqrt{5}$ 80
29. $6\sqrt{t} = 18\sqrt{7}$ 63
30. $6\sqrt{y} = 5\sqrt{10}$ $\frac{125}{18}$
31. $\sqrt{2a^2 - 5} = 11$
32. $2\sqrt{3c^2 + 2} = 10$
33. $4\sqrt{4y^2 + 5} = 36$
34. $\sqrt{x^2 + 4} = 2 - x$ 0
35. $\sqrt{5b^2 - 36} = 2b$ 6
36. $\sqrt{12m^2 - 45} = 3m$
37. $\sqrt{x^2 + 1} = 1 - x$ 0
38. $\sqrt{3a^2 - 32} = a$ 4
39. $\sqrt{7b^2 + 14} = 3b\sqrt{7}$

C

40. $\sqrt{a^2 + 8a} = 3$ $\{1, -9\}$
41. $\sqrt{15x^2 - 12x} = 9x$ 0
42. $\sqrt{x} + 2 = \sqrt{9x}$ 1
43. $\sqrt{c^2 + 3c} = 2$ $\{-4, 1\}$
44. $\sqrt{10y^2 - 16y} = 4y$ 0
45. $\sqrt{a} + 1 = \sqrt{4a}$ 1

Solve the following systems of equations.

46. $2\sqrt{a} + 3\sqrt{b} = 13$
$4\sqrt{a} - 3\sqrt{b} = -1$ (4, 9)

47. $5\sqrt{a} - 2\sqrt{b} = 4\sqrt{2}$
$2\sqrt{a} + 3\sqrt{b} = 13\sqrt{2}$ (8, 18)

Supplementary Materials

Practice Master 70
Test 40
Resource Book, p. 123

Additional A Exercises

Solve.

1. $\sqrt{z} = 16$ 256
2. $\sqrt{2m} = 4$ 8
3. $\sqrt{x} + 6 = 14$ 64
4. $\sqrt{\frac{x}{3}} = 7$ 147
5. $\sqrt{z + 2} = 3$ 7
6. $\sqrt{5x} - 6 = 4$ 20
7. $\sqrt{4m - 3} + 6 = 10$ $\frac{19}{4}$
8. $\sqrt{\frac{5p}{3}} - 8 = -7$ $\frac{3}{5}$

Common Errors

Students may give incorrect solutions because they have forgotten that checking the solutions of radical equations is not only helpful but necessary. (See the explanation that follows the solution to Example 2.) However, students who do check their solutions may not discard extraneous roots such as -4 in Example 3, because they think that statements such as $\sqrt{64} + 8 = 0$ are true. Remind students that $\sqrt{a} \neq \pm\sqrt{a}$ (see p. 510).

Some students may have difficulty with exercises such as Written Exercises 34 and 37. In solving the radical equation in Exercise 34, for example, students may write $2 - x$ or $4 - x^2$ for $(2 - x)^2$. Remind them that $(a - b)^2 = a^2 - 2ab + b^2$.

Mixed Review Exercises

1. It takes Molly $1\frac{1}{2}$ h to package 100 pounds of meat and it takes Micky $1\frac{1}{3}$ h to do the same job. How long will it take them to do the job together? $\frac{12}{17}$ h
2. Express 0.00096 in scientific notation. 9.6×10^{-4}
3. Simplify $(3x^{-7})^2$. Give your answer in terms of positive exponents. $\frac{9}{x^{14}}$
4. Multiply: $(\sqrt{5} - \sqrt{3})(\sqrt{5} + \sqrt{3})$ 2

Problems

Solve.

A 1. The square root of twice a number is 14. Find the number. 98

2. Twice the square root of a number is 22. Find the number. 121
3. One sixth of the square root of a number is 5. Find the number. 900
4. The square root of one sixth of a number is 5. Find the number. 150
5. When 4 times a number is increased by 5, the square root of the result is 11. Find the number. 29
6. When 6 is subtracted from the square root of twice a number, the result is 58. Find the number. 2048

B 7. The radius of a circle is related to the area of a circle by the formula $r = \sqrt{\frac{A}{\pi}}$. Find the area of a circle whose radius is 15 cm. Express your answer in terms of π. 225π cm^2

8. The radius of a cylinder is related to its volume and its height by the formula $r = \sqrt{\frac{V}{\pi h}}$. Find the volume of a cylinder whose radius is 12 cm and whose height is 25 cm. Express your answer in terms of π. 3600π cm^3
9. The velocity of a free-falling object can be found by using the formula $v = \sqrt{2gd}$, where v is in m/s, $g = 9.8$ m/s^2, and d is the distance in meters. Find the distance a ball falls if its velocity is 14 m/s. 10 m

C 10. The current I that flows through an electrical appliance is determined by $I = \sqrt{\frac{P}{R}}$, where P is the power required and R is the resistance of the appliance. To use this formula, express the current in amperes (A), the power in watts (W), and the resistance in ohms (Ω). If an electric hair dryer has a resistance of 60 Ω and draws 4.5 A of current, how much power does it use? 1215 W

11. The geometric mean of two numbers is the positive square root of their product. Find two consecutive even integers whose geometric mean is $10\sqrt{26}$. -52 and -50 or 50 and 52
12. The period of a pendulum (T) is the amount of time (in seconds) it takes the pendulum to make a complete swing back and forth. The period is determined by the formula $T = 2\pi\sqrt{\frac{l}{9.8}}$ where l is the length of the pendulum in meters. Find the length of a pendulum with a period of 6 seconds. Express your answer to the nearest tenth. (Use $\pi \approx 3.14$.) 8.9 m

Self-Test 3

Vocabulary simplest form of a radical (p. 527)
rationalizing the denominator (p. 527)
conjugate (p. 531)
radical equation (p. 534)

Express in simplest form.

1. $2\sqrt{3} \cdot 5\sqrt{3}$ 30 **2.** $\sqrt{\frac{7}{9}} \cdot \sqrt{\frac{27}{21}}$ 1 **Obj. 11-7, p. 527**

3. $4\sqrt{5} + \sqrt{11} - 3\sqrt{11} + \sqrt{5}$ $5\sqrt{5} - 2\sqrt{11}$ **4.** $5\sqrt{48} - 8\sqrt{27}$ $-4\sqrt{3}$ **Obj. 11-8, p. 529**

5. $(3 - \sqrt{6})^2$ $15 - 6\sqrt{6}$ **6.** $(\sqrt{5} - \sqrt{2})(\sqrt{5} + \sqrt{2})$ 3 **Obj. 11-9, p. 531**

Rationalize the denominator.

7. $\frac{4}{\sqrt{5} + 1}$ $\sqrt{5} - 1$ **8.** $\frac{\sqrt{3}}{\sqrt{3} - 2}$ $-3 - 2\sqrt{3}$

Solve.

9. $\sqrt{y} + 3 = 5$ 4 **10.** $\sqrt{5x - 2} + 3 = 6$ $\frac{11}{5}$ **Obj. 11-10, p. 534**

Check your answers with those at the back of the book.

Extra / Fractional Exponents

In Chapter 4 you learned the Rule of Exponents for Multiplication, which states that for all positive integers m and n, $a^m \cdot a^n = a^{m+n}$. Thus, you can simplify $2^3 \cdot 2^4$ as follows.

$$2^3 \cdot 2^4 = 2^{3+4} = 2^7$$

If the Rule of Exponents for Multiplication were to hold for all positive numbers, and not just for positive integers, what would be the value of n in the equation $2^n \cdot 2^n = 2$?

Since $$2^n \cdot 2^n = 2^{n+n} = 2^{2n},$$

you have $$2^{2n} = 2.$$

The bases are equal (and not -1, 0, or 1); therefore, the exponents must be equal. Thus, $2n = 1$, or $n = \frac{1}{2}$; and you have $2^{\frac{1}{2}} \cdot 2^{\frac{1}{2}} = 2$.

Because $\sqrt{2} \cdot \sqrt{2} = 2$ and $(-\sqrt{2})(-\sqrt{2}) = 2$, it makes sense to define $2^{\frac{1}{2}}$ as either the positive or the negative square root of 2. Selecting the positive, or principal, square root, we define

$$2^{\frac{1}{2}} = \sqrt{2}.$$

Quick Quiz

Express in simplest form.

1. $4\sqrt{5} \cdot 3\sqrt{5}$ 60

2. $\sqrt{\frac{5}{16}} \cdot \sqrt{\frac{12}{15}}$ $\frac{1}{2}$

3. $2\sqrt{6} - \sqrt{10} + 4\sqrt{10} - \sqrt{6}$ $\sqrt{6} + 3\sqrt{10}$

4. $6\sqrt{45} - 2\sqrt{80}$ $10\sqrt{5}$

5. $(4 + \sqrt{5})^2$ $21 + 8\sqrt{5}$

6. $(\sqrt{6} + \sqrt{3})(\sqrt{6} - \sqrt{3})$ 3

Rationalize the denominator.

7. $\frac{2}{\sqrt{7} + 2}$ $\frac{2\sqrt{7} - 4}{3}$

8. $\frac{\sqrt{6}}{5 + \sqrt{6}}$ $\frac{5\sqrt{6} - 6}{19}$

Solve.

9. $4 + \sqrt{x} = 9$ 25

10. $\sqrt{4x + 1} + 2 = 9$ 12

Radicals are not restricted to square roots. The symbol $\sqrt[n]{a}$ is used to indicate the principal nth root of a, where n is a positive integer. Thus, you can have third (or cube) roots, fourth roots, fifth roots, and so on. As you have seen, the *root index, n,* is omitted when $n = 2$.

Just as the inverse of squaring a number is finding the square root of that number, the inverse of cubing a number is finding its cube root. For example, since $2^3 = 8$, $\sqrt[3]{8}$, read "the cube root of 8," is 2. Likewise, since $(-2)^3 = -8$, $\sqrt[3]{-8} = -2$.

Notice that it is possible to find the cube root of a negative number. In fact, if the root index is any odd positive integer, it is possible to find that root of a negative number. In general,

If n is an odd positive integer, $\sqrt[n]{a^n} = a$.

If n is an even positive integer, $\sqrt[n]{a^n} = |a|$.

Example 1 Solve $5^n \cdot 5^n \cdot 5^n = 5$.

Solution

$$5^n \cdot 5^n \cdot 5^n = 5$$
$$5^{3n} = 5$$

Since the bases are equal the exponents are equal.

Thus,
$$3n = 1$$
$$n = \frac{1}{3}$$

Is it always possible to find the nth root of a? Think of a^n. Since a^n is always positive when n is an even integer, $\sqrt[n]{a}$, and hence $a^{\frac{1}{n}}$, its *exponential* form, do not name a real number if n is even and $a < 0$. For example, since $2^4 = (-2)^4 = 16$, $\sqrt[4]{-16}$, or $(-16)^{\frac{1}{4}}$, does not name a real number. Thus, we have the following definition.

For all integers $n > 1$,

$$a^{\frac{1}{n}} = \sqrt[n]{a},$$

unless $a < 0$ and n is even.

Example 2 Write each of the following radicals in exponential form.

a. $\sqrt{3}$ **b.** $\sqrt[3]{6}$ **c.** $\sqrt[4]{2}$ **d.** $\sqrt[5]{-10}$

Solution

a. $\sqrt{3} = \sqrt[2]{3^1} = 3^{\frac{1}{2}}$ **b.** $\sqrt[3]{6} = \sqrt[3]{6^1} = 6^{\frac{1}{3}}$

c. $\sqrt[4]{2} = \sqrt[4]{2^1} = 2^{\frac{1}{4}}$ **d.** $\sqrt[5]{-10} = \sqrt[5]{(-10)^1} = (-10)^{\frac{1}{5}}$

Example 3 Simplify.

a. $36^{\frac{1}{2}}$ **b.** $27^{\frac{1}{3}}$ **c.** $(-32)^{\frac{1}{5}}$ **d.** $(-256)^{\frac{1}{4}}$

Solution

a. $36^{\frac{1}{2}} = \sqrt{36} = \sqrt{6^2} = 6$

b. $27^{\frac{1}{3}} = \sqrt[3]{27} = \sqrt[3]{3^3} = 3$

c. $(-32)^{\frac{1}{5}} = \sqrt[5]{-32} = \sqrt[5]{(-2)^5} = -2$

d. $(-256)^{\frac{1}{4}} = \sqrt[4]{-256}$, which does not name a real number.

You know that $\sqrt[3]{5} = 5^{\frac{1}{3}}$. But how would you write $(\sqrt[3]{5})^2$ in exponential form? If the Rule of Exponents for a Power of a Power is to be true for all positive exponents, then

$$(\sqrt[3]{5})^2 = (5^{\frac{1}{3}})^2 = 5^{2 \cdot \frac{1}{3}} = 5^{\frac{2}{3}}.$$

This suggests the following definition.

If $\sqrt[n]{a}$ is a real number and m and n are positive integers, then $(\sqrt[n]{a})^m = a^{\frac{m}{n}}$.

Example 4 Write each of the following radicals in exponential form.

a. $(\sqrt[3]{3})^2$ **b.** $(\sqrt{3})^3$ **c.** $(\sqrt[4]{2})^3$ **d.** $(\sqrt[5]{6})^4$

Solution

a. $(\sqrt[3]{3})^2 = (3^{\frac{1}{3}})^2 = 3^{\frac{2}{3}}$ **b.** $(\sqrt{3})^3 = (3^{\frac{1}{2}})^3 = 3^{\frac{3}{2}}$

c. $(\sqrt[4]{2})^3 = (2^{\frac{1}{4}})^3 = 2^{\frac{3}{4}}$ **d.** $(\sqrt[5]{6})^4 = (6^{\frac{1}{5}})^4 = 6^{\frac{4}{5}}$

Example 5 Simplify.

a. $9^{\frac{3}{2}}$ **b.** $81^{\frac{3}{4}}$ **c.** $(-8)^{\frac{2}{3}}$ **d.** $(-9)^{\frac{5}{2}}$

Solution

a. $9^{\frac{3}{2}} = (9^{\frac{1}{2}})^3 = (\sqrt[2]{9})^3 = (\sqrt{3^2})^3 = 3^3 = 27$

b. $81^{\frac{3}{4}} = (81^{\frac{1}{4}})^3 = (\sqrt[4]{81})^3 = (\sqrt[4]{3^4})^3 = 3^3 = 27$

c. $(-8)^{\frac{2}{3}} = [(-8)^{\frac{1}{3}}]^2 = (\sqrt[3]{-8})^2 = [\sqrt[3]{(-2)^3}]^2 = (-2)^2 = 4$

d. $(-9)^{\frac{5}{2}} = [(-9)^{\frac{1}{2}}]^5 = (\sqrt{-9})^5$, which does not name a real number.

Exercises

Write each of the following radicals in exponential form.

1. $\sqrt{5}$ $5^{\frac{1}{2}}$ **2.** $\sqrt[5]{7}$ $7^{\frac{1}{5}}$ **3.** $\sqrt[4]{3}$ $3^{\frac{1}{4}}$ **4.** $\sqrt[3]{-10}$ $(-10)^{\frac{1}{3}}$

5. $(\sqrt[3]{6})^2$ $6^{\frac{2}{3}}$ **6.** $(\sqrt[4]{5})^3$ $5^{\frac{3}{4}}$ **7.** $(\sqrt{2})^3$ $2^{\frac{3}{2}}$ **8.** $(\sqrt[3]{3})^5$ $3^{\frac{5}{3}}$

Simplify. If the expression does not represent a real number, indicate this.

12. Not a real number 16. Not a real number

9. $49^{\frac{1}{2}}$ 7 **10.** $64^{\frac{1}{3}}$ 4 **11.** $(-27)^{\frac{1}{3}}$ -3 **12.** $(-81)^{\frac{1}{4}}$

13. $16^{\frac{3}{4}}$ 8 **14.** $9^{\frac{5}{2}}$ 243 **15.** $81^{\frac{1}{4}}$ 3 **16.** $(-9)^{\frac{3}{2}}$

17. $(25)^{\frac{3}{2}}$ 125 **18.** $(-64)^{\frac{2}{3}}$ 16 **19.** $27^{\frac{4}{3}}$ 81 **20.** $(-32)^{\frac{3}{5}}$ -8

Application / Boyle's Gas Law

Air and other gases have characteristics of temperature, pressure, and volume much the same as do liquids, such as water. Air temperature is measured in degrees, volume in cubic centimeters or liters, and pressure in millimeters.

Robert Boyle, a seventeenth-century English scientist, investigated many properties of air and gases. He conducted experiments to see how the pressure of a gas in an enclosed space is related to its volume. His discovery is used today in the modern internal combustion engine and in a simple basketball or bicycle pump.

Boyle observed that pressure on a confined gas reduces its volume. In fact, he found that with a constant temperature, the volume of a gas varies inversely with the pressure exerted on it. This statement, known as Boyle's Law, can be written in these two ways.

$pV = k$, where k is a constant, V is the volume, and p is the pressure.

or $pV = p'V'$, where p' and V' are the new pressure and the new volume, respectively.

Example A gas has a volume of 600 mL at a pressure of 760 mm. What is the volume of the gas at a pressure of 800 mm?

Solution

$$pV = p'V'$$
$$760 \times 600 = 800V'$$
$$\frac{760 \times 600}{800} = V'$$
$$570 = V'$$

$\therefore$ the volume is 570 mL.

Exercises

1. A certain gas has a volume of 420 cm^3 at a pressure of 720 mm. What will its volume be if the pressure is increased to 840 mm? 360 cm^3

2. A gas kept at 760 mm of pressure occupies 2 L. What pressure must be exerted for the volume to decrease to 1.9 L? 800 mm

3. A certain gas has a volume of 500 cm^3 at a pressure of 750 mm. If the pressure is decreased to 625 mm, what is the resulting volume? 600 cm^3

4. A gas occupies 2 m^3 of space at 760 mm of pressure. It is compressed to 1 m^3 of space. What is the new pressure? 1520 mm

5. An underinflated balloon contains 9 m^3 of helium when the pressure is 760 mm. What is the volume of the balloon when it reaches an altitude where the pressure is 304 mm? 22.5 m^3

Career Note / Architect

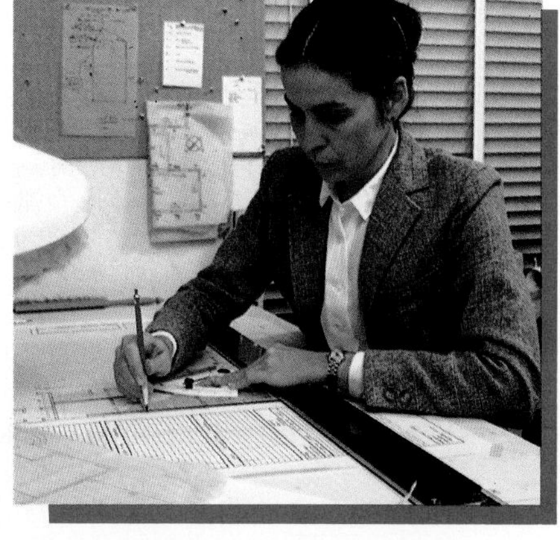

An architect must design offices, shopping malls, and other buildings to be safe and functional as well as attractive. Thus, architects must be able to solve engineering and technical problems in addition to being talented in architectural design.

Architecture involves a variety of skills. Architects are involved in all phases of the development of a structure. They draw detailed plans, specify building materials, and may assist in negotiating, hiring, and supervising contractors. The buildings they design must meet fire and building codes as well as other local standards.

All states require architects to pass a licensing examination. A bachelor's degree and three years experience in an architect's office or a master's degree and two years experience usually qualify a person to take the licensing exam.

Chapter Summary

1. A rational number can be expressed as a fraction in simplest form, $\frac{a}{b}$, where a and b are integers and $b > 0$. Rational numbers in fractional form can be expressed as either terminating or repeating decimals by dividing.
2. Irrational numbers are represented by nonterminating, nonrepeating decimals which may be rounded to a convenient number of places for use in computation. These numbers cannot be represented in fraction form.
3. Square roots may be rational or irrational. Irrational square roots may be approximated using a table of square roots or a calculator.
4. Some quadratic equations can be solved using the property of square roots of equal numbers (page 517).
5. Many problems involving right triangles can be solved using the Pythagorean theorem:

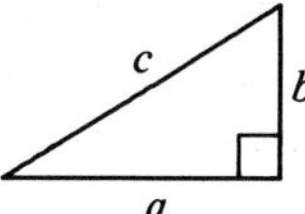

$$a^2 + b^2 = c^2$$

6. Radical expressions can be added, subtracted, multiplied, and divided. The product and quotient properties of square roots (pages 510, 511) are useful in simplifying expressions involving radicals. Divisions can often be simplified by rationalizing the denominator.

Supplementary Materials

Practice Masters 71–72
Test 41
Resource Book,
pp. 54–57, 119–123, 159

Extra Practice

Skills, pp. 628–631
Problems, pp. 647–648

Chapter Review

Give the letter of the correct answer.

1. Find the rational number halfway between $\frac{1}{2}$ and $\frac{7}{8}$. 11-1

a. $\frac{3}{4}$ **b.** $\frac{11}{16}$ **c.** $\frac{2}{3}$ **d.** $\frac{5}{8}$

2. Compare $\frac{3}{4}$ and $\frac{9}{13}$.

a. $\frac{3}{4} > \frac{9}{13}$ **b.** $\frac{9}{13} > \frac{3}{4}$ **c.** $\frac{3}{4} = \frac{9}{13}$

3. Express $\frac{5}{11}$ as a decimal. 11-2

a. 0.45 **b.** $0.\overline{454}$ **c.** $0.\overline{45}$ **d.** $0.0\overline{45}$

4. Express $0.\overline{57}$ as a fraction in simplest form.

a. $\frac{57}{100}$ **b.** $\frac{57}{99}$ **c.** $\frac{575}{1000}$ **d.** $\frac{19}{33}$

5. Find $\sqrt{5184}$. 11-3

a. 720 **b.** 7.2 **c.** 72 **d.** 0.72

6. Find $\sqrt{\frac{256}{400}}$.

a. $\frac{7}{10}$ **b.** $\frac{3}{4}$ **c.** $\frac{6}{5}$ **d.** $\frac{4}{5}$

7. Approximate $\sqrt{2700}$ to the nearest hundredth using the Table of Square Roots on page 650. 11-4

a. 5.196 **b.** 51.96 **c.** 519.6 **d.** 51.9

8. Simplify $\sqrt{88}$.

a. 8 **b.** $8\sqrt{11}$ **c.** $4\sqrt{22}$ **d.** $2\sqrt{22}$

9. Simplify $\sqrt{2.25a^4b^2c^6}$. 11-5

a. $1.5a^2|bc^3|$ **b.** $1.5\sqrt{a^4b^2c^6}$ **c.** $1.5a^2bc^3$

10. Solve $5z^2 - 405 = 0$.

a. $\{9\}$ **b.** $\{9, -9\}$ **c.** $\{3, -3\}$ **d.** $\{81, -81\}$

11. The shorter sides of a right triangle are 16 cm and 30 cm long. Find the length of the hypotenuse. 11-6

a. 14 cm **b.** 46 cm **c.** 34 cm **d.** 1156 cm

12. Can a right triangle have sides 15 m, 36 m, and 39 m long?

a. yes **b.** no

13. Simplify $\sqrt{15} \cdot \sqrt{50}$. 11-7

a. $\sqrt{750}$ **b.** $5\sqrt{30}$ **c.** $6\sqrt{125}$ **d.** $5\sqrt{6}$

14. Simplify $\sqrt{16} + 3\sqrt{8} - 2\sqrt{2}$. 11-8

a. $4 + 3\sqrt{8} - 2\sqrt{2}$ **b.** $4 + 5\sqrt{2}$ **c.** $4 + 4\sqrt{2}$ **d.** $8\sqrt{2}$

15. Multiply $(3 + \sqrt{7})(3 - \sqrt{7})$. 11-9

a. $9 - \sqrt{7}$ **b.** -40 **c.** $9 - 2\sqrt{7}$ **d.** 2

16. Rationalize the denominator of $\frac{\sqrt{3}}{\sqrt{3}-2}$.

a. $\frac{\sqrt{3}}{5}$ (b.) $-3 - 2\sqrt{3}$ c. $\frac{3 + 2\sqrt{3}}{5}$ d. $3 + 2\sqrt{3}$

17. Solve $\sqrt{5x + 1} - 6 = 8$. 11-10

(a.) 39 b. 3 c. 51 d. $\frac{13}{5}$

Chapter Test

Alternate Test p. T20

1. Find the rational number halfway between $\frac{5}{16}$ and $\frac{1}{32}$. $\frac{11}{64}$ 11-1

2. Arrange $\frac{77}{32}, \frac{56}{25}, \frac{64}{27}$, in order from least to greatest. $\frac{56}{25}, \frac{64}{27}, \frac{77}{32}$

3. Express $\frac{7}{12}$ as a decimal. $0.58\overline{3}$ 11-2

4. Express $0.1\overline{6}$ as a fraction in simplest form. $\frac{1}{6}$

5. Find the indicated square roots. 11-3

a. $\sqrt{\frac{169}{2304}}$ $\frac{13}{48}$ b. $\sqrt{0.0036}$ 0.06

6. Use the Table of Square Roots on page 650 to approximate $\sqrt{4400}$ to the nearest tenth. 66.3 11-4

7. Simplify: a. $\sqrt{150}$ $5\sqrt{6}$ b. $4\sqrt{216}$ $24\sqrt{6}$

8. Simplify $\sqrt{121a^4b^{10}}$. $11a^2|b^5|$ 11-5

9. Solve $5a^2 - 80 = 0$. $\{-4, 4\}$

10. In a right triangle, the hypotenuse is 19 m long, and one of the shorter sides is 8 m long. Find the length of the other side to the nearest hundredth. 17.23 m 11-6

11. Is a triangle with sides 14 units, 48 units, and 50 units long a right triangle? yes

Express in simplest form.

12. $6\sqrt{243}$ $54\sqrt{3}$

13. $\frac{6\sqrt{12}}{12\sqrt{6}}$ $\frac{\sqrt{2}}{2}$ 11-7

14. $4\sqrt{2} + \sqrt{72}$ $10\sqrt{2}$

15. $3\sqrt{32} - 5\sqrt{8}$ $2\sqrt{2}$ 11-8

16. $(\sqrt{5} + 3)^2$ $14 + 6\sqrt{5}$

17. $(\sqrt{7} - \sqrt{2})(\sqrt{7} + \sqrt{2})$ 5 11-9

18. Rationalize the denominator of $\frac{6}{2\sqrt{5} - 3}$. $\frac{12\sqrt{5} + 18}{11}$

19. Solve $\sqrt{3x + 2} = 4$. $\frac{14}{3}$ 11-10

Cumulative Review (Chapters 1–11)

Simplify. Assume that no denominator is zero.

1. $-27 \div 3 + 6 \times (-2)$ **2.** $(2ab^2)^2(3a^2 + 5ab + b^2)$ **3.** $(4a^3b + 9c^2)^2$

4. $(-12x + 7y)(x - 5y)$ **5.** $(3.2 \times 10^{-4})^2$ **6.** $(6x^2 + 10x + 9) \div (3x - 1)$

7. $\frac{7x^2 + 50x + 7}{x^2 + 6x + 9} \cdot \frac{2x^2 + 7x + 3}{2x^2 + 15x + 7}$ **8.** $\frac{3x^2 - 14x + 15}{x^2 + 10x + 25} \div \frac{3x^2 + 10x - 25}{x^2 - 25}$

9. $\frac{t-2}{t+4} + \frac{1}{t-2} + 3$ **10.** $\sqrt{4225}$ **11.** $\sqrt{112} - \sqrt{63}$ **12.** $2\sqrt{3}(5\sqrt{6} + 4\sqrt{2})$

13. $\frac{5\sqrt{75}}{\sqrt{90}}$ $\frac{5\sqrt{30}}{6}$ **14.** $\frac{4}{\sqrt{7} - 1}$ $\frac{2\sqrt{7} + 2}{3}$ **15.** $\sqrt{\frac{2}{3}} + \sqrt{\frac{5}{6}}$ $\frac{2\sqrt{6} + \sqrt{30}}{6}$

Factor completely.

16. $16x^4 - 72x^2y^2 + 81y^4$ $(2x - 3y)^2(2x + 3y)^2$ **17.** $4c^2 - 4cd + d^2 - 9$ $(2c - d - 3)(2c - d + 3)$ **18.** $22b^2 + 5b - 3$ $(2b + 1)(11b - 3)$

Graph the solution set. (In Ex. 19, use a number line.)

19. $|2 - x| \le 4$ **20.** $4x + 3y = 3$ **21.** $x + 2y > 6$

22. Write an equation in standard form of the line that contains (0, 4) and (1, −1). $5x + y = 4$

23. Find the least value of the function $f: x \to x^2 - 4x + 4$. 0

24. Express $0.\overline{5}$ and $0.\overline{15}$ as fractions. Then find their sum. $0.\overline{5} = \frac{5}{9}$, $0.\overline{15} = \frac{5}{33}$; $0.\overline{70}$

25. Graph the solution set of the system: $x - y < 3$
$2x + y > -1$

Solve each equation, inequality, or system. Assume that no denominator is zero. If there is no solution, state that fact.

26. $2y - 3 = |-15|$ 9 **27.** $y\%$ of 80 = 12 15 **28.** $\frac{1}{3}y - 2 = \frac{1}{2}$ $\frac{15}{2}$

29. $4y^2 + 20y + 25 = 0$ $-\frac{5}{2}$ **30.** $6t^2 + 7t = 3$ $\left\{\frac{1}{3}, -\frac{3}{2}\right\}$ **31.** $\frac{1}{x} + \frac{2-x}{x+3} = \frac{1}{x+3}$ $\{3, -1\}$

32. $x - 2y = 8$; $3x + 2y = 9$ $\left(\frac{17}{4}, -\frac{15}{8}\right)$ **33.** $2x - 5y = -1$; $3x - 10y = -1$ $\left(-1, -\frac{1}{5}\right)$ **34.** $2x + 11y = 3$; $5x + 28y = 7$ $(7, -1)$

35. $4 \le 2x - 3 \le 9$ **36.** $3|y - 1| > 12$ **37.** $7 - 3b < 9$

38. $2\sqrt{t} = 3\sqrt{2}$ $\frac{9}{2}$ **39.** $\sqrt{y - 1} = y - 3$ $\{5\}$ **40.** $\sqrt{z^2 + 7} = z - 1$ no sol.

41. The hypotenuse of a right triangle is 18 cm long and another side is 9 cm long. Find the length of the third side to the nearest hundredth. (Use the Table of Square Roots on page 650.) 15.59 cm

42. Two groups entering a museum each paid \$63. One group included ten adults and nine children. The other included six adults and eighteen children. Find the admission price for children and for adults.
adults, \$4.50; children, \$2

Additional Answers Cumulative Review

1. -21
2. $12a^4b^4 + 20a^3b^5 + 4a^2b^6$
3. $16a^6b^2 + 72a^3bc^2 + 81c^4$
4. $-12x^2 + 67xy - 35y^2$
5. 1.024×10^{-7}
6. $2x + 4 + \frac{13}{3x - 1}$
7. $\frac{7x + 1}{x + 3}$
8. $\frac{(x - 3)(x - 5)}{(x + 5)^2}$
9. $\frac{4t^2 + 3t - 16}{(t + 4)(t - 2)}$
10. 65 11. $\sqrt{7}$
12. $30\sqrt{2} + 8\sqrt{6}$
19. −3 −2 −1 0 1 2 3 4 5 6 7

20.
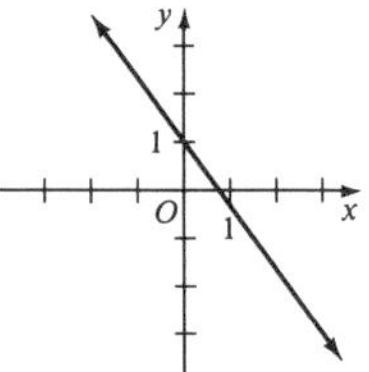

21.
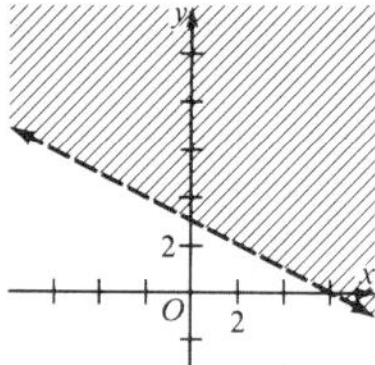

25.
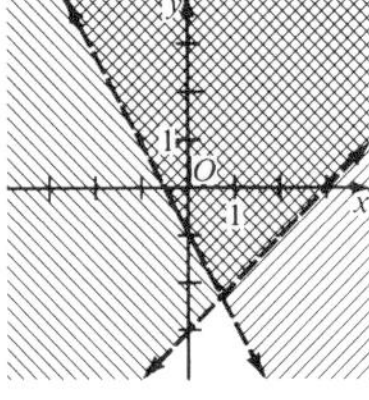

35. $\left\{\frac{7}{2}, 6\right.$, and the real numbers between $\frac{7}{2}$ and $\left.6\right\}$

Maintaining Skills

Solve each system.

Example 1 (Substitution Method) $x - 2y = 1$
$3x - 5y = 6$

Solution Solve one equation for one of the variables (in this case, x) and substitute in the other equation.

$$\begin{aligned} x - 2y = 1 &\longrightarrow x = 2y + 1 \\ 3x - 5y = 6 \quad & \quad 3(2y + 1) - 5y = 6 \\ & \quad 6y + 3 - 5y = 6 \\ & \quad y + 3 = 6 \\ & \quad y = 3 \end{aligned}$$

$x - 2(3) = 1;\ x - 6 = 1;\ x = 7$

The check is left to you. The solution is (7, 3).

Example 2 (Multiplication with the Addition-or-Subtraction Method) $7x - 2y = 4$
$3x + y = 11$

Solution

$$\begin{aligned} 7x - 2y &= 4 & 7x - 2y &= 4 \\ 3x + y &= 11 \ \xrightarrow{\times 2} & 6x + 2y &= 22 \\ & & 13x \quad &= 26;\ x = 2 \end{aligned}$$

$7(2) - 2y = 4;\ 14 - 2y = 4;\ -2y = -10;\ y = 5$

The check is left to you. The solution is (2, 5).

1. $x + y = 1$, $2x + y = 0$ $(-1, 2)$
2. $x + y = 3$, $2x - y = 6$ $(3, 0)$
3. $2x + y = 15$, $x + 2y = 15$
4. $3x + 4y = -2$, $4x + 3y = -12$ $(-6, 4)$
5. $2x + 3y = 2$, $8x + 9y = 7$ $\left(\frac{1}{2}, \frac{1}{3}\right)$
6. $9x + 4y = 5$, $y = 4x$
7. $4x + 5 = y$, $2x + y = 1$ $\left(-\frac{2}{3}, \frac{7}{3}\right)$
8. $y - x = 20$, $2x + 3y = 10$ $(-10, 10)$
9. $3x - 4y = 9$, $x + 2y = 13$
10. $5x - 6y = 2$, $4y - 5x = 12$ $(-8, -7)$
11. $x + 10y = 2$, $\frac{1}{3}x + y = 3$ $(12, -1)$
12. $\frac{4}{5}x - \frac{1}{2}y = 18$, $\frac{1}{2}x - \frac{3}{4}y = 20$
13. $y = 7x$, $5x - 8y = 0$ $(0, 0)$
14. $x - 2y = 5$, $-2x + 3y = -5$ $(-5, -5)$
15. $2x + 3y = 11$, $3x + 14y = 7$
16. $5x + 6y = 4$, $3x + 6y = 3$ $\left(\frac{1}{2}, \frac{1}{4}\right)$
17. $4x + 3y = 8$, $5x + 4y = 13$ $(-7, 12)$
18. $5x - 6y = 1$, $2x - 3y = 7$
19. $6x - 5y = 0$, $5x - 3y = 7$ $(5, 6)$
20. $2x - 7y = 9$, $x + 8y = 16$ $(8, 1)$
21. $3x - 5y = 7$, $-2x + 7y = 10$

36. {the real numbers greater than 5 or less than -3}.

37. $\left\{\text{the real numbers greater than } -\frac{2}{3}\right\}$

Additional Answers
Maintaining Skills

3. (5, 5)
6. $\left(\frac{1}{5}, \frac{4}{5}\right)$
9. (7, 3)
12. (10, −20)
15. (7, −1)
18. (−13, −11)
21. (9, 4)

About the Photo

The bridge shown in the photograph is an example of an arch bridge. Other types of bridges include suspension, cantilever, truss, and trestle, bridges.

Many factors are considered when the construction of a bridge is planned. These factors take into account the nature of the ground or the depth of the water, the length to be spanned, the availability of certain types of materials such as concrete, wood, masonry, or steel, and the type of load that the bridge is to bear. Arch bridges require particularly strong vertical supporting structures because the arch exerts an outward, as well as a downward, force.

Roman bridgebuilders were famous for bridges with circular arches, some of which are still standing. Other bridges have been built with pointed arches. Concrete and masonry are suitable materials for arch bridges since compression further holds the construction materials together. Metal and metal cable, on the other hand, are ideal construction materials for suspension bridges because metals can withstand stretching forces.

12 Quadratic Functions

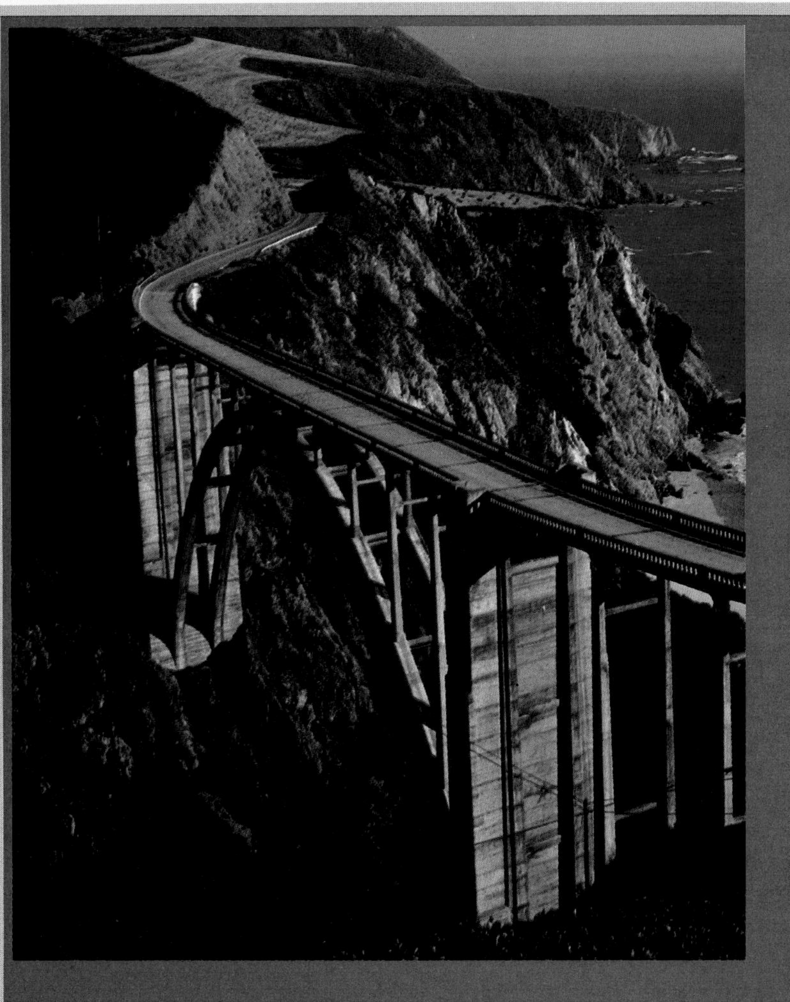

Parabolic curves, often used in bridge designs because of their strength and beauty, can be seen in this arch bridge on Coastal Highway 1 near Big Sur, California.

Quadratic Equations

12-1 Quadratic Equations with Perfect Squares

Objective To solve quadratic equations involving perfect squares.

You learned in Chapter 5 how to solve certain quadratic equations by factoring. In Chapter 11 you learned how to solve quadratic equations of the form $x^2 = k$. This section extends what you learned in Chapter 11 to any quadratic equation involving a perfect square. Later in this chapter you will learn more general methods that can be used to solve any quadratic equation or to determine that the equation has no real-number solutions.

The property of square roots of equal numbers enables you to analyze equations of the form $x^2 = k$ as follows:

If $k > 0$, then $x^2 = k$ has two real-number roots: $x = \pm\sqrt{k}$

If $k = 0$, then $x^2 = k$ has one real-number root: $x = 0$

If $k < 0$, then $x^2 = k$ has no real-number roots.

The property of square roots of equal numbers also suggests a basic strategy for solving quadratic equations such as the one in the following example.

Example 1 Solve $(x + 2)^2 = 49$.

Solution

$$(x + 2)^2 = 49$$
$$x + 2 = \pm 7$$
$$x = -2 \pm 7$$
$$x = 5 \text{ or } x = -9$$

Check: $(5 + 2)^2 \stackrel{?}{=} 49$; $(7)^2 \stackrel{?}{=} 49$; $49 = 49$ ✓

$(-9 + 2)^2 \stackrel{?}{=} 49$; $(-7)^2 \stackrel{?}{=} 49$; $49 = 49$ ✓

$\therefore$ the solution set is $\{5, -9\}$. ***Answer***

An expression such as $(x + 2)^2$, x^2, or $(3x - 2)^2$ is called a **perfect square.** Whenever an equation can be expressed in the form

$$\text{perfect square} = k \quad (k \geq 0)$$

you can solve it by the method shown above. (You may find it helpful to reread Section 5-6 about squaring binomials.)

Teaching References

Lesson Commentary, pp. T126–T128

Assignment Guide, pp. T66–T67

Supplementary Materials
- Practice Masters 73–80
- Tests 42–46
- Resource Book
  - Practice Exercises, pp. 124–130
  - Tests, pp. 58–66
  - Enrichment Activity, p. 160
  - Mixed Review, p. 142
- Algebra Action

Extra Practice
- Skills, pp. 631–632
- Problems, p. 648

Alternate Test, p. T21

Cumulative Review, p. T28

Problem Solving Strategies

Generalizing from Specific
In Section 12-2 students learn the method of completing the square by first studying numerical examples.

Solve a Simpler Problem / Deduction
Deductive reasoning is used to derive the quadratic formula in Section 12-3, using the generalized method for completing the square discussed in Section 12-2.

Word Problem Plan
The course concludes in Section 12-6 with the use of the five-step plan to solve word problems involving quadratic equations.

Teaching Suggestions
p. T126

Suggested Extensions
p. T126

Chalkboard Examples

Solve.

1. $(x+4)^2 = 81$
$x + 4 = \pm 9$
$x = -4 \pm 9$
$\{5, -13\}$
2. $3y^2 - 1 = 8$
$3y^2 = 9$
$y^2 = 3$
$y = \pm\sqrt{3}$
$\{\sqrt{3}, -\sqrt{3}\}$
3. $2(m-3)^2 - 1 = 11$
$2(m-3)^2 = 12$
$(m-3)^2 = 6$
$m - 3 = \pm\sqrt{6}$
$m = 3 \pm \sqrt{6}$
$\{3+\sqrt{6}, 3-\sqrt{6}\}$
4. $5(c+3)^2 + 2 = 0$
$5(c+3)^2 = -2$
$(c+3)^2 = -\frac{2}{5}$
$\emptyset$
5. $a^2 - 12a + 36 = 25$
$(a-6)^2 = 25$
$a - 6 = \pm 5$
$a = 6 \pm 5$
$\{11, 1\}$

Suggested Assignments

Minimum
549/1–37 odd

Average
Day 1: 549/1–45 odd
Day 2: 549/46–53
552/2–12 even
Day 2 finishes Sec. 12-1 and starts Sec. 12-2.

Maximum
Day 1: 549/1–51 odd
Day 2: 549/52–57
552/2–18 even
Day 2 finishes Sec. 12-1 and starts Sec. 12-2.

Example 2 Solve: **a.** $3(x-2)^2 = 42$ **b.** $y^2 + 8y + 16 = 36$

Solution **a.** $3(x-2)^2 = 42$
$(x-2)^2 = 14$
$x - 2 = \pm\sqrt{14}$
$x = 2 \pm \sqrt{14}$

The check is left to you.

$\therefore$ the solution set is $\{2+\sqrt{14}, 2-\sqrt{14}\}$. ***Answer***

b. $y^2 + 8y + 16 = 36$
$(y+4)^2 = 36$
$y + 4 = \pm\sqrt{36}$
$y = -4 \pm 6$

The check is left to you.

$\therefore$ the solution set is $\{2, -10\}$. ***Answer***

The perfect squares occurring in Example 2 are $(x-2)^2$ and $(y+4)^2$. You should note that Example 2(b) could have been solved by factoring.

An equation that has a negative number as one side and a perfect square as the other side has no real-number solutions. The reason for this is that the square of any real number is always a nonnegative real number.

Example 3 Solve $3(2x-6)^2 + 17 = 2$.

Solution $3(2x-6)^2 + 17 = 2$
$3(2x-6)^2 = -15$
$(2x-6)^2 = -5$

$\therefore$ there is no real-number solution. ***Answer***

Oral Exercises

Express each trinomial as the square of a binomial.

Example $x^2 + 6x + 9 = (x+3)^2$

1. $x^2 + 4x + 4$ $(x+2)^2$
2. $x^2 - 6x + 9$ $(x-3)^2$
3. $x^2 + 12x + 36$ $(x+6)^2$
4. $x^2 - 16x + 64$ $(x-8)^2$
5. $x^2 - 10x + 25$ $(x-5)^2$
6. $x^2 - 24x + 144$ $(x-12)^2$

Solve.

7. $3r^2 = 75$ $\{-5, 5\}$
8. $y^2 = \frac{1}{64}$ $\left\{-\frac{1}{8}, \frac{1}{8}\right\}$
9. $5x^2 - 35 = 0$ $\{-\sqrt{7}, \sqrt{7}\}$

Written Exercises

Solve. Express irrational solutions in simplest radical form. If the equation has no solution, write "no solution."

15. $\{\pm\sqrt{6}\}$

A 1. $x^2 = 49$ $\{\pm 7\}$
2. $y^2 = \frac{36}{64}$ $\left\{\pm\frac{3}{4}\right\}$
3. $t^2 = \frac{121}{144}$ $\left\{\pm\frac{11}{12}\right\}$
4. $a^2 = -4$ no sol.
5. $3x^2 = 108$ $\{\pm 6\}$
6. $5r^2 = 175$ $\{\pm\sqrt{35}\}$
7. $13x^2 = 52$ $\{\pm 2\}$
8. $x^2 - 32 = 0$ $\{\pm 4\sqrt{2}\}$
9. $x^2 + 32 = 0$ no sol.
10. $m^2 - 48 = 0$ $\{\pm 4\sqrt{3}\}$
11. $6x^2 - 18 = 0$ $\{\pm\sqrt{3}\}$
12. $9m^2 - 63 = 0$ $\{\pm\sqrt{7}\}$
13. $4y^2 + 7 = 19$ $\{\pm\sqrt{3}\}$
14. $3r^2 - 5 = 7$ $\{\pm 2\}$
15. $2z^2 - 13 = -1$
16. $6y^2 - 2 = 16$ $\{\pm\sqrt{3}\}$
17. $2x^2 + 8 = 30$ $\{\pm\sqrt{11}\}$
18. $2t^2 + 8 = 1$ no sol.
19. $(x + 3)^2 = 9$ $\{0, -6\}$
20. $(r - 5)^2 = 8$ $\{5 \pm 2\sqrt{2}\}$
21. $(y + 2)^2 = 12$
22. $(t - 4)^2 = 24$ $\{4 \pm 2\sqrt{6}\}$
23. $(z - 3)^2 = 32$ $\{3 \pm 4\sqrt{2}\}$
24. $3(x - 1)^2 = 12$
25. $5(m - 8)^2 = 25$ $\{8 \pm \sqrt{5}\}$
26. $7(x + 2)^2 = 42$ $\{-2 \pm \sqrt{6}\}$
27. $4(z + 3)^2 = 24$
28. $(3x + 2)^2 = 64$ $\left\{2, -\frac{10}{3}\right\}$
29. $2(6r - 1)^2 = 32$ $\left\{\frac{5}{6}, -\frac{1}{2}\right\}$
30. $6(5z - 3)^2 = 96$

B 31. $r^2 + 4r + 4 = 9$ $\{1, -5\}$
32. $x^2 - 14x + 49 = 64$ $\{15, -1\}$
33. $t^2 + 20t + 100 = 121$
34. $y^2 - 18y + 81 = 144$
35. $\frac{1}{3}x^2 - \frac{3}{16} = 0$ $\left\{\pm\frac{3}{4}\right\}$
36. $\frac{1}{4}t^2 - \frac{9}{64} = 0$ $\left\{\pm\frac{3}{4}\right\}$
37. $\frac{1}{4}r^2 - 4 = \frac{3}{4}$ $\{\pm\sqrt{19}\}$
38. $\frac{1}{6}x^2 - 4 = \frac{5}{6}$ $\{\pm\sqrt{29}\}$
39. $1.69y^2 + 5 = 5.64$
40. $0.49x^2 + 2 = 3.96$ $\{\pm 2\}$
41. $0.64z^2 - 0.91 = -0.55$ $\left\{\pm\frac{3}{4}\right\}$
42. $5(t + 2)^2 = \frac{3}{5}$
43. $4(x - 3)^2 = \frac{1}{36}$ $\left\{\frac{37}{12}, \frac{35}{12}\right\}$
44. $\left(y - \frac{3}{7}\right)^2 = -\frac{8}{9}$ no sol.
45. $\left(z - \frac{4}{9}\right)^2 = \frac{3}{16}$ $\left\{\frac{16 \pm 9\sqrt{3}}{36}\right\}$

Solve each equation by factoring.

46. $5y^3 - 45y = 0$ $\{0, \pm 3\}$
47. $7a^3 - 175a = 0$ $\{0, \pm 5\}$
48. $\frac{1}{3}t^3 - 12t = 0$ $\{0, \pm 6\}$
49. $4b^3 - \frac{1}{4}b = 0$ $\left\{0, \pm\frac{1}{4}\right\}$
50. $6x^3 = 216x$ $\{0, \pm 6\}$
51. $8x^3 = 512x$ $\{0, \pm 8\}$

Solve.

C 52. $6(2x + 3)^2 = 24$ $\left\{-\frac{1}{2}, -\frac{5}{2}\right\}$
53. $5(6x - 1)^2 = 5$ $\left\{\frac{1}{3}, 0\right\}$
54. $3(5x - 3)^2 + 2 = 8$ $\left\{\frac{3 \pm \sqrt{2}}{5}\right\}$
55. $4(7x + 5)^2 + 9 = 1$ no sol.
56. $x^2 + 2x\sqrt{3} + 3 = 0$ $\{-\sqrt{3}\}$
57. $y^2 - 2y\sqrt{5} + 5 = 3$ $\{\sqrt{5} \pm \sqrt{3}\}$
58. How many real-number solutions are there to the equation $a(x - b)^2 = c$ if:
   a. $a > 0$ and $c > 0$? 2
   b. $a < 0$ and $c < 0$? 2
   c. $a < 0$ and $c > 0$? none
   d. $a > 0$ and $c = 0$? 1

Additional A Exercises

Solve. Express irrational solutions in simplest radical form.

1. $x^2 = 81$ ± 9
2. $m^2 = \frac{49}{169}$ $\pm\frac{7}{13}$
3. $15x^2 = 120$ $\pm 2\sqrt{2}$
4. $x^2 - 54 = 0$ $\pm 3\sqrt{6}$
5. $9m^2 + 1 = 28$ $\pm\sqrt{3}$
6. $(y - 2)^2 = 48$ $2 \pm 4\sqrt{3}$
7. $7(3z - 1)^2 = 252$ $\frac{7}{3}, -\frac{5}{3}$

Mixed Review Exercises

1. Graph $3x - 7y = 21$.

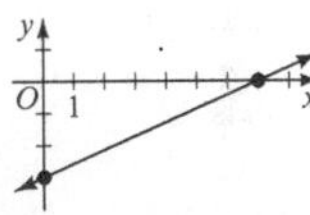

2. Solve by the substitution method:
   $4x - y = 4$
   $x + 2y = 10$ (2, 4)
3. Solve by the addition-or-subtraction method:
   $2x + 5y = 23$
   $3x - 7y = 20$ (9, 1)
4. Solve $\sqrt{4x + 1} + 4 = 9$. 6

Additional Answers Written Exercises

21. $\{-2 \pm 2\sqrt{3}\}$
24. $\{-1, 3\}$
27. $\{-3 \pm \sqrt{6}\}$
30. $\left\{-\frac{1}{5}, \frac{7}{5}\right\}$
33. $\{1, -21\}$
34. $\{21, -3\}$
39. $\left\{\pm\frac{8}{13}\right\}$
42. $\left\{-2 \pm \frac{\sqrt{3}}{5}\right\}$

Teaching Suggestions
p. T127

Chalkboard Examples

Complete the square. Then write the trinomial as the square of a binomial.

1. $x^2 + 10x + \underline{?}$
   $25;\ (x+5)^2$
2. $x^2 - 5x + \underline{?}$
   $\frac{25}{4};\ \left(x - \frac{5}{2}\right)^2$
3. $x^2 + \underline{?} + 144$
   $24x;\ (x+12)^2$

Solve by completing the square.

4. $y^2 + 6y + 2 = 0$
   $y^2 + 6y = -2$
   $y^2 + 6y + 9 = 7$
   $(y+3)^2 = 7$
   $y + 3 = \pm\sqrt{7}$
   $y = -3 \pm \sqrt{7}$
   $\{-3 + \sqrt{7}, -3 - \sqrt{7}\}$
5. $2n^2 - 8n - 11 = 0$
   $n^2 - 4n - \frac{11}{2} = 0$
   $n^2 - 4n = \frac{11}{2}$
   $n^2 - 4n + 4 = \frac{19}{2}$
   $(n-2)^2 = \frac{19}{2}$
   $n - 2 = \pm\frac{\sqrt{38}}{2}$
   $n = 2 \pm \frac{\sqrt{38}}{2}$
   $\left\{2 + \frac{\sqrt{38}}{2}, 2 - \frac{\sqrt{38}}{2}\right\}$
6. $x^2 + 4x - 320 = 0$
   $x^2 + 4x = 320$
   $x^2 + 4x + 4 = 324$
   $(x+2)^2 = 324$
   $x + 2 = \pm 18$
   $x = -2 \pm 18$
   $\{16, -20\}$

12-2 Completing the Square

Objective To "complete the square" and to use the result to solve quadratic equations.

In Section 12-1 you learned that it is always possible to solve a quadratic equation that has the form:

$$\text{perfect square} = k \quad (k \geq 0)$$

If a quadratic equation does not have the form perfect square $= k$, it may be possible to transform it into one that does by a method called **completing the square.**

Study the perfect squares shown at the right. The main idea behind completing the square is shown.

Notice that in each case the coefficient of x^2 is 1, and that the constant term is the square of half the coefficient of x. This observation leads to the method described below. This method can be used to solve certain quadratic equations, as illustrated in Example 2.

$$(x+5)^2 = x^2 \underbrace{+ 10x}_{} + 25 \qquad \left(\frac{10}{2}\right)^2 = 25$$

$$(x-3)^2 = x^2 \underbrace{- 6x}_{} + 9 \qquad \left(-\frac{6}{2}\right)^2 = 9$$

$$(x+a)^2 = x^2 \underbrace{+ 2ax}_{} + a^2 \qquad \left(\frac{2a}{2}\right)^2 = a^2$$

Method of Completing the Square

For $x^2 + bx + \underline{?}$:

1. Find half the coefficient of x.
2. Square the result of Step 1.
3. Add the result of Step 2 to $x^2 + bx$.

Example 1 Complete the square.

a. $x^2 + 20x + \underline{?}$ **b.** $x^2 - 7x + \underline{?}$

Solution **a.** $x^2 \underbrace{+ 20x}_{} + 100 = (x+10)^2$; $\left(\frac{20}{2}\right)^2 = 100$

b. $x^2 \underbrace{- 7x}_{} + \frac{49}{4} = \left(x - \frac{7}{2}\right)^2$; $\left(-\frac{7}{2}\right)^2 = \frac{49}{4}$

Example 2 Solve $x^2 - 16x - 17 = 0$ by completing the square.

Solution

$$x^2 - 16x - 17 = 0$$
$$x^2 - 16x = 17$$
$$x^2 - 16x + \left(-\frac{16}{2}\right)^2 = 17 + \left(-\frac{16}{2}\right)^2 \quad \{\text{Complete the square.}$$
$$x^2 - 16x + 64 = 17 + 64$$
$$(x - 8)^2 = 81$$
$$x - 8 = \pm\sqrt{81}$$
Solve using the method of Section 12-1.
$$x = 8 \pm 9$$
$$x = 17 \text{ or } x = -1$$

The check is left to you.
$\therefore$ the solution set is $\{17, -1\}$. ***Answer***

Example 3 Solve $5x^2 + 7x - 2 = 0$ by completing the square.

Solution After adding 2 to both sides of the equation, divide both sides by 5 so that the coefficient of x^2 will be 1.

$$5x^2 + 7x - 2 = 0$$
$$5x^2 + 7x = 2$$
$$x^2 + \frac{7}{5}x = \frac{2}{5}$$
$$x^2 + \frac{7}{5}x + \left(\frac{7}{10}\right)^2 = \frac{2}{5} + \left(\frac{7}{10}\right)^2$$
$$x^2 + \frac{7}{5}x + \frac{49}{100} = \frac{2}{5} + \frac{49}{100}$$
$$\left(x + \frac{7}{10}\right)^2 = \frac{89}{100}$$
$$x + \frac{7}{10} = \pm\frac{\sqrt{89}}{10}$$
$$x = -\frac{7}{10} \pm \frac{\sqrt{89}}{10} = \frac{-7 \pm \sqrt{89}}{10}$$
$$x = \frac{-7 + \sqrt{89}}{10} \text{ or } x = \frac{-7 - \sqrt{89}}{10}$$

The check is left to you.

$\therefore$ the solution set is $\left\{\frac{-7 + \sqrt{89}}{10}, \frac{-7 - \sqrt{89}}{10}\right\}$. ***Answer***

You can use your calculator or a table of square roots to obtain decimal approximations to the irrational roots in Example 3. Using the Table of Square Roots on page 650,

$$\frac{-7 + \sqrt{89}}{10} \approx \frac{-7 + 9.43}{10} = \frac{2.43}{10} = 0.243 \approx 0.2$$
$$\frac{-7 - \sqrt{89}}{10} \approx \frac{-7 - 9.43}{10} = \frac{-16.43}{10} = -1.643 \approx -1.6$$

Thus, to the nearest tenth, the roots are 0.2 and -1.6.

Common Errors

In completing the square, some students may not take half the coefficient of the middle term, especially if it is odd or a fraction. Encourage such students to write their work, $\frac{1}{2} \cdot \frac{7}{5} = \frac{7}{10}$, for example, off to the side.

When students take the square root of both sides of equations such as the one in Example 3, they may sometimes forget to write $\pm$ in front of $\frac{\sqrt{89}}{10}$, for example. Thus, they may write $x = \frac{\sqrt{89}}{10} \pm \frac{7}{10}$, instead of $x = -\frac{7}{10} \pm \frac{\sqrt{89}}{10}$.

Supplementary Materials

Practice Master 73
Resource Book, p. 124

Suggested Assignments

Minimum
Day 1: 552/1–10
S 549/20–30 even
Day 2: 552/11–27

Average
552/14–36 even
S 549/40, 42, 49, 51
Day 2 of Sec. 12-1 finishes Sec. 12-1 and starts Sec. 12-2.

Maximum
552/20–38 even
S 549/58
Day 2 of Sec. 12-1 finishes Sec. 12-1 and starts Sec. 12-2.

Additional A Exercises

Solve by completing the square. Give irrational roots in simplest radical form.

1. $x^2 - 5x = 23$ $\frac{5 \pm 3\sqrt{13}}{2}$
2. $m^2 - 7m + 10 = 0$ 5, 2
3. $4a^2 + 8a = 27$ $\frac{-2 \pm \sqrt{31}}{2}$

Additional Answers Written Exercises

1. $\{1 \pm \sqrt{21}\}$; $\{5.6, -3.6\}$
2. $\{-4 \pm \sqrt{26}\}$; $\{-9.1, 1.1\}$
3. $\{-6 \pm \sqrt{34}\}$; $\{-11.8, -0.2\}$
4. $\{5 \pm 2\sqrt{5}\}$; $\{9.5, 0.5\}$
5. $\{2 \pm \sqrt{7}\}$; $\{4.6, -0.6\}$
6. $\{-7 \pm 2\sqrt{11}\}$; $\{-0.4, -13.6\}$
7. $\{-22, 6\}$ 8. $\{19, 1\}$
9. $\{3 \pm 4\sqrt{21}\}$; $\{21.3, -15.3\}$
10. $\{-9 \pm 5\sqrt{11}\}$; $\{7.6, -25.6\}$
11. $\{-3 \pm 3\sqrt{2}\}$; $\{-7.2, 1.2\}$
12. $\{2 \pm \sqrt{6}\}$; $\{-0.4, 4.4\}$
13. $\left\{\frac{-1 \pm \sqrt{21}}{2}\right\}$; $\{1.8, -2.8\}$
14. $\left\{\frac{5 \pm \sqrt{33}}{2}\right\}$; $\{5.4, -0.4\}$
15. $\left\{\frac{9 \pm \sqrt{109}}{2}\right\}$; $\{9.7, -0.7\}$
16. $\{24, -22\}$
17. $\{31, -37\}$
18. $\{-2 \pm 2\sqrt{39}\}$; $\{10.5, -14.5\}$

Oral Exercises

Complete the square.

1. $x^2 + 6x + \underline{\ ?\ } = (x + \underline{\ ?\ })^2$ 9; 3
2. $x^2 + 14x + \underline{\ ?\ } = (x + \underline{\ ?\ })^2$ 49; 7
3. $y^2 - 4y + \underline{\ ?\ } = (y - \underline{\ ?\ })^2$ 4; 2
4. $y^2 - 18y + \underline{\ ?\ } = (y - \underline{\ ?\ })^2$ 81; 9
5. $m^2 + 3m + \underline{\ ?\ } = (m + \underline{\ ?\ })^2$ $\frac{9}{4}; \frac{3}{2}$
6. $r^2 - 11r + \underline{\ ?\ } = (r - \underline{\ ?\ })^2$ $\frac{121}{4}; \frac{11}{2}$
7. $t^2 + 1.6t + \underline{\ ?\ } = (t + \underline{\ ?\ })^2$ 0.64; 0.8
8. $q^2 - \frac{1}{3}q + \underline{\ ?\ } = (q - \underline{\ ?\ })^2$ $\frac{1}{36}$; $\frac{1}{6}$

Written Exercises

Solve by completing the square. Give irrational roots in simplest radical form and then approximate them to the nearest tenth.

A

1. $x^2 - 2x = 20$
2. $x^2 + 8x = 10$
3. $x^2 + 12x = -2$
4. $r^2 - 10r = -5$
5. $s^2 - 4s - 3 = 0$
6. $q^2 + 14q + 5 = 0$
7. $c^2 + 16c - 132 = 0$
8. $v^2 - 20v + 19 = 0$
9. $z^2 - 6z - 321 = 6$
10. $y^2 + 18y + 32 = 226$
11. $2b^2 + 12b = 18$
12. $5x^2 - 20x = 10$
13. $w^2 + w = 5$
14. $x^2 - 5x = 2$
15. $c^2 - 9c - 4 = 3$
16. $j^2 - 2j - 528 = 0$
17. $s^2 + 6s - 1147 = 0$
18. $3a^2 + 12a = 456$

Solve the equations using two methods: (a) completing the square and (b) factoring.

19. $x^2 - 14x + 45 = 0$ $\{9, 5\}$
20. $y^2 + 18y + 56 = 0$ $\{-4, -14\}$
21. $a^2 + 28a - 60 = 0$ $\{-30, 2\}$
22. $3c^2 - 7c = 6$ $\left\{3, -\frac{2}{3}\right\}$
23. $5k^2 - 4k = 1$ $\left\{-\frac{1}{5}, 1\right\}$
24. $4m^2 + 12m + 5 = 0$ $\left\{-\frac{5}{2}, -\frac{1}{2}\right\}$

Solve. Write irrational roots in simplest radical form.

B

25. $\frac{x^2}{2} - 3x = 8$ $\{8, -2\}$
26. $\frac{2y^2}{3} - y - 3 = 0$ $\left\{-\frac{3}{2}, 3\right\}$
27. $m^2 - 2 = \frac{7m}{2}$ $\left\{-\frac{1}{2}, 4\right\}$
28. $a^2 + \frac{a}{3} = 3$ $\left\{\frac{-1 \pm \sqrt{109}}{6}\right\}$
29. $\frac{2m^2}{3} - 2 = \frac{m}{2}$ $\left\{\frac{3 \pm \sqrt{201}}{8}\right\}$
30. $\frac{y^2}{2} - \frac{y}{4} = 3$ $\left\{\frac{1 \pm \sqrt{97}}{4}\right\}$
31. $x + 2 = \frac{3 + x}{6x}$ $\left\{\frac{-11 \pm \sqrt{193}}{12}\right\}$
32. $y - 3 = \frac{4y - 4}{5y}$ $\left\{\frac{19 \pm \sqrt{281}}{10}\right\}$
33. $7t = \frac{20t - 2}{t + 1}$ $\left\{\frac{13}{14} \pm \frac{\sqrt{113}}{14}\right\}$
34. $3m = \frac{m - 5}{m + 4}$ $\left\{\frac{-11 \pm \sqrt{61}}{6}\right\}$
35. $3 + \frac{7r - 2}{r - 1} = -4r$ $\left\{\frac{-3 \pm \sqrt{29}}{4}\right\}$
36. $2m - 5 = \frac{6}{m + 3}$ $\left\{3, -\frac{7}{2}\right\}$

Solve for x in terms of a, b, and c. State the conditions on a, b, and c for the equation to have real roots.

C

37. $x^2 + bx + 1 = 0$ $\left\{\frac{-b \pm \sqrt{b^2 - 4}}{2}\right\}$; $b \geq 2$ or $b \leq -2$
38. $x^2 + bx + c = 0$ $\left\{\frac{-b \pm \sqrt{b^2 - 4c}}{2}\right\}$; $b^2 - 4c \geq 0$
39. $ax^2 + bx + c = 0$ $\left\{\frac{-b \pm \sqrt{b^2 - 4ac}}{2a}\right\}$; $a \neq 0$, $b^2 - 4ac \geq 0$

12-3 The Quadratic Formula

Objective: To learn the quadratic formula and use it to solve equations.

Recall from Section 5–12 (page 223) that the general form of the quadratic equation is

$$ax^2 + bx + c = 0$$

where $a \neq 0$. You can solve this equation by the method of completing the square.

$$ax^2 + bx + c = 0$$

$$ax^2 + bx = -c$$

$$x^2 + \frac{b}{a}x = -\frac{c}{a}$$

$$x^2 + \frac{b}{a}x + \left(\frac{b}{2a}\right)^2 = -\frac{c}{a} + \left(\frac{b}{2a}\right)^2 \quad \text{\{Complete the square.}$$

$$\left(x + \frac{b}{2a}\right)^2 = -\frac{c}{a} + \frac{b^2}{4a^2}$$

$$\left(x + \frac{b}{2a}\right)^2 = \frac{b^2 - 4ac}{4a^2}$$

$$x + \frac{b}{2a} = \pm\sqrt{\frac{b^2 - 4ac}{4a^2}} \quad \text{\{If } b^2 - 4ac \geq 0$$

$$x = -\frac{b}{2a} \pm \sqrt{\frac{b^2 - 4ac}{4a^2}}$$

$$x = -\frac{b}{2a} \pm \frac{\sqrt{b^2 - 4ac}}{2a}$$

$$x = \frac{-b \pm \sqrt{b^2 - 4ac}}{2a}$$

The last equation in the solution above is called the **quadratic formula.** It gives the roots of $ax^2 + bx + c = 0$ in terms of the coefficients a, b, and c. In this solution, notice the assumptions that $a \neq 0$ and that $b^2 - 4ac \geq 0$.

The Quadratic Formula

If $ax^2 + bx + c = 0$, $a \neq 0$, and $b^2 - 4ac \geq 0$,

then $$x = \frac{-b \pm \sqrt{b^2 - 4ac}}{2a}.$$

Teaching Suggestions
p. T127

Suggested Extensions
p. T127

Chalkboard Examples

Solve by using the quadratic formula.

1. $x^2 - 3x - 6 = 0$

$$x = \frac{-(-3) \pm \sqrt{9 - 4(-6)}}{2}$$

$$= \frac{3 \pm \sqrt{33}}{2}$$

$$\left\{\frac{3 + \sqrt{33}}{2}, \frac{3 - \sqrt{33}}{2}\right\}$$

2. $2y^2 + 2y = 3$

$$2y^2 + 2y - 3 = 0$$

$$y = \frac{-2 \pm \sqrt{4 - 4(2)(-3)}}{4}$$

$$= \frac{-2 \pm \sqrt{28}}{4}$$

$$= \frac{-2 \pm 2\sqrt{7}}{4}$$

$$= \frac{-1 \pm \sqrt{7}}{2}$$

$$\left\{\frac{-1 + \sqrt{7}}{2}, \frac{-1 - \sqrt{7}}{2}\right\}$$

Common Error

Students may confuse the values of a, b, and c if the quadratic equation is not given in the standard form $ax^2 + bx + c = 0$ (emphasize the last paragraph of page 554). Students may also be confused about the values of b and c if the quadratic equation lacks either a linear or a constant term or both. Point out that $b = 0$ if there is no linear term and that $c = 0$ if there is no constant term.

Supplementary Materials

Test 42
Resource Book, p. 125

Suggested Assignments

Minimum
Day 1: 554/1–12
S 552/28–30
Day 2: 554/13–15
R 561/*Self-Test 1*, 1–6
569/Chapter Review, 1–6

Average
554/1–23 odd, 24
S 552/31, 33, 35

Maximum
554/1–21 odd, 23–25
S 552/37, 39

Additional Answers Written Exercises

1. $\left\{\frac{-3 \pm \sqrt{5}}{2}\right\}$; $\{-0.4, -2.6\}$
2. $\left\{\frac{-5 \pm \sqrt{13}}{2}\right\}$; $\{-0.7, -4.3\}$
3. $\{-2 \pm \sqrt{10}\}$; $\{1.2, -5.2\}$
4. $\{4, -1\}$ 5. $\{6, -1\}$
6. $\{-1, -7\}$
7. $\left\{-1, -\frac{1}{4}\right\}$
8. $\left\{\frac{1 \pm \sqrt{3}}{2}\right\}$; $\{1.4, -0.4\}$
9. no real-number solution
10. $\left\{\frac{5 \pm \sqrt{5}}{4}\right\}$; $\{1.8, 0.7\}$
11. $\left\{\frac{4}{3}, 1\right\}$
12. $\left\{\frac{-7 \pm \sqrt{149}}{10}\right\}$; $\{0.5, -1.9\}$
13. $\left\{\frac{-9 \pm \sqrt{41}}{20}\right\}$

Example Solve $3x^2 - 8x + 2 = 0$ using the quadratic formula.

Solution

$$3x^2 - 8x + 2 = 0$$

$$x = \frac{-b \pm \sqrt{b^2 - 4ac}}{2a} \quad \text{where } a = 3,\ b = -8, \text{ and } c = 2$$

$$x = \frac{-(-8) \pm \sqrt{(-8)^2 - 4(3)(2)}}{2(3)} = \frac{8 \pm \sqrt{64 - 24}}{6}$$

$$= \frac{8 \pm \sqrt{40}}{6} = \frac{8 \pm 2\sqrt{10}}{6} = \frac{4 \pm \sqrt{10}}{3}$$

The check is left to you.

$\therefore$ the solution set is $\left\{\frac{4 + \sqrt{10}}{3}, \frac{4 - \sqrt{10}}{3}\right\}$. ***Answer***

Remember to express a quadratic equation in the form $ax^2 + bx + c = 0$ before using the quadratic formula. For example, to solve $3x^2 = 7x - 1$, first express the equation as $3x^2 - 7x + 1 = 0$ so that you can easily identify the values of a, b, and c.

Oral Exercises

State the values of *a*, *b*, and *c* for each equation.

1. $2x^2 + 7x + 3 = 0$ 2, 7, 3
2. $3x^2 - 9x + 5 = 0$ 3, −9, 5
3. $4x^2 + 8x - 3 = 0$ 4, 8, −3
4. $6x^2 + 11x = 3$ 6, 11, −3
5. $x^2 - 7x = 4$ 1, −7, −4
6. $y^2 = 5y - 5$ 1, −5, 5
7. $7m^2 = m + 3$ 7, −1, −3
8. $9 - q^2 = 2q$ −1, −2, 9
9. $5x^2 = 7x$ 5, −7, 0
10. $z = 8z^2$ 8, −1, 0
11. $4x^2 = 5$ 4, 0, −5
12. $11t^2 = 0$ 11, 0, 0

Written Exercises

Use the quadratic formula to solve each equation. Give irrational roots in simplest radical form; also approximate them to the nearest tenth.

A

1. $x^2 + 3x + 1 = 0$
2. $x^2 + 5x + 3 = 0$
3. $x^2 + 4x - 6 = 0$
4. $2y^2 - 6y - 8 = 0$
5. $z^2 - 5z - 6 = 0$
6. $m^2 + 8m + 7 = 0$
7. $4t^2 + 5t + 1 = 0$
8. $2q^2 - 2q - 1 = 0$
9. $5a^2 - 6a + 2 = 0$
10. $4x^2 = 10x - 5$
11. $3b^2 + 4 = 7b$
12. $7r = 5 - 5r^2$

Solve.

B

13. $a^2 + 0.9a + 0.1 = 0$
14. $3x^2 - 1.8x + 0.03 = 0$
15. $2x^2 - 0.8x - 0.5 = 0$
16. $x^2 + \frac{3}{2}x + \frac{2}{3} = 0$
17. $\frac{1}{5}y^2 - \frac{5}{4}y = 1$
18. $2c^2 + \frac{1}{2}c + \frac{2}{3} = 0$

19. $\dfrac{x+4}{2x} = \dfrac{x-1}{x+1}$ $\left\{\dfrac{7 \pm \sqrt{65}}{2}\right\}$

20. $\dfrac{1}{3} - \dfrac{2}{2x+1} = \dfrac{3}{x}$ $\left\{\dfrac{23 \pm \sqrt{601}}{4}\right\}$

21. $\dfrac{1.5}{x-3} = 2x$ $\left\{\dfrac{3 \pm 2\sqrt{3}}{2}\right\}$

22. $\dfrac{x+3}{x-1} - \dfrac{7}{x+5} = 3$ $\left\{\dfrac{-11 \pm \sqrt{417}}{4}\right\}$

The roots of a quadratic equation $ax^2 + bx + c = 0$ are

$$\frac{-b + \sqrt{b^2 - 4ac}}{2a} \quad \text{and} \quad \frac{-b - \sqrt{b^2 - 4ac}}{2a}.$$

C 23. Find the sum of the roots. $-\frac{b}{a}$

24. Find the product of the roots. $\frac{c}{a}$

25. Write a quadratic equation whose roots are $3 \pm \sqrt{2}$. (*Hint:* Find the sum and the product of the roots. Then use the results of Exercises 23 and 24 to find values for a, b, and c.)
Answers may vary. Example: $x^2 - 6x + 7 = 0$

Computer Key-In

Exercises

1. Write a program that will solve quadratic equations by using the quadratic formula. Provide an output if the discriminant is negative.

Answers may vary slightly. Irrational answers are given to the nearest hundredth.

Use your program to solve the following equations.

2. $2x^2 + 7x + 3 = 0$ $\{-0.5, -3\}$
3. $4x^2 - 7x + 3 = 0$ $\{1, 0.75\}$
4. $3x^2 - 8x + 2 = 0$ $\{2.39, 0.28\}$
5. $x^2 - 4x + 2 = 0$ $\{3.41, 0.59\}$
6. $x^2 - 6x + 9 = 0$ $\{3\}$
7. $x^2 - 2x + 3 = 0$ no real-number solution

Note: The program of Exercise 1 above can be used to do Exercises 1–12 on page 554.

Extra / *Imaginary Numbers*

You know that there are no real-number solutions to the equation $x^2 = -9$. If you take another course in algebra, you will learn that equations like this have solutions that are *imaginary numbers*. Imaginary numbers involve the *imaginary unit, i,* defined to be the square root of -1.

$$i = \sqrt{-1} \qquad i^2 = -1$$

14. $\left\{\dfrac{3 \pm 2\sqrt{2}}{10}\right\}$

15. $\left\{\dfrac{2 \pm \sqrt{29}}{10}\right\}$

16. no real-number solution

17. $\left\{\dfrac{25 \pm 3\sqrt{105}}{8}\right\}$

18. no real-number solution

Additional A Exercises

Use the quadratic formula to solve each equation. Give irrational roots in simplest radical form.

1. $a^2 + 5a - 16 = 0$ $\dfrac{-5 \pm \sqrt{89}}{2}$
2. $x^2 - 3x - 7 = 0$ $\dfrac{3 \pm \sqrt{37}}{2}$
3. $m^2 + 4m + 3 = 0$ $-1, -3$
4. $3t^2 - 5t - 3 = 0$ $\dfrac{5 \pm \sqrt{61}}{6}$
5. $16s = 4s^2 + 5$ $\dfrac{4 \pm \sqrt{11}}{2}$
6. $8p - p^2 = 16$ 4

Mixed Review Exercises

1. Write an equation in standard form of the line that passes through (6, 2) and (4, 4). $x + y = 8$
2. Find the least value of the function $f: x \to x^2 - 6x - 7$. -16
3. Find the missing value if (35, 49) and (?, 14) are ordered pairs of the same inverse variation. 122.5
4. Solve $x^2 - 11x - 15 = 0$ by completing the square. $\frac{11 \pm \sqrt{181}}{2}$

The definition of i allows us to solve $x^2 = -9$ over the set of imaginary numbers. Thus:

$$\begin{aligned} x^2 &= -9 \\ x &= \pm\sqrt{-9} \\ &= \pm 3\sqrt{-1} \\ &= \pm 3i \end{aligned}$$

In general,

If $r > 0$: $\sqrt{-r} = i\sqrt{r}$

We write $i\sqrt{r}$ rather than $\sqrt{r}\,i$ to avoid confusion with $\sqrt{ri}$.

An interesting pattern occurs when we find i^n for increasing powers of n:

$i^1 = \sqrt{-1}$	i	$i^5 = i^2 \cdot i^3 = (-1)(-i) = i$	i
$i^2 = -1$	-1	$i^6 = i^3 \cdot i^3 = (-i)(-i) = i^2 = -1$	-1
$i^3 = i \cdot i^2 = i(-1) = -i$	$-i$	$i^7 = i^3 \cdot i^4 = (-i)1 = -i$	$-i$
$i^4 = i^2 \cdot i^2 = (-1)(-1) = 1$	1	$i^8 = i^4 \cdot i^4 = 1(1) = 1$	1

Likewise, it can be shown that $i^9 = i$, $i^{10} = -1$, $i^{11} = -i$, $i^{12} = 1$, and so on.

Exercises

Simplify to i, -1, $-i$, or 1.

1. i^{13} i **2.** i^{22} -1 **3.** i^{15} $-i$ **4.** i^{24} 1 **5.** i^{17} i **6.** i^{19} $-i$

Example Simplify: **a.** $-\sqrt{-18}$ **b.** $\sqrt{20}\sqrt{-45}$ **c.** $\sqrt{\frac{-9}{16}}$

Solution

a. $-\sqrt{-18} = -\sqrt{-1 \cdot 2 \cdot 3^2} = -3i\sqrt{2}$

b. $\sqrt{20}\sqrt{-45} = \sqrt{2^2 \cdot 5}\sqrt{-1 \cdot 3^2 \cdot 5} = 2\sqrt{5} \cdot 3i\sqrt{5} = 6i \cdot 5 = 30i$

c. $\sqrt{\frac{-9}{16}} = \frac{\sqrt{-9}}{\sqrt{16}} = \frac{\sqrt{-1 \cdot 3^2}}{\sqrt{4^2}} = \frac{3i}{4}$

Simplify.

7. $\sqrt{-36}$ $6i$ **8.** $-\sqrt{-75}$ $-5i\sqrt{3}$ **9.** $\sqrt{-80}$ $4i\sqrt{5}$ **10.** $-\sqrt{-100}$ $-10i$

11. $\sqrt{8}\sqrt{-50}$ $20i$ **12.** $\sqrt{-3}\sqrt{27}$ $9i$ **13.** $\sqrt{12}\sqrt{-48}$ $24i$ **14.** $(\sqrt{-4}\sqrt{9})^2$ 14. -36

15. $\sqrt{\frac{25}{-49}}$ $-\frac{5i}{7}$ **16.** $-\sqrt{\frac{-16}{81}}$ $-\frac{4i}{9}$ **17.** $-\sqrt{\frac{-36}{100}}$ $-\frac{3i}{5}$ **18.** $\frac{\sqrt{-150}}{-\sqrt{54}}$ $-\frac{5i}{3}$

Solve.

19. $x^2 = -121$ $\{\pm 11i\}$ **20.** $x^2 + 28 = 0$ $\{\pm 2i\sqrt{7}\}$ **21.** $x^2 = -98$ $\{\pm 7i\sqrt{2}\}$ **22.** $x^2 + 240 = 0$ $\{\pm 4i\sqrt{15}\}$

12-4 Graphs of Quadratic Equations: The Discriminant

Objective To use the discriminant to determine the number of roots of the equation $ax^2 + bx + c = 0$ and the number of x-intercepts of the graph of the related equation $y = ax^2 + bx + c$.

Teaching Suggestions p. T128

Suggested Extensions p. T128

In Section 9-6 (page 412), you learned that the graph of the function defined by the quadratic equation

$$y = x^2 + 2x - 3$$

is the parabola shown at the right. The x-coordinate of a point where the curve intersects the x-axis is called an **x-intercept** of the curve. This parabola has two x-intercepts, -3 and 1, because $y = 0$ for these values of x. You can also see that the equation

$$x^2 + 2x - 3 = 0$$

has -3 and 1 as roots.

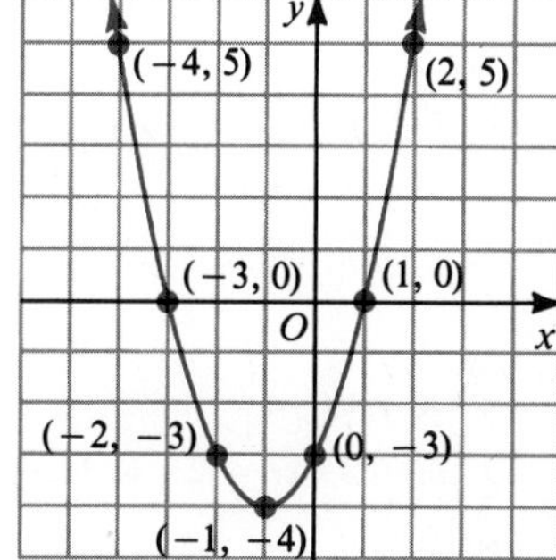

The roots of any quadratic equation of the form

$$ax^2 + bx + c = 0$$

are the x-intercepts of the graph of the related equation,

$$y = ax^2 + bx + c.$$

The algebraic fact that a quadratic equation can have two, one, or no real-number roots corresponds to the geometric fact that a parabola can have two, one, or no x-intercepts, as illustrated in the following examples.

Example 1

Equation: $x^2 - 4x + 2 = 0$

Related equation: $y = x^2 - 4x + 2$

Solution:

$$x = \frac{-(-4) \pm \sqrt{(-4)^2 - 4(1)(2)}}{2(1)}$$

$$= \frac{4 \pm \sqrt{8}}{2}$$

$$= 2 \pm \sqrt{2}$$

$\therefore$ the solution set is $\{2 + \sqrt{2}, 2 - \sqrt{2}\}$.

Graph:

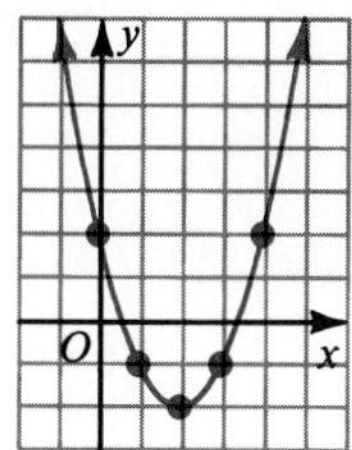

Number of roots: Two real-number roots

Number of x-intercepts: Two

Chalkboard Examples

Find the value of the discriminant of each equation. Without solving, state how many real roots each equation has.

1. $x^2 - 6x + 3 = 0$
   $b^2 - 4ac = 36 - 4(1)(3) = 24$; two real roots
2. $x^2 - 6x + 10 = 0$
   $b^2 - 4ac = 36 - 4(1)(10) = -4$; no real roots

For each of the following quadratic functions:

a. State the number of real roots.
b. Find the x-intercepts.
c. Graph the function.

3. $f(x) = x^2 - 2x - 4$
   a. $b^2 - 4ac = 4 - 4(1)(-4) = 20$; two real roots
   b. $x^2 - 2x - 4 = 0$
   $x^2 - 2x + 1 = 5$
   $(x - 1)^2 = 5$
   $x - 1 = \pm\sqrt{5}$
   $x = 1 \pm \sqrt{5}$
   ∴ the x-intercepts are $1 + \sqrt{5}$ and $1 - \sqrt{5}$.
   c. 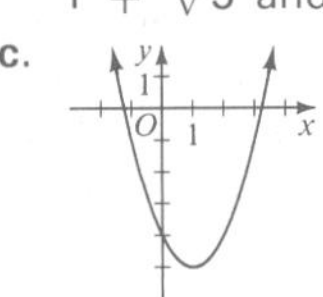
4. $f(x) = -(x - 2)^2$
   a. $-(x - 2)^2 = -x^2 + 4x - 4$; $b^2 - 4ac = 16 - 4(-1)(-4) = 0$; one real root
   b. $-(x - 2)^2 = 0$
   $(x - 2)^2 = 0$
   $x - 2 = 0$
   $x = 2$
   ∴ the x-intercept is 2.
   c. 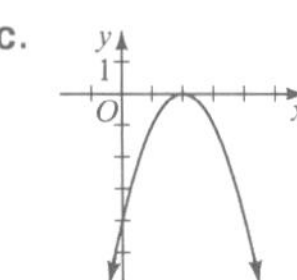

Example 2

Equation: $x^2 - 6x + 9 = 0$

Solution:

$$x = \frac{-(-6) \pm \sqrt{(-6)^2 - 4(1)(9)}}{2(1)}$$

$$= \frac{6 \pm \sqrt{0}}{2}$$

$$= 3$$

∴ the solution set is {3}.

Number of roots: One real-number root

Related equation: $y = x^2 - 6x + 9$

Graph:

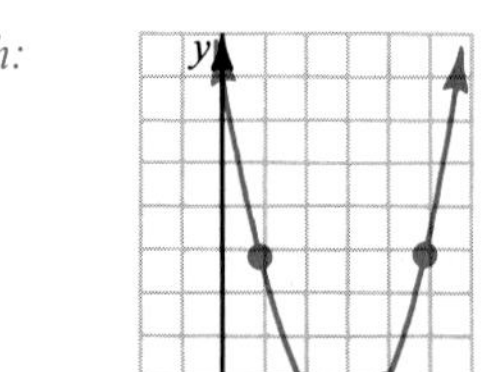

Number of x-intercepts: One

Example 3

Equation: $x^2 - 2x + 3 = 0$

Solution:

$$x = \frac{-(-2) \pm \sqrt{(-2)^2 - 4(1)(3)}}{2(1)}$$

$$= \frac{2 \pm \sqrt{-8}}{2}$$

There is no real-number root since $\sqrt{-8}$ does not exist in the set of real numbers.

Number of roots: No real-number roots

Related equation: $y = x^2 - 2x + 3$

Graph:

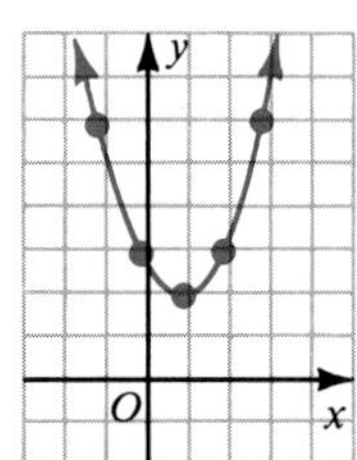

Number of x-intercepts: None

In each of Examples 1–3, the value of $b^2 - 4ac$ in the quadratic formula is shown in color. This value is the key to the number of real roots, as shown in the following chart.

	Value of $b^2 - 4ac$	Number of different real roots of $ax^2 + bx + c = 0$	Number of x-intercepts of the graph of $y = ax^2 + bx + c$
Case 1	positive	2	2
Case 2	zero	1 (a double root)	1
Case 3	negative	0	0

Note that when $b^2 - 4ac$ is negative, no real-number root of the equation exists because square roots of negative numbers do not exist in the set of real numbers.

Because the value of $b^2 - 4ac$ discriminates, or distinguishes, the three cases, it is called the **discriminant** of the quadratic equation.

Oral Exercises

The value of the discriminant of an equation is given. Tell how many different real-number roots there are.

1. 22 two
2. -5 none
3. 0 one
4. 1 two
5. 36 two

Find the value of the discriminant.

6. $x^2 - 3x + 4 = 0$ -7
7. $-2x^2 + 7x - 3 = 0$ 25
8. $4x^2 - 3x - 7 = 0$ 121

Written Exercises

Write the value of the discriminant of each equation. Then use it to decide how many different real-number roots the equation has. (Do not solve.)

A

1. $x^2 - 4x + 3 = 0$ 4; two
2. $x^2 - 5x + 7 = 0$ -3; none
3. $x^2 + 12x + 36 = 0$ 0; one
4. $2y^2 + 5y - 4 = 0$ 57; two
5. $9y^2 - 12y + 4 = 0$ 0; one
6. $4t^2 - 3t + 5 = 0$ -71; none
7. $2y^2 + 12y + 18 = 0$ 0; one
8. $2a^2 - a - 6 = 0$ 49; two
9. $-3b^2 + 4b + 2 = 0$ 40; two
10. $4q^2 - 3q + 3 = 0$ -39; none
11. $2c^2 - 1.4c + 0.1 = 0$ 1.16; two
12. $\frac{1}{4}z^2 - 2z + 4 = 0$ 0; one

Without drawing the graph of the given equation, determine (a) how many points the parabola has in common with the x-axis, and (b) whether its vertex lies above, below, or on the x-axis.

Example $y = 4x - x^2 + 5$

a. The x-intercepts of the graph are the roots of the equation

$$4x - x^2 + 5 = 0, \quad \text{or} \quad -x^2 + 4x + 5 = 0.$$

Its discriminant is $(4)^2 - (4)(-1)(5) = 36$ and therefore it has two real-number roots. The parabola has two points in common with the x-axis.

b. Since the coefficient of x^2 is negative, the parabola opens downward (see page 413). Its vertex must be above the x-axis (otherwise the parabola would not intersect the x-axis in two points).

B

13. $y = x^2 - 5x + 5$ two; below
14. $y = 2x^2 + 4x - 3$ two; below
15. $y = 3 + 3x - x^2$ two; above
16. $y = x^2 + 9 - 6x$ one; on
17. $y = 4x - 3 - 2x^2$ none; below
18. $y = 3x + 9 - 2x^2$ two; above

C

19. Find k so that the equation $9x^2 + 12x + k = 0$ has one real-number (double) root. 4
20. Find k so that the equation $x^2 - kx + 25 = 0$ has one real-number (double) root. $\{-10, 10\}$

Common Errors

Some students may think that the discriminant is a root of a quadratic equation. Point out the discriminant in the quadratic formula (note the use of color in examples) and discuss how the discriminant helps one determine the nature of the roots.

Some students may think that the discriminant is $\sqrt{b^2 - 4ac}$. Emphasize that it is the radicand of the radical in the quadratic formula.

Supplementary Materials

Practice Master 74
Resource Book, p. 126

Suggested Assignments

Average
559/2–20 even
R 561/*Self-Test 1*

Maximum
559/2–20 even

Additional A Exercises

Write the value of the discriminant of each equation. Then use it to decide how many different real-number roots the equation has. (Do not solve.)

1. $x^2 - 3x + 4 = 0$ -7, no real roots
2. $a^2 + 4a - 5 = 0$ 36, 2 real roots
3. $3b^2 - 2b + 16 = 0$ -188, no real roots
4. $9 - 4m - m^2 = 0$ 52, 2 real roots
5. $6x^2 + 7x + 5 = 0$ -71, no real roots
6. $10x^2 - x - 3 = 0$ 121, 2 real roots

Mixed Review Exercises

1. Find the constant of variation if y varies directly as x and $y = 132$ when $x = 33$. 4
2. If z varies jointly as m and n and $z = 150$ when $m = 10$ and $n = 10$, find z when $m = 6$ and $n = 12$. 108
3. Solve the inequality $6 \leq 3x - 2$ and graph its solution set on a number line. $x \geq \frac{8}{3}$

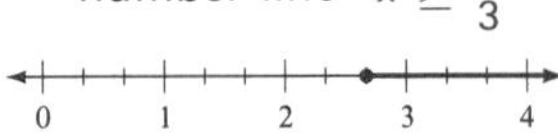

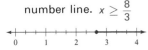

4. Solve $x^2 + x - 1 = 0$ by using the quadratic formula. $\frac{-1 \pm \sqrt{5}}{2}$

Computer Exercises

For students with some programming experience

1. Write a BASIC program that computes the value of the discriminant of a quadratic equation $AX^2 + BX + C = 0$, where the values of A, B, and C are entered with INPUT statements. The program should then report the number of real roots of the equation.
2. Write a BASIC program that computes the sum and the product of the roots of a quadratic equation $AX^2 + BX + C = 0$, where the values of A, B, and C are entered with INPUT statements.

Computer Key-In

The program on page 491 can be modified to graph equations of the form

$$y = Ax^2 + Bx + C, \quad (A \neq 0).$$

First change lines 10 and 15:

```
10  PRINT "TO GRAPH THE PARABOLA"
15  PRINT "FOR Y = AX↑2 + BX + C:"
```

Copy lines from the program on page 433 into this program as shown:

```
20  Copy line 40
25  Copy line 50
30  IF A = 0 THEN 20
35  Copy line 70
40  Copy line 110
```

Add these lines:

```
45  LET M = X1 - 10
50  LET N = X1 + 10
```

Change line 80 to:

```
80  IF Y = A*X↑2 + B*X + C THEN 110
```

Exercises

RUN the revised program for each of the following.

1. $y = x^2 + 2x - 8$
2. $y = x^2 - 4x + 2$
3. $y = x^2 - 6x + 9$
4. $y = x^2 - 2x + 3$
5. $y = x^2$
6. $y = 0.5x^2$
7. $y = 0.25x^2$
8. $y = 0.25x^2 - 8$

Note: The program above can be used to do Exercises 7–18 on page 416.

Self-Test 1

Vocabulary perfect square (p. 547) · completing the square (p. 550) · quadratic formula (p. 553) · x-intercept (p. 557) · discriminant (p. 558)

Solve by using perfect squares.

1. $6x^2 = 54$ $\{-3, 3\}$ **2.** $(x - 3)^2 = 7$ $\{3 \pm \sqrt{7}\}$ **Obj. 12-1, p. 547**

Solve by completing the square.

3. $a^2 - 12a + 35 = 0$ $\{5, 7\}$ **4.** $x^2 - 6x - 16 = 0$ $\{8, -2\}$ **Obj. 12-2, p. 550**

Solve by the quadratic formula.

5. $2x^2 - 3x - 2 = 0$ $\left\{2, -\frac{1}{2}\right\}$ **6.** $t^2 - 3t - 6 = 0$ $\left\{\frac{3 \pm \sqrt{33}}{2}\right\}$ **Obj. 12-3, p. 553**

Give the number of real roots.

7. $2y^2 - 2y + 8 = 0$ none **8.** $c^2 - c + 3 = 0$ none **Obj. 12-4, p. 557**

Check your answers with those at the back of the book.

Career Note / *Welder*

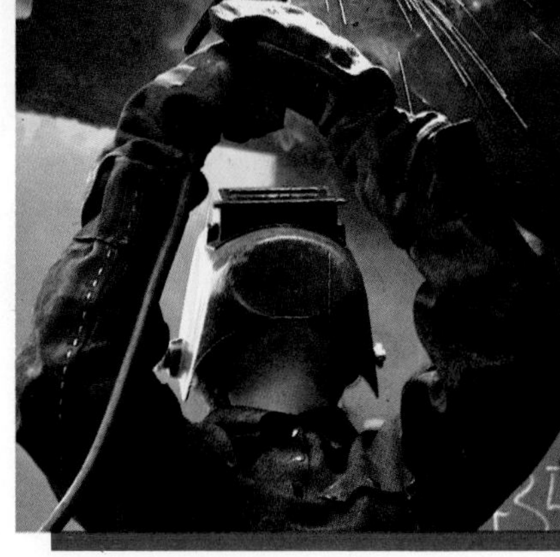

Welders are responsible for repairing and joining metal parts and products. Usually, a welder heats and fuses the metal pieces to be joined and may sometimes add a filler material to strengthen a joint. Welders must apply the correct amount of heat from the correct distance to accurately repair the break or strengthen the bond.

Some welders are employed in the construction of ships. Others construct bridges or weld pipes. Welders are highly skilled workers who must be knowledgeable about the melting properties of various metals.

Welders often have had some high school or vocational training in welding. Some companies prefer to train their own welders through apprenticeship programs. There is also an increasing demand for experienced welders with college training to work in researching and developing new applications.

Quick Quiz

Solve by using perfect squares.

1. $5x^2 = 180$ $\{-6, 6\}$

2. $(y - 3)^2 = 16$ $\{7, -1\}$

Solve by completing the square.

3. $a^2 - 14a + 13 = 0$ $\{13, 1\}$

4. $x^2 + 4x - 12 = 0$ $\{2, -6\}$

Solve by the quadratic formula.

5. $2m^2 + 5m - 1 = 0$ $\left\{\frac{-5 + \sqrt{33}}{4}, \frac{-5 - \sqrt{33}}{4}\right\}$

6. $c^2 - 4c - 2 = 0$ $\{2 + \sqrt{6}, 2 - \sqrt{6}\}$

Give the number of real roots.

7. $3n^2 - 4n + 1 = 0$ two

8. $y^2 - 2y + 4 = 0$ none

Teaching Suggestions
p. T128

Chalkboard Examples

Solve by the most efficient method.

1. $6x^2 + 5x = 4$

$6x^2 + 5x - 4 = 0$
$(2x - 1)(3x + 4) = 0$
$x = \frac{1}{2}$ or $x = -\frac{4}{3}$
$\left\{\frac{1}{2}, -\frac{4}{3}\right\}$

2. $x^2 = 8(x + 3)$

$x^2 = 8x + 24$
$x^2 - 8x = 24$
$x^2 - 8x + 16 = 40$
$(x - 4)^2 = 40$
$x - 4 = \pm\sqrt{40}$
$x = 4 \pm 2\sqrt{10}$
$\{4 + 2\sqrt{10}, 4 - 2\sqrt{10}\}$

3. $5x^2 - 1 = 49$

$5x^2 = 50$
$x^2 = 10$
$x = \pm\sqrt{10}$
$\{\sqrt{10}, -\sqrt{10}\}$

4. $x^2 - 4x - 396 = 0$

$x^2 - 4x = 396$
$x^2 - 4x + 4 = 400$
$(x - 2)^2 = 400$
$x - 2 = \pm 20$
$x = 2 \pm 20$
$\{22, -18\}$

5. $4x^2 + x + 2 = 0$

$x = \frac{-1 \pm \sqrt{1 - 4(4)(2)}}{8}$
$= \frac{-1 \pm \sqrt{-31}}{8}$
no real solutions

12-5 Methods of Solution

Objective To choose the best method for solving a quadratic equation.

You have learned the following four methods for solving quadratic equations.

Methods for Solving a Quadratic Equation

1. Factoring
2. Using the property of square roots of equal numbers
3. Completing the square
4. Using the quadratic formula

Although the quadratic formula can be used to solve any quadratic equation in the form

$$ax^2 + bx + c = 0,$$

one of the other methods may be easier. Here are some guidelines that suggest when one of the other methods may be easier:

1. If the equation is in the form $ax^2 + bx = 0$ or if the factors are easily seen, use factoring;
2. If the equation is in the form $ax^2 + c = 0$, use the property of square roots of equal numbers;
3. If the equation is in the form $x^2 + bx + c = 0$ and b is an even number, use the method of completing the square.

Example Solve each quadratic equation using the most convenient method.

a. $5x^2 - 80 = 0$ **b.** $3x^2 - 4x - 1 = 0$
c. $3t^2 - 36t = 0$ **d.** $n^2 + 6n - 3 = 0$

Solution **a.** $5x^2 - 80 = 0$ Use the property of square roots of equal numbers.

$5x^2 = 80$
$x^2 = 16$
$x = \pm 4$

$\therefore$ the solution set is $\{4, -4\}$. ***Answer***

b. $3x^2 - 4x - 1 = 0$
Since no other method suggests itself, use the quadratic formula.

$$x = \frac{-(-4) \pm \sqrt{(-4)^2 - 4(3)(-1)}}{2(3)} = \frac{4 \pm \sqrt{28}}{6} = \frac{4 \pm 2\sqrt{7}}{6} = \frac{2 \pm \sqrt{7}}{3}$$

$\therefore$ the solution set is $\left\{\frac{2 + \sqrt{7}}{3}, \frac{2 - \sqrt{7}}{3}\right\}$. ***Answer***

c. $3t^2 - 36t = 0$ Factor.
$3t(t - 12) = 0$
$3t = 0$ or $t - 12 = 0$

$\therefore$ the solution set is $\{0, 12\}$. ***Answer***

d. $n^2 + 6n - 3 = 0$ Complete the square.
$n^2 + 6n = 3$
$n^2 + 6n + 9 = 12$
$(n + 3)^2 = 12$
$n + 3 = \pm\sqrt{12}$
$n = -3 \pm 2\sqrt{3}$

$\therefore$ the solution set is $\{-3 + 2\sqrt{3}, -3 - 2\sqrt{3}\}$. ***Answer***

Oral Exercises

a = the property of square roots of equal numbers
b = the quadratic formula
c = factoring d = completing the square

For each of the following quadratic equations, state which method you would use to solve the equation. Answers may vary. Likely choices are given.

1. $x^2 + 5x + 4 = 0$ c
2. $x^2 - 4x = 32$ c
3. $x^2 + 8x - 3 = 0$ d
4. $8x^2 + 11x = 0$ c
5. $11x^2 = 44$ a
6. $3x^2 - 5x = 4$ b
7. $x^2 + 7x + 2 = 0$ b
8. $2x^2 + 7x + 3 = 0$ c
9. $x^2 + 6x = 5$ d
10. $(x - 2)^2 = 7$ a
11. $5x^2 - 20x = 0$ c
12. $4x^2 - 2x - 3 = 0$ b

Written Exercises

A **1-12.** Solve the quadratic equations given in Oral Exercises 1-12. Write the answers in simplest radical form.

Solve by the most efficient method. Write irrational answers in simplest radical form.

13. $4x^2 + 7x = 2$ $\left\{\frac{1}{4}, -2\right\}$

14. $\frac{(y + 3)^2}{2} = 10$ $\{-3 \pm 2\sqrt{5}\}$

15. $5x^2 + 4x = 3$ $\left\{\frac{-2 \pm \sqrt{19}}{5}\right\}$

Suggested Assignments

Average
Day 1: 563/1-27 odd
S 559/19
Day 2: 563/22-30 even
566/*P*:1, 3, 8-10
Day 2 finishes Sec. 12-5 and starts Sec. 12-6.

Maximum
563/1-31 odd
R 561/*Self-Test 1*

Additional Answers Written Exercises

1. $\{-4, -1\}$
2. $\{8, -4\}$
3. $\{-4 \pm \sqrt{19}\}$
4. $\left\{-\frac{11}{8}, 0\right\}$
5. $\{-2, 2\}$
6. $\left\{\frac{5 \pm \sqrt{73}}{6}\right\}$
7. $\left\{\frac{-7 \pm \sqrt{41}}{2}\right\}$
8. $\left\{-\frac{1}{2}, -3\right\}$
9. $\{-3 \pm \sqrt{14}\}$
10. $\{2 \pm \sqrt{7}\}$
11. $\{0, 4\}$
12. $\left\{\frac{1 \pm \sqrt{13}}{4}\right\}$

Additional Answers Written Exercises

23. $\left\{\frac{-2 \pm 3\sqrt{6}}{5}\right\}$

25. $\left\{5, \frac{37}{8}\right\}$

27. $\left\{-\frac{5}{3}, \frac{1}{11}\right\}$

Additional A Exercises

Solve by the most efficient method. Write irrational answers in simplest radical form.

1. $x^2 + 4x - 5 = 0$ $-5, 1$
2. $12x^2 = 108$ ± 3
3. $x^2 + 8x = 5$ $-4 \pm \sqrt{21}$
4. $3x^2 + 10x - 6 = 0$ $\frac{-5 \pm \sqrt{43}}{3}$
5. $6x^2 - 30x = 0$ $0, 5$
6. $(x + 9)^2 = 27$ $-9 \pm 3\sqrt{3}$

Mixed Review Exercises

1. Solve $|3m + 1| > 6$ and graph its solution set.
   $m < \frac{-7}{3}$ or $m > \frac{5}{3}$
   -3 -2 -1 0 1 2
2. Express $\frac{3}{11}$ as a decimal. $0.\overline{27}$
3. How many real roots does $x^2 - 3x + 5 = 7$ have? 2

Solve by the most efficient method. Write irrational answers in simplest radical form.

16. $x^2 - 8x = 11$ $\{4 \pm 3\sqrt{3}\}$

17. $\frac{2}{5}x^2 + \frac{2}{3}x = 1$ $\left\{\frac{-5 \pm \sqrt{115}}{6}\right\}$

18. $\frac{1}{3x} = \frac{2x - 3}{2}$ $\left\{\frac{9 \pm \sqrt{129}}{12}\right\}$

19. $\frac{x - 2}{3x - 1} = \frac{2x + 1}{5x - 1}$ $\{-6 \pm \sqrt{39}\}$

20. $0.75x^2 - 0.3x + 0.03 = 0$ $\left\{\frac{1}{5}\right\}$

21. $1.6x^2 - 0.6x = 0.4$ $\left\{\frac{3 \pm \sqrt{73}}{16}\right\}$

B

22. $5x(x - 3) + 4(x + 4) = 31 - 7x^2$ $\left\{-\frac{3}{4}, \frac{5}{3}\right\}$

23. $4x(x + 2) + 6(x^2 - 1) = 14$

24. $(x + 3)^2 + 6(x + 3) = 16$ $\{-1, -11\}$

25. $8(x - 5)^2 + 3(x - 5) = 0$

26. $(3x + 2)(x - 1) - 13 = 2x(2 - x)$ $\left\{\frac{1 \pm \sqrt{13}}{2}\right\}$

27. $(4x - 3)^2 = (7x + 2)^2$

Solve. Be sure that you have found all real roots of each equation. Write irrational answers in simplest form. (*Hint:* Substitute y for x^2.)

C

28. $12x^4 - 23x^2 + 10 = 0$ $\left\{\pm\frac{\sqrt{5}}{2}, \pm\frac{\sqrt{6}}{3}\right\}$

29. $4x^4 + 21x^2 - 18 = 0$ $\left\{\pm\frac{\sqrt{3}}{2}\right\}$

30. $2x^4 - 5x^2 = 0$ $\left\{0, \pm\frac{\sqrt{10}}{2}\right\}$

31. $8x^4 + 5x^2 + 4 = 0$ no real-number solution

Biographical Note / *Srinivasa Ramanujan*

Srinivasa Ramanujan (1887–1920) was a self-taught mathematician who made a number of contributions to modern mathematics. At age 16 he was awarded a scholarship to Government College in India for his proficiency in mathematics. However, he became so absorbed in his mathematical studies that he neglected to study English and lost his scholarship. He continued to study mathematics on his own, discovering over one hundred theorems.

Friends interested in his mathematical work convinced Ramanujan to write to G. H. Hardy, one of the leading specialists in number theory, at Cambridge University in England. Ramanujan enclosed about 120 of the theorems he had discovered. Convinced of his exceptional ability, Hardy brought Ramanujan to England, where he was admitted to Trinity College. Hardy was not always sure how to teach a student possessing such profound mathematical insight, but so lacking in formal training; nevertheless Ramanujan progressed rapidly. While in England, Ramanujan did a great deal of work in number theory. In 1918 he was elected a fellow of the Royal Society and of Trinity College.

12-6 Solving Problems Involving Quadratic Equations

Objective To use quadratic equations to solve problems.

Example

An architect wishes to design a rectangular building such that the area of the floor is 3 km^2. The length of the floor is to be 1 km longer than the width. To the nearest tenth of a kilometer what will be the length and the width of the floor?

Solution

Step 1 The problem asks for the length and the width of the floor.

Step 2 Let x = the width in kilometers.
Then $(x + 1)$ = the length.

Step 3 Use the formula for the area of a rectangle to write an equation.

$$x(x + 1) = 3$$

Step 4 Solve $x(x + 1) = 3$.

$$x^2 + x = 3$$
$$x^2 + x - 3 = 0$$

Use the quadratic formula.

$$x = \frac{-1 \pm \sqrt{(1)^2 - 4(1)(-3)}}{2(1)} = \frac{-1 \pm \sqrt{13}}{2}$$

From the Table of Square Roots on page 650:

$$\frac{-1 + \sqrt{13}}{2} \approx \frac{-1 + 3.61}{2} = \frac{2.61}{2} = 1.305 \approx 1.3$$
$$\frac{-1 - \sqrt{13}}{2} \approx \frac{-1 - 3.61}{2} = \frac{-4.61}{2} = -2.305 \approx -2.3$$

Step 5 Discard the negative root since a negative length has no meaning.
Check 1.3.

$$1.3(1.3 + 1) \stackrel{?}{=} 3$$
$$1.3(2.3) \stackrel{?}{=} 3$$
$$2.99 \approx 3 \checkmark$$

The numbers are approximately equal so the approximate solution is correct.
∴ the width of the floor is 1.3 km and the length is 2.3 km. ***Answer***

Teaching Suggestions
p. T128

Chalkboard Examples

Solve.

1. The sum of three times a number and its square is 28. Find the number.
   Let n = the number.
   $3n + n^2 = 28$
   $n^2 + 3n - 28 = 0$
   $(n + 7)(n - 4) = 0$
   $n = -7$ or 4
   The number is -7 or 4.
2. The altitude of a triangle is 2 cm less than twice the length of the base. If the triangle has an area of 6 cm^2, find the length of its base and its altitude.
   Let x = the base. Then $2x - 2$ = the altitude.
   $\frac{1}{2}x(2x - 2) = 6$
   $x(x - 1) = 6$
   $x^2 - x = 6$
   $x^2 - x - 6 = 0$
   $(x - 3)(x + 2) = 0$
   $x = 3$ or -2
   -2 cannot be a solution.
   ∴ the base is 3 cm and the altitude is 4 cm.

Common Error

Students who mean to discard a negative root of a quadratic equation because such a value does not make sense in the context of a problem, sometimes discard solutions such as $\frac{3 - \sqrt{8}}{2}$. Point out that since $3 > \sqrt{8}$, $\frac{3 - \sqrt{8}}{2}$, for example, is positive. Emphasize that not all expressions that contain a negative term are negative.

Supplementary Materials

Practice Master 75
Test 43
Resource Book, p. 127

Suggested Assignments

Average
566/*P*: 2, 5, 7, 11–14
S 554/20, 22
R 568/*Self-Test 2*
Day 2 of Sec. 12-5 finishes Sec. 12-5 and starts Sec. 12-6.

Maximum
Day 1: 566/*P*: 3–5, 8–11
S 564/28, 30
Day 2: 566/*P*: 2, 6, 7, 12–15
R 568/*Self-Test 2*

Problems

Solve. Give irrational roots to the nearest tenth. Use the Table of Square Roots on page 650 or a calculator as necessary.

A

1. The length of a rectangular park is 6 m longer than the width. If the area of the park is 135 m^2, find the length and the width. 15 m, 9 m
2. The length of a rectangle is 3 times the width. The area of the rectangle is 75 cm^2. Find the length and the width. 15 cm, 5 cm
3. The sum of a number and its square is 72. Find the number. 8 or -9
4. The difference of a number and its square is 182. Find the number. 14 or -13
5. The length of the base of a triangle is twice its altitude. If the area of the triangle is 100 cm^2, find the altitude. (*Hint:* Area of a triangle = $\frac{1}{2}\cdot$ base $\cdot$ altitude.) 10 cm
6. The altitude of a triangle is 5 m less than its base. The area of the triangle is 80 m^2. Find the base. 15.4 m
7. If the sides of a square are increased by 2 cm, its area becomes 81 cm^2. Find the length of the sides of the original square. 7 cm
8. Rudolph has a rectangular garden that measures 20 m by 16 m. Next year he wants to increase the area to 396 m^2 by increasing the width and length by the same amount. What will be the dimensions of the garden next year? length 22 m, width 18 m
9. The perimeter of the large rectangular fish tank at the Seaside Aquarium is 172 m and its area is 1800 m^2. Find the length and the width of the fish tank. width 36 m, length 50 m

B

10. Working alone, Marcia can paint a house in 3 hours less than Joe. Together Marcia and Joe can paint a house in 8 hours. How long does it take Joe to paint a house working alone? 17.6 h
11. Together Sara and Mary can mow the golf course in 15 hours. Alone it takes Mary 2 hours less than Sara. Find the time it takes each of them to mow the course alone. Sara, 31.0 h; Mary, 29.0 h
12. A mathematics class planned a field trip to a computer center. The trip cost \$240 to be paid for equally by each student. The day before the trip, 4 students decided not to go. This increased the cost by \$2 per student. How many students went to the computer center? 20 students

13. The Calculator Club bought a $54 calculator for club use. If there had been 3 more students in the club, each would have had to donate 20 cents less. How many students were in the club? 27 students

14. Carla can ride her bike 2 mph faster than Karen. It takes Carla 48 minutes less to travel 50 miles than it does Karen. What is Carla's rate in miles per hour? 12.2 mph

C 15. Pipe A can fill a tank in 2 hours, and pipe B can fill the tank in half the time it takes pipe C, a drain pipe, to empty the tank. When all 3 pipes are open, it takes 1.5 hours to fill the tank. How much time is required for pipe C to empty the tank? 6 h

Computer Exercises

For students with some programming experience

Write a BASIC program that finds the largest or smallest value of $AX^2 + BX + C$. The values of A, B, and C should be entered with INPUT statements.

Extra / *Quadratic Inequalities*

The graph of the quadratic function $y = x^2 - 4x + 3$ can be used to illustrate the solutions of the following:

(1) $x^2 - 4x + 3 = 0$
(2) $x^2 - 4x + 3 > 0$
(3) $x^2 - 4x + 3 < 0$

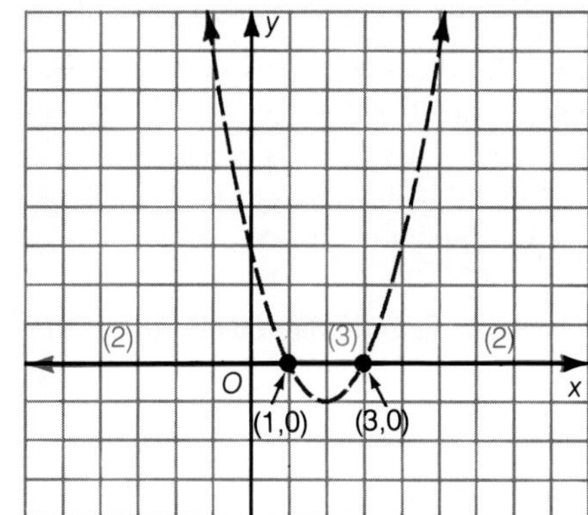

The solution set of the quadratic equation **(1)** is $\{1, 3\}$. These two values of x are called the *zeros* of the quadratic function.

To solve the quadratic inequality (2) reason as follows:

a. If (x, y) is on the graph, then
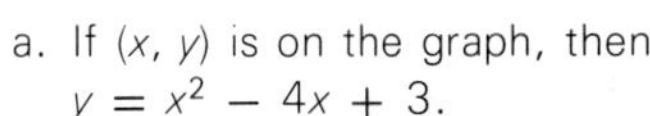
$y = x^2 - 4x + 3$.

b. If (x, y) is *above* the x-axis, then $y > 0$.

c. Therefore, if (x, y) is on the graph *and* above the x-axis, then $y = x^2 - 4x + 3 > 0$.

d. $\therefore$ the solution set for **(2)** is $\{x < 1 \text{ or } x > 3\}$ because these values of x give points that are on the graph above the x-axis.

Similar reasoning shows that the solution set for **(3)** is $\{1 < x < 3\}$ because these values of x give points on the graph *below* the x-axis.

Additional A Exercises

Solve. Give irrational roots to the nearest tenth. Use the Table of Square Roots on p. 650 or a calculator as necessary.

1. The length of a rectangular table is 5 in. more than twice its width. Its area is 1950 in.^{2}. Find its measurements. 30 in. by 65 in.
2. The sum of a number and its square is 156. Find the number. 12 or −13
3. The altitude of a triangle is 9 cm less than the base. The area is 143 cm^2. What are the altitude and the base? alt., 13 cm; base, 22 cm
4. If the side of a square is increased by 3 m, its area is 121 m^2. Find the length of a side of the original square. 8 m
5. If you square a positive number, add twelve times the number and subtract 105, the result is 300. What is the number? 15

Additional Answers
Extra

1.
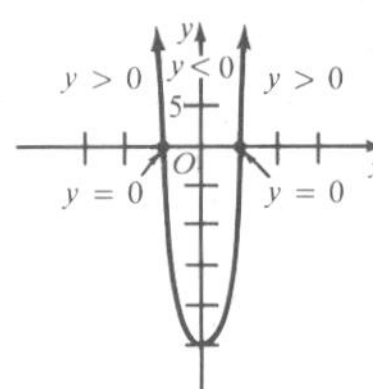

2.
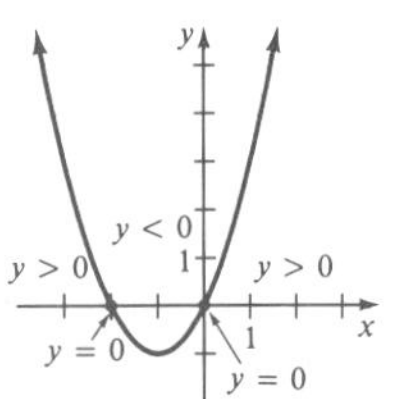

3.
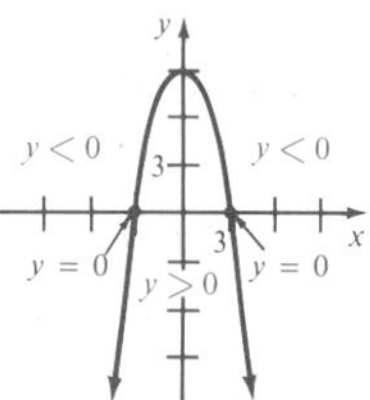

4.
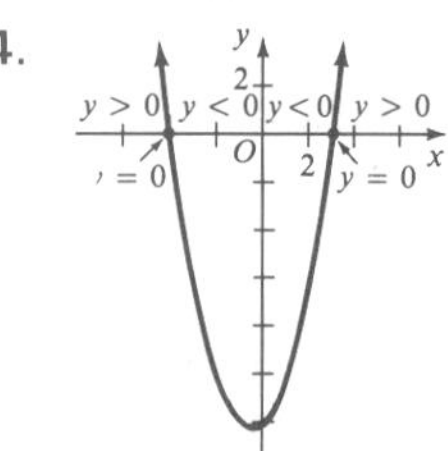

5.
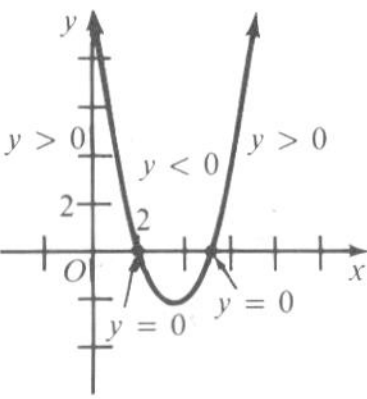

6.
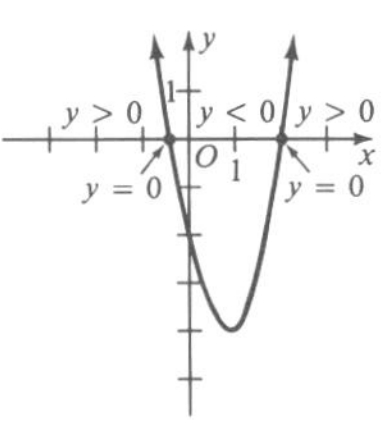

Example Solve for x.

(1) $x^2 + 6x + 9 = 0$
(2) $x^2 + 6x + 9 > 0$
(3) $x^2 + 6x + 9 < 0$

Solution Use the graph of $y = x^2 + 6x + 9$.

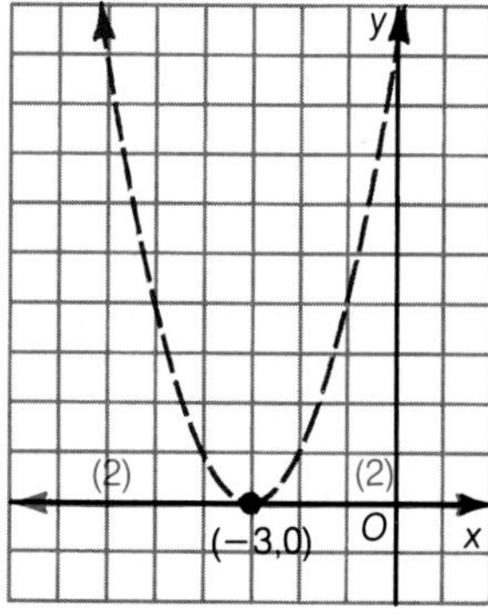

(1) Factor the quadratic equation
$x^2 + 6x + 9 = 0$.
Since $(x + 3)(x + 3) = 0$,
$\mathbf{x = -3}$.

(2) Since the graph lies above the x-axis for all x except -3,
$x^2 + 6x + 9 > 0$ for all $\mathbf{x \neq -3}$.

(3) There are **no values of x** for which $x^2 + 6x + 9 < 0$, since the graph does not go below the x-axis.

Graph each equation and mark the sections of the x-axis which correspond to $y = 0$, $y > 0$, and $y < 0$.

1. $y = x^2 - 25$
2. $y = 2x + x^2$
3. $y = 9 - x^2$
4. $y = x^2 + x - 12$
5. $y = x^2 - 7x + 10$
6. $y = 3x^2 - 5x - 2$

Find the values of x for which each expression represents a real number.

7. $\sqrt{x^2 - 5x}$ $x \leq 0$ or $x \geq 5$
8. $\sqrt{x^2 + 6x + 8}$ $x \leq -4$ or $x \geq -2$
9. $\sqrt{x^2 - 10x + 21}$ $x \leq 3$ or $x \geq 7$

Self-Test 2

Solve the following quadratic equations using the most convenient method. **Obj. 12-5, p. 562**

1. $3(x + 2)^2 = 12$ $\{-4, 0\}$
2. $2x^2 + 6x + 3 = 0$ $\left\{\frac{-3 \pm \sqrt{3}}{2}\right\}$
3. $x^2 - 10x = 20$ $\{5 \pm 3\sqrt{5}\}$
4. $3x^2 + 9x = 0$ $\{0, -3\}$

Solve. Give irrational roots to the nearest tenth. Use the Table of Square Roots on page 650 or a calculator as necessary.

5. The length of a rectangle is twice the width. The area of the rectangle is 200 cm^2. Find the length and width. **Obj. 12-6, p. 565** length, 20 cm; width, 10 cm

6. A rectangular wading pool measures 50 m by 40 m. How wide must a concrete walk of uniform width around the pool be if the walk is to cover an area of 784 m^2? 4 m

Check your answers with those at the back of the book.

Chapter Summary

1. Any quadratic equation can be solved using the quadratic formula (see item 2 below). Some quadratic equations, however, may be more easily solved by factoring, applying the property of square roots of equal numbers, or by completing the square.
2. When $ax^2 + bx + c = 0$ and $a \neq 0$, the quadratic formula is expressed as follows:

$$x = \frac{-b \pm \sqrt{b^2 - 4ac}}{2a}$$

3. The graph of a quadratic equation of the form $y = ax^2 + bx + c$ is a parabola. The x-intercepts of the parabola correspond to the roots of the related quadratic equation $ax^2 + bx + c = 0$.
4. The discriminant, $b^2 - 4ac$, is used to determine the number of roots of a quadratic equation.

   If $b^2 - 4ac > 0$, there are two real-number roots.

   If $b^2 - 4ac = 0$, there is one (double) real-number root.

   If $b^2 - 4ac < 0$, there are no real-number roots.

Chapter Review

Give the letter of the correct answer.

Solve.

1. $2x^2 - 128 = 0$ 12-1
   a. $\{64\}$ b. $\{64, -64\}$ c. $\{8\}$ (d.) $\{8, -8\}$
2. $(a + 3)^2 = 25$
   a. $\{22, 28\}$ (b.) $\{2, -8\}$ c. $\{2, -2\}$ d. $\{2, 8\}$

Solve by completing the square.

3. $x^2 + 4x - 77 = 0$ 12-2
   a. $\{11, 7\}$ b. $\{-11, -7\}$ c. $\{11, -7\}$ (d.) $\{-11, 7\}$
4. $c^2 - 10c - 20 = 0$
   a. $\{-5 + 3\sqrt{5}, -5 - 3\sqrt{5}\}$ b. $\{3\sqrt{5} + 5, 3\sqrt{5} - 5\}$
   (c.) $\{5 + 3\sqrt{5}, 5 - 3\sqrt{5}\}$ d. $\{-3\sqrt{5} + 5, -3\sqrt{5} - 5\}$

Solve by the quadratic formula.

5. $5z^2 - 11z + 2 = 0$ 12-3
   a. $\left\{-2, -\frac{1}{5}\right\}$ (b.) $\left\{2, \frac{1}{5}\right\}$ c. $\left\{2, -\frac{1}{5}\right\}$ d. $\left\{-2, \frac{1}{5}\right\}$

Mixed Review Exercises

1. Approximate $\sqrt{567}$ to the nearest hundredth, using the table on page 650. 23.81
2. Simplify $\sqrt{15} \cdot \sqrt{20} + 2\sqrt{12} - 5\sqrt{75}$. $-11\sqrt{3}$
3. Simplify $\sqrt{0.81b^4c^2d^4}$. $0.9b^2d^2|c|$
4. Solve $3x^2 - 4x - 12 = 0$. $\frac{2 \pm 2\sqrt{10}}{3}$

Quick Quiz

Solve the following quadratic equations using the most efficient method.

1. $2(x - 3)^2 = 18$ $\{6, 0\}$
2. $3x^2 + 12x + 7 = 0$ $\left\{\frac{-6 + \sqrt{15}}{3}, \frac{-6 - \sqrt{15}}{3}\right\}$
3. $x^2 - 16x = 26$ $\{8 + 3\sqrt{10}, 8 - 3\sqrt{10}\}$
4. $16x^2 + 9x = 0$ $\left\{0, -\frac{9}{16}\right\}$

Solve.

5. Find two integers whose difference is 4 and the sum of whose squares is 106. -9 and -5 or 5 and 9
6. A rectangular rug has an area of 21 m². If the width is 2 m less than three times the length, find the perimeter of the rug. 20 m

Supplementary Materials

Practice Masters 76–80
Tests 44–46
Resource Book, pp. 58–66, 128–132, 160

Extra Practice

Skills, pp. 631–632
Problems, p. 648

Alternate Test p. T21

Solve by the quadratic formula.

6. $10y^2 - y - 3 = 0$
   a. $\left\{-\frac{3}{5}, -\frac{1}{2}\right\}$ b. $\left\{\frac{3}{5}, \frac{1}{2}\right\}$ c. $\left\{-\frac{3}{5}, \frac{1}{2}\right\}$ (d.) $\left\{\frac{3}{5}, -\frac{1}{2}\right\}$

7. Give the discriminant of $2x^2 - 3x - 2 = 0$. 12-4
   a. -25 (b.) 25 c. -5 d. 5

8. How many real roots does $x^2 - 5x + 2 = 0$ have?
   a. 0 b. 1 (c.) 2 d. 3

9. Give the best method for solving $2y^2 + 8y = 0$. 12-5
   (a.) Factoring
   b. Property of square roots of equal numbers
   c. Completing the square
   d. Quadratic formula

Solve.

10. The dimensions of a sheet of paper can be represented by consecutive odd integers. If the area of the paper is 99 cm^2, find the dimensions. 12-6
    a. $l = 9$ cm, $w = 7$ cm (b.) $l = 11$ cm, $w = 9$ cm c. $l = 13$ cm, $w = 11$ cm d. $l = 11$ cm, $w = 13$ cm

Chapter Test

Solve.

1. $25x^2 = 121$ $\left\{-\frac{11}{5}, \frac{11}{5}\right\}$
2. $3(a - 5)^2 = 21$ $\{5 \pm \sqrt{7}\}$ 12-1

Solve by completing the square.

3. $c^2 + 8c + 15 = 0$ $\{-3, -5\}$
4. $b^2 - 4b - 10 = 0$ $\{2 \pm \sqrt{14}\}$ 12-2

Solve by the quadratic formula.

5. $2z^2 - 8z + 6 = 0$ $\{3, 1\}$
6. $y^2 - 8y - 4 = 0$ $\{4 \pm 2\sqrt{5}\}$ 12-3

State the number of real roots.

7. $2x^2 - 3x - 2 = 0$ two
8. $x^2 - 4x + 4 = 0$ one 12-4

Solve by the easiest method.

9. $9x^2 + 8x = 0$ $\left\{0, -\frac{8}{9}\right\}$
10. $3x^2 - 10x - 4 = 0$ $\left\{\frac{5 \pm \sqrt{37}}{3}\right\}$ 12-5

Solve. Approximate irrational roots to the nearest tenth.

11. A garden is currently 5 m wide and 8 m long. If the area of the garden is to be doubled by increasing the width and the length by the same number of meters, find the new dimensions of the garden. length, 10.6 m; width, 7.6 m 12-6

Cumulative Review (Chapters 1–12)

Evaluate if $a = -1$, $b = 1$, $c = 0$, $d = 3$, and $e = -\frac{5}{2}$.

1. $a(b + e)$ $\frac{3}{2}$
2. $(b \div d + e)^a$ $-\frac{6}{13}$
3. $c \div e$ 0
4. $(ab)^3 - (ab)^2$ -2
5. $(de + ab)^c$ 1
6. $e \div e^a$ $\frac{25}{4}$

Simplify. Assume that no denominator is zero. Each variable represents a positive real number.

7. $2 \cdot 58 - 7 \cdot 58 - (-58)$ -232
8. $6^2 \div 3^2 + 4 \div 3$ $\frac{16}{3}$
9. $(6 - 13)(6 + 13)$ -133
10. $4x - (0.4x + 1.2y)$
11. $15(3c - 4) + 5 - 9c$ $36c - 55$
12. $\left(-\frac{1}{8}x^5y^3z\right)(-16xy^2)$
13. $-\frac{4}{5}a^3b(-20ab^2 + 35b^3)$ $16a^4b^3 - 28a^3b^4$
14. $(5x^3y^2)^2(3x^4y^3)^3$ $675x^{18}y^{13}$
15. $\frac{-72wx^4y^5z}{-96x^3y^7z}$ $\frac{3wx}{4y^2}$
16. $\frac{(3r^3s^4)^3}{(-9r^5s^6)^2}$ $\frac{1}{3r}$
17. $(4u^2 - 2u + 1)(2u + 1)$ $8u^3 + 1$
18. $a - 2(a - 9)$ $-a + 18$
19. $(9z - 5)(3z + 4)$ $27z^2 + 21z - 20$
20. $(3a^3 - 2)^2$ $9a^6 - 12a^3 + 4$
21. $(8r^3t - 3v)(8r^3t + 3v)$ $64r^6t^2 - 9v^2$
22. $(3.4 \times 10^{12})(0.3 \times 10^{-3})$
23. $\frac{12c^2 - 26cd + 12d^2}{12c^2 - 44cd + 24d^2}$ $\frac{2c - 3d}{2(c - 3d)}$
24. $(18x^2 - x - 4) \div (2x - 1)$
25. $(27x^3 + 64) \div (3x + 4)$ $9x^2 - 12x + 16$
26. $\frac{b^2 + b - 12}{b + 2} \cdot \frac{b^2 - 4}{b^2 + 2b - 8}$
27. $\frac{3z^2 + 16z + 16}{z^2 + 6z + 9} \div \frac{z^2 + 3z - 4}{z + 3}$ $\frac{3z + 4}{(z + 3)(z - 1)}$
28. $\frac{85k^8 + 51k^4 - 17k^2}{-17k^4}$
29. $\frac{a - 1}{3} - \frac{5 - 2a}{3}$ $a - 2$
30. $\frac{n + 1}{2n - 3} + \frac{4}{n + 1} - 3$
31. $\frac{3}{m - 3} - \frac{1}{2m + 6}$
32. $-\sqrt{2.25x^6z^3}$ $-1.5x^3z\sqrt{z}$
33. $3\sqrt{5}(\sqrt{80} - \sqrt{64})$ $60 - 24\sqrt{5}$
34. $(3\sqrt{2} - 1)^2$ $19 - 6\sqrt{2}$
35. $\sqrt{\frac{18a^7}{7}} \cdot \sqrt{\frac{112}{2a^5}}$ $12a$
36. $\sqrt{108} - \sqrt{27} + \sqrt{6}$ $3\sqrt{3} + \sqrt{6}$
37. $3\sqrt{80} + \frac{2\sqrt{35}}{\sqrt{7}}$ $14\sqrt{5}$
38. $(2\sqrt{5} + 5\sqrt{2})(8\sqrt{5} - 4\sqrt{2})$ $40 + 32\sqrt{10}$
39. $\frac{3\sqrt{5} - 4}{\sqrt{2} + 3}$ $\frac{-3\sqrt{10} + 4\sqrt{2} + 9\sqrt{5} - 12}{7}$

Factor completely. If the polynomial cannot be factored, write "prime."

40. $49r^2 + 56rs + 16s^2$
41. $4t^5 - 9t^3$
42. $30x^2 - 91x - 30$
43. $-16z^4 + 80z^3 - 64z^2$
44. $125a^4 + 45a^2$
45. $12a^2 - 5a - 12$
46. $2a^2 - ab + 6a - 3b$
47. $c^2 - 8c + 16$
48. $-10p^2 + 27p + 28$

Cumulative Review p. T28

Additional Answers
Cumulative Review

10. $3.6x - 1.2y$
12. $2x^6y^5z$
22. 1.02×10^9
24. $9x + 4$
26. $b - 3$
28. $-5k^4 - 3 + \frac{1}{k^2}$
30. $\frac{-5n^2 + 13n - 2}{(2n - 3)(n + 1)}$
31. $\frac{5m + 21}{2(m - 3)(m + 3)}$
40. $(7r + 4s)^2$
41. $t^3(2t - 3)(2t + 3)$
42. $(10x + 3)(3x - 10)$
43. $-16z^2(z - 4)(z - 1)$
44. $5a^2(25a^2 + 9)$
45. prime
46. $(2a - b)(a + 3)$
47. $(c - 4)^2$
48. $-(5p + 4)(2p - 7)$

Additional Answers
Cumulative Review

57. $\left\{\frac{1}{4}, -\frac{2}{3}\right\}$

58. $\left\{-\frac{7}{12}, 1\right\}$

63. {the real numbers between −2 and 8}

64. $\left\{-3, \frac{8}{3}\right.$, and the real numbers between −3 and $\left.\frac{8}{3}\right\}$

65. $\left\{-\frac{3}{2}\right.$, 2, and the real numbers between $-\frac{3}{2}$ and $\left.2\right\}$

66. $\left\{-\frac{1}{3}\right.$ and the real numbers greater than $\left.-\frac{1}{3}\right\}$

73. {the real numbers greater than 2 or less than −4}

74.

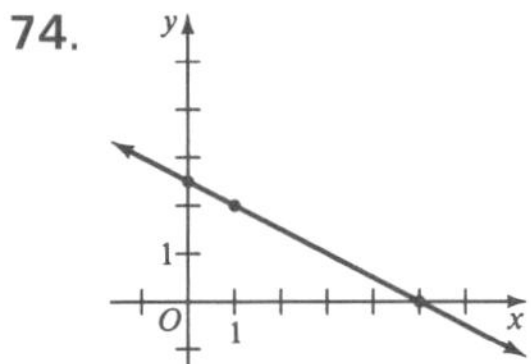

75.

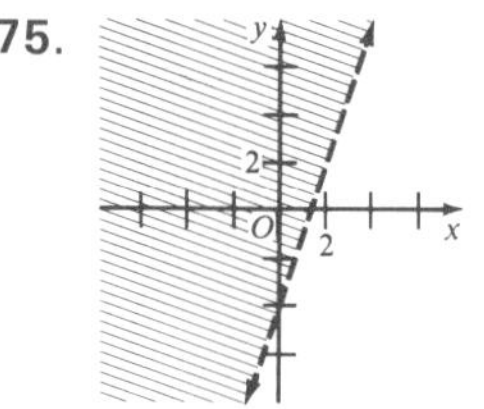

77.

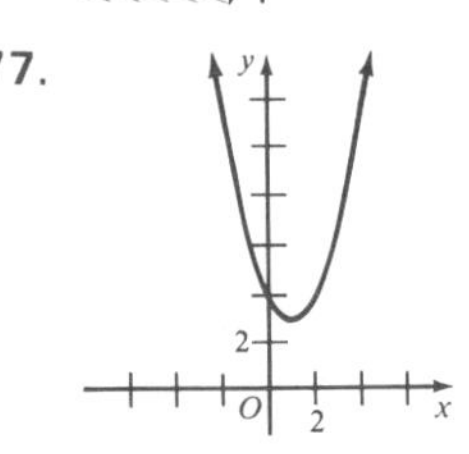

Solve each equation, inequality, or system. Assume that no denominator is zero. If there is no solution, state that fact.

49. $\frac{1}{4}x - 3 = \frac{2}{3}$ $\frac{44}{3}$

50. $15 - 3(y + 1) = 14 - 5y$ 1

51. $7w + 4 = |-56|$ $\frac{52}{7}$

52. $16 = 4.8x - 2.48$ 3.85

53. 27% of $t = 54$ 200

54. $3|x| + 5 = 9$ $\left\{\pm\frac{4}{3}\right\}$

55. $z^2 + 4z - 5 = 0$ $\{-5, 1\}$

56. $4t^2 - 20t + 25 = 0$ $\frac{5}{2}$

57. $12b^2 + 5b = 2$

58. $(3a - 2)(4a + 1) = 5$

59. $3x + 4y = 2$
$5x + 4y = -2$ $(-2, 2)$

60. $2x + y = 7$
$x - 2y = 11$ $(5, -3)$

61. $\frac{x - 2}{8} - \frac{2x + 1}{12} = \frac{1}{3}$ -16

62. $\frac{3x + 2}{x - 1} = \frac{3x + 4}{x + 1}$ $-\frac{3}{2}$

63. $|t - 3| < 5$

64. $-4 \le 3t + 5 \le 13$

65. $0 \le 4 - 2t \le 7$

66. $\frac{7}{2}t + \frac{1}{3} \ge -\frac{5}{6}$

67. $2\sqrt{t + 1} = 6$ 8

68. $\sqrt{x^2 + 3} = x - 3$ no sol.

69. $\sqrt{3r + 1} = 2r - 6$ 5

70. $\frac{1}{2}m^2 + 2m + 2 = 0$ -2

71. $2t^2 + 5t + 1 = 0$ $\left\{\frac{-5 \pm \sqrt{17}}{4}\right\}$

72. $3t^2 + 2t - 7 = 0$ $\left\{\frac{-1 \pm \sqrt{22}}{3}\right\}$

Graph the solution set. (In Exercise 73, use a number line.)

73. $|x + 1| > 3$

74. $x + 2y = 5$

75. $3x - y < 4$

76. Write an equation in standard form of the line that contains (1, 1) and (6, −1). $2x + 5y = 7$

77. Graph the function $f(x) = x^2 - 2x + 4$.

78. Write $0.4\overline{25}$ as a fraction in simplest form. $\frac{421}{990}$

79. Graph the solution set of the system:

$$y > 2x - 3$$
$$2x - 2y < 1$$

80. Find the length, to the nearest hundredth of a meter, of the diagonal of a rectangle that is 12 m by 8 m. (Use the Table of Square Roots on page 650 or a calculator.) 14.42 m

81. A plumber and an assistant finished a job in 4 hours. The job would have taken the plumber 6 hours working alone. How long would the job have taken the assistant working alone? 12 h

82. If a varies directly as b and inversely as the square of c, and $a = 10$ when $b = 8$ and $c = 2$, find a when $b = 20$ and $c = 5$. 4

83. During a canoe trip, Roberto paddled twice as many hours as Edward, and Jim paddled for one hour. If the three of them paddled less than a total of 10 hours, what is the number of hours that Roberto could have paddled? less than 6 h

84. During a 3000-mile flight, a plane encountered a strong tail wind that increased its speed by 100 mph. This increase in speed shortened the flying time by one hour. Find the speed of the plane relative to the ground. 500 mph

Mixed Review

Skills and Problem Solving

1. Find the coordinates of the vertex and the equation of the axis of symmetry of the graph of $f(x) = x^2 - 6x + 14$. (3, 5); $x = 3$

2. The legs of a right triangle are 100 m and 50 m long. Find the length of the hypotenuse as a radical in simplest form. $50\sqrt{5}$ m

3. How many liters of water must be added to 24 L of a 15% acid solution to make a solution that is 5% acid? 48 L

4. The sum of three consecutive odd integers is one third the square of the second. Find all such integers. 7, 9, 11

Simplify. Assume that no denominator equals zero. Each variable represents a positive real number.

5. $\frac{\sqrt{5} - 2}{\sqrt{6} + 1}$ $\frac{\sqrt{30} - 2\sqrt{6} - \sqrt{5} + 2}{5}$

6. $(7x - 3)(2x + 9)$ $14x^2 + 57x - 27$

7. $\frac{3a^2b^4}{12c^4} \div \frac{9ab^3}{3c^4b}$ $\frac{ab^2}{12}$

8. $9 \cdot 8 \div 4 + 36 \div 2 + 4$ 40

9. $\frac{b}{b + 1} + \frac{5}{4b + 4}$ $\frac{4b + 5}{4(b + 1)}$

10. $(3^{-1} - 3^{-2})^{-2}$ $\frac{81}{4}$

11. $(6.2 \times 10^4)(3.1 \times 10^3)$ 1.922×10^8

12. $\frac{2x + 12}{x^2 + 10x + 24}$ $\frac{2}{x + 4}$

13. $4\sqrt{2}(2\sqrt{6} - 6\sqrt{3})$ $16\sqrt{3} - 24\sqrt{6}$

14. $\frac{z^2}{z^2 - 1} - \frac{1}{z + 1}$ $\frac{z^2 - z + 1}{(z - 1)(z + 1)}$

15. $-\frac{3}{4}mn^2(12m^2n - 8n^3)$ $-9m^3n^3 + 6mn^5$

16. $\frac{3c^2 - 27}{15} \cdot \frac{5}{c^2 - 3c}$

17. $\frac{1}{4}\sqrt{8} - \frac{1}{2}\sqrt{12} + \frac{3}{4}\sqrt{27}$

18. $\frac{49a^2 - 14ab + b^2}{49a^2 - 7ab - 2b^2}$

19. $\sqrt{\frac{27c^5}{5}} \cdot \sqrt{\frac{170}{3c}}$ $3c^2\sqrt{34}$

Factor completely, if possible. If not, write "prime."

20. $24y^3 - 3y^2$ $3y^2(8y - 1)$

21. 360 $2^3 \cdot 3^2 \cdot 5$

22. $3x^2 - 27$ $3(x - 3)(x + 3)$

23. $35a^2 - 2ab - 6b^2$ prime

24. $x^4 - 25x^2 + 144$

25. $4\pi r^2 - 2\pi rh$ $2\pi r(2r - h)$

26. $x^2 - 0.09$ $(x - 0.3)(x + 0.3)$

27. $18t^3 + 39t^2 - 15t$

28. 1080 $3^3 \cdot 2^3 \cdot 5$

29. Arrange in order from least to greatest: 4.0×10^{-2}, $\frac{43}{99}$, $0.\overline{4}$, $-\frac{4}{9}$, $\frac{1}{2}$, $\frac{2}{5}$

30. Two trains leave a station at noon traveling in opposite directions. One train is traveling at 100 km/h, the other at 80 km/h. At what time will they be 270 km apart? 1:30 P.M.

31. The Mas bought furniture at 25% off the regular price. Their total cost, including a 4% tax on the sale price, was \$1170. What was the regular price, excluding tax? \$1500

Graph each solution set.

32. $3x - 2y \leq 4$
$2x + 3y \geq 7$

33. $3x - y = 1$

34. $x + 3y < 3$

35. $3y - 1 > 5$ or $2 - 3y > -1$

36. $-9 \leq -2x + 1 < 3$

79.

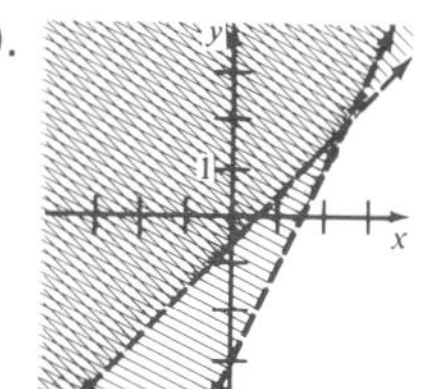

Additional Answers Mixed Review

16. $\frac{c + 3}{c}$ 17. $\frac{2\sqrt{2} + 5\sqrt{3}}{4}$

18. $\frac{(7a - b)^2}{(7a + b)(7a - 2b)}$

24. $(x - 3)(x + 3)(x - 4) \cdot (x + 4)$

27. $3t(3t - 1)(2t + 5)$

29. $-\frac{4}{9}$, 4.0×10^{-2}, $\frac{2}{5}$, $\frac{43}{99}$, $0.\overline{4}$, $\frac{1}{2}$

32.

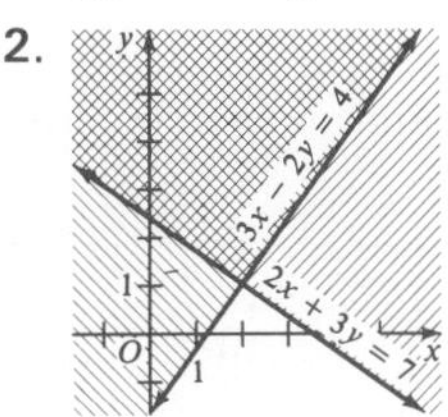

33.

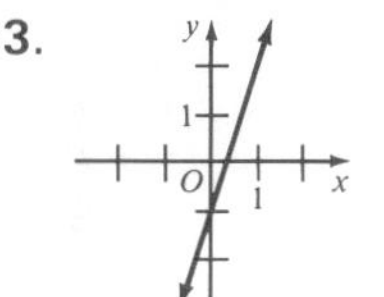

34.

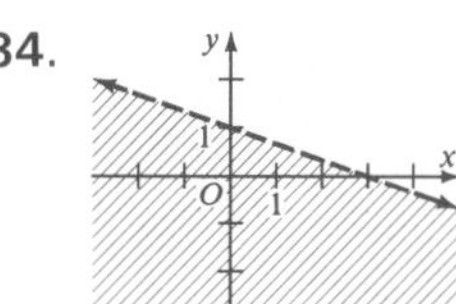

35.

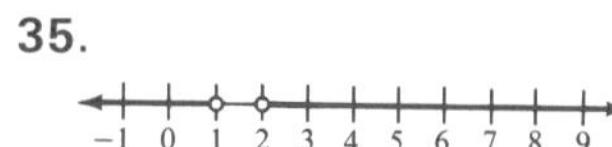

36.

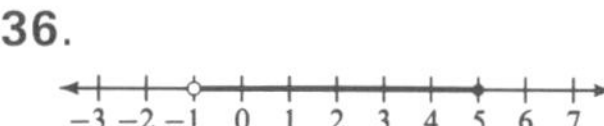

Additional Answers
Mixed Review

42. {the real numbers greater than $\frac{8}{3}$}

48. {2 and the real numbers greater than 2, except for 3}

50. $\left\{\frac{1 \pm \sqrt{13}}{2}\right\}$

51. {the real numbers less than 10 or greater than 18}

Solve each equation, inequality, or system.

37. $7w + 1 = -|-125|$ -18

38. $2a - 1 = 3a + 4$ -5

39. $\frac{1}{2m} - \frac{1}{5m} = \frac{1}{10}$ 3

40. $3x + 4y = 7$
$2x + 5y = 14$ $(-3, 4)$

41. $\frac{4}{3x + 2} + \frac{1}{x} = 1$ $\left\{-\frac{1}{3}, 2\right\}$

42. $\frac{5}{2}y + \frac{1}{3} > 7$

43. $\sqrt{1 - 5x} = 4$ -3

44. $2c^2 + 5c + 3 = 0$ $\left\{-\frac{3}{2}, -1\right\}$

45. $x - 2y = 16$
$x + y = 10$ $(12, -2)$

46. $d^2 - 6d = 15$ $\{3 \pm 2\sqrt{6}\}$

47. $6 - n^2 = 0$ $\{\pm\sqrt{6}\}$

48. $\frac{1}{(x - 3)^2} + \frac{1}{x - 3} \geq 0$

49. $\sqrt{4a + 5} = 2a + 1$ 1

50. $\frac{2a + 1}{a + 2} + \frac{a}{a + 1} = 2$

51. $\left|\frac{1}{2}x - 7\right| > 2$

52. Find an equation of the line through $(-4, 3)$ and $(2, 6)$. $x - 2y = -10$

53. The sum of twice one number and five times a second number is 5. The sum of three times the first number and twice the second number is -9. Find the numbers. -5 and 3

54. A painter can finish a job in 2 hours less than the assistant. Together they finish in 1 hour and 20 minutes. How long would the painter take working alone? 2 h

55. A street 6 m wide and 200 m long can be plowed in 20 min. How long will it take to plow a street 12 m wide and 300 m long? 60 min, or 1 h

56. Find 120% of 45. 54

57. Find $7\frac{1}{3}\%$ of 150. 11

58. If c varies inversely as d, and $c = 3$ when $d = 1$, find d when $c = 9$. $\frac{1}{3}$

59. If x varies directly as y^2 and inversely as z, and $x = 75$ when $y = 5$ and $z = 2$, find x when $y = 4$ and $z = 3$. 32

60. Write $0.5\overline{27}$ as a fraction in lowest terms. $\frac{29}{55}$

61. Find an equation in standard form of the line with slope 2 passing through the point $(-1, -1)$. $2x - y = -1$

62. Find an equation in standard form of the line parallel to $x - y = 5$ passing through $(3, 3)$. $x - y = 0$

63. If $f(x) = x^2 + 6$, find $f(2)$ and $f(-4)$. $f(2) = 10$; $f(-4) = 22$

64. If $f(x) = 8x + 4x^2 - 7$, find $f\left(\frac{1}{2}\right)$ and $f(-5)$. $f\left(\frac{1}{2}\right) = -2$; $f(-5) = 53$

65. Sandra Chu invests a total of \$2800, part at 9% and the rest at $9\frac{1}{2}\%$. If she receives \$258.50 in annual interest, how much is invested at each rate? \$1300 at $9\frac{1}{2}\%$, \$1500 at 9%

66. If the sides of a square are increased by 2 cm, the area is increased by 100 cm^2. Find the area of the original square. 576 cm^2

67. The average distance from the sun to Earth is 1.496×10^8 km. The average distance from the sun to Pluto is 5.090×10^9 km. What is the average distance from Earth's orbit to Pluto's orbit? 4.940×10^9 km

Preparing for College Entrance Exams

Strategy for Success

Take your time and be sure to read each question and all the possible answers carefully. Although it is important to work quickly, you must be sure not to work so quickly that you lose accuracy. Remember that no partial credit is given.

Decide which is the best of the choices given and write the corresponding letter on your answer sheet.

1. Which number is $\frac{3}{5}$ of the way from $-\frac{4}{7}$ to $1\frac{1}{8}$? D

   (A) $\frac{31}{56}$ **(B)** $\frac{95}{56}$ **(C)** $\frac{93}{280}$ **(D)** $\frac{25}{56}$ **(E)** $\frac{57}{56}$

2. The length of a rectangle is five times the width. The area is 336.2 m^2. Find the width of the rectangle to the nearest tenth of a meter. B

   (A) 9.1 m **(B)** 8.2 m **(C)** 8.9 m **(D)** 9.0 m **(E)** 7.8 m

3. Two sides of a right triangle are 5 cm and 12 cm long. Find the length of the hypotenuse to the nearest tenth of a centimeter. A

   (A) 13.0 cm **(B)** 10.9 cm **(C)** 7.0 cm
   (D) No such triangle is possible.
   (E) Cannot be determined from the given information.

4. Evaluate $\frac{x(x+1)}{x+2}$ if $x = \sqrt{3}$. A

   (A) $3 - \sqrt{3}$ **(B)** $\sqrt{3} - 3$ **(C)** $-3 - \sqrt{3}$ **(D)** $\frac{1+\sqrt{3}}{2}$

5. The sum of a positive integer and the square of the next consecutive integer is 131. Find the sum of the two integers. C

   (A) 19 **(B)** 20 **(C)** 21 **(D)** 22 **(E)** 23

6. The graph of an equation of the form $y = ax^2 + bx + c$ is shown at the right. Identify the true statement(s). D

   I. $0 < a < 1$
   II. $b^2 > 4ac$
   III. $c > 0$

   (A) I only **(B)** II only **(C)** III only
   (D) I and II only **(E)** I, II, and III

   $y = \frac{1}{2}x^2 - 2$

7. The equation $ax^2 + 3x + c = 0$ has two distinct roots. Which of the following is (are) possible? E

   I. $a = 1, c = 2$ II. $a = -1, c = -2$ III. $a = -1, c = 2$

   (A) I only **(B)** II only **(C)** III only
   (D) I and II only **(E)** I, II, and III

Teaching References

Lesson Commentary, pp. T129–T132

Assignment Guide, p. T67

Teaching Suggestions

p. T129

Chalkboard Examples

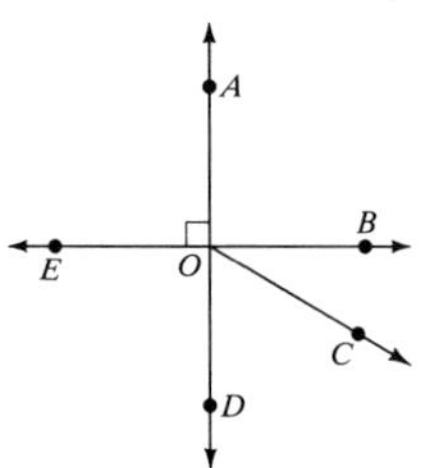

1. In the diagram above, $\overleftrightarrow{AD}$ and $\overleftrightarrow{BE}$ intersect at O. Name:

a. the points
A, B, C, D, E, O

b. the line segments
$\overline{AO}, \overline{AD}, \overline{BO}, \overline{BE}, \overline{CO}, \overline{DO}, \overline{EO}$

c. the rays
$\overrightarrow{OA}, \overrightarrow{OB}, \overrightarrow{OC}, \overrightarrow{OD}, \overrightarrow{OE}, \overrightarrow{AD}, \overrightarrow{DA}, \overrightarrow{BE}, \overrightarrow{EB}$

d. the right angles
$\angle AOB, \angle BOD, \angle DOE, \angle AOE$

e. the acute angles
$\angle BOC, \angle COD$

f. the obtuse angles
$\angle AOC, \angle COE$

Identify each graph as a point, a line, a ray, or a segment.

A B C
−5 −4 −3 −2 −1 0 1 2 3 4 5

2. $x = 2$ point, B

3. $x \geq -3$ ray, $\overrightarrow{AC}$ or $\overrightarrow{AB}$

4. $-3 \leq x \leq 2$
line segment, $\overline{AB}$

Looking Ahead

Geometry

Points, Lines, and Angles

Objective To represent points, lines, and angles and to measure angles.

You have illustrated relationships among numbers by representing them as points on a number line. Similarly, you have illustrated relationships among ordered pairs of numbers by representing them as points in a coordinate plane. The study of *points, lines,* and *planes* is the subject of the branch of mathematics called *geometry.*

Geometric points and *lines* are abstract ideas, not concrete objects. A point has no size; a line has no thickness. To illustrate these abstract ideas, however, you draw figures that do have size and thickness. To represent the idea of a geometric point, you draw a dot. To represent the idea of a geometric line, you draw a straight line.

A line determined by points A and B is denoted by $\overleftrightarrow{AB}$, or $\overleftrightarrow{BA}$. The arrowheads indicate that the line extends in both directions without ending.

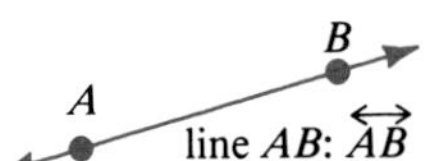

The part of $\overleftrightarrow{AB}$ that consists of points A and B and all points of $\overleftrightarrow{AB}$ between A and B is called a **line segment,** or a **segment.** The segment is denoted by $\overline{AB}$, or $\overline{BA}$. The length of $\overline{AB}$ is denoted by AB.

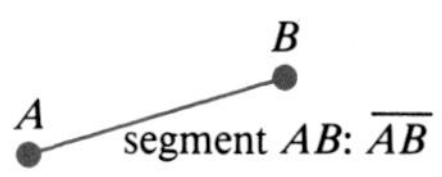

The part of $\overleftrightarrow{AB}$ that starts at point A and extends without ending through point B is a **ray,** denoted by $\overrightarrow{AB}$. A is called the **endpoint** of $\overrightarrow{AB}$.

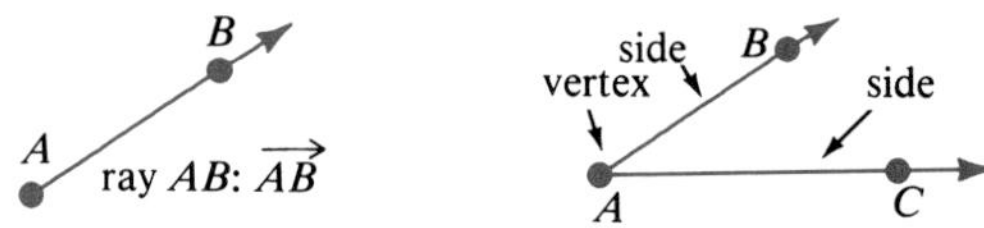

An **angle** is a figure formed by two different rays that have the same endpoint. The rays are called the **sides** of the angle and the common endpoint is called the **vertex** of the angle. The angle shown above is formed by $\overrightarrow{AB}$ and $\overrightarrow{AC}$. It is denoted by $\angle A$, $\angle BAC$, or $\angle CAB$.

To find the **degree measure** of an angle, you use a protractor. Using the outer scale, you can see that the degree measure of $\angle NOL$ is 40. You may write this fact as $m\angle NOL = 40$, or $\angle NOL = 40°$. Also, $m\angle NOK = 90$ and $m\angle NOM = 130$.

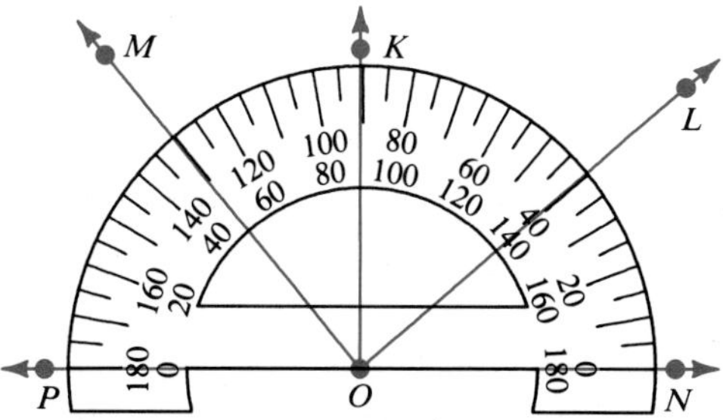

Angles are classified according to their measures.

An **acute angle** has measure between 0 and 90.
A **right angle** has measure 90.
An **obtuse angle** has measure between 90 and 180.
A **straight angle** has measure 180.

You can find the degree measure of $\angle LOK$ in the diagram above by subtracting 40 from 90: $m\angle LOK = 50$. Do you see that $\angle LOM$ is a right angle? that $m\angle KOM = 40$? To state that $\angle NOL$ and $\angle KOM$ have equal measures, you write $m\angle NOL = m\angle KOM$.

Oral Exercises

Exercises 1–8 refer to the diagram below. Name each angle whose measure is given.

1. 145° $\angle FOA$ **2.** 55° $\angle COA$, $\angle DOF$ **3.** 115° $\angle EOA$ **4.** 90° $\angle DOA$, $\angle DOH$, $\angle FOC$

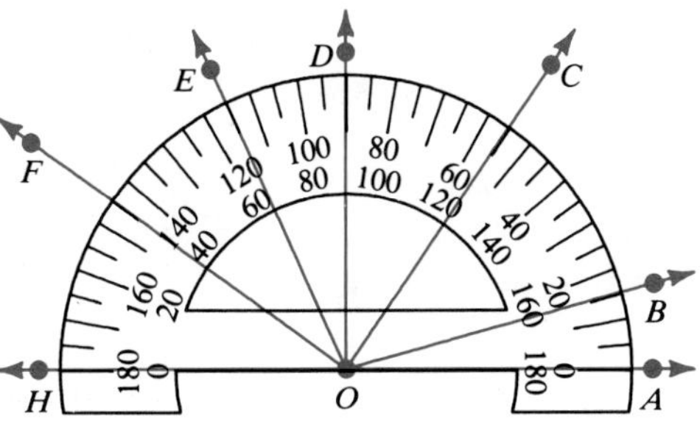

State the measure of each angle.

5. $\angle DOF$ 55° **6.** $\angle BOD$ 75° **7.** $\angle COH$ 125° **8.** $\angle EOH$ 65°

5. $x > 2$ or $x < 3$
line, $\overleftrightarrow{AB}$ or $\overleftrightarrow{AC}$ or $\overleftrightarrow{BC}$

6. $x \leq 3$ and $x \geq 3$
point, C

Suggested Assignment

Maximum
578/1–20

Additional Answers Written Exercises

13.

14.

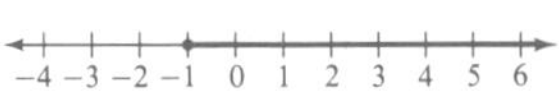

15.

16.

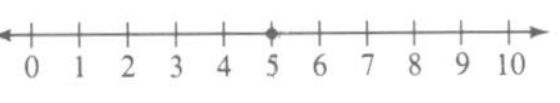

17.

18.

19.

20.

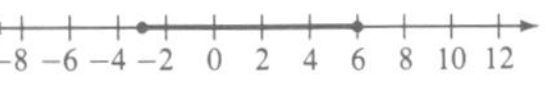

21.

22.

Written Exercises

For Exs. 1–4, students may give any five of the line segments given.

In Exercises 1-4, name five different line segments in each diagram.

A **1.**

$\overline{LM}$, $\overline{LN}$, $\overline{LP}$, $\overline{MN}$, $\overline{MP}$, $\overline{NP}$

2.

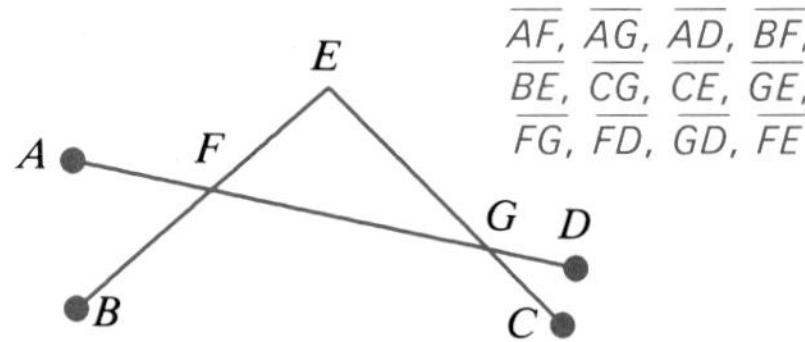

$\overline{AF}$, $\overline{AG}$, $\overline{AD}$, $\overline{BF}$, $\overline{BE}$, $\overline{CG}$, $\overline{CE}$, $\overline{GE}$, $\overline{FG}$, $\overline{FD}$, $\overline{GD}$, $\overline{FE}$

3.

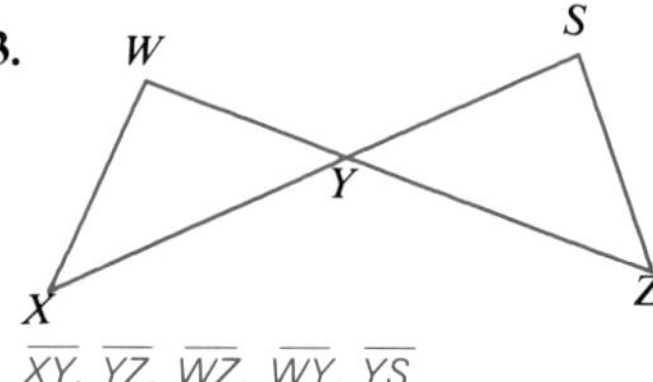

$\overline{XY}$, $\overline{YZ}$, $\overline{WZ}$, $\overline{WY}$, $\overline{YS}$, $\overline{XS}$, $\overline{WX}$, $\overline{SZ}$

4.

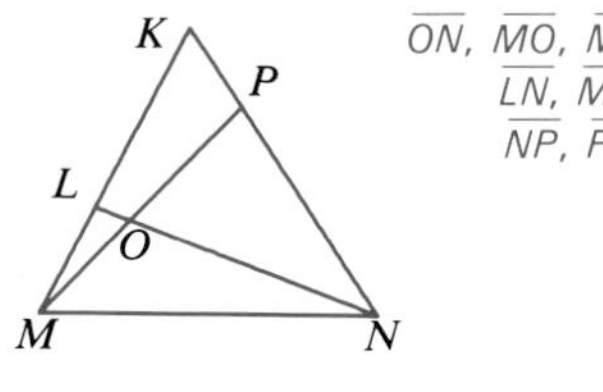

$\overline{ON}$, $\overline{MO}$, $\overline{MP}$, $\overline{OP}$, $\overline{LO}$, $\overline{LN}$, $\overline{ML}$, $\overline{LK}$, $\overline{MK}$, $\overline{NP}$, $\overline{PK}$, $\overline{NK}$, $\overline{MN}$

Measure the given angle and classify it as acute, obtuse, or right.

5. $\angle AOB$ acute

6. $\angle AOD$ right

7. $\angle AOC$ acute

8. $\angle EOG$ acute

9. $\angle BOE$ obtuse

10. $\angle COH$ acute

11. $\angle DOG$ obtuse

12. $\angle EOH$ obtuse

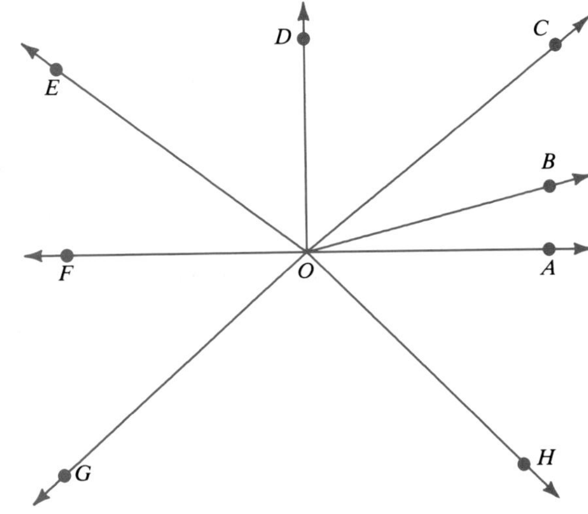

Graph the solution set of each sentence on a number line. Identify the graph as a point, a line, a line segment, or a ray.

B **13.** $x = 5$ point **14.** $x \geq -1$ ray **15.** $-3 \leq x \leq 2$ line segment

16. $x - 4 = 1$ point **17.** $-6 \leq x - 2 \leq 0$ line segment **18.** $x + 4 = 7 + x - 3$ line

C **19.** $x - 2 \leq 6$ or $x + 1 \leq 4$ ray **20.** $x - 4 \geq -7$ and $x + 2 \leq 7$ line segment

21. $3x > 6$ or $4x \leq 16$ line **22.** $2x + 5 \leq 1$ and $3x + 10 \geq 1$ line segment

Pairs of Angles

Objective To learn the names and properties of special pairs of angles.

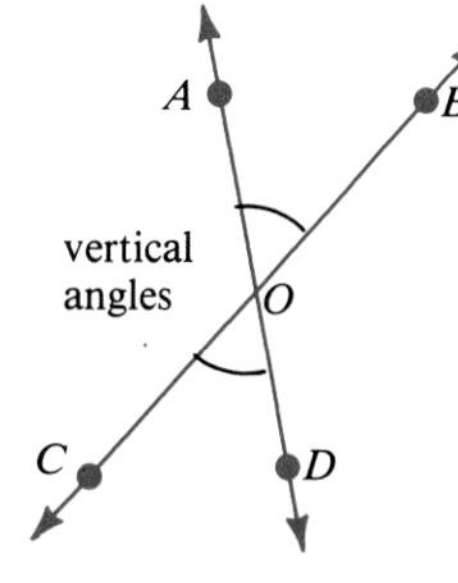

Certain pairs of angles whose measures are related are given special names.

The diagram at the right shows two lines intersecting at O and forming $\angle AOB$, $\angle AOC$, $\angle COD$, and $\angle DOB$. Two angles, such as $\angle AOB$ and $\angle COD$, whose sides are rays in the same lines, but in opposite directions are called **vertical angles.** $\angle AOC$ and $\angle BOD$ are also a pair of vertical angles.

Vertical angles have equal measures. You can use a protractor to see that $m\angle AOB = m\angle COD$ and $m\angle AOC = m\angle BOD$.

Two angles are **complementary angles** if the sum of their measures is 90. Each angle is called a **complement** of the other. The diagram at the left below shows a pair of complementary angles.

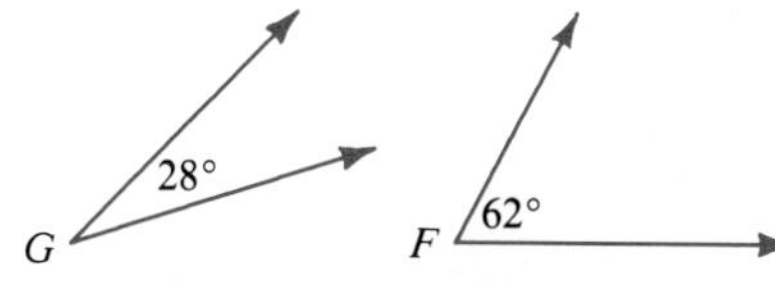

R 27° S 153°

$\angle G$ and $\angle F$ are complementary.
$\angle G$ is a complement of $\angle F$.

$\angle R$ and $\angle S$ are supplementary.
$\angle R$ is a supplement of $\angle S$.

Two angles are **supplementary angles** if the sum of their measures is 180. Each angle is called a **supplement** of the other. The diagram at the right above shows a pair of supplementary angles.

Example The measure of an angle is 32 less than the measure of its supplement.

Find: **a.** the measure of the angle.
b. the measure of its supplement.
c. the measure of its complement.

Solution Let n = the measure in degrees of the angle.
Then $n + 32$ = the measure of its supplement.

$$n + (n + 32) = 180$$
$$2n + 32 = 180$$
$$2n = 148$$
$$n = 74$$

a. The measure of the angle is 74.
b. The measure of its supplement is $(74 + 32)$, or 106.
c. The measure of its complement is $(90 - 74)$, or 16.

Teaching Suggestions
p. T129

Suggested Extensions
p. T129

Chalkboard Examples

1. Find the measure of the complement and the supplement of each angle.

a. 36° 54°; 144°
b. 3° 87°; 177°
c. $x°$ $(90 - x)°$; $(180 - x)°$
d. 120° none; 60°
e. $(90 - y)°$ $y°$; $(90 + y)°$

2. The product of the measures of two vertical angles is 36 less than twenty times the measure of one vertical angle. Find the measure of each.

Let n = the measure of each of the vertical angles. $n^2 + 36 = 20n$
$n^2 - 20n + 36 = 0$
$(n - 2)(n - 18) = 0$
$n = 2$ or $n = 18$
(both answers check)
The vertical angles are each 2° or each 18°.

3. The measure of the supplement of an angle is 10° more than twice the measure of its complement. What is the measure of the angle?

Let x = the measure of the angle.
$$180 - x - 10 = 2(90 - x)$$
$$170 - x = 180 - 2x$$
$$x = 10$$
The measure of the angle is 10°

Suggested Assignment

Maximum
580/1–10
S 578/21, 22

Oral Exercises

State the measure of the complement of an angle with the given measure.

1. 12° 78° **2.** 68° 22° **3.** 45° 45° **4.** 84° 6° **5.** x° $(90 - x)$° **6.** $25y$° $(90 - 25y)$°

State the measure of the supplement of an angle with the given measure.

7. 30° 150° **8.** 150° 30° **9.** 85° 95° **10.** 125° 55° **11.** x° $(180 - x)$° **12.** $12y$° $(180 - 12y)$°

Classify each statement as true or false.

13. The measures of two supplementary angles are never equal. false

14. If two angles have equal measures, then their complements have equal measures. true

15. If an angle is obtuse, its supplement is obtuse. false

16. If an angle is acute, its complement is acute. true

17. A supplement of a right angle is also a right angle. true

Written Exercises

In Exercises 1–4 use the diagram at the right. Assume that the measures of $\angle BCJ$ and $\angle EIJ$ are equal.

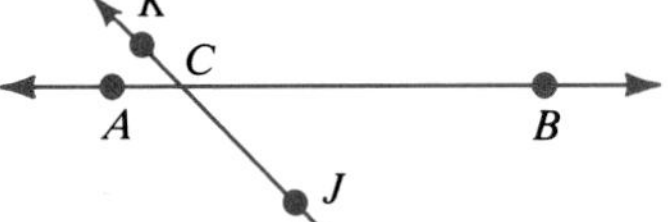

A **1.** List all the angles with measures equal to the measure of $\angle EIJ$. $\angle FIH$, $\angle BCJ$, $\angle KCA$

2. List all the angles that are supplementary to $\angle EIJ$. $\angle JIF$, $\angle EIH$, $\angle ACJ$, $\angle KCB$

3. If $m\angle EIJ = 30$, then $m\angle JIF =$ _?_. 150

4. If $m\angle BCK = 125$, then $m\angle ACK =$ _?_. 55

5. The smaller of two supplementary angles has a measure that is 40 less than the larger. Find the measures of the two angles. 70, 110

6. What are the measures of two supplementary angles, the larger of which measures 5 times the smaller? 30, 150

7. Find the measure of an angle that measures 56 more than its complement. 73

8. Find the measure of an angle that measures one third of its supplement. 45

B **9.** The sum of the measures of the complement and the supplement of an angle is 106. Find the measure of the angle. 82

10. The measure of the supplement of an angle exceeds six times the measure of the complement of the angle by 30. Find the measure of the angle. 78

Triangles

Objective To learn some properties of triangles.

A **triangle** is the figure formed by three segments joining three points not on the same line. Each segment is a **side** of the triangle. Each of the three points is a **vertex** of the triangle.

"Triangle ABC" can be written $\triangle ABC$.
Sides of $\triangle ABC$: $\overline{AB}$, $\overline{BC}$, $\overline{CA}$
Vertices of $\triangle ABC$: A, B, C
Angles of $\triangle ABC$: $\angle A$, $\angle B$, $\angle C$

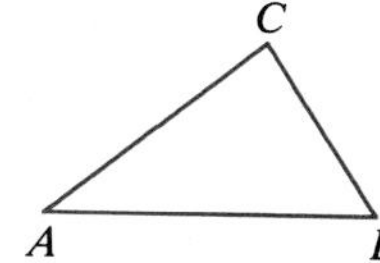

In any triangle, the sum of the measures of the angles is 180°. To check this statement for a particular triangle, measure each angle with a protractor and then find the sum of the measures. You can also show this by tearing off the corners of a paper triangle and fitting them together so that they form a straight angle, as shown below.

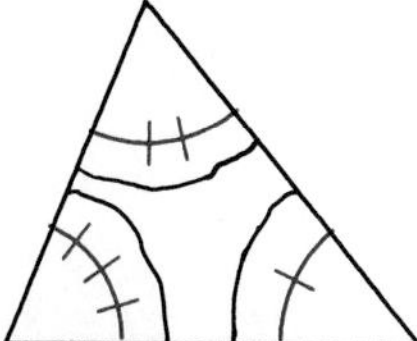

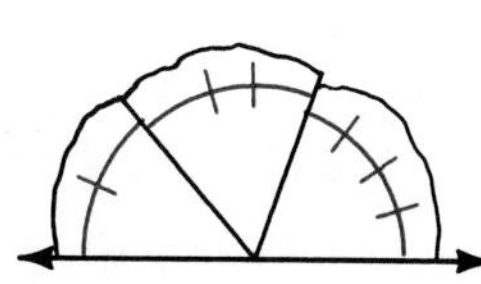

Here are some special triangles:

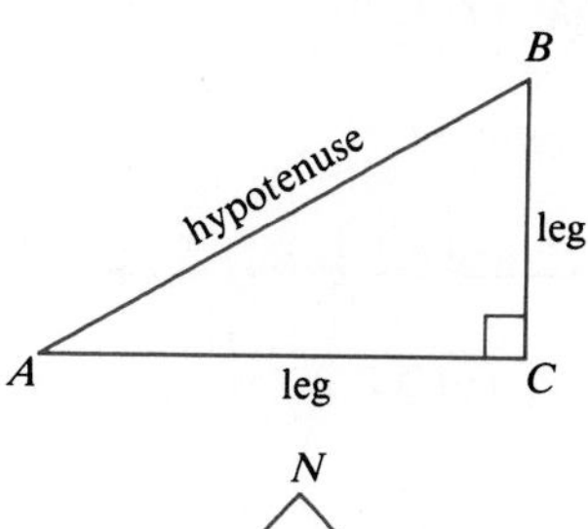

Right triangle
$m\angle C = 90$
$(AC)^2 + (BC)^2 = (AB)^2$
(Pythagorean theorem, p. 520, converse p. 521.)

The small square in the right triangle indicates the right angle.

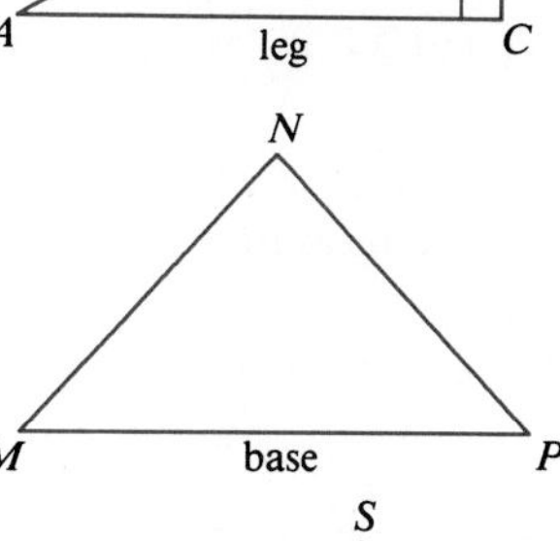

Isosceles triangle
$MN = NP$; $m\angle M = m\angle P$
Base: $\overline{MP}$
Base angles: $\angle M$ and $\angle P$

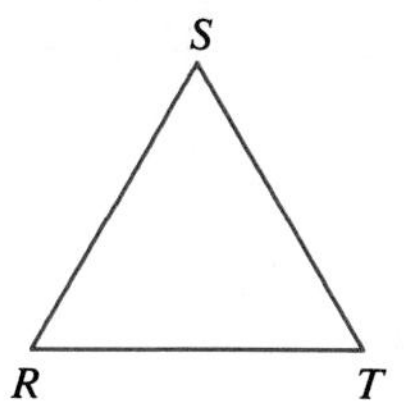

Equilateral triangle
$RS = ST = TR$
$m\angle R = m\angle S = m\angle T$
$= 60$

Teaching Suggestions
p. T130

Suggested Extensions
p. T130

Chalkboard Examples

Find the value of x.

1.

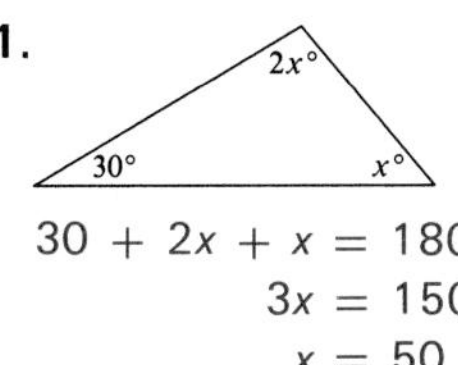

$$30 + 2x + x = 180$$
$$3x = 150$$
$$x = 50$$

2.

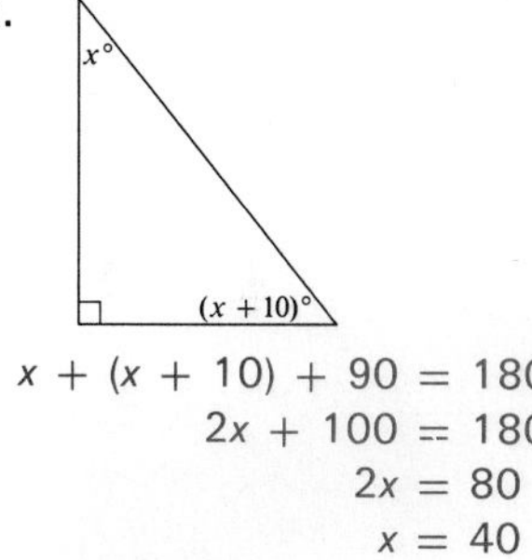

$$x + (x + 10) + 90 = 180$$
$$2x + 100 = 180$$
$$2x = 80$$
$$x = 40$$

3.

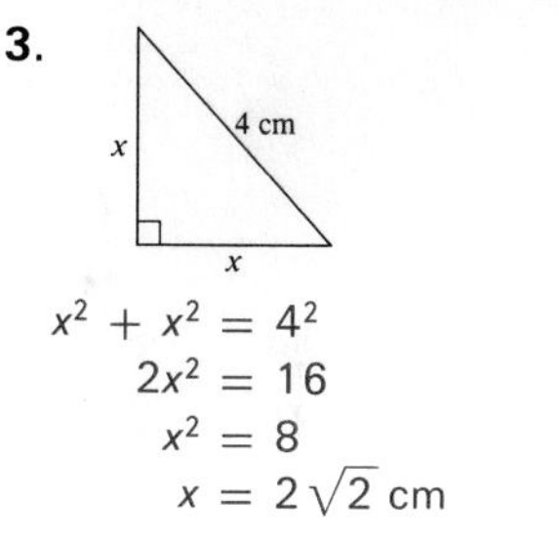

$$x^2 + x^2 = 4^2$$
$$2x^2 = 16$$
$$x^2 = 8$$
$$x = 2\sqrt{2} \text{ cm}$$

Suggested Assignment

Maximum
582/1–22
583/*P*: 1–11 odd

Oral Exercises

Identify $\triangle ABC$ as right, isosceles, or equilateral.

1. $AB = 10$, $BC = 10$ isosceles

2. $AB = BC = CA$ equilateral

3. $m\angle B = 90$ right

4. $AB = 3$, $BC = 4$, $AC = 5$ right

5. $AC = BC$ isosceles

6. $m\angle C = 23$, $m\angle A = 67$ right

7. $m\angle B = 60$, $m\angle C = 60$ equilateral

8. $m\angle A = 40$, $m\angle B = 100$ isosceles

Written Exercises

The measures of two angles of a triangle are given. Find the measure of the third angle.

A **1.** 37°, 74° 69°

2. 111°, 43° 26°

3. 84°, 48° 48°

4. 90°, 29° 61°

5. 23°, 34° 123°

6. 63°, 57° 60°

In Exercises 7-12, use the converse of the Pythagorean theorem to determine whether the triangle is a right triangle.

7. $\triangle ABC$: $AB = 7$, $BC = 4$, $AC = 3$ no

8. $\triangle DEF$: $EF = 8$, $FD = 10$, $DE = 6$ yes

9. $\triangle GHI$: $GH = 7$, $HI = 25$, $GI = 24$ yes

10. $\triangle JKL$: $JK = 15$, $KL = 17$, $JL = 8$ yes

11. $\triangle MNO$: $MN = 26$, $NO = 24$, $MO = 10$ yes

12. $\triangle PQR$: $PQ = 10$, $QR = 12$, $PR = 8$ no

13. If $\triangle RST$ is a right triangle with $m\angle S = 90$, $RS = 6$, and $ST = 8$, find RT. 10

14. If $\triangle STU$ is a right triangle with $m\angle S = 90$, $SU = 12$, and $ST = 5$, find TU. 13

15. If $\triangle XYZ$ is a right triangle with $m\angle Y = 90$, $YZ = 12$, and $XZ = 15$, find XY. 9

16. If $\triangle DEF$ is isosceles, $m\angle D = 40$, and $DE = DF$, find the measure of $\angle E$. 70

17. If $\triangle MNO$ is isosceles, $m\angle N = 50$, and $MN = MO$, find the measure of $\angle M$. 80

18. If $\triangle PQR$ is a right isosceles triangle, and $m\angle Q = 90$, find the measures of $\angle P$ and $\angle R$. $m\angle P = m\angle R = 45$

In Exercises 19-24, $m\angle C = 90$ in $\triangle ABC$. Find the length of the third side in simplest radical form given the lengths of the other two sides.

B **19.** $AC = 4$, $BC = 12$ $4\sqrt{10}$

20. $AC = 3$, $BC = 6$ $3\sqrt{5}$

21. $AC = 6$, $AB = 9$ $3\sqrt{5}$

22. $BC = 16$, $AB = 24$ $8\sqrt{5}$

C **23.** $AC = BC = x$ $x\sqrt{2}$

24. $AC = y$, $AB = 2y$ $y\sqrt{3}$

Problems

Solve.

A 1. In a right triangle, the measure of one acute angle is 5 times the measure of the other. Find the measure of each angle. 90, 15, 75

2. Find the measure of each angle of an isosceles triangle if the measure of the third angle is 10 times the measure of each base angle. 15, 15, 150

3. Find the measure of each angle of a triangle if the measure of the second angle is 4 times the measure of the first angle and the measure of the third angle is 7 times the measure of the first angle. 15, 60, 105

4. The measures of the angles of a triangle are in the ratio 4:5:6. Find the measure of each angle. 48, 60, 72

5. The measure of the second angle of a triangle is twice the measure of the first angle, and the measure of the third angle is 6 times the measure of the second angle. Find the measure of each angle. 12, 24, 144

6. The measure of the second angle of a triangle is 4 times the measure of the first angle and the measure of the third angle is 63 less than the measure of the second angle. Find the measure of each angle. 27, 108, 45

7. The measures of two angles of a triangle are equal. The measure of the third angle is $\frac{7}{8}$ of the sum of the measures of the first two angles. Find the measure of each angle. 48, 48, 84

8. How many degrees are there in each angle of a triangle if the measure of the second of the angles is twice that of the first, and the measure of the third is 5 more than 4 times that of the first? 25°, 50°, 105°

B 9. The measure of the second angle of a triangle is 4 more than 3 times the measure of the first angle, and the measure of the third angle is 12 less than twice the measure of the second angle. Find the measure of each angle. 18, 58, 104

10. The sum of the measures of four angles is 360. The measure of the second angle is 3 more than twice the measure of the first angle, the measure of the third angle is 3 times the measure of the second angle, and the measure of the fourth angle is 9 more than the measure of the third angle. Find the measure of each angle. 22, 47, 141, 150

C 11. The measure of the second angle of a triangle is 18 less than the measure of the complement of the first angle, and the measure of the third angle is 30 more than one half the measure of the supplement of the first angle. Find the measure of each angle. 24, 48, 108

12. Find the number of degrees in each angle of a triangle if the number of degrees in the first angle is 2 less than twice the number of degrees in the second angle, and the number of degrees in the third angle is 35 more than half the number of degrees in the first. 37°, 71°, 72°

Teaching Suggestions
p. T130

Suggested Extensions
p. T130

Chalkboard Examples

1.

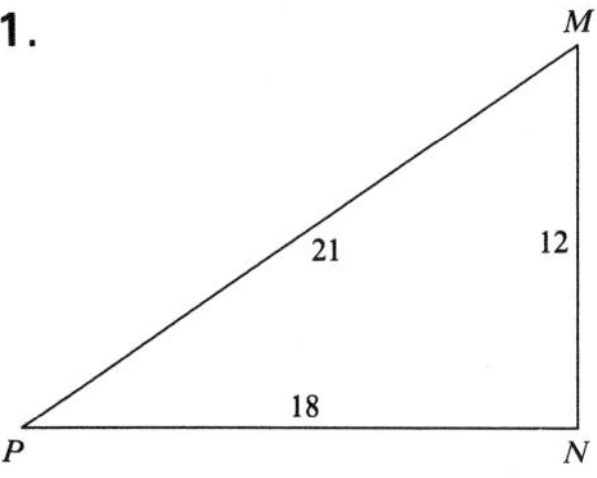

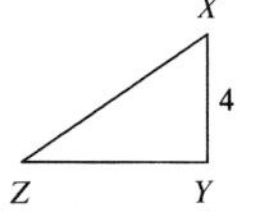

If $\triangle MNP \sim \triangle XYZ$, find YZ and ZX.

$\frac{YZ}{18} = \frac{4}{12}$, $YZ = 6$

$\frac{ZX}{21} = \frac{4}{12}$, $ZX = 7$

2.

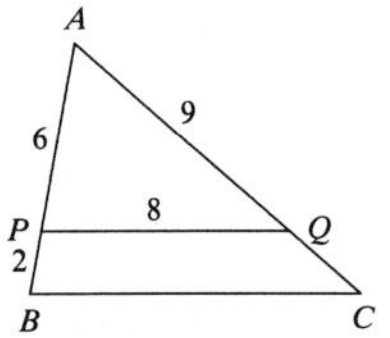

If $\triangle APQ \sim \triangle ABC$, find QC and BC.

$\frac{AP}{AB} = \frac{AQ}{AC}$, $\frac{6}{8} = \frac{9}{AC}$,

$AC = 12$, $QC = 3$

$\frac{AP}{PQ} = \frac{AB}{BC}$, $\frac{6}{8} = \frac{8}{BC}$,

$BC = \frac{32}{3}$, or $10\frac{2}{3}$

Similar Triangles

Objective To solve problems involving similar triangles.

An object viewed under a magnifying lens appears larger than it is, but its shape is not changed. Two figures that have the same shape are called *similar.*

Two triangles are **similar triangles** when the measures of two angles of one triangle equal the measures of two angles of the other triangle. (Since the sum of the measures of the angles of a triangle is 180°, it follows that the remaining angles also have equal measures.) The triangles shown below are similar.

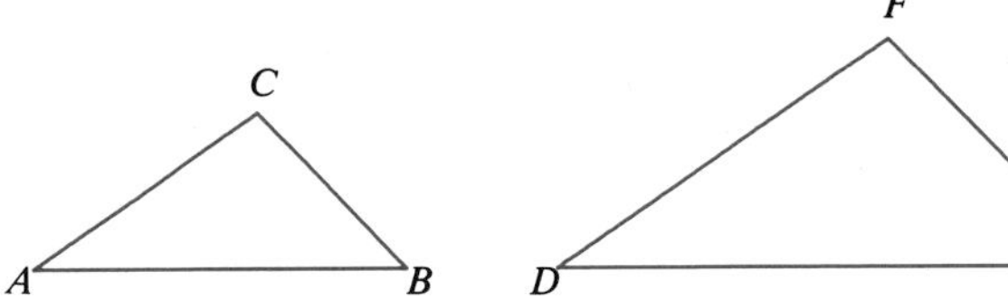

$$m\angle A = m\angle D,\ m\angle B = m\angle E,\ m\angle C = m\angle F$$

You indicate that triangles ABC and DEF are similar by writing

$$\triangle ABC \sim \triangle DEF.$$

Here angles with equal measures are listed in corresponding positions. They are called **corresponding angles.** The sides opposite corresponding angles are called **corresponding sides.** $\overline{AB}$ corresponds to $\overline{DE}$, and so on. *It is a geometric fact that the lengths of corresponding sides of similar triangles are proportional.* Thus,

$$\frac{AB}{DE} = \frac{BC}{EF} = \frac{CA}{FD}.$$

Example 1 In the diagram, $\triangle ABC \sim \triangle DEF$. Find AB and BC.

Solution Corresponding sides are proportional:

$\frac{AB}{45} = \frac{8}{24}$ and $\frac{BC}{36} = \frac{8}{24}$

Solving each proportion, you have

$AB = 15$ and $BC = 12$. ***Answer***

Example 2 In the diagram, $\triangle ABC \sim \triangle EDC$. Find BC and DE.

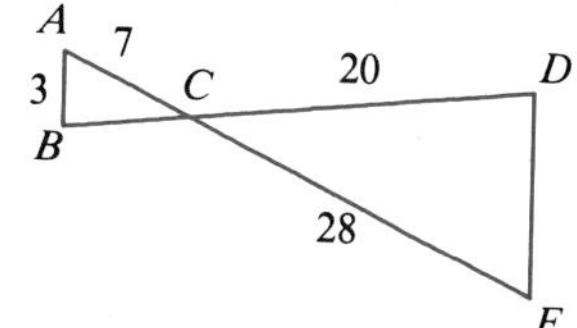

Solution Corresponding sides are proportional:

$$\frac{BC}{20} = \frac{7}{28} \quad \text{and} \quad \frac{3}{DE} = \frac{7}{28}$$

Solving each proportion, you have

$BC = 5$ and $DE = 12$. ***Answer***

Oral Exercises

In the diagram for Exercises 1-3, $\triangle XYZ \sim \triangle XWV$.

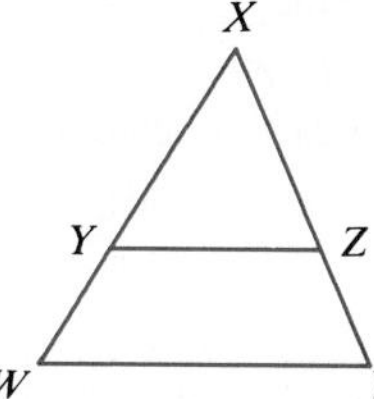

1. Name the corresponding angles. $\angle W$ and $\angle XYZ$, $\angle XZY$ and $\angle V$, $\angle X$ and $\angle X$
2. Name the corresponding sides. 2. $\overline{XY}$ and $\overline{XW}$, $\overline{XZ}$ and $\overline{XV}$, $\overline{YZ}$ and $\overline{WV}$
3. Name three equal ratios. $\frac{XY}{XW} = \frac{XZ}{XV} = \frac{YZ}{WV}$

Written Exercises

A 1. In $\triangle ABC$, $m\angle A = 60$ and $m\angle C = 80$. In $\triangle DEF$, $m\angle F = 60$ and $m\angle E = 80$. Write the corresponding angles and sides. $\angle A$ and $\angle F$, $\angle C$ and $\angle E$, $\angle B$ and $\angle D$, $\overline{AB}$ and $\overline{FD}$, $\overline{AC}$ and $\overline{EF}$, $\overline{BC}$ and $\overline{ED}$

2. In $\triangle JKL$ and $\triangle MNP$, $m\angle J = m\angle P$ and $m\angle K = m\angle M$. Write three equal ratios. $\frac{LJ}{NP} = \frac{JK}{PM} = \frac{KL}{NM}$

Classify each statement as true or false.

3. All right triangles are similar. false
4. All isosceles triangles are similar. false
5. All equilateral triangles are similar. true
6. All isosceles right triangles are similar. true

In Exercises 7-10, $\triangle ABC \sim \triangle DEF$. Find the lengths of the sides not given.

7. $AB = 3$, $BC = 5$, $AC = 6$, $DE = 6$ $EF = 10$, $FD = 12$
8. $DE = 6$, $EF = 9$, $DF = 12$, $BC = 12$ $AC = 16$, $AB = 8$
9. $AB = 20$, $BC = 10$, $AC = 15$, $DE = 8$ $DF = 6$, $FE = 4$
10. $AB = 6$, $BC = AC = 8$, $EF = 12$ $DF = 12$, $DE = 9$

3. Suppose that $\triangle ABC \sim \triangle DEF$. If $\angle B = 35°$ and $\angle E = (5x^2 - 18x)°$, what is the value of x?

$$5x^2 - 18x = 35$$
$$5x^2 - 18x - 35 = 0$$
$$(5x + 7)(x - 5) = 0$$
$$x = -\frac{7}{5} \text{ or } x = 5$$

4.

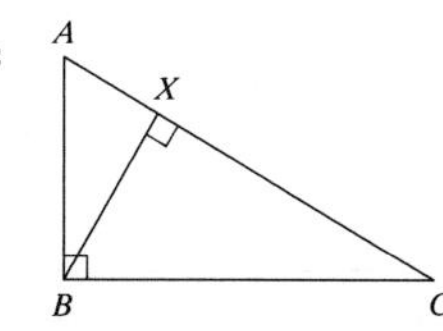

a. Name three similar triangles.
$\triangle ABC \sim \triangle AXB \sim \triangle BXC$

b. If $AX = 9$ cm and $XC = 15$ cm, find XB.
Since $\triangle AXB \sim \triangle BXC$,

$$\frac{AX}{XB} = \frac{XB}{XC}$$
$$\frac{9}{XB} = \frac{XB}{15}$$
$$(XB)^2 = 9 \cdot 15$$
$$XB = 3\sqrt{15} \text{ cm}$$

Suggested Assignment

Maximum
585/1-6, 7-13 odd
586/*P*: 2, 5-8
S 582/23, 24

In Exercises 11–14, $\triangle ABC \sim \triangle DEF$. Find the lengths of the sides not given.

B **11.** $AB = 6$, $BC = 8$, $DE = 9$, $DF = 15$ $AC = 10$, $EF = 12$

12. $AB = 12$, $BC = 18$, $DE = 8$, $DF = 16$ $AC = 24$, $EF = 12$

13. $BC = 14$, $AC = 35$, $EF = 6$, $DE = 12$ $AB = 28$, $FD = 15$

14. $AB = 16$, $BC = 14$, $DE = 28$, $DF = 49$ $AC = 28$, $FE = 24.5$

Problems

Solve.

A **1.** A triangle has sides with lengths of 8 cm, 12 cm, and 16 cm. If the shortest side of a similar triangle is 14 cm, find its longest side. 28 cm

2. A vertical pole 3 m long casts a shadow 1 m long at the same time a building casts a shadow 12 m long. How tall is the building? 36 m

3. A bush 2 m tall casts a shadow 3 m long at the same time a tree casts a shadow 18 m long. Find the height of the tree. 12 m

4. An isosceles triangle has sides with lengths 12 cm, 12 cm, and 15 cm. The base of a similar triangle is 20 cm. Find the perimeter of the larger triangle. 52 cm

5. To find the length of a swamp, two similar triangles were roped off. The measurements are shown on the diagram. How long is the swamp? 225 m

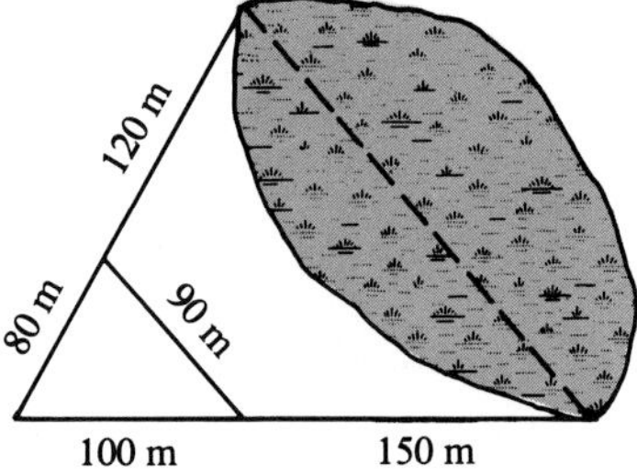

B **6.** Given: S is on $\overline{RU}$, T is on $\overline{RV}$, $\triangle RST \sim \triangle RUV$. If $RS = 3x$, $SU = x$, $RT = 12$, and $ST = 15$, find UV. 20

7. Sara walks 4 m up a ramp and is 1 m above the ground. If she were to walk 8 m farther, how far above the ground would she be? 3 m

8. From a point on the ground 5 m from the base of a 6 m tree, it is possible to see the top of a 300 m building just over the top of the tree. How far is the point from the base of the building? 250 m

C **9.** A boy whose eye level is 1.5 m above the ground wants to find the height of a tree ED. He places a plane mirror horizontally on the ground 15 m from the tree. If he stands at a point B which is 2 m from the mirror C, he can see the reflection of the top of the tree. Find the height of the tree. 11.25 m

Trigonometry

Trigonometric Ratios

Objective To find the sine, cosine, and tangent of an acute angle.

In the branch of mathematics called *trigonometry* you learn more about the measurement of triangles.

Any acute angle, such as $\angle A$ in the diagram, can be made an angle of a right triangle ABC. The legs opposite and adjacent to this angle are labeled. Ratios of the lengths of the sides of $\triangle ABC$ are called **trigonometric ratios** of $\angle A$. These ratios have special names and symbols.

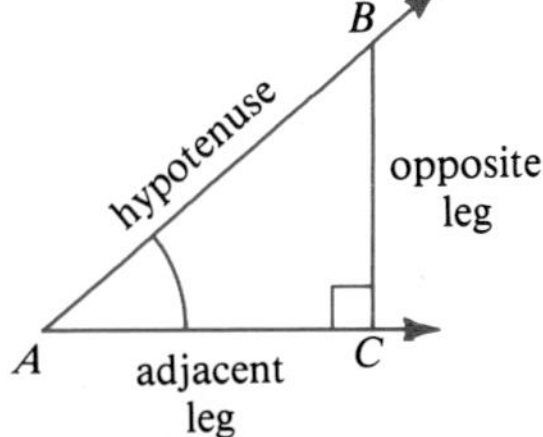

sine of $\angle A$ (symbol, $\sin A$) $= \dfrac{\text{length of leg opposite } \angle A}{\text{length of hypotenuse}} = \dfrac{BC}{AB}$

cosine of $\angle A$ (symbol, $\cos A$) $= \dfrac{\text{length of leg adjacent to } \angle A}{\text{length of hypotenuse}} = \dfrac{AC}{AB}$

tangent of $\angle A$ (symbol, $\tan A$) $= \dfrac{\text{length of leg opposite } \angle A}{\text{length of leg adjacent to } \angle A} = \dfrac{BC}{AC}$

Example 1 Find the sine, cosine, and tangent of $\angle A$ and of $\angle B$.

Solution

$\sin A = \frac{5}{13}$ $\quad \sin B = \frac{12}{13}$

$\cos A = \frac{12}{13}$ $\quad \cos B = \frac{5}{13}$

$\tan A = \frac{5}{12}$ $\quad \tan B = \frac{12}{5}$

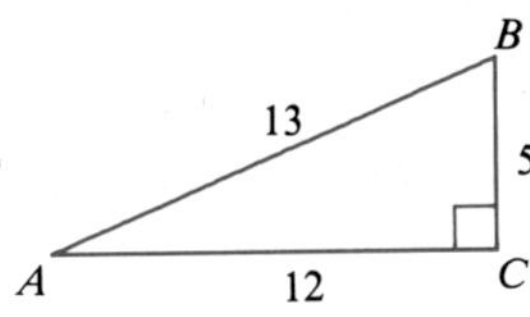

Example 2 Find the sine, cosine, and tangent of $\angle P$.

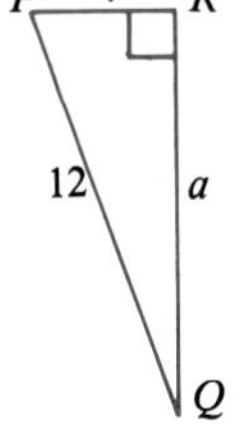

Solution First use the Pythagorean theorem to find RQ.

$$a^2 + 4^2 = 12^2$$
$$a^2 + 16 = 144$$
$$a^2 = 128$$
$$a = \sqrt{128} = 8\sqrt{2}$$

$\sin P = \dfrac{8\sqrt{2}}{12} = \dfrac{2\sqrt{2}}{3}$ $\quad \cos P = \dfrac{4}{12} = \dfrac{1}{3}$ $\quad \tan P = \dfrac{8\sqrt{2}}{4} = 2\sqrt{2}$

Teaching Suggestions
p. T130

Chalkboard Examples

1. Find the sine, cosine, and tangent of $\angle M$.

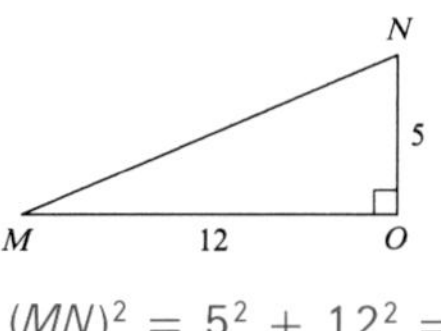

$(MN)^2 = 5^2 + 12^2 = 169$
$MN = 13$
$\sin M = \frac{5}{13}$
$\cos M = \frac{12}{13}$
$\tan M = \frac{5}{12}$

2.

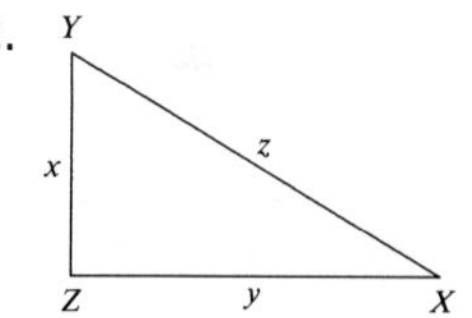

Find (in terms of x, y, and z):

a. $\tan X$ $\frac{x}{y}$

b. $\cos X$ $\frac{y}{z}$

c. $\sin Y$ $\frac{y}{z}$

d. $\cos Y$ $\frac{x}{z}$

e. $(\sin Y)^2 + (\cos Y)^2$
$\left(\frac{y}{z}\right)^2 + \left(\frac{x}{z}\right)^2 =$
$\frac{y^2}{z^2} + \frac{x^2}{z^2} =$
$\frac{y^2 + x^2}{z^2} = \frac{z^2}{z^2} = 1$

(continued)

Chalkboard Examples
(continued)

3.

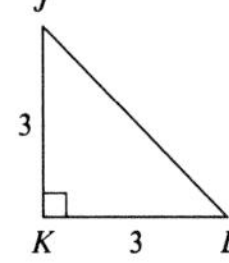

a. Find the length of the hypotenuse of the isosceles right triangle pictured.

$3^2 + 3^2 = (JL)^2$
$18 = (JL)^2$
$JL = 3\sqrt{2}$

b. Find the measure of each base angle of the isosceles right triangle pictured.

$x + x + 90 = 180$
$2x = 90$
$x = 45$
$\angle J = \angle L = 45°$

c. Using the information obtained in parts a and b, evaluate sin 45°, cos 45°, and tan 45°.

$\sin 45° = \frac{3}{3\sqrt{2}} = \frac{\sqrt{2}}{2}$

$\cos 45° = \frac{3}{3\sqrt{2}} = \frac{\sqrt{2}}{2}$

$\tan 45° = \frac{3}{3} = 1$

Suggested Assignments

Maximum
589/1–16
S 583/*P*: 12

Additional Answers Written Exercises

2. $\sin A = \frac{35}{37}$

$\cos A = \frac{12}{37}$

$\tan A = \frac{35}{12}$

$\sin B = \frac{12}{37}$

$\cos B = \frac{35}{37}$

$\tan B = \frac{12}{35}$

The values of the trigonometric ratios of an angle depend only on the measure of the angle and not on the particular right triangle that contains the angle. For example, in the two right triangles below, $\angle A$ and $\angle D$ have equal measures. It can be shown that the trigonometric ratios of $\angle A$ and $\angle D$ are also equal.

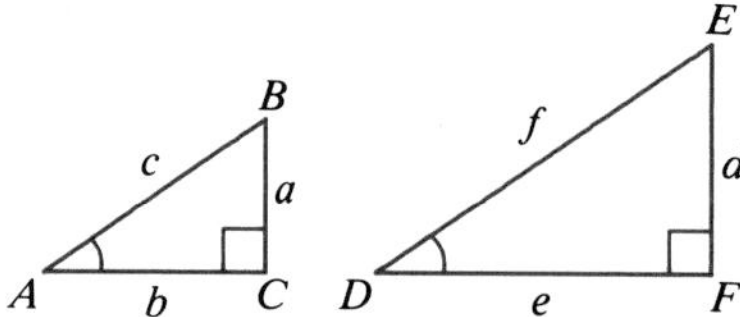

Since $m\angle A = m\angle D$ and $m\angle C = m\angle F = 90$, the triangles are similar and their corresponding sides are proportional:

$$\frac{a}{d} = \frac{c}{f}$$

Multiplying both ratios by $\frac{d}{c}$, you obtain the equivalent proportion

$$\frac{a}{c} = \frac{d}{f}, \text{ or } \sin A = \sin D.$$

You can show similarly that $\cos A = \cos D$ and $\tan A = \tan D$.

Because the values of $\sin A$, $\cos A$, and $\tan A$ depend only on the measure of $\angle A$ and not on the triangle containing $\angle A$, you can think of these trigonometric ratios as the values of three functions each having the set of acute angles as its domain. These functions are called **trigonometric functions.**

Oral Exercises

State the value of each trigonometric ratio for the triangle shown.

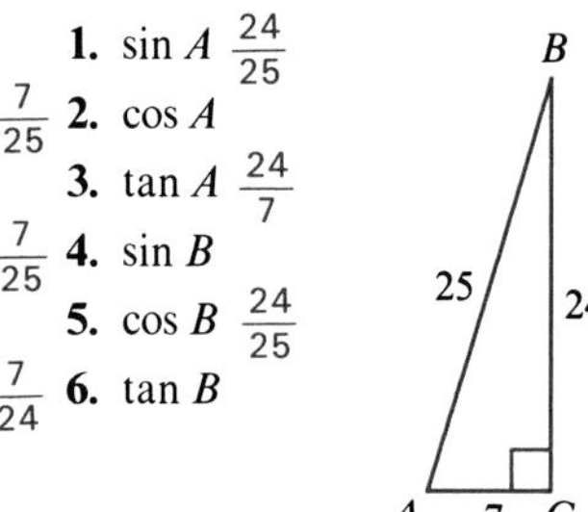

1. $\sin A$ $\frac{24}{25}$
2. $\cos A$ $\frac{7}{25}$
3. $\tan A$ $\frac{24}{7}$
4. $\sin B$ $\frac{7}{25}$
5. $\cos B$ $\frac{24}{25}$
6. $\tan B$ $\frac{7}{24}$

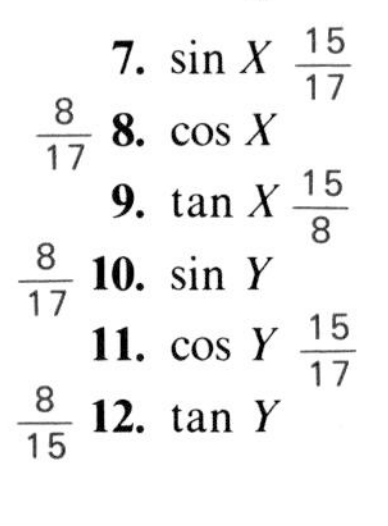

7. $\sin X$ $\frac{15}{17}$
8. $\cos X$ $\frac{8}{17}$
9. $\tan X$ $\frac{15}{8}$
10. $\sin Y$ $\frac{8}{17}$
11. $\cos Y$ $\frac{15}{17}$
12. $\tan Y$ $\frac{8}{15}$

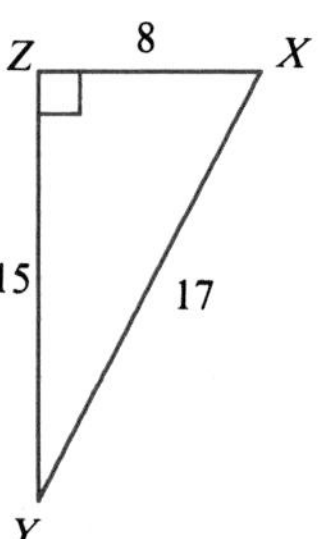

Written Exercises

For each right triangle shown, find sin A, cos A, tan A, sin B, cos B, and tan B. Write irrational answers in simplest radical form.

A **1.**

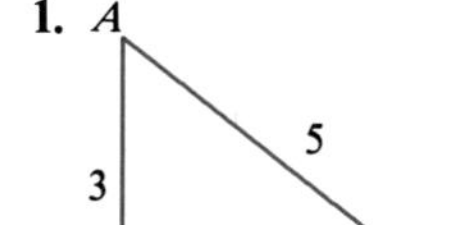

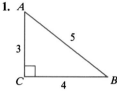

2.

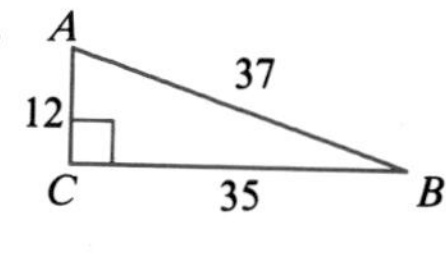

3.

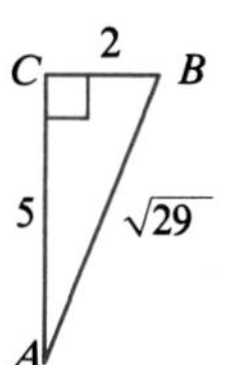

4.

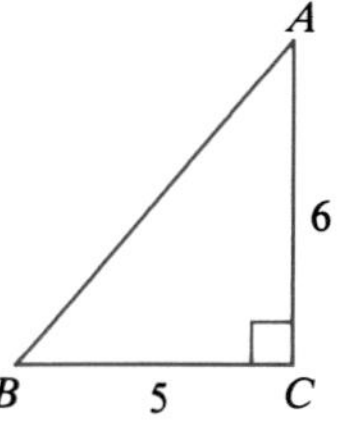

5.

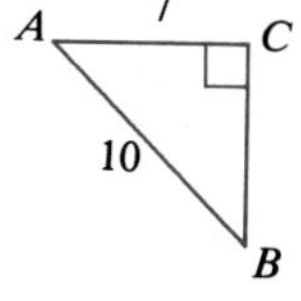

6.

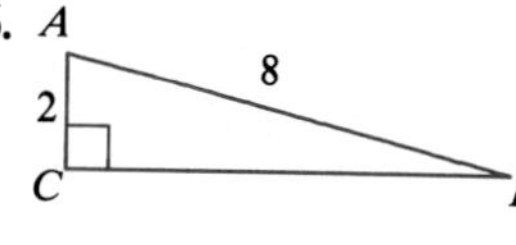

7.

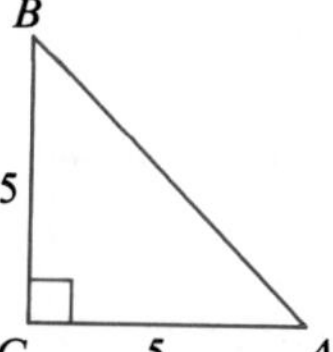

8.

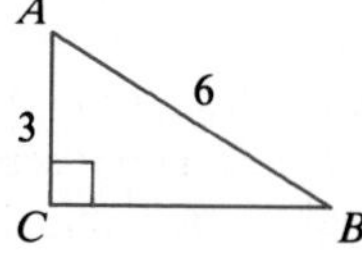

9.

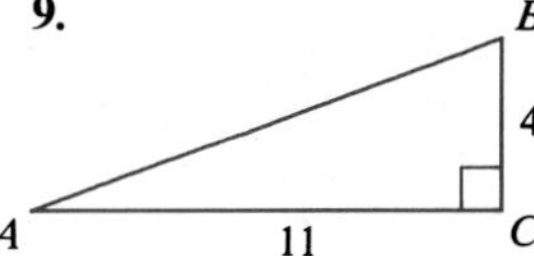

In Exercises 10–13 $\triangle ABC$ is a right triangle with $\angle C$ as the right angle. Show that the following statements are true.

B **10.** $\sin A = \cos B$

11. $\cos A = \sin B$

12. $(\sin A)^2 + (\cos A)^2 = 1$

13. $\tan A = \dfrac{\sin A}{\cos A}$

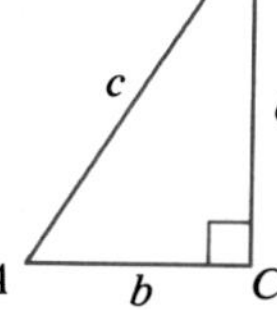

C **14.** If $\cos Y = \frac{4}{5}$, find $\sin Y$. $\frac{3}{5}$

15. If $\sin Z = \frac{5}{8}$, find the sine of the complement of $\angle Z$. $\frac{\sqrt{39}}{8}$

16. If $\tan X = \frac{9}{40}$, find $\sin Z$ and $\cos X$. $\sin Z = \frac{40}{41}$, $\cos X = \frac{40}{41}$

4. $\sin A = \frac{5\sqrt{61}}{61}$

$\cos A = \frac{6\sqrt{61}}{61}$

$\tan A = \frac{5}{6}$

$\sin B = \frac{6\sqrt{61}}{61}$

$\cos B = \frac{5\sqrt{61}}{61}$

$\tan B = \frac{6}{5}$

6. $\sin A = \frac{\sqrt{15}}{4}$

$\cos A = \frac{1}{4}$

$\tan A = \sqrt{15}$

$\sin B = \frac{1}{4}$

$\cos B = \frac{\sqrt{15}}{4}$

$\tan B = \frac{\sqrt{15}}{15}$

8. $\sin A = \frac{\sqrt{3}}{2}$

$\cos A = \frac{1}{2}$

$\tan A = \sqrt{3}$

$\sin B = \frac{1}{2}$

$\cos B = \frac{\sqrt{3}}{2}$

$\tan B = \frac{\sqrt{3}}{3}$

10. $\sin A = \frac{a}{c}$, $\cos B = \frac{a}{c}$; thus, $\sin A = \cos B$

11. $\cos A = \frac{b}{c}$, $\sin B = \frac{b}{c}$; thus, $\cos A = \sin B$

12. $(\sin A)^2 + (\cos A)^2 = \left(\frac{a}{c}\right)^2 + \left(\frac{b}{c}\right)^2 = \frac{a^2}{c^2} + \frac{b^2}{c^2} = \frac{a^2 + b^2}{c^2} = \frac{c^2}{c^2} = 1$

13. $\frac{\sin A}{\cos A} = \frac{\frac{a}{c}}{\frac{b}{c}} = \frac{a}{c} \cdot \frac{c}{b} = \frac{a}{b} = \tan A$

Teaching Suggestions
p. T131

Chalkboard Examples

1. Use the table on page 651 to find the values of:
   a. tan 58° 1.6003
   b. sin 10° 0.1736
   c. cos 83° 0.1219
2. Use the table on page 651 to find the values of the trigonometric functions for angles of degree measure 45°, 30°, and 60°.
   tan 30° = 0.5774
   sin 30° = 0.5000
   cos 30° = 0.8660
   tan 60° = 1.7321
   sin 60° = 0.8660
   cos 60° = 0.5000
   tan 45° = 1
   sin 45° = 0.7071
   cos 45° = 0.7071
3. Use the table on page 651 to estimate $\angle A$ to the nearest degree if tan A = 0.6494.
   $\angle A \approx 33°$
4. Use the table on page 651 to estimate $\angle B$ to the nearest degree if cos B = 0.4000.
   $\angle B \approx 66°$
5. Find the measure of an angle of a right triangle if the ratio of the adjacent leg to the hypotenuse is 1 : 2.

$\cos A = \frac{x}{2x} = \frac{1}{2} = 0.5000$

$\angle A = 60°$

Using Trigonometric Tables

Objective To find values of trigonometric ratios for given angles, and measures of angles for given trigonometric ratios.

Values of the trigonometric ratios for degree measures of angles are needed to solve practical problems involving right triangles. A few values can be easily computed using the properties of special triangles and the Pythagorean theorem. For an isosceles right triangle:

$$\sin 45° = \frac{1}{\sqrt{2}} = \frac{\sqrt{2}}{2} \approx 0.707$$

$$\cos 45° = \frac{1}{\sqrt{2}} = \frac{\sqrt{2}}{2} \approx 0.707$$

$$\tan 45° = \frac{1}{1} = 1$$

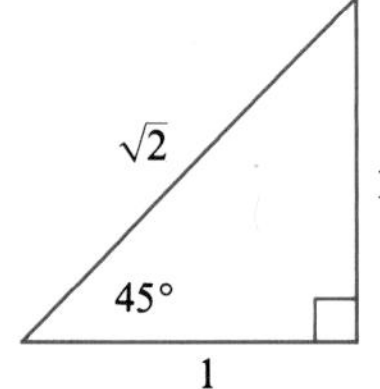

Most values of trigonometric ratios have to be computed by advanced methods. Approximate values are listed in the table of trigonometric ratios at the back of the book. You can use the table to find sin A, cos A, and tan A for any angle with whole-number measure from 1° to 89°.

To find the values of sin 72°, cos 72°, and tan 72°, locate 72° in the left-hand column of the portion of the table shown below and then read across the row to find:

$\sin 72° \approx 0.9511$

$\cos 72° \approx 0.3090$

$\tan 72° \approx 3.0777$

For convenience you may write = instead of $\approx$ in equations such as these.

Angle	*Sine*	*Cosine*	*Tangent*
1°	.0175	.9998	.0175
70°	.9397	.3420	2.7475
71°	.9455	.3256	2.9042
72°	.9511	.3090	3.0777
73°	.9563	.2924	3.2709
74°	.9613	.2756	3.4874

The trigonometric table can also be used to approximate the measure of an angle if one of its trigonometric ratios is given. For example, the table indicates that an angle whose cosine is approximately 0.3420 has a measure of 70°.

Suppose that sin A = 0.9571, a number not listed in the table. To find the approximate measure of $\angle A$, locate in the sine column the entries between which 0.9571 lies:

$$\sin 73° = 0.9563 \text{ and } \sin 74° = 0.9613.$$

$$73° < m\angle A < 74°$$

Since 0.9571 is closer to 0.9563 than it is to 0.9613, $m\angle A = 73°$, to the nearest degree.

Oral Exercises

For Exercises 1-12, use the portion of the table of trigonometric ratios shown on the previous page.

State the value of each trigonometric ratio.

1. sin 1° 0.0175
2. cos 71° 0.3256
3. tan 73° 3.2709
4. cos 74° 0.2756
5. tan 71° 2.9042
6. sin 70° 0.9397

Find the measure of ∠A to the nearest degree.

7. cos A = 0.9998 1°
8. sin A = 0.9563 73°
9. tan A = 2.9042 71°
10. tan A = 3.4000 74°
11. sin A = 0.9430 71°
12. cos A = 0.2932 73°

Written Exercises

Use the table at the back of the book to find sin A, cos A, and tan A for the given measure of ∠A.

A

1. 10°
2. 50°
3. 85°
4. 28°
5. 45°
6. 62°
7. 18°
8. 81°
9. 34°
10. 53°
11. 7°
12. 66°

Find the measure of ∠A to the nearest degree.

18. 81° 21. 77° 24. 49°

13. sin A = 0.9962 85°
14. cos A = 0.8660 30°
15. tan A = 2.0503 64°
16. cos A = 0.4372 64°
17. sin A = 0.6840 43°
18. tan A = 6.5328
19. tan A = 0.4897 26°
20. cos A = 0.9714 14°
21. sin A = 0.9751
22. tan A = 1.3821 54°
23. sin A = 0.7985 53°
24. cos A = 0.6555
25. tan A = 4.0940 76°
26. cos A = 0.0710 86°
27. sin A = 0.6939 44°

Challenge

Is the reasoning logical in each case?

1. The sum of the measures of the angles of a triangle is 180°. The sum of the measures of ∠A, ∠R, and ∠Z is 180°. Therefore, ∠A, ∠R, and ∠Z are the angles of a triangle. no
2. A square is a rectangle with four sides of equal length. A rectangle has four right angles. Therefore, a square has four right angles. yes

6. Using the table on page 651, show by example that, in general, tan A + tan B ≠ tan (A + B).
Answers will vary; for example:
tan 20° + tan 30° = 0.3640 + 0.5774 = 0.9414 ≠ tan 50° = 1.1918

Suggested Assignment

Maximum
591/1–27 odd
S 586/*P*: 9

Additional Answers Written Exercises

1. 0.1736, 0.9848, 0.1763
2. 0.7660, 0.6428, 1.1918
3. 0.9962, 0.0872, 11.4301
4. 0.4695, 0.8829, 0.5317
5. 0.7071, 0.7071, 1
6. 0.8829, 0.4695, 1.8807
7. 0.3090, 0.9511, 0.3249
8. 0.9877, 0.1564, 6.3138
9. 0.5592, 0.8290, 0.6745
10. 0.7986, 0.6018, 1.3270
11. 0.1219, 0.9925, 0.1228
12. 0.9135, 0.4067, 2.2460

Teaching Suggestions
p. T131

Suggested Extensions
p. T131

Chalkboard Examples

1. Find x to the nearest centimeter.

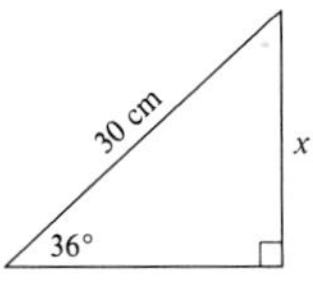

$\sin 36° = \frac{x}{30}$

$0.5878 = \frac{x}{30}$

$x = 30(0.5878) = 17.634$

$\therefore x \approx 18$ cm

2. Find angle A to the nearest degree.

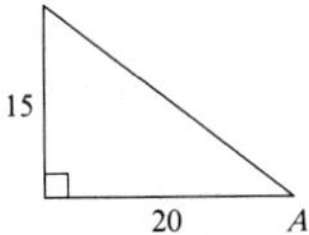

$\tan A = \frac{15}{20}$

$\tan A = 0.75$

$\therefore \angle A \approx 37°$

Numerical Trigonometry

Objective To use trigonometric ratios to solve problems.

Trigonometric ratios can be used to solve practical problems involving right triangles. You can find values for these ratios from the table at the back of the book or from a scientific calculator.

Example 1 During a severe storm, a radio mast broke 39.6 m from the ground. The top of the mast now makes a 47° angle with the ground. How high was the radio mast?

Solution Draw a triangle showing the known values. First find x, the length of the mast from the point where it broke to its top. Since $\triangle ABC$ is a right triangle,

$$\sin 47° = \frac{39.6}{x}, \quad \text{or} \quad x = \frac{39.6}{\sin 47°}.$$

From the table, $\sin 47° = 0.7314$.

Then $x = \frac{39.6}{0.7314} \approx 54.1$.

$\therefore$ to the nearest tenth of a meter, the radio mast was $54.1 + 39.6 = 93.7$ m tall. ***Answer***

In surveying and navigation problems involving right triangles, the terms *angle of elevation* and *angle of depression* are used.

In the diagram below, $\angle CBA$ is an angle of elevation, since the point A is elevated with respect to an observer at B. $\angle DAB$ is an angle of depression, since the point B is depressed with respect to an observer at A.

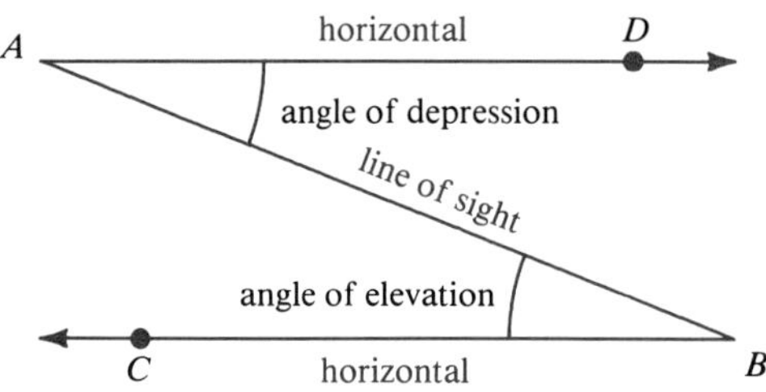

Example 2 At a point 86 m from the base of the Washington Monument, the angle of elevation to the top is 63°. To the nearest meter, what is the height of the Washington Monument?

Solution Draw a triangle. You want to find x, the height of the Washington Monument.

Since $\triangle ABC$ is a right triangle,

$\tan 63° = \frac{x}{86}$.

$x = 86(\tan 63°)$

From the table, $\tan 63° = 1.9626$.

Then $x = 86(1.9626) = 168.7836$.

$\therefore$ to the nearest meter, the Washington Monument is 169 m high. ***Answer***

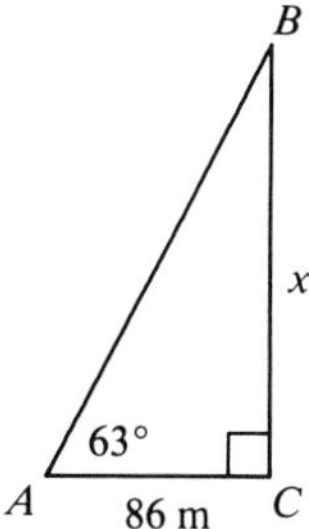

Oral Exercises

State whether you would use the sine, the cosine, or the tangent ratio to find x for each figure.

1.

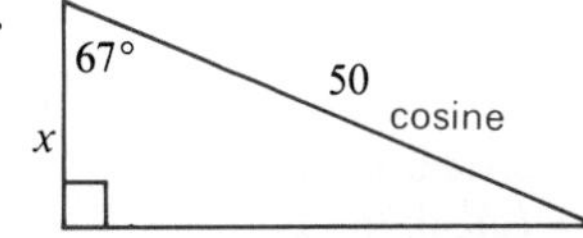

cosine

2.

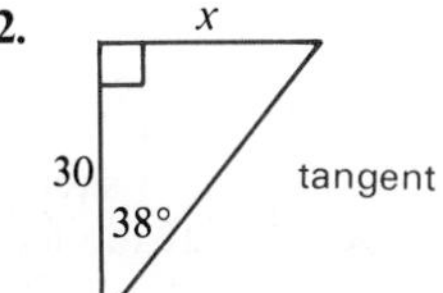

tangent

3.

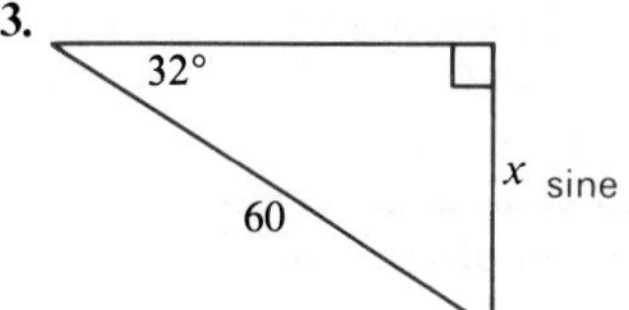

sine

4. tangent

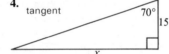

70° 15 x

5.

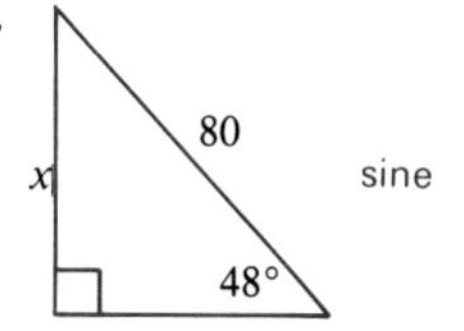

sine

6.

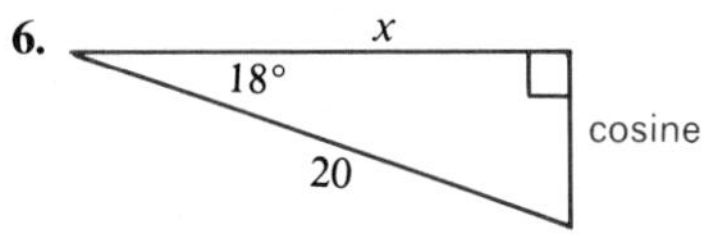

cosine

Written Exercises

Use the table at the back of the book or a calculator as needed.

A **1-6.** In Oral Exercises 1-6, find x to the nearest whole number.

1. 20 2. 23 3. 32 4. 41 5. 59 6. 19

3. The angle of elevation to the top of a tree, from a point 16 m from the base of the tree, is 48°. Find the height of the tree to the nearest meter.

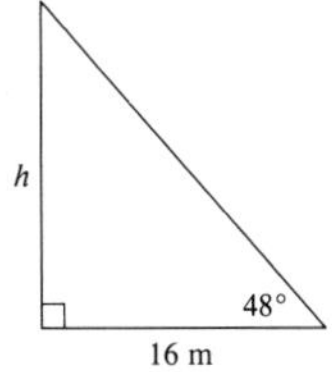

$\tan 48° = \frac{h}{16}$

$1.1106 = \frac{h}{16}$

$h = 16(1.1106) = 17.7696$

$\therefore$ to the nearest meter, the height of the tree is 18 m.

4. A 12 m ladder rests against the side of a house. If the foot of the ladder is 5 m away from the house, find, to the nearest degree, the angle that the ladder makes with the ground.

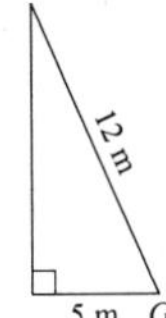

$\cos G = \frac{5}{12} = 0.4167$

$\angle G \approx 65°$

$\therefore$ to the nearest degree, the ladder makes an angle of 65° with the ground.

Suggested Assignment

Maximum
593/2–18 even
594/*P*: 1, 2, 4, 9–11

In right triangle ABC, with $m\angle C = 90$, find the other sides of the triangle to the nearest whole number from the following facts.

7. $m\angle A = 56$, $AB = 48$ $BC \approx 40$, $AC \approx 27$
8. $m\angle B = 21$, $AB = 72$ $AC \approx 26$, $BC \approx 67$
9. $m\angle B = 11$, $BC = 85$ $AC \approx 17$, $AB \approx 87$
10. $m\angle A = 65$, $AC = 28$ $BC \approx 60$, $AB \approx 66$

In right triangle DEF, $m\angle E = 90$. Find the measures of $\angle D$ and $\angle F$ to the nearest degree from the following facts.

B 11. $EF = 42$, $ED = 36$ $\angle D \approx 49°$, $\angle F \approx 41°$
12. $ED = 45$, $FD = 63$ $\angle D \approx 44°$, $\angle F \approx 46°$
13. $FE = 32$, $FD = 48$ $\angle D \approx 42°$, $\angle F \approx 48°$
14. $EF = 50$, $ED = 45$ $\angle D \approx 48°$, $\angle F \approx 42°$

In right triangle XYZ, $m\angle X = 90$. Find the measures of the other sides of the triangle to the nearest whole number from the following facts.

15. $m\angle Z = 41$, $XY = 65$ $XZ \approx 75$, $YZ \approx 99$
16. $m\angle Y = 64$, $XY = 70$ $XZ \approx 144$, $YZ \approx 160$
17. $m\angle Y = 27$, $ZX = 25$ $YZ \approx 55$, $XY \approx 49$
18. $m\angle Z = 58$, $ZX = 90$ $YZ \approx 170$, $XY \approx 144$

Problems

Solve each problem, drawing a sketch for each. Express distances to the nearest unit. Use the table at the back of the book or a calculator as needed.

A 1. To the nearest meter, how far is it across the river? 18 m

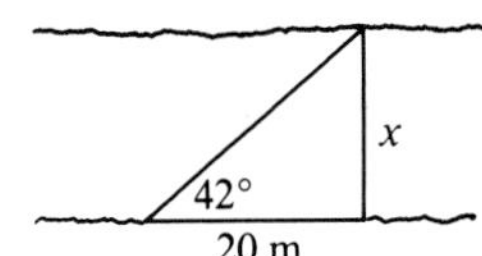

2. To the nearest centimeter, how long is the cable that supports the pole? 1478 cm

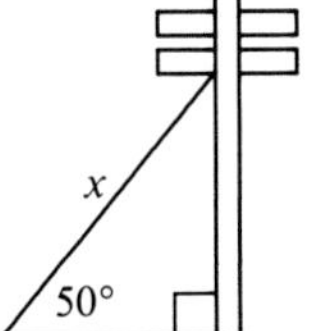

3. To the nearest meter, how high is the cliff? 226 m

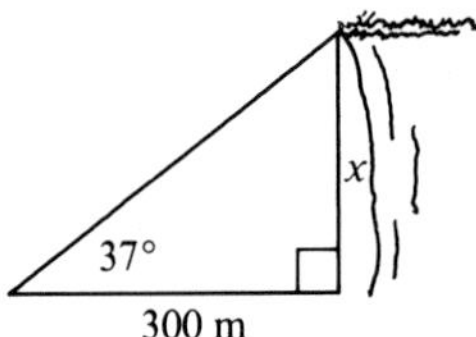

4. To the nearest meter, how far is the car from the tower? 79 m

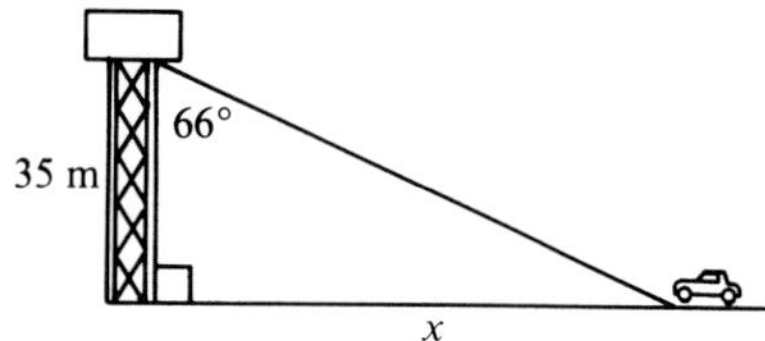

5. How deep will a submarine be if it travels 250 m at a 28° angle of depression? 117 m

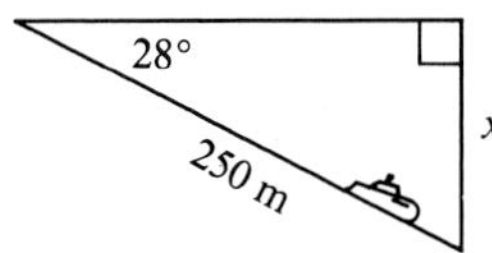

6. The length of a water ski jump is 720 cm and the angle of elevation is 35°. Find the height of the ski jump. 413 cm

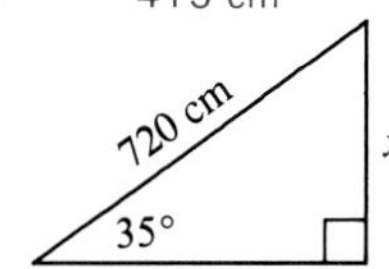

7. A road rises 12 m vertically over a horizontal distance of 180 m. What is the angle of elevation? approx. 4°

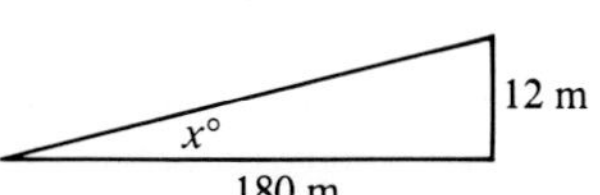

8. If a plane flies 1° off course for 6000 km, how far away from the correct path will the plane be? 105 km

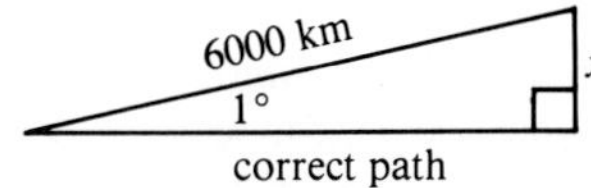

B 9. A train travels 600 m on a track with an 18° incline. How high above its starting point is the train? 185 m

10. From the top of a 20 m lighthouse, the angle of depression of the nearest point on the beach is 8°. Find the distance from the bottom of the lighthouse to the beach. 142 m

11. An airplane, at an altitude of 700 m, is directly over a water dam. The navigator finds the angle of depression of the airport to be 18°. How far is it from the dam to the airport? 2154 m

12. A submarine travels through the water at a steady rate of 360 m/min on a diving path that forms a 4° angle of depression with the surface of the water. After 5 min, how far below the surface is the submarine? 126 m

C 13. The pilot of a hot air balloon at an altitude of 80 m sees landing sites in opposite directions. The angles of depression of the sites are 34° and 11°, respectively. How far apart are the sites? 530 m

14. A car is traveling on a level road toward a 2-km high mountain. The angle of elevation from the car to the top of the mountain changes from 6° to 15°. How far has the car traveled? 11,565 m

15. From the top of an office building, the angle of depression to the top of a motel is 23°. From the bottom of the office building, the angle of elevation to the top of the motel is 17°. The distance from the office building to the motel is 250 m. Find the height of the office building. 182 m

16. Two support cables to a TV antenna are anchored to the same spot on the ground 40 feet from the base of the tower. If one cable is fastened to the tower 40 feet above the ground and the other is fastened to the tower 60 feet above the ground, what is the measure of the angle between the cables? approx. 11°

Teaching Suggestions
p. T131

Chalkboard Examples

1. A taste test is done for Hot Stuff Soup, which comes in vegetable beef, chicken noodle, chicken vegetable and mushroom varieties. Specify:
   a. the sample space for the test.
   b. the event that mushroom soup is chosen.
   c. the event that a chicken soup is chosen.
   d. the event that a vegetable soup is chosen.
   a. {veg. beef, chicken noodle, chicken veg., mushroom}
   b. {mushroom}
   c. {chicken noodle, chicken veg.}
   d. {veg. beef, chicken veg.}
2. Campers at Super Sports Camp are randomly assigned a morning activity and an afternoon activity. If basketball (B), soccer (SO) and tennis (T) take place in the morning, and swimming (SW), hiking (HI) and horseback riding (HO) take place in the afternoon, specify:
   a. the sample space for an activity schedule.
   b. the event that a camper plays soccer.
   c. the event that a camper goes hiking.
   d. the event that a camper plays basketball and swims.

(continued)

Probability

Sample Spaces and Events

Objective To list the sample space and events for a random experiment.

You have been solving mathematical problems that dealt with definite situations. You will now consider the branch of mathematics called **probability** that deals with the possibility, or likelihood, of an event occurring.

Suppose you toss a coin repeatedly in exactly the same manner. You know that on each toss it will land with either a head or a tail showing, but you cannot predict with certainty which it will be. An activity, such as tossing a coin, for which you cannot predict the outcome when you repeat the activity under essentially the same conditions is called a **random experiment.**

Although you do not know prior to each toss whether the result will be a head or a tail, you do know that only these two outcomes are possible. The set of all possible outcomes of a random experiment is called the **sample space** of the experiment. For the coin-tossing experiment, if the outcomes are denoted by H and T, then the sample space is $\{H, T\}$.

Any possible subset of the sample space resulting from an experiment is called an **event.** When an event involves a single member of the sample space, it is called a **simple event.** In the coin-tossing experiment, there are two simple events: $\{H\}$ and $\{T\}$.

Example 1 For the experiment of turning the pointer on the spinner at the right, specify:

a. the sample space for the experiment.
b. the event that an odd number results.
c. the event that a number less than 3 results.

Solution **a.** $\{1, 2, 3, 4, 5, 6\}$
b. $\{1, 3, 5\}$
c. $\{1, 2\}$

Suppose you now have two spinners, one blue and one green. A simple event in this experiment can be represented by the ordered pair (b, g), where b is the number from the blue spinner and g is the number from the green spinner. The ordered pair (3, 1) denotes the simple event "blue spinner shows 3 and green spinner shows 1."

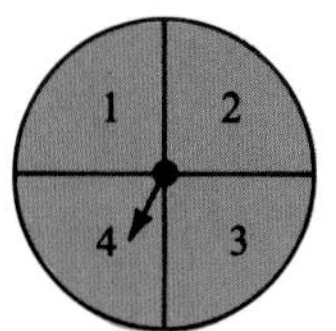

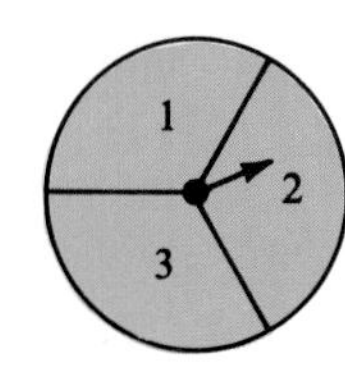

Example 2 For the two-spinner experiment, specify:

a. the sample space for the experiment.
b. the event that the sum of the numbers on the two spinners equals 3.
c. the event that the sum of the numbers on the two spinners is greater than 5.

Solution

a. {(1, 1), (1, 2), (1, 3), (2, 1), (2, 2), (2, 3), (3, 1), (3, 2), (3, 3), (4, 1), (4, 2), (4, 3)}
b. {(1, 2), (2, 1)}
c. {(3, 3), (4, 2), (4, 3)}

a. {(B, SW), (B, HI), (B, HO), (SO, SW), (SO, HI), (SO, HO), (T, SW), (T, HI), (T, HO)}
b. {(SO, SW), (SO, HI), (SO, HO)}
c. {(B, HI), (SO, HI), (T, HI)}
d. {(B, SW)}

Suggested Assignment

Maximum
597/1, 2, 5, 7–11
S 595/*P*: 12–14

Oral Exercises

A penny and a nickel are tossed. The sample space is {(*H*, *H*), (*H*, *T*), (*T*, *H*), (*T*, *T*) . Specify the following events.

1. Two tails up {(*T*, *T*)}
2. One head up and one tail up {(*H*, *T*), (*T*, *H*)}
3. Exactly one head up {(*H*, *T*), (*T*, *H*)}
4. At least one tail up {(*H*, *T*), (*T*, *H*), (*T*, *T*)}

Each letter of the word BASKET is written on a separate card. The cards are shuffled, and one card is drawn.

5. Give the sample space for this experiment. {B, A, S, K, E, T}
6. Give the event that the letter on the card is a vowel. {A, E}
7. Give the event that the letter on the card is neither B nor T. {A, S, K, E}

Each letter of the word TRIANGLE is written on a separate card. The cards are shuffled, and one card is drawn.

8. Give the sample space for this experiment. {T, R, I, A, N, G, L, E}
9. Give the event that the letter on the card is a vowel. {I, A, E}
10. Give the event that the letter on the card is neither R nor L. {T, I, A, N, G, E}

Written Exercises

A **1.** Each of the letters *A*, *B*, *C*, *D*, *E*, *F*, *G*, *H*, *I*, *J*, and *K* is written on a card. The cards are shuffled and one card is drawn. For this experiment, specify:

a. the sample space. {*A*, *B*, *C*, *D*, *E*, *F*, *G*, *H*, *I*, *J*, *K*}
b. the event that the letter is a vowel. {*A*, *E*, *I*}
c. the event that the letter is *C*, *F*, *G*, or *I*. {*C*, *F*, *G*, *I*}
d. the event that the letter is not *B*, *E*, *G*, *J*. {*A*, *C*, *D*, *F*, *H*, *I*, *K*}

Additional Answers
Written Exercises

3. a. {(2, 1), (2, 4), (2, 9), (4, 1), (4, 4), (4, 9), (8, 1), (8, 4), (8, 9), (15, 1), (15, 4), (15, 9)}
   d. {(4, 9), (8, 9), (15, 1), (15, 4), (15, 9)}
4. a. {(1, 1), (1, 5), (1, 10), (1, 15), (2, 1), (2, 5), (2, 10), (2, 15), (3, 1), (3, 5), (3, 10), (3, 15), (4, 1), (4, 5), (4, 10), (4, 15)}
   d. {(1, 10), (2, 10), (3, 5), (3, 10), (4, 5), (4, 10)}
5. a. {(on, on, on), (on, on, off), (on, off, off), (on, off, on), (off, on, on), (off, on, off), (off, off, off), (off, off, on)}
   b. {(on, on, on), (on, on, off), (on, off, on), (off, on, on)}
   c. {(on, on, off), (on, off, off), (on, off, on), (off, on, on), (off, on, off), (off, off, off), (off, off, on)}
   d. {(off, off, off)}
10. {(1, 1), (1, 2), (2, 1), (2, 2), (3, 1), (3, 2), (3, 3), (4, 1), (4, 2), (4, 3)}
11. {(2, 1), (2, 2), (2, 3), (4, 1), (4, 2), (4, 3), (1, 1), (1, 3), (3, 1), (3, 3)}

2. A bowl contains a yellow marble and a white marble. A second bowl contains a yellow, a green, a blue, and a red marble. One marble is taken from each bowl. For this experiment, specify:
a. the sample space. {(Y, Y), (Y, G), (Y, B), (Y, R), (W, Y), (W, G), (W, B), (W, R)}
b. the event that one marble is green. {(Y, G), (W, G)}
c. the event that at least one marble is yellow. {(Y, Y), (Y, G), (Y, B), (Y, R), (W, Y)}
d. the event that neither marble is yellow. {(W, G), (W, B), (W, R)}

3. A hat contains cards numbered 2, 4, 8, and 15. A second hat contains cards numbered 1, 4, and 9. One card is drawn from each hat. For this experiment, specify:
a. the sample space.
b. the event that both numbers are the same. {(4, 4)}
c. the event that both numbers are odd. {(15, 1), (15, 9)}
d. the event that the sum of the numbers is greater than 12.
e. the event that the sum of the numbers is less than 6. {(2, 1), (4, 1)}

4. A spinner is divided into four equal sections numbered 1, 2, 3, and 4. A second spinner is divided into four equal sections numbered 1, 5, 10, and 15. Each pointer is turned. For this experiment specify:
a. the sample space.
b. the event that both numbers are even. {(2, 10), (4, 10)}
c. the event that neither number is odd. {(2, 10), (4, 10)}
d. the event that the sum of the numbers is between 7 and 15.
e. the event that the product of the numbers is greater than 30. {(3, 15), (4, 10), (4, 15)}

B

5. There are three on-off switches on a light panel.
a. List the sample space.
b. Write the event that at least two lights are on.
c. Write the event that at least one light is off.
d. Write the event that all three lights are off.

6. Li has a \$10 bill and a \$20 bill in his wallet. Cara has a \$1 bill and a \$20 bill in her wallet. Sid has a \$5 bill in his wallet. A bill is randomly selected from each wallet. For this experiment, specify:
a. the sample space. {(\$10, \$1, \$5), (\$10, \$20, \$5), (\$20, \$1, \$5), (\$20, \$20, \$5)}
b. the event that the sum is even. {(\$10, \$1, \$5), (\$20, \$1, \$5)}
c. the event that the sum is odd. {(\$10, \$20, \$5), (\$20, \$20, \$5)}
d. the event that the sum is less than \$30. {(\$10, \$1, \$5), (\$20, \$1, \$5)}

For Exercises 7-11 refer again to the two-spinner experiment. The ordered pair (*b*, *g*) denotes a simple event, as before.

7. Specify the event that $b + g = 4$. {(1, 3), (2, 2), (3, 1)}

8. Specify the event that $b < g$. {(1, 2), (1, 3), (2, 3)}

9. Specify the event that $b + g$ is an even number. {(1, 1), (1, 3), (2, 2), (3, 1), (3, 3), (4, 2)}

C

10. Specify the event that $b > 2$ or $g \leq 2$.

11. Specify the event that b is an even number or g is an odd number.

Probability

Objective To find the probability that an event will occur.

Suppose you toss a single coin repeatedly. The sample space consists of two simple events, $\{H\}$ and $\{T\}$. Assuming that the coin is fair, the two simple events are **equally likely** to occur. That is, for large numbers of tosses, you would expect the number of heads, or the number of tails, appearing to be about one half the number of tosses.

The **probability** of an event is the ratio of the number of outcomes favoring the event to the total number of outcomes. Thus, in the case of a tossed coin, the probability of the simple event $\{H\}$ equals the probability of the simple event $\{T\}$. If the probability of $\{H\}$ is denoted by $P(H)$ and the probability of $\{T\}$ by $P(T)$, then,

$$P(H) = P(T) = \frac{1}{2}.$$

In general, for any probability P, $0 \leq P \leq 1$. If an event can never occur, it is assigned a probability of 0. If an event will always occur, the probability is 1.

Consider the spinner shown at the right. The sample space consists of five simple events, $\{Y, R, G, B, W\}$. If the spinner is fair, the five simple events are equally likely to occur.

Thus, $P(Y) = P(R) = P(G) = P(B) = P(W) = \frac{1}{5}$.

In general, if $\{a_1, a_2, a_3, \ldots, a_n\}$ is a sample space containing n equally likely simple events, then:

$$P(a_1) = P(a_2) = P(a_3) = \cdots = P(a_n) = \frac{1}{n}$$

The sum of all probabilities assigned to all simple events in the sample space of a random experiment is 1. Thus,

$$P(a_1) + P(a_2) + P(a_3) + \cdots + P(a_n) = 1.$$

Example A cube whose sides are numbered 1, 2, 3, 4, 5, and 6 is rolled. Find the probability of each event.
Event A: The number turned up is greater than 3.
Event B: The number turned up is greater than 2 and less than 5.

Solution The sample space is $\{1, 2, 3, 4, 5, 6\}$. Since each simple event is equally likely to occur, the probability of each simple event is $\frac{1}{6}$.

Event A $= \{4, 5, 6\}$ *Event B* $= \{3, 4\}$

$P(A) = \frac{3}{6} = \frac{1}{2}$ $P(B) = \frac{2}{6} = \frac{1}{3}$

Teaching Suggestions
p. T132

Suggested Extensions
p. T132

Chalkboard Examples

1. A spinner has 8 equal sections numbered 1, 2, 3, . . . , 8. Find the probability of each event.

   Event A: The spinner stops on an odd number.
   Event A = $\{1, 3, 5, 7\}$;
   $P(A) = \frac{4}{8} = \frac{1}{2}$

   Event B: The spinner stops on a number less than 6.
   Event B = $\{1, 2, 3, 4, 5\}$;
   $P(B) = \frac{5}{8}$

   Event C: The spinner stops on a prime number.
   Event C = $\{2, 3, 5, 7\}$;
   $P(C) = \frac{4}{8} = \frac{1}{2}$

   Event D: The spinner stops on a perfect square.
   Event D = $\{1, 4\}$;
   $P(D) = \frac{2}{8} = \frac{1}{4}$

(continued)

Chalkboard Examples
(continued)

2. A nickel, a dime and a quarter are tossed. Find the probability of each event.
Event A: exactly 2 heads
Event B: all tails
Event C: 1 head or 1 tail
First list the sample space: {(H, H, H), (H, T, T), (H, H, T), (H, T, H), (T, H, H), (T, T, H), (T, H, T), (T, T, T)}
Event A = {(H, H, T), (H, T, H), (T, H, H)};
$P(A) = \frac{3}{8}$
Event B = {(*T, T, T*)};
$P(B) = \frac{1}{8}$
Event C = {(H, T, T), (H, H, T), (H, T, H), (T, H, H), (T, T, H), (T, H, T)}; $P(C) = \frac{6}{8} = \frac{3}{4}$

Suggested Assignment
Maximum
600/2–4, 6, 8
S 595/*P*: 15, 16

Additional Answers Written Exercises
4. (6, 3) (6, 4) (6, 5) (6, 6)
(5, 3) (5, 4) (5, 5) (5, 6)
(4, 3) (4, 4) (4, 5) (4, 6)
(3, 3) (3, 4) (3, 5) (3, 6)
(2, 5) (2, 6)
(1, 6)

Oral Exercises

A letter is selected randomly from the word ALGEBRA. Name the probability of each event.

1. It is a vowel. $\frac{3}{7}$
2. It is a consonant. $\frac{4}{7}$
3. It is a G. $\frac{1}{7}$
4. It is an A. $\frac{2}{7}$

A cube whose sides are numbered 1, 2, 3, 4, 5, and 6 is tossed. Name the probability of each event.

5. The number is even. $\frac{1}{2}$
6. The number is 3 or 4. $\frac{1}{3}$
7. The number is greater than 6. 0
8. The number is less than 7. 1

Written Exercises

A

1. A jar contains 4 red marbles, 6 white marbles, and 2 blue marbles. A marble is drawn at random from the jar. Find the probability of each event.
   a. The marble is red. $\frac{1}{3}$
   b. The marble is blue. $\frac{1}{6}$
   c. The marble is either blue or red. $\frac{1}{2}$
   d. The marble is green. 0
   e. The marble is either blue or white. $\frac{2}{3}$
2. One card is drawn at random from a 52-card deck. Find the probability of each event.
   a. It is the 3 of diamonds. $\frac{1}{52}$
   b. It is a black 10. $\frac{1}{26}$
   c. It is a king. $\frac{1}{13}$
   d. It is a heart. $\frac{1}{4}$
   e. It is a 6 or 7. $\frac{2}{13}$
   f. It is an 8, 9, or 10. $\frac{3}{13}$
3. There are 25 students in a public speaking class. The order of speeches is determined by having students select a number from a box containing the numbers 1–25. Find the probability of each event.
   a. Being the first person to give a speech. $\frac{1}{25}$
   b. Being one of the last 10 people to give a speech. $\frac{2}{5}$
   c. Selecting a number between 10 and 16. $\frac{1}{5}$
   d. Selecting a number divisible by 4. $\frac{6}{25}$
4. The results of rolling two numbered cubes are shown in the table at the right. Copy and complete the table and then use it to find the probability of each event shown on the next page. $P(6)$ means "the probability of getting a sum of 6."

6	(6, 1)	(6, 2)	(?)	(?)	(?)	(?)
5	(5, 1)	(5, 2)	(?)	(?)	(?)	(?)
4	(4, 1)	(4, 2)	(?)	(?)	(?)	(?)
3	(3, 1)	(3, 2)	(?)	(?)	(?)	(?)
2	(2, 1)	(2, 2)	(2, 3)	(2, 4)	(?)	(?)
1	(1, 1)	(1, 2)	(1, 3)	(1, 4)	(1, 5)	(?)
	1	2	3	4	5	6

a. $P(6)$ $\frac{5}{36}$

b. $P(\text{not } 6)$ $\frac{31}{36}$

c. $P(4 \text{ or } 7)$ $\frac{1}{4}$

d. $P(11)$ $\frac{1}{18}$

e. $P(12)$ $\frac{1}{36}$

f. $P(2 \text{ or } 8)$ $\frac{1}{6}$

g. $P(5)$ $\frac{1}{9}$

h. $P(\text{not } 5)$ $\frac{8}{9}$

i. $P(\text{even number})$ $\frac{1}{2}$

j. $P(\text{odd number})$ $\frac{1}{2}$

5. A penny, a nickel, and a dime are tossed. Find the probability of each event.

a. 3 heads $\frac{1}{8}$

b. exactly 2 tails $\frac{3}{8}$

c. at least 2 heads $\frac{1}{2}$

d. one or two heads $\frac{3}{4}$

B 6. A penny, a nickel, a dime, and a quarter are tossed. Find the probability of each event.

a. 4 tails $\frac{1}{16}$

b. exactly 2 heads $\frac{3}{8}$

c. at least 3 tails $\frac{5}{16}$

d. 2 or 3 heads $\frac{5}{8}$

e. no heads $\frac{1}{16}$

f. exactly 1 tail $\frac{1}{4}$

7. A spinner is divided into three equal sections numbered 1, 2, and 3. A second spinner is divided into four equal sections numbered 2, 4, 6, and 7. Each pointer is turned. Find the probability of each event.

a. $P(1, 4)$ $\frac{1}{12}$

b. $P(2, \text{not } 2)$ $\frac{1}{4}$

c. $P(3, 6)$ $\frac{1}{12}$

d. $P(\text{even number, even number})$ $\frac{1}{4}$

e. $P(\text{sum is } 7)$ $\frac{1}{6}$

f. $P(\text{sum is less than } 8)$ $\frac{7}{12}$

C 8. A bag contains 1 red marble, 2 green marbles, and 3 white marbles. Two marbles are randomly selected. Find the probability of each event.

a. 1 green and 1 white marble $\frac{2}{5}$

b. 2 white marbles $\frac{1}{5}$

c. 2 green marbles $\frac{1}{15}$

d. 2 marbles of the same color $\frac{4}{15}$

e. 1 red marble and a green or a white marble $\frac{1}{3}$

Calculator Key-In

Answers may vary slightly. The answers given have been rounded to the nearest hundredth.

Use a calculator and the formula $A = \sqrt{s(s - a)(s - b)(s - c)}$ (page 519) to find the approximate area of each triangle whose sides are given.

1. 7 cm, 11 cm, 14 cm 37.95 cm²
2. 13 mm, 18 mm, 27 mm 101.03 mm²
3. 12 m, 12 m, 16 m 71.55m²
4. 48 mm, 64 mm, 84 mm 1527.22 mm²
5. 2.8 m, 3.9 m, 5.7 m 4.92 m²
6. 15.8 cm, 16.9 cm, 23.4 cm 133.47 cm²
7. 9.2 cm, 11.8 cm, 17.1 cm 51.51 cm²
8. 37.1 m, 46.4 m, 69.7 m 794.04 m²

Teaching Suggestions
p. T132

Suggested Extensions
p. T132

Chalkboard Examples

For each set of data, find (a) the mean, (b) the median, (c) the mode and (d) the range.

1. $\frac{1}{2}, \frac{1}{3}, \frac{1}{6}$

a. mean $= \dfrac{\frac{1}{2} + \frac{1}{3} + \frac{1}{6}}{3} = \dfrac{\frac{3}{6} + \frac{2}{6} + \frac{1}{6}}{3} = \dfrac{\frac{6}{6}}{3} = \frac{1}{3}$

b. Arrange the numbers in order: $\frac{1}{6}, \frac{1}{3}, \frac{1}{2}$

The median is the middle number, $\frac{1}{3}$.

c. Each number occurs the same number of times (once), so there is no mode.

d. Subtract the lowest number from the highest number.

range $= \frac{1}{2} - \frac{1}{6} = \frac{3}{6} - \frac{1}{6} = \frac{2}{6} = \frac{1}{3}$

602

Statistics

Frequency Distributions

Objective To recognize and characterize frequency distributions.

The results of a test are of little value until they have been summarized and then analyzed. One way to summarize data is shown in the table at the right. The table shows the scores that were received on a test and how many students received each score. This table is called a **frequency distribution.**

Another way to summarize data is shown in the graph below. This type of graph is called a **histogram.** In a histogram, data is grouped into convenient intervals. The intervals in this histogram of the test scores are 60–65, 65–70, and so on. A test score of 75 is considered to be in the interval 70–75, while a score of 80 is in the interval 75–80. In general, a "boundary" score is included in the interval to its left.

Score	Number of Students
100	1
98	2
95	3
93	1
91	1
89	5
87	2
86	1
84	3
83	2
82	1
80	1
79	2
76	2
75	1
71	1
68	1
65	2
62	1

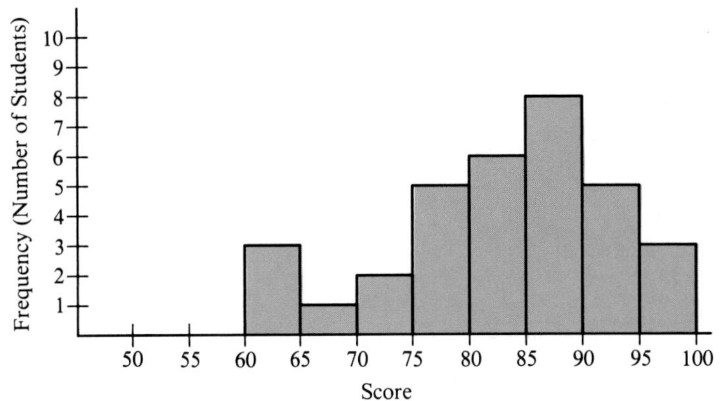

Frequency distributions are often analyzed by using numbers called *statistics.* One statistic used to indicate the center of a distribution is called the **mean.** The **mean** of a collection of data is the sum of the numbers divided by the number of numbers.

Example 1 The number of home runs that led the National League during five consecutive years was 40, 54, 47, 42, and 37. What is the mean (M) of the number of home runs?

Solution $M = \frac{40 + 54 + 47 + 42 + 37}{5} = \frac{220}{5} = 44$ ***Answer***

Other important numbers for analyzing a set of data are the *median,* the *mode,* and the *range.*

The **median** of a frequency distribution is the middle number when the data are arranged in order. If the number of data is even, the average of the two numbers closest to the middle is the median. Arranging the data from the test score table in increasing order gives a median of 84.

The **mode** is the most frequently occurring number in a frequency distribution. A set of data may have more than one, one, or no modes. From the table, the mode of the test scores is 89. The mode is most useful in analyzing nonnumerical data, such as color or taste preferences.

The **range** of a frequency distribution is the difference between the highest and the lowest values. For example, the range of the data in the table is 100 − 62, or 38.

Example 2 Three numbered cubes are rolled 10 times. The sums of the numbers after each roll are, in ascending order, 6, 7, 9, 10, 10, 12, 13, 14, 15, and 17. Find the median, the mode, and the range of the data.

Solution Since there is an even number of data, the median is the average of the middle two scores.

$$\frac{10 + 12}{2} = \frac{22}{2} = 11$$

Since 10 is the score that occurs most frequently, it is the mode.

The range is the difference between 17 and 6, or 11.

Oral Exercises

1. The heights of three students are 60 in., 68 in., and 70 in. For the heights, find:

a. the mean 66 in. **b.** the median 68 in. **c.** the range 10 in.

2. In four days, Rachel earned \$7, \$5, \$1, and \$7. For her earnings, find:

a. the mean \$5 **b.** the mode \$7 **c.** the median \$6 **d.** the range \$6

3. In five successive hockey games, the Fraser Flags scored 3, 2, 0, 1, and 4 goals, respectively. For this goal distribution, find:

a. the mean 2 goals **b.** the median 2 goals **c.** the mode none **d.** the range 4 goals

2. The ages of the members of the Statistics Club are 15, 14, 14, 13, and 15.

a. mean = $\frac{15 + 14 + 14 + 13 + 15}{5} = \frac{71}{5} = 14\frac{1}{5}$

b. 13, 14, 14, 15, 15; the median is the middle number, 14.

c. The most frequently a number occurs is twice. ∴ there are two modes, 14 and 15.

d. range = 15 − 13 = 2

Suggested Assignment

Maximum
604/1–7 odd, 8, 10–15

Additional Answers Written Exercises

3. $64\frac{2}{3}$, $62\frac{1}{2}$, 62, 15

4. $10\frac{1}{7}$, 10, 9, 4

5. $27\frac{6}{7}$, 26, 25 and 33, 11

6. $65\frac{4}{7}$, 66, none, 32

10.

Score	Number of Students
100	2
98	1
96	1
95	1
94	1
90	4
88	2
85	1
84	1
82	1
81	3
80	1
79	1
78	1
76	2
74	1
65	1

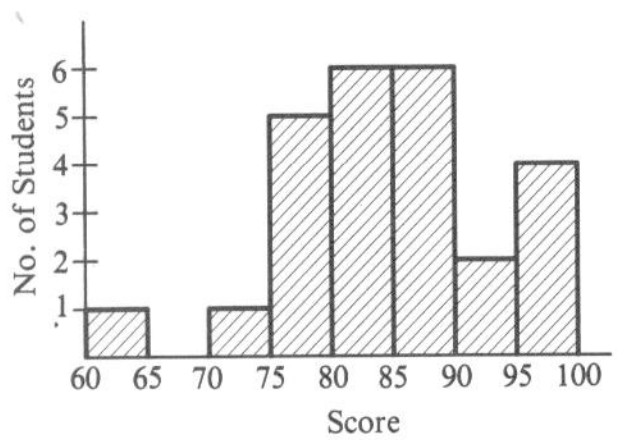

Written Exercises

For the data given in Exercises 1-6, find the mean, the median, the mode, and the range.

A

1. 24, 53, 38, 39, 51 41, 39, none, 29
2. 8, 15, 42, 31, 15 22.2, 15, 15, 34
3. 58, 62, 63, 70, 62, 73
4. 11, 9, 10, 9, 10, 9, 13
5. 25, 31, 22, 33, 33, 26, 25
6. 72, 78, 63, 49, 81, 50, 66
7. In six debate matches, Dana scored 28, 25, 28, 30, 24, and 29. Find the mean, the median, the mode, and the range of her scores. $27\frac{1}{3}$, 28, 28, 6
8. Find the mean and the range for the average monthly temperatures given in degrees Celsius: $-1.5°$, $-2°$, $-1°$, $5°$, $24.5°$, $28°$, $33.5°$, $34°$, $28.5°$, $18.5°$, $6°$, $1.5°$. $14.58\overline{3}°$, 36°
9. In ten basketball games, Kim scored 9, 12, 11, 8, 11, 15, 15, 16, 15, and 19 points. To the nearest tenth of a point, find the mean, the median, the mode, and the range. 13.1, 13.5, 15.0, 11.0
10. In a class of 25 students, the test scores were 78, 90, 95, 76, 65, 80, 90, 96, 100, 98, 84, 88, 81, 76, 100, 94, 90, 82, 74, 85, 90, 81, 79, 81, 88. First make a frequency table and then draw a histogram for the data.

B

11. Yon needs an average bowling score of 165 to bowl in a spring tournament. If he has scores of 150, 155, 177, and 161 in the first four games, what does he have to bowl in the fifth game to be eligible for the tournament? at least a score of 182
12. If each score on an algebra test is increased by 10 points, how does this affect the:
    a. mean? **b.** mode? **c.** median? **d.** range?
13. If each entry in a set of data is multiplied by four, how does this affect the:
    a. mean? **b.** mode? **c.** median? **d.** range?
14. The mean of 6 numbers is 18. What is the sum of the numbers? 108

C

15. Find the mean of twelve numbers if the mean of the first five numbers is 20 and the mean of the last seven numbers is 32. 27
16. In an algebra class, Sherm has a score of 89 for each of the first eight weeks. For the ninth week, his score is 96. What does his score for the tenth week have to be in order for him to have a final mean score of 90? 92

12. a. increases 10 points
b. increases 10 points (if there was one)
c. increases 10 points
d. remains the same

13. a. quadruples
b. quadruples (if there was one)
c. quadruples
d. quadruples

Summary

1. Geometry is the branch of mathematics that deals with the properties of sets of points such as lines, rays, angles, and triangles.
2. Two angles whose sides are rays in the same lines but in opposite directions are called vertical angles. Two angles are complementary if the sum of their measures is 90. Two angles are supplementary if the sum of their measures is 180.
3. The sum of the measures of the angles of a triangle is 180. Some special triangles are right triangles, isosceles triangles, and equilateral triangles.
4. Similar triangles have the same shape but not necessarily the same size. Their corresponding angles have the same measure and corresponding sides are proportional.
5. Trigonometry is the branch of mathematics involved with the measurement of triangles. Three trigonometric ratios are

   $\sin A = \frac{a}{c}$, $\cos A = \frac{b}{c}$, and $\tan A = \frac{a}{b}$.

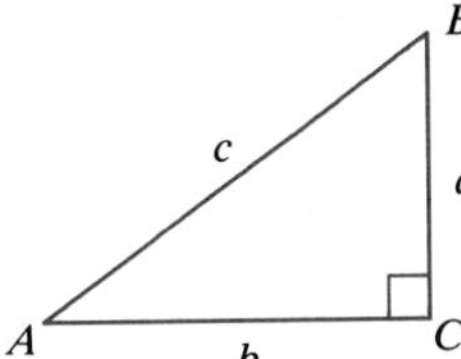

   Approximate values for these ratios are given in the table at the back of the book. Trigonometric ratios can be used to solve problems involving right triangles.
6. Probability is the branch of mathematics that is concerned with the possibility of an event occurring. For any event with probability P, $0 \leq P \leq 1$.
7. Statistics is involved with summarizing and analyzing data. This can be done by using histograms and frequency distributions.

Review

Give the letter of the correct answer.

1. Which symbol denotes the line segment joining points A and B?
   a. AB (b.) $\overline{AB}$ c. $\overrightarrow{AB}$ d. $\overleftrightarrow{AB}$
2. Which angle is a right angle?
   a. $\angle A = 99°$ b. $\angle B = 89°$ (c.) $\angle C = 90°$ d. $\angle D = 100°$
3. Find the measure of the supplement of an angle with measure 49.
   a. 41 b. 141 (c.) 131 d. 51
4. Find the complement of an angle with measure x.
   (a.) $(90 - x)$ b. $(90 + x)$ c. $(180 - x)$ d. $(180 + x)$

5. Find the sum of the measures of the angles of a right triangle.
a. 45° b. 90° (c.) 180° d. 360°

6. If $\triangle ABC \sim \triangle DEF$, $\frac{AB}{DE} = \frac{8}{5}$, and $CA = 12$, find FD.
a. 10 b. $\frac{96}{5}$ c. $\frac{2}{15}$ (d.) $\frac{15}{2}$

7. Use the diagram to find cos B.
a. $\frac{3}{4}$ b. $\frac{4}{5}$
(c.) $\frac{3}{5}$ d. $\frac{4}{3}$

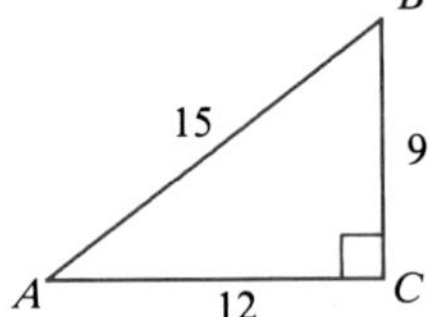

8. Use the table at the back of the book to find sin 54°.
a. 1.3764 b. 0.5878 (c.) 0.8090 d. 0.1584

9. The angle of elevation of the top of a tree from a point on the ground 800 cm from the base of the tree is 47°. Find the height of the tree.
a. 600 cm (b.) 858 cm c. 585 cm d. 546 cm

10. A cube with the letters A, B, C, D, E, and F is rolled. Specify the event that the letter turned up is a vowel.
a. $\{A, B, C, D, E, F\}$ b. $\{A, E, I, O, U\}$
(c.) $\{A, E\}$ d. $\{B, C, D, F\}$

11. A spinner is divided into five equal sections, numbered 1, 2, 3, 4, and 5. The pointer is turned. Find the probability that the number the pointer stops on is even.
a. 0 b. 1 c. $\frac{1}{5}$ (d.) $\frac{2}{5}$

12. Find the mean of 39, 43, 46, 52, 55.
(a.) 47 b. 46 c. 16 d. 55

13. Find the range of 33, 43, 57, 61, 76.
a. 54 b. 57 (c.) 43 d. 76

14. The histogram at the right shows the frequency distribution for the number of points scored in a game by a high-school basketball team for a season of 18 games. In how many games did the team score between 60 and 80 points?
a. 9 b. 6
(c.) 11 d. 5

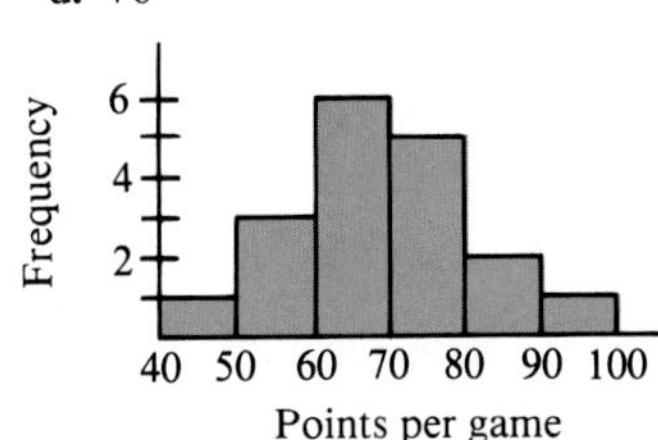

Extra Practice: Skills

Chapter 1

Simplify each expression. (1-1, 1-2)

1. $5 + (4 \times 8)$ 37
2. $(3 + 7) \times 2$ 20
3. $(30 \times 3) + (5 \times 2)$ 100
4. $(40 \div 4) - (9 - 5)$ 6
5. $(30 + 3) \times (4 + 2)$ 198
6. $(40 - 4) \div (9 - 5)$ 9
7. $9 + 7 - 2 \times 8 \div 4$ 12
8. $32 \div 8 + 3 \times 7 - 6$ 19
9. $4 \times 6 - 16 \div 2 + 7$ 23

Evaluate each expression if $e = 2, f = 3, g = 4, u = 0, v = 5$, and $w = 1$. (1-1, 1-2)

10. $ev - f$ 7
11. $5g + 4w$ 24
12. $(uv) + (fg)$ 12
13. $w(v - f) + g$ 6
14. $(3g) \cdot (e + u)$ 24
15. $(v - u)w + g$ 9
16. $(e + f)(g + v)$ 45
17. $e(u + v - w)$ 8
18. $(4e - 2f)(v + w)$ 12
19. $\frac{e + g}{v - f}$ 3
20. $\frac{gv - 5e}{5 - 3u}$ 2
21. $f(we + v) + \frac{g}{e}$ 23

Solve each equation if $x \in \{0, 1, 2, 3, 4, 5, 6\}$. (1-3)

22. $7 + x = 12$ 5
23. $x - 4 = 2$ 6
24. $8 - x = 3$ 5
25. $x - x = 0$ {0, 1, 2, 3, 4, 5, 6}
26. $6x = 18$ 3
27. $0 = 5x$ 0
28. $8x = 32$ 4
29. $x \cdot x = 36$ 6
30. $x \cdot x = 1$ 1
31. $\frac{1}{2}x = 2$ 4
32. $\frac{1}{3}x = 2$ 6
33. $x \cdot x = 5x$ {0, 5}
34. $3x + 9 = 26$ no solution
35. $15 = 9x - 3$ 2
36. $4x = x \cdot 4$ {0, 1, 2, 3, 4, 5, 6}
37. $x(9 - x) = 0$ 0

Represent the required numbers in terms of the given variables. (1-4)

38. What number is three more than twice the number m? $2m + 3$
39. What number is four less than half the number z? $\frac{1}{2}z - 4$
40. What number is two more than eight times the number k? $8k + 2$
41. What number is the difference of five times a number w and one? $5w - 1$
42. What number is three times the sum of a number h and six? $3(h + 6)$

Using the given variable, write an expression for the measure required to complete each statement. (1-4)

43. In x weeks there are __?__ days. $7x$
44. In y yards there are __?__ feet. $3y$
45. Barbara is x years old. Four years ago she was __?__ years old. $x - 4$
46. Tony weighs w lb. Ray is 7 lb heavier than Tony. Ray weighs __?__ lb. $w + 7$
47. Claudia is 5 years older than Carl. If Claudia is n years old, then Carl is __?__ years old. $n - 5$

Use the given facts to state an equation that represents the third statement. (1-5)

48. The Lions scored 7 points less than the Bears. The Bears scored x points. The Lions scored 73 points. $x - 7 = 73$

49. Henry is 4 years older than Celia. Celia is m years old. The product of their ages is 140. $(4 + m)m = 140$

50. The length of a rectangle is 5 cm more than its width. Its width is t cm. The area of the rectangle is 176 cm^2. $(5 + t)t = 176$

Write an equation, using a variable you have chosen, that represents the given information. (1-5)

51. A package of a dozen pencils costs \$1.39. (Cost of one pencil) $12p = 1.39$

52. The perimeter of a square is 52 m. (Length of a side) $4s = 52$

53. All but 5 of the 34 invited guests came to the party. (Number of guests at the party) $g + 5 = 34$

Use the five-step plan to solve each problem. Write out each step. (1-6)

54. If half of a number is decreased by 12, the result is 30. Find the number. 84

55. A store has twice as many blue T-shirts as red T-shirts on a sale rack holding 48 red and blue T-shirts. How many red T-shirts are on the rack? 16

56. If 6 times a number is increased by 3, the result is 27. Find the number. 4

Write a positive or negative number for each measurement. (1-7)

57. 400 ft above sea level 400

58. A bank withdrawal of \$50 $^-50$

59. Ten losses $^-10$

60. Seven floors up 7

61. 2 points under par $^-2$

62. 5 m underground $^-5$

Graph the given numbers on a number line. (1-7)

63. $5, -2, \frac{1}{2}, 3, -4$

64. $-3, 0, 1, -2.5, 2$

Additional Answers

63.

−5 −4 −3 −2 −1 0 1 2 3 4 5

64.

−5 −4 −3 −2 −1 0 1 2 3 4 5

Simplify. (1-8)

65. $-(7 - 4)$ -3

66. $-(5 - 5)$ 0

67. $[-(-8)] + 10$ 18

68. $3 + [-(-6)]$ 9

69. $2 + |-9|$ 11

70. $|-8| + |5|$ 13

71. $|-3| + |0|$ 3

72. $|6| - |6|$ 0

73. $|5| - |-5|$ 0

74. $|-3.2| + |-0.8|$ 4

75. $|-4.7| + |4.7|$ 9.4

76. $|-2| - |0|$ 2

Replace each _?_ with one of the symbols $<$ or $>$ to make a true statement. (1-9)

77. $9 - 8$ _?_ -1 $>$

78. 7 _?_ $6 + 5$ $<$

79. $|0|$ _?_ 1 $<$

80. -4.3 _?_ -4.4 $>$

81. $|-2|$ _?_ $-(-4)$ $<$

82. $|-6|$ _?_ $|-8|$ $<$

83. $-(7 + 3)$ _?_ $|-14|$ $<$

84. $-\frac{3}{7}$ _?_ $-\frac{2}{7}$ $<$

85. $-\frac{5}{8}$ _?_ $\frac{3}{8}$ $<$

Chapter 2

Simplify. (2-1)

1. $237 + 75 + 13 + 25$ 350
2. $456 + 29 + 44 + 21$ 550
3. $0.2 + 16.4 + 2.8 + 0.6$ 20
4. $3.75 + 4.85 + 1.25 + 3.15$ 13
5. $6\frac{3}{8} + 1\frac{2}{7} + 4\frac{5}{8} + 3\frac{5}{7}$ 16
6. $25\frac{3}{4} + \frac{4}{5} + \frac{1}{4} + 2\frac{1}{5}$ 29
7. $8 + 3m + 4$ $3m + 12$
8. $15 + 5f + 7$ $5f + 22$
9. $9 + 6w + 3$ $6w + 12$
10. $5(7u)$ $35u$
11. $(8n)(11)$ $88n$
12. $(4b)9$ $36b$
13. $(3p)(4q)(5r)$ $60pqr$
14. $(2x)(5k)(7l)$ $70xkl$
15. $(10w)(3h)(2m)$ $60whm$

Simplify. If necessary, draw a number line to help you. (2-2)

16. $(-4 + 8) + 9$ 13
17. $(-7 + 10) + (-3)$ 0
18. $[16 + (-21)] + 4$ -1
19. $[-5 + (-13)] + 6$ -12
20. $[0 + (-7)] + [-8 + (-22)]$ -37
21. $[27 + (-7)] + [1 + (-1)]$ 20
22. $-3 + (-4) + (-9)$ -16
23. $(-5) + (-8) + (-6)$ -19
24. $-7.2 + (-3.5) + 10.7$ 0
25. $5.4 + (-3.1) + (-7.9)$ -5.6

Add. (2-3)

26. $9 + 8 + (-3) + 4$ 18
27. $-6 + (-7) + 10 + 2$ -1
28. $112 + (-32) + (-40) + (-25)$ 15
29. $-265 + (-88) + 105 + 95$ -153
30. $-[24 + (-8)] + [-(-4 + 6)]$ -18
31. $[-9 + (-2)] + [-(-9 + 2)]$ -4

Replace each __?__ with a number to make a true statement. (2-3)

32. __?__ $+ (-8) = 2$ 10
33. $-14 +$ __?__ $= 5$ 19
34. $3 +$ __?__ $= -10$ -13
35. __?__ $+ (-5) = 4$ 9
36. $0.7 +$ __?__ $= -1$ -1.7
37. __?__ $+ 0.35 = -0.65$ -1

Simplify. (2-4, 2-5)

38. $48 - 218$ -170
39. $53 - (-47)$ 100
40. $-18 - (-5)$ -13
41. $-27 - 56$ -83
42. $133 - (62 - 59)$ 130
43. $186 - (40 - 69)$ 215
44. $(33 - 44) - (66 - 77)$ 0
45. $(54 - 32) - (-8 + 13)$ 17
46. $14 - (-8) - [6 - (-3)]$ 13
47. $-18 - 7 - [-6 - (-11)]$ -30
48. $6 + x - (6 - x) - x$ x
49. $y - (-4) - [y + (-4)] - 4$ 4
50. $30\left(\frac{1}{6} + \frac{1}{3}\right)$ 15
51. $\frac{1}{5}(24) + \frac{1}{5}(16)$ 8
52. $\frac{1}{4}(16 + 12)$ 7
53. $(0.25)(34) + (0.75)(34)$ 34
54. $(37 \times 22) - (7 \times 22)$ 660
55. $(16 \times 58) - (6 \times 58)$ 580
56. $14m + 7m$ $21m$
57. $15q + (-8)q$ $7q$
58. $53n - 110n$ $-57n$
59. $79a - 37a$ $42a$
60. $3u + 7u + 8$ $10u + 8$
61. $7(c + 3) + 6$ $7c + 27$

Simplify. 88. $5l + 5$ (2-5, 2-6)

62. $26 + 4(h + 3)$ $4h + 38$ **63.** $8(j - 4) + 17$ $8j - 15$ **64.** $23 + 6(t - 2)$ $6t + 11$

65. $5x + 9 + 3x + 11$ $8x + 20$ **66.** $(-5)m + 3 + 13m + 17$ $8m + 20$

67. $14u - 8 - 12u + 13$ $2u + 5$ **68.** $4h + 8k + (-2)h + 12k$ $2h + 20k$

69. $9f + 3g - 7f + 7g$ $2f + 10g$ **70.** $10x + 14y - 6x - 3y$ $4x + 11y$

71. $(-27)(-5)$ 135 **72.** $38(-2)$ -76 **73.** $(-4)45$ -180

74. $(-8)(-6)(30)$ 1440 **75.** $(-5)(-9)(-3)$ -135 **76.** $(-13)(-14)(0)$ 0

77. $5(-4)(-12)(-2)$ -480 **78.** $-3(-2 - 9)$ 33 **79.** $(-17 + 6)(-1)$ 11

80. $(-6 \times 13) + (-6 \times 15)$ -168 **81.** $[27 \times (-5)] - (27 \times 5)$ -270

82. $-16 \times (-1) - [-16 \times (-11)]$ -160 **83.** $7(-m + 6p)$ $-7m + 42p$

84. $-5(2u - h)$ $-10u + 5h$ **85.** $-4(6n - 9v)$ $-24n + 36v$

86. $-x + 7 + 6x - 5$ $5x + 2$ **87.** $4 - t - 8 - 7t$ $-4 - 8t$ **88.** $-l + 9 + 6l - 4$

89. $3(x + 4y) + (-4)(8x - y)$ $-29x + 16y$ **90.** $-4(2u + v) + 5(u - v)$ $-3u - 9v$

91. $-2(3c + d) - 3(5d - c)$ $-3c - 17d$ **92.** $7(e - f) - 3(2e - 3f)$ $e + 2f$

Write an equation to represent the stated relationship. Answers may vary. (2-7)

93. The sum of three consecutive integers is 75. $n + (n + 1) + (n + 2) = 75$

94. The sum of three consecutive odd integers is 87. $n + (n + 2) + (n + 4) = 87$

95. The sum of three consecutive even integers is 138. $n + (n + 2) + (n + 4) = 138$

96. The product of two consecutive integers is 156. $n(n + 1) = 156$

97. The greater of two consecutive odd integers is eight more than three times the lesser. $n + 2 = 3n + 8$

98. The smaller of two consecutive even integers is one less than half of the greater. $n = \frac{1}{2}(n + 2) - 1$

Simplify each expression. (2-8, 2-9)

99. $-\frac{1}{11}(55)$ -5 **100.** $-5000\left(\frac{1}{50}\right)$ -100 **101.** $-\frac{1}{9}(-63)$ 7

102. $112\left(-\frac{1}{7}\right)\left(-\frac{1}{2}\right)$ 8 **103.** $-\frac{1}{5}(80)\frac{1}{4}$ -4 **104.** $6uv\left(-\frac{1}{6}\right)$ $-uv$

105. $44xy\left(\frac{1}{4}\right)$ $11xy$ **106.** $\frac{1}{m}(3mn),\ m \neq 0$ $3n$ **107.** $(8fg)\left(\frac{1}{f}\right),\ f \neq 0$ $8g$

108. $\frac{1}{5}(-35a + 15)$ $-7a + 3$ **109.** $(27h - 18)\frac{1}{3}$ $9h - 6$ **110.** $-\frac{1}{4}(-32e + 40f)$ $8e - 10f$

111. $(42x - 63y)\left(-\frac{1}{7}\right)$ $-6x + 9y$ **112.** $\frac{1}{12}(-480 - 144m)$ $-12m - 40$ **113.** $(-50p - 100q)\left(-\frac{1}{10}\right)$ $5p + 10q$

114. $-392 \div 56$ -7 **115.** $216 \div (-27)$ -8 **116.** $55 \div \left(-\frac{1}{5}\right)$ -275 **117.** $0 \div (-29)$ 0

118. $\frac{-36}{-\frac{1}{6}}$ 216 **119.** $\frac{8}{-\frac{1}{5}}$ -40 **120.** $\frac{-12}{\frac{1}{4}}$ -48 **121.** $\frac{0}{-\frac{1}{3}}$ 0

122. $\frac{168m}{-12}$ $-14m$ 123. $\frac{252a}{-8}$ $-31.5a$ 124. $\frac{-756x}{7x}$, $x \neq 0$ -108 125. $\frac{-253u}{-23u}$, $u \neq 0$ 11

126. $-\frac{c}{17}(-17)$ c 127. $-9 \cdot \frac{x}{9}$ $-x$ 128. $\frac{8w}{7} \cdot 7$ $8w$ 129. $-\frac{5h}{3}(-3)$ $5h$

Chapter 3

Solve. (3-1, 3-2, 3-3)

1. $a - 13 = 17$ 30
2. $c + 8 = 22$ 14
3. $s - 20 = -12$ 8
4. $t + 14 = -33$ -47
5. $15 + h = 0$ -15
6. $0 = k - 13$ 13
7. $f - 4 = |16|$ 20
8. $g + 7 = |-2|$ -5
9. $-x + 6 = 9$ -3
10. $23 - y = 47$ -24
11. $-5 - m = 7$ -12
12. $13 = -q + 8$ -5
13. $(e + 4) + 3 = 9$ 2
14. $6 = 10 + (n + 3)$ -7
15. $-5 + (1 + z) = 8$ 12
16. $13u = 338$ 26
17. $-396 = 22a$ -18
18. $-12x = -444$ 37
19. $126 = -9w$ -14
20. $\frac{1}{7}t = 13$ 91
21. $\frac{1}{8}h = -8$ -64
22. $11 = -\frac{1}{4}v$ -44
23. $-10 = -\frac{1}{5}m$ 50
24. $-42 = \frac{n}{7}$ -294
25. $-\frac{c}{4} = 32$ -128
26. $-\frac{m}{27} = 0$ 0
27. $-\frac{m}{3} = -40$ 120
28. $4x = -\frac{2}{7}$ $-\frac{1}{14}$
29. $-\frac{3}{2} = -9z$ $\frac{1}{6}$
30. $\frac{1}{4}v = 2\frac{3}{4}$ 11
31. $3\frac{1}{2} = \frac{1}{2}u$ 7
32. $5k + 8 = 43$ 7
33. $7h - 6 = 36$ 6
34. $-3 + 3m = -45$ -14
35. $2z + 8z = 80$ 8
36. $9v - 5v = 44$ 11
37. $3l - 8l = 65$ -13
38. $\frac{n}{5} + 9 = -11$ -100
39. $-\frac{x}{3} - 2 = 7$ -27
40. $\frac{5}{6}u + 15 = 0$ -18
41. $x - 5 - 6x = -25$ 4
42. $0 = y - 14 - 3y$ -7
43. $e + 3e + 4e = 48$ 6
44. $5(k + 3) = -10$ -5
45. $-\frac{4}{3}(n - 6) = 12$ -3
46. $2(v + 7) - 9 = 19$ 7

Use the five-step plan to solve each problem. (3-4)

47. The sum of 37 and three times a number is 67. Find the number. 10
48. Four times a number, decreased by 24, is -20. Find the number. 1
49. The perimeter of a rectangle is 108. If the length is 33, find the width. 21
50. An eighteen-year-old camp counselor is 6 years younger than three times the age of the girls in her cabin. How old are the campers? 8 years old
51. The lengths, in meters, of the sides of a triangle are consecutive even integers. The perimeter is 18 m. How long are the sides? 4 m, 6 m, 8 m
52. Bruce's savings account contains \$122 more than his younger brother's account. Together, they have \$354. Find the amount in each account. Bruce's, \$238; his brother's, \$116

Solve each equation. If the equation is an identity or if it has no root, state that fact. (3-5)

58. no root
64. $-\frac{5}{3}$

53. $10w = 8w + 14$ 7
54. $x = 45 - 4x$ 9
55. $48 - 6k = -12k$ −8
56. $9m + 3 = 6m + 21$ 6
57. $27 + u = 3 - 3u$ −6
58. $4n + 1 = -1 + 4n$
59. $2(v - 8) = 6v$ −4
60. $3l = 5(l - 6)$ 15
61. $7t - 3 = 6(t + 2)$ 15
62. $\frac{1}{3}(18 - 9c) = 6 - 3c$ identity
63. $m - 5 = \frac{1}{2}(12 - 14m)$ $\frac{11}{8}$
64. $\frac{4}{5}(25x - 15) = 50x + 38$
65. $5(3 + h) = 4(h + 2)$ −7
66. $(6t - 3)2 = (4t + 7)3$ no root
67. $7(n - 3) = 5(n - 3)$ 3

Use the five-step plan to solve each problem. (3-6, 3-7)

68. Jason is one fifth as old as his grandfather. In 4 years the sum of their ages will be 80. How old is each now? Jason, 12; grandfather, 60
69. The ages, in years, of three sisters are consecutive odd integers. Three years ago, the oldest sister was three times as old as the youngest. How old is each now? 5 y old, 7 y old, 9 y old
70. Julius weighs twice as much as each of his twin brothers. If each of the twins gains 5 pounds and Julius gains twice that amount, the sum of the three brothers' weights will be 240 pounds. How much does each weigh now? twins, 55 lb; Julius, 110 lb
71. The width of a rectangle is 6 cm shorter than the length. A second rectangle, with a perimeter of 54 cm, is 3 cm wider and 2 cm shorter than the first. What are the dimensions of each rectangle? 16 cm by 10 cm; 14 cm by 13 cm
72. Martha has some nickels and dimes worth $6.25. She has three times as many nickels as dimes. How many nickels does she have? 75 nickels
73. Elliot paid $1.50 a dozen for some flowers. He sold all but 5 dozen of them for $2 a dozen, making a profit of $18. How many dozen flowers did he buy? 56 dozen
74. Rachel spent $16.18 for some cans of dog food costing 79 cents each and some cans of cat food costing 69 cents each. She bought two more cans of cat food than of dog food. How many cans of each did she buy? 10 cans of dog food, 12 cans of cat food
75. Victor earns $3 an hour working after school and $4 an hour working on Saturdays. Last week he earned $43, working a total of 13 hours. How many hours did he work on Saturday? 4 h

State a reason for each step in Exercises 76–78. (3-8)

76. $6 + (15 + 4) = 6 + (4 + 15)$ ___?___ Comm. ax. for add.
$= (6 + 4) + 15$ ___?___ Assoc. ax. for add.
$= 10 + 15 = 25$ ___?___ Substitution principle

77. $20 + (-4) = (16 + 4) + (-4)$ ___?___ Substitution principle
$= 16 + [4 + (-4)]$ ___?___ Assoc. ax. for add.
$= 16 + 0$ ___?___ Axiom of opposites
$= 16$ ___?___ Identity ax. for add.

78. $-7 + 19 = 19 + (-7)$ — ? Comm. ax. for add.
$= 12 + 7 + (-7)$ — ? Substitution principle
$= 12 + 0$ — ? Axiom of opposites
$= 12$ — ? Identity ax. for add.

Chapter 4

Simplify. (4-1)

1. 7^3 343
2. $(-5)^4$ 625
3. $-3 \cdot 2^4$ -48
4. $(-2 \cdot 5)^3$ -1000
5. $7 + 5^2$ 32
6. $(8 - 4)^3$ 64
7. $6 - 2^5$ -26
8. $(4 + 7)^2$ 121
9. $5^3 \div (3^2 + 4^2)$ 5
10. $(8^2 - 6^2) \div 7$ 4
11. $4(9^2 - 4^3)$ 68

Evaluate if $a = -3$ and $b = 2$. (4-1)

12. $3a + b^2$ -5
13. $(3a + b)^2$ 49
14. $4a - b^3$ -20
15. $(4a - b)^3$ -2744
16. $7 + ab^2$ -5
17. $(7 + ab)^2$ 1
18. $-\frac{3a}{b^2}$ $\frac{9}{4}$
19. $\left(-\frac{3a}{b}\right)^2$ $\frac{81}{4}$

Add. (4-2)

20. $4x - 3$ / $7x + 8$ — $11x + 5$
21. $3b + 4$ / $-2b - 6$ — $b - 2$
22. $5m + 8$ / $4m + 3$ — $9m + 11$
23. $-2t - 7$ / $6t - 3$ — $4t - 10$
24. $5k - 6l + 4$ / $-5k + 8l + 2$ — $2l + 6$
25. $6x^2 - 2xy + 3y^2$ / $4x^2 - xy - y^2$ — $10x^2 - 3xy + 2y^2$
26. $2m^2 - 3mn - 5n$ / $-8m^2 \quad - n$ — $-6m^2 - 3mn - 6n$
27. $5a^2 - 6ab$ / $-2a^2 + 9ab - b^2$ — $3a^2 + 3ab - b^2$

28–35. In Exercises 20–27, subtract the lower polynomial from the upper one.

Simplify. (4-3, 4-4)

36. $e^6 \cdot e^3 \cdot e$ e^{10}
37. $(4f^3)(2f^4)$ $8f^7$
38. $(-3c^2d)(-4cd^2)$ $12c^3d^3$
39. $(-2gh^2)(5g^3h)$ $-10g^4h^3$
40. $(3mn)(6m^2n)(2n^2)$ $36m^3n^4$
41. $(-5j^4k^2)(4jl^3)(-3kl^2)$
42. $\left(\frac{8}{3}x^5y\right)\left(\frac{9}{2}xy^6\right)$ $12x^6y^7$
43. $(-6a^3)\left(\frac{1}{6}a^3\right)$ $-a^6$
44. $(3u^2v)(-7v^3)\left(\frac{4}{9}u^2\right)$
45. $3^w \cdot 3^{5-w} \cdot 3$ 3^6
46. $4^2 \cdot 4^{a+1} \cdot 4^a$ 4^{2a+3}
47. $2^5 \cdot 2^{b+3} \cdot 2^{3-b}$ 2^{11}
48. $(3p^5)(5p^2) + (7p^3)(2p^4)$ $29p^7$
49. $(8d^3)(2d^7) - (3d^6)(4d^4)$ $4d^{10}$
50. $(w^5)^2$ w^{10}
51. $(x^2)^5$ x^{10}
52. $y^2 \cdot y^5$ y^7
53. $z^n \cdot z^n$ z^{2n}
54. $(a^n)^3$ a^{3n}
55. $(b^3)^n$ b^{3n}
56. $c^3 \cdot c^n$ c^{n+3}
57. $d^n \cdot d^n \cdot d^n$ d^{3n}
58. $(5f)^2$ $25f^2$
59. $(gh)^4$ g^4h^4
60. $(6m^3)^2$ $36m^6$
61. $(4mn^5)^3$ $64m^3n^{15}$
62. $(2u^3v)^5$ $32u^{15}v^5$
63. $(3a^5b^4)^2$ $9a^{10}b^8$
64. $(-7x^4)^2$ $49x^8$
65. $-(8x^5)^3$ $-512x^{15}$
66. $(3k)^2(3k)^4$ $729k^6$
67. $(-2l^3)^3 \cdot (5l^2)^2$ $-200l^{13}$
68. $-(4t^2)^2(3t)^3$ $-432t^7$
69. $(5x^2y)^3 \cdot 3xy^2$ $375x^7y^5$

Additional Answers

28. $-3x - 11$
29. $5b + 10$
30. $m + 5$
31. $-8t - 4$
32. $10k - 14l + 2$
33. $2x^2 - xy + 4y^2$
34. $10m^2 - 3mn - 4n$
35. $7a^2 - 15ab + b^2$
41. $60j^5k^3l^5$
44. $-\frac{28u^4v^4}{3}$

Additional Answers

74. $3n^2 + 15n$
75. $-12t + 8t^2$
76. $12k^2 - 42k$
77. $-40h^2 - 15h$
81. $5u^3v^2 - 2u^2v^3 + 4uv^4$
82. $m^2 + 6m + 8$
83. $n^2 + 2n - 15$
84. $a^2 - 13a + 42$
85. $5x^2 + 33x - 14$
86. $12y^2 - 10y + 2$
87. $30b^2 + 38b + 12$
88. $u^3 + 5u^2 + 11u + 15$
89. $3v^3 + v^2 + 3v - 7$
90. $6c^3 - 13c^2 + 29c - 40$
94. $15m^3 - 17m^2n + mn^2 + n^3$
99. $r = \sqrt{\frac{A}{\pi}}, A \geq 0$
100. $n = \frac{S + 360}{180}$

Multiply. (4-5, 4-6)

70. $7(x + 3)$ $7x + 21$
71. $5(y - 4)$ $5y - 20$
72. $-3(z - 2)$ $-3z + 6$
73. $-8(1 + 4m)$ $-8 - 32m$
74. $3n(n + 5)$
75. $-4t(3 - 2t)$
76. $6k(2k - 7)$
77. $-5h(8h + 3)$
78. $9a(a^2 - 3a - 4)$ $9a^3 - 27a^2 - 36a$
79. $-5b^2(3b^2 - 2b + 6)$ $-15b^4 + 10b^3 - 30b^2$
80. $\frac{1}{3}c(6c^2 - 3cd + 9d^2)$ $2c^3 - c^2d + 3cd^2$
81. $\frac{1}{2}uv^2(10u^2 - 4uv + 8v^2)$
82. $(m + 4)(m + 2)$
83. $(n - 3)(n + 5)$
84. $(a - 6)(a - 7)$
85. $(5x - 2)(x + 7)$
86. $(4y - 2)(3y - 1)$
87. $(6b + 4)(5b + 3)$
88. $(u + 3)(u^2 + 2u + 5)$
89. $(v - 1)(3v^2 + 4v + 7)$
90. $(3c - 5)(2c^2 - c + 8)$
91. $\begin{array}{r} 7x - 4y \\ 3x - 2y \\ \hline \end{array}$ $21x^2 - 26xy + 8y^2$
92. $\begin{array}{r} 5a - 8b \\ 4a + b \\ \hline \end{array}$ $20a^2 - 27ab - 8b^2$
93. $\begin{array}{r} e^2 + ef + f^2 \\ e + f \\ \hline \end{array}$ $e^3 + 2e^2f + 2ef^2 + f^3$
94. $\begin{array}{r} 3m^2 - 4mn + n^2 \\ 5m + n \\ \hline \end{array}$

Solve for the given variable. State the restrictions, if any, for the formula obtained to be meaningful. (4-7)

95. $A = \frac{1}{2}ap$; a $a = \frac{2A}{p}$; $p \neq 0$
96. $V = \frac{1}{3}Bh$; h $h = \frac{3V}{B}$; $B \neq 0$
97. $A = \frac{1}{2}h(b_1 + b_2)$; b_1 $b_1 = \frac{2A - b_2h}{h}$; $h \neq 0$
98. $y = mx + b$; b $b = y - mx$
99. $A = \pi r^2$; r
100. $S = (n - 2)180$; n
101. $F = \frac{9}{5}C + 32$; C $C = \frac{5}{9}(F - 32)$
102. $P = \frac{A}{1 + rt}$; A $A = P + Prt$
103. $r = \frac{I}{Pt}$; t $t = \frac{I}{Pr}$; $P \neq 0$, $r \neq 0$

Make a chart for each problem. Then solve. (4-8)

104. Two buses leave a depot at the same time, one traveling north and the other south. The speed of the northbound bus is 15 mph greater than the speed of the southbound bus. After 3 hours on the road, the buses are 255 miles apart. What are their speeds? southbound, 35 mph; northbound, 50 mph

105. Exactly 10 min after Alex left his grandparents' house, his cousin Alison set out from there to overtake him. Alex drives at 36 mph. Alison drives at 40 mph. How long did it take Alison to overtake Alex? $1\frac{1}{2}$ h

106. A plane flew from the Sky City airport to the Plainsville airport at 800 km/h and then returned to Sky City at 900 km/h. The return trip took 30 min less than the flight to Plainsville. How far apart are the airports and how long did the trip to Plainsville take? 3600 km; 4.5 h

107. A poster is three times as long as it is wide. It is framed by a mat such that there is a 4 in. border around the poster. Find the dimensions of the poster if the area of the mat is 488 in^2. 13.25 in. by 39.75 in.

108. A square piece of remnant material is on sale. A rectangular piece of the same material, whose length is 1 yd longer than a side of the square and whose width is $\frac{5}{9}$ yd shorter than a side of the square, is also on sale. If the square and the rectangle have the same area and you purchase both remnants, how much material will you get? $3\frac{1}{8}$ yd^2

Chapter 5

List all the pairs of integral factors of each integer. (5-1)

1. 42 **2.** 80 **3.** 91 **4.** 72 **5.** 52

6–10. Give the prime factorization of each integer in Exercises 1–5.
6. $2 \cdot 3 \cdot 7$ 7. $2^4 \cdot 5$ 8. $7 \cdot 13$ 9. $2^3 \cdot 3^2$ 10. $2^2 \cdot 13$

Give the GCF of each group of numbers. (5-1)

11. 126, 168 42 **12.** 144, 84 12 **13.** 65, 52 13 **14.** 90, 330 30

Simplify each expression, assuming that no denominator equals zero. (5-2)

15. $\frac{12x^5}{4x}$ $3x^4$ **16.** $\frac{25m^4n}{-15mn^6}$ $-\frac{5m^3}{3n^5}$ **17.** $\frac{-7ab}{21ab^5}$ $-\frac{1}{3b^4}$ **18.** $\frac{-8(uv)^7}{-10(uv)^5}$ $\frac{4u^2v^5}{5}$

19. $\frac{(w^4)^2}{(w^5)^4}$ $\frac{1}{w^{12}}$ **20.** $\frac{(5k)^2}{5k^2}$ 5 **21.** $\frac{(-3y)^3}{(y^3)^2}$ $-\frac{27}{y^3}$ **22.** $\frac{(2c^5)(4c^3)}{(8c^2)^3}$ $\frac{c^2}{64}$

Divide. Assume that no denominator equals zero. (5-3)

23. $\frac{12e+8}{4}$ $3e+2$ **24.** $\frac{6x-9y+12}{3}$ $2x-3y+4$ **25.** $\frac{2x^3+6x^2+x}{x}$ $2x^2+6x+1$

26. $\frac{18ab-24a^2}{-6a}$ $-3b+4a$ **27.** $\frac{15m-25m^2-5m^3}{5m}$ $3-5m-m^2$ **28.** $\frac{28h^5k^3-35hk^2}{7hk^2}$ $4h^4k-5$

Factor each polynomial as the product of its greatest monomial factor and another polynomial. (5-3)

29. $15w^2-10w+5$ $5(3w^2-2w+1)$ **30.** $9x^2+18x$ $9x(x+2)$ **31.** $7u^3+14u^2$ $7u^2(u+2)$

32. $12a^3-6a^2+18a$ $6a(2a^2-a+3)$ **33.** $15c^2+3cd$ $3c(5c+d)$ **34.** $8m^2n-24mn^2$ $8mn(m-3n)$

Write each product as a trinomial. (5-4)

35. $(x+5)(x+3)$ $x^2+8x+15$ **36.** $(b-2)(b-4)$ b^2-6b+8 **37.** $(n-3)(n+7)$ $n^2+4n-21$

38. $(e-8)(e+6)$ **39.** $(3+m)(2+m)$ **40.** $(3f+2)(f+5)$

41. $(4y-3)(2y-1)$ **42.** $(8z+7)(z-2)$ **43.** $(5n-3)(4n-2)$

44. $a(6a-4)(5a-3)$ $30a^3-38a^2+12a$ **45.** $h(3h+7)(4h+9)$ $12h^3+55h^2+63h$ **46.** $2x(9x-1)(2x+3)$ $36x^3+50x^2-6x$

Express each product as a binomial. (5-5)

47. $(k-5)(k+5)$ k^2-25 **48.** $(3-t)(3+t)$ $9-t^2$ **49.** $(4d-8)(4d+8)$ $16d^2-64$

50. $(w^2-6)(w^2+6)$ w^4-36 **51.** $(5m^2+n)(5m^2-n)$ $25m^4-n^2$ **52.** $(ab+c^2)(ab-c^2)$ $a^2b^2-c^4$

Factor completely, using the table of squares. (5-5)

53. $16e^2-9$ **54.** $36u^2-25$ **55.** $81-f^2$ $(9-f)(9+f)$ **56.** $144a^2-64b^2$ $16(3a-2b)(3a+2b)$

57. $49-100y^2$ $(7-10y)(7+10y)$ **58.** v^4-w^4 $(v-w)(v+w)(v^2+w^2)$ **59.** s^6-4 $(s^3-2)(s^3+2)$ **60.** $16x^8-625$

Additional Answers

1. 1, 42; 2, 21; 3, 14; 6, 7; −1, −42; −2, −21; −3, −14; −6, −7
2. 1, 80; 2, 40; 4, 20; 5, 16; 8, 10; −1, −80; −2, −40; −4, −20; −5, −16; −8, −10
3. 1, 91; 7, 13; −1, −91; −7, −13
4. 1, 72; 2, 36; 3, 24; 4, 18; 6, 12; 8, 9; −1, −72; −2, −36; −3, −24; −4, −18; −6, −12; −8, −9
5. 1, 52; 2, 26; 4, 13; −1, −52; −2, −26; −4, −13

38. $e^2-2e-48$
39. $6+5m+m^2$
40. $3f^2+17f+10$
41. $8y^2-10y+3$
42. $8z^2-9z-14$
43. $20n^2-22n+6$
53. $(4e-3)(4e+3)$
54. $(6u-5)(6u+5)$
60. $(2x^2-5)(2x^2+5)\cdot(4x^4+25)$

Additional Answers

75. $(k+7)(k+1)$
76. $(v-5)(v-4)$
77. $(a-1)^2$
78. $(7+u)(5+u)$
79. $(b-12)(b-4)$
80. $(w+8)(w+10)$
81. $(x+6y)(x+7y)$
82. $(m-7n)(m-3n)$
83. $(e-4f)(e-11f)$
84. $(c+6)(c-3)$
85. $(x-7)(x+5)$
86. prime
87. $(h-9)(h+2)$
88. $(b+10)(b-3)$
89. $(t-9)(t+5)$
90. $(a-3b)(a+b)$
91. $(u+4v)(u-v)$
92. $(m-5n)(m+4n)$
93. $(2x+3)(x+4)$
94. prime
95. $(5d+3)(2d-1)$
96. $-2(5+3y)(1+2y)$
97. prime
98. $-2(2z-1)(2z-5)$
99. $(5x+y)(3x+2y)$
100. $2(a-2b)(4a-3b)$
101. $(7m+3n)(2m-n)$
102. $(m-3)(8+5m)$
103. $2(a+2)(3a+2)$
104. $(u+1)(u-2v)$
105. $(b+1)^2(b-3)$
106. $(a+2)(a+b)$
107. $(7w+3)(c-w)$
108. $(n+1)(n^2-6)$
109. $(1-m)(1+m)\cdot(64+m^4)$
110. $2x(3x+4)(7x+2)$
111. $6y(5y+1)(2y-1)$
112. $x^3(6x-1)(2x-3)$

Express each square as a trinomial. (5-6)

61. $(g+7)^2$ $g^2+14g+49$
62. $(k-3)^2$ k^2-6k+9
63. $(2x+6)^2$ $4x^2+24x+36$
64. $(5y-3)^2$ $25y^2-30y+9$
65. $(2m+3n)^2$ $4m^2+12mn+9n^2$
66. $(7a-5b)^2$ $49a^2-70ab+25b^2$
67. $(ef-8)^2$ $e^2f^2-16ef+64$
68. $(-4+9f)^2$ $81f^2-72f+16$

Factor each trinomial as the square of a binomial. (5-6)

69. x^2-6x+9 $(x-3)^2$
70. $e^2+18e+81$ $(e+9)^2$
71. $4-28h+49h^2$ $(2-7h)^2$
72. $64x^2+80xy+25y^2$ $(8x+5y)^2$
73. $4m^2-36mn+81n^2$ $(2m-9n)^2$
74. $16w^2+24wz+9z^2$ $(4w+3z)^2$

Factor completely, if possible. Check by multiplying the factors. If the polynomial is not factorable, write "prime." (5-7, 5-8, 5-9)

75. k^2+8k+7
76. $v^2-9v+20$
77. a^2-2a+1
78. $35+12u+u^2$
79. $b^2-16b+48$
80. $w^2+18w+80$
81. $x^2+13xy+42y^2$
82. $m^2-10mn+21n^2$
83. $e^2-15ef+44f^2$
84. $c^2+3c-18$
85. $x^2-2x-35$
86. $k^2+8k-32$
87. $h^2-7h-18$
88. $b^2+7b-30$
89. $t^2-4t-45$
90. $a^2-2ab-3b^2$
91. $u^2+3uv-4v^2$
92. $m^2-mn-20n^2$
93. $2x^2+11x+12$
94. $10e^2-12e+3$
95. $10d^2+d-3$
96. $-10-26y-12y^2$
97. $-7-39z-18z^2$
98. $-10+24z-8z^2$
99. $15x^2+13xy+2y^2$
100. $8a^2-22ab+12b^2$
101. $14m^2-mn-3n^2$

Factor by grouping. Check by multiplying. (5-10)

102. $8(m-3)-5m(3-m)$
103. $6a(a+2)+4(a+2)$
104. $u(u-2v)-(2v-u)$
105. $b(b-2)(b+1)-3-3b$
106. $a^2+2a+ab+2b$
107. $7cw+3c-7w^2-3w$
108. n^3+n^2-6n-6
109. $64-64m^2+m^4-m^6$

Factor completely. Check by multiplying. (5-11)

110. $42x^3+68x^2+16x$
111. $60y^3-18y^2-6y$
112. $12x^5-20x^4+3x^3$
113. $16a^4-144a^2$
114. $4n^5-100n$
115. $28w^7-102w^5$
116. $36m^2+24mn+4n^2$
117. $24cd-12c^2-12d^2$
118. $-7x^3+14x^2y-7xy^2$

Solve and check. (5-12)

119. $(a+13)(a+8)=0$ $\{-13,-8\}$
120. $(f-16)(f-27)=0$ $\{16,27\}$
121. $(2x-4)(3x-5)=0$ $\left\{2,\frac{5}{3}\right\}$
122. $(6h-5)(6h+5)=0$
123. $7w(4w+3)=0$
124. $m(2m+7)(3m-4)=0$
125. $a^2+7a+6=0$ $\{-6,-1\}$
126. $q^2-21q=-20$ $\{20,1\}$
127. $d^2=14d-45$ $\{5,9\}$
128. $y^2-7y-18=0$ $\{9,-2\}$
129. $c^2-36=-5c$ $\{-9,4\}$
130. $h^2=-3h+54$ $\{-9,6\}$
131. $6-23z-4z^2=0$ $\left\{-6,\frac{1}{4}\right\}$
132. $3m^2+1=4m$ $\left\{\frac{1}{3},1\right\}$
133. $2t^2=10+t$ $\left\{-2,\frac{5}{2}\right\}$
134. $e^2-49=0$ $\{7,-7\}$
135. $36g^2=16$ $\left\{\frac{2}{3},-\frac{2}{3}\right\}$
136. $w^3-9w=0$ $\{0,-3,3\}$

(5-13)

137. The sum of a number and its square is 56. Find the number. 7 or -8

138. Find two consecutive negative odd integers whose product is 143. $-13, -11$

139. The length of a rectangle is 5 cm less than twice the width. If the area of the rectangle is 88 cm², find the dimensions of the rectangle. 8 cm by 11 cm

140. Find two numbers that total 12 and whose squares total 74. 5, 7

Chapter 6

(6-1)

Express in simplest form, noting any restrictions on the variable.

1. $\frac{5m - 15}{m - 3}$ 5; $m \neq 3$ **2.** $\frac{2a + 1}{6a + 3}$ $\frac{1}{3}$; $a \neq -\frac{1}{2}$ **3.** $\frac{7c - 7d}{7c + 7d}$ $\frac{c - d}{c + d}$; $c \neq -d$ **4.** $\frac{6k - k^2}{36 - k^2}$ $\frac{k}{6 + k}$; $k \neq -6, 6$

5. $\frac{3uv}{u^2v - v^2u}$ **6.** $\frac{8w^3}{8w^2 - 12w}$ **7.** $\frac{x^2 - 64}{x^2 - x - 56}$ **8.** $\frac{(e - 7)^2}{49 - e^2}$

9. $\frac{15m + 6n}{25m^2 - 4n^2}$ $\frac{3}{5m - 2n}$; $m \neq \frac{2}{5}n$, $m \neq -\frac{2}{5}n$ **10.** $\frac{a^2 + ab}{a^2 - ab}$ $\frac{a + b}{a - b}$; $a \neq 0$, $a \neq b$

11. $\frac{(k - 3)(7k - 2)}{(2 - 7k)(k - 3)}$ -1; $k \neq 3$, $k \neq \frac{2}{7}$ **12.** $\frac{3x^2 + 17xy + 20y^2}{3x^2 - xy - 10y^2}$

13. $\frac{14 - 9t + t^2}{t^2 - 4}$ $\frac{t - 7}{t + 2}$; $t \neq 2$, $t \neq -2$ **14.** $\frac{u^2 - v^2}{u^2 + 2uv + v^2}$ $\frac{u - v}{u + v}$; $u \neq -v$

15. $\frac{(5w - x)^5}{(x - 5w)^7}$ $-\frac{1}{(5w - x)^2}$; $w \neq \frac{x}{5}$ **16.** $\frac{(4s - 6)^2(3s - 2)}{(2 - 3s)(6 - 4s)}$ $4s - 6$; $s \neq \frac{2}{3}$, $s \neq \frac{3}{2}$

(6-2)

Express each product as a fraction in simplest form.

17. $\frac{5}{8} \cdot \frac{32}{25}$ $\frac{4}{5}$ **18.** $\frac{4}{3} \cdot \frac{3}{5} \cdot \frac{5}{7}$ $\frac{4}{7}$ **19.** $\left(\frac{-2}{5}\right)^2 \cdot \frac{15}{16}$ $\frac{3}{20}$ **20.** $\left(-\frac{3}{2}\right)^3 \cdot \frac{24}{9}$ -9

21. $\frac{e}{f} \cdot \frac{f}{g} \cdot \frac{g}{h}$ $\frac{e}{h}$ **22.** $\frac{5}{w} \cdot \frac{w^2}{10}$ $\frac{w}{2}$ **23.** $\frac{8m}{3} \cdot \frac{9}{12m}$ 2 **24.** $\frac{a^2}{3b} \cdot \frac{b^2}{4a}$ $\frac{ab}{12}$

25. $\frac{14v}{12v^2} \cdot \frac{4uw^2}{7v^2}$ $\frac{2uw^2}{3v^3}$ **26.** $\frac{a + 5}{a} \cdot \frac{a^2}{a^2 - 25}$ $\frac{a}{a - 5}$

27. $\frac{4x - xy}{8x^2y} \cdot \frac{2}{16 - y^2}$ $\frac{1}{4xy(4 + y)}$ **28.** $\frac{m + n}{m - n} \cdot \frac{m^2 - n^2}{3m + 3n}$ $\frac{m + n}{3}$

(6-2)

Simplify using the rules of exponents for the power of a product and the power of a quotient.

29. $(5k^3)^2$ $25k^6$ **30.** $\left(\frac{x}{7}\right)^2$ $\frac{x^2}{49}$ **31.** $\left(\frac{3x}{4}\right)^2$ $\frac{9x^2}{16}$ **32.** $\left(\frac{2m}{3n^2}\right)^3$ $\frac{8m^3}{27n^6}$

33. $\left(-\frac{x^2}{5}\right)^3$ $-\frac{x^6}{125}$ **34.** $\left(\frac{e}{f}\right)^3 \cdot \frac{e}{f}$ $\frac{e^4}{f^4}$ **35.** $\left(\frac{4c}{d}\right)^3 \cdot \frac{c^2}{8}$ $\frac{8c^5}{d^3}$ **36.** $\left(\frac{7a}{b}\right)^2 \cdot \frac{3ab}{14}$ $\frac{21a^3}{2b}$

113. $16a^2(a - 3)(a + 3)$
114. $4n(n^2 - 5)(n^2 + 5)$
115. $2w^5(14w^2 - 51)$
116. $4(3m + n)^2$
117. $-12(c - d)^2$
118. $-7x(x - y)^2$
122. $\left\{\frac{5}{6}, -\frac{5}{6}\right\}$
123. $\left\{0, -\frac{3}{4}\right\}$
124. $\left\{0, -\frac{7}{2}, \frac{4}{3}\right\}$

Additional Answers

5. $\frac{3}{u - v}$; $u \neq 0$, $v \neq 0$, $u \neq v$

6. $\frac{2w^2}{2w - 3}$; $w \neq 0$, $w \neq \frac{3}{2}$

7. $\frac{x + 8}{x + 7}$; $x \neq 8$, $x \neq -7$

8. $\frac{7 - e}{7 + e}$; $e \neq 7$, $e \neq -7$

12. $\frac{x + 4y}{x - 2y}$; $x \neq 2y$, $x \neq -\frac{5y}{3}$

Additional Answers

70. $\frac{7ef}{ef(e+f)}$, $\frac{5ef+5f^2}{ef(e+f)}$, $\frac{6e^2+6ef}{ef(e+f)}$

71. $\frac{2wx+6w}{3(x-3)(x+3)}$, $\frac{3}{3(x-3)(x+3)}$

76. $\frac{2c-7}{c-3}$

Divide. Express the answers in simplest form. (6-3)

37. $\frac{4}{9} \div \frac{16}{3}$ $\frac{1}{12}$
38. $\frac{a^2}{4} \div \frac{a}{12}$ $3a$
39. $\frac{m}{3n} \div \frac{mn}{6}$ $\frac{2}{n^2}$
40. $\frac{8x^2}{5y} \div 4xy$ $\frac{2x}{5y^2}$

41. $\frac{e+f}{5} \div \frac{3e+3f}{15}$ 1
42. $\frac{u^2-v^2}{u^2+v^2} \div (u+v)$ $\frac{u-v}{u^2+v^2}$

43. $\frac{5}{n^2-25} \div \frac{5n-15}{n+5}$ $\frac{1}{(n-3)(n-5)}$
44. $\frac{4n-12}{4} \div \frac{5n-15}{8}$ $\frac{8}{5}$

45. $\frac{x^4-y^4}{2x^2+8x} \div \frac{x^2+y^2}{x^2-16}$ $\frac{(x-y)(x+y)(x-4)}{2x}$
46. $\frac{4a^2-25}{6a^2} \div \frac{12a-30}{3a^4}$ $\frac{a^2(2a+5)}{12}$
47. $\frac{m^2+n^2}{8s-10t} \div \frac{7m+7n}{4t-6s}$ $\frac{(2t-3s)(m^2+n^2)}{7(4s-5t)(m+n)}$

Simplify. (6-3)

48. $\frac{1}{3} \div \frac{2}{6} \cdot \frac{5}{7}$ $\frac{5}{7}$
49. $\frac{x}{7} \div \frac{y^2}{x} \cdot \frac{7}{y}$ $\frac{x^2}{y^3}$
50. $\frac{e^2}{3} \cdot \frac{f^2}{e} \div \frac{e}{f}$ $\frac{f^3}{3}$

51. $\left(\frac{c}{3}\right)^2 \div \frac{c}{9} \cdot \frac{c}{3}$ $\frac{c^2}{3}$
52. $\left(\frac{w}{4}\right)^2 \div \left(\frac{w}{8} \cdot \frac{w}{2}\right)$ 1
53. $\frac{a-b}{a+3b} \cdot \frac{3b+a}{b+a} \div \frac{b-a}{b+a}$ -1

Find the missing numerator. (6-4)

54. $\frac{5x}{11} = \frac{?}{33}$ $15x$
55. $\frac{h-4}{7} = \frac{?}{14}$ $2h-8$
56. $\frac{3k-5}{2} = \frac{?}{8}$ $12k-20$
57. $\frac{6m-n}{7} = \frac{?}{35}$ $30m-5n$

58. $\frac{c}{d} = \frac{?}{c^3d}$ c^4
59. $\frac{4s}{5t} = \frac{?}{15st^2}$ $12s^2t$

60. $\frac{8}{7d+2} = \frac{?}{(7d+2)^2}$ $56d+16$
61. $\frac{5}{e-1} = \frac{?}{e^2-1}$ $5e+5$

62. $\frac{3}{h-2} = \frac{?}{2-h}$ -3
63. $\frac{5}{z-3} = \frac{?}{z^2-3z}$ $5z$

64. $\frac{w}{w+4} = \frac{?}{w^2+4w}$ w^2
65. $\frac{3}{a^2b} = \frac{?}{a^3b^2}$ $3ab$

Express each group of fractions with their LCD. (6-4)

66. $\frac{2}{3}, \frac{4}{5}, \frac{3}{7}$ $\frac{70}{105}, \frac{84}{105}, \frac{45}{105}$
67. $\frac{x-2}{16}, \frac{x+3}{12}$ $\frac{3x-6}{48}, \frac{4x+12}{48}$
68. $\frac{3m-n}{10}, \frac{3m+n}{15}$ $\frac{9m-3n}{30}, \frac{6m+2n}{30}$

69. $\frac{1}{3cd}, \frac{4}{cd^2}$ $\frac{d}{3cd^2}, \frac{12}{3cd^2}$
70. $\frac{7}{e+f}, \frac{5}{e}, \frac{6}{f}$
71. $\frac{2w}{3x-9}, \frac{1}{x^2-9}$

Simplify. (6-5)

72. $\frac{3}{a} + \frac{5}{a} - \frac{4}{a}$ $\frac{4}{a}$
73. $\frac{7}{2x} + \frac{6}{2x} - \frac{5}{2x}$ $\frac{4}{x}$
74. $\frac{u}{7} - \frac{3u+5}{7}$ $\frac{-2u-5}{7}$

75. $\frac{k+3}{5} - \frac{2k+7}{5}$ $\frac{-k-4}{5}$
76. $\frac{c}{c-3} + \frac{1}{c-3} - \frac{8-c}{c-3}$
77. $\frac{4}{g-3} - \frac{3}{3-g}$ $\frac{7}{g-3}$

78. $\frac{3m}{m-n} + \frac{3n}{n-m}$ 3
79. $\frac{5}{t^2} + \frac{3}{t}$ $\frac{5+3t}{t^2}$
80. $\frac{4}{5x} - \frac{1}{15x^2}$ $\frac{12x-1}{15x^2}$

81. $\frac{1}{5wx} - \frac{3}{10w}$ $\frac{2-3x}{10wx}$
82. $\frac{3k-2}{2k^3} + \frac{6}{k^2}$ $\frac{15k-2}{2k^3}$
83. $\frac{2}{3(x+2)} + \frac{x}{x+2}$ $\frac{2+3x}{3(x+2)}$

84. $\dfrac{5a-4}{6}+\dfrac{a-2}{9}$ $\dfrac{17a-16}{18}$ 85. $\dfrac{2h+4}{8}-\dfrac{h}{4}+\dfrac{3h-2}{10}$ $\dfrac{3(h+1)}{10}$ 86. $\dfrac{4(m-n)}{16}-\dfrac{3(m+n)}{12}$ $-\dfrac{n}{2}$

87. $\dfrac{3}{x+2}-\dfrac{1}{x+3}$ $\dfrac{2x+7}{(x+2)(x+3)}$ 88. $\dfrac{3z}{z^2-16}+\dfrac{z}{z-4}$ $\dfrac{z(z+7)}{(z+4)(z-4)}$ 89. $\dfrac{u}{u-4}+\dfrac{3}{4-u}$ $\dfrac{u-3}{u-4}$

Write each expression as a fraction in simplest form. (6-6)

90. $7\frac{1}{3}$ $\frac{22}{3}$ 91. $5+\frac{1}{n}$ $\frac{5n+1}{n}$ 92. $4m-\frac{3}{m}$ $\frac{4m^2-3}{m}$ 93. $\frac{x}{y}+3$ $\frac{x+3y}{y}$

94. $6-\frac{5}{k+3}$ $\frac{6k+13}{k+3}$ 95. $\frac{z}{z-2}+7$ $\frac{8z-14}{z-2}$ 96. $\frac{x+3}{x}-2$ $\frac{-x+3}{x}$ 97. $8h-\frac{h}{h+3}$

98. $3t+\frac{t}{2t+7}$ 99. $5-\frac{e+3}{e^2-1}$ 100. $a+\frac{5a+3}{a+3}$ 101. $2w-\frac{w+3}{w-3}$

102. $n-\frac{7}{n+2}-\frac{3n-1}{n+2}$ 103. $\frac{v}{u+v}+\frac{u}{v-u}+1$ 104. $\frac{x}{x-4}+\frac{x}{x+4}-3$

Divide. Write your answer as a polynomial or mixed expression. Check. (6-7)

105. $\frac{x^2+7x+10}{x+2}$ 106. $\frac{z^2-2z-35}{z-7}$ 107. $\frac{a^2-5a-3}{a+2}$ 108. $\frac{n^2-16}{n+4}$

109. $\frac{7+k^2-4k}{k-5}$ 110. $\frac{8y^2+6}{2y-1}$ 111. $\frac{b^3-1}{b+1}$ 112. $\frac{x^3+5}{x+3}$

113. $\frac{w^3+w^2+2w-4}{w-1}$ 114. $\frac{u^3+2u^2-16}{u-2}$ 115. $\frac{2t^2-13t+20}{2t-5}$

116. $\frac{2-9h+7h^2}{7h-2}$ 117. $\frac{v^3+v^2+v+1}{v-2}$ 118. $\frac{5n^2+6n^3+9}{3+2n}$

Chapter 7

State each ratio in simplest form. (7-1)

1. 40 s:2 min 1:3 2. 4 m:250 cm 8:5 3. 3 kg:45 g 200:3
4. $6y:15y$ 2:5 5. $36d^2:10d$ $18d:5$ 6. $(4a)^2:6a$ $8a:3$
7. The ratio of old cars to new cars if there are 180 cars and 55 are new. 25:11
8. The ratio of wins to losses for a baseball team that played 84 games and won 48 of them. 4:3

Solve each proportion. (7-2)

9. $\frac{3}{5}=\frac{x}{15}$ 9 10. $\frac{5}{7}=\frac{25}{a}$ 35 11. $\frac{24}{7}=\frac{4}{c}$ $\frac{7}{6}$

12. $\frac{3x}{2}=\frac{2}{5}$ $\frac{4}{15}$ 13. $\frac{15a}{64}=\frac{45}{32}$ 6 14. $\frac{17d}{25}=\frac{51}{125}$ $\frac{3}{5}$

15. $\frac{x-4}{x}=\frac{7}{9}$ 18 16. $\frac{3w}{10w+2}=\frac{2}{7}$ 4 17. $\frac{8a-5}{5a-4}=\frac{13}{8}$ 12

97. $\frac{h(8h+23)}{h+3}$
98. $\frac{2t(3t+11)}{2t+7}$
99. $\frac{5e^2-e-8}{(e+1)(e-1)}$
100. $\frac{a^2+8a+3}{a+3}$
101. $\frac{2w^2-7w-3}{w-3}$
102. $n-3$
103. $\frac{2v^2}{(v+u)(v-u)}$
104. $\frac{-x^2+48}{(x+4)(x-4)}$
105. $x+5$
106. $z+5$
107. $a-7+\frac{11}{a+2}$
108. $n-4$
109. $k+1+\frac{12}{k-5}$
110. $4y+2+\frac{8}{2y-1}$
111. $b^2-b+1-\frac{2}{b+1}$
112. $x^2-3x+9-\frac{22}{x+3}$
113. w^2+2w+4
114. u^2+4u+8
115. $t-4$
116. $h-1$
117. $v^2+3v+7+\frac{15}{v-2}$
118. $3n^2-2n+3$

(7-3, 7-4)

23. -7
26. 1

Solve each equation.

18. $\frac{a}{3} - \frac{a}{9} = 2$ 9
19. $\frac{2x}{3} - \frac{x}{2} = 12$ 72
20. $\frac{6}{7}b - \frac{1}{2}b = 5$ 14
21. $\frac{2}{3}x - \frac{5}{9}x = -1$ -9
22. $\frac{y+2}{2} = \frac{2y}{3}$ 6
23. $\frac{x+1}{5} - \frac{3}{2} = \frac{3x-6}{10}$
24. $\frac{12}{z} = \frac{4+4z}{z}$ 2
25. $\frac{1}{x} + \frac{1}{3} = \frac{1}{2}$ 6
26. $\frac{4}{5y} + \frac{y-2}{y} = -\frac{1}{5}$
27. $\frac{c}{c+3} = \frac{2}{5}$ 2
28. $\frac{3m+5}{6} - \frac{10}{m} = \frac{m}{2}$ 12
29. $\frac{h}{2h+4} - \frac{1}{h+2} = 1$ -6

Evaluate. (7-5)

30. 80% of 700 560
31. 45% of 450 202.5
32. 3.25% of 48 1.56
33. 18 is 60% of what number? 30
34. 63 is 150% of what number? 42
35. What percent of 180 is 45? 25%
36. What percent of 36 is 54? 150%

Solve. (7-5, 7-6, 7-7, 7-8)

37. $1.2x = 48$ 40
38. $0.6z = 180$ 300
39. $0.08y = 64$ 800
40. $0.4a - 0.7 = 2.9$ 9
41. $0.3b + 0.03b = 99$ 300
42. $0.05c = 6.6 - 0.06c$ 60
43. How many kilograms of zinc are contained in 30 kg of an alloy containing 28% zinc? 8.4 kg
44. Ed Jefferson bought a new suit that cost \$140. If he also paid \$6.30 in sales tax, find the sales tax rate. 4.5%
45. A camera that originally cost \$150 is on sale at 15% off the original price. Find the sale price. \$127.50
46. How many kilograms of water must be added to 12 kg of a 30% salt solution to produce a 20% solution? 6 kg
47. How many kilograms of water must be evaporated from 40 kg of a 10% salt solution to produce a 25% solution? 24 kg
48. A coin-sorting machine can sort a certain number of coins in 15 minutes. A second machine can sort the same number of coins in 30 minutes. How long would it take both machines working together to do the job? 10 min
49. An air conditioner takes 20 minutes to cool a room. If a second air conditioner is used together with the first, it takes only 12 minutes to cool the room. How long would it take the second air conditioner alone to cool the room? 30 min

Express each of the following numbers in scientific notation. (7-9)

50. 64,800,000 6.48×10^7
51. 147,000,000 1.47×10^8
52. 643 billion 6.43×10^{11}
53. 0.0000098 9.8×10^{-6}
54. 0.000000006 6×10^{-9}
55. 0.00000000001 1×10^{-11}

Additional Answers p. 621

13.
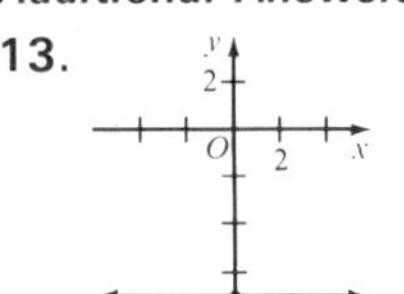

14.
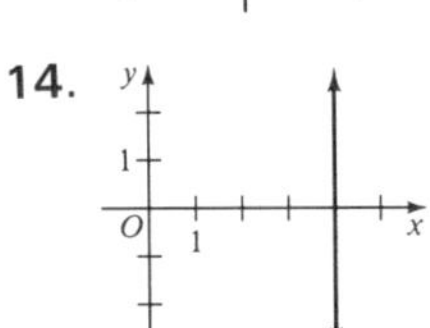

Evaluate. (7-10)

56. 6^{-2} $\frac{1}{36}$ **57.** 5^{-3} $\frac{1}{125}$ **58.** 7^{-2} $\frac{1}{49}$ **59.** 9^{-3} $\frac{1}{729}$

60. $2^{-4} \cdot 2^{-3}$ $\frac{1}{128}$ **61.** $(6^{-2})^{-1}$ 36 **62.** $\frac{3^{-4}}{3^{-3}}$ $\frac{1}{3}$ **63.** $\frac{8^{-2}}{8^{-4}}$ 64

Simplify. Give answers in terms of positive exponents. (7-10)

64. $5z^{-2}$ $\frac{5}{z^2}$ **65.** $(9y)^{-3}$ $\frac{1}{729y^3}$ **66.** x^2y^{-5} $\frac{x^2}{y^5}$ **67.** $a^{-2}b^{-3}$ $\frac{1}{a^2b^3}$

68. $uv^{-2}w^{-1}$ $\frac{u}{v^2w}$ **69.** $d^{-4}e^2f^{-2}$ $\frac{e^2}{d^4f^2}$ **70.** $(a^{-2}b^3)^2$ $\frac{b^6}{a^4}$ **71.** $(x^{-4}y^{-5}z^3)^{-3}$ $\frac{x^{12}y^{15}}{z^9}$

Chapter 8

State whether each ordered pair of numbers is a solution of the given equation. (8-1)

1. $x - 2y = 6$
$(3, 0), (0, -3)$ no; yes

2. $x + 3y = 9$
$(3, 2), (-3, 4)$ yes; yes

3. $2x - y = 5$
$(4, -1), (1, -7)$ no; no

4. $2x + 3y = 7$
$(1, 2), (5, -1)$ no; yes

5. $4x + 2y = 6$
$\left(\frac{3}{2}, 0\right), (1, 1)$ yes; yes

6. $-3x + 4y = -7$
$(1, -1), \left(2, \frac{1}{4}\right)$ yes; no

Solve each equation for y in terms of x. (8-1)

7. $x + 2y = 8$ $y = \frac{8 - x}{2}$ **8.** $12x - 4y = 1$ $y = \frac{12x - 1}{4}$ **9.** $3x + 4y = 6$ $y = \frac{6 - 3x}{4}$

10. $2x - 3y = 7$ $y = \frac{2x - 7}{3}$ **11.** $4x + 3y = 0$ $y = -\frac{4x}{3}$ **12.** $\frac{5}{x + y} = 8$ $y = \frac{5 - 8x}{8}$

Graph each equation. (8-2)

13. $y = -7$ **14.** $x = 4$ **15.** $y = 3x + 2$

16. $y = 2x - 5$ **17.** $5x = 3y$ **18.** $8x - 2y = 0$

19. $3x + y = -6$ **20.** $4x + 3y = 12$ **21.** $2x + 3y = 7$

Solve each system by the graphic method. (8-3)

22. $x + y = 6$
$x - y = 2$

23. $x + y = 9$
$y = 2x$

24. $x + y = 0$
$x + 2y = 2$

25. $y = 3 - x$
$x + y = 5$

26. $y = \frac{2}{3}x + 1$
$y = -\frac{2}{3}x + 5$

27. $y = \frac{1}{2}x + 1$
$x + 2 = 2y$

Solve by the substitution method. (8-4)

28. $3x + y = 5$
$y = 2x$ (1, 2)

29. $m - 3n = -4$
$2m + 6n = 5$ $\left(-\frac{3}{4}, \frac{13}{12}\right)$

30. $2a + b = 4$
$b = 1 - a$ (3, −2)

31. $4c - 3d = 9$
$2c - d = 5$ (3, 1)

32. $x + 3y = 2$
$2x + 3y = 7$ (5, −1)

33. $3t - 2s = 5$
$t + 2s = 15$ (5, 5)

15. 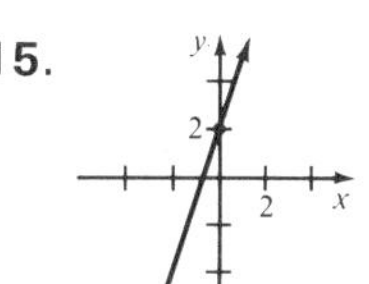

16. 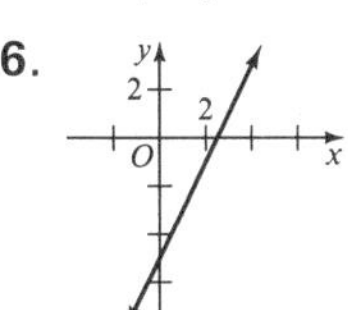

17. 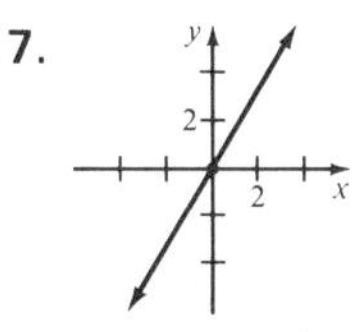

18. 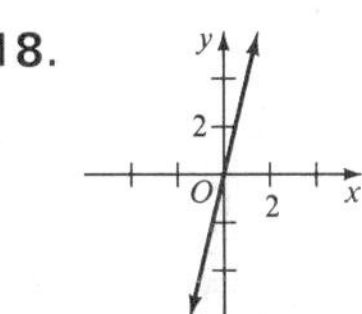

19. 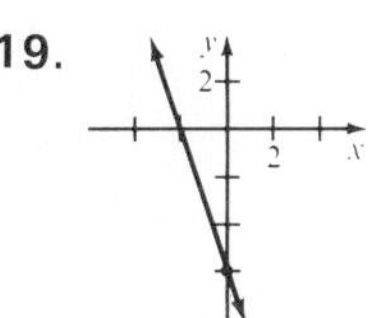

20. 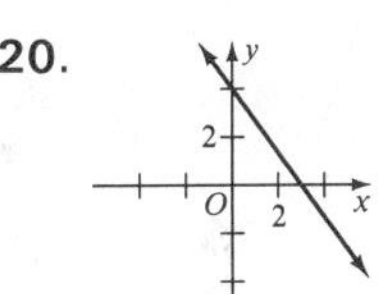

21. 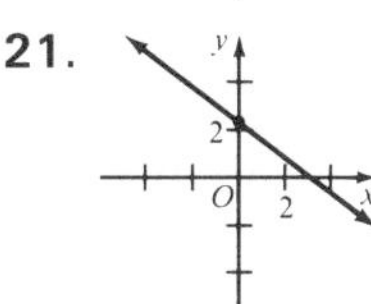

22. (4, 2)
23. (3, 6)
24. (−2, 2)
25. no solution
26. (3, 3)
27. infinite number of sols.

Solve by using a system of two equations in two variables. (8-5)

34. On a jury there are 3 fewer men than twice the number of women. If there were 2 more women on the jury, the numbers of men and women would be equal. How many men are on the jury? 7 men

35. Janet and Lynn live 8 miles apart in opposite directions from their office. If Lynn lives 1 mile less than twice as far from the office as Janet does, how far does each live from the office? Janet, 3 mi; Lynn, 5 mi

Solve by the addition-or-subtraction method. (8-6)

36. $r - s = -3$; $r + s = 9$ $(3, 6)$

37. $c + 2n = -20$; $c - 2n = 30$ $\left(5, -\frac{25}{2}\right)$

38. $x - 3y = 2$; $x + 4y = 16$ $(8, 2)$

39. $6r + 5s = -8$; $2r - 5s = -16$ $(-3, 2)$

40. $12m + 3n = 51$; $7m - 3n = 44$ $(5, -3)$

41. $8g + 7h = 26$; $8g - 10h = 60$ $(5, -2)$

Solve by using multiplication with the addition-or-subtraction method. (8-7)

42. $v + w = 3$; $3v - 5w = 17$ $(4, -1)$

43. $4a - 3b = -1$; $a - b = -1$ $(2, 3)$

44. $3x - y = 3$; $x + 3y = 11$ $(2, 3)$

45. $3x + 4y = -25$; $2x - 3y = 6$ $(-3, -4)$

46. $2w - 3z = -1$; $3w + 4z = 24$ $(4, 3)$

47. $5a - 2b = 0$; $2a - 3b = -11$ $(2, 5)$

Solve by using a system of two equations in two variables. (8-8, 8-9)

48. A plane can fly 1120 km in 80 min with the wind. Flying against the same wind, the plane travels the same distance in 84 min. Find the speed of the wind and the speed of the plane in still air. wind, 20 km/h; plane, 820 km/h

49. The sum of the digits of a two-digit number is 7. With the digits reversed the number is 5 times the tens digit of the original number. Find the original number. 52

50. In five years Jenny will be two thirds as old as her aunt. Three years ago she was half as old as her aunt is now. How old are Jenny and her aunt now? Jenny is 17 y old; her aunt is 28 y old.

51. The numerator of a fraction is 1 less than the denominator. If 1 is subtracted from the numerator, and the denominator is unchanged, the resulting fraction has a value of $\frac{3}{4}$. Find the original fraction. $\frac{7}{8}$

Chapter 9

In each exercise, the coordinates of two points of a line are given. Find the slope of the line. (9-1)

1. (1, 2), (4, 6) $\frac{4}{3}$

2. (−7, 1), (−1, 2) $\frac{1}{6}$

3. (−1, 6), (0, 0) −6

4. (−4, −3), (2, −3) 0

5. (2, 1), (8, −2) $-\frac{1}{2}$

6. (−7, −7), (6, −4) $\frac{3}{13}$

Additional Answers p. 623

17.

18.

19.

20.

21.

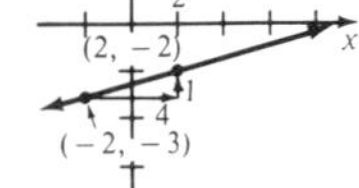

22.

29. $y = -x - 3$

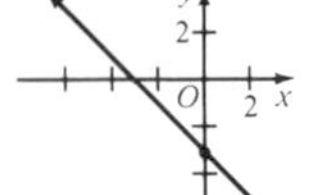

Find the slope of each line whose equation is given. (9-1)

7. $y = 7x - 3$ 7
8. $y = \frac{1}{4}x + 2$ $\frac{1}{4}$
9. $3x - 2y = 8$ $\frac{3}{2}$
10. $y - 9 = 0$ 0
11. $5x + 4y = 16$ $-\frac{5}{4}$
12. $y = 1 - x$ -1

Determine whether the points in each exercise are collinear. If they are, find the slope of the line. (9-1)

13. (2, 1), (0, −3), (4, 5), (−2, −7) yes; 2
14. (0, 4), (9, −2), (−3, 6), (6, 0) yes; $-\frac{2}{3}$
15. (−3, −2), (2, −4), (6, −5), (−5, 2) no
16. (−5, 3), (0, 3), (5, 3), (−2, 3) yes; 0

Through the given point, draw a line with the given slope. (9-1)

17. $P(3, 1)$; slope 2
18. $P(-4, 5)$; slope 0
19. $P(0, -6)$; slope 5
20. $P(7, 0)$; slope −3
21. $P(-2, -3)$; slope $\frac{1}{4}$
22. $P(3, 4)$; slope $-\frac{2}{3}$

Write an equation in standard form of the line that has the given slope and y-intercept. (9-2)

23. $m = 3, b = \frac{1}{2}$ $6x - 2y = -1$
24. $m = -4, b = \frac{3}{5}$ $20x + 5y = 3$
25. $m = \frac{1}{3}, b = 6$ $x - 3y = -18$
26. $m = 0, b = -3.5$ $y = -3.5$
27. $m = -\frac{3}{7}, b = \frac{3}{8}$ $24x + 56y = 21$
28. $m = -1.5, b = 2.7$ $15x + 10y = 27$

Change each equation to the slope-intercept form. Then draw the graph, using only the slope and y-intercept. (9-2)

29. $x + y = -3$
30. $7x = 2y$
31. $4x - y = 3$
32. $2x + 2y = 6$
33. $-x + 5y = 10$
34. $3x - 4y - 5 = 0$

Use the slope-intercept form of the equations to determine whether or not each system has a solution. (9-2)

35. $x - y = 2$
$y - x = -2$ yes (infinite number)
36. $3x - 2y = 6$
$-2x - 3y = -12$ yes (one point)
37. $x - 5y = -1$
$5x + y = 3$ yes (one point)

Write an equation in standard form of the line that has the given slope and passes through the given point. (9-3)

38. $m = 3$; $(-3, -5)$ $3x - y = -4$
39. $m = -2$; $(3, -4)$ $2x + y = 2$
40. $m = \frac{3}{4}$; $(0, -2)$ $3x - 4y = 8$
41. $m = 0$; $\left(\frac{1}{2}, 3\right)$ $y = 3$
42. $m = -\frac{1}{5}$; $(-5, 0)$ $x + 5y = -5$
43. $m = \frac{7}{3}$; $(3, 7)$ $7x - 3y = 0$

Write an equation in standard form of the line passing through the points. (9-3)

44. (2, 1), (6, 4)
45. (2, −1), (1, −7)
46. (0, 0), (6, −1)
47. (−3, 2), (−3, −4)
48. (−2, 8), (1, 2)
49. (6, −4), (−7, −7)

30. $y = \frac{7}{2}x$

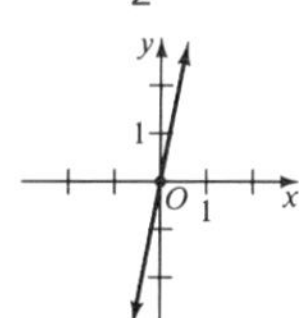

31. $y = 4x - 3$

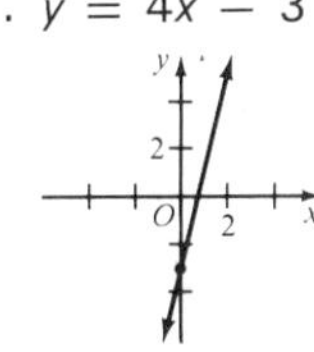

32. $y = -x + 3$

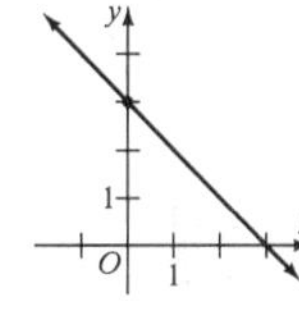

33. $y = \frac{1}{5}x + 2$

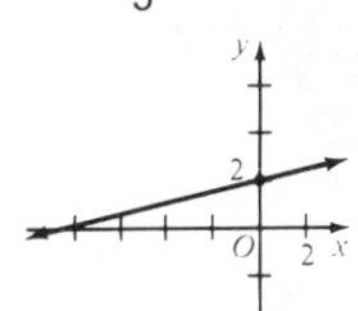

34. $y = \frac{3}{4}x - \frac{5}{4}$

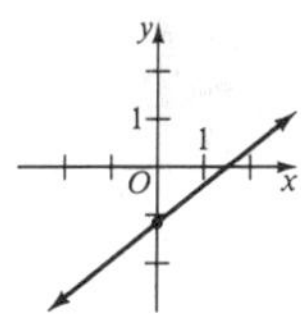

44. $3x - 4y = 2$
45. $6x - y = 13$
46. $x + 6y = 0$
47. $x = -3$
48. $2x + y = 4$
49. $3x - 13y = 70$

Given $f: x \to 5 - 3x$, find the following values of f. (9-4)

50. $f(4)$ -7 **51.** $f\left(-\frac{1}{3}\right)$ 6 **52.** $f(0)$ 5 **53.** $f(-5)$ 20

Given $G(n) = n^3 + 2n$, find the following values of G. (9-4)

54. $G(0)$ 0 **55.** $G(-2)$ -12 **56.** $G\left(\frac{1}{2}\right)$ $\frac{9}{8}$ **57.** $G(3)$ 33

Find all the values of each function. (9-4)

58. $h(x) = 5 - 2x - x^2$, $D = \{1, 2, 3\}$
$h(1) = 2$, $h(2) = -3$, $h(3) = -10$

59. $M(u) = \frac{6}{4u + 2}$, $D = \{-1, 0, 1\}$
$M(-1) = -3$, $M(0) = 3$, $M(1) = 1$

Find the range of each function. (9-4)

60. $r: z \to -3 - 4z$, $D = \{-2, -1, 0\}$ $\{5, 1, -3\}$

61. $N: s \to \frac{10}{s - 3}$, $D = \{2, 4, 8\}$ $\{-10, 10, 2\}$

62. $G: w \to (w - 1)(w + 1)$, $D = \{-2, 0, 2\}$ $\{-1, 3\}$

63. $k: v \to v^2 - 4v + 2$, $D = \{3, 4, 5\}$ $\{-1, 2, 7\}$

State the domain and range of the function shown by each table. (9-5)

64.

Longest Suspension Bridges	
Mackinac Straits	3800 ft
Humber Estuary	4626 ft
Golden Gate	4200 ft
Ataturk	3524 ft
Verrazano Narrows	4260 ft

65.

Airports in U.S.	
1930	1782
1940	2331
1950	6403
1960	6881
1970	11,261

66. Make a bar graph for the function shown in Exercise 64.
67. Make a broken-line graph for the function shown in Exercise 65.

Find the coordinates of the vertex and the equation of the axis of symmetry of the graph of each equation. Use the vertex and at least six other points to graph the equation. (9-6)

68. $y = 4x^2$ $(0, 0)$, $x = 0$ **69.** $y = -2x^2$ $(0, 0)$, $x = 0$ **70.** $y = \frac{1}{5}x^2$ $(0, 0)$, $x = 0$

71. $y = -x^2 + 3x$
$\left(\frac{3}{2}, \frac{9}{4}\right)$, $x = \frac{3}{2}$

72. $y = x^2 - 2x + 5$
$(1, 4)$, $x = 1$

73. $y = 4 - \frac{1}{2}x^2$
$(0, 4)$, $x = 0$

Find the least value of each function. (9-6)

74. $f: x \to x^2 + 7x$ $-\frac{49}{4}$ **75.** $g: x \to x^2 - 3x - 4$ $-\frac{25}{4}$ **76.** $h: x \to \frac{1}{2}x^2$ 0

Find the greatest value of each function. (9-6)

77. $f(x) = x - 3x^2$ $\frac{1}{12}$ **78.** $g(x) = 2 - \frac{1}{3}x^2$ 2 **79.** $h(x) = -x^2 - x - 1$ $-\frac{3}{4}$

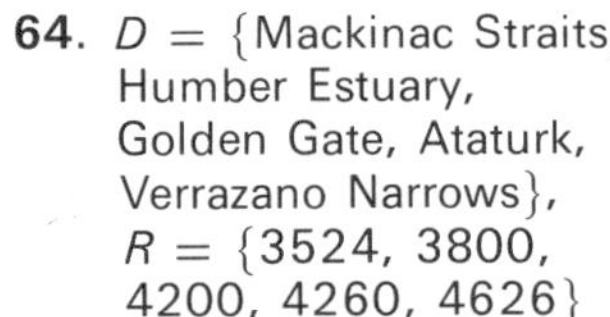
64. $D = \{$Mackinac Straits, Humber Estuary, Golden Gate, Ataturk, Verrazano Narrows$\}$, $R = \{3524, 3800, 4200, 4260, 4626\}$

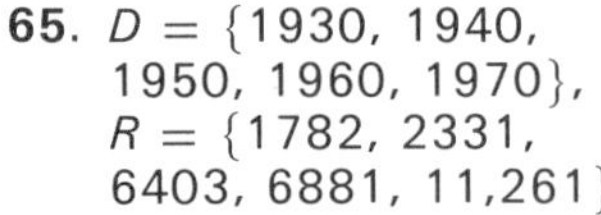
65. $D = \{1930, 1940, 1950, 1960, 1970\}$, $R = \{1782, 2331, 6403, 6881, 11{,}261\}$

66.
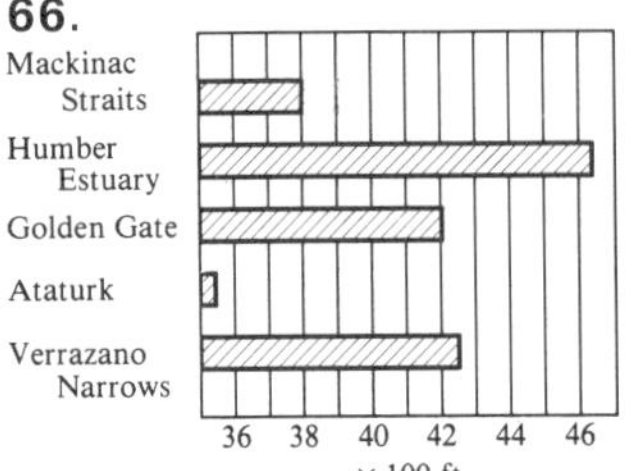

67.
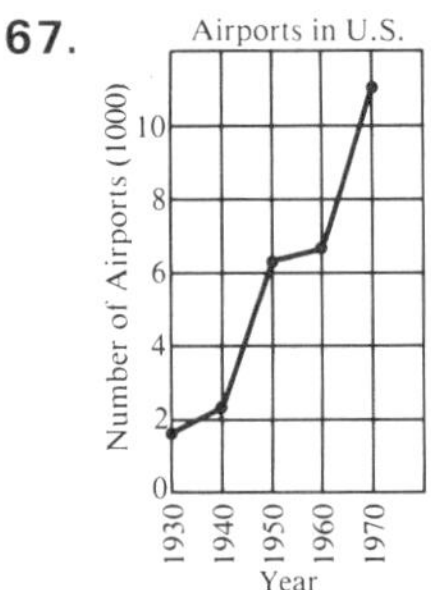

68.
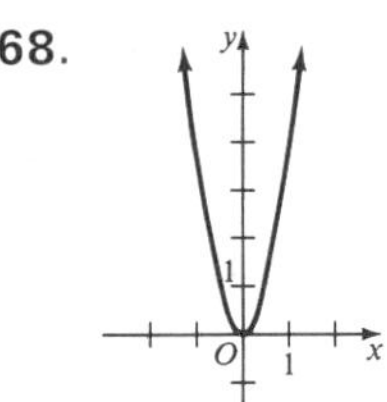

69.
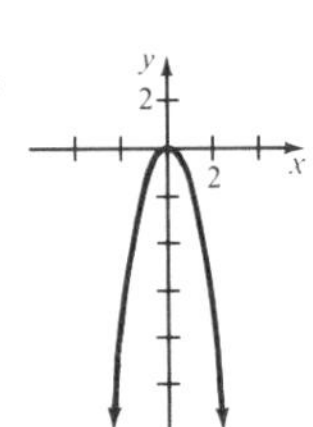

70.
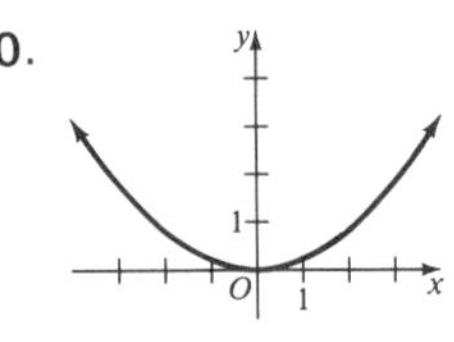

In Exercises 80 and 81, find the constant of variation. (9-7)

80. y varies directly as x, and $y = 12$ when $x = 60$. $\frac{1}{5}$

81. q is directly proportional to p, and $q = 144$ when $p = 24$. 6

82. If n varies directly as m, and $n = 300$ when $m = 5$, find n when $m = 15$. 900

83. If b is directly proportional to a, and $b = 28.7$ when $a = 4.1$, find b when $a = 13$. 91

In each exercise find the missing value if (x_1, y_1) and (x_2, y_2) are ordered pairs of the same direct variation. (9-7)

84. $x_1 = 35$, $y_1 = 7$
$x_2 = 105$, $y_2 = \underline{\ ?\ }$ 21

85. $x_1 = 5.2$, $y_1 = 5$
$x_2 = \underline{\ ?\ }$, $y_2 = 1$ 1.04

86. $x_1 = \frac{3}{8}$, $y_1 = \underline{\ ?\ }$ $\frac{3}{32}$
$x_2 = \frac{2}{5}$, $y_2 = \frac{1}{10}$

For the variation described, state (a) a formula and (b) a proportion. Use k as the constant of variation. (9-7, 9-8)

87. The circumference, C, of a circle is directly proportional to the diameter, d, of the circle. $C = kd$; $\frac{C_1}{d_1} = \frac{C_2}{d_2}$

88. The elongation, e, of a coil spring varies directly as the mass, m, suspended from it. $e = km$; $\frac{e_1}{m_1} = \frac{e_2}{m_2}$

89. The length, l, of the shadow of a vertical object at a given time and location varies directly with the height, h, of the object. $l = kh$; $\frac{l_1}{h_1} = \frac{l_2}{h_2}$

90. The monthly rent, r, for each roommate in an apartment is inversely proportional to the number, n, of roommates. $nr = k$; $\frac{n_1}{r_2} = \frac{n_2}{r_1}$

91. The height, h, of a triangle of constant area varies inversely as the base length, b. $hb = k$; $\frac{b_1}{h_2} = \frac{b_2}{h_1}$

92. The number of tickets remaining to be sold, n, varies inversely as the number of tickets sold, s. $ns = k$; $\frac{s_1}{n_2} = \frac{s_2}{n_1}$

Graph each equation if the domain and the range are both limited to the set of positive numbers. (9-8)

93. $xy = 4$ **94.** $3xy = 1$ **95.** $x = \frac{10}{y}$ **96.** $\frac{x}{2} = \frac{4}{y}$

Find the missing value if (x_1, y_1) and (x_2, y_2) are ordered pairs of the same inverse variation. (9-8)

97. $x_1 = 5$, $y_1 = 8$
$x_2 = 4$, $y_2 = \underline{\ ?\ }$ 10

98. $x_1 = 0.6$, $y_1 = 1.2$
$x_2 = \underline{\ ?\ }$, $y_2 = 0.4$ 1.8

99. $x_1 = \frac{1}{4}$, $y_1 = \underline{\ ?\ }$ $\frac{1}{3}$
$x_2 = \frac{1}{6}$, $y_2 = \frac{1}{2}$

71.
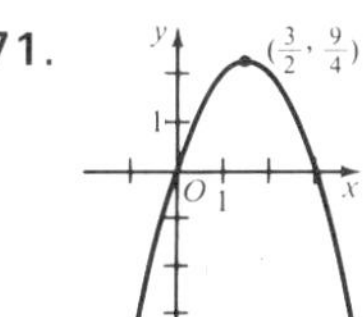

72.
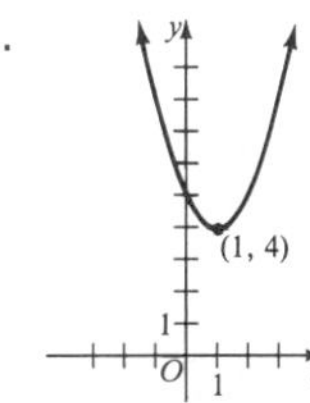

73.
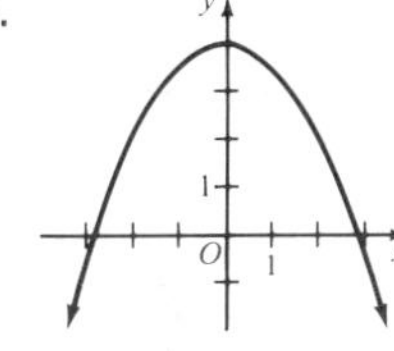

93.
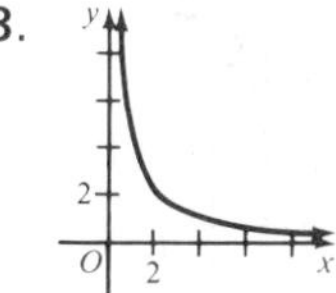

94.
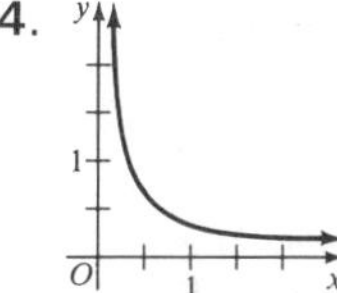

95.
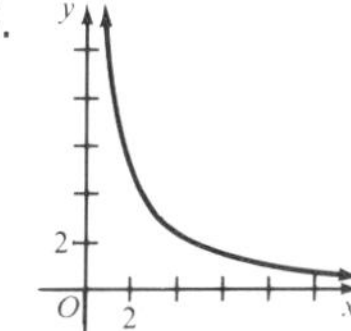

96.
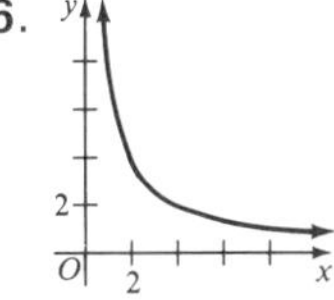

625

Additional Answers

14. {the real numbers greater than 4}

−1 0 1 2 3 4 5 6 7 8 9

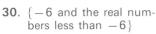

16. {−4, −3, −2, −1, 0, 1, 2}

−6 −5 −4 −3 −2 −1 0 1 2 3 4

18. {the real numbers greater than 20}

0 5 10 15 20 25 30 35 40 45 50

20. {the real numbers less than −5}

−9 −8 −7 −6 −5 −4 −3 −2 −1 0 1

22. {the real numbers greater than 9}

5 6 7 8 9 10 11 12 13 14 15

24. {the real numbers greater than 3}

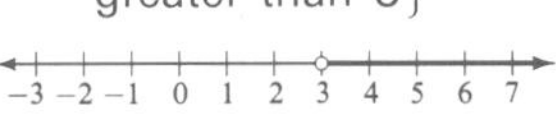

26. {the real numbers less than 8}

0 1 2 3 4 5 6 7 8 9 10

28. {−4 and the real numbers greater than −4}

−8 −7 −6 −5 −4 −3 −2 −1 0 1 2

30. {−6 and the real numbers less than −6}

−10 −9 −8 −7 −6 −5 −4 −3 −2 −1 0

32. $\left\{\text{the real numbers greater than } \frac{8}{5}\right\}$

−2 −1 0 1 2 3

38. {the real numbers between −8 and 2}

−14 −12 −10 −8 −6 −4 −2 0 2 4 6

Translate each statement into a formula. Use k as the constant of variation where needed. (9-9, 9-10)

100. The height, h, of a right circular cylinder of a given volume is inversely proportional to the square of the radius, r. $hr^2 = k$

101. Wind pressure, p, on a flat surface varies directly as the square of the wind velocity, v. $\frac{p}{v^2} = k$

102. The lateral area, L, of a cylinder varies jointly as the radius, r, of the base, and the height, h. $L = krh$

103. The volume, V, of a cone varies jointly as the height, h, and the square of the radius, r, of the base. $V = kr^2h$

104. The rate of speed, r, of a moving body varies inversely as the time traveled, t, and directly as the distance traveled, d. $\frac{rt}{d} = k$

105. Centrifugal force, F, varies inversely as the radius, r, of the circular path, and directly as the square of the velocity, v, of a moving body. $\frac{Fr}{v^2} = k$

Chapter 10

Classify each statement as true or false. (10-1)

1. $-8 > 7 > 6$ false
2. $-5 < -4 < 5$ true
3. $-1.5 < -1 < -0.05$ true
4. $-\frac{1}{2} < 0 < 1$ true
5. $7 > 0 > 2$ false
6. $-10 < -15 < -20$ false
7. $|-0.6| < 0.4$ false
8. $\left|-\frac{1}{3}\right| \geq 0$ true
9. $|5 - 3| \leq |3 - 5|$ true

Solve each inequality if $x \in \{-4, -3, -2, -1, 0, 1, 2, 3, 4\}$. (10-1)

10. $5x \leq 15$ {−4, −3, −2, −1, 0, 1, 2, 3}
11. $-7x > 14$ {−4, −3}
12. $-4 - x \geq 0$ {−4}
13. $x^2 < 10$ {−3, −2, −1, 0, 1, 2, 3}

Solve each inequality over the given domain and draw its graph. (10-1)

14. $32 < 8x$; {the positive numbers}
15. $-6 \leq k < 2$; {the negative integers}
16. $3 > t \geq -4$; {the integers}
17. $-2 < n < 2$; {the real numbers}

Solve each inequality and draw its graph. (10-2)

18. $e - 8 > 12$
19. $13 > n + 9$
20. $4q < -20$
21. $-\frac{x}{7} < 14$
22. $\frac{m}{3} - 5 > -2$
23. $-3 > 7 + \frac{4}{5}k$
24. $5v + 3 > 18$
25. $48 - 6y < 0$
26. $7t < 6t + 8$
27. $8f - 5 > 4f + 11$
28. $-6(v - 3) \leq 42$
29. $5(m + 2) > 4(m - 1)$
30. $\frac{4}{9}h + 3 \leq \frac{1}{3}$
31. $2(w - 1) < \frac{3}{2}w$
32. $2z - \frac{1}{4}(3z + 8) > 0$

In Exercises 33–37: (10-3)

a. Choose a variable to represent the number shown in color.

b. Use the variable to write an inequality based on the given information. (Do not solve.)

33. Marquita sold 9 fewer magazine subscriptions than twice the number Juanita sold. Marquita sold at most 43 subscriptions. $j;\ 2j - 9 \leq 43$

34. Rick, who is not yet 16 years old, is 3 years older than Sam. (Sam's age) $s;\ s + 3 < 16$

35. Andrea lives 10 miles less than half as far as Roger lives from the beach. Andrea lives at least 25 miles from the beach. $r;\ \frac{1}{2}r - 10 \geq 25$

36. The number of San Marcos High School students who ride the bus is one third the number who walk or ride their bikes. The total number of students is at least 1800. $w;\ \frac{1}{3}w + w \geq 1800$

37. Six years ago, Buford was less than half as old as he is now. (His present age) $p;\ p - 6 < \frac{1}{2}p$

Solve each open sentence and graph each solution set that is not empty. (10-4)

38. $-3 < n + 5 < 7$

39. $-6 < -6 + w \leq 2$

40. $-4 \leq 3a - 1 < 5$

41. $-1 \leq 8m + 7 \leq 23$

42. $u - 2 < -5$ or $u - 2 \geq 4$

43. $k + 6 \leq -3$ or $k + 6 > 2$

44. $4t + 3 < -1$ or $4t + 3 > 7$

45. $2x - 2 \leq -8$ or $8 < 2x - 2$

46. $-5e < 15$ and $6 + 3e < 0$

47. $h - 4 \geq 2$ or $4 - h \geq 2$

Solve each open sentence and draw its graph. (10-5, 10-6)

48. $|v - 6| = 3$

49. $|8 - k| = 5$

50. $|m| > 2\frac{1}{2}$

51. $|x| \leq 1.5$

52. $|y + 5| > 2$

53. $|3 + z| \leq 4$

54. $|7 - f| < 6$

55. $|-4 - g| > 7$

56. $|-a - 2| \geq 1$

57. $4|s| + 2 \leq 8$

58. $5 - 3|z| < 14$

59. $9 - |3 - b| > 2$

60. $|8k| = 16$

61. $\left|\frac{a}{2}\right| \geq 3$

62. $\left|\frac{c}{4}\right| \leq 1$

63. $|5x - 3| = 17$

64. $|7 + 6n| < 19$

65. $|2w - 3| > 5$

66. $\left|\frac{u}{3} + 4\right| = 1$

67. $\left|\frac{v}{2} - 1\right| \leq 3$

68. $\left|\frac{a}{4} + 2\right| \geq 1$

69. $|5 - (3 - 2x)| < 6$

70. $7 + 3|2m + 1| = 13$

71. $10 - 6|2 - k| \geq 22$

Graph each inequality. (10-7)

72. $x < 3$

73. $x \geq -4$

74. $y > 0$

75. $y \leq -2$

76. $y > x - 1$

77. $y \leq -x + 2$

78. $y < 3 + 4x$

79. $y \geq -5x - 1$

40. {−1 and the real numbers between −1 and 2}

42. {the real numbers less than −3 or greater than or equal to 6}

44. {the real numbers less than −1 or greater than 1}

46. {the real numbers between −3 and −2}

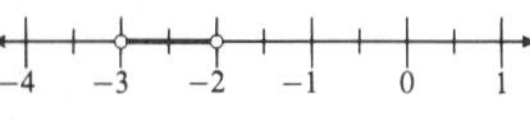

48. {3, 9}

50. {the real numbers greater than $2\frac{1}{2}$ or less than $-2\frac{1}{2}$}

52. {the real numbers less than −7 or greater than −3}

54. {the real numbers between 1 and 13}

56. {−3, −1, and the real numbers greater than −1 or less than −3}

58. {all the real numbers}

(continued)

Additional Answers
(continued)

60. $\{-2, 2\}$

62. $\{-4, 4$, and the real numbers between -4 and $4\}$

64. {the real numbers between $-\frac{13}{3}$ and 2}

66. $\{-15, -9\}$

68. $\{-12, -4$, and the real numbers less than -12 or greater than $-4\}$

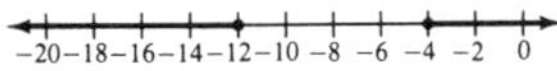

70. $\left\{-\frac{3}{2}, \frac{1}{2}\right\}$

(continued on p. 634)

Transform each inequality into an equivalent inequality with y as one side. Then graph the inequality. (10-7)

80. $x - y \geq 5$ **81.** $4x + y \leq -2$ **82.** $x - 3y > 6$
83. $6x - y < 2$ **84.** $y - 5x \geq 3$ **85.** $4y - 5x < 0$
86. $7x + 6y \geq x - 3$ **87.** $3y - 2 > 6x - 4$ **88.** $8y - 7 \leq 3(x + 2y)$

Graph each pair of inequalities and indicate the solution set of the system with crosshatching or shading. (10-8)

89. $y \leq 0$, $x > 0$ **90.** $y \geq -3$, $x \leq 2$ **91.** $y > 4x$, $x < 3$ **92.** $x \geq -1$, $y < 2x - 5$

93. $y < x + 3$, $y > 3 - x$ **94.** $y \leq 5x - 4$, $y \geq 2x + 1$ **95.** $x + y > 2$, $x - y < 6$ **96.** $3x - 4y \leq 0$, $x - 2y \geq -6$

Chapter 11

Replace the ___?___ with <, =, or > to make a true statement. (11-1)

1. $\frac{17}{23}$ ___?___ $\frac{15}{19}$ <
2. $-\frac{87}{29}$ ___?___ $-\frac{39}{13}$ =
3. $\frac{197}{6}$ ___?___ $33\frac{2}{7}$ <

Arrange each group of numbers from least to greatest. (11-1)

4. $-\frac{39}{8}, -4.7, -\frac{41}{9}$ $-\frac{39}{8}, -4.7, -\frac{41}{9}$
5. $\frac{5}{7}, \frac{2}{3}, \frac{11}{15}, \frac{12}{17}$ $\frac{2}{3}, \frac{12}{17}, \frac{5}{7}, \frac{11}{15}$
6. $-\frac{4}{9}, -\frac{5}{8}, -\frac{6}{11}, -\frac{5}{7}$ $-\frac{5}{7}, -\frac{5}{8}, -\frac{6}{11}, -\frac{4}{9}$

Find the number halfway between the given numbers. (11-1)

7. $\frac{27}{41}, \frac{31}{37}$ $\frac{1135}{1517}$
8. $-\frac{17}{140}, -\frac{11}{32}$ $-\frac{521}{2240}$
9. $-5\frac{2}{7}, 9\frac{1}{4}$ $\frac{111}{56}$

If $x \in \{0, 1, 2, 3\}$ state whether each fraction increases or decreases in value as x takes on the values in increasing order. (11-1)

10. $\frac{5}{x + 1}$ decreases
11. $\frac{x - 3}{7}$ increases
12. $\frac{8}{x + 2}$ decreases
13. $\frac{6 - x}{4}$ decreases
14. $\frac{10}{5 + 2x}$ decreases

Express each rational number as a terminating or repeating decimal. (11-2)

15. $\frac{4}{9}$ $0.\overline{4}$
16. $-\frac{29}{24}$ $-1.208\overline{3}$
17. $3\frac{11}{20}$ 3.55
18. $-7\frac{5}{11}$ $-7.\overline{45}$
19. $\frac{41}{55}$ $0.7\overline{45}$

Express each rational number as a fraction in simplest form. (11-2)

20. 0.77 $\frac{77}{100}$
21. $0.\overline{6}$ $\frac{2}{3}$
22. $-0.31\overline{8}$ $-\frac{287}{900}$
23. $2.\overline{37}$ $\frac{235}{99}$
24. $0.\overline{4135}$ $\frac{4135}{9999}$

Find the difference of the given numbers. Then find the number halfway between them. (11-2)

25. $\frac{5}{8}$ and 0.63
$0.00\overline{5}$; 0.6275

26. 0.66 and $0.\overline{6}$
$0.00\overline{6}$; $0.66\overline{3}$

27. $\frac{7}{11}$ and $0.6\overline{28}$
$0.0\overline{08}$; $0.6\overline{32}$

Express both numbers as fractions and find their product. (11-2)

28. $\frac{2}{5}$ and 0.85
$\frac{2}{5}, \frac{85}{100}; \frac{17}{50}$

29. $0.\overline{4}$ and $\frac{2}{3}$
$\frac{4}{9}, \frac{2}{3}; \frac{8}{27}$

30. -2.2 and $0.\overline{3}$
$-\frac{22}{10}, \frac{1}{3}; -\frac{11}{15}$

Find the indicated square roots. (11-3)

31. $\sqrt{441}$ 21
32. $\sqrt{784}$ 28
33. $\sqrt{2704}$ 52
34. $\sqrt{5184}$ 72
35. $\sqrt{10816}$ 104
36. $\sqrt{0.04}$ 0.2
37. $\sqrt{0.64}$ 0.8
38. $\sqrt{1.96}$ 1.4
39. $\sqrt{0.0144}$ 0.12
40. $\sqrt{0.0036}$
41. $\sqrt{\frac{81}{225}}$ $\frac{3}{5}$
42. $\sqrt{\frac{1}{289}}$ $\frac{1}{17}$
43. $\sqrt{\frac{324}{1936}}$ $\frac{9}{22}$
44. $\sqrt{\frac{32}{50}}$ $\frac{4}{5}$
45. $\sqrt{\frac{320}{405}}$ $\frac{8}{9}$

Simplify. (11-4)

46. $\sqrt{63}$ $3\sqrt{7}$
47. $\sqrt{176}$ $4\sqrt{11}$
48. $2\sqrt{52}$ $4\sqrt{13}$
49. $4\sqrt{99}$ $12\sqrt{11}$
50. $5\sqrt{175}$ $25\sqrt{7}$
51. $10\sqrt{162}$ $90\sqrt{2}$
52. $\sqrt{192}$ $8\sqrt{3}$
53. $\sqrt{672}$ $4\sqrt{42}$
54. $\sqrt{224}$ $4\sqrt{14}$
55. $\sqrt{2646}$ $21\sqrt{6}$

Approximate to the nearest tenth by using the square root table. (11-4)

56. $\sqrt{720}$ 26.8
57. $-\sqrt{800}$ -28.3
58. $\sqrt{440}$ 21.0
59. $\sqrt{8400}$ 91.7
60. $-\sqrt{5400}$ -73.5

Simplify. (11-5)

61. $\sqrt{169m^2}$ $13|m|$
62. $\sqrt{48a^2}$ $4|a|\sqrt{3}$
63. $\sqrt{125x^4}$ $5x^2\sqrt{5}$
64. $\sqrt{54e^3}$ $3e\sqrt{6e}$
65. $-\sqrt{36t^6}$ $-6|t^3|$
66. $\sqrt{98u^2v^2}$
67. $-2\sqrt{72x^3y^2}$
68. $\sqrt{324r^4s^6}$
69. $-\sqrt{4.84w^4}$
70. $\sqrt{5.76c^6}$
71. $\sqrt{\frac{a^4b^6}{12c^2}}$
72. $\sqrt{\frac{48u^5v^2}{4uv^4}}$
73. $\sqrt{\frac{144k^8}{256}}$
74. $\sqrt{\frac{3600}{81m^{36}}}$
75. $\sqrt{\frac{225x^{40}}{16}}$
76. $\sqrt{x^2 + 8x + 16}$ $|x + 4|$
77. $\sqrt{a^2 - 4a + 4}$ $|a - 2|$
78. $\sqrt{81 + 18k + k^2}$ $|9 + k|$

Solve. (11-5)

79. $g^2 = 49$ $\{-7, 7\}$
80. $h^2 - 64 = 0$ $\{-8, 8\}$
81. $25m^2 = 16$ $\left\{-\frac{4}{5}, \frac{4}{5}\right\}$
82. $9x^2 - 4 = 0$ $\left\{-\frac{2}{3}, \frac{2}{3}\right\}$
83. $6y^2 - 54 = 0$ $\{-3, 3\}$
84. $32t^2 - 27 = 0$ $\left\{-\frac{3\sqrt{6}}{8}, \frac{3\sqrt{6}}{8}\right\}$

Find both roots of each equation to the nearest tenth. (11-5)

85. $a^2 = 132$ $\{-11.5, 11.5\}$
86. $b^2 - 208 = 0$ $\{-14.4, 14.4\}$
87. $11c^2 = 473$ $\{-6.6, 6.6\}$

State whether or not the three numbers given could represent the lengths of the sides of a right triangle. (11-6)

88. 21, 28, 35 yes
89. 9, 9, 12 no
90. 45, 60, 75 yes
91. 31, 41, 51 no
92. $6a$, $8a$, $10a$, $a > 0$ yes
93. $5a$, $7a$, $9a$, $a > 0$ no

Additional Answers

40. 0.06
66. $7|uv|\sqrt{2}$
67. $-12|xy|\sqrt{2x}$
68. $18r^2|s^3|$
69. $-2.2w^2$
70. $2.4|c^3|$
71. $\frac{a^2|b^3|\sqrt{3}}{6|c|}$ $(c \neq 0)$
72. $\frac{2u^2\sqrt{3}}{|v|}$ $(u \neq 0, v \neq 0)$
73. $\frac{3k^4}{4}$
74. $\frac{20}{3m^{18}}$ $(m \neq 0)$
75. $\frac{15x^{20}}{4}$

In Exercises 94–101, refer to the right triangle shown at the right. Find the missing length correct to the nearest hundredth. (11-6)

94. $a = 3$, $b = 4$, $c = \underline{\ ?\ }$ 5.00
95. $a = 5$, $b = 8$, $c = \underline{\ ?\ }$ 9.43
96. $a = \underline{\ ?\ }$, $b = 9$, $c = 13$ 9.38
97. $a = \underline{\ ?\ }$, $b = 10$, $c = 15$ 11.18
98. $a = 8$, $b = \underline{\ ?\ }$, $c = 16$ 13.86
99. $a = 20$, $b = \underline{\ ?\ }$, $c = 30$ 22.36
100. $a = 12$, $b = \frac{3}{4}a$, $c = \underline{\ ?\ }$ 15.00
101. $a = \frac{2}{3}b$, $b = 15$, $c = \underline{\ ?\ }$ 18.03

Express in simplest form. (11-7)

102. $\sqrt{3} \cdot 4\sqrt{3}$ 12
103. $2\sqrt{5} \cdot 3\sqrt{5}$ 30
104. $\sqrt{7} \cdot \sqrt{6} \cdot \sqrt{2}$ $2\sqrt{21}$
105. $\sqrt{7} \cdot \sqrt{7} \cdot \sqrt{4}$ 14
106. $5\sqrt{2} \cdot \sqrt{3}$ $5\sqrt{6}$
107. $8\sqrt{162}$ $72\sqrt{2}$
108. $\sqrt{\frac{5}{9}} \cdot \sqrt{\frac{9}{5}}$ 1
109. $\sqrt{\frac{7}{5}} \cdot \sqrt{\frac{45}{14}}$ $\frac{3\sqrt{2}}{2}$
110. $\sqrt{5\frac{5}{6}} \cdot \sqrt{2\frac{4}{7}}$ $\sqrt{15}$
111. $\frac{1}{4}\sqrt{\frac{16}{3}} \cdot \frac{1}{2}\sqrt{\frac{3}{2}}$ $\frac{\sqrt{2}}{4}$
112. $\frac{12\sqrt{20}}{4\sqrt{3}}$ $2\sqrt{15}$
113. $\frac{11\sqrt{6}}{\sqrt{98}}$ $\frac{11\sqrt{3}}{7}$

Simplify. Assume the radicands are nonnegative real numbers. (11-7)

114. $(3\sqrt{y})(-5\sqrt{x^2y})$ $-15xy$
115. $\sqrt{n}(\sqrt{n^3} + 3)$ $n^2 + 3\sqrt{n}$
116. $(7\sqrt{3})(-4\sqrt{6})(5\sqrt{22})$ $-840\sqrt{11}$

Simplify. (11-8)

117. $9\sqrt{3} - 5\sqrt{3}$ $4\sqrt{3}$
118. $7\sqrt{2} + 6\sqrt{2}$ $13\sqrt{2}$
119. $3\sqrt{54} - 2\sqrt{6}$ $7\sqrt{6}$
120. $4\sqrt{28} + 6\sqrt{112}$ $32\sqrt{7}$
121. $-10\sqrt{18} - 5\sqrt{32}$
122. $\sqrt{242} - 3\sqrt{363}$
123. $\sqrt{8} - \sqrt{\frac{5}{6}}$
124. $\sqrt{\frac{2}{3}} - \sqrt{\frac{3}{2}}$
125. $5\sqrt{\frac{16}{7}} + \sqrt{\frac{9}{8}}$
126. $3\sqrt{63} + 2\sqrt{28} - \sqrt{35}$ $13\sqrt{7} - \sqrt{35}$
127. $\sqrt{120} - \sqrt{270} + \sqrt{300}$ $-\sqrt{30} + 10\sqrt{3}$
128. $2\sqrt{\frac{5}{3}} + 4\sqrt{\frac{3}{8}} - \frac{1}{2}\sqrt{68}$ $\frac{2\sqrt{15}}{3} + \sqrt{6} - \sqrt{17}$
129. $3\sqrt{5}(\sqrt{75} - 2\sqrt{12})$ $3\sqrt{15}$

Express in simplest form. (11-9)

130. $(5 - \sqrt{3})(5 + \sqrt{3})$ 22
131. $(\sqrt{7} + 6)(\sqrt{7} - 6)$ -29
132. $(\sqrt{6} - \sqrt{5})(\sqrt{6} + \sqrt{5})$ 1
133. $(4 + \sqrt{2})^2$ $18 + 8\sqrt{2}$
134. $(5 - \sqrt{5})^2$ $30 - 10\sqrt{5}$
135. $(3\sqrt{2} - 4)^2$ $34 - 24\sqrt{2}$
136. $(\sqrt{11} + 3\sqrt{7})^2$ $74 + 6\sqrt{77}$
137. $2\sqrt{6}(5\sqrt{2} - 4\sqrt{3})$ $20\sqrt{3} - 24\sqrt{2}$
138. $(4\sqrt{5} - 6)(2\sqrt{7} + 7)$ $8\sqrt{35} - 12\sqrt{7} + 28\sqrt{5} - 42$
139. $(3\sqrt{14} + 2\sqrt{7})(5\sqrt{14} + 3\sqrt{7})$ $252 + 133\sqrt{2}$

Rationalize the denominator of each fraction. (11-9)

140. $\frac{5}{3 + \sqrt{7}}$ $\frac{15 - 5\sqrt{7}}{2}$
141. $\frac{2 + \sqrt{3}}{1 - \sqrt{5}}$ $\frac{2 + \sqrt{3} + 2\sqrt{5} + \sqrt{15}}{-4}$

Additional Answers

121. $-50\sqrt{2}$
122. $11\sqrt{2} - 33\sqrt{3}$
123. $2\sqrt{2} - \frac{\sqrt{30}}{6}$
124. $-\frac{\sqrt{6}}{6}$
125. $\frac{80\sqrt{7} + 21\sqrt{2}}{28}$

Solve. (11-10)

142. $\sqrt{m} = 7$ 49 **143.** $\sqrt{6x} = \frac{3}{2}$ $\frac{3}{8}$ **144.** $\sqrt{a} - 5 = 4$ 81

145. $\frac{1}{5} + \sqrt{y} = 1$ $\frac{16}{25}$ **146.** $\sqrt{\frac{x}{3}} = 6$ 108 **147.** $\sqrt{n - 2} = 9$ 83

148. $4\sqrt{5t} = 8$ $\frac{4}{5}$ **149.** $\sqrt{3z} + 2 = 5$ 3 **150.** $\sqrt{4k - 5} + 1 = 8$ $\frac{27}{2}$

151. $\sqrt{\frac{5u}{2}} - 3 = -2$ $\frac{2}{5}$ **152.** $\sqrt{\frac{4c - 3}{7}} = 3$ $\frac{33}{2}$ **153.** $8\sqrt{n} = 24\sqrt{5}$ 45

Chapter 12

Solve. Express irrational solutions in simplest radical form. If the equation has no solution, write "no solution." (12-1)

1. $m^2 = \frac{25}{49}$ $\left\{-\frac{5}{7}, \frac{5}{7}\right\}$ **2.** $5a^2 = 60$ $\{-2\sqrt{3}, 2\sqrt{3}\}$ **3.** $w^2 + 52 = 0$ no solution

4. $x^2 - 108 = 0$ $\{-6\sqrt{3}, 6\sqrt{3}\}$ **5.** $7u^2 - 112 = 0$ $\{-4, 4\}$ **6.** $4c^2 + 7 = 23$ $\{-2, 2\}$

7. $3t^2 - 12 = -3$ $\{-\sqrt{3}, \sqrt{3}\}$ **8.** $2n^2 + 9 = 4$ no solution **9.** $(v + 5)^2 = 16$

10. $(z - 5)^2 = 6$ $\{5 \pm \sqrt{6}\}$ **11.** $3(k + 4)^2 = 81$ $\{-4 \pm 3\sqrt{3}\}$ **12.** $4(f - 1)^2 = 60$

13. $2(h + 7)^2 = 42$ $\{-7 \pm \sqrt{21}\}$ **14.** $(2x + 3)^2 = 100$ $\left\{\frac{7}{2}, -\frac{13}{2}\right\}$ **15.** $7(3y - 1)^2 = 168$

16. $e^2 + 6e + 9 = 64$ $\{5, -11\}$ **17.** $a^2 - 12a + 36 = 49$ $\{13, -1\}$ **18.** $m^2 + 18m + 81 = 36$ $\{-3, -15\}$

Solve by completing the square. Give irrational roots in simplest form and then approximate them to the nearest tenth. (12-2)

19. $x^2 + 16x = -15$ $\{-15, -1\}$ **20.** $y^2 - 8y + 7 = 0$ $\{7, 1\}$ **21.** $z^2 - 12z - 202 = 8$ $\{6 \pm \sqrt{246}\}$; $\{21.7, -9.7\}$

22. $4a^2 + 10a = 12$ $\left\{\frac{-5 \pm \sqrt{73}}{4}\right\}$; $\{0.9, -3.4\}$ **23.** $b^2 - 3b = 5$ $\left\{\frac{3 \pm \sqrt{29}}{2}\right\}$; $\{4.2, -1.2\}$ **24.** $3c^2 + 6c - 1233 = 0$ $\{-1 \pm 2\sqrt{103}\}$; $\{-21.3, 19.3\}$

Solve by (a) completing the square and (b) factoring. (12-2)

25. $e^2 - 10e + 21 = 0$ $\{7, 3\}$ **26.** $4f^2 - 18f = 10$ $\left\{5, -\frac{1}{2}\right\}$ **27.** $6h^2 + 9h - 42 = 0$ $\left\{2, -\frac{7}{2}\right\}$

Solve. Write irrational roots in simplest radical form. (12-2)

28. $\frac{m^2}{3} - 2m = 7$ $\{3 \pm \sqrt{30}\}$ **29.** $n^2 + \frac{n}{2} = 5$ $\left\{2, -\frac{5}{2}\right\}$ **30.** $\frac{x^2}{2} - \frac{x}{4} = 2$ $\left\{\frac{1 \pm \sqrt{65}}{4}\right\}$

Use the quadratic formula to solve each equation. Give irrational roots in simplest radical form; also approximate them to the nearest tenth. (12-3)

31. $z^2 + 7z + 3 = 0$ **32.** $w^2 + 8w - 4 = 0$ **33.** $2u^2 - 10u - 6 = 0$

34. $5t^2 = -9t - 1$ **35.** $3k^2 + 2 = 5k$ **36.** $6m = 3 - 2m^2$

37. $x^2 + 0.3x - 0.2 = 0$ **38.** $n^2 + \frac{2}{3}n - \frac{1}{2} = 0$ **39.** $\frac{1}{2}y^2 - \frac{7}{2}y = 1$

Additional Answers

9. $\{-1, -9\}$
12. $\{1 \pm \sqrt{15}\}$
15. $\left\{\frac{1 \pm 2\sqrt{6}}{3}\right\}$
31. $\left\{\frac{-7 \pm \sqrt{37}}{2}\right\}$; $\{-6.6, -0.5\}$
32. $\{-4 \pm 2\sqrt{5}\}$; $\{-8.5, 0.5\}$
33. $\left\{\frac{5 \pm \sqrt{37}}{2}\right\}$; $\{5.5, -0.5\}$
34. $\left\{\frac{-9 \pm \sqrt{61}}{10}\right\}$; $\{-1.7, -0.1\}$
35. $\left\{1, \frac{2}{3}\right\}$
36. $\left\{\frac{-3 \pm \sqrt{15}}{2}\right\}$; $\{-3.4, 0.4\}$
37. $\left\{\frac{-3 \pm \sqrt{89}}{20}\right\}$; $\{-0.6, 0.3\}$
38. $\left\{\frac{-2 \pm \sqrt{22}}{6}\right\}$; $\{-1.1, 0.4\}$
39. $\left\{\frac{7 \pm \sqrt{57}}{2}\right\}$; $\{7.3, -0.3\}$

Additional Answers

49. $\{-4, -3\}$

50. $\{-2, 2\}$

51. $\left\{0, \frac{9}{5}\right\}$

52. $\left\{\frac{11 \pm \sqrt{145}}{6}\right\}$

53. $\{-4 \pm \sqrt{13}\}$

54. $\{3 \pm \sqrt{6}\}$

55. $\left\{\frac{-2 \pm \sqrt{10}}{6}\right\}$

56. $\{-4 \pm 2\sqrt{6}\}$

57. $\left\{\frac{4 \pm 2\sqrt{31}}{9}\right\}$

58. $\left\{\frac{2 \pm \sqrt{22}}{6}\right\}$

59. $\left\{\frac{1 \pm \sqrt{7}}{6}\right\}$

60. $\left\{\frac{7 \pm \sqrt{51}}{2}\right\}$

61. $\left\{\frac{-5 \pm \sqrt{13}}{2}\right\}$

62. $\{-7 \pm 2\sqrt{7}\}$

Write the value of the discriminant of each equation. Then use it to decide how many different real-number roots the equation has. (Do not solve the equations.) (12-4)

40. $x^2 - 6x + 2 = 0$ 28; two

41. $5n^2 + 3n + 7 = 0$ −131; none

42. $-2t^2 + 4t - 2 = 0$ 0; one

43. $3k^2 - 1.2k + 1.1 = 0$ −11.76; none

44. $3s^2 + 6s + 3 = 0$ 0; one

45. $\frac{1}{3}b^2 - b - 3 = 0$ 5; two

Without drawing the graph of the given equation, determine (a) how many points the parabola has in common with the *x*-axis, and (b) whether its vertex lies above, below, or on the *x*-axis. (12-4)

46. $y = 3x^2 + 2x - 5$ two; below

47. $y = -6 + 3x - 2x^2$ none; below

48. $y = x^2 - 4x + 16$ none; above

Solve by the most efficient method. Write irrational answers in simplest radical form. (12-5)

49. $x^2 + 7x + 12 = 0$

50. $13x^2 = 52$

51. $5x^2 - 9x = 0$

52. $3x^2 - 11x = 2$

53. $x^2 + 8x + 3 = 0$

54. $(x - 3)^2 = 6$

55. $6x^2 + 4x = 1$

56. $\frac{(x + 4)^2}{3} = 8$

57. $\frac{3}{4}x^2 - \frac{2}{3}x = 1$

58. $\frac{1}{2x} = \frac{3x - 2}{3}$

59. $1.2x^2 - 0.4x = 0.2$

60. $\frac{2x - 1}{4x + 3} = \frac{x + 1}{3x - 2}$

61. $4x(x - 2) + 3(x + 8) = 27 + 5x^2$

62. $(x + 6)^2 + 2(x - 1) = 13$

Solve. Give irrational roots to the nearest tenth. Use the Table of Square Roots on page 650 or a calculator as necessary. (12-6)

63. The length of a rectangle is 6 times the width. The area of the rectangle is 84 cm^2. Find the length and width. length, 22.2 cm; width, 3.7 cm

64. The difference of a number and its square is 56. Find the number. 8 or −7

65. The altitude of a triangle is 2 m less than the base. The area of the triangle is 84 m^2. Find the base. 14 m

66. Theresa is crocheting an afghan that is already 30 inches wide by 40 inches long. If she continues to crochet by increasing the width and the length by the same number of inches until the afghan's area is doubled, what will be the new dimensions? 44.2 in. by 54.2 in.

Extra Practice: Problem-Solving

Chapter 1

Use the five-step plan to solve each problem.

1. A train is traveling at an average speed of 90 km/h. How far will it travel in 2.5 h? 225 km **(1-6)**
2. If a number is decreased by 27, the result is 36. Find the number. 63
3. A football team finished its 12-game season with no ties. The team won twice as many games as it lost. How many games did the team win? 8 games
4. A store sold 102 record albums during a two-day sale. Twice as many albums were sold the second day as the first. How many albums were sold the first day? 34 albums
5. If three times a number is increased by 11, the result is 68. Find the number. 19
6. A bank contains 57 nickels, dimes, and quarters. There are 8 more dimes than quarters and 5 more nickels than dimes. How much money is in the bank? $6.25 (12 quarters, 20 dimes, and 25 nickels)

Chapter 2

Solve.

1. A football team gained 23 yards on one play. However, the ball was brought back to the line of scrimmage and then the team was given a 15 yard penalty. How far was the ball from where it would have been had no penalty been assessed? 38 yd **(2-3)**
2. An elevator left the twenty-sixth floor of a building and went up eight floors, then down twelve, and back up four. Where was the elevator then? 26th floor
3. At the beginning of the month the Cranes had $250 in their vacation fund. They were able to add $10 per week for four weeks. Then they had to take out $85 for emergency household repairs. How much was in the fund at the end of the month? $205
4. A neighborhood association collected $85 in dues, earned $280 at a garage sale, and got $124 in donations. The association needs $500 to build a playground. How much more must it collect? $11
5. An 8:00 A.M. flight from Boston to Minneapolis took three hours. The time in Minneapolis is one hour earlier than in Boston. What time was it in Minneapolis when the flight arrived? 10 A.M.

Additional Answers
(continued from p. 628)

72. 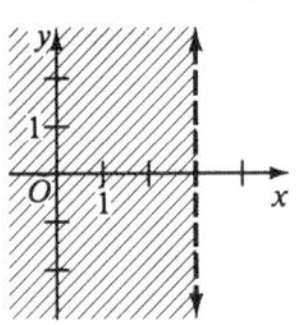

74. 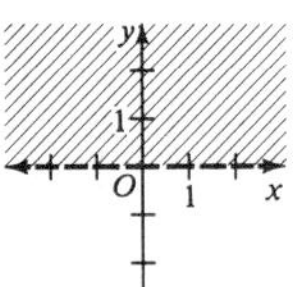

76. 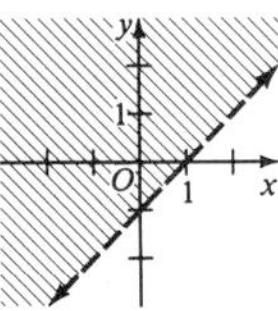

78. 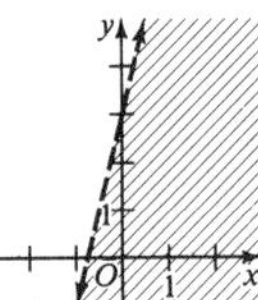

80. $y \leq x - 5$

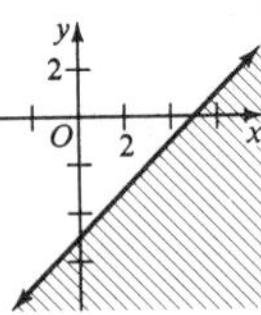

82. $y < \frac{1}{3}x - 2$

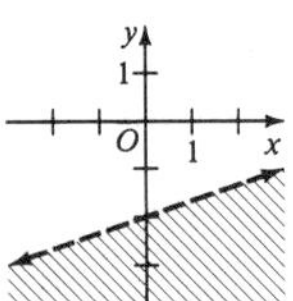

84. $y \geq 5x + 3$

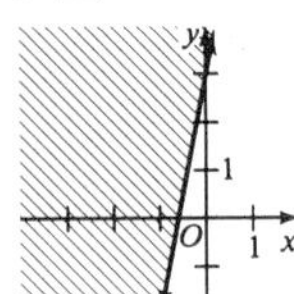

6. A train is traveling at the rate of 100 km/h. A conductor is walking toward the back of the train at 5 km/h. What is the conductor's speed relative to the ground? 95 km/h

Solve.

1. Neon freezes at −248.61°C and boils at −246.09°C. Find the difference between the boiling point and the freezing point. 2.52°C (2-4)

2. The highest point in California is Mount Whitney at 4418 m above sea level. The lowest is Death Valley at 86 m below sea level. Find the difference in altitude. 4504 m

3. A candidate goes door to door along Main Street from a point 16 blocks west of campaign headquarters to a point 12 blocks east of headquarters. How many blocks has she gone? 28 blocks

4. Find the difference in degrees of longitude between Chicago at about 88°W and Rome at about 12°E. 100°

5. Mount Everest at 8848 m above sea level is 9245 m higher than the Dead Sea. Find the altitude of the Dead Sea. 397 m below sea level

6. One winter day the temperature in Marshview reached a record high of 18.3°C. That was 22.7° higher than the average temperature for that day. Find the average temperature. −4.4°C

Chapter 3

Solve.

1. A number increased by 13 is −5. Find the number. −18 (3-1)

2. A glass of milk costs 55¢. If a glass of milk and a sandwich cost $1.90, how much does the sandwich cost? $1.35

3. Fifteen less than a number is 43. Find the number. 58

4. A plane flew 145 km/h faster when it was flying with the wind than it would have flown in still air. If its speed with the wind was 970 km/h, find the speed of the plane in still air. 825 km/h

5. The Booster Club had $425 in its treasury. The members earned $642 selling refreshments. They donated $320 to the football team for bus rentals. How much money did they have left? $747

6. Seventy-six tickets were sold in advance for a museum field trip. Thirteen tickets were sold the day of the trip. Seven people had to return their tickets and did not go. How many people went altogether? 82 people

Solve.

1. The opposite of seven times a number is 238. Find the number. −34 (3-2)

2. One fourth of a number is 73. Find the number. 292

3. A 2.5 kg bag of apples costs 75¢. Find the cost per kilogram of the apples. 30¢
4. Frank works the same number of hours each week at a part-time job. In the first 8 weeks he worked 68 hours. How many hours did he work each week? $8\frac{1}{2}$ h
5. A rectangle is 24 cm long and has a perimeter of 72 cm. Find the width. 12 cm
6. A restaurant cuts its large pizza into 8 slices and sells them for 75¢ each. If the pizzas were cut into 6 slices, how much would the restaurant have to charge for each slice to make the same amount? $1.00

Solve.

(3-4)

1. If you subtract 34 from the product of 15 and a number, you get 146. Find the number. 12
2. The perimeter of a rectangle is 152 m. The width is 35 cm. Find the length. 41 m
3. Carlene paid $131.44, including tax, for a desk. The tax was 31 cents less than $\frac{1}{16}$ the cost of the desk. Find the cost of the desk. $124
4. Twin Cinema I seats 150 more people than Twin Cinema II. If together they seat 1250 people, find the number of seats in Twin Cinema II. 550 seats
5. A bank contains 36 nickels, dimes, and quarters. There are 4 more dimes than quarters and twice as many nickels as quarters. How many of each coin are in the bank? 8 quarters, 12 dimes, 16 nickels
6. The longest side of a triangle is 8 cm longer than the shortest side and 5 cm longer than the third side. If the perimeter of the triangle is 56 cm, find the lengths of the three sides. 23 cm, 15 cm, 18 cm

Solve.

(3-5)

1. The larger of two consecutive integers is 10 more than twice the smaller. Find the integers. -9, -8
2. Find a number whose product with 6 is the same as its sum with 45. 9
3. Five times a number, increased by 3, is the same as three times the number, increased by 27. Find the number. 12
4. The sum of two numbers is 20. Twice one number is 4 more than four times the other. Find the numbers. 14, 6
5. The lengths of the sides of a triangle are consecutive odd integers. If the perimeter is 1 less than four times the shortest side, find the length of each side. 7, 9, 11
6. A sandwich costs 20¢ more than a salad plate. Six sandwiches cost as much as seven salad plates. Find the cost of each. salad plate, $1.20; sandwich, $1.40

86. $y \geq -x - \frac{1}{2}$

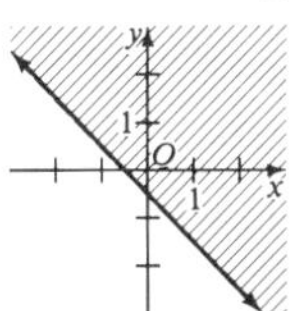

88. $y \leq \frac{3}{2}x + \frac{7}{2}$

90.

92.

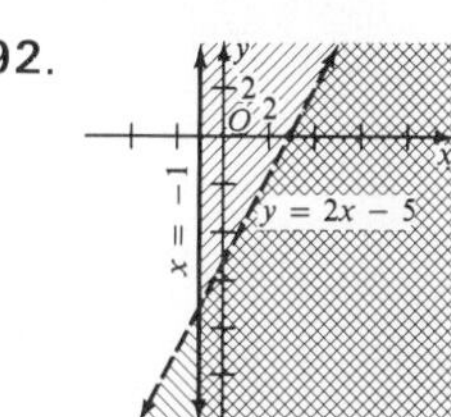

94.

96.

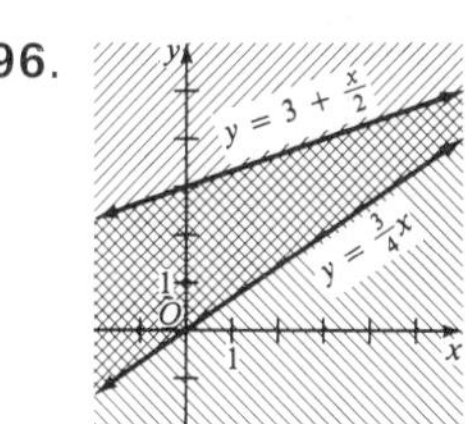

Solve.

1. Kevin is three times as old as Karen. In 6 years he will be twice as old as she. How old are both now? Kevin, 18 y old; Karen, 6 y old (3-6)
2. Aaron, Betsy, and Charita work part-time at the public library. Betsy works 4 hours more each week than Aaron, and together they work half as many hours as Charita. How long does each person work if their total time is 45 hours? Aaron, $5\frac{1}{2}$ h; Betsy, $9\frac{1}{2}$ h; Charita, 30 h
3. In ten years Zachary will be half his father's age. If his father was 25 years old when he was born, how old is each now? Zachary, 15 y; father, 40 y
4. The length of a rectangle is 18 cm more than the width. A second rectangle is 6 cm shorter and 3 cm wider than the first and has a perimeter of 126 cm. Find the dimensions of each rectangle. 42 cm by 24 cm; 36 cm by 27 cm
5. Becky's age is the sum of the ages of Ryan and Amy. Ryan is 2 years older than Amy, and Amy is one third as old as Becky. How old is each now? Becky, 6 y old; Amy, 2 y old; Ryan, 4 y old
6. A cup of skim milk has 10 more than half the calories of a cup of whole milk. A cup of whole milk has 40 more calories than a glass of apple juice. If the total number of calories in one cup of each is 370, find the number of calories in each.
whole milk, 160 calories; apple juice, 120 calories; skim milk, 90 calories

Solve.

1. A collection of quarters and dimes is worth \$6.75. The number of dimes is 4 less than three times the number of quarters. How many of each are there? 13 quarters, 35 dimes (3-7)
2. A total of 720 people attended a basketball game. Adult tickets cost \$2.50 each and student tickets cost \$1.50 each. If \$1220 worth of tickets were sold, how many students and how many adults attended? 580 students, 140 adults
3. A worker earns \$9 per hour for a regular workday and \$13.50 per hour for additional hours. If the worker was paid \$114.75 for an 11-hour workday, what is the length of a regular workday? $7\frac{1}{2}$ h
4. Carrots cost 75¢ per kilogram and potatoes cost 70¢ per kilogram. A shopper bought 9 kg of the vegetables for \$6.60. How many kilograms of each did the shopper buy? carrots, 6 kg; potatoes, 3 kg
5. A collection of 102 nickels, dimes, and quarters is worth \$13.60. There are 14 more nickels than dimes. How many quarters are there? 36 quarters

Chapter 4

Solve.

1. Two trains leave a station at the same time, heading in opposite directions. One train is traveling at 80 km/h, the other at 90 km/h. How long will it take for the trains to be 425 km apart? 2.5 h (4-8)

2. Grace leaves home at 8:00 A.M. Ten minutes later, Will notices Grace's lunch and begins bicycling after her. If Grace walks at 5 km/h and Will cycles at 15 km/h, how long will it take him to catch up with her? 5 min

3. A jet took one hour longer flying to Lincoln from Adams at 800 km/h than to return at 1200 km/h. Find the distance from Lincoln to Adams. 2400 km

4. Gene spent 10 min riding his bicycle to a friend's house. He left his bike there and, with his friend, walked for 15 min to the gym. Gene rides his bicycle 10 km/h faster than he walks. If the entire trip covered a distance of 2.75 km, how far is it from his friend's house to the gym? 0.65 km

5. At noon, Sheila left a boat landing and paddled her canoe 20 km downstream and back. If she traveled 10 km/h downstream and 4 km/h upstream, what time did she arrive back at the landing? 7 P.M.

Solve.

1. A rectangle is 4 m longer than it is wide. If the length and width are both increased by 5 m, the area is increased by 115 m^2. Find the original dimensions. 7 m by 11 m **(4-9)**

2. A rectangle is 3 cm longer and 2 cm narrower than a square with the same area. Find the dimensions of each. 6 cm by 6 cm; 9 cm by 4 cm

3. A rectangular swimming pool is 4 m longer than it is wide. It is surrounded by a cement walk 1 m wide. The area of the walk is 32 m^2. Find the dimensions of the pool. 5 m by 9 m

4. When the length of a square is increased by 6 and the width is decreased by 4, the area remains unchanged. Find the dimensions of the square. 12 by 12

5. A print is 10 cm longer than it is wide. It is mounted in a frame 1.5 cm wide. The area of the frame is 339 cm^2. Find the dimensions of the print. 50 cm by 60 cm

Solve.

1. Find two consecutive integers whose sum is 104. no solution **(4-10)**

2. A plane averaged 1000 km/h on the first half of a round trip, but heavy winds slowed its speed on the return trip to 600 km/h. If the entire trip took 6 h, find the total distance. 4500 km

3. Jill is 12 years older than Jack. In 8 years she will be three times his age. How old is Jack? no solution

4. The side of a square is 2 cm longer than the side of a second square. If the area of the first square exceeds that of the second by 220 cm^2, find the side of each square. first, 56 cm; second, 54 cm

5. Find three consecutive integers whose sum is four times the greatest integer. -5, -4, -3

Chapter 5

Solve.

1. The sum of a number and its square is 132. Find the number. -12 or 11 (5-13)
2. The sum of the squares of two consecutive positive odd integers is 202. Find the numbers. 9, 11
3. A rectangle is 8 cm longer than it is wide. The area is 240 cm^2. Find the dimensions. 12 cm by 20 cm
4. The sum of two numbers is 12 and the sum of their squares is 74. Find the numbers. 5, 7
5. A rectangular flower garden is planted in a rectangular yard that is 16 m by 12 m. The garden occupies $\frac{1}{6}$ of the area of the yard and leaves a uniform strip of grass around the edges. Find the dimensions of the garden. 4 m by 8 m
6. The edge of one cube is 4 cm longer than the edge of a second cube. The volumes of the cubes differ by 316 cm^3. Find the length of the edge of each cube. first, 3 cm; second, 7 cm

Chapter 7

Solve.

1. Two numbers are in the ratio 2:3 and their sum is 125. Find the numbers. 50, 75 (7-1)
2. The measures of the angles of a triangle are in the ratio 2:3:5. Recall that the sum of the measures of the angles of a triangle is 180°. Find the measure of each angle. 36, 54, 90
3. Three numbers are in the ratio 2:3:5 and their sum is 200. Find the numbers. 40, 60, 100
4. The ratio of teachers to assistants to children at a day care center is 2:1:9. Of the 96 people at the center, how many are children? 72
5. A collection of quarters, dimes, and nickels is worth $22.80. If the ratio of quarters to dimes to nickels is 5:3:7, how many coins are there? 180 coins
6. Two planes leave an airport at the same time heading in opposite directions. After 2 h, the planes are 376 km apart. If the ratio of their speeds is 22:25, find the speed of each plane. 88 km/h, 100 km/h

Solve.

1. A 1.5 pound steak costs $5.25. Find the cost of a 2 pound steak. $7 (7-2)
2. A poll showed that 400 voters out of 625 favor Question 1 in the town elections. If there are 7500 voters altogether, how many can be expected to vote in favor of the question? 4800 voters

3. Group-rate admissions to a museum cost \$140.70 for a group of 42. How much would it have cost for a group of 50? \$167.50
4. The tax on a restaurant meal that costs \$24 is \$1.44. Find the tax on a meal that costs \$35. \$2.10
5. The Sommers' scale is inaccurate. If it registers 120 lb for Karen, who actually weighs 116 lb, how much will it register for Neil, who actually weighs 174 lb? 180 lb
6. On a wall map, 1 cm represents 25 km. Colorado is represented by a rectangle 25.8 cm long and 18.4 cm wide. Find the approximate area of Colorado in square kilometers. 296,700 km^2

Solve.

1. Juan is 2 years older than Sylvia. Four years ago Sylvia's age was five sixths of Juan's age. How old are both now? Juan, 16 y; Sylvia, 14 y (7-3)
2. Three fifths of a number added to one fourth of the number is 51. Find the number. 60
3. Bart's age is one third of his mother's age. Seven years ago, his age was one fifth of hers. How old are both now? Bart, 14 y; mother, 42 y
4. A rectangle is 11 cm narrower than it is long. The length is two sevenths of the perimeter. Find the length and the width. 44 cm, 33 cm
5. Two thirds of the coins in a collection of quarters and dimes are quarters. The collection is worth \$12. How many dimes are there? 20 dimes
6. A bus, traveling at 90 km/h, takes 15.2 hours longer to get from Ardmore to Zephyr than a plane flying at 850 km/h. How far is it from Ardmore to Zephyr? 1530 km

Solve.

1. The sum of a number and its reciprocal is $\frac{25}{12}$. Find the number. $\frac{3}{4}$ or $\frac{4}{3}$ (7-4)
2. The sum of a number and its reciprocal is $\frac{29}{10}$. Find the number. $\frac{2}{5}$ or $\frac{5}{2}$
3. The denominator of a fraction is 2 more than the numerator. If the numerator and denominator are increased by 2, the new fraction is $\frac{4}{15}$ greater than the original fraction. Find the original fraction. $\frac{1}{3}$
4. The denominator of a fraction is 2 more than the numerator. The sum of the fraction and its reciprocal is $\frac{34}{15}$. Find the fraction. $\frac{3}{5}$
5. If the speed limit is decreased by 10 km/h on a 100 km stretch of a highway, the trip will take a half hour longer than usual. What is the usual speed limit? 50 km/h
6. I can ride my bike 14 km/h faster than I can walk. It takes 17.5 min longer to walk 2.5 km than to ride. Find my walking speed. 6 km/h

Solve.

1. If there is a 6% tax on clothing, find the tax on a suit that costs \$175. \$10.50 (7-5)
2. A real estate agent makes a 4% commission on all sales. How much does the agent make on a sale of \$82,500? \$3300
3. A discount store sold a sweater for \$32. If the discount was 20%, find the original price. \$40
4. If the Ghannams' \$84 monthly gas bill goes up 8%, what will be their new monthly payment? \$90.72
5. An \$840 personal computer is discounted 25%. What is the final cost? \$630
6. How much greater is the income on \$3600 invested at 12% than on \$4200 invested at 8%? \$96

Solve.

1. Last season, when a football team was doing poorly, weekly attendance averaged 42,000. This season attendance averages 56,700. What is the percent of increase? 35% (7-6)
2. A single monthly issue of *Sports Spotlight* costs \$2.25 at the newsstand. A yearly subscription costs \$21.60. Find the percent of discount from the newsstand price. 20%
3. Enrollment in the summer recreation program this year increased by 16% to 1711 people. How many people enrolled last year? 1475 people
4. The Kerchners invested \$7500 at 8% and \$3500 at 5%. Find the total annual income from the two investments. \$775
5. The Jokis invested a sum of money at 10%. They could have earned the same interest by investing \$1600 less at 12%. How much did they invest? \$9600
6. The Sanjurjos invested three fourths of their money at 12% and the rest at 8%. If their annual income from the investment is \$1320, how much have they invested? \$12,000

Chemistry

Solve.

1. How many liters of water must be added to 20 L of a 75% acid solution to produce a solution that is 15% acid? 80 L (7-7)
2. How many liters of acid should be added to 4 L of a 10% acid solution to make a solution that is 80% acid? 14 L
3. A chemist mixes 16 L of a 40% acid solution and 24 L of a 16% acid solution. What is the percent of acid of the mixture? 25.6%
4. How many kilograms of water must be evaporated from 84 kg of a 5% salt solution to produce a solution that is 35% salt? 72 kg

Grocery

Solve.

1. Students working at a refreshment stand mix cranberry juice at 50¢ per liter and apple juice at 35¢ per liter to make 120 L of a fruit drink worth 40¢ per liter. How many liters of each did they use? cranberry, 40 L; apple, 80 L
2. A grocer mixes a premium blend worth $17 per kilogram with a blend worth $7 per kilogram to make 36 kg of a blend worth $11 per kilogram. How many kilograms of each type are included? premium, 14.4 kg; other, 21.6 kg
3. A butcher mixes 12 pounds of ground pork at $1.25 per pound with 24 pounds of ground beef at $2 per pound to sell as meat loaf mix. What should be the cost per pound of the mixture? $1.75
4. How many kilograms of cranberries at $2.10 per kilogram should a grocer mix with 10 kg of pineapple chunks at $1.20 per kilogram to make a relish worth $1.35 per kilogram? 2 kg

Investment and Wages

Solve.

1. A worker earns $1\frac{1}{2}$ times the regular wage for overtime. In one week the worker's total income was $625 for 35 hours of regular work plus 10 hours of overtime. What is the regular hourly wage? $12.50
2. The Esperanzas invested part of their $8000 at 12% and part at 8%. If their annual investment income is $825, how much is invested at each rate? $4625 at 12%, $3375 at 8%
3. The Lees invested two thirds of their money at 12.5%, one fourth at 8%, and the rest at 6%. If their annual investment income is $1625, how much did they invest altogether? $15,000
4. An investor has $10,000 invested in two stocks. If one pays 15% and the other 16%, and the total annual income is $1520, how much is invested in each? $8000 at 15%, $2000 at 16%

Solve.

1. Joe can do a job in 6 h and Charlie can do the same job in 5 h. What part of the job can they finish by working together for 2 h? $\frac{11}{15}$ **(7-8)**
2. Charlotte can finish her paper route in 2 h. When Ralph helps, they finish in 45 min. How long would it take Ralph working alone? 1 h 12 min
3. A crew of 2 could put siding on a house in 30 h. Another crew of 3 could do the same job in 24 h. How long would it take all 5 people working together? 13 h 20 min
4. Flora can finish her chores in 4 h. One week after Flora worked alone for 1 h, she was joined by her younger sister Fiona and they finished the job in 2 h. How long would it have taken Fiona working alone? 8 h

5. One pipe can fill a tank in 50 min and a second pipe can fill it in 90 min. When the tank was empty, the first pipe was opened for 20 min, then shut. How long will it take the second pipe to finish the job? 54 min
6. One machine can produce an order of Wonder Widgets in 45 min. A second machine takes 60 min, and a third takes 90 min. How long would it take all three working together? 20 min

Solve.

(7-9)

1. The speed of light is about 3.00×10^5 km/s. The average distance from Earth to the moon is about 3.84×10^5 km. How long does it take light reflected from Earth to reach the moon? 1.28 s
2. At its farthest, the moon is about 4.07×10^5 km from Earth. At its closest, it is about 3.56×10^5 km from Earth. Find the difference between the two distances. 5.1×10^4 km
3. The average distance from the sun to Pluto is about 6.10×10^9 km. About how long does it take light from the sun to reach Pluto? (See Exercise 1 above.) 2.03×10^4 s
4. **a.** A parsec is about 3.3×10^3 light years. The star Deneb is about 5.0×10^2 parsecs from the sun. How many light years is that? 1.65×10^6
   b. A light year is about 9.5×10^{12} km. Find the distance from Deneb to the sun in kilometers. 1.5675×10^{19} km
5. The approximate wavelength of visible light is 6.0×10^3 Angstrom units. An Angstrom unit is equal to 1.0×10^{-8} cm. Find the wavelength of visible light in centimeters. 6×10^{-5} cm

Solve.

2. a. 0.09766 g b. 102,400 g

(7-10)

1. The population of a certain area in t years is expected to be $10(1.03)^t$ thousand people. Find the population (a) now (b) last year (c) next year. 10,000 people; 9709 people; 10,300 people
2. A certain isotope has a half-life of 100 years. Starting with 100 g of the isotope, in t years there will be $100(0.5)^{\frac{t}{100}}$ grams left. (a) How much will be left in 1000 years? (b) How much was there 1000 years ago?
3. A certain bacteria culture quadruples every 2 days. The number present t days from now will be $1{,}000{,}000\ (4)^{\frac{t}{2}}$. How many bacteria were there 2 weeks ago? 61 bacteria
4. A \$10,000 investment earning 8%, compounded annually, will be worth $\$10{,}000(1.08)^t$ in t years. What was the amount 4 years ago? \$7350.29
5. The growth rate of a certain city is such that its population t years from now is given by the formula $12{,}000(1.06)^t$. What was the population 10 years ago? 6701 people
6. In one country the cost of living has been increasing so that an item costing one dollar now will cost $(1.05)^t$ dollars t years from now. How much did today's one-dollar item cost 5 years ago? \$.78

Chapter 8

Solve.

(8-5)

1. A collection of 77 quarters and dimes is worth \$12.50. How many quarters are there? 32 quarters
2. The sum of two numbers is 32. One number is 4 more than the other. Find the numbers. 14, 18
3. The length of a rectangle is 3 less than twice the width. The perimeter is 54. Find the dimensions. 10 by 17
4. The sum of two numbers is 66. If the smaller number is subtracted from two thirds of the larger number, the result is one third the positive difference of the original numbers. Find the numbers. 22, 44
5. If 1 is subtracted from the numerator of a fraction, the resulting fraction is $\frac{1}{3}$. If 2 is subtracted from the denominator, the resulting fraction is $\frac{1}{2}$. Find the original fraction. $\frac{5}{12}$
6. If 2 is added to the numerator of a fraction, the resulting fraction is $\frac{2}{3}$. If 1 is subtracted from the denominator, the resulting fraction is $\frac{1}{2}$. Find the original fraction. $\frac{4}{9}$

Solve.

(8-6)

1. The sum of two numbers is 36 and their difference is 6. Find the numbers. 21, 15
2. The sum of two numbers is 73. When the smaller number is subtracted from twice the greater number, the result is 50. Find the numbers. 41, 32
3. There are 158 members in the soccer program. There are 16 more boys than girls. How many boys are there? 87 boys
4. If Cathy walks for 2 h and rides her bicycle for 1 h, she can travel 36 km. If she walks for 2 h and rides her bicycle for 2 h, she can travel 56 km. How fast can she walk? How fast can she ride her bicycle? 8 km/h; 20 km/h
5. Craig has 38 quarters and dimes. If he had twice as many quarters, he would have \$11. How many of each coin does he have? 18 quarters, 20 dimes
6. Olivia's father is 30 years older than she. Seven years ago, the sum of their ages was equal to his age now. How old is each now? Olivia, 14 y; father, 44 y

Solve.

(8-7)

1. The sum of two numbers is 51 and their difference is 13. Find the numbers. 32, 19
2. A collection of 27 nickels and dimes is worth \$1.95. How many of each coin are there? 15 nickels, 12 dimes

3. The side of a square house is 24 ft long, and the house is located on a lot which is 50 ft longer than it is wide. The perimeter of the lot is 20 ft more than 5 times the perimeter of the house. Find the length of the lot. 150 ft

4. Museum passes cost $5 for adults and $2 for children. One day the museum sold 1820 passes for $6100. How many of each type were sold? adults, 820; children, 1000

5. In a math contest, each team is asked 50 questions. The teams earn 15 points for each correct answer and lose 8 for each incorrect answer. One team finished with a score of 566. How many questions did this team answer correctly? 42 questions

6. A grocer mixes two types of nuts, Brand A and Brand B. If the mix includes 4 kg of Brand A and 6 kg of Brand B, the mix will cost $6.20 per kilogram. If it includes 2 kg of Brand A and 8 kg of Brand B, it will cost $5.60 per kilogram. Find the cost per kilogram of each brand. Brand A, $8.00 per kg; Brand B, $5.00 per kg

Solve. 2. wind, 175 km/h; jet, 925 km/h

1. A boat can travel 16 km/h against the current. The same boat can travel 30 km/h with the current. Find the rate of the boat in still water and the rate of the current. boat, 23 km/h; current, 7 km/h **(8-8)**

2. A jet flies with the wind at 1100 km/h and against the wind at 750 km/h. Find the rate of the wind and the ground speed of the jet.

3. A swimmer can swim 4 km with the current in 24 min. The same distance would take 40 min against the current. Find the rate of the current and the speed of the swimmer. current, 2 km/h; swimmer, 8 km/h

4. A plane flies the first half of a 5600 km flight into the wind in 3.5 h. The return trip, with the same wind, takes 2.5 h. Find the speed of the wind and the ground speed of the plane. wind, 160 km/h; plane, 960 km/h

5. A plane has a ground speed of 840 km/h. It can travel 3120 km with the wind in the same time it would take to travel 1920 km against the wind. Find the speed of the wind. 200 km/h

6. A rowboat can travel a distance of 66 km in 3 h with the current. The rowboat can travel 33 km in 3 h against the current. Find the rate of the current and the rate of the rowboat in still water. current, 5.5 km/h; rowboat, 16.5 km/h

Chapter 9

Solve.

1. A beam bends 1.6 cm with a mass of 32 kg on it. If the amount of bending is directly proportional to the mass, find the amount of bending caused by a mass of 62 kg. 3.1 cm **(9-7)**

2. A baker uses 18 cups of flour to make 48 sandwich rolls. How many cups of flour are needed to make 104 sandwich rolls? 39 cups

3. A grocer uses 22 kg of premium nuts in making 54 kg of a mixture. How much of the premium nuts is needed for 81 kg of the mixture? 33 kg

4. On a scale drawing, a child 4 ft tall is represented by a figure 6 in. tall. How tall a figure should be used to represent an 11 ft elephant? $16\frac{1}{2}$ in.

5. On a map, 1 cm represents 60 km. Find the actual area of a region represented on the map by a rectangle 7.5 cm by 8.4 cm. 226,800 km^2

6. A factory is to be built in the shape of a rectangular solid. The actual building will be 62 m long, 30 m wide, and 12 m high. A scale model is built with a scale of 1 cm to 5 m. Find the volume of the model. 178.56 cm^3

Solve. (9-8)

1. The time required to drive a given distance is inversely proportional to the speed. If it takes 7.5 hours to cover a distance at 84 km/h, how long will it take at 90 km/h? 7 h

2. A gear with 36 teeth revolves at 800 rpm and meshes with a gear with 24 teeth. Find the speed of the second gear if the speed varies inversely as the number of teeth. 1200 rpm

3. How much would you have to invest at 8% to earn as much interest as $1250 invested at 12%? $1875

4. A room is to be partitioned into a row of carrels. If each carrel is 1.8 m wide, there will be room for 16 carrels. How many carrels will fit if each is 1.92 m wide? 15 carrels

5. A mass of 18 g and a mass of 22 g are on the ends of a meter stick. Where should a fulcrum be placed to balance the meter stick? 55 cm from the 18 g mass

6. A lever has a mass of 400 g on one end and a mass of 250 g on the other. The lever is balanced when the mass of 400 g is 0.75 m closer to the fulcrum than the other mass. How far from the fulcrum is the mass of 250 g? 2 m

Solve. (9-9)

1. The stopping distance of a car varies directly as the square of its speed. If the stopping distance is 112 m at 64 km/h, find the stopping distance at 56 km/h. 85.75 m

2. The price of a diamond varies directly as the square of its mass. If a 1.4 carat diamond costs $1764, find the cost of a similar stone with a mass of 1.7 carats. $2601

3. The height of a cone of given volume is inversely proportional to the square of the radius of the base. If a cone that is 4 units high has a base with radius 3 units, find the height of a cone of equal volume with a base of radius 6 units. 1 unit

4. The time needed to fill a tank varies inversely as the square of the radius of the hose. If a hose of radius 3.5 cm takes 8 min to fill a tank, how long will it take using a hose of radius 2 cm? 24.5 min

It is $\frac{1}{9}$ as large as it was.

5. The force between two magnets varies inversely as the square of the distance between them. Two magnets are initially 4 cm apart. They are moved 8 cm farther apart. What is the effect on the force?
6. The distance an object falls varies directly as the square of the time it falls. If an object falls 175.5 m in 6 s, how long would it take to fall 487.5 m? 10 s

Solve.

1. The cost of operating an appliance varies jointly as the number of watts, hours of operation, and the cost per kilowatt-hour. It costs 45¢ to operate a 3000-watt air conditioner for 2 h at 7.5¢ per kilowatt-hour. Find the cost of operating a 1200-watt dishwasher for 40 min. 6¢ **(9-10)**
2. The number of persons needed to do a job varies directly as the amount of work to be done and inversely as the time in which the job is to be done. If 8 factory workers can produce 520 items in 4 days, how many workers will be needed to produce 585 items in 3 days? 12 workers
3. If 2 painters can cover 320 ft^2 in 3 h, how long will it take 3 painters to cover 840 ft^2? (See Exercise 2 above.) 5.25 h
4. The mass of a metal disc varies directly as the thickness and the square of the radius. A disc 2 cm thick with radius 5 cm has a mass of 840 g. Find the mass of a disc of the same metal that has radius 3 cm and is 0.5 cm thick. 75.6 g

Chapter 10

Solve.

1. The sum of two consecutive integers is less than 83. Find the pair of such integers with the greatest sum. 40, 41 **(10-3)**
2. A collection of quarters and dimes is worth more than \$20. There are twice as many quarters as dimes. At least how many dimes are there? 34 dimes
3. Four members of a bowling team had scores of 240, 180, 220, and 200. Find the lowest score a fifth person must get to maintain an average for the group of at least 220. 260
4. The sum of three consecutive even integers is less than 80. Find the greatest such integers. 24, 26, 28
5. When road repairs begin, the current speed limit will be cut by 40 km/h. It will then take at least 3.6 h to cover the same distance that can be covered in 2 h now. What is the speed limit now? at most, 90 km/h
6. The length of a rectangle is 1 cm greater than twice the width. If each dimension were increased by 5 cm, the area would be at least 150 cm^2 greater. Find the least possible dimensions. 8 cm by 17 cm

Chapter 11

Solve.

1. A square has an area of 184 cm^2. Find the length of a side to the nearest tenth of a centimeter. 13.6 cm (11-5)
2. A square has the same area as a rectangle that is 25 m by 18 m. Find the length of a side of the square to the nearest tenth of a meter. 21.2 m
3. A square has the same area as a triangle that has a base of 8 cm and a height of 5 cm. Find the length of a side of the square to the nearest tenth of a centimeter. 4.5 cm
4. A circle inside a square just touches its sides. The area of the circle is 226.08 m^2. Find the length of a side of the square to the nearest tenth of a meter. Use 3.14 for π. 17.0 m
5. A circular pool covers an area of 34.54 m^2. Find the radius of the pool to the nearest tenth of a meter. Use 3.14 for π. 3.3 m
6. A circular flower bed is surrounded by a walk that is 1 m wide. If the area of the whole region is 21.98 m^2, find the radius of the flower bed to the nearest tenth of a meter. Use 3.14 for π. 1.6 m

Solve. Approximate each square root to the nearest hundredth.

1. A state park in the shape of a rectangle has dimensions 50 m by 20 m. A road through the park follows the diagonal of the rectangle. Find the length of the road. 53.85 m (11-6)
2. A rope from the top of a mast of a sailboat is attached to a point 2 m from the mast. If the rope is 6 m long, how tall is the mast? 5.66 m
3. The length of one side of a right triangle is one centimeter less than twice the length of the second side. The hypotenuse is one centimeter more than twice the length of the second side. Find the length of each side. 8 cm, 15 cm, 17 cm
4. The bottom of a 7 m ramp is 5 m from the base of a loading platform. Find the height of the platform. 4.90 m
5. The length of the longer side of a right triangle is 3 cm more than the length of the shorter side. The length of the hypotenuse is 3 cm more than the length of the longer side. Find the length of each side. 9 cm, 12 cm, 15 cm

Solve.

1. One fourth the square root of a number is 7. Find the number. 784 (11-10)
2. When 8 is subtracted from 3 times a number, the square root of the result is 10. Find the number. 36
3. Four times the square root of a number is 28. Find the number. 49
4. When 5 is subtracted from the square root of twice a number, the result is 9. Find the number. 98

5. The geometric mean of two positive numbers is the positive square root of their product. Find two consecutive even integers whose geometric mean is $8\sqrt{15}$. 30, 32

6. Find two consecutive positive odd integers whose geometric mean is $15\sqrt{3}$. 25, 27

Chapter 12

Solve.

1. The sum of a number and its square is 30. Find the number. 5 or -6 **(12-6)**
2. The foundation of a house is 13 m by 7 m. If the builder increases each dimension by the same amount, the area of the foundation will increase to 135 m^2. Find the new dimensions. 15 m by 9 m
3. The perimeter of a rectangular yard is 138 m and the area is 540 m^2. Find the dimensions of the yard. 60 m by 9 m
4. The sum of the squares of two consecutive even integers is 340. Find the integers. -14 and -12 or 12 and 14
5. One work crew can finish a job in 18 h less than a second crew. Working together, they can finish the job in 40 h. How long would each crew take working alone? first crew, 90 h; second crew, 72 h
6. One number is 2 more than 3 times another. The sum of their squares is 212. Find the numbers. 4 and 14 or -5.2 and -13.6

Table of Squares of Integers from 1 to 100

Number	Square	Number	Square	Number	Square	Number	Square
1	1	**26**	676	**51**	2601	**76**	5776
2	4	**27**	729	**52**	2704	**77**	5929
3	9	**28**	784	**53**	2809	**78**	6084
4	16	**29**	841	**54**	2916	**79**	6241
5	25	**30**	900	**55**	3025	**80**	6400
6	36	**31**	961	**56**	3136	**81**	6561
7	49	**32**	1024	**57**	3249	**82**	6724
8	64	**33**	1089	**58**	3364	**83**	6889
9	81	**34**	1156	**59**	3481	**84**	7056
10	100	**35**	1225	**60**	3600	**85**	7225
11	121	**36**	1296	**61**	3721	**86**	7396
12	144	**37**	1369	**62**	3844	**87**	7569
13	169	**38**	1444	**63**	3969	**88**	7744
14	196	**39**	1521	**64**	4096	**89**	7921
15	225	**40**	1600	**65**	4225	**90**	8100
16	256	**41**	1681	**66**	4356	**91**	8281
17	289	**42**	1764	**67**	4489	**92**	8464
18	324	**43**	1849	**68**	4624	**93**	8649
19	361	**44**	1936	**69**	4761	**94**	8836
20	400	**45**	2025	**70**	4900	**95**	9025
21	441	**46**	2116	**71**	5041	**96**	9216
22	484	**47**	2209	**72**	5184	**97**	9409
23	529	**48**	2304	**73**	5329	**98**	9604
24	576	**49**	2401	**74**	5476	**99**	9801
25	625	**50**	2500	**75**	5625	**100**	10,000

Table of Square Roots of Integers from 1 to 100

Exact square roots are shown in red. For the others, rational approximations are given correct to three decimal places.

Number N	Positive Square Root $\sqrt{N}$	Number N	Positive Square Root $\sqrt{N}$	Number N	Positive Square Root $\sqrt{N}$	Number N	Positive Square Root $\sqrt{N}$
1	1	26	5.099	51	7.141	76	8.718
2	1.414	27	5.196	52	7.211	77	8.775
3	1.732	28	5.292	53	7.280	78	8.832
4	2	29	5.385	54	7.348	79	8.888
5	2.236	30	5.477	55	7.416	80	8.944
6	2.449	31	5.568	56	7.483	81	9
7	2.646	32	5.657	57	7.550	82	9.055
8	2.828	33	5.745	58	7.616	83	9.110
9	3	34	5.831	59	7.681	84	9.165
10	3.162	35	5.916	60	7.746	85	9.220
11	3.317	36	6	61	7.810	86	9.274
12	3.464	37	6.083	62	7.874	87	9.327
13	3.606	38	6.164	63	7.937	88	9.381
14	3.742	39	6.245	64	8	89	9.434
15	3.873	40	6.325	65	8.062	90	9.487
16	4	41	6.403	66	8.124	91	9.539
17	4.123	42	6.481	67	8.185	92	9.592
18	4.243	43	6.557	68	8.246	93	9.644
19	4.359	44	6.633	69	8.307	94	9.695
20	4.472	45	6.708	70	8.367	95	9.747
21	4.583	46	6.782	71	8.426	96	9.798
22	4.690	47	6.856	72	8.485	97	9.849
23	4.796	48	6.928	73	8.544	98	9.899
24	4.899	49	7	74	8.602	99	9.950
25	5	50	7.071	75	8.660	100	10

Table of Trigonometric Ratios

Angle	Sine	Cosine	Tangent	Angle	Sine	Cosine	Tangent
1°	.0175	.9998	.0175	46°	.7193	.6947	1.0355
2°	.0349	.9994	.0349	47°	.7314	.6820	1.0724
3°	.0523	.9986	.0524	48°	.7431	.6691	1.1106
4°	.0698	.9976	.0699	49°	.7547	.6561	1.1504
5°	.0872	.9962	.0875	50°	.7660	.6428	1.1918
6°	.1045	.9945	.1051	51°	.7771	.6293	1.2349
7°	.1219	.9925	.1228	52°	.7880	.6157	1.2799
8°	.1392	.9903	.1405	53°	.7986	.6018	1.3270
9°	.1564	.9877	.1584	54°	.8090	.5878	1.3764
10°	.1736	.9848	.1763	55°	.8192	.5736	1.4281
11°	.1908	.9816	.1944	56°	.8290	.5592	1.4826
12°	.2079	.9781	.2126	57°	.8387	.5446	1.5399
13°	.2250	.9744	.2309	58°	.8480	.5299	1.6003
14°	.2419	.9703	.2493	59°	.8572	.5150	1.6643
15°	.2588	.9659	.2679	60°	.8660	.5000	1.7321
16°	.2756	.9613	.2867	61°	.8746	.4848	1.8040
17°	.2924	.9563	.3057	62°	.8829	.4695	1.8807
18°	.3090	.9511	.3249	63°	.8910	.4540	1.9626
19°	.3256	.9455	.3443	64°	.8988	.4384	2.0503
20°	.3420	.9397	.3640	65°	.9063	.4226	2.1445
21°	.3584	.9336	.3839	66°	.9135	.4067	2.2460
22°	.3746	.9272	.4040	67°	.9205	.3907	2.3559
23°	.3907	.9205	.4245	68°	.9272	.3746	2.4751
24°	.4067	.9135	.4452	69°	.9336	.3584	2.6051
25°	.4226	.9063	.4663	70°	.9397	.3420	2.7475
26°	.4384	.8988	.4877	71°	.9455	.3256	2.9042
27°	.4540	.8910	.5095	72°	.9511	.3090	3.0777
28°	.4695	.8829	.5317	73°	.9563	.2924	3.2709
29°	.4848	.8746	.5543	74°	.9613	.2756	3.4874
30°	.5000	.8660	.5774	75°	.9659	.2588	3.7321
31°	.5150	.8572	.6009	76°	.9703	.2419	4.0108
32°	.5299	.8480	.6249	77°	.9744	.2250	4.3315
33°	.5446	.8387	.6494	78°	.9781	.2079	4.7046
34°	.5592	.8290	.6745	79°	.9816	.1908	5.1446
35°	.5736	.8192	.7002	80°	.9848	.1736	5.6713
36°	.5878	.8090	.7265	81°	.9877	.1564	6.3138
37°	.6018	.7986	.7536	82°	.9903	.1392	7.1154
38°	.6157	.7880	.7813	83°	.9925	.1219	8.1443
39°	.6293	.7771	.8098	84°	.9945	.1045	9.5144
40°	.6428	.7660	.8391	85°	.9962	.0872	11.4301
41°	.6561	.7547	.8693	86°	.9976	.0698	14.3007
42°	.6691	.7431	.9004	87°	.9986	.0523	19.0811
43°	.6820	.7314	.9325	88°	.9994	.0349	28.6363
44°	.6947	.7193	.9657	89°	.9998	.0175	57.2900
45°	.7071	.7071	1.0000				

Appendix: Divide-and-Average Method

Objective To use the divide-and-average method.

If you do not have access to a calculator or a square-root table, you can still find an approximation to an irrational square root by using the divide-and-average method. This method is based upon the following.

If you divide a positive number by a positive number that is smaller than the positive square root of that number, the quotient will be larger than the square root.

Example Approximate $\sqrt{51}$ to the nearest ten-thousandth.

Solution

1. Select the integer whose square is nearest 51 as your first approximation, a. Since $7^2 = 49$, let $a = 7$.
2. Divide 51 by a, carrying out the division to two more digits than are in the divisor: $51 \div 7 \approx 7.28$
3. Find the average of a and $\frac{51}{a}$: $\frac{1}{2}(7 + 7.28) \approx 7.14$
4. Use the average as the new value for a. Continue repeating steps 2 and 3 as often as necessary.

   (Step 2) (Step 3)

   $51 \div 7.14 \approx 7.1428 \rightarrow \frac{1}{2}(7.14 + 7.1428) \approx 7.1414$

   $51 \div 7.1414 \approx 7.141456$
5. The approximation is accurate to at least as many digits as match in a and $51 \div a$.

   $\therefore\ \sqrt{51} \approx 7.1414$. ***Answer***

Written Exercises

11. 3.8730 12. −4.7958 13. −6.2450 16. 13.7840 17. 20.1990 18. 3.4496 19. −6.3797 20. 5.6480

Approximate each square root to the nearest hundredth.

1. $\sqrt{29}$ 5.39 **2.** $\sqrt{13}$ 3.61 **3.** $-\sqrt{47}$ −6.86 **4.** $-\sqrt{83}$ −9.11 **5.** $\sqrt{350}$ 18.71

6. $\sqrt{223}$ 14.93 **7.** $-\sqrt{167}$ −12.92 **8.** $-\sqrt{42.3}$ −6.50 **9.** $\sqrt{23.8}$ 4.88 **10.** $\sqrt{18.6}$ 4.31

Approximate each square root to the nearest ten thousandth.

11. $\sqrt{15}$ **12.** $-\sqrt{23}$ **13.** $-\sqrt{39}$ **14.** $\sqrt{45}$ 6.7082 **15.** $-\sqrt{273}$ −16.5227

16. $\sqrt{190}$ **17.** $\sqrt{408}$ **18.** $\sqrt{11.9}$ **19.** $-\sqrt{40.7}$ **20.** $\sqrt{31.9}$

Appendix: Summary of BASIC

BASIC is one of the so-called "higher-level" languages in which programs may be written for computers. It is translated by a *compiler* or *interpreter* inside the computer into a "machine language," which tells the computer what to do.

BASIC is essentially linear in character. Each *statement* is numbered in succession, often 10, 20, 30, . . . (page 9). The computer follows through the statements in numerical order and carries out the instruction in each statement as it comes to it. Some versions of BASIC require an

END statement

for each program (page 9).

BASIC also includes several *commands*, which are not parts of programs and so do not have line numbers.

The command RUN

This command tells the computer to RUN (or execute) the program (page 9).

The command LIST

This command tells the computer to list the statements in numerical order. This is especially useful after changes have been made in a program and you want to see a clean copy of it (page 79).

A program must include both *input* and *output*. In the two-line program on page 9, the input and output are both in one statement, line 10. The input is the arithmetical expression and the output is its value, given by the PRINT statement. See later in this section for more information about PRINT statements.

The symbols for operations (pages 9 and 226) are:

+ for addition	* for multiplication
− for subtraction	/ for division
( ) for grouping	↑ or ^ for raising to a power

The same order-of-operations rule is followed as in algebra. (See page 138.)

Other symbols used in BASIC are:

= for equals	< for less than
> for greater than	< > for not equal
< = for less than or equal	> = for greater than or equal

Very large and very small numbers are stated in E-notation, which is a version of scientific notation. (See page 322.)

BASIC handles variables much as you do in algebra. A variable may be denoted by a letter, a letter followed by a digit, or possibly other combinations of symbols as allowed by the various versions of BASIC. Values are given to variables, and operations are performed on them.

The *input* for a program often involves giving values to variables. There are several ways of doing this.

(1) The INPUT statement

```
INPUT A
```

This statement will cause the computer to print a question mark and wait for the user to type in a value (page 17).

```
INPUT A, B
```

This statement will print only one question mark, but the computer will expect two values to be typed in, separated by a comma (page 107).

(2) The LET statement

```
LET S = 0
```

This statement will give the value 0 to the variable *S* (page 58).

```
LET S = A + B
```

This statement will find the sum of the values of *A* and *B* and give this value to *S*.

```
LET S = S + N
```

This statement will take the value of *S*, add to it the value of *N*, and give *S* this new value (page 58).

Notice that the LET statement is not an equation. It should be read from right to left.

(3) READ and DATA statements

A DATA statement contains a list of values that are to be given to one or more variables by a READ statement.

```
DATA 2, 5, 25, -10
READ N
```

This statement will read one value at a time from the DATA statement.

```
READ M, N
```

This statement will read two values in succession from the list of DATA (page 141).

The list of DATA may be broken up into several DATA statements. The DATA will be read as if there were one continuous list (page 141). DATA statements may be put anywhere in a program. They are usually put near the beginning or near the end for convenience.

If the list of DATA is to be read more than once, a

RESTORE statement

will be needed to direct the computer to start again at the beginning of the list (page 170).

Output is handled by

PRINT statements.

`PRINT A`

This statement will print the value of *A*.

`PRINT "A"`

This statement will print the letter A. Any expression in quotation marks will be printed exactly as it appears—including spaces. (See page 17.)

`PRINT "A = ";A`

The *semicolon* will cause the value of *A* to be printed immediately following the expression in quotation marks. (See pages 17 and 58.)

`PRINT A, B`

The *comma* will cause the values of *A* and *B* to be printed spaced apart. (See page 117.)

`PRINT`

(a) This statement will cancel the effect of a semicolon or a comma at the end of the preceding line (page 186).
(b) By itself, the statement will print a blank line (page 17).

Sometimes it is helpful to separate blocks of a program with

REM statements.

REM means *remark*. A REM statement may contain any comment that you wish to use to clarify the program (page 170). It will appear in the LISTing but have no effect on the program itself. A long comment may run over several lines (page 171), but each line must begin with REM. Any letters or symbols may follow the REM.

Sometimes in the construction of a program, it is necessary to change the line-by-line flow of the program. This is done by using

Transfer statements.

`GOTO 00`

This is an *unconditional transfer* statement. It will transfer the execution to line 00. (See page 58.)

`IF` (expression or relation) `THEN 00`

This is a *conditional transfer* statement. If the expression or relation is true, (THEN) the execution will be transferred to line 00. Otherwise (ELSE), the execution will go ahead to the following line. (See pages 58 and 107.)

These transfers are often used together to form a *branched* program. (See page 107.)

An especially useful construction is a *loop;* that is, passing through the same block of steps several times. One form of a loop simply uses a

GOTO statement to return the execution to the beginning of the block of statements (page 58). Some provision must be made for ending such a loop. One way is to provide an ending number, such as the -1 on page 58. Sometimes such a loop requires the use of a *counter:*

```
LET C = 0
. . . . . .
LET C = C + 1
```

This counter can be used to record the number of passes through the loop. (See page 79.)

When the number of passes through a loop is known ahead of time, a

FOR-NEXT loop

may be used. For a simple counter, use

```
FOR I = 1 to N
. . . . . . . .
NEXT I
```

which will go through a block of statements N times. (See page 117.)

If a sequence of values is to be given to a variable X, this form may be used:

```
FOR X = M TO N STEP S
. . . . . . . . . . . .
NEXT X
```

This construction will give values to X as follows (page 247):

$$M, M + S, M + 2 * S, \text{ and so on, up to } N.$$

IF $M < N$, then $S > 0$, but if $M < N$, then $S < 0$ (page 491). If $S = 1$, then the STEP portion may be omitted.

When one loop is contained within another loop, the loops are said to be *nested.* (See page 186.)

When a block of statements is to be used in several places in a program, it is often convenient to set off that block of statements as a *subroutine.* This is done by using

GOSUB . . . RETURN statements.

```
GOSUB 00
```

This statement will transfer the execution to line 00 (page 217). The block of statements forming the subroutine must end with:

```
RETURN
```

This statement will transfer the execution back to the line following GOSUB 00. (See page 217.)

BASIC has several special functions. Three of these are:

```
ABS(X)
```

This function gives $|X|$. (See page 217.)

```
SQR(X)
```

This function gives $\sqrt{X}$. (See page 526.)

INT(X)

This function gives the greatest integer less than or equal to X (page 186).

The following function is used in PRINT statements to adjust the spacing (page 171).

PRINT TAB(00);"A"

This statement will skip over 00 spaces from the left margin before printing the letter A.

This TAB function can also be used to print out a table with computed spacing as shown in the multiplication table below. (Note also the uses of FOR-NEXT loops and REM statements.)

```
5 REM---PRINTS COLUMN HEADINGS
10 FOR I=0 TO 9
20 PRINT TAB(I*3+3);I;
30 NEXT I
40 PRINT
45 REM---PRINTS HORIZONTAL LINE
50 FOR I=1 TO 34
60 PRINT "-";
70 NEXT I
80 PRINT
85 REM---PRINTS ROW HEADINGS
86 REM---AND TABLE ENTRIES
90 FOR I=0 TO 9
100 PRINT I;"!";
110 FOR J=0 TO 9
120 PRINT TAB(J*3+3);I*J;
130 NEXT J
140 PRINT
150 NEXT I
160 END
RUN

     0  1  2  3  4  5  6  7  8  9
----------------------------------
0!  0  0  0  0  0  0  0  0  0  0
1!  0  1  2  3  4  5  6  7  8  9
2!  0  2  4  6  8  10 12 14 16 18
3!  0  3  6  9  12 15 18 21 24 27
4!  0  4  8  12 16 20 24 28 32 36
5!  0  5  10 15 20 25 30 35 40 45
6!  0  6  12 18 24 30 36 42 48 54
7!  0  7  14 21 28 35 42 49 56 63
8!  0  8  16 24 32 40 48 56 64 72
9!  0  9  18 27 36 45 54 63 72 81
```

PRINT TAB statements may also be used in plotting graphs of functions. In doing this, the x-values are plotted vertically and the function values (y-values) are plotted horizontally. The following simple program will plot graphs on a 21 by 21 "grid" with the x-axis running vertically at TAB(13)—see lines 30, 140, and 200. The y-axis is suggested in lines 40 and 160. Lines 90 and 120 keep the graph within the chosen grid.

Copy and RUN this program. Then, by changing line 50, RUN it also for $y = x^2 - 9$, $y = x^3$, and $y = x^2 - 2x$.

```
10  PRINT "GRAPH OF A FUNCTION"
20  FOR X=-10 TO 10
30  IF X <> 0 THEN 50
40  PRINT "---";
50  LET Y=X
60  IF Y<0 THEN 120
70  IF Y=0 THEN 100
80  PRINT TAB(13);"!";
90  IF Y>10 THEN 150
100  PRINT TAB(Y+13);"*";
110  GOTO 150
120  IF Y<-10 THEN 140
130  PRINT TAB(Y+13);"*";
140  PRINT TAB(13);"!";
150  IF X <> 0 THEN 180
160  PRINT TAB(24);"---Y"
170  GOTO 190
180  PRINT
190  NEXT X
200  PRINT TAB(13);"X"
210  END
```

Subscripted variables are used to represent *lists,* or *arrays,* of values. For example,

$$A(1),\ A(2),\ A(3)$$

are often more convenient to use than A, B, C. (See page 171.)

If more than 10 (or in some cases 11) values are to be used, then a *dimension statement* is needed. For example,

```
DIM A(15)
```

will allow for values $A(1), A(2), \ldots, A(15)$ or, in some cases, $A(0), A(1), \ldots, A(15)$.

A *string* is a set of characters (including spaces) generally enclosed in quotation marks. A *string variable* is a variable having strings as values. Its name must end with $.

As with numeric variables, values may be given to string variables by INPUT (page 107), LET, or READ . . . DATA statements.

Here is a portion of a program that shows how strings and string variables may be used in chatty kinds of programs.

```
10  REM---CHATTY PROGRAM
20  PRINT "WHAT IS YOUR NAME";
30  INPUT N$
40  PRINT "HELLO ";N$;"!"
50  PRINT "I AM GLAD TO MEET YOU."
60  PRINT "DO YOU ENJOY WORKING WITH ";
70  PRINT "ME (YES/NO)";
80  INPUT A$
90  IF A$="YES" THEN 120
100  PRINT "I AM VERY SORRY, ";N$;"."
110  GOTO 130
120  PRINT "I AM VERY GLAD, ";N$;"."
130  END
```

Preparing for College Entrance Exams

If you plan to attend college, you will most likely be required to take college entrance examinations. Some of these exams attempt to measure the extent to which your verbal and mathematical reasoning skills have been developed. Others test your knowledge of specific subject areas. Usually, the best preparation for college entrance examinations is to follow a strong academic program in school, to study, and to read as extensively as possible.

The following test-taking strategies may prove useful:

- Familiarize yourself with the test you will be taking well in advance of the test date. Sample tests, with accompanying explanatory material, are available for many standardized tests. By working through this sample material, you become comfortable with the types of questions and directions that will appear on the test and you develop a feeling for the pace at which you must work in order to complete the test.
- Find out how the test is scored so that you know whether it is advantageous to guess.
- Skim sections of the test before starting to answer the questions, to get an overview of the questions. You may wish to answer the easiest questions first. In any case, do not waste time on questions you do not understand; go on to those that you do.
- Mark your answer sheet carefully, checking the numbering on the answer sheet about every five questions to avoid errors caused by misplaced answer markings.
- Write in the test booklet if it is helpful; for example, cross out incorrect alternatives and do mathematical calculations.
- Work carefully, but do not take time to double-check your answers unless you finish before the deadline and have extra time.
- Arrive at the test center early and come well prepared with any necessary supplies such as sharpened pencils and a watch.

College entrance examinations that test general reasoning abilities, such as the Scholastic Aptitude Test, usually include questions dealing with basic algebraic concepts and skills. The College Board Achievement Tests in mathematics (Level I and Level II) include many questions on algebra. The following first-year algebra topics often appear on these exams. For each of the topics listed on pages 661–663, a page reference to the place in your textbook where this topic is discussed has been provided. As you prepare for college entrance exams, you may wish to review the topics on these pages.

Types of Numbers (pages 30–31, 72, 183)

Positive integers	$\{1, 2, 3, 4, \ldots\}$
Negative integers	$\{-1, -2, -3, -4, \ldots\}$
Integers	$\{\ldots, -4, -3, -2, -1, 0, 1, 2, 3, 4, \ldots\}$
Odd numbers	$\{1, 3, 5, 7, 9, \ldots\}$
Even numbers	$\{0, 2, 4, 6, 8, \ldots\}$
Consecutive integers	$\{n, n + 1, n + 2, \ldots\}$ (n = an integer)
Consecutive even integers	$\{n, n + 2, n + 4, \ldots\}$ (n = even integer)
Consecutive odd integers	$\{n, n + 2, n + 4, \ldots\}$ (n = odd integer)
Prime numbers	$\{2, 3, 5, 7, 11, 13, \ldots\}$

Properties and Axioms (pages 45–81)

Closure Axioms (p. 45)
Commutative Axioms (p. 45)
Associative Axioms (p. 46)
Reflexive Property (p. 47)
Symmetric Property (p. 47)
Transitive Property (p. 47)
Identity Axioms (pp. 50, 68)
Axiom of Opposites (p. 50)
Property of the Opposite of a Sum (p. 53)
Distributive Axiom (p. 64)
Multiplicative Property of Zero (p. 68)
Multiplicative Property of -1 (p. 68)
Property of Opposites in Products (p. 69)
Axiom of Reciprocals (p. 76)
Property of the Reciprocal of a Product (p. 77)

Rules for Operations on Positive and Negative Numbers (pages 54, 69)

If $a > 0$, $b > 0$, then $a + b = |a| + |b|$.
If $a < 0$, $b < 0$, then $a + b = -(|a| + |b|)$.
If $a > 0$, $b < 0$, and $|a| > |b|$, then $a + b = |a| - |b|$.
If $a > 0$, $b < 0$, and $|a| < |b|$, then $a + b = -(|b| - |a|)$.
If $a > 0$, $b < 0$, then $ab < 0$.
If $a > 0$, $b > 0$, then $ab > 0$.

Percents (pages 295–296, 300–301)

Converting decimals and fractions to percents
Percents greater than 100
Percents less than 1
Percent problems

Solving Equations (pages 94, 99, 104, 223–224, 547, 553–554)

Transformation by substitution (p. 94)
Transformation by addition (p. 94)
Transformation by subtraction (p. 94)
Transformation by multiplication (p. 99)
Transformation by division (p. 99)
Factoring (pp. 223–224)
$x^2 = k$ (p. 547)
Quadratic formula (p. 553)
Discriminant (p. 558)

Graphing (pages 30–37, 339–341, 412–415, 449–455, 468–469, 480–482, 484)

Points on a number line
Inequalities on a number line
Points and lines in a number plane
Inequalities in a number plane
Quadratic functions

Factoring (pages 183–221)

Integers
$a^2 - b^2$
$ax^2 + bx$
$a^2 + 2ab + b^2$
$a^2 - 2ab + b^2$
$ax^2 + bx + c$

Variation (pages 418–435)

Direct variation
Inverse variation
Direct variation involving powers
Inverse variation involving powers
Joint variation
Combined variation

Simultaneous Equations (pages 346–351, 358–363)

The graphic method
The substitution method
The addition-or-subtraction method
Multiplication with the addition-or-subtraction method

Algebraic Fractions (pages 239–268)

Simplification
Addition
Multiplication
Division

Word Problems (pages 26, 72–73, 118–124, 146–147, 163–174, 194–195, 230–231, 278–286, 300–316, 378–380)

Age
Area
Consecutive integers
Cost and value
Digit
Fraction
Investment
Mixture
Percent
Proportion
Rate-of-work
Ratio
Uniform motion
Without solutions

Appendix: Presenting Statistical Data

Objective To construct stem-and-leaf plots and box-and-whisker plots.

Statisticians need to organize the data they have collected so that the information can be presented in a useful form. You have learned that bar graphs, broken-line graphs (pages 408–409), and histograms (page 602) can be used to summarize data.

Another way to organize data is by a **stem-and-leaf plot.** In this type of display, the raw data values themselves are incorporated into a frequency distribution. The method may be illustrated for the following set of thirty test scores:

83	72	91	80	73	81	62	87	85	73
100	82	93	99	78	63	49	83	55	68
74	87	82	100	95	58	53	68	97	45

First the **stems,** derived by dropping the units digit from each score, are written in order, to the left of a vertical line.

4	
5	
6	
7	
8	
9	
10	

For each score, the **leaf** or units digit is then recorded to the right of the corresponding stem. For the score 83, for example, the leaf 3 is recorded to the right of the stem 8.

4	9, 5
5	8, 3, 5
6	3, 2, 8, 8
7	4, 2, 3, 8, 3
8	3, 2, 7, 2, 0, 1, 7, 3, 5
9	1, 3, 9, 5, 7
10	0, 0

The leaves are separated by commas, using equal space for each leaf. With equal spacing, the plot can be rotated to become a histogram, displaying the shape of the frequency distribution. Unlike a standard histogram, however, the stem-and-leaf plot still retains every individual score in coded form.

Researchers often wish to compare pairs of data, such as these semester mathematics (M) and English (E) averages collected from twenty students.

M	83	91	63	40	72	82	70	61	78	63	84	73	77	67	92	83	75	86	65	78
E	75	86	74	68	87	91	87	79	89	58	92	72	95	72	90	55	80	79	80	83

Each pair of points can be plotted on a scatter diagram to investigate the relationship between the two grades. (See *Application,* page 411.)

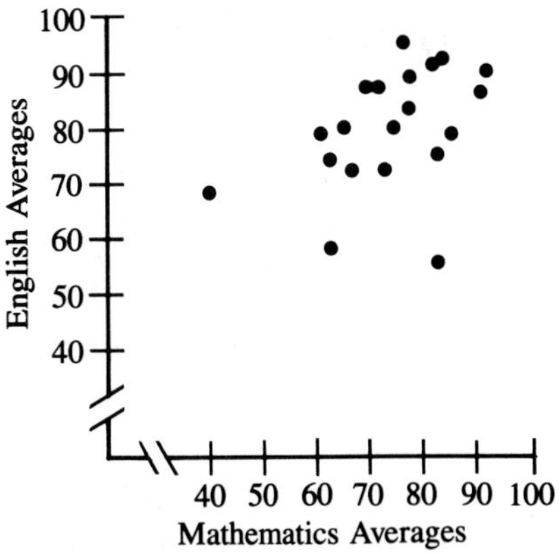

The averages can also be compared by using **box-and-whisker plots.** To construct a box-and-whisker plot, the following values must be identified for each set of data: highest score, lowest score, median score, first and third quartile scores.

Recall that the median of a set of scores is the middle score when the data are arranged in order. The *first quartile score* is the median of the bottom half of the data, and the *third quartile score* is the median of the upper half of the data. In the example above, the mathematics averages, in order, are:

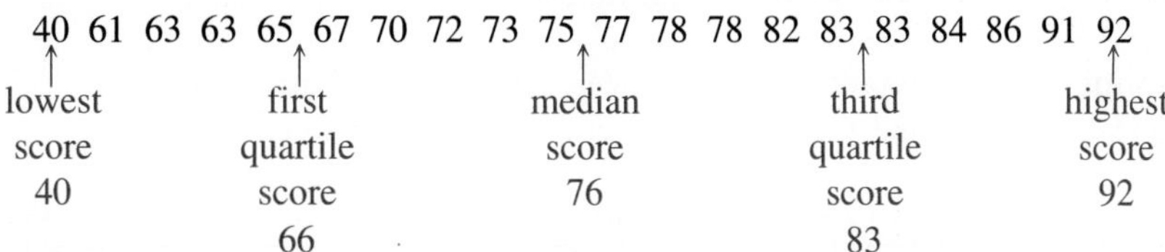

Identify these five special values with dots below a number line.

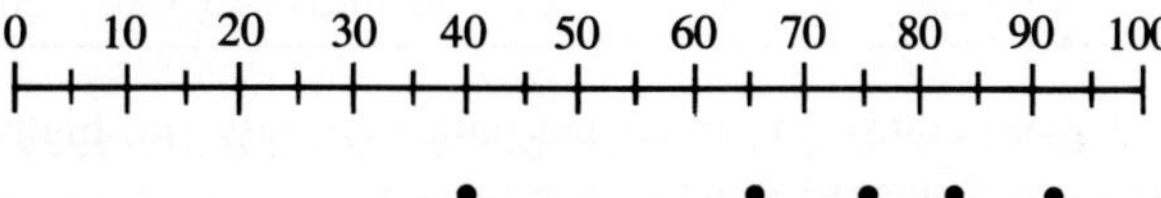

Next, make a box with the two quartile values on the outer sides. Draw a line inside the box, through the median dot. Finally, draw the ''whiskers'' from the sides of the box to the dots of the lowest and highest scores.

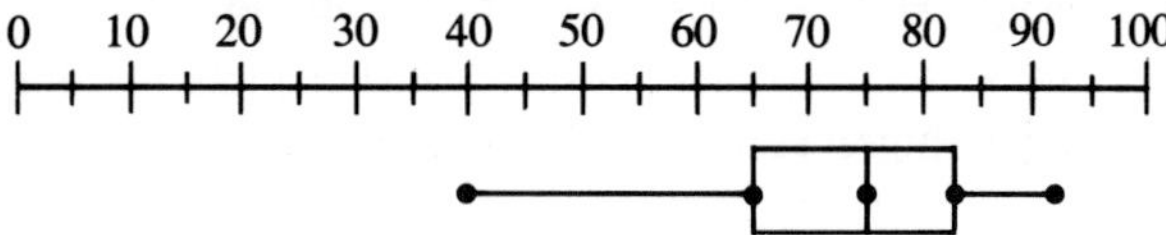

Verify the given box-and-whisker plot for the set of English averages (median: 80; lowest score: 55; highest score: 95; first quartile: 73; third quartile: 88).

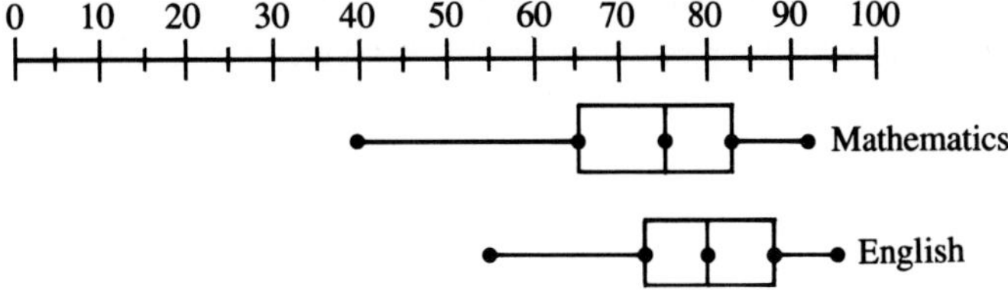

Notice that the box encloses the middle half of the data while the whiskers show the range. By studying the box-and-whisker plot for each set of data, you can easily compare the ranges and the locations of the middle halves of the distributions.

Written Exercises

3.
2	7, 9
3	8, 9, 6, 9
4	2, 5, 4, 7, 0, 9
5	3, 0, 6

For Exercises 1 and 2, use the distribution of scores given by the stem-and-leaf plot at the right.

1	3, 8, 5
2	7, 5, 1, 0, 2
3	3, 6, 4, 2, 7, 5, 4
4	1, 0, 2, 7

1. List the original scores of the distribution in order. **13, 15, 18, 20, 21, 22, 25, 27, 32, 33, 34, 34, 35, 36, 37, 40, 41, 42, 47**
2. What is the median of the scores in the distribution? **33**
3. A department store had 15 applications for the position of store manager. The ages of the 15 applicants were: 38, 42, 53, 39, 27, 45, 50, 36, 44, 47, 39, 40, 56, 49, and 29. Construct a stem-and-leaf plot for their ages. **See above.**
4. Twenty students reported the amount of money they earned last week in their part-time jobs. They earned (in dollars): 102, 115, 87, 91, 80, 73, 114, 145, 137, 135, 127, 120, 86, 100, 134, 129, 133, 88, 75, and 109. Construct a stem-and-leaf plot for their earnings. **See below.**

7	3, 5
8	7, 0, 6, 8
9	1
10	2, 0, 9
11	5, 4
12	7, 0, 9
13	7, 5, 4, 3
14	5

Use the following data for Exercises 5–8: Fifteen cars were road tested on both city streets and highways, and the resulting fuel economy data were recorded.

Miles per Gallon

City	22	21	28	19	28	30	21	20	19	28	22	24	21	24	28
Highway	24	27	32	23	29	38	24	25	24	30	23	26	26	26	31

5. Construct a scatter diagram comparing miles per gallon for city and highway driving. **See Answers to Selected Exercises on p. 37.**
6. For the city driving test, determine the median, first quartile score, third quartile score, highest score, and lowest score. **22, 21, 28, 30, 19**
7. For the highway driving test, determine the median, first quartile score, third quartile score, highest score, and lowest score. **26, 24, 30, 38, 23**
8. On the same number-line scale, construct box-and-whisker plots to compare the mpg figures for city and highway driving. **See Solution Key.**

For Exercises 9 and 10, collect the date of birth from all the students in your class.

9. Construct a stem-and-leaf plot using the month of birth as the stem and the day of the month as the leaf. **Answers will vary.**
10. Construct a box-and-whisker plot for the set of birthdays you collected. **Answers will vary.**

Appendix: Measures of Variation

Objective: To calculate measures of variation for a given distribution.

You learned previously (pages 602–603) that the mean, median, and mode are important numbers for analyzing a set of data. These statistics are used to identify the centers of a distribution. Statisticians are also interested in how the scores are dispersed, or spread throughout the distribution. The statistics used to measure this dispersion are called *measures of variation*.

The range (page 603) is a *weak* measure of variation because it uses only two values of the distribution. Consider, for example, the following two groups of scores:

Group A: 1, 1, 2, 2, 2, 2, 9
Group B: 1, 3, 4, 5, 6, 7, 8

For Group A, the range is $9 - 1 = 8$; for Group B, the range is $8 - 1 = 7$. These groups have almost the same range, but the scores in Group A are more clustered together than those in Group B. Although the range is easy to calculate, it can be a misleading measurement of variation.

Strong measurements of variation use the distance of each value of the distribution from the mean, $\overline{x}$. ($\overline{x}$, pronounced "x bar", is commonly used to designate the mean of a distribution.) The **variance,** denoted by s^2, is the mean of the squares of the distance of each score (x_i) from the mean. For a distribution of n scores,

$$s^2 = \frac{(x_i - \overline{x})^2 + (x_2 - \overline{x})^2 + \cdots + (x_n - \overline{x})^2}{n}.$$

The **standard deviation,** denoted by s, is the principal square root of the variance.

Example 1 Calculate the variance and the standard deviation for the data:

2, 4, 5, 6, 8

Solution First find the mean: $\overline{x} = \dfrac{2 + 4 + 5 + 6 + 8}{5} = 5.$

x_i	$x_i - \overline{x}$	$(x_i - \overline{x})^2$
2	−3	9
4	−1	1
5	0	0
6	1	1
8	3	9

Use $\overline{x}$ to calculate the variance.

$$s^2 = \frac{9 + 1 + 0 + 1 + 9}{5} = 4$$

Find the standard deviation.

$$s = \sqrt{s^2} = \sqrt{4} = 2$$

The **standard score** is a useful statistic for identifying the relative position of an individual value within the distribution. Often called a ***z*-score,** the standard score gives the distance from the mean to the score, *in terms of the standard deviation*. For a distribution with mean $\bar{x}$ and standard deviation s, a score x_i has standard score given by

$$z = \frac{x_i - \bar{x}}{s}.$$

Example 2 Find the standard score for each individual score in the distribution in Example 1.

Solution In Example 1, $\bar{x} = 5$ and $s = 2$. The standard scores are computed:

x_i	$\frac{x_i - \bar{x}}{s}$ = *standard score*
2	$\frac{2-5}{2} = -1.5$
4	$\frac{4-5}{2} = -0.5$
5	$\frac{5-5}{2} = 0.0$
6	$\frac{6-5}{2} = 0.5$
8	$\frac{8-5}{2} = 1.5$

Written Exercises

In Exercises 1–3, calculate the range, mean, and standard deviation for each set of data.

1. The number of broken light bulbs found in each of five cases: 5, 9, 6, 7, 3. **6, 6, 2**
2. The number of hours of sleep a student had each night of a week: 4, 7, 4, 7, 8, 6, 6. **4, 6, $\sqrt{2}$**
3. The number of home runs hit in six baseball games: 4, 4, 4, 4, 4, 4. **0, 4, 0**
4. Explain your answer to Exercise 3. When will the standard deviation of a distribution be zero? **When the range is 0.**
5. A set of test scores had a mean of 26 and a standard deviation of 5. Find the standard score of the following scores from the distribution.
   a. 31 **b.** 22 **c.** 17 **d.** 29 **e.** 26 **f.** 40 **1 −0.8 −1.8 0.6 0 2.8**

6. A distribution of student heights had a mean of 66 inches and a standard deviation of 2 inches. Find the standard score of each of the following individual student heights (in inches).
a. 70 **b.** 64 **c.** 66 **d.** 61 **e.** 71 **f.** 50 **2** **−1** **0** **−2.5** **2.5** **−8**

7. Two algebra classes took the same test with the following results:

$$\text{Class A: } \bar{x} = 76, \ s = 3$$
$$\text{Class B: } \bar{x} = 76, \ s = 5$$

If your grade on the test was 82, in which class would your relative position be higher? Explain. **Class A**

8. Two factories compared the number of items their workers could produce in an hour:

$$\text{Factory I: } \bar{x} = 235, \ s = 14$$
$$\text{Factory II: } \bar{x} = 235, \ s = 6$$

In which factory were the production rates of the workers more nearly alike? How do you know? **See below.**

9. On a chapter test, you received a standard score of 2.5. If the mean score was 79 and the standard deviation was 6, what was your actual score? **94**

10. A distribution has a mean of 45. If the score 39 is equivalent to a standard score of −1.2, what is the standard deviation of the distribution? **5**

8. Factory II. The lower standard deviation indicates less dispersion about the mean.

Glossary

abscissa (p. 339): The first coordinate in an ordered pair of numbers that is associated with a point in the coordinate plane. Also called the *x-coordinate.*

absolute value (p. 35): The positive number of any pair of opposite nonzero real numbers. The absolute value of a number a is denoted by $|a|$. The absolute value of 0 is 0.

acute angle (p. 577): An angle having a measure between 0 and 90.

addition axiom of order (p. 454): For all real numbers a, b, and c:
1. If $a < b$, then $a + c < b + c$;
2. If $a > b$, then $a + c > b + c$.

addition property of equality (p. 93): If a, b, and c are any real numbers and $a = b$, then $a + c = b + c$ and $c + a = c + b$.

additive inverse (p. 50): The additive inverse of the real number a is the real number $-a$ such that $a + (-a) = 0$ and $(-a) + a = 0$. Also called *opposite of a.*

addition-or-subtraction method (p. 358): A method for solving a system of equations whereby the equations are added or subtracted to obtain a new equation with just one variable. Sometimes one or both equations must be multiplied by a number.

angle (p. 576): A figure formed by two different rays with the same endpoint. The rays are the *sides* of the angle and the common endpoint is called the *vertex.*

angles of a triangle (p. 581): *See under* triangle.

area: The area of a region is the number of unit squares it contains.

arrow notation (p. 404): A notation used in defining a function as $f\colon x \longrightarrow 7x + 1$.

associative axioms (p. 46): For all real numbers a, b, c:
Addition: $(a + b) + c = a + (b + c)$
Multiplication: $(ab)c = a(bc)$

average (p. 82): The average of n numbers is the sum of the numbers divided by n.

axes (p. 340): *See under* coordinate axes.

axioms (p. 45): Statements that are assumed to be true. Also called *postulates.*

axiom of comparison (p. 453): For all real numbers a and b, one and only one of the following statements is true: $a < b$, $a = b$, $b < a$.

axiom of opposites (p. 50): For every real number a, there is a unique real number $-a$ such that $a + (-a) = 0$ and $(-a) + a = 0$.

axiom of reciprocals (p. 76): For every nonzero real number a, there is a real number $\frac{1}{a}$ such that

$$a \cdot \frac{1}{a} = 1 \text{ and } \frac{1}{a} \cdot a = 1.$$

axioms of closure (p. 45): For all real numbers a and b:
Addition: $a + b$ is a unique real number.
Multiplication: ab is a unique real number.

axis of symmetry (of a parabola) (p. 413): If the graph of a parabola is folded so that its two halves coincide, the line on which the fold occurs is the axis of symmetry. For $y = ax^2 + bx + c$ $(a \neq 0)$, this axis is the line $x = -\frac{b}{2a}$.

base (of a power) (p. 137): One of the equal factors. In b^n, b is the base.

base angles of an isosceles triangle (p. 581): *See under* isosceles triangle.

base of an isosceles triangle (p. 581): *See under* isosceles triangle.

BASIC (p. 9): A programming language.

between (p. 449): b is between a and c if $a < b < c$ or $c > b > a$.

binomial (p. 143): A polynomial of two terms.

boundary line (p. 480): A line which separates the plane into two half-planes.

circumference: The perimeter of a circle.

closed half-plane (p. 480): The union of an open half-plane and its boundary.

coefficient (p. 143): In a monomial such as $-8x^2y$, the number -8 is called the coefficient, or numerical coefficient.

combined variation (p. 434): A function defined by an equation of the form $z = \frac{kx}{y}$, k a nonzero constant.

common factor (p. 184): A factor of two or more integers.

commutative axioms (p. 45): For all real numbers a and b:
Addition: $a + b = b + a$
Multiplication: $ab = ba$

complementary angles (p. 579): Two angles with 90 as the sum of their measures. Each is the *complement* of the other.

completing the square (p. 551): A method for transforming a quadratic equation into one with the form perfect square $= k$ $(k \geq 0)$.

complex fraction (p. 267): A fraction whose numerator or denominator contains one or more fractions.

conjugates (p. 531): If b and d are both nonnegative, the binomials $a\sqrt{b} + c\sqrt{d}$ and $a\sqrt{b} - c\sqrt{d}$ are conjugates of one another.

conjunction (p. 468): A sentence formed by joining two open sentences by the word *and.*

consecutive even integers (p. 72): Obtained by counting by twos from any even integer.

consecutive integers (p. 72): Obtained by counting by ones from any given integer.

consecutive odd integers (p. 72): Obtained by counting by twos from any odd integer.

constant monomial (p. 143): A numerical term with no variable expression.

constant of variation (p. 418): In a direct variation expressed by $y = kx$, k is the constant of variation. Also called *constant of proportionality.*

converse (p. 223): The converse of a statement is obtained by interchanging the "if" and "then" parts.

coordinate (p. 30): The number paired with a point on the number line.

coordinate axes (p. 340): The x- and y-axes in the number plane.

coordinate plane (p. 340): A plane in which a coordinate system has been set up.

coordinate system (pp. 339–340): A system of graphing ordered pairs of numbers in relation to two axes (horizontal and vertical) that intersect at right angles at their zero point (the origin).

coordinates of a point (p. 339): The abscissa and ordinate of the point, written as an ordered pair of numbers.

corresponding angles (p. 584): *See under* similar triangles.

corresponding sides (p. 584): *See under* similar triangles.

cosine (p. 587): The cosine of $\angle A$ of a right triangle $= \dfrac{\text{length of leg adjacent to } \angle A}{\text{length of hypotenuse}}$.

cubic equation (p. 223): A polynomial equation of degree three.

degree (measure of an angle) (p. 577): $\frac{1}{180}$ of the rotation of a ray from one direction to its opposite.

degree of a monomial (p. 143): The number of times that a variable occurs as a factor in a monomial is the degree of the monomial in that variable. The sum of the degrees in each of the variables is the degree of the monomial. A nonzero constant has degree 0. 0 has no degree.

degree of a polynomial (p. 144): The greatest of the degrees of its terms after it has been simplified.

denominator: In the fraction $\frac{a}{b}$, b is the denominator.

density property (p. 500): Between every pair of different rational numbers there is another rational number.

difference (p. 59): For any two real numbers a and b, the difference $a - b$ is the number whose sum with b is a.

directly proportional (p. 419): y is directly proportional to x if (x_1, y_1) and (x_2, y_2) are ordered pairs of a function, neither of which is $(0, 0)$, and this statement is true: $\frac{y_1}{x_1} = \frac{y_2}{x_2}$.

direct variation (p. 418): A function defined by an equation of the form $y = kx$, where k is a nonzero constant.

discriminant (p. 558): The value of $b^2 - 4ac$ is called the discriminant of the quadratic equation $ax^2 + bx + c = 0$.

disjoint sets (p. 465): Sets with no members in common.

disjunction (p. 468): A sentence formed by joining two open sentences with the word *or*.

distance formula (p. 526): For any points $P_1(x_1, y_1)$ and $P_2(x_2, y_2)$: $P_1P_2 = \sqrt{(x_2 - x_1)^2 + (y_2 - y_1)^2}$.

distributive axiom of multiplication with respect to addition (p. 64): For all real numbers a, b, and c:

$$a(b + c) = ab + ac$$
$$(b + c)a = ba + ca.$$

divide-and-average method (p. 652): A way to find closer and closer approximations to the square root of a number that is not a perfect square by continuing to average pairs of factors.

divisible (p. 191): One polynomial is said to be evenly divisible, or simply divisible, by another polynomial if the quotient is also a polynomial.

domain of a function (p. 404): One of the sets comprising a function, as the values of x in $y = 7x + 1$.

domain of a variable (p. 10): The given set of numbers the variable may represent.

double root (p. 224): *See under* multiple root.

empty set (p. 112): The set with no members. Also called the *null set*.

equal expressions (p. 2): Expressions that name the same number.

equation (p. 10): An equation is formed by placing an equals sign between two numerical or variable expressions.

equilateral triangle (p. 581): A triangle with all sides of equal length.

equivalent equations (p. 94): Equations having the same solution set over a given domain.

equivalent expressions (p. 65): Expressions that represent the same number for all values of the variable that they contain.

equivalent inequalities (p. 454): Inequalities having the same solution set over a given domain.

equivalent systems (p. 351): Systems of equations having the same solution set.

evaluating a variable expression (p. 2): Replacing each variable in the expression by a given value and simplifying the result.

even integers (p. 72): The integers that are the products of 2 and any integer.

event (p. 596): Any possible subset of the sample space resulting from an experiment.

expanded notation (p. 319): Used to express a number as the sum of the digits associated with integral powers of 10.

exponent (p. 137): In a power, the number of times the base occurs as a factor.

exponential form (p. 138): The expression "x^3" is the exponential form of the third power of x.

expressing in simplest form (p. 239): Dividing the numerator and the denominator of a fraction by their greatest common factor.

extremes (p. 282): In the proportion $\frac{a}{b} = \frac{c}{d}$, a and d are the extremes.

factor (p. 46): When two or more numbers are multiplied, each of the numbers is a factor of the product.

factored form (p. 138): The expression "$x \cdot x \cdot x$" is the factored form of the third power of x, that is, x^3.

factoring (pp. 183, 191): Finding the factors of a number or an expression over a specified factor set.

factor set (p. 183): The name given to the set over which a number is factored.

factored completely (p. 221): Term used to describe a polynomial when it is expressed as the product of prime polynomials and a monomial.

formula (p. 13): An equation that states a rule about quantities such as measurements.

fraction (p. 239): An expression in the form $\frac{a}{b}$, $b \neq 0$.

fractional equation (p. 291): An equation that has a variable in the denominator of one or more terms.

frequency distribution (p. 602): A table summarizing data.

function (p. 404): A function consists of two sets, the *domain* and the *range,* and a *rule* that assigns to each member of the domain exactly one member of the range. Each member of the range must be assigned to at least one member of the domain.

graph of an equation (p. 340): Consists of all the points associated with the solutions of the equation.

graph of a function (p. 412): The graphs in the coordinate plane of all the ordered pairs that form the function.

graph of a number (p. 30): The point on the number line paired with a number.

graph of an ordered pair of numbers (p. 339): The point in the plane paired with an ordered pair of real numbers.

graphic method (p. 346): The method of solving a system of equations by using graphs.

greatest common factor of integers (p. 184): The greatest integer that is a factor of two or more integers.

greatest common factor of two or more monomials (p. 188): The common factor that has the greatest coefficient and the greatest degree in each variable.

greatest monomial factor of a polynomial (p. 191): The greatest common monomial factor of its terms.

grouping symbol (p. 5): A device used to enclose an expression. Parentheses, brackets, and fraction bars are grouping symbols.

half-plane (p. 480): *See under* closed half-plane and open half-plane.

histogram (p. 602): A bar graph used to summarize a large set of data.

horizontal axis (p. 339): The horizontal number line in the number plane. Also called the *x-axis.*

hyperbola (p. 424): The graph of $xy = k$ for every nonzero value of k.

hypotenuse (p. 520): The side of a right triangle opposite the right angle.

identity (p. 113): An equation that is true for every value of the variable(s).

identity axioms (pp. 50, 68): For any real number a:
Addition: $a + 0 = 0 + a = a$
Multiplication: $a \cdot 1 = 1 \cdot a = a$.

identity elements (pp. 50, 68): 0 is the identity element for addition. 1 is the identity element for multiplication.

imaginary numbers (p. 555): Numbers involving the imaginary unit, i, which is defined to be $\sqrt{-1}$.

inequality (p. 450): A statement formed by placing an inequality symbol between two numerical or variable expressions.

inequality symbols (p. 37): Symbols used to show the order of pairs of real numbers. The symbol $\neq$ (p. 2) means "is not equal to."

integers (p. 30): The numbers in the set $\{\ldots, -3, -2, -1, 0, 1, 2, 3, \ldots\}$.

intersection of sets (p. 465): For any two sets A and B, the set consisting of all members belonging to both A and B is the intersection of A and B.

inverse operations (p. 103): Operations that "undo" each other; for example, addition and subtraction.

inverse variation (p. 424): A function defined by an equation of the form $xy = k$, where k is a nonzero constant.

inverse variation as the square (p. 430): A function defined by an equation of the form $x^2y = k$, where k is a nonzero constant.

irrational numbers (p. 515): Real numbers that cannot be expressed in the form $\frac{a}{b}$, where a and b are integers.

irreducible polynomial (p. 209): A polynomial that cannot be rewritten as a product of polynomials of lower degree.

isosceles triangle (p. 581): A triangle having two sides equal in length. The third side is called the *base* and the adjoining angles are the *base angles.*

joint variation (p. 434): A function defined by the equation $z = kxy$, where k is a nonzero constant.

least common denominator (LCD) (p. 251): The least positive common multiple of the denominators of the given fractions.

leg of a right triangle (p. 581): One of the two sides that form the right angle.

linear direct variation (p. 418): *See under* direct variation.

linear equation in one variable (p. 223): A polynomial equation of degree one.

linear equation in two variables (p. 340): Any equation equivalent to one of the form $ax + by = c$, where a, b, and c are real numbers with a and b not both zero.

linear function (p. 412): A function f given by $f(x) = mx + b$.

linear programming (p. 487): A branch of mathematics concerned with maximizing or minimizing certain quantities.

linear term (p. 196): A term of degree one in the variable.

line segment (p. 576): A part of a line that consists of two points and all points between them.

maximum point of a quadratic function (p. 413): The point whose y-coordinate is the greatest value the function can have.

mean (p. 602): A statistic indicating the center of a distribution.

means (p. 282): In the proportion $\frac{a}{b} = \frac{c}{d}$, b and c are the means.

mean proportional (p. 285): When the means of a proportion are the same, the mean is called the mean proportional between the two extremes.

median (p. 603): The middle number of a frequency distribution when data are arranged in order.

member of a set (p. 10): Any object in the set.

minimum point of a quadratic function (p. 413): A point whose y-coordinate is the least value the function can have.

mixed expression (p. 260): A sum or difference of a polynomial and a fraction.

mixed numeral (p. 260): A numeral, like $3\frac{2}{5}$, that denotes the sum of an integer and a fraction.

mode (p. 603): The most frequently occurring number in a frequency distribution.

monomial (p. 143): An expression that is either a numeral, a variable, or a product of a numeral and one or more variables.

multiple (p. 75): The product of any real number and an integer is called a multiple of the real number.

multiple root (p. 224): A solution to an equation that occurs more than once.

multiplication axiom of order (p. 454): For all real numbers a, b, and c:
1. If $a < b$ and $c > 0$, then $ac < bc$; if $a > b$ and $c > 0$, then $ac > bc$.
2. If $a < b$ and $c < 0$, then $ac > bc$; if $a > b$ and $c < 0$, then $ac < bc$.

multiplication property of equality (p. 99): If $a = b$, then $ac = bc$ and $ca = cb$.

multiplicative inverse (p. 76): For a nonzero real number b, the real number $\frac{1}{b}$, for which $b \cdot \frac{1}{b} = 1$ and $\frac{1}{b} \cdot b = 1$. Also called *reciprocal.*

multiplicative property of -1 (p. 68): For all real numbers a, $a(-1) = -a$ and $(-1)a = -a$.

multiplicative property of zero (p. 68): For all real numbers a, $a \cdot 0 = 0$ and $0 \cdot a = 0$.

negative number (p. 30): A number paired with a point on the negative side of a number line.

nonterminating decimal (p. 504): A decimal for which the division process is unending.

numeral (p. 1): An expression that names a particular number. Also called *numerical expression.*

numerator: In the fraction $\frac{a}{b}$, a is the numerator.

numerical coefficient (p. 143): In a term, the factor that is not a variable; for example, 5 in $5xy$.

obtuse angle (p. 577): An angle with measure between 90 and 180.

odd integer (p. 72): An integer that is not even.

open half-plane (p. 480): One of the two regions into which a line separates the plane. The boundary line is not a member of either open half-plane.

open sentences (p. 10): Equations or inequalities containing variables.

open sentence in two variables (p. 335): An equation or inequality that contains two variables.

opposite of a number (p. 34): *See under* additive inverse.

ordered pair (p. 335): A pair of numbers, such as (1, 2), for which the order of the numbers is important.

ordinate (p. 339): The second coordinate in an ordered pair of numbers that is associated with a point in a coordinate plane. Also called *y-coordinate.*

origin (pp. 30, 339): The zero point on a number line. The zero point of the intersecting axes in a number plane.

parabola (p. 413): A graph of the equation $y = ax^2 + bx + c$ $(a \neq 0)$ where the domain is the set of real numbers.

parallel lines (p. 346): Lines in the same plane that do not intersect.

percent (p. 295): A notation for a ratio with the denominator 100. The word means "hundredths" or "divided by 100."

perfect square (p. 547): An expression such as $(x + 2)^2$, x^2, or $(3x - 2)^2$.

perimeter: The perimeter of a geometric figure is the distance around it.

plotting a point (p. 339): Locating the graph of an ordered pair of real numbers on the coordinate plane.

polynomial (p. 143): A sum of monomials.

polynomial equation (p. 223): An equation whose sides are both polynomials.

positive number (p. 30): A number paired with a point on the positive side of a number line.

postulate (p. 45): *See under* axiom.

power (p. 137): Exponential expressions such as 3^2 and 3^4 are powers of 3. The nth power of b is defined as $b^n = \underbrace{b \cdot b \cdot b \cdot \ldots \cdot b}_{n \text{ factors}}$.

prime factorization (p. 183): The expression of a positive integer as a product of prime factors.

prime factors (p. 183): Factors that are prime numbers or prime polynomials.

prime number (p. 183): An integer greater than 1 that has no positive integral factor other than itself and 1.

prime polynomial (p. 209): An irreducible polynomial whose greatest monomial factor is 1.

principal square root (p. 510): The positive square root, denoted by $\sqrt{\ }$.

probability of an event (p. 599): The ratio of the number of outcomes favoring an event to the total number of outcomes.

proof (p. 126): Logical reasoning using definitions, given facts, and axioms to show a theorem is true.

property of completeness (p. 515): Every decimal represents a real number, and every real number can be represented as a decimal.

property of the opposite of a sum (p. 53): $-(a + b) = (-a) + (-b)$.

property of square roots of equal numbers (p. 517): If r and s are any real numbers, then $r^2 = s^2$ if and only if $r = s$ or $r = -s$.

proportion (p. 282): An equation that states that two ratios are equal.

protractor (p. 577): An instrument used to find the degree measure of an angle.

Pythagorean theorem (p. 520): In any right triangle, the square of the length of the hypotenuse equals the sum of the squares of the lengths of the other two sides.

quadrants (p. 340): The four regions formed by the coordinate axes.

quadratic direct variation (p. 430): A function defined by an equation of the form $y = kx^2$, where k is a nonzero constant.

quadratic equation (p. 223): A polynomial equation of degree two.

quadratic formula (p. 553): Given $ax^2 + bx + c = 0$, $a \neq 0$, $b^2 - 4ac \geq 0$, the formula is $x = \frac{-b \pm \sqrt{b^2 - 4ac}}{2a}$.

quadratic function (p. 413): A function f given by $f(x) = ax^2 + bx + c$ $(a \neq 0)$.

quadratic polynomial (p. 196): A trinomial, such as $8x^2 + 2x - 21$, whose term of greatest degree is quadratic.

quadratic term (p. 196): A term of degree two.

quotient (p. 80): The quotient $a \div b$, $b \neq 0$, is the number whose product with b is a.

radical (p. 510): An expression of the form $\sqrt{a}$.

radical equation (p. 534): An equation that has a variable in the radicand.

radical sign (p. 510): The symbol $\sqrt{\ }$.

radicand (p. 510): An expression beneath a radical sign.

random experiment (p. 596): An activity for which you cannot predict with certainty the outcome when the activity is repeated.

range (p. 603): The difference between the highest and lowest values in a frequency distribution.

range of a function (p. 404): One of the sets comprising a function, as the values of y in $y = 7x - 1$.

ratio (p. 277): The ratio of one number to another (not zero) is the quotient of the first divided by the second.

rational expression (pp. 239, 499): A fraction; an expression for a rational number.

rational number (p. 499): A real number that can be written as the quotient of two integers.

rationalizing a denominator (p. 527): The process of expressing a fraction with an irrational denominator as an equal fraction with a rational denominator.

ray (p. 576): The part of a line that consists of a point A and all points on the line on one side of A.

real numbers (p. 31): Any number that is either a positive number, a negative number, or zero.

reciprocals (p. 76): *See under* multiplicative inverse.

reflexive property of equality (p. 47): $a = a$.

repeating decimal (p. 504): A nonterminating decimal in which the same digit or block of digits repeats unendingly. Also called *periodic decimal.*

relation (p. 440): Any set of ordered pairs. Its *domain* is the set of first coordinates in its ordered pairs; its *range* is the set of second coordinates. Its *graph* comprises the graphs of all these ordered pairs.

right angle (p. 577): An angle with measure 90.

right triangle (p. 581): A triangle having one right angle.

root of an open sentence (p. 10): A solution of the sentence.

rounding a decimal (p. 506): Breaking off a decimal to achieve an approximation, by adding 1 to the value of the last digit kept if the first digit dropped is 5 or more, or, otherwise, by leaving unchanged the digits that are kept.

sample space (p. 596): The set of all possible outcomes of a random experiment.

satisfy (p. 10): Each member of the solution set of an open sentence satisfies that sentence.

scientific notation (p. 317): A number is written in this notation when it is expressed as a product of a number greater than or equal to 1, but less than 10, and an integral power of 10.

set (p. 10): Collection of objects.

sides of an angle (p. 576): *See under* angle.

sides of an equation (p. 10): The expressions joined by the symbol of equality.

sides of an inequality (p. 450): The expressions joined by an inequality symbol.

sides of a triangle (p. 581): *See under* triangle.

similar terms (p. 143): Terms that are exactly alike or that differ only in their numerical coefficients.

similar triangles (p. 584): $\triangle ABC$ and $\triangle DEF$ are similar triangles if $m\angle A = m\angle D$, $m\angle B = m\angle E$, and $m\angle C = m\angle F$. $\angle A$ and $\angle D$ are *corresponding angles* (as are $\angle B$ and $\angle E$, $\angle C$ and $\angle F$). The sides opposite corresponding angles are *corresponding sides.*

simple interest (p. 4): Simple interest I on an investment of P dollars at the interest rate R for T years is given by the formula $I = PRT$.

simplest form of a fraction (p. 239): The fraction $\frac{a}{b}$ is in simplest form when a and b have no common factor other than 1 and -1.

simplest form of a polynomial (p. 143): A polynomial is in simplest form if no two of its terms are similar.

simplest form of a radical (p. 527): The radical contains no integral radical with a square factor other than 1, no fractions under a radical sign, and no radicals in a denominator.

simplifying a numerical expression (p. 2): Replacing a numerical expression by the simplest form of its value.

simplifying a variable expression (p. 65): Replacing a variable expression by an equivalent expression having as few terms as possible.

simultaneous equations (p. 346): *See under* system of equations.

sine (p. 587): The sine of $\angle A$ of a right triangle =

$$\frac{\text{length of leg opposite } \angle A}{\text{length of hypotenuse}}.$$

slope of a line (p. 392): If (x_1, y_1) and (x_2, y_2) are two different points on a line, then slope $= \frac{y_2 - y_1}{x_2 - x_1} (x_1 \neq x_2)$. A horizontal line has slope 0; a vertical line has no slope.

slope-intercept form (p. 397): The equation of a line in the form $y = mx + b$ where the slope is m and the y-intercept is b.

solution (p. 10): A value of a variable that converts an open sentence into a true statement.

solution of an open sentence in two variables (p. 335): An ordered pair of values for which the sentence becomes a true sentence.

solution of a system of two equations in two variables (p. 346): An ordered pair of numbers that satisfies both equations.

solution set of an open sentence (p. 10): The set that consists of the members of the domain of the variable for which the sentence is true is called the solution set of the sentence over that domain.

solve (p. 10): Find the solution set of an open sentence over a given domain.

square root (p. 510): The number a is a square root of the number b if $a^2 = b$.

standard form of a linear equation (p. 340): The form $ax + by = c$ where a, b, and c are integers with a and b not both zero.

standard form of polynomial equation (p. 224): A polynomial equation where one side is 0 and the other side is a simplified polynomial arranged in descending powers of the variable.

straight angle (p. 577): An angle with measure 180.

substitution method (p. 350): A method for finding the solution of a pair of linear equations in two variables by: (1) solving one equation for one of the variables, (2) substituting the resulting expression in the other equation, (3) solving this derived equation, (4) finding the corresponding value of the other variable.

substitution principle (p. 2): Changing the numeral by which a number is named in an expression does not change the value of the expression.

subtraction property of equality (p. 93): If a, b, and c are any real numbers and $a = b$, then $a - c = b - c$.

supplementary angles (p. 579): Two angles with 180 as the sum of their measures. Each is the *supplement* of the other.

symmetric property of equality (p. 47): If $a = b$, then $b = a$.

system of equations (p. 346): A set of equations in the same variables. Also called *simultaneous equations*.

tangent (p. 587): The tangent of $\angle A$ of a right triangle = $\dfrac{\text{length of leg opposite } \angle A}{\text{length of leg adjacent to } \angle A}$.

term (p. 46): A mathematical expression using numerals or variables or both to indicate a product or a quotient.

terminating decimals (p. 504): A decimal in which the division process stops because a remainder of zero has been reached. Also called *finite* or *ending*.

theorem (p. 126): A statement that is shown to be true by using axioms, definitions, and other proved theorems in a logical development.

transformation: Each of the following always produces an equation equivalent to the original equation:

by addition (p. 94): Adding the same number to each side.

by division (p. 99): Dividing each side by the same nonzero number.

by multiplication (p. 99): Multiplying each side by the same nonzero number.

by substitution (p. 94): Replacing either side by an expression equivalent to it.

by subtraction (p. 94): Subtracting the same number from each side.

transitive axiom of order (p. 453): For all real numbers a, b, and c:

1. If $a < b$ and $b < c$, then $a < c$.
2. If $c > b$ and $b > a$, then $c > a$.

transitive property of equality (p. 47): If $a = b$ and $b = c$, then $a = c$.

triangle (p. 581): A figure formed by connecting three points not on a line by segments. In $\triangle ABC$: $\overline{AB}$, $\overline{BC}$, and $\overline{CA}$ are the *sides* of the triangle; A, B, and C are the *vertices* of the triangle; and $\angle BAC$, $\angle ACB$, and $\angle CBA$ are the *angles* of the triangle.

trigonometric functions (p. 588): The functions having the set of acute angles as domain. $\sin A$, $\cos A$, $\tan A$.

trigonometric ratios (p. 587): Ratios of the lengths of the sides of a right triangle. *See* sine, cosine, and tangent.

trinomial (p. 143): A polynomial of three terms.

trinomial square (p. 204): A trinomial that is the square of a binomial.

uniform motion (p. 163): A term used to describe motion of an object when it moves without changing its speed or rate.

union of sets (p. 465): For any two sets A and B, the set consisting of all members belonging to at least one of the sets A and B is the union of A and B.

unit distance (p. 30): The distance between 0 and 1 on a number line.

values of a function (p. 405): Members of the range of the function.

values of a variable (p. 1): Numbers in the domain of the variable.

variable (p. 1): A symbol used to represent one or more numbers.

variable expression (p. 1): An expression that contains a variable. Also called an open expression.

vertex of an angle (p. 576): *See under* angle.

vertex of a parabola (p. 414): The minimum or maximum point of the graph of $y = ax^2 + bx + c$ $(a \neq 0)$.

vertical angles (p. 579): Two angles whose sides are rays in the same lines but in opposite directions.

vertical axis (p. 339): The vertical number line in the number plane. Also called the *y-axis.*

vertices of a triangle (p. 581): *See under* triangle.

volume: The volume of a solid is the number of unit cubes it contains.

whole numbers (p. 30): The set made up of the positive integers and zero; $\{0, 1, 2, 3, \ldots\}$.

***x*-coordinate** (p. 339): *See under* abscissa.

***x*-intercept** (p. 557): The x-coordinate of a point where a graph intersects the x-axis.

***y*-coordinate** (p. 339): *See under* ordinate.

***y*-intercept** (p. 396): The y-coordinate of a point where a graph intersects the y-axis.

zero of a function (p. 567): A zero of a function f is a solution of the equation $f(x) = 0$.

zero-product property (p. 223): For all real numbers a and b, $ab = 0$ if and only if $a = 0$ or $b = 0$.

Index

Acknowledgments

Mechanical art: ANCO/Boston. Cover: Skolos, Wedell, & Raynor. Page xiv, Jeff Rotman; 18, Donald Dietz/Stock Boston; 22, NASA; 27, Henry Ford Museum, The Edison Institute; 28, The Bettmann Archives; 33, Lee Foster/Alpha; 44, H. Wendler/The Image Bank; 56, Focus on Sports Inc.; 57, Marc Solomon/The Image Bank; 62 top, B. Evans/Peter Arnold, Inc.; 62 bot., J. McNee/FPG; 64, Chris Brown/Stock Boston; 92 Pat Goudvis/Picture Group; 97, Focus on Sports Inc.; 102 top, Bill Gallery/Stock Boston; 102 bot., David York/MediChrome Div., The Stock Shop; 108, Tim Courlas; 121, Alvis Upitis/The Image Bank; 136, Richard L. Miller/The Picture Cube; 150, Tom Tracy/The Stock Shop; 161, Philip Jon Bailey/Stock Boston; 166, Tom Walker/Stock Boston; 167, Ellis Herwig/Stock Boston; 168, Alan C. Ross/Photo Researchers, Inc.; 169, Ulrike Welsch/Stock Boston; 173 bot., Tom Stack/Tom Stack & Assoc.; 182, Dick Pietrzyk/Alpha; 194, The Image Bank; 195, Gary Milburn/Tom Stack & Assoc.; 206, Brian Seed/Click/Chicago; 207, Michal Heron; 230, Jerry Wachter/Focus on Sports Inc.; 231, Colonial Homes Magazine; 238, Clyde H. Smith/Peter Arnold, Inc.; 257 top, J. Holland/Stock Boston; 257 bot., ALON/Leo deWys Inc.; 259, V. Phillips/Leo deWys Inc.; 261, Mike Mazzaschi/Stock Boston; 266, Don Carstens/Folio; 276, NASA; 278, Grant Heilman; 294, R. Valentine Atkinson/Focus on Sports Inc.; 299, Tcherevkoff Studio/The Image Bank; 313, Sepp Seitz/Woodfin Camp & Assoc.; 315, Lou Jones; 320, California Institue of Technology; 321, Eastman Kodak Co.; 328, Peter F. Palmisano; 334, Gary Milburn/Tom Stack & Assoc.; 338, Robert McKenzie/Tom Stack & Assoc.; 349, Michal Heron; 356, Ted Spiegel/Black Star; 361, Duane Bradford/Black Star; 367, Michael Melford/The Image Bank; 374, Dennis J. Cipnic/Photo Researchers, Inc.; 378, Grant Heilman; 390, Lou Jones; 391, Scott Dietrich/Click/Chicago; 400, Malcolm S. Kirk/Peter Arnold, Inc.; 413, Riley Caton/Alpha; 418, G. C. Gladstone/The Image Bank; 423, Sherman Hines/Masterfile; 429, Gregg Mancuso/Stock Boston; 430, Aileen Soslas/Tom Stack & Assoc.; 448, Phillip A. Harrington/Fran Heyl Assocs., Courtesy of I.B.M.; 461, Focus on Sports Inc.; 464, Mike Yamashita/The Stock Shop; 478, Hallinan/FPG; 488, Michael Philip Manheim/Photo Researchers, Inc.; 498, David Madison/Bruce Coleman Inc.; 502, Clyde H. Smith/Peter Arnold, Inc.; 519, D. P. Hershkowitz/Bruce Coleman Inc.; 536, Tim Courlas; 541, Michal Heron; 546, C. Seghers/Leo deWys Inc.; 561, John McGrail/Wheeler Pictures; 566, Katrina Thomas/Photo Researchers, Inc.; Biography portraits: Gary Torrisi

Answers to Self-Tests

Chapter 1, Self-Test 1, page 12

1. 34 **2.** 8 **3.** 6 **4.** 1 **5.** 3 **6.** 3

Chapter 1, Self-Test 2, page 28

1. $9(n - 1)$ **2.** $60(t + 3)$ **3.** $\frac{1}{2}a = a - 7$
4. $c + (2c + 10) = 100$
5. 2.5 h

Chapter 1, Self-Test 3, page 40

1. 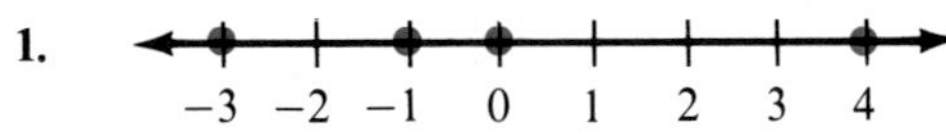

2. 16 **3.** 5 **4.** Negative two is less than one. **5.** $-5, -1, 0, 6$

Chapter 2, Self-Test 1, page 63

1. 9700 **2.** $20 + 3x$ **3.** 0 **4.** -5 **5.** -6
6. -27 **7.** -9 **8.** -11 **9.** 2

Chapter 2, Self-Test 2, page 75

1. $6y + 7$ **2.** $4x - 11$ **3.** $22 + 7z$
4. $18 + 5t$ **5.** -270 **6.** $a - 21$
7. $-18a + 30b$ **8.** -70 **9.** $n - 1$; $n + 1$
10. $x + (x + 2) = -44$

Chapter 2, Self-Test 3, page 84

1. -6 **2.** $\frac{1}{2x}$ **3.** n **4.** $-6c + 8$ **5.** -16
6. -6 **7.** 2 **8.** $-9y$

Chapter 3, Self-Test 1, page 106

1. 42 **2.** 13 **3.** -17 **4.** -90 **5.** 375 containers of juice **6.** 7 **7.** 3

Chapter 3, Self-Test 2, page 116

1. 108 min **2.** 9 **3.** -5 **4.** Eagles, 14 hits; Hawks, 17 hits

Chapter 3, Self-Test 3, page 131

1.

	Now	2 yr. ago	3 yr. from now
Kay	$x - 5$	$x - 7$	$x - 2$
Sid	x	$x - 2$	$x + 3$

2. Marcia, \$6680; Dora, \$3340 **3.** 96 dimes
4. (1) Assoc. axiom for add.; (2) Axiom of opposites; (3) Identity axiom

Chapter 4, Self-Test 1, page 147

1. a^3 **2.** $(xy)^3$ **3.** 1 **4.** -8 **5. a.** $6x^2 - 12$
b. $4x^2 + 12x - 4$ **6. a.** $-8x^2y + 3$
b. $10x^2y - 6xy^2 + 11$ **7.** 19, 21, 23

Chapter 4, Self-Test 2, page 160

1. $-2x^7$ **2.** $18a^9$ **3.** $-2a^5$ **4.** 4^{2x}
5. $-8x^{12}$ **6.** $-8x^{12}y^3$ **7.** $-16x^{12}y^4$
8. $16x^{12}$ **9.** $-32c + 4c^2$
10. $8x^3y^2 - 7x^2y^3 + \frac{1}{7}xy^4$ **11.** 13
12. $7a^2 - 62a + 48$
13. $-56t^3 + 114t^2 - 103t + 63$

Chapter 4, Self-Test 3, page 174

1. $V = \frac{kT}{P}$ **2.** 20 km/h **3.** 10 ft by 17 ft
4. no solution, contradictory facts

Chapter 5, Self-Test 1, page 195

1. $2^3 \cdot 3^2$ **2.** (1)(44), (2)(22), (4)(11), $(-1)(-44)$, $(-2)(-22)$, $(-4)(-11)$ **3.** 4
4. $-\frac{3x}{y}$ **5.** $\frac{m^4}{4k}$ **6.** $12t^2$ **7.** $-5ab^4$
8. $7t^2 + 5t - 3$ **9.** $2xy^2(2x^3y - 4x + 3)$

Chapter 5, Self-Test 2, page 207

1. $6y^2 - 8y - 30$ **2.** $6x^3 - 28x^2 + 16x$
3. $x^2 - 49$ **4.** $81a^2 - 4b^2$
5. $(2x - 7)(2x + 7)$ **6.** $9(2x^2 - 3)(2x^2 + 3)$
7. $4y^2 + 20y + 25$ **8.** $9z^2 - 30zk + 25k^2$
9. $(3a + 2)^2$ **10.** $(4m - 3n)^2$

Chapter 5, Self-Test 3, page 216

1. $(y + 5)(y + 3)$ **2.** $(x - 8)(x - 2)$
3. $(n - 7)(n + 4)$ **4.** $(v + 12t)(v - 3t)$
5. $(2x - 3)(3x - 5)$ **6.** $(3x - 2y)(x + 4y)$

Chapter 5, Self-Test 4, page 232

1. $(a + b)(5 - 2c)$
2. $(n - 1 - 10t^2)(n - 1 + 10t^2)$
3. $2a(3a - 1)^2$ **4.** $-3(2x - y)(3x - 2y)$
5. 8, -4 **6.** -2 **7.** 0, 11, -11 **8.** 0, 6, -5
9. 11 cm

Chapter 6, Self-Test 1, page 250

1. -3; $a \neq 0$, $a \neq 2$ **2.** $\frac{2a - 3}{3a + 2}$; $a \neq -\frac{3}{2}$, $a \neq -\frac{2}{3}$ **3.** $\frac{1}{12ab^2c}$ **4.** $\frac{x^2}{6}$ **5.** $-\frac{1}{2}$ **6.** $\frac{1}{3r^2}$

Chapter 6, Self-Test 2, page 258

1. $15a^2b^2$ **2.** $-5a$ **3.** $\frac{3}{4(x - 2y)}, \frac{48}{4(x - 2y)}$
4. $\frac{2y(x + y)}{xy(x + y)}, \frac{3x(x + y)}{xy(x + y)}, \frac{5xy}{xy(x + y)}$ **5.** $\frac{4a + 1}{a}$
6. $\frac{4(7b - 6)}{21ab^2}$ **7.** 1 **8.** $\frac{9x - 1}{9(x - 1)}$

Chapter 6, Self-Test 3, page 266

1. $\frac{9b + a}{b}$ **2.** $\frac{(2x - 1)(2x + 1)}{x}$ **3.** $\frac{a^2 + 1}{a + 1}$
4. $2x - 5$ **5.** $2b^2 - 3b + 7 + \frac{2}{b + 2}$

Chapter 7, Self-Test 1, page 286

1. 3:5 **2.** 40:1 **3.** 63 questions **4.** 54
5. $\frac{1}{16}$ **6.** 26

Chapter 7, Self-Test 2, page 294

1. -8 **2.** 18 **3.** -1 **4.** -6 **5.** -5
6. no solution **7.** 2, 3

Chapter 7, Self-Test 3, page 305

1. $\frac{14}{25}$ **2.** $\frac{7}{8}$ **3.** $\frac{21}{20}$ **4.** 13.6 **5.** 6.25 **6.** 250%
7. 25% **8.** \$2160 **9.** $33\frac{1}{3}$%

Chapter 7, Self-Test 4, page 316

1. 24 kg **2.** 0.2 kg **3.** 18 days **4.** $34\frac{2}{7}$ s

Chapter 7, Self-Test 5, page 327

1. 1.5×10^8 **2.** 9×10^{-9} **3.** 1 **4.** $\frac{1}{8}$
5. -16 **6.** $\frac{1}{x^5}$ **7.** $\frac{4}{a^2}$ **8.** $\frac{9}{a^8}$

Chapter 8, Self-Test 1, page 345

1. yes; no **2.** no; yes **3.** $y = \frac{2x - 6}{3}$
4. $y = \frac{10 - 2x}{5}$

5–7.

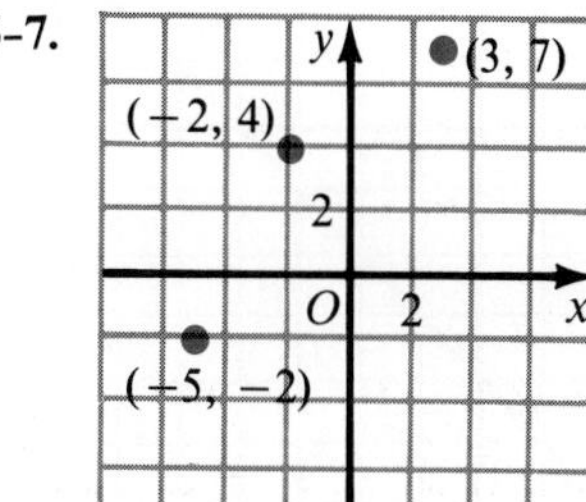

8.

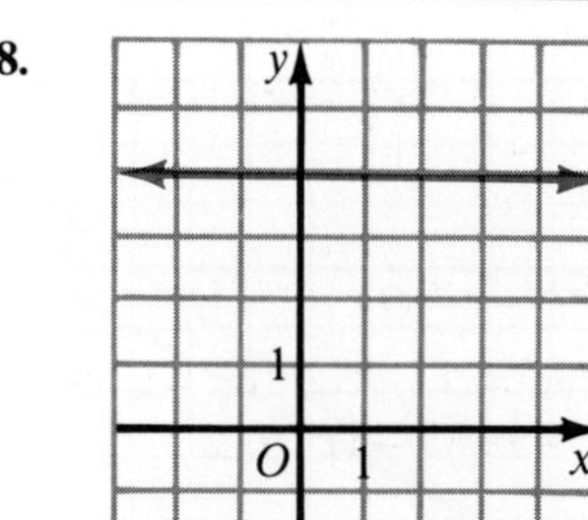

9.

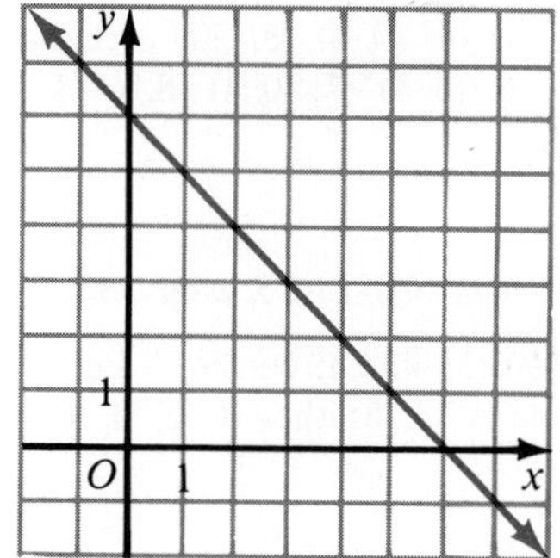

10.

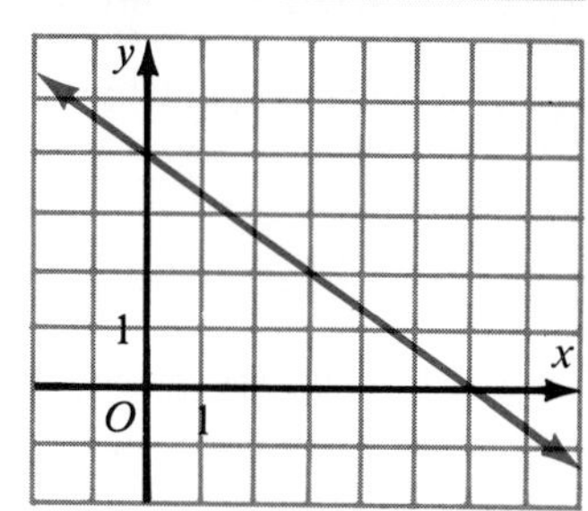

Chapter 8, Self-Test 2, page 369

1. (6,2) 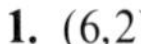

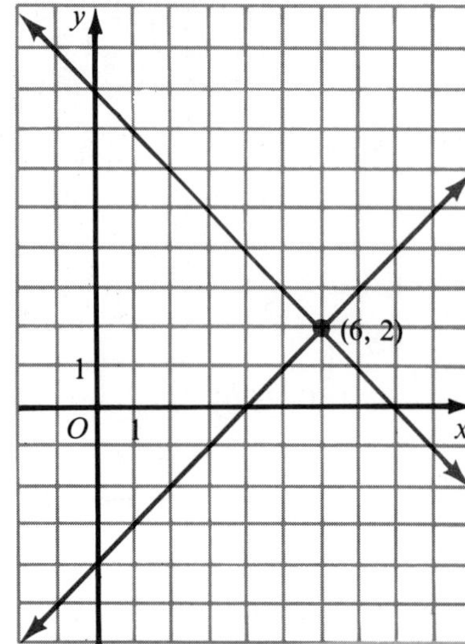

2. (−1, −2)

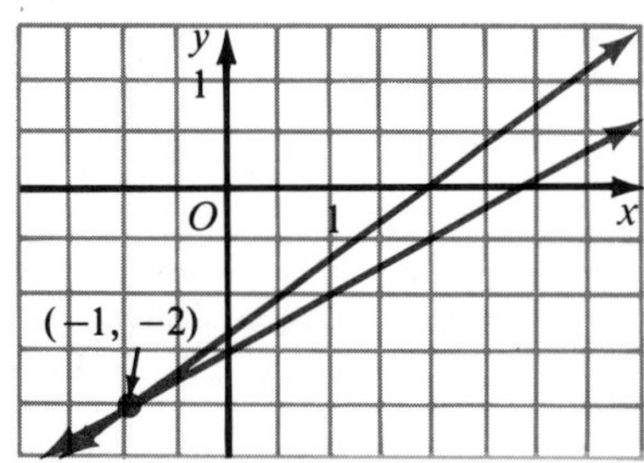

3. (6, 4) **4.** (0, 4) **5.** 500 orchestra, 400 balcony **6.** (6, 3) **7.** (0, 4) **8.** (−3, −2) **9.** (3, 2)

Chapter 8, Self-Test 3, page 382

1. boat, 23 km/h; current 7 km/h **2.** 96 **3.** Ella is 18; brother is 12 **4.** $\frac{4}{7}$

Chapter 9, Self-Test 1, page 403

1. $\frac{3}{2}$ **2.** 0 **3.** slope, $\frac{3}{7}$; y-intercept, −4 **4.** $-3x + y = 5$ **5.** $x - y = 5$

Chapter 9, Self-Test 2, page 417

1. 9 **2.** {2, 3, 6, 11, 18} **3.** D = {boric acid, salt, sodium nitrate, sugar}; R = {4.8, 36, 88, 203.9}

Amount of Substance Dissolved in 100 g Water at 20°C

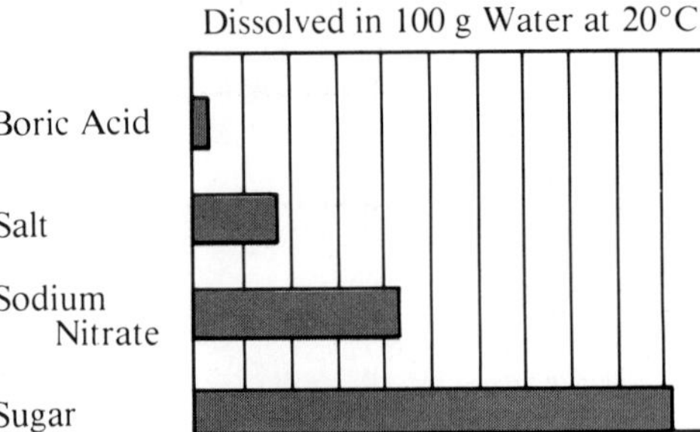

4. (1, −1); $x = 1$ **5.** 1

Chapter 9, Self-Test 3, page 438

1. $259 **2.** 7 people **3.** 196 km **4.** 158.4 g

Chapter 10, Self-Test 1, page 464

1. $-5 < -2 < -1$ **2.** {−3, −2, −1, 0, 1, 2}
3. {the real numbers less than 8}

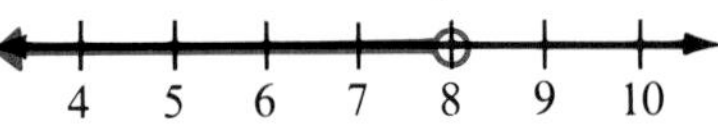

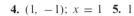

4. {the real numbers greater than or equal to −5}

5. at least 9 dimes

Chapter 10, Self-Test 2, page 478

1. {the real numbers greater than 3 or less than 2}

2. {−6, and the real numbers between −6 and 1}

3. {−2, 2, and the real numbers less than −2 or greater than 2}

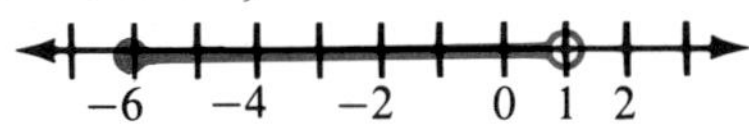

4. {−2, and the real numbers between −2 and 1}

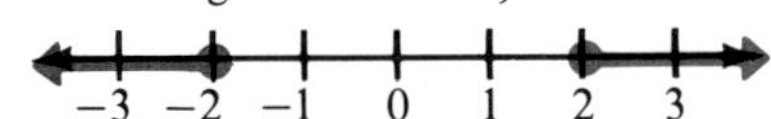

5. 8, 0

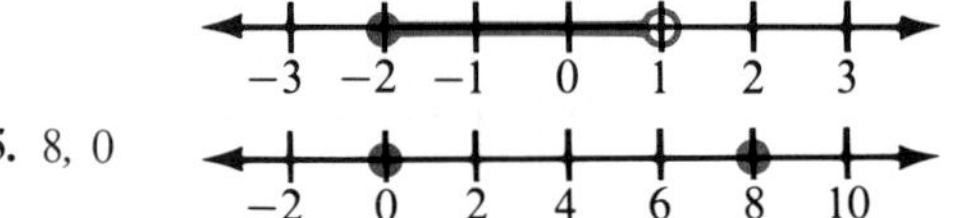

6. {1, 5, and the real numbers less than 1 or greater than 5}

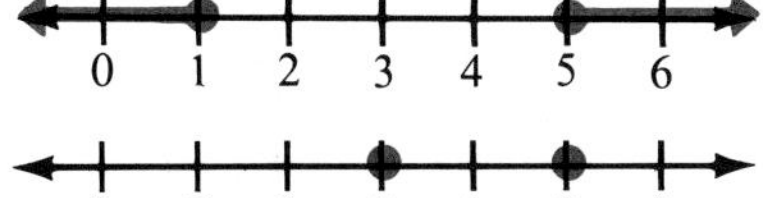

7. 0, 2

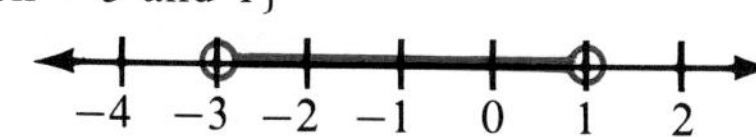

8. {the real numbers between −3 and 1}

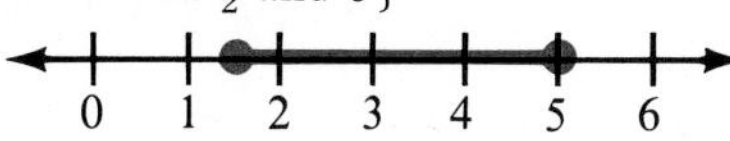

9. {$\frac{3}{2}$, 5, and the real numbers between $\frac{3}{2}$ and 5}

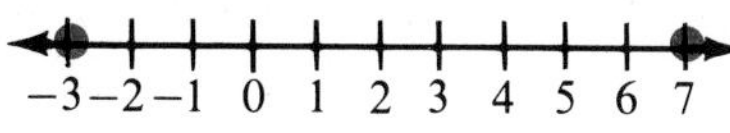

10. 7, −3

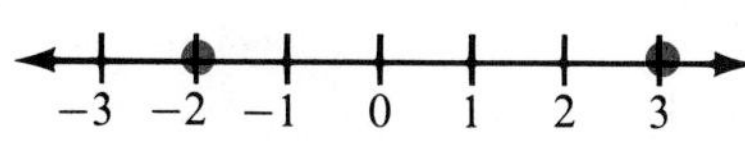

11. 3, −2

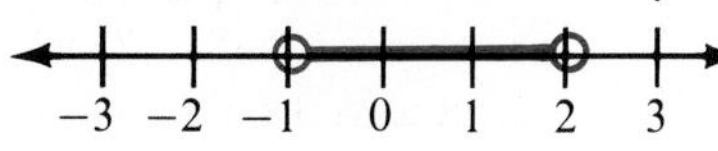

12. {the real numbers between −1 and 2}

Chapter 10, Self-Test 3, page 487

1.

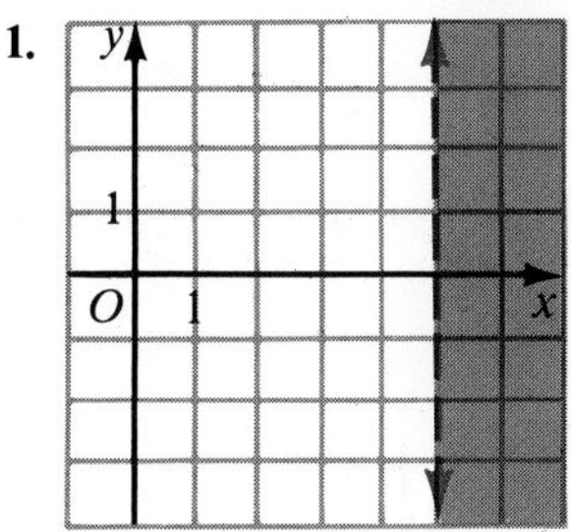

2. $y \leq 3 - \frac{x}{2}$

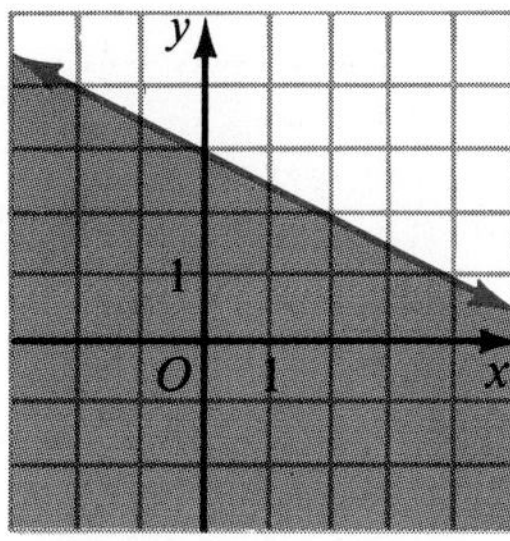

3. $y < x - 5, y \geq -3x - 1$

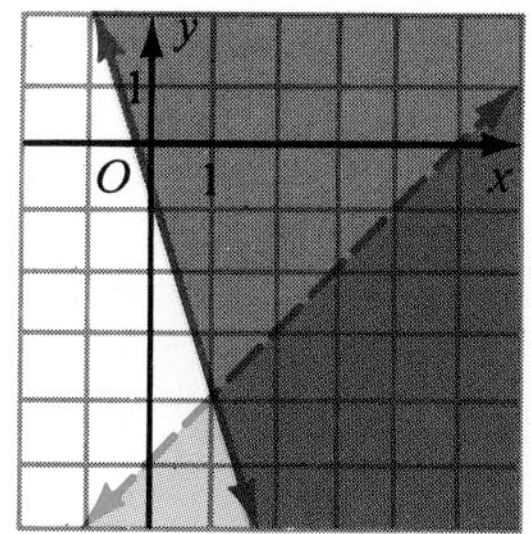

Chapter 11, Self-Test 1, page 513

1. $\frac{71}{126}$ **2.** $\frac{31}{24}$ **3.** $\frac{223}{48}$ **4.** $\frac{3}{5}$ **5.** $-\frac{33}{20}$ **6.** $\frac{13}{12}$ **7.** 0.24 **8.** 1.375 **9.** $0.2\overline{3}$ **10.** $0.6\overline{857142}$ **11.** $\frac{20}{99}$ **12.** 32 **13.** $\frac{8}{45}$ **14.** 1.6

Chapter 11, Self-Test 2, page 524

1. 9.84 **2.** 41.23 **3.** −0.94 **4.** $9|xy|$ **5.** $-12|a^3|b^4$ **6.** $0.5c^2$ **7.** {7, −7} **8.** {8, −8} **9.** $\{\frac{5}{6}, -\frac{5}{6}\}$ **10.** 22.02 **11.** no

Chapter 11, Self-Test 3, page 537

1. 30 **2.** 1 **3.** $5\sqrt{5} - 2\sqrt{11}$ **4.** $-4\sqrt{3}$ **5.** $15 - 6\sqrt{6}$ **6.** 3 **7.** $\sqrt{5} - 1$ **8.** $-3 - 2\sqrt{3}$ **9.** 4 **10.** $\frac{11}{5}$

Chapter 12, Self-Test 1, page 561

1. {3, −3} **2.** $\{3 + \sqrt{7}, 3 - \sqrt{7}\}$ **3.** {5, 7} **4.** {8, −2} **5.** $\{2, -\frac{1}{2}\}$ **6.** $\left\{\frac{3 + \sqrt{33}}{2}, \frac{3 - \sqrt{33}}{2}\right\}$ **7.** no real roots **8.** no real roots

Chapter 12, Self-Test 2, page 568

1. {−4, 0} **2.** $\left\{\frac{-3 + \sqrt{3}}{2}, \frac{-3 - \sqrt{3}}{2}\right\}$ **3.** $\{5 + 3\sqrt{5}, 5 - 3\sqrt{5}\}$ **4.** {0, −3} **5.** 10 cm by 20 cm **6.** 4 m wide

Answers to Selected Exercises

CHAPTER 1 INTRODUCTION TO ALGEBRA

Written Exercises, pages 3–4 **1.** 8 **3.** 60 **5.** 6 **7.** 29 **9.** 170 **11.** 2 **13.** 2 **15.** 3 **17.** 10 **19.** 6 **21.** 55 **23.** 1 **25.** $=$ **27.** $\neq$ **29.** 300 **31.** 65 **33.** 59 **35.** \$1250 **37.** 1 **39.** $\frac{1}{2}$ **41.** 0, 2

Written Exercises, pages 7–8 **1.** 8 **3.** 1 **5.** 69 **7.** 34 **9.** 25 **11.** $\frac{1}{2}$ **13.** 0 **15.** 8 **17.** 12 **19.** 61.6 **21.** 315 **23.** 16.28 **25.** $\neq$ **27.** $=$ **29.** $\neq$ **31.** $=$ **33.** $=$ **35.** $\neq$

Computer Key-In, page 9 **1.** 300 **3.** 1180 **5.** (21 + 33)/6; 9 **7.** (24 + 10)*(24 − 10); 476

Written Exercises, page 11 **1.** {4} **3.** {5} **5.** {5} **7.** {6} **9.** {2} **11.** {0} **13.** {3} **15.** {4} **17.** {1} **19.** {0, 1, 2, 3, 4, 5, 6, 7} **21.** {4} **23.** {2} **25.** {8} **27.** {7} **29.** {0, 2} **31.** {0, 6} Answers may vary for Exs. 33 and 35 **33.** $x + 5 = 8$; $3z = 9$ **35.** $4k - 2 = 2(2k - 1)$; $2x + 1 = 2x + 1$

Calculator Key-In, page 12 **1.** 0 **3.** 0.1 **5.** 333,333

Written Exercises, pages 15–17 **1.** d **3.** a **5.** e **7.** $2a + 2$ **9.** $\frac{1}{3}y - 6$ **11.** $30 - x$ **13.** $t - 6$ **15.** $12x$ **17.** $2w - 15$; $2(2w - 15) + 2w$, or $6w - 30$ **19.** $a + 4$ **21.** $10s$; $10(s - 5)$ **23.** $y + 8y$, or $9y$ cents **25.** $n - 5$ **27.** $r + 240$ **29.** $2(t - 6)$ **31.** $2s + (s - 6)$, or $3s - 6$ **33.** $c + 2(c - 29) + (c + 13)$, or $4c - 45$

Written Exercises, pages 20–23 **1.** $p + (p - 150) = 675$ **3.** $c + 5.5c = 105{,}000$ **5.** $2x - 1 = 47$ **7.** $t + (t + 3) = 29$ **9.** $74 = 2z + \frac{1}{2}$ **11.** s; $4s = 68$ **13.** a; $a - 10 = 7$ **15.** c; $285 - c = 14$ **17.** p; $\frac{1}{8}p = 0.95$ **19.** h; $132h = 462$ **21.** l; $\frac{1}{100}l = 8.5$ **23.** d; $d + 3.2 = 42.8$ **25.** r; $r + (2r + 3) = 24$ **27.** s; $s + s + (s + 9) = 54$ **29.** a; $a + 10 = 3(a - 8)$ **31.** m; $m + 5 = 1 + 2m$ **33.** s; $(3s - 6) + s + (3s + 2) = 80$

Problems, pages 26–27 **1.** 8.6 units **3.** 985.3 **5. a.** 24 **b.** 6 **7.** 9 men **9.** 36 white eggs **11.** 72 games **13.** 105.5 m by 68.5 m **15.** 110 wpm

Reading Algebra, page 29 **1.** $a = \frac{3}{2}x$ **3.** $0.8n + 100 = 660$ **5.** $\frac{2}{3}$ the total number of cartons of milk and fruit juice served **7.** yes; $c = 0.45(660)$ **9.** $x + \frac{1}{2}x + \frac{1}{3}x = 660$

Written Exercises, pages 32–33 **1.** 5, −5; 5 floors down **3.** 190, −190; 190 m below sea level **5.** 18, −18; \$18 loss **7.** 15, −15; 15 km west **9.** 85, −85; payments of \$85 **11.** 1, −1; one second before liftoff **13.** 50, −50; a debit of \$50 **15.** −1, 0, 1 **17.** −1, 2, 4 **19.** −5, −3, −1, 0 **21.** $-\frac{1}{2}$, $\frac{1}{2}$ **23.** S, F **25.** N, R **27.** Q, A, U **29.** M, P, T

31. −2 −1 0 1 2

33. −4 −3 −2 −1 0 1

35. −3 −2 −1 0

37. −2 −1 0 1 2

39. 7 **41.** −4 **43.** −1 **45.** 3

Written Exercises, page 36 **1.** −13 **3.** 0 **5.** 19 **7.** 8 **9.** 11 **11.** 14 **13.** $\frac{3}{2}$ **15.** 4 **17.** 1 **19.** 0 **21.** {0} **23.** $\{\frac{1}{2}, -\frac{1}{2}\}$ **25.** no solution; there is no real number whose absolute value is negative. **27.** {1, −1} **29.** {5, −5} **31.** {5, −5} **33.** {2, −2} **35.** 1.8 **37.** 2.3 **39.** 6.3 **41.** 5.2 **43.** 1.7

Written Exercises, pages 38–39 **1.** $6 > -9$ **3.** $-8 > -20$ **5.** $6 < 6.5$ **7.** $-13 < 0$ **9.** $|-5| > 2$ **11.** $-(-2) > -(-1)$ **13.** $<$ **15.** $<$ **17.** $>$ **19.** $>$ **21.** $<$ **23.** $<$ **25.** $<$ **27.** $<$ **29.** −7, −5, 0, 8 **31.** −3, −1, 2, 5 **33.** $-\frac{1}{2}, -\frac{1}{3}, -\frac{1}{4}, -\frac{1}{6}$ **35.** −1.5, −0.7, 0.3, 1.4 **37.** −3.141, 3.14, 3.1416 **39.** $-4\frac{1}{2}, -4\frac{1}{3}, -4\frac{1}{6}$ **41.** $-(-1)$, $-(-2)$, $|-3|$, $|-6|$ **43.** Cal, Flo, Sal, Nell **45.** false **47.** true **49.** false **51.** true **53.** true **55.** false; negative numbers are less than their opposites.

Challenge, page 39 **1.** 21, 28, 36, 45, 55

Chapter Review, page 41 **1.** d **3.** a **5.** c **7.** b **9.** d **11.** a

Maintaining Skills, page 43 **1.** 29.9476 **3.** 377.7 **5.** 1653.6 **7.** 16.522 **9.** 989.04 **11.** 45.79 **13.** $\frac{5}{8}, \frac{6}{8}$ **15.** $\frac{6}{21}, \frac{14}{21}$ **17.** $\frac{47}{45}$ **19.** $\frac{67}{72}$ **21.** $\frac{15}{52}$ **23.** $\frac{5}{6}$ **25.** $\frac{23}{21}$ **27.** $\frac{49}{64}$

CHAPTER 2 WORKING WITH REAL NUMBERS

Written Exercises, page 48 **1.** 550 **3.** 810 **5.** 5300 **7.** 13 **9.** 8 **11.** $10 + 2p$ **13.** $30x$ **15.** $96t$ **17.** $m + f + g + 11$ **19.** $110\ mkh$ **21.** $10{,}500\ cde$ **23.** no **25.** no; $2 \div 4 = 4 \div 2$ is false **27. a.** 13 **b.** yes **c.** no

Written Exercises, pages 51–52 **1.** 10 **3.** 0 **5.** -1 **7.** -8 **9.** 28 **11.** -36 **13.** 20 **15.** -38 **17.** -13 **19.** -11 **21.** 0 **23.** 0 **25.** 6 **27.** -15 **29.** 9 **31.** -38 **33.** -0.5 **35.** 0

Challenge, page 52 Fill 5 L container, pour it in 8 L container; next fill the 5 L container again, pour enough in 8 L container to fill it; the remainder in 5 L container is 2 L.

Written Exercises, pages 55–56 **1.** 19 **3.** 49 **5.** 107 **7.** 14 **9.** -12 **11.** -26 **13.** 24.8 **15.** -35 **17.** 0 **19.** $\frac{1}{2}$ **21.** $-\frac{9}{4}$ **23.** 2 **25.** -4 **27.** -11 **29.** 10 **31.** -15 **33.** -1.6

Problems, pages 56–58 **1.** \$818 **3.** 20th floor **5.** \$600 **7.** 12 fewer guests **9.** 3 blocks east, 9 blocks south **11.** 101 m below sea level **13.** 12:30 P.M. **15.** \$121.75

Computer Key-In, page 58 **1.** 110 **3.** 17.62

Written Exercises, pages 60–61 **1.** -260 **3.** 71 **5.** -16 **7.** -7.2 **9.** 184 **11.** 2.94 **13.** -25 **15.** -25 **17.** 121 **19.** 337 **21.** 0 **23.** -9 **25.** 1350 **27.** 12 **29.** 21 **31.** -9 **33.** 3 **35.** 116 **37.** -84 **39.** y **41.** 17 **43.** -19 **45.** -11 **47.** -5 **49.** 0 **51.** -14 **53. a.** (1) definition of subtraction, (2) commutative axiom of addition, (3) associative axiom of addition, (4) axiom of opposites, (5) identity axiom for addition

Problems, pages 62–63 **1.** 4 h **3.** 85 years old **5.** 3.8°C **7.** 91 blocks west **9.** -88.3°C

Challenge, page 63 **1.** $4 = 1 + 3$; $9 = 3 + 6$; $16 = 6 + 10$; $25 = 10 + 15$; $36 = 15 + 21$; $49 = 21 + 28$; $64 = 28 + 36$; $81 = 36 + 45$; $100 = 45 + 55$

Written Exercises, pages 66–67 **1.** 27 **3.** 5 **5.** 830 **7.** $17a$ **9.** $25n$ **11.** $9t$ **13.** $-67q$ **15.** $9x + 12$ **17.** $9r + 34$ **19.** $7 + 6w$ **21.** $13a + 13$ **23.** $11x + 31$ **25.** $8p$ **27.** $4n$ **29.** $h - 10$ **31.** $4e + 20f$ **33.** $8x + 11y + 9$ **35.** $21a + 17b$ **37.** $11r + 12$ **39.** $34c + 14d + 50$ **41.** $7(c + d) + 2(3c + 2d)$; $13c + 11d$ **43.** $(-5 + 15y) + 8 + \frac{1}{2}(12y - 8)$; $21y - 1$ **45.** $69.95x + 69.95(x + 3)$; $(139.90x + 209.85)$ dollars **47.** $248x + 160$ **49.** $113n - 9p - 99$

Written Exercises, pages 70–71 **1.** 84 **3.** 480 **5.** -84 **7.** 0 **9.** -300 **11.** 420 **13.** 18 **15.** -80 **17.** -90 **19.** $-8a + 40d$ **21.** $2r + 10s$ **23.** $4x + 4$ **25.** $6u - 11p$ **27.** $5.3t - 2s$ **29.** $-\frac{1}{3}m + 2n$ **31.** $-19x + 13y$ **33.** $3q - 9w$ **35.** $e + 3f$ **37.** $-22r - 31s$ **39.** $33 - 12g$ **41.** $-500p - 500$ **43.** (1) identity axiom of multiplication, (2) distributive axiom, (3) axiom of opposites, (4) multiplicative property of 0

Written Exercises, pages 74–75

1. $x + (x + 1) = 87$

3. $x + (x + 1) + (x + 2) + (x + 3) = -106$

5. $x + (x + 2) + (x + 4) = 81$

7. $x(x + 2) = 168$ **9.** $x + 2 = 2x - 6$

11. $x + (x + 2) + (x + 4) + (x + 6) = 36$

13. $x + (x + 1) + (x + 2) + (x + 3) = 100 - 2[(x + 3) - 2x]$

15. $(x + 1) + (x + 2) = \frac{1}{2}x - 6$

17. $2[x + (x + 1)] - [(x + 2) + (x + 3)] = 15$

19. $\frac{1}{2}(x + 1) = (x + 2) - 80$

21. $(x - 5) + (x + 2) + (x + 9) = 195$

Written Exercises, page 78 **1.** -5 **3.** -10 **5.** 1 **7.** -3 **9.** $-rs$ **11.** $5y$ **13.** $-8a + 10$ **15.** $9c - 2d$ **17.** $6m + 13k$ **19.** $-u + 6v$ **21.** $-4x - 17y$ **23.** $-27m$ **25.** $-r$ **27.** t **29.** -4 **31.** π **33.** 2

Computer Key-In, page 79 **1.** 11 **3.** 3.524

Calculator Key-In, page 79 **1.** 16 **3.** 0.00032 **5.** that number

Written Exercises, pages 82–83 **1.** −8 **3.** −99 **5.** 343 **7.** −80 **9.** −12a **11.** −142 **13.** w **15.** 5c **17.** $-5\frac{1}{2}$ **19.** −1 **21.** −3 **23.** −1 **25.** −3 **27.** 0 **29.** 16 **31.** $\frac{a-b}{c} = (a-b)\cdot\frac{1}{c} = a\cdot\frac{1}{c} - b\cdot\frac{1}{c} = \frac{a}{c} - \frac{b}{c}$

Chapter Review, pages 85–86 **1.** d **3.** c **5.** b **7.** d **9.** b **11.** c **13.** d **15.** d **17.** a **19.** d

Cumulative Review, page 88 **1.** 2 **3.** 6 **5.** 57 **7.** 32 **9.** −15 **11.** $13x + 11y$ **13.** $-a - 11b$ **15.** 0 **17.** −4 **19.** −3, −2, $-\frac{1}{2}$, 0, 5, 7
21. 

23. {10, −10} **25.** {−12} **27.** {0} **29.** $[(-2 + b) - 5] + 2(12b)$ **31.** $x + (x + 2) = 2(x + 2) - 2$

Maintaining Skills, page 89 **1.** 11.32 **3.** 291.82 **5.** 2.5996 **7.** 0.757 **9.** 55 **11.** 662 **13.** 0.0025 **15.** 192 **17.** $\frac{2}{7}$ **19.** $\frac{3}{4}$ **21.** $\frac{9}{11}$ **23.** $\frac{1}{21}$ **25.** $\frac{1}{3}$ **27.** $\frac{1}{28}$ **29.** $\frac{1}{4}$ **31.** 1 **33.** $\frac{100}{49}$ **35.** $\frac{4}{5}$ **37.** $\frac{10}{21}$

Mixed Review, page 90 **1.** −15y **3.** $\frac{3}{2}$ **5.** 117
7. 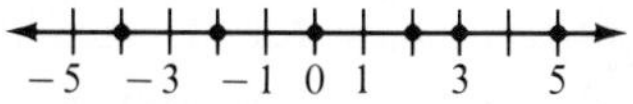

9. $-\frac{1}{2}$ **11.** −5 **13.** $2x + 7 = (x - 3) + 5$ **15.** $|-x| - 8 = 4$; −12 **17.** −155 **19.** −7, −6, $-\frac{1}{2}$, 0, $\frac{1}{5}$, 0.3, $\frac{1}{2}$

Preparing for College Entrance Exams, page 91 **1.** D **3.** A **5.** E **7.** C

CHAPTER 3 SOLVING EQUATIONS AND PROBLEMS

Written Exercises, page 96 **1.** 26 **3.** 22 **5.** 168 **7.** 11 **9.** −50 **11.** −24 **13.** −17 **15.** −10 **17.** 29 **19.** −4 **21.** −4 **23.** 0 **25.** 2 **27.** −6 **29.** −16 **31.** −4 **33.** −11 **35.** 6 **37.** 109 **39.** −2 **41.** 7 **43.** 10, −10 **45.** 7, −7 **47.** 6, −6 **49.** 5, −5 **51.** 8, −8 **53.** 0 **55.** no solution

Problems, pages 97–98 **1.** 49 **3.** −23 **5.** 44 points **7.** 15 members **9.** 94°C **11.** 64° **13.** 454 employees **15.** $.35

Calculator Key-In, page 98 **1.** 0.75 **3.** −0.4375 **5.** 0.025 **7.** −0.24 **9.** 0.96875 **11.–20.** Answers are the same.

Written Exercises, page 101 **1.** 31 **3.** −32 **5.** −256 **7.** 169 **9.** 384 **11.** −18 **13.** −24 **15.** −245 **17.** −297 **19.** 0 **21.** 66 **23.** $-\frac{2}{7}$ **25.** 7 **27.** −0.4 **29.** 34 **31.** −11 **33.** 15, −15 **35.** 16, −16

Problems, pages 101–102 **1.** −47 **3.** −2736 **5.** $24.50 **7.** 39 m **9.** 48 years old **11.** 44 h **13.** 0.02 mps; 72 mph **15.** $78,750

Written Exercises, page 105 **1.** 3 **3.** −6 **5.** 24 **7.** −175 **9.** −2 **11.** −7 **13.** −4 **15.** 0 **17.** −105 **19.** −7 **21.** −1 **23.** −16 **25.** 6 **27.** −8 **29.** −12 **31.** −2 **33.** −4 **35.** −4 **37.** 6 **39.** 2 **41.** −34 **43.** 4 **45.** 0 **47.** −18 **49.** 5 **51.** 7, −7

Computer Exercises, page 106 **1. a.** 8 **b.** 2 **c.** −10 **d.** 33 **e.** 30 **f.** 18 **3. a.** 2, −2 **b.** no solution **c.** 0.5; −0.5 **d.** 30, −30 **e.** 18, −18 **f.** 18, −18

Computer Key-In, page 107 **1.** 16 **3.** 5 **5.** 10

Problems, pages 110–111 **1.** 76 **3.** 15 **5.** 87 **7.** 69 **9.** boat, $1250; motor, $250 **11.** 12 years **13.** 7 years old **15.** 26, 27, 28 **17.** −31, −29, −27, −25 **19.** 68 m, 70 m, 72 m **21.** 16, 19 **23.** 2 waterfalls **25.** 529 cm^2 **27.** Carol, $24; Nina, $12; Lynn, $18 **29.** Sally is 12; Tilly is 29; Angie is 19 **31.** A, 15,800 bottles; B, 7900 bottles; C, 16,300 bottles **33.** 88, 89

Written Exercises, pages 113–114 **1.** 8 **3.** 19 **5.** 12 **7.** −13 **9.** −14 **11.** −13 **13.** −2 **15.** no solution **17.** −19 **19.** −16 **21.** −5 **23.** identity **25.** 4 **27.** −3 **29.** identity **31.** −1 **33.** identity **35.** −1 **37.** −2 **39.** 1

Problems, pages 114–115 **1.** 48 **3.** 7 **5.** 23 **7.** 7, 8 **9.** −14, −13 **11.** 25 g **13.** 10 units **15.** 6 years **17.** $56 **19.** 8, 12, 16, 20

Computer Exercises, page 115 **1.** -3 **3.** no solution **5.** 3

Computer Key-In, page 117 **1.** Line 110 adds the overtime pay to the regular wages. **3.** 7890, \$375.38; 9870, \$479.54; 7809, \$438.07

Problems, pages 120–121 **1.** Toby is 21. Sarah is 18. **3.** Bob is 22. Father is 46. **5.** 15 years **7.** first: length, 24 cm; width, 9 cm; second: length, 22 cm; width, 14 cm **9.** 125 lb **11.** Jack is 29. Jill is 16. **13.** Susan is 16. Ralph is 10. Neil is 5. **15.** Washington was 18. Jefferson was 7. **17.** juice, \$1.25; soup, \$1.75; fruit, \$2.25 **19.** 65 calories **21.** Paul is 58. Matt is 10.

Challenge, page 121 90186 or 60189

Problems, pages 123–124 **1.** 5 notebooks

	Number	× Price	= Cost
Pencils	$x + 7$	20	$20(x + 7)$
Notebooks	x	120	$120x$

3. 12 quarters, 24 dimes, 14 nickels

	Number	× Value of coin	= Total value
Nickels	$50 - 3q$	5	$5(50 - 3q)$
Dimes	$2q$	10	$20q$
Quarters	q	25	$25q$

5. 8 people **7.** apprentice, \$15.50; plumber, \$20 **9.** 7 quarters **11.** \$5.50 **13.** The number of half-dollars is not a natural number. **15.** 68 pennies, 34 nickels, 30 dimes, 15 quarters **17.** 13 nickels, 9 dimes, 4 quarters

Written Exercises, pages 128–129 **1. a.** (1) Associative axiom for multiplication (2) Axiom of reciprocals (3) Identity axiom for multiplication **b.** (4) Commutative axiom for multiplication (5) Commutative axiom for multiplication **3.** (2) Addition property of equality (3) Definition of subtraction (4) Associative axiom; Axiom of opposites **5.** (1) Definition of subtraction (2) Distributive axiom (3) Multiplicative property of -1

Application, page 130 **1.** \$2.40 **3.** \$.68 **5.** total amount, \$3420; interest, \$420

Chapter Review, page 132 **1.** a **3.** c **5.** a **7.** d **9.** a **11.** b

Cumulative Review, page 134 **1.** 1 **3.** 4 **5.** 46 **7.** -20 **9.** $17\frac{1}{4}$ **11.** $2x - 2$ **13.** -28 **15.** $24y$ **17.** 8 **19.** -2 **21.** -5 **23.** -4 **25.** 1 **27.** no solution **29.** -4 **31.** 16 **33.** 18 **35.** 24 **37.** 11 **39.** $\frac{9}{5}$ **41.** 36 years old **43.** \$7.80

Maintaining Skills, page 135 **1.** $2\frac{1}{12}$ **3.** $5\frac{1}{5}$ **5.** $7\frac{7}{12}$ **7.** $9\frac{1}{4}$ **9.** $\frac{25}{6}$ **11.** $\frac{25}{9}$ **13.** $\frac{47}{13}$ **15.** $\frac{119}{12}$ **17.** $18\frac{1}{5}$ **19.** $-\frac{22}{21}$ **21.** 3 **23.** $3\frac{9}{40}$ **25.** $4\frac{3}{10}$ **27.** $21\frac{27}{35}$ **29.** $-2\frac{13}{22}$ **31.** $1\frac{11}{36}$ **33.** $-1\frac{13}{21}$ **35.** $26\frac{1}{12}$

CHAPTER 4 POLYNOMIALS

Written Exercises, page 140 **1.** a^5 **3.** $5y^3$ **5.** $-8x^2$ **7.** $-7x^2$ **9.** $x + y^2$ **11.** $(x + y)^2$ **13.** $\frac{1}{2}t^6$ **15.** $(\frac{1}{3}r)^2$ **17. a.** -25 **b.** 25 **19. a.** -40 **b.** -1000 **21. a.** 16 **b.** 1000 **23. a.** -10 **b.** 4 **25.** 18 **27.** 9 **29.** -13 **31. a.** 12 **b.** 36 **33. a.** 16 **b.** 1000 **35.** 0 **37.** 256 **39.** 0 **41.** 5

Computer Exercises, pages 140–141 **1.** 1, 4, 27, 256, 3125 **3.** For $n > 1$, $n^n > n!$

Computer Key-In, page 141 **1.** 1234, \$425.50; 3412, \$400; 4321, \$516

Reading Algebra, page 142 **1.** To add and subtract polynomials; to multiply monomials. **3.** A monomial is an expression that is either a numeral, a variable, or a product of a numeral and one or more variables. A sum of monomials is called a polynomial. **5.** $3x^2 + 5x - 4$ **7.** index, table of contents

Written Exercises, pages 145–146
1. $\underline{2a} - \underline{\underline{3b}} + \underline{4a} + \underline{\underline{7b}}$; $6a + 4b$
3. $\underline{7x^2} - \underline{\underline{3xy}} + \underline{\underline{5xy}} - \underline{4x^2}$; $3x^2 + 2xy$
5. $\underline{x^2y} + xy^2 - \underline{3x^2y} + xy$; $-2x^2y + xy^2 + xy$ **7.** $8a + 5$ **9.** $3y + 5$ **11.** $7a^2 - 7a + 2$ **13.** $-2a^2 - 2ab - 8b$ **15.** $7x - 2y - 6z + 8$ **17.** $-2a - 9$ **19.** $6x - 11y - 1$ **21.** $-a^2 - 3a - 16$ **23.** $8a^2 - 2ab - 6b$ **25.** $12a - 9b - 1$ **27.** $8a^2 + 2a - 8$ **29.** xy^2 **31.** $2a - 7$ **33.** $x - 2y$ **35.** $4x^2 - 11$ **37.** $n^2 - 9m^2 + mn$ **39.** 1 **41.** 4 **43.** $\frac{4}{3}$ **45.** 8 **47.** -3 **49.** no solution

Problems, pages 146–147 **1.** 25, 26 **3.** 58, 60, 62, 64 **5.** 22 **7.** 8, 9 **9.** 7, 9, 11 **11.** 17, 18, 19, 20 **13.** length, 25 m; width, 23 m

Written Exercises, pages 149–150 **1.** b^{10} **3.** $15a^8$ **5.** $6x^3y^3$ **7.** $24a^3b^4$ **9.** $-24c^5d^7$ **11.** $6a^5b^9$ **13.** x^6 **15.** $2y^5$ **17.** $4p^5r^3$ **19.** b^{n+3} **21.** 32 **23.** $7ay^{a+7}$ **25.** -128, 128 **27.** $26a^4$ **29.** $-14x^9$ **31.** $-2x^3y^3$ **33.** $8x^5y^6$ **35.** $10ab$, $6a^2b^2$ **37.** $18a$, $10a^2$ **39.** $46x^2$ **41.** $6a^3$ **43.** $18a^3$

Written Exercises, pages 152–153 **1. a.** x^{12} **b.** x^{12} **c.** x^7 **3. a.** a^{2n} **b.** a^{2n} **c.** a^{2+n} **5. a.** 16 **b.** 64 **c.** 64 **7. a.** 18 **b.** 36 **c.** 36 **9.** $64n^2$ **11.** $32x^5$ **13.** $81n^8$ **15.** $\frac{1}{1000}x^{30}$ **17.** $16a^4b^8$ **19.** $8a^6b^{18}$ **21. a.** $9x^{10}$ **b.** $-9x^{10}$ **23. a.** $-27x^{15}$ **b.** $-27x^{15}$ **25.** $32a^5$ **27.** $10{,}000b^8$ **29.** $108x^7y^6$ **31.** $-\frac{1}{2}c^{15}d^8$ **33.** $72a^{5n}$ **35.** $2y^{2mn}$ **37.** $2x^4y^6$ **39.** $4c^5d^2$ **41. a.** $8x^3$, $64x^3$ **b.** 8 times **43.** $2^{4x} \cdot 2^{4x} = 2^{8x}$

Challenge, page 153 Dividing by $(r - s)$ is not defined because if $r = s$, then $r - s = 0$.

Written Exercises, pages 155–156 **1.** $5a + 10$ **3.** $-8a + 24$ **5.** $4x^2 + 8x$ **7.** $-6b + 15b^2$ **9.** $5x^3 - 10x^2 - 15x$ **11.** $-16x^4 + 24x^3 - 32x^2$ **13.** $2a^3 - a^2b + 4ab^2$ **15.** $6b^3 - 15b^2 - 27b$ **17.** $-6n^4 + 8n^3 + 12n^2$ **19.** $11x^2 - 9x$ **21.** $2y^3$ **23.** $14x^3 - 14x^2$ **25.** $7x - 6$ **27.** 3 **29.** -1 **31.** $-\frac{5}{2}$ **33.** 7 **35.** 1 **37.** $\frac{2}{3}$ **39.** 64; $80 - L$; $W + 50 - L$; $W + 60 - L$; $W + G - L$ **41.** $2x^2 + 5x$ **43.** $2x^2 + 8x + 8$ **45.** $2x^{2n} - 3x^{n+1} + 4x^n$ **47.** $2b^{2n+2} + 3b^{n+3}$

Challenge, page 156 $x = 12$

Written Exercises, pages 158–159 **1.** $a^2 + 8a + 15$ **3.** $c^2 - 3c - 10$ **5.** $2a^2 + 9a - 18$ **7.** $12t^2 + 7t - 10$ **9.** $x^3 + 5x^2 + 10x + 8$ **11.** $2a^3 + 5a^2 + 11a - 7$ **13.** $24x^3 - 23x^2 + 37x - 20$ **15.** $8 + 4t^2 - 3t^3$ **17.** $6n^2 + 3n - 45$ **19.** $16y^3 - 34y^2 + 11y + 6$ **21.** $6c^2 - 11cd - 7d^2$ **23.** $4x^3 - 4x^2y - xy^2 + y^3$ **25.** ac, bc, ad, bd; $ac + bc + ad + bd = (a + b)(c + d)$; $ac + bc + ad + bd = ac + bc + ad + bd$ **27.** $12 + 14n - 12n^2 + 16n^3$ **29.** $14 - 73y + 73y^2 - 20y^3$ **31.** $8c^3 - 55c^2d - 8cd^2 + 7d^3$ **33.** $24x^3 + 4x^2y - 16xy^2 + 4y^3$ **35.** $2y^4 - y^3z + 2y^2z^2 - 5yz^3 + 2z^4$ **37.** $\frac{1}{3}$ **39.** 5 **41.** $\frac{23}{5}$ **43.** $x^3 + 9x^2 + 27x + 27$ **45.** $2y^2 - xy - 5x^2$ **47. a.** (1) $x^3 + 1$ (2) $x^4 - 1$ (3) $x^5 + 1$ **b.** (4) $x^6 - 1$ (5) $x^7 + 1$

Computer Exercises, page 159
1. $4 + 11x + 3x^2$; $2 - 3x + 7x^2$
3. $5x^3 + 9x^2 + 4x$; $4x + 9x^2 - 5x^3$

Written Exercises, page 162 **1.** $r = \frac{C}{2\pi}$ **3.** $g = \frac{2s}{t^2}$, $t \neq 0$ **5.** $z = a$ **7.** $h = \frac{2A}{b + c}$, $b + c \neq 0$ **9.** $F = \frac{9}{5}C + 32$ **11.** $t = \frac{A - P}{Pr}$, $P \neq 0$, $r \neq 0$ **13.** $d = 4A - a - b - c$ **15.** $x = \frac{4}{a}$, $a \neq 0$ **17.** $w = -\frac{4}{a}$, $a \neq 0$ **19.** $l = \frac{2s}{n} - a$, $n \neq 0$ **21.** $n = \frac{360}{180 - a}$, $a \neq 180$ **23.** $u = \frac{2b}{a}$, $a \neq 0$ **25.** $L = \frac{a + sr - s}{r}$, $r \neq 0$ **27.** $P = \frac{A}{1 + rt}$, $r \neq -\frac{1}{t}$ **29.** $R = \frac{Cr}{C - Kr}$, $Kr \neq C$

Problems, pages 166–167 **1.** 24 km/h **3.** 2:30 P.M. **5.** 4:30 P.M. **7.** 360 km **9.** 4 km **11.** 400 m **13.** 215 km **15.** $\left(\frac{b}{s - r}\right)$ hours **17.** 5:00 P.M.

Problems, pages 169–170 **1.** length, 9 m; width, 4 m **3.** Both are 400 cm² **5.** 3500 cm² **7.** length, 20 m; width, 15 m **9.** 6 m **11. a.** $[8r + 2\pi r + \pi]$ m **b.** 6π m

Computer Key-In, pages 170–171

1.

ITEM	NO. SOLD	PRICE	COST
2341	7	8.25	57.75
7204	4	10.95	43.80
3475	12	9.68	116.16
5068	15	11.49	172.35

Problems, pages 172–174 **1.** no solution; impossible to have the same number of dimes as quarters and have \$8 **3.** no solution; need to know either the amount of her gains or the amount of her losses **5.** 90 km/h **7.** no solution; six years ago Barbara had not been born according to the information in problem **9.** no solution; there are no three consecutive integers whose sum is 36 more than the greatest consecutive integer **11.** no solution; need to know the time traveled by automobile **13.** 7 cm **15.** no solution; the sum of their ages two years ago was greater than 10

Chapter Review, pages 175–176 **1.** d **3.** b **5.** d **7.** d **9.** d **11.** b **13.** a **15.** b **17.** b

Cumulative Review, page 178 **1.** -72 **3.** 0 **5.** -14 **7.** 45 **9.** $8z - 5$ **11.** $1600a^{5n}$ **13.** $-12x^4 + 8x^3 + 20x^2$ **15.** $15 - 2x - 8x^2$ **17.** 0 **19.** 0 **21.** no solution **23.** -12 **25.** -1 **27.** -3 **29.** 11 **31.** 4 **33.** -10 **35.** $m = \frac{bn + c}{a}$ **37.** \$1.50 **39.** 15 cm × 13 cm

Maintaining Skills, page 179 **1.** 1045 **3.** -44 **5.** -23 **7.** -85 **9.** $\frac{5}{8}$ **11.** 19.15 **13.** 72 **15.** -92 **17.** -21.275 **19.** 3.282 **21.** -28.96 **23.** $-\frac{7}{15}$ **25.** $\frac{19}{17}$ **27.** 13 **29.** -0.45 **31.** $\frac{1}{2}$

Mixed Review, page 180 **1.** 4 **3.** no solution **5.** $2x^2 + 2x - 12$ **7.** $3x - 1$ **9.** 1 year old **11.** identity axiom for multiplication **13.** associative axiom for multiplication **15.** identity axiom for addition **17.** 8 **19.** 18.75 km/h **21.** $h = \frac{2A}{b_1 + b_2}$ **23.** 9, 11, 13, 15

Preparing for College Entrance Exams, page 181 **1.** B **3.** B **5.** A **7.** C

CHAPTER 5 FACTORING POLYNOMIALS

Written Exercises, pages 184–185 **1.** (1)(18), (2)(9), (3)(6), (−1)(−18), (−2)(−9), (−3)(−6) **3.** (1)(37), (−1)(−37) **5.** (1)(64), (2)(32), (4)(16), (8)(8), (−1)(−64), (−2)(−32), (−4)(−16), (−8)(−8) **7.** (1)(101), (−1)(−101) **9.** (1)(83), (−1)(−83) **11.** (−1)(18), (−2)(9), (−3)(6), (1)(−18), (2)(−9), (3)(−6) **13.** (−1)(37), (1)(−37) **15.** (−1)(64), (−2)(32), (−4)(16), (−8)(8), (1)(−64), (2)(−32), (4)(−16) **17.** (−1)(101), (1)(−101) **19.** (−1)(83), (1)(−83) **21.** $3^2 \cdot 11$ **23.** $2^3 \cdot 13$ **25.** $3^3 \cdot 7$ **27.** $2^2 \cdot 7 \cdot 17$ **29.** $2^3 \cdot 3 \cdot 17$ **31.** $2 \cdot 11^2$ **33.** $5 \cdot 7 \cdot 13$ **35.** $2^3 \cdot 3 \cdot 5^2$ **37.** 14 **39.** 36 **41.** 36 **43.** 175 **45.** 1 **47.** 13

Challenge, page 185 Browns' rate = 3 m/s; Coles' rate = 4 m/s; pond is 360 m wide

Written Exercises, pages 189–190 **1.** $3a^3$ **3.** $\frac{1}{3y^2}$ **5.** $\frac{3x^2y^2}{4}$ **7.** $\frac{2}{3b^4}$ **9.** $\frac{1}{x}$ **11.** $\frac{1}{3y}$ **13.** 8 **15.** $-\frac{8}{y^3}$ **17.** $\frac{4b^2}{a^5}$ **19.** $\frac{c^5}{13d^4}$ **21.** $3a^4$ **23.** $-2c^2d$ **25.** $-8x^4y^2$ **27.** $7b^3$ **29.** a^4b^2 **31.** x^4y **33.** $2a^3b^2$ **35.** $8rs^2t^2$ **37.** ab^2 **39.** $x + y$ **41.** $\frac{8x^{n-1}}{7}$ **43.** $-x^{2n}y^n$ **45.** (1) Def. of division, (2) Prop. of the recip. of a product, (3) Comm. ax. for mult.; Assoc. ax. for mult., (4) Def. of division

Calculator Key-In, page 190 **1.** 3; $\frac{3}{13}$ **3.** 5; $\frac{5}{11}$ **5.** 26; $\frac{13}{18}$

Written Exercises, pages 192–193 **1.** $a + 2$ **3.** $6x - 3$ **5.** $x - 2y + 3$ **7.** $2y - 3x$ **9.** $2 - 3y - y^2$ **11.** $-4d^3 + 3cd + 2$ **13.** $6s^3t^2 - 5$ **15.** $3d^2k^2 - 5dk + 2d^2$ **17.** 780 **19.** 380 **21.** 8100 **23.** 850 **25.** 770 **27.** $3(3p - 2q + 1)$ **29.** $3a(5a - 3)$ **31.** $4a^2(a + 2)$ **33.** $5y(2y^2 - y + 3)$ **35.** $\frac{1}{2}h(b - a)$ **37.** $6a^2x(4a^2 - 3a + 2x)$ **39.** $8a(ab - 2b - 3)$ **41.** $-8r^8s^5(5s + 2r)$ **43.** $42w^2yz(3x^3 + 5wy^3z)$ **45.** $5x - 4$ **47.** $6x - 2$ **49.** $a + 5ab - a^2$

Problems, pages 194–195 **1.** $r^2(4 - \pi)$ **3.** $r^2(4 + \pi)$ **5.** $4r^2(4 - \pi)$ **7.** $2r^2(2\pi - 1)$ **9.** $r^2(4 + 3\pi)$

Written Exercises, pages 197–198 **1.** $x^2 + 9x + 14$ **3.** $a^2 - 9a + 20$ **5.** $c^2 + 10c + 21$ **7.** $a^2 - 14a + 45$ **9.** $2a^2 + 11a + 5$ **11.** $2a^2 + 3a - 27$ **13.** $x^2 - 2x - 63$ **15.** $b^2 + 5b - 24$ **17.** $6k^2 + 17k + 5$ **19.** $35a^3 - 74a^2 + 35a$ **21.** $12x^3 - 26x^2 - 10x$

23. $14k^3 - 27k^2 - 20k$
25. $6x^2 + 16xy + 8y^2$
27. $27a^2 - 51ab + 10b^2$ **29.** $2a^4 + a^2 - 21$
31. $x^6 + 4x^4 - 21x^2$
33. $3a^8 - 11a^4b^2 + 10b^4$ **35.** 26 **37.** 3
39. 1 **41.** $a = 9$, $b = 2$, $c = -6$
43. $x^{2n} - 16y^{2n}$

Computer Exercises, page 198
1. $x^2 + 8x + 15$ **3.** $8x^2 - 14x - 15$
5. $9x^2 - 4$

Calculator Key-In, page 198 **1.** 44 **3.** 11
5. 600 **7.** 728 **9.** 17.5

Written Exercises, pages 200–201 **1.** $a^2 - 9$
3. $9b^2 - 25$ **5.** $81a^2 - 49$ **7.** $64a^2 - 25b^2$
9. $9u^4 - v^2$ **11.** $r^2s^2 - t^4$ **13.** 391 **15.** 3596
17. 2499 **19.** 39,984 **21.** $(5y - 3)(5y + 3)$
23. $(12 - x)(12 + x)$
25. $(3a - bc)(3a + bc)$
27. $(x^3 - y^3)(x^3 + y^3)$
29. $(5t^3 - 12)(5t^3 + 12)$
31. $(15 - ab^2)(15 + ab^2)$
33. $(ab - c^2)(ab + c^2)(a^2b^2 + c^4)$
35. $(a - 1)(a + 1)(a^2 + 1)(a^4 + 1)(a^8 + 1)$
37. $3(2x + 3)$ **39.** $2(2a)$
41. $9(2x - 3y)(2x + 3y)$
43. $2xy(1 - 6x)(1 + 6x)$
45. $9t(3t^4 - 1)(3t^4 + 1)$
47. $2a(15a^2 - 2)(15a^2 + 2)$
49. $(x^n - y^n)(x^n + y^n)$
51. $(b^n - c^{2n})(b^n + c^{2n})$
53. $(a^{2n} - b^{3n})(a^{2n} + b^{3n})$
55. $y^3(y^n - 1)(y^n + 1)$

Extra, page 202 **1.** $x^3 + y^3$
3. $(w + 2)(w^2 - 2w + 4)$
5. $(n + 5)(n^2 - 5n + 25)$
7. a. $(z^2 - 1)(z^4 + z^2 + 1) =$
$(z - 1)(z + 1)(z^4 + z^2 + 1)$
b. $(z^3 - 1)(z^3 + 1) =$
$(z - 1)(z^2 + z + 1)(z + 1)(z^2 - z + 1)$
c. $z^4 + z^2 + 1 =$
$z^4 + z^2 + z^2 + 1 - z^2 =$
$(z^4 + 2z^2 + 1) - z^2 =$
$(z^2 + 1)^2 - z^2 =$
$(z^2 + 1 - z)(z^2 + 1 + z) =$
$(z^2 - z + 1)(z^2 + 1 + z)$

Challenge, page 202 **1.** 6 times

Written Exercises, pages 205–206
1. $x^2 + 4x + 4$ **3.** $a^2 - 8a + 16$
5. $4x^2 + 12x + 9$ **7.** $16k^2 - 40k + 25$
9. $16p^2 + 24pq + 9q^2$
11. $9x^2 + 42xy + 49y^2$
13. $a^2b^2 - 10ab + 25$ **15.** $4s^2t^2 - 28st + 49$
17. $9 - 30a + 25a^2$ **19.** $64x^4 - 16x^2 + 1$
21. $(n - 1)^2$ **23.** $(r - 2)^2$ **25.** $(9 - b)^2$
27. $(2x + 1)^2$ **29.** $(6 - 5a)^2$ **31.** $(8x - y)^2$
33. $(x^2 + 1)^2$ **35.** $(ab - 6)^2$ **37.** $(a^2 - 12)^2$
39. $(5x - 2)^2 = 25x^2 - 20x + 4$;
$(2 - 5x)^2 = 4 - 20x + 25x^2$
b. $(2 - 5x)^2 = (-1)(5x - 2)(-1)(5x - 2) =$
$(5x - 2)^2$ **41.** $(x^2 - 9)(x^2 - 9) = (x + 3)$
$(x - 3)(x + 3)(x - 3) = (x + 3)^2(x - 3)^2$
43. $3(z + 3)^2$ **45.** $2(3y - 1)^2$
47. $5(2x^2 + 3)^2$ **49.** $4k(2k^2 - 3)^2$
51. $(w + 3 - 2q)(w + 3 + 2q)$
53. $(5c - 2d - 1)(5c + 2d + 1)$ **55.** -9
57. -1 **59.** 7, 8, 9
61. $a^2 + 2ab + b^2 - (a^2 - 2ab + b^2) \stackrel{?}{=} 4ab$;
$a^2 + 2ab + b^2 - a^2 + 2ab - b^2 \stackrel{?}{=} 4ab$;
$4ab = 4ab$ **63. a.** 1225; 3025; 7225
b. $(10t + 5)^2 = 100t^2 + 100t + 25 =$
$[t(t + 1) \times 100] + 25$

Written Exercises, pages 209–210
1. $(x + 5)(x + 1)$ **3.** $(a - 3)(a - 1)$
5. $(r + 6)(r + 3)$ **7.** $(k - 4)(k - 7)$
9. $(z - 6)(z - 7)$ **11.** prime
13. $(y + 11)(y + 5)$ **15.** $(p - 9)(p - 8)$
17. $(10 - c)(2 - c)$ **19.** $(x - 7y)(x - 5y)$
21. $(s - 5t)(s - 6t)$ **23.** $(b + 8c)(b + 5c)$
25. $(s - 6t)(s - 7t)$ **27.** prime
29. $(d + 9e)(d + 3e)$ **31.** $(a - 8)(a - 15)$
33. $(9 - a)(12 - a)$ **35.** $(7n - x)(14n - x)$
37. 7, 11, -7, -11 **39.** 8, 16, -8, -16
41. 7, 8, 13, -7, -8, -13
43. $(x + 6)(x + 3)$
45. $(a + b - 4)(a + b - 2)$
47. $(a + 3)(a - 3)(a + 1)(a - 1)$
49. $(c + 3)(c - 3)(c^2 - 3)$
51. $(x^n - 19y^{2n})(x^n - 23y^{2n})$

Computer Exercises, page 210 **1.** yes **3.** no
5. no

Written Exercises, pages 212–213
1. $(a + 5)(a - 1)$ **3.** $(y - 6)(y + 1)$
5. prime **7.** prime **9.** $(a + 7)(a - 5)$
11. $(z + 9)(z - 4)$ **13.** $(p - 7)(p + 3)$
15. prime **17.** $(a - 6b)(a + 5b)$

19. $(p - 10q)(p + 5q)$
21. $(k - 15d)(k + 4d)$
23. $(x - 11y)(x + 2y)$
25. $(1 - 10ab)(1 + 2ab)$
27. $(1 - 8ab)(1 + 7ab)$ **29.** $(r - 24)(r + 6)$
31. $(40 + b)(20 - b)$ **33.** $(40 + x)(8 - x)$
35. $-27, 27, -3, 3, -12, 12$ Answers may vary for Exs. 37–41. **37.** $-18, -10$
39. $-140, -96$ **41.** $-26, -60$
43. $(x - 4)(x + 4)$
45. $(2x - y + 10)(2x - y - 6)$
47. $(x - 3)(x + 3)(x^2 + 1)$
49. $3(a^2 + 4)(a - 5)(a + 5)$

Written Exercises, page 216
1. $(2x + 3)(x + 1)$ **3.** $(5a + 1)(a + 1)$
5. $(7n - 1)(n - 1)$ **7.** $(5y - 1)(y - 3)$
9. prime **11.** $(2t + 3)(t - 2)$
13. $(8y - 9)(y + 1)$ **15.** $(k + 3)(7k - 2)$
17. prime **19.** $-(2y - 5)(y + 2)$
21. $(a + 2b)(a - b)$ **23.** $(9r + 2s)(r - 3s)$
25. $(5a - b)(5a + 3b)$
27. $(3x - 2y)(4x + 9y)$
29. $-(2x - 3)(6x + 7)$
31. $-(3c + 1)(16c - 15)$
33. $(3x + 1)(36x - 7)$
35. $(14y + 9)(3y + 1)$ **37.** $(2y + 5)(y + 5)$
39. $x^2(x - 4)(x + 4)$
41. $(5a - 5b + 2)(2a - 2b - 3)$

Computer Key-In, page 217 **1.** $(1)(36)$, $(-1)(-36)$, $(2)(18)$, $(-2)(-18)$, $(3)(12)$, $(-3)(-12)$, $(4)(9)$, $(-4)(-9)$, $(6)(6)$, $(-6)(-6)$; $(1)(-36)$, $(-1)(36)$, $(2)(-18)$, $(-2)(18)$, $(3)(-12)$, $(-3)(12)$, $(4)(-9)$, $(-4)(9)$, $(6)(-6)$, $(-6)(6)$ **3.** $(1)(87)$, $(-1)(-87)$, $(3)(29)$, $(-3)(-29)$; $(1)(-87)$, $(-1)(87)$, $(3)(-29)$, $(-3)(29)$

Written Exercises, pages 219–220
1. $(n - 3)(2t + 1)$ **3.** $(x + y)(3 - y)$
5. $(x^2 + 1)(2d - e + f)$ **7.** $(g + h)(z - 1)$
9. $(2 + x)(x - y + 2z)$
11. $(2m + n)(p - 4r)$ **13.** $(2w - 1)(z^2 - 6)$
15. $(2r + 5)(s - 6)$ **17.** $(p + q)(2 + a)$
19. $(q + r)(p + 2r)$ **21.** $(b + c)(a - 2)$
23. $(x^2 + 4)(2x + 1)$ **25.** $(4x - 3)(x - 2y)$
27. $(4y - 1)(y + 2a)$ **29.** $(2x + 7z)(2x - y)$
31. $(a - 2b - 3c)(a + 2b + 3c)$
33. $(6k - 2a + c)(6k + 2a - c)$
35. $(x - 4y - 3)(x - 4y + 3)$
37. $(x + 3 - y)(x + 3 + y)$
39. $(h - 6 - k)(h - 6 + k)$
41. $(5 - a - 2b)(5 + a + 2b)$
43. $(4y + 1 - 4z)(4y + 1 + 4z)$
45. $(a - 2b + 2)(a + 2b - 2)$
47. $(a - b - 5c)(a + b + 5c)$
49. $9(a - b - c)(a - b + c)$
51. $(a - b)(a - b - 3)$
53. $(2x^2 - 2x + 1)(2x^2 + 2x + 1)$
55. $(a - 2b^{2n})(a^{3n} - b)$

Written Exercises, pages 222–223
1. $5(a + b)^2$ **3.** $-7z(2z + 1)(z - 3)$
5. $8x(5x^2 + 7x - 2)$ **7.** $t^2(t - 3)(t + 1)$
9. $(x + 5)(y - 2)$ **11.** $36z(2z + q)(2z - q)$
13. $(x - y)(x + y)(x^2 + y^2)$
15. $2(x - 3)(x + 3)(x^2 + 9)$
17. $(a - 2b - 1)(a + 2b + 1)$
19. $(y - 2)(y + 2)(y - 1)(y + 1)$
21. $(b - 3)^2(b + 3)^2$ **23.** $5k(2k - 5)(k + 1)$
25. $2(x - 2y + 2)(x + 2y - 2)$
27. $4(a - 4)(a - 2)$ **29.** $(x - 1)(x - 2)(x + 2)$
31. $(m - k)(m + k + 1)$
33. $c(a - 2b - 3c)(a - 2b + 3c)$
35. $(x - a)(ax + a^2 - x)$
37. $(b - 3c)(a - 3b)(a + 3b)$
39. $2(1 - 2x - y)(1 + 2x + y)$
41. $(x + 1)^2(x - 2)$
43. $(x + 2y)(a - 3x + 6y)$
45. $2(p + 1)(p - 4)(p - 2)$
47. $(p - 2q - r + 2s)(p - 2q + r - 2s)$
49. $3(15x + y)(x - 4y)$
51. $-(b - c - a)(b - c + a)(b + c - a)(b + c + a)$
53. $(a + 3b)^2(1 - a + 3b)(1 + a - 3b)$
55. $(x + y - x^2 + 2y^2)(x + y + x^2 - 2y^2)$
57. $(x - 1)(x - 2)(x + 2)$

Written Exercises, page 225 **1.** $\{-17, -7\}$ **3.** $\{0, 35\}$ **5.** $\{-\frac{1}{2}, 3\}$ **7.** $\{0, 4, -\frac{7}{2}\}$ **9.** $\{0, \frac{8}{3}, -\frac{1}{3}\}$ **11.** $\{-9, 7\}$ **13.** $\{2, 3\}$ **15.** $\{5\}$ **17.** $\{1, 9\}$ **19.** $\{4, -4\}$ **21.** $\{2\}$ **23.** $\{0, 1, -1\}$ **25.** $\{6, -5\}$ **27.** $\{0, 5\}$ **29.** $\{\frac{5}{2}, -\frac{1}{2}\}$ **31.** $\{-8, 3\}$ **33.** $\{-\frac{1}{3}, \frac{1}{2}\}$ **35.** $\{3, -1\}$ **37.** $\{\frac{1}{4}, 7\}$ **39.** $\{-\frac{9}{2}, \frac{8}{3}\}$ **41.** $\{0, 7\}$ **43.** $\{-1, -2, 2\}$ **45.** $\{1, -1, 3, -3\}$ **47.** $\{0, 5, 9\}$ **49.** $\{-4, 3\}$ **51.** $\{2, -2\}$

Computer Key-In, pages 226–227 **1.** A-loop: 80–160, 410, C-loop: 190–260; 400
3. $(x + 7)(x + 4)$ **5.** $(2x + 7)(2x + 3)$
7. $(2x + 1)(3x - 5)$ **9.** when the factors are in reverse order

Problems, pages 229–232 **1.** 8 or −9 **3.** −6 **5.** 10 or −2 **7.** 16 cm by 7 cm **9.** 13 cm by 8 cm **11.** 11 m by 11 m **13.** 15 or −2 **15.** 2 s, 3 s **17.** 30 s **19. a.** 3 s **b.** The 44.1 m height is reached only at 3 s. If it was less than the maximum height, it would be reached once going up and again coming down. **21.** 6 **23.** 2 m **25.** 5 m **27.** 40 cm by 60 cm

Chapter Review, pages 233–234 **1.** c **3.** c **5.** c **7.** d **9.** d **11.** b **13.** b **15.** d **17.** c **19.** b **21.** b **23.** a

Cumulative Review, page 236 **1.** −12.7 **3.** $-5t$ **5.** $5z - 7$ **7.** $216a^{12}b^6$ **9.** $3x^2y - x + \frac{8}{9}$ **11.** $25y^2 + 60y + 36$ **13.** −4 **15.** 1 **17.** $2p^2(3p - pr^2 + 4r^3st)$ **19.** $(2a + 3b)^2$ **21.** $(m - 6)(m - 3)$ **23.** $(3y - 1)(2y + 5)$ **25.** $(a + b)^2(a - b)$ **27.** −6, 6 **29.** 4 **31.** 10 **33.** $\{-3, 3\}$ **35.** $\{3\}$ **37.** $\{-\frac{1}{4}, \frac{3}{2}\}$ **39.** 60 km/h **41.** 11 cm by 2 cm

Maintaining Skills, page 237 **1.** 0.92 **3.** 2.5 **5.** 3.24 **7.** 1.7 **9.** 2.33 **11.** 0.68 **13.** $\frac{31}{50}$ **15.** $\frac{17}{20}$ **17.** $\frac{3}{10{,}000}$ **19.** 91% **21.** 80% **23.** 3.2% **25.** 27.2 **27.** 0.08 **29.** 52 **31.** 70 **33.** 12 **35.** 450 **37.** 60 **39.** 20 **41.** 34

CHAPTER 6 FRACTIONS

Written Exercises, pages 240–241 **1.** 3, $a \neq 2$ **3.** $\frac{1}{3}$, $n \neq -\frac{1}{3}$ **5.** $\frac{2}{x + 1}$, $x \neq 1$, $x \neq -1$ **7.** $\frac{2}{x - y}$, $x \neq y$, $x \neq 0$, $y \neq 0$ **9.** $\frac{a + 4}{4 - a}$, $a \neq 4$, $a \neq -4$ **11.** $\frac{1}{y - 5}$, $y \neq 5$, $y \neq -5$ **13.** $-\frac{1}{y - 2}$, $y \neq 2$ **15.** $\frac{1}{2x - y}$, $y \neq 2x$ **17.** $\frac{x + y}{x - y}$, $x \neq y$, $x \neq 0$ **19.** $\frac{x - 2}{x + 2}$, $x \neq -\frac{5}{2}$, $x \neq -2$ **21.** $\frac{n - 3}{2n - 5}$, $n \neq -\frac{1}{2}$, $n \neq \frac{5}{2}$ **23.** $\frac{3x}{3x - 1}$, $x \neq \frac{1}{3}$, $x \neq 5$ **25.** $\frac{a - 5}{a + 2}$, $a \neq 2$, $a \neq -2$ **27.** $\frac{x + y}{x + 3y}$, $x \neq -3y$, $x \neq y$ **29.** $x = c - d$, $c \neq -d$ **31.** $x = a + b$, $a \neq b$ **33.** $x = 5k - 1$, $k \neq \frac{1}{5}$ **35.** $x = c - 2d$, $c \neq d$ **37.** $x = a - 6$, $a \neq -6$ **39.** The correct answer is 22. The values $x = 4$ and $y = 6$ make the denominator of the original fraction equal to 0, thus the fraction is not defined for these values. **41. a.** 0 **b.** 4 **c.** undefined **43.** $\frac{4x + 7y}{4x - 7y}$ **45.** $\frac{a}{2(3a - 5)}$ **47.** $1 + x$ **49.** $\frac{5 - x}{x + 5}$ **51.** $\frac{a - 3b}{a + 3b + 2}$ **53.** $\frac{a - 3b + 3}{3}$ **55.** 0 **57.** −3 **59.** $\frac{5}{2}$

Application, page 243 **1.** 4¢ **3.** 387.5 kW · h; $372

Written Exercises, pages 246–247 **1.** $\frac{3}{2}$ **3.** $\frac{9}{5}$ **5.** $\frac{1}{3}$ **7.** $\frac{1}{6}$ **9.** $\frac{x}{2}$ **11.** $\frac{a}{d}$ **13.** $\frac{pq}{4}$ **15.** $\frac{2df}{27}$ **17.** $9a^{10}$ **19.** $\frac{a^2}{36}$ **21.** $\frac{125a^3}{27b^6}$ **23.** $\frac{x^8}{10{,}000}$ **25.** $\frac{a}{b}$ **27.** $\frac{24x}{5}$ **29.** $\frac{4x^2}{49}$ in.² **31.** $\frac{x^2}{6}$ **33.** $\frac{dy}{9}$ dollars **35.** $\frac{y}{y - 3}$ **37.** $-\frac{a + x}{3a}$ **39.** $\frac{(x - 2)(x - 4)}{x^2}$ **41.** $\frac{1}{2xy(3 + y)}$ **43.** $(2n - 1)^2$ **45.** $2x(2a - x)$ **47.** 1 **49.** $\frac{(2a + b)(d - 2c)}{(2c + d)(b - 2a)}$ **51.** 6 **53.** $\frac{3(a - b + c)}{(b - a + c)}$

Computer Key-In, page 247 **1.** 1 is a factor of every integer. **3.** 1, 3, 5, 7, 9, 11, 13, 15, 17, 19, 21, 23, 25

Written Exercises, pages 249–250 **1.** $\frac{5}{6}$ **3.** $\frac{1}{2}$ **5.** $\frac{a^2}{3}$ **7.** $\frac{2n}{3}$ **9.** $\frac{2x}{3y}$ **11.** $\frac{25}{9x^2}$ **13.** 1 **15.** $\frac{2}{3}$ **17.** $\frac{c(a - b)}{abd}$ **19.** $-\frac{1}{(x + 1)^2}$ **21.** $\frac{a^2 + b^2}{a + b}$ **23.** $-\frac{3}{2(n + 3)(n - 1)}$ **25. a.** $\frac{15}{8}$ **b.** $\frac{10}{3}$ **c.** $\frac{r^2}{t^3}$ **27. a.** $\frac{n^2}{3}$ **b.** 3 **c.** 4 **29.** $\frac{1}{6a^5}$ **31.** $\frac{x(2x - 5)}{3(x - 4)}$ **33.** $a + b$ **35.** −1 **37.** $\frac{1}{4(3n - 5)}$ **39.** $\frac{5(s - 2)}{s - 4}$ **41.** $\frac{2(a + 3)}{a - 2}$

Challenge, page 250 16,807 hekats of grain

Written Exercises, pages 253–254 **1.** 15 **3.** $6x$ **5.** $3(x - 3)$ **7.** $5(4 - a)$ **9.** a^3 **11.** $4mn^2$ **13.** $5(2n - 3)$ **15.** −4 **17.** $2(x - 1)$ **19.** $3y$ **21.** $6(x + 2)$

23. $2(x + 5)$ **25.** 18 **27.** 36 **29.** 12 **31.** 24
33. 100 **35.** $3(x - 2)$ **37.** $48x^2y^3$
39. $2(x - 1)(x + 1)$ **41.** $8a^2b^2$
43. $y(y - 3)(y + 3)$ **45.** $(a - 1)(a + 1)$
47. $12(y + 2)(y + 3)(y + 4)$

Written Exercises, pages 256–258 **1.** $\frac{1}{n}$ **3.** $\frac{1}{a}$
5. $\frac{x + 1}{3}$ **7.** $-x - 1$ **9.** $\frac{3 - 2n}{n - 2}$ **11.** $\frac{5}{2y - 7}$
13. $\frac{2x + 3}{x^2}$ **15.** $\frac{8x - 1}{6x^2}$ **17.** $\frac{12n - 1}{2n^3}$
19. $\frac{5x - 6}{6}$ **21.** $\frac{7y}{18}$ **23.** $\frac{8x + 9}{15}$ **25.** $\frac{n + 23}{24}$
27. $\frac{17a - 12b}{12}$ **29.** $\frac{7x + 1}{3}$; $\frac{x^2 - 1}{3}$
31. $\frac{9}{2}x + 2$; $\frac{7x(x + 1)}{12}$ **33.** $\frac{6(x - 1)}{(x - 3)(x + 3)}$
35. $\frac{3(x - 3)}{(x + 1)(x - 2)}$
37. $\frac{-y(y + 3)}{(y - 5)(y + 5)}$ **39.** $\frac{x^2 + y^2}{(x + y)(x - y)}$ **41.** 1
43. $\frac{z^2 + z - 1}{z(1 - z)(1 + z)}$ **45.** $\frac{a + b}{ab}$
47. $\frac{4}{(n - 5)(n + 5)}$ **49.** $\frac{3(3c + 2)}{(c + 1)(c + 2)^2}$
51. $\frac{2x - 1}{2x + 1}$ **53.** $\frac{-(2x^2 + 15x + 9)}{3(x - 3)(x + 3)}$ **55.** $\frac{-3}{cd}$
57. $\frac{-4}{(y + 1)^2(y - 1)^2}$

Written Exercises, pages 261–262 **1.** $\frac{21}{5}$
3. $\frac{6x + 1}{x}$ **5.** $\frac{3a^2 - 2}{a}$ **7.** $\frac{a + 2b}{b}$ **9.** $\frac{5x + 6}{x + 2}$
11. $\frac{-4x - 15}{x + 3}$ **13.** $\frac{6x^2 + 5x}{x + 1}$ **15.** $\frac{3n^2 - n - 5}{n^2 - 1}$
17. $\frac{n^2 + n - 2}{n + 1}$ **19.** $\frac{a^2 + 5a + 2}{a + 2}$ **21.** $x - 6$
23. $\frac{2x^2 - 1}{x(x + 1)}$ **25.** $\frac{4x}{x + 1}$ **27.** $\frac{-a + 15}{a - 3}$
29. $\frac{5x^2 + 5x - 6}{2x + 3}$ **31.** $\frac{a^4 - 2a^2 - 8}{a^2}$ **33.** $\frac{a + b}{a}$
35. $a - b$ **37.** $\frac{a}{a + 2}$ **39.** All three denominators used are common denominators and yield an answer of $\frac{3x - 9}{x - 1}$. **41.** $\frac{10y^2 + 18y - 400}{y}$
43. -1 **45.** $C = 4$, $D = 2$

Computer Key-In, page 262 **1.** 72 **3.** 195
9. The RUNs that have the smaller denominator first.

Written Exercises, pages 265–266 **1.** $x + 5$
3. $n + 6$ **5.** $y + 4 + \frac{2}{y + 2}$ **7.** $x - \frac{9}{x - 3}$
9. $n + 2 + \frac{18}{n - 5}$ **11.** $x - 2 + \frac{8}{x + 2}$
13. $x - 3 + \frac{2}{2x - 1}$ **15.** $2x - 1 + \frac{9}{2x + 1}$
17. $n^2 + 2n + 1$ **19.** $a^2 - 2a + 4$
21. $8x^2 + 6x + 4 - \frac{7}{3x - 2}$
23. $a^2 + 5ab - 7b^2$ **25.** $2x^3 - x^2 - 3x + 2$
27. $n^3 - 1$ **29.** $n^2 + 3n + 4$ **31.** $3n + 2$
33. $(3n + 2)(n - 1)(n - 2)$
35. $(2x + 1)(2x + 3)(x - 5)$ **37.** -6 **39.** 1
41. a. $x^{99} + x^{98} + \ldots + 1$
b. $x^{n-1} + x^{n-2} + \ldots + 1$
43. a. $x^{100} - x^{99} + x^{98} - x^{97} + \ldots + 1$
b. $x^{n-1} - x^{n-2} + x^{n-3} - \ldots + 1$

Extra, pages 267–268 **1.** $\frac{1}{5}$ **3.** $\frac{1}{v}$ **5.** 3
7. $\frac{1}{13}$ **9.** $\frac{6}{d}$ **11.** $\frac{r + 2s}{s - r}$ **13.** $\frac{z - 5}{z + 5}$ **15.** $\frac{k + 3}{k + 2}$
17. 1 **19.** $\frac{2z^2 - 2z}{2z^2 + z - 4}$ **21.** $x = \frac{z}{2 - z}$
25. $\frac{5n}{5 - n}$ articles **27.** $\frac{w + 6}{3(w - 2)}$
29. $n^2 + 1$ **31.** $\frac{54e^2 - e - 29}{6(3e - 1)(3e + 1)}$ **33.** $\frac{1}{2s}$
35. $-\frac{1}{c - 3}$

Chapter Review, pages 269–270 **1.** c **3.** a
5. b **7.** d **9.** a **11.** d **13.** c

Cumulative Review, page 272 **1.** 0.64
3. $-27a^6b^9c^{12}$ **5.** $20x^2 + 3x - 9$
7. $-17t - 3s$ **9.** $16t^4s^2 - 81$ **11.** 0
13. $a^2b(6a + 5ab - 3b)$ **15.** $2t(2t - 7)^2$
17. prime **19.** $y(y + 8)(y - 4)$
21. $(2x - y + 1)(2x + y - 1)$ **23.** 36
25. -6 **27.** $\frac{4}{3}$, $-\frac{4}{3}$ **29.** 7, -1 **31.** $\frac{1}{a + 4}$
33. $\frac{a - b}{cd^2}$ **35.** $3b^2 - 2b + 1 - \frac{8}{2b - 3}$
37. twins, 16; mother, 40 **39.** 5 km

Maintaining Skills, page 273 **1.** 14 cm by 2 cm **3.** 9 cm by 6 cm **5.** 5 km

Mixed Review, page 274 **1.** 2 cm by 7 cm
3.
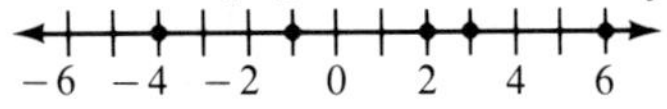

5. no solution **7.** -3 **9.** home team; 2 points **11.** $3a^2 + 8ab - 3b^2$ **13.** -12 **15.** $(2x + 1)(2x + 3)$ **17.** 10, -8 **19.** 34 **21.** -16

Preparing for College Entrance Exams, page 275 **1.** E **3.** D **5.** D **7.** B

CHAPTER 7 APPLYING FRACTIONS

Written Exercises, pages 279–280 **1.** 1:6 **3.** 1:100 **5.** 14:1 **7.** 22:1 **9.** 2:1 **11.** 4:3:1 **13. a.** 14:19 **b.** 8:15 **15. a.** 24:19 **b.** 4:3 **17.** 5:8 **19.** 2:1 **21.** 3:1 **23.** 1:2 **25.** $(a + b):1$ **27.** 2:1

Problems, pages 280–281 **1.** 18, 48 **3.** 360 girls **5.** 200, 240, 280 **7.** 150 m^3 cement, 300 m^3 sand, 400 m^3 gravel **9.** 88 km/h, 66 km/h **11.** 24 dimes, 16 nickels **13.** 200 pencils **15.** 900 full size cars

Written Exercises, pages 284–285 **1.** $\frac{15}{4}$ **3.** 3 **5.** $\frac{28}{15}$ **7.** $\frac{15}{4}$ **9.** $\frac{2}{3}$ **11.** $\frac{6}{7}$ **13.** 9 **15.** $\frac{3}{2}$ **17.** $\frac{4}{5}$ **19.** -14 **21.** 11 **23.** 18 **25.** 3 **27.** -1 **29.** 0 **31.** 9 **33.** 0 **35.** $\frac{7}{20}$ **37.** $\frac{c(c + d)}{d}$ **39.** $m = \frac{F}{r}$, $r = \frac{F}{m}$ **41.** $V = \frac{KT}{P}$, $T = \frac{PV}{K}$ **43.** 16

Problems, pages 285–286 **1.** \$5.85 **3.** 20 L **5.** $3\frac{3}{4}$ doz **7.** 69 dentists **9.** 5 acres **11.** 262,995 km^2

Computer Exercises, page 286 **1. a.** $0.\overline{6}$ **b.** 2.5 **c.** $0.\overline{45}$ **d.** $0.\overline{135}$

Computer Key-In, page 287 **1.** $\frac{3}{5}$, $\frac{6}{10}$, $\frac{9}{15}$, $\frac{12}{20}$, $\frac{15}{25}$, $\frac{18}{30}$, and so on. **5.** For $A = 3$, $B = 5$ the areas are 15, 60, 135, 240, 375; for $A = 2$, $B = 6$, the areas are 12, 48, 108, 192, 300 **7.** For $A = 3$, $B = 5$ the ratio is 25:1; for $A = 2$, $B = 6$, the ratio is 25:1.

Written Exercises, pages 289–290 **1.** $\frac{6}{5}$ **3.** 4 **5.** -1 **7.** 8 **9.** 1 **11.** $\frac{12}{5}$ **13.** 11 **15.** $-\frac{2}{5}$ **17.** $\frac{1}{2}$ **19.** 0 **21.** 12 **23.** 5 **25.** 4 **27.** -5 **29.** 1 **31.** $\frac{1}{3}$ **33.** -4 **35.** $-\frac{7n}{13}$ **37.** $\frac{a + 3}{a}$

Problems, pages 289–290 **1.** 48 **3.** 15, 6 **5.** Jill is 15; Jack is 18 **7.** 15 cm by 6 cm **9.** 8 km **11.** 24 quarters, 8 dimes **13.** 6 apples

Written Exercises, pages 292–293 **1.** 4 **3.** 9 **5.** 12 **7.** 2 **9.** 9 **11.** no solution **13.** 0 **15.** no solution **17.** all real numbers except $y = 2$ **19.** $y = 2$ **21.** $\{-\frac{1}{2}, 1\}$ **23.** all values except $n = -\frac{1}{2}$ **25.** 12 **27.** $\{0, 4\}$ **29.** no solution **31.** $\frac{7}{13}$ **33.** 3 **35.** 1 **37.** 9 **39.** 8 **41.** $\{1, 4\}$ **43.** $\{4, -2\}$

Problems, pages 293–294 **1.** $\frac{2}{3}$ or $\frac{3}{2}$ **3.** $\frac{3}{2}$ **5.** 26, 14 **7.** $5\frac{1}{2}$ h **9.** 24 people **11.** 12 km/h

Computer Exercises, page 294 **1.** 60 **3.** 50

Written Exercises, pages 297–298 **1.** $\frac{1}{4}$ **3.** $\frac{1}{3}$ **5.** $\frac{3}{5}$ **7.** $\frac{1}{8}$ **9.** $\frac{1}{25}$ **11.** $\frac{5}{4}$ **13.** 96 **15.** 190 **17.** 0.06 **19.** 89 **21.** 483 **23.** 3000 **25.** 40 **27.** 180 **29.** 5.6 **31.** 80% **33.** 2% **35.** $33\frac{1}{3}$% **37.** \$3, \$9 **39.** \$24, \$136 **41.** \$11, \$55 **43.** \$120, \$300 **45.** 20 **47.** 8 **49.** 20 **51.** 10 **53.** 86.25 **55.** 9.6 **57.** $x = -64{,}000$ **59.** $-56\frac{2}{3}$ **61.** \$1230 **63.** 0.11 **65.** \$2000

Problems, page 299 **1.** 60% **3.** \$85,000 **5.** \$9500 **7.** \$18.70 **9.** \$39 **11.** \$126 **13.** rural, 68 million people; urban, 153 million people **15.** 360 calories

Written Exercises, pages 302–303 **1.** 10% **3.** 5% **5.** $12\frac{1}{2}$% **7.** \$3.64 **9.** \$6.40 **11.** \$50 **13.** 20% **15.** 15% **17.** \$25.60 **19.** \$7 **21.** \$70

Problems, pages 303–304 **1.** $33\frac{1}{3}$% **3.** 8% **5.** 20% **7.** \$10,800 **9.** \$42 **11.** \$1600 at 6%, \$4400 at 11% **13.** \$20,000 **15.** \$1440

Problems, pages 309–311 **1.** 2 kg of cashews, 6 kg pecans **3.** 50 g **5.** \$3.00 **7.** 13% **9.** 25 g **11.** 2 kg **13.** 8 kg of apples, 12 kg of apricots **15.** 65 km/h **17.** 3.2 L acid, 4.8 L water **19.** 8 kg **21.** \$5500 at 12%, \$8500 at $5\frac{1}{2}$% **23. a.** 25 km/h **b.** 24 km/h **25. a.** $2sx + rx$ **b.** $\frac{2s + r}{3}$ **27. a.** $0.05a + 0.10b$ **b.** $\frac{0.05a + 0.1b}{a + b}$

Calculator Key-In, page 311 **1.** 969.4 **3.** 637.5 **5.** 1625 **7.** \$1816.83

Challenge, page 311 30 km

Problems, pages 315-316 **1.** $\frac{2}{5}$; $\frac{x}{5}$ **3.** $\frac{11}{20}$; $\frac{11x}{30}$ **5.** 1 h 12 min **7.** 30 min **9.** 36 min **11.** 24 min **13.** $13\frac{1}{3}$ min **15.** 30 min **17.** 12 h **19.** 2 h **21.** 2 h

Written Exercises, pages 319-320
1. 300,000,000 m/s
3. 2,000,000,000,000,000,000,000,000,000,000 kg
5. 0.00000136 cm
7. 0.00000000000000005 cm **9. a.** 10^3 **b.** 10^{-3} **11. a.** 10^6 **b.** 10^{-6} **13.** 10^6
15. a. 4.7×10^3
b. $4 \cdot 10^3 + 7 \cdot 10^2 + 0 \cdot 10^1 + 0 \cdot 10^0$
17. a. 9.081×10^8
b. $9 \cdot 10^8 + 0 \cdot 10^7 + 8 \cdot 10^6 + 1 \cdot 10^5 + 0 \cdot 10^4 + 0 \cdot 10^3 + 0 \cdot 10^2 + 0 \cdot 10^1 + 0 \cdot 10^0$
19. a. 2.1×10^{-4}
b. $0 \cdot 10^{-1} + 0 \cdot 10^{-2} + 0 \cdot 10^{-3} + 2 \cdot 10^{-4} + 1 \cdot 10^{-5}$ **21. a.** 1.02×10^{-8}
b. $0 \cdot 10^{-1} + 0 \cdot 10^{-2} + 0 \cdot 10^{-3} + 0 \cdot 10^{-4} + 0 \cdot 10^{-5} + 0 \cdot 10^{-6} + 0 \cdot 10^{-7} + 1 \cdot 10^{-8} + 0 \cdot 10^{-9} + 2 \cdot 10^{-10}$ **23. a.** 9.944×10^{-1}
b. $9 \times 10^{-1} + 9 \times 10^{-2} + 4 \times 10^{-3} + 4 \times 10^{-4}$
25. a. 1.7×10^{10} **b.** $1 \cdot 10^{10} + 7 \cdot 10^9$
27. 2×10^6 **29.** 1.6×10^9 **31.** 1

Problems, pages 320-321
1. 9.4608×10^{12} km **3.** 4.3 years
5. 1.695×10^{13} cm; yes; yes; yes; yes; yes

Written Exercises, pages 325-326 **1.** $\frac{1}{5}$ **3.** $\frac{1}{25}$ **5.** $\frac{1}{81}$ **7.** $\frac{1}{729}$ **9.** $\frac{1}{16}$ **11.** $\frac{1}{32}$ **13.** 64 **15.** 81 **17.** 27 **19.** 64 **21.** $\frac{1}{81}$ **23.** 729 **25. a.** $\frac{4}{3}$ **b.** 8 **27. a.** 16 **b.** $\frac{16}{9}$ **29.** Division by zero is not defined **31.** $\frac{7}{x}$ **33.** $\frac{y^2}{x}$ **35.** $\frac{1}{a^6}$ **37.** $\frac{27}{x^6}$ **39.** $\frac{1}{x^2}$ **41.** $\frac{1}{a^6}$ **43.** a^8 **45.** $\frac{1}{c^7}$ **47.** x^6 **49.** n^8 **51.** 25 **53.** 0.0000128 **55.** 0.0000128 **57.** 625 **59.** 3 **61.** 2 **63.** $\frac{1}{\sqrt{x}}$; $\frac{1}{\sqrt[3]{x}}$

Problems, page 327 **1.** 0.7084252 kg; 0.5018663 kg **3. a.** 15 million **b.** 22 million **c.** 10 million **5. a.** $100(2.72)^4 \approx 5474$
b. $100(2.72)^{-4} \approx 2$
c. $100(2.72)^{12} = 16{,}399{,}358$
d. $100(2.72)^{-12} = 0$

Calculator Key-In, page 328 **1.** 0.6 **3.** 0.9 **5.** $68.\overline{3}$ **7.** −5.75

Chapter Review, pages 329-330 **1.** d **3.** a **5.** d **7.** b **9.** b **11.** a **13.** d **15.** c

Cumulative Review, page 332 **1.** 12
3. $-16m^8n^7$ **5.** $25a^6b^2c^8$
7. $36t^2v^4 - 60tv^2 + 25$
9. $2x^3 - 11x^2y - 11xy^2 - 3y^3$
11. $\frac{1}{x^2z(3z + 1)}$ **13.** $5b + 3$ **15.** $x^{14}(x - 4)^2$
17. 12% **19.** $(7z - 2)^2$
21. $(3b + 7)(2b + 3)$ **23.** $(12x - 1)(x + 4)$
25. 30 **27.** $-\frac{9}{2}$ **29.** {0, 1, 11} **31.** 1
33. 7.4×10^{-5} **35.** 14, 16 **37.** 12%
39. 56 min

Maintaining Skills, page 333
1. $9a^2 - 5a + 8$ **3.** $12 - 5x$ **5.** $12x - 20z$
7. $2x - 8y - 6$ **9.** $-\frac{13}{6}b$ **11.** $-6a^3b^4c$
13. $-m^5n^2p^3$ **15.** $16x^8y^{12}$ **17.** $r^{15}s^{11}t^7$
19. $64c^{12}d^{12}e^6 - 8c^{12}d^{12}r^6$
21. $3a^3b^2 - 3a^2b^3 + 3ab^4$
23. $c^2d^7 - 2c^3d^5 + c^5d^3$ **25.** $z^2 + 5z - 24$
27. $y^2 - 8y - 20$ **29.** $12z^2 - 9z - 3$
31. $81d^2 - 9$ **33.** $x^4 - 36$
35. $-2b^3 + 19b^2 - 37b + 14$

CHAPTER 8 LINEAR EQUATIONS AND SYSTEMS

Written Exercises, pages 337-338 **1.** yes, yes **3.** yes, yes **5.** no, no **7.** yes, no **9.** $y = \frac{3x - 7}{2}$ **11.** $y = \frac{7x^2 - 4}{3}$ **13.** $y = \frac{4 - 3x}{3}$ **15.** $a = \frac{7 + 3b}{2}$ **17.** $q = \frac{4p}{3}$ **19.** $a = 8b$
21. (1, 4), (3, 3), (5, 2), (7, 1), (9, 0)
23. (1, 11), (3, 6), (5, 1) **25.** (0, 5), (3, 4), (4, 3), (5, 0) **27.** (1, 6), (2, 3), (3, 2), (6, 1)
29. 13 45's, 1 LP; 9 45's, 2 LP's; 5 45's, 3 LP's; 1 45, 4 LP's **31.** 4 pigs, 40 chickens
33. (3, 9) **35.** (19, 8) **37.** $y = \frac{2x}{x - 2}$

Computer Exercises, page 338 **1.** yes **3.** yes **5.** no

Written Exercises, pages 343–344

1–11.

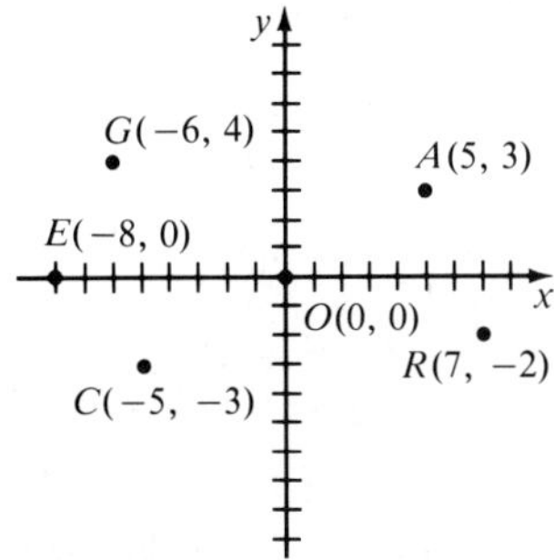

13. parallelogram

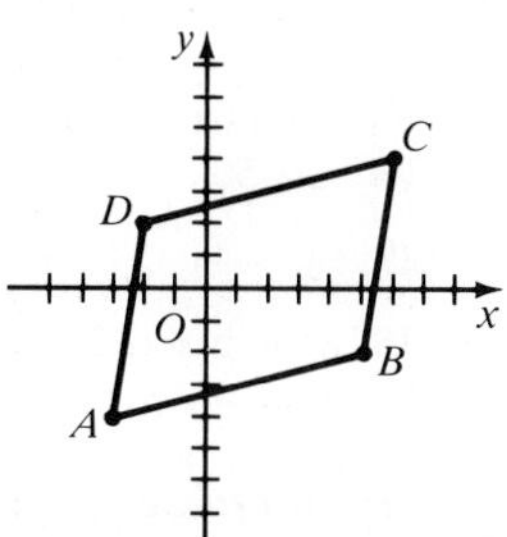

15. rectangle

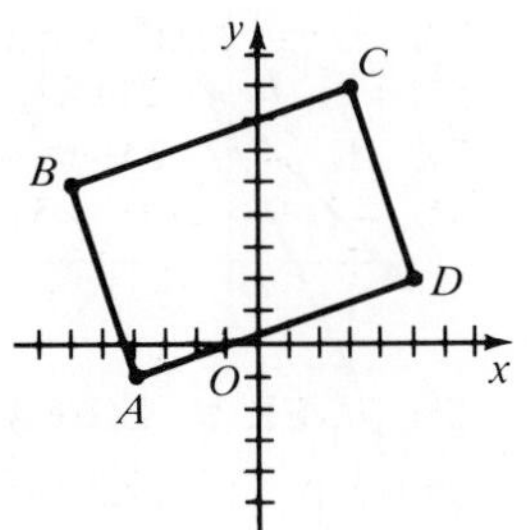

17. *E* **19.** *Z, O* **21.** *P, O, X, I* **23.** *B*

25.

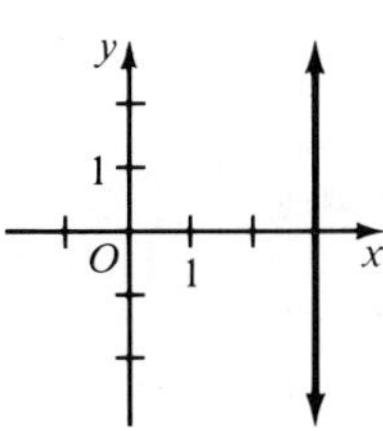

27.

29.

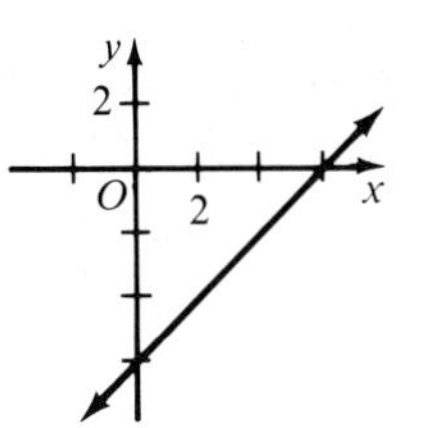

31.

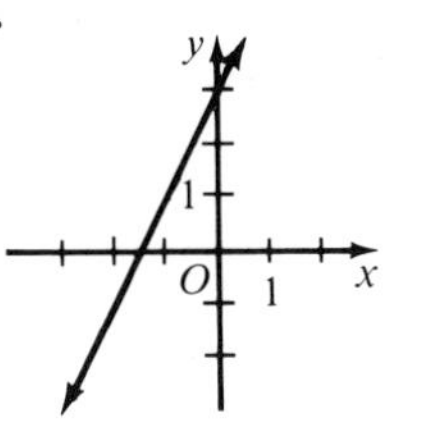

33.

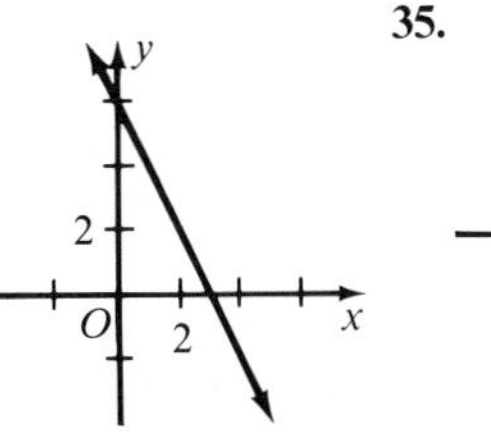

35.

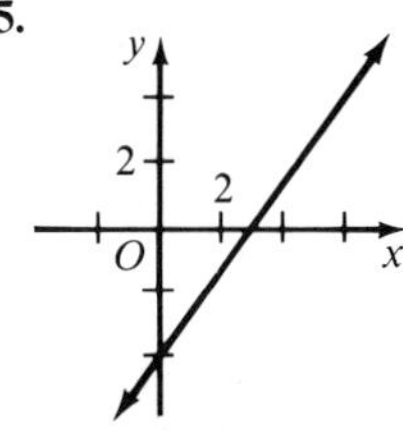

37.

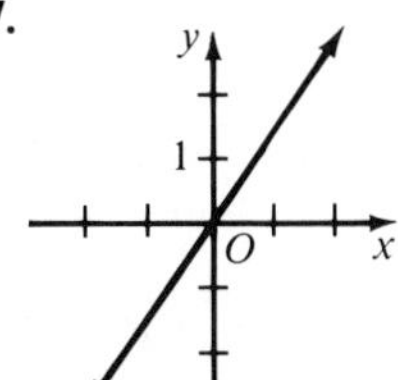

39.

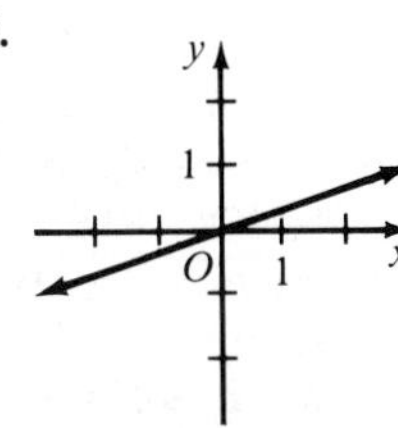

41.

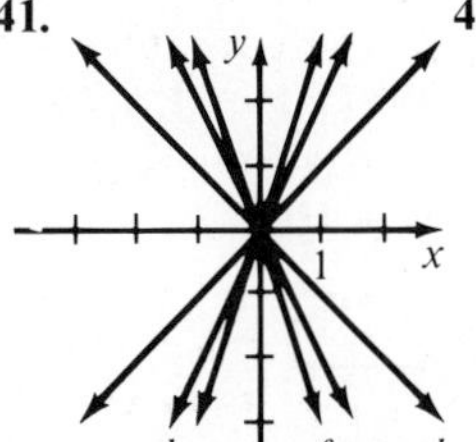

43.

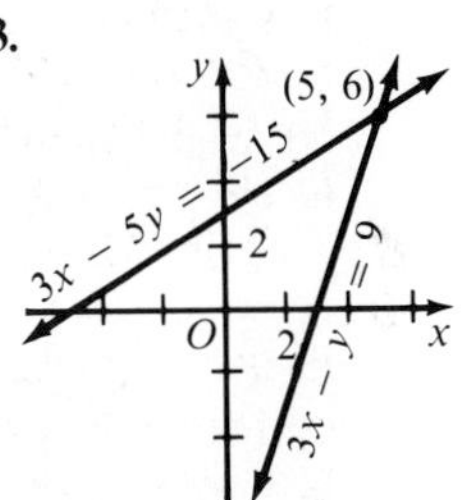

Computer Exercises, page 344 **1. a.** yes **b.** no **c.** yes

Challenge, page 345 41

Written Exercises, pages 348–349

1.

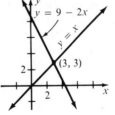

3.

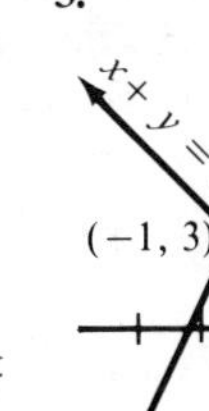

5.

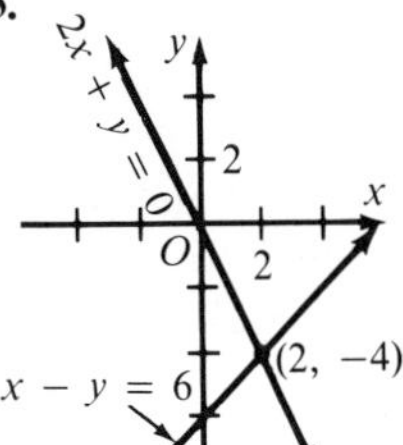

7.

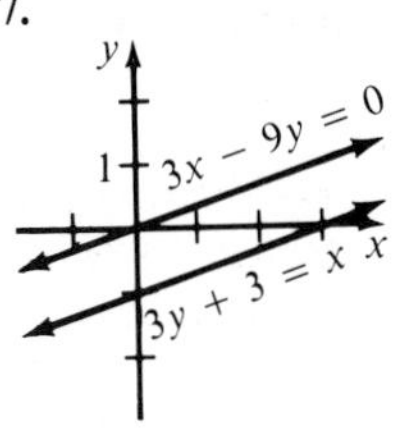

9. 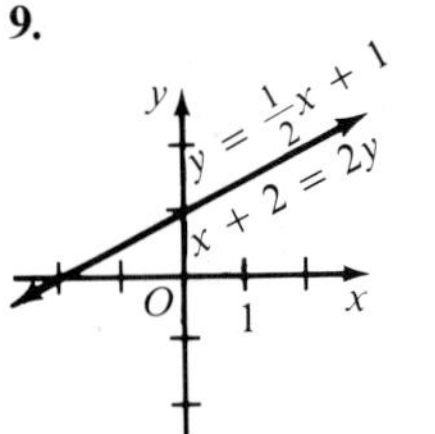

11. 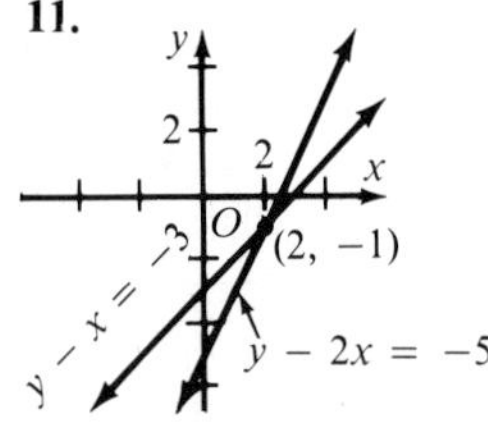

13. 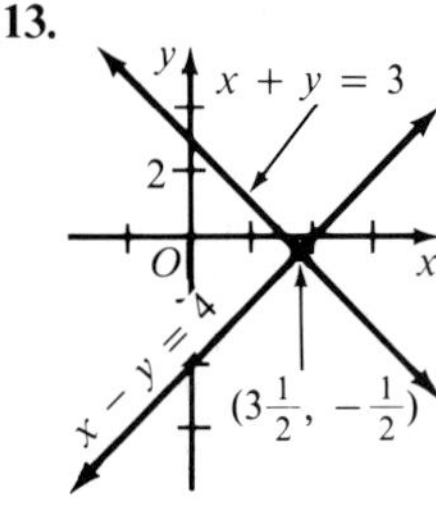

15. 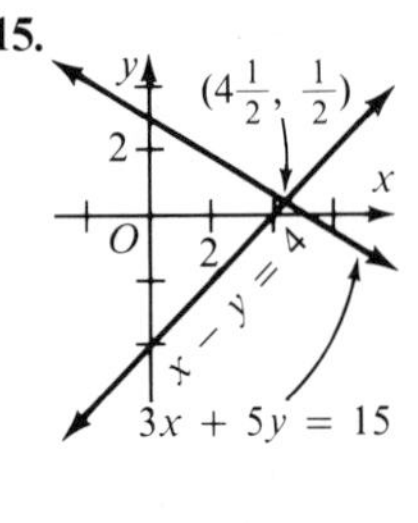

17. (2, 4), (−2, 4) **19.** (5, 5) **21.** (−2, −4)
23. 12

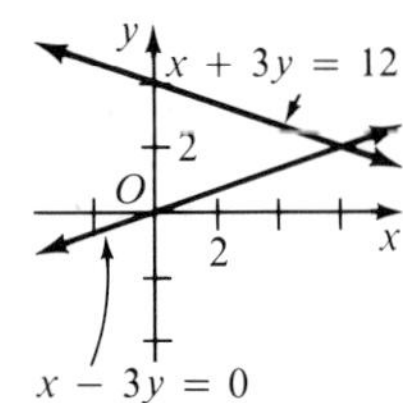

Written Exercises, pages 352–353 **1.** (5, 25) **3.** (8, 2) **5.** (1, 4) **7.** (3, −1) **9.** $(\frac{1}{14}, \frac{5}{28})$ **11.** $(\frac{8}{11}, \frac{13}{11})$ **13.** (1, −1) **15.** (3, 5) **17.** (5, −3) **19.** (8, −2) **21.** (12, 8) **23.** (4, −3) **25.** (3, −1) **27.** (5, −26) **29.** infinite number; (1, 10), (0, 8), (−4, 0) **31.** $A = 3$, $B = -1$ **33.** The equations have no common solution, so their graphs are parallel lines. **35.** $a = 5$, $b = 2$ **37.** yes **39.** $a = 19$, $b = 31$, $c = 12$ **41.** $x = 5$, $y = -1$, $z = 2$ **43.** $a = 1$, $b = 2$, $c = 3$, $d = -4$

Computer Exercises, page 353 **1.** (1, −1) **3.** no solution

Problems, page 357 **1.** 12 nickels **3.** 18 quarters **5.** Connie, \$26.50; Dick, \$9.50 **7.** Tracy, \$32; Connie, \$20 **9.** Pat, \$52.50; Mike, \$35.50 **11.** 13 cm by 7 cm **13.** \$1000 **15.** 18, 20 **17.** \$1.10 **19.** \$5970 **21.** 8, 24 **23.** Carl, \$9.60; Diane, \$19.20; Ed, \$17.20

Written Exercises, pages 359–360 **1.** (5, 4) **3.** (4, −3) **5.** (10, −2) **7.** $(\frac{23}{4}, -\frac{1}{2})$ **9.** (3, −2) **11.** $(-\frac{1}{3}, \frac{2}{3})$ **13.** $(\frac{1}{2}, \frac{1}{4})$ **15.** $(\frac{9}{2}, \frac{1}{4})$ **17.** (5, −1) **19.** (0, −1) **21.** (1, −3) **23.** (6, 4) **25.** $(24, \frac{5}{3})$ **27.** $a = 4$, $b = -3$ **29.** Both equations can be simplified to $x - 4y = 0$.

Problems, pages 360–361 **1.** 8, 13 **3.** 424 girls **5.** 14 bull's eye **7.** walking, 8 km/h; cycling, 30 km/h **9.** Tom, \$1.80; Maria, \$1.20 **11.** 15 3000-lb car, 3 5000-lb cars

Challenge, page 361 8 roosters, 11 hens, 81 chicks, or 12 roosters, 4 hens, 84 chicks

Written Exercises, pages 364–365 **1.** (3, 2) **3.** (1, 2) **5.** (2, −2) **7.** (1, −1) **9.** (5, 4) **11.** (−5, −3) **13.** (2, 1) **15.** (4, 1) **17.** (−6, 0) **19.** (4, 3) **21.** (3, 4) **23.** (20, 50) **25.** (6, −9) **27.** yes **29.** $(\frac{1}{2}, -1)$ **31.** $(\frac{2}{3}, \frac{5}{7})$ **33.** $\left(\frac{6}{5a}, -\frac{1}{5b}\right)$ **35.** $x = 1$, $y = 2$, $z = 4$ **37.** infinite number of solutions in the form $(x, 8 - x, 6 - x)$

Mixed Practice, pages 365–366
1. (1, 6)

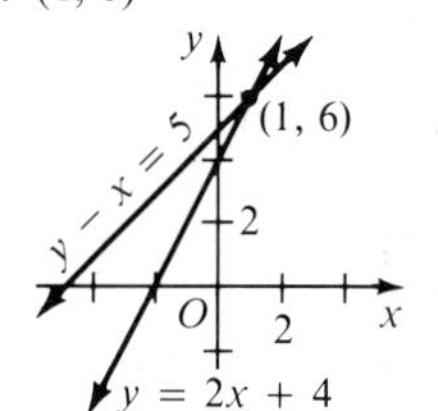

3. (2, 1)

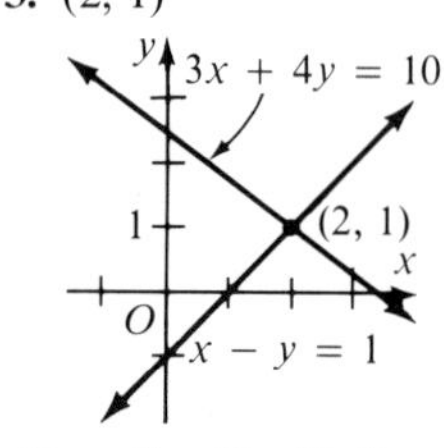

5. (3, 1) **7.** (1, −1) **9.** (1, −1) **11.** (7, 1) **13.** (2, 0) **15.** (14, 10) **17.** (7, 4) **19.** (5, 3) **21.** (7, 3) **23.** (4, 3) **25.** (2, −1) **27.** (−4, −6) **29.** $r = 90$, $s = 72$, $t = 18$ **31.** $(\frac{1}{4}, \frac{1}{5})$ **33.** $x = -\frac{46}{9}$, $y = -\frac{14}{9}$, $z = \frac{20}{3}$

Problems, pages 366–368 **1.** 16, 34 **3.** Al is 38; Jack is 25 **5.** 8000 cm² **7.** 24 dimes, 76 quarters **9.** 15 boys, 9 girls **11.** 100 children **13.** 480 g **15.** grape, \$1.20; orange, \$1.50 **17.** 280 kg cement, 210 kg sand, 140 kg water **19.** 120

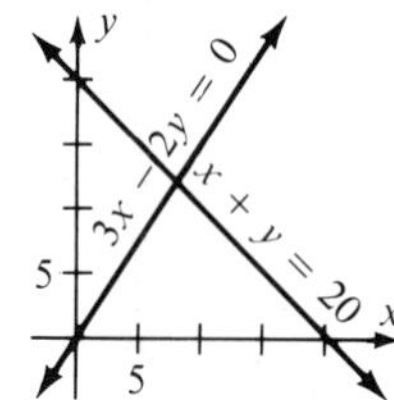

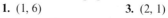

21. stock A, \$2000; stock B, \$3000 **23.** 2 kg **25.** \$4500 **27.** 7 plums **29.** 30 by 28

Calculator Key-In, page 369 **1.** (2, 3)

Reading Algebra, page 370 **1.** 85 dimes, 72 quarters **3.** 800 km/h **5.** 12 cm by 7 cm **7.** 4 cm, 6 cm

Problems, pages 373–374

No current

1.

	Rate × Time = Distance		
Downstream	10	3	30
Upstream	10	3	30

Total time = 6 h
Average speed = 10 km/h

5 km/h current

Rate × Time = Distance		
15	2	30
5	6	30

Total time = 8 h
Average speed = 7.5 km/h

3. $5.\overline{3}$ km **5.** 17 km/h, 5 km/h **7.** 500 km/h, 100 km/h **9.** 770 km/h, 70 km/h **11.** 15 km/h **13.** 5 km/h

Problems, pages 378–380 **1.** 38 **3.** 79 **5.** 72 **7.** Alicia is 13. **9.** Karen is 22. **11.** Eiffel Tower was 95; Washington Monument was 100. **13.** $\frac{5}{13}$ **15.** $\frac{5}{8}$ **17.** $\frac{12}{18}$ **19.** 360 **21.** 342 **23.** James is 18 **25.** $\frac{18}{81}$ **27.** $\frac{37}{73}$ **29.** $\frac{21}{12}, \frac{42}{24}, \frac{63}{36}, \frac{84}{48}$ **31.** father is 39; son is 16

Challenge, page 380 $a = 7$, $b = 6$, $c = 5$

Chapter Review, pages 383–384 **1.** c **3.** b **5.** c **7.** d **9.** c **11.** b **13.** d

Cumulative Review, page 386
1. $7p^2q + 4p - 21q^3$
3. $-3j^4k^4 + 24j^4k^3 - 27j^3k^4$
5. $42z^2 - 78z - 12$ **7.** $7t + 5$ **9.** $\frac{1}{5(x-3)}$
11. 7.2×10^{11} **13.** $(8z + 9y)^2$ **15.** prime
17. $(2y + 1)(3y - 10)$ **19.** 16 **21.** 11 **23.** $\frac{6}{5}$
25. $\{\frac{1}{15}, -4\}$ **27.** -160 **29.** $(2, \frac{4}{3})$
31. (2, 1) **33.** 660 km/h, 180 km/h **35.** 7, 9 or −1, 1

Maintaining Skills, page 387
1. $5b^2c^3(5 + 3b^3c)$ **3.** $3u^4v(3u + 12v - 5v^2)$
5. $-8x^2y^3(3x^5y^2 - 4x^4 + y)$
7. $z(z - 11)(z + 11)$ **9.** $(7 - x^3)(7 + x^3)$
11. prime **13.** $(4a - 5)^2$ **15.** $(5x + 3)^2$
17. $(b + 9)(b + 2)$ **19.** $(7d - c)(2d + c)$
21. $(x + 7)(x + 3)$ **23.** $(n - 2p)(n - 3p)$
25. $(t + 3)(r - 2s)$
27. $(s - 2t - 3)(s + 2t + 3)$
29. $(4a - 3b + 5)(4a + 3b - 5)$
31. $(3b + 5)(b - 1)$ **33.** $2(3m + 2)(m - 2)$
35. $z(5z + 1)(5z + 2)$ **37.** $(1 - 7y)(y + 3)$
39. $2(2b + 1)(3b - 5)$

Mixed Review, page 388
1. (1, 2)

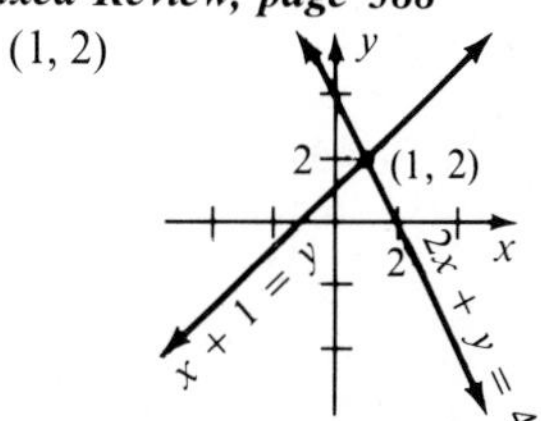

3. 14 **5.** 4 **7.** 8 **9.** $(3x + 5)^2$ **11.** 3 km/h, 6 km/h
13. $(n)^2 + (n + 2)^2 = 8(n + n + 2) + 2$
15. 1.25×10^6 **17.** (2, −2) **19.** $(\frac{1}{3}, \frac{1}{2})$

Preparing for College Entrance Exams, page 389 **1.** A **3.** A **5.** C

CHAPTER 9 INTRODUCTION TO FUNCTIONS

Written Exercises, pages 394–395 **1.** $-\frac{1}{2}$ **3.** 1 **5.** $\frac{2}{11}$ **7.** 1 **9.** no slope **11.** 0 **13.** 5 **15.** −3 **17.** 1 **19.** $-\frac{2}{3}$ **21.** $\frac{8}{3}$ **23.** 0 **25.** −2 **27.** not collinear

29.

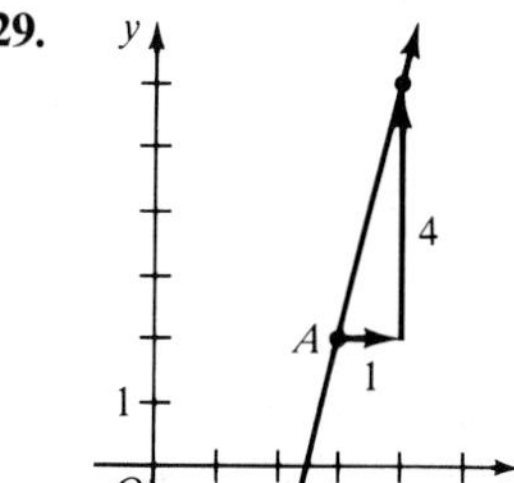

31. **33.**

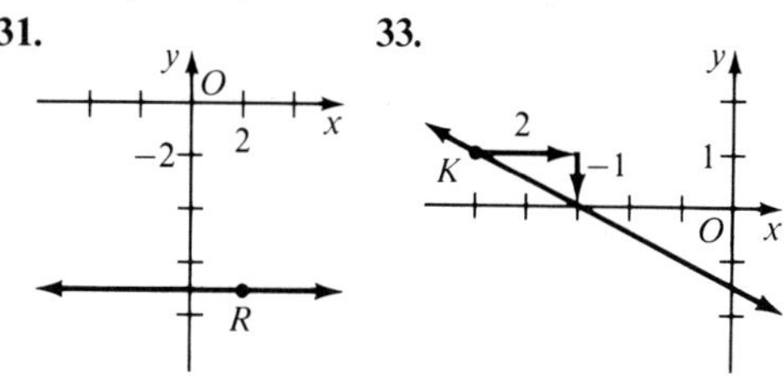

35. AB, 0; BC, $\frac{8}{9}$; AC, no slope **37.** $\frac{1}{2}$, $y = 8$ **39.** $c = -16$ **41.** slope $AM = -\frac{5}{3}$; slope $AC = -\frac{5}{3}$; thus M lies on AC: slope $DB = \frac{3}{5}$; slope $DM = \frac{3}{5}$; thus M lies on DB

Computer Exercises, page 395 **1.** (0, −1), (1, 1), (2, 3), (3, 5), (4, 7) **3.** (1, 5.5), (2, 5), (3, 4.5), (4, 4), (5, 3.5), (6, 3), (7, 2.5), (8, 2), (9, 1.5), (10, 1)

Written Exercises, pages 399–400
1. $-6x + 3y = 1$ **3.** $x - 5y = -20$
5. $30x - 5y = 3$ **7.** $14x - 6y = 1$
9. $y = -6$ **11.** $21x + 10y = -4$
13. $y = -x + 5$ **15.** $y = x - 4$

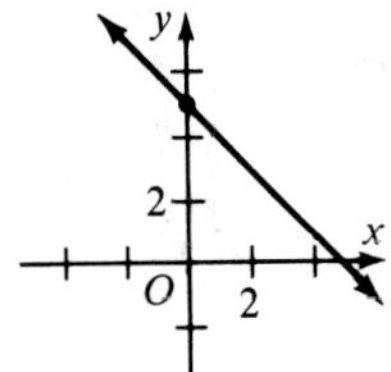

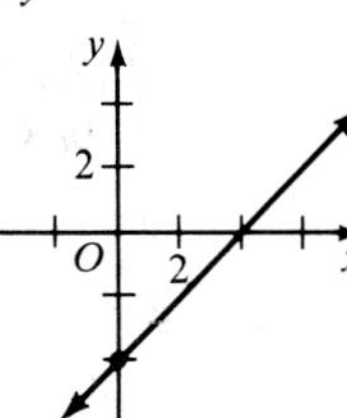

17. $y = \frac{1}{2}x - 3$

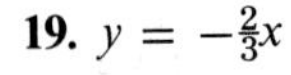

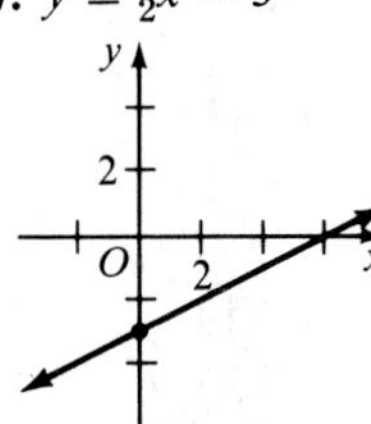

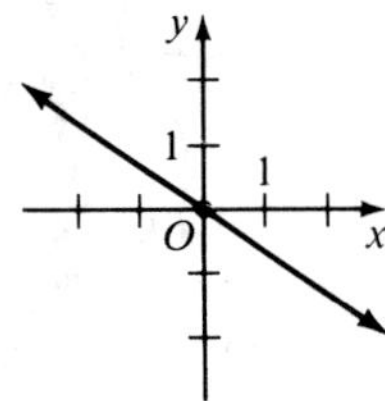

21. $y = \frac{4}{5}x + 3$ **23.** $y = \frac{2}{3}x - 2$

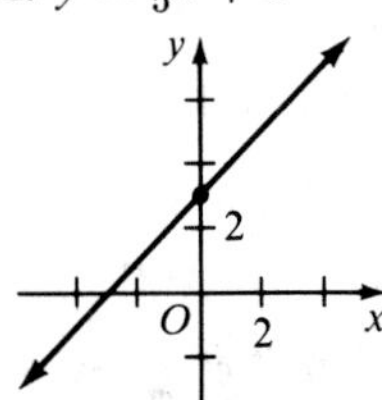

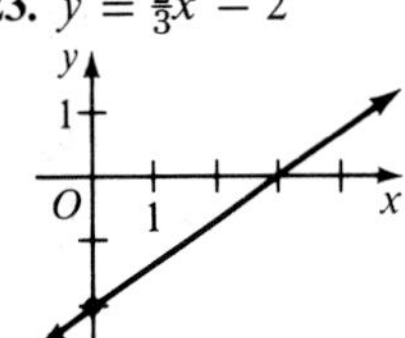

25. no solution **27.** infinite number of solutions **29.** no solution **31.** $y = 3x - 4$ **33.** −3; 3 **35.** −9 **37.** 3 **39.** slope, $-\frac{A}{B}$; y-intercept, $\frac{C}{B}$

Written Exercises, page 402 **1.** −5 **3.** −7 **5.** $-2x + y = 7$ **7.** $3x + y = 18$ **9.** $-3x + 2y = 6$ **11.** $4x + 5y = -34$ **13.** $x + 2y = 0$ **15.** $y = -4$ **17.** $-7x + 4y = -11$ **19.** $y = 1$ **21.** $2x + y = 10$ **23.** $-8x + 3y = -27$ **25.** $-5x + y = -1$ **27.** $3x + 4y = -6$ **29.** $3x - y = -6$ **31.** $-x + 2y = -6$ **33.** $-x + 3y = -7$ **35.** $x - 3y = -6$

Computer Key-In, page 403 **1. a.** slope $= \frac{y_2 - y_1}{x_2 - x_1}$; when $x_2 = x_1$ **b.** −2, 0.75, no slope, 0 **3. b.** $y = 1.5x - 3$; $x = 2$; $y = 3$

Written Exercises, pages 406–407 **1.** 7 **3.** 9 **5.** 15 **7.** 6 **9.** 0 **11.** 4 **13.** −2 **15.** $-\frac{14}{9}$ **17.** −4, 1, 6 **19.** 0, −6, −24 **21.** 5, 7, $6\frac{1}{2}$ **23.** {13, 5, −3} **25.** {10, 5, −2} **27.** $\{-\frac{1}{2}, -1, 1\}$ **29.** {3, −1} **31.** {0, 2} **33.** {0, 9, 64} **35. a.** −12 **b.** 6 **37. a.** 0 **b.** 0, 1, −1 **39. a.** $-\frac{1}{2}$ **b.** −1 **41.** −18 **43.** 6 **45. a.** 2 **b.** 1 **c.** 2 **d.** 4 **47.** 0

Computer Exercises, page 407 **1.** −13, −7, −4, 23 **3.** 0.0625, 0.5, 1, 2, 4, 16

Challenge, page 407 **1. a.** $\frac{2}{3}, \frac{3}{4}, \frac{4}{5}$ **b.** $\frac{100}{101}$ **c.** $\frac{n}{n + 1}$

Written Exercises, pages 410–411

1.

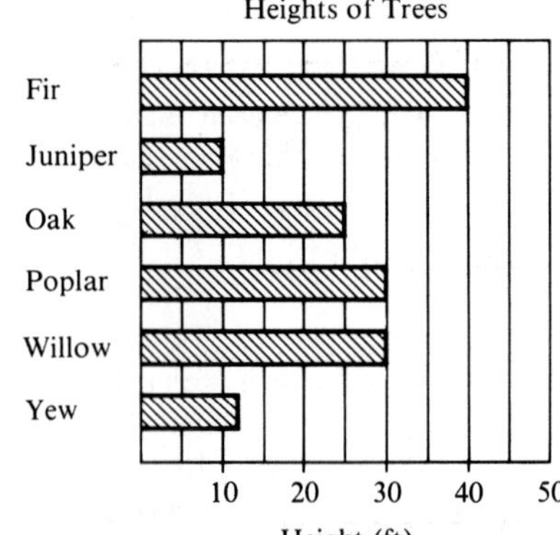

3.

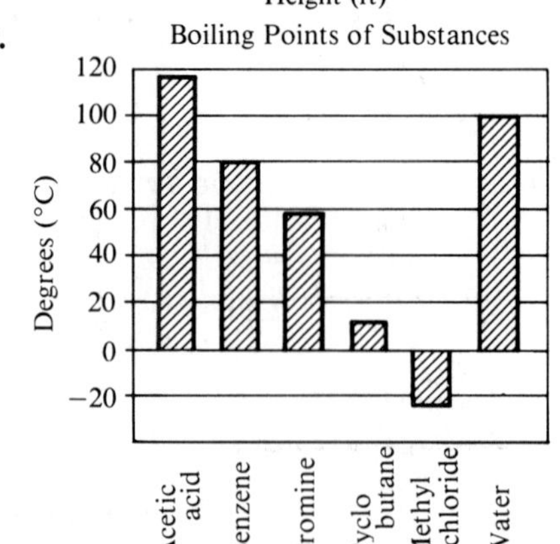

5. Cost of a Barrel of Crude Oil

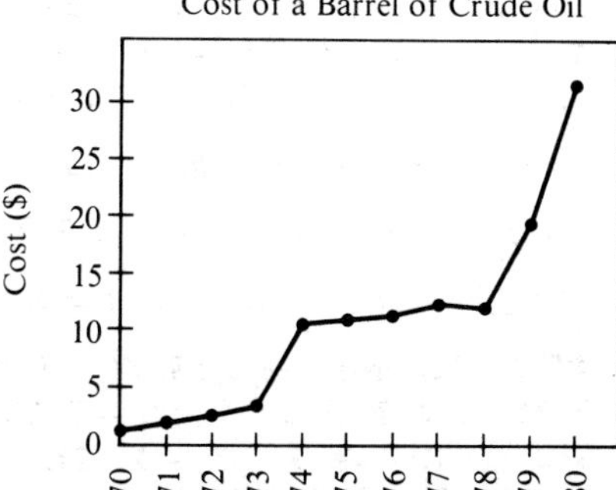

7. Average Monthly Temperature in Greenough

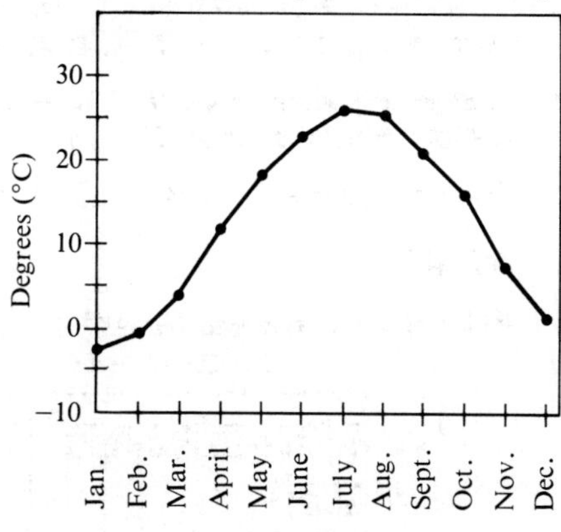

9. Answers may vary.

Written Exercises, pages 416–417

1.

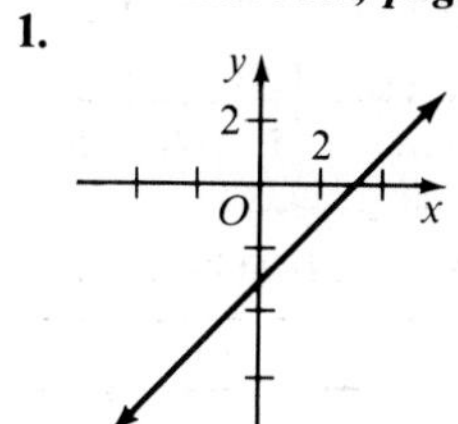

3.

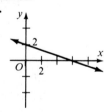

5.

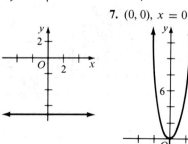

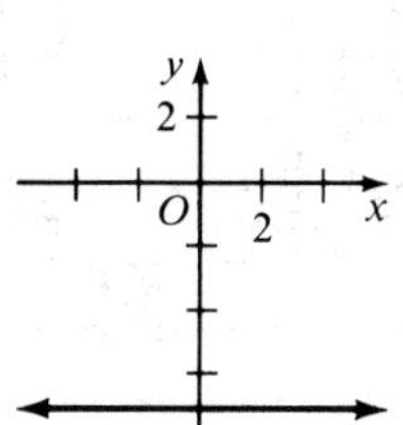

7. (0, 0), $x = 0$

9. (0, 0), $x = 0$

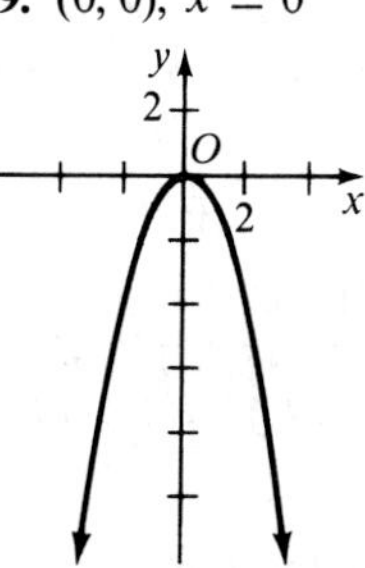

11. (0, 0), $x = 0$

13. (1, −1), $x = 1$

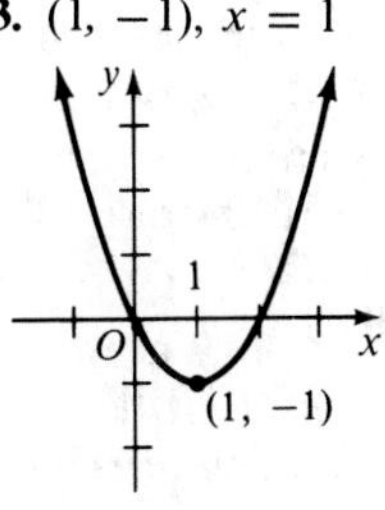

15. $(-\frac{5}{2}, \frac{49}{4})$, $x = -\frac{5}{2}$

17. (0, 2), $x = 0$

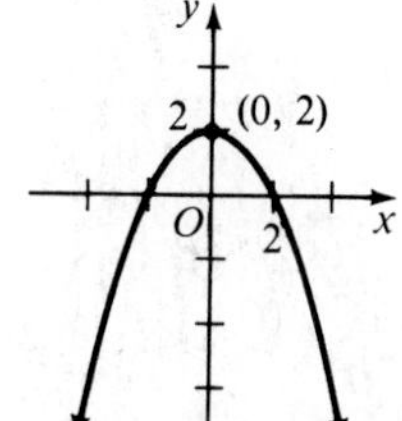

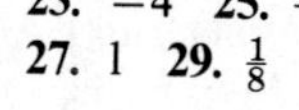
19. $-\frac{25}{4}$ **21.** $-\frac{49}{4}$
23. −4 **25.** $\frac{49}{4}$
27. 1 **29.** $\frac{1}{8}$

31. a.

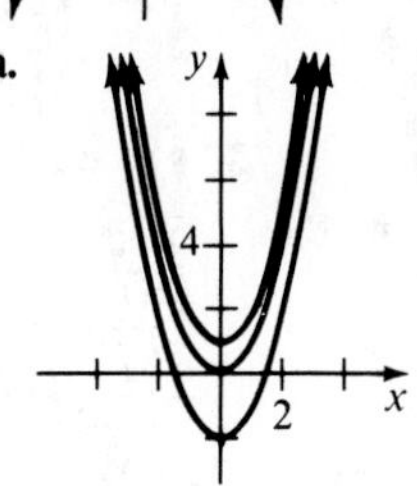

b. graph moves up; graph moves down

33. a. −4 **b.** −4, 1 **35.** The zeros are where the graph of f crosses the x-axis.

Written Exercises, pages 421–422 **1.** $\frac{1}{4}$ **3.** 7 **5.** 25 **7.** 1500 **9.** 600 **11.** 24 **13.** 1.2 **15.** $\frac{2}{3}$ **17. a.** $H = 49m$ **b.** $\frac{49}{1} = \frac{H_2}{m_2}$

19. a. $M = \frac{1}{6}E$ **b.** $\frac{M_1}{E_1} = \frac{14}{84}$

21. a. $R = 0.02059l$ **b.** $\frac{10.295}{500} = \frac{R_2}{l_2}$

Problems, pages 422–423 **1.** 243 m² **3.** 80 g **5.** 40 g **7.** 227 g **9.** 5:162 **11.** 37 units **13.** 1,125,000 m²

Challenge, page 423 5 pennies, 1 nickel, 9 dimes

Written Exercises, pages 426–427
1. **3.**

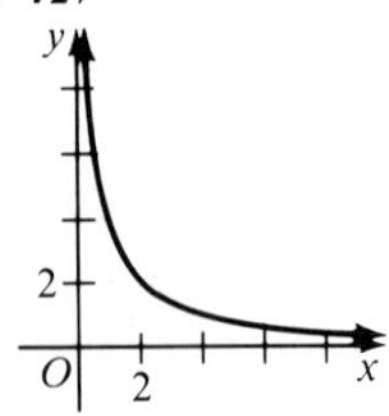

5. 81 **7.** 6.3 **9.** 18 **11. a.** $lw = 60$ **b.** $\frac{15}{w_2} = \frac{l_2}{4}$ **13. a.** $fl = 1.5$ **b.** $\frac{2.5}{l_2} = \frac{f_2}{0.6}$ **15. a.** $VP = 337{,}125$ **b.** $\frac{465}{P_2} = \frac{V_2}{725}$

Problems, pages 427–429 **1.** 9 people **3.** 80 cm **5.** 900 rpm **7.** 60 shares **9.** 3.8 cm **11.** $2\frac{2}{3}$ yd **13.** The distance of the 12 g mass from the fulcrum is 70 cm. **15.** $\frac{1}{2}$ **17.** 0.4 m

Computer Exercises, page 429 **1.** direct **3.** neither

Problems, pages 432–433 **1.** 3850 cm^2 **3.** 63 m **5.** 562.5 lm/m^2 **7.** $\frac{1}{16}$ of the strength at the first position **9.** $\sqrt{2}$ times **11.** 64:27

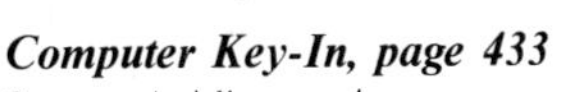

Computer Key-In, page 433 **1.**

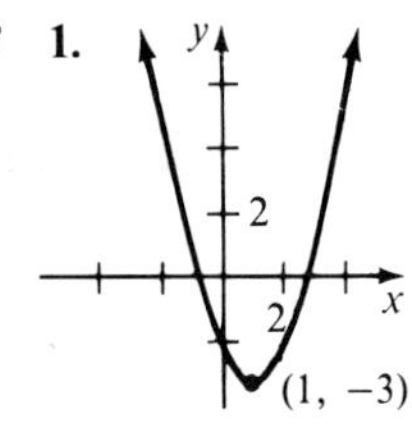

3.

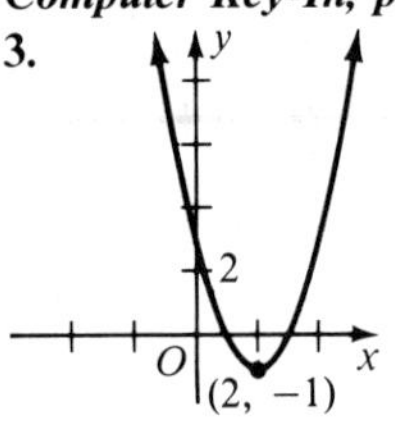

5.

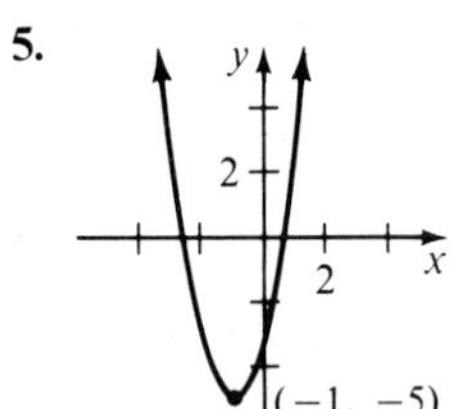

Written Exercises, page 436 **1.** 16 **3.** 60 **5.** 2.5 **7.** x is quadrupled; x remains the same **9.** h is 12 times bigger.

Problems, pages 436–437 **1.** 175 cm^3 **3.** 10 ohms **5.** 10 students **7.** 558 kg **9.** 5.30 **11.** 18 joules **13. a.** 4 times **b.** halved **c.** no change

Application, page 439 **1.** 10 lx **3.** 3 m **5.** 20 lx

Extra, pages 440–441 **1.** $D = \{3, 2\}$, $R = \{4, 3, 6, 0\}$, relation **3.** $D = \{2, 3, 4, 1\}$, $R = \{-1, 0, 6, -3\}$, function **5.** $D = \{-1, 1, 2, -2\}$, $R = \{1, 4\}$, function **7.** $D = \{-1, 1, 2, 4\}$, $R = \{1, 2\}$, function **9.** $D = \{-2, 2, 4\}$, $R = \{1, -1, 0, -3\}$ relation **11.** $D = \{-3, -2, -1, 0, 1, 2, 3\}$, $R = \{1, 0, -1, -2\}$, function **13.** not a function because of (4, 4), (4, −3)

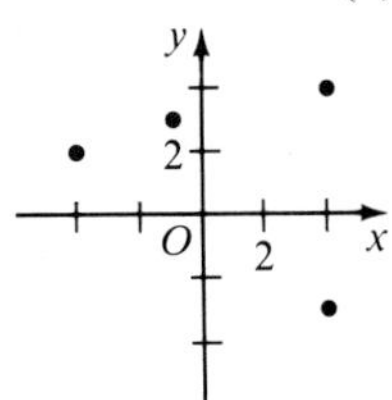

15. not a function because of (−3, 0), (−3, −2)

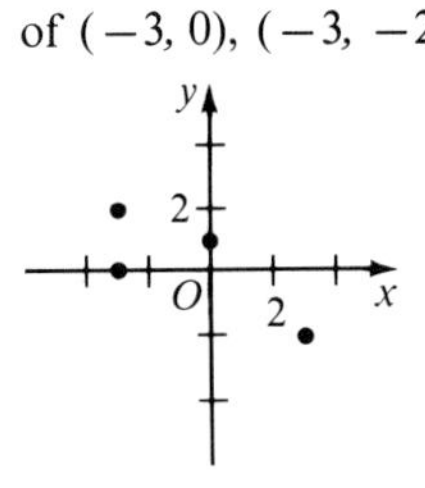

17. function

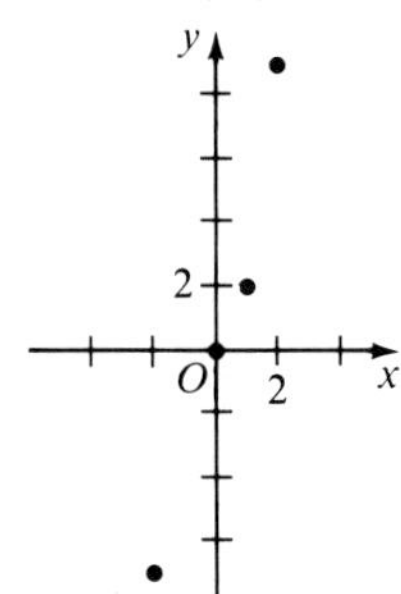

19. relation **21.** relation **23.** function

Chapter Review, pages 442–443 **1.** c **3.** d **5.** a **7.** c **9.** d **11.** b **13.** a **15.** d

Cumulative Review, page 446 **1.** $6z + y$ **3.** $20m^4n + 6m^3n^2 + 10m^2n^3$ **5.** $25b^2 - 80bc + 64c^2$ **7.** $(4x + 7)(3x - 1)$ **9.** $3(z - 8)(z + 1)$ **11.** $\frac{(x + 3)(x - 1)}{2x - 1}$ **13.** $\frac{-3t^2 + 4t + 12}{(t - 2)(t + 2)}$ **15.** $x + y = 7$ **17.** $\{13, 7, 3, 1\}$ **19.**

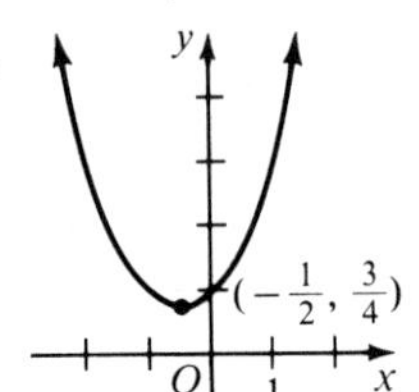

21. 21 **23.** 54% **25.** $\{\frac{5}{6}, -\frac{5}{6}\}$ **27.** $\{0, -2\}$ **29.** $\{0, \frac{1}{3}\}$ **31.** $(\frac{3}{2}, \frac{7}{8})$ **33.** 102.4

Maintaining Skills, page 447 **1.** $\frac{a}{4}$ **3.** 8

5. $\frac{3(z-3)}{5z}$ **7.** $\frac{3t-1}{t-2}$ **9.** $5ab$ **11.** $\frac{2b+3}{b+1}$

13. $\frac{c+2}{c+1}$ **15.** $\frac{(r-6)(r+6)^2}{(r-3)(r+3)^2}$ **17.** $\frac{2x+3y}{x-y}$

19. $\frac{-2-w^2}{w-3}$ **21.** $\frac{v^2-v+8}{(v-1)(v+1)}$ **23.** $\frac{2b(2-b)}{2b-1}$

25. $\frac{d^2-2}{(2d+1)(d+1)}$ **27.** $\frac{6t}{t^2-4}$

29. $\frac{2x^2+13x-28}{(x-4)(x+3)}$

CHAPTER 10 INEQUALITIES

Written Exercises, pages 451–452 **1.** $6 > -7$
3. $-12 \le -9$ **5.** $2 < 3 < 3.5$
7. $-20 < -15 < -10$ **9.** $2.8 > 2 > 0$
11. $|n| \ge n$ **13.** false **15.** true **17.** true
19. $\{-4, -3, -2, -1, 0, 1\}$
21. $\{-2, -1, 0, 1, 2, 3, 4\}$
23. $\{-4, -3, -2, -1, 0, 1, 2, 3, 4\}$
25. $\{-4, 4\}$
27.
−4 −3 −2 −1 0 1 2 3 4 5

29.
−6 −5 −4 −3 −2 −1 0 1 2 3 4

31.
−2 −1 0 1 2 3 4 5 6 7

33.
−7 −6 −5 −4 −3 −2 −1 0 1 2

Answers may vary for Exercises 35 and 37.
35. a. $x = -2, y = -3$ **b.** $x = 3, y = 2$
37. a. $x = 3, y = 2$ **b.** $x = 3, y = -2$

Computer Exercises, page 452
1. $\{0, 1, 2, 3, 4, 5\}$ **3.** $\{4, 5\}$
5. $\{-3, -2, -1, 0, 1\}$

Written Exercises, pages 456–457 **1.** d **3.** c
5. b **7.** e **9.** {the real numbers greater than 15}
11 12 13 14 15 16 17 18 19 20 21

11. {the real numbers less than −8}
−13 −11 −9 −7 −5 −3

13. {the real numbers less than −324}
−328 −327 −326 −325 −324 −323

15. {−1, and the real numbers less than −1}
−6 −5 −4 −3 −2 −1 0 1 2 3 4

17. {the real numbers greater than −4}
−8 −7 −6 −5 −4 −3 −2 −1 0 1 2

19. {0, and the real numbers less than 0}
−5 −4 −3 −2 −1 0 1 2 3 4 5

21. {the real numbers less than 6}
−2 −1 0 1 2 3 4 5 6 7 8

23. {the real numbers greater than −15}
−17 −15 −13 −11 −9 −7

25. {the real numbers less than 8}

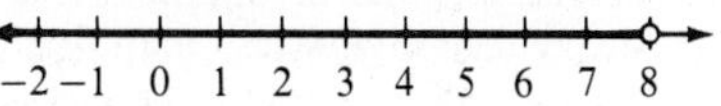

27. {the real numbers less than 6}
29. {the real numbers greater than −12}
31. {4, and the real numbers less than 4}
33. {the real numbers less than 0}
35. {−7, and the real numbers less than −7}
37. $\{\frac{2}{5}$, and the real numbers greater than $\frac{2}{5}\}$
39. $\{\frac{4}{3}$, and the real numbers greater than $\frac{4}{3}\}$

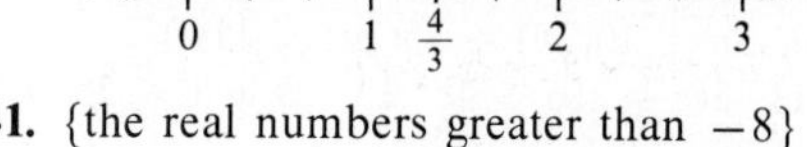

41. {the real numbers greater than −8}
−13 −11 −9 −7 −5 −3

43. {the real numbers greater than −2}
−6 −5 −4 −3 −2 −1 0 1 2 3 4

45. {−4, and the real numbers greater than −4}
−7 −6 −5 −4 −3 −2 −1 0 1 2 3

47. $\{-\frac{3}{2}$, and the real numbers less than $-\frac{3}{2}\}$
−7 −6 −5 −4 −3 −2 −1 0 1 2 3

49. positive real numbers **51.** zero **53.** negative real numbers **55.** none **57.** true
59. true **61.** false **63.** true

Reading Algebra, page 458 **1. a.** greater than
b. open; right **c.** {the real numbers greater than 15}

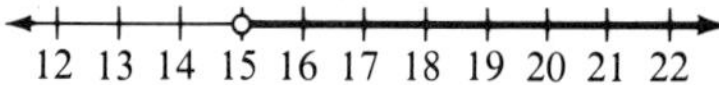

3. a. greater than or equal to **b.** closed; left **c.** {4, and the real numbers less than 4}

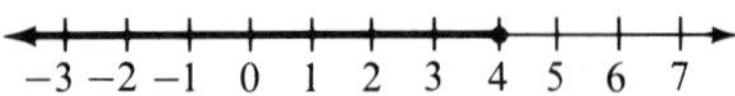

5. a. less than **b.** open; right **c.** {the real numbers greater than −15}

−17 −15 −13 −11 −9 −7

7. a. greater than **b.** open; left **c.** {the real numbers less than 6}

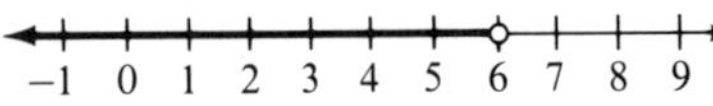

9. a. less than **b.** open; right **c.** {the real numbers greater than −4}

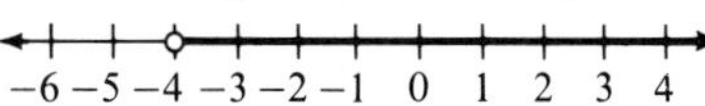

11. a. greater than **b.** open; left **c.** {the real numbers less than 7}

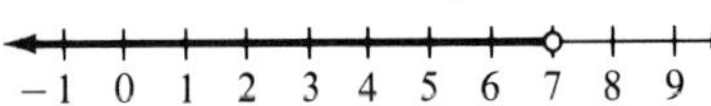

Written Exercises, pages 461-462

1. $i + 2 < 21$ **3.** $a + \frac{a}{10} > 3000$

5. $\frac{1}{2}k + 15 \leq 36$

7. $(m - 2) + m + (m + 2) \geq 51$

9. $5n + 10(2n) + 25(\frac{1}{2}n) \leq 1140$

11. $3(r + 10) > 4r$ **13.** $2s + 1 \leq 25 - s$

15. $n - 2 \geq \frac{1}{4}n + 15$

17. $5(n + 2) - (n + 1) \geq 9 + 2n$

19. $|a + b| \leq |a| + |b|$

Problems, pages 462-464 **1.** 10 kg **3.** 36, 37 **5.** 41, 43 **7.** Jane, at least 21; Terry, at most 29 **9.** 25 cm, 25 cm, 45 cm **11.** 23 years old **13.** 3 PM **15.** at least 4 kg **17.** 4, 5 **19.** 38 **21.** 10.92 km **23.** $1999 **25.** 42, 43, 44

Extra, pages 465-466 **1.** {6, 9} **3.** {0, 3, 4, 5, 6, 7, 8, 9} **5.** {6} **7.** {5, 6, 9} **9.** {5, 6, 7, 8} **11.** {−4, −3, −2, −1, 0}; {−3, −2} **13.** {3, 4, 5, 6, 7, 8}; disjoint sets **15.** {2, 3, 4, 6, 8, 10, 12}; {4, 6, 8} **17.** {the real numbers between −1 and 2} **19.** {the real numbers greater than −3} **21.** {the real numbers between −3 and 2} **23.** {the real numbers between −1 and 2}

25.

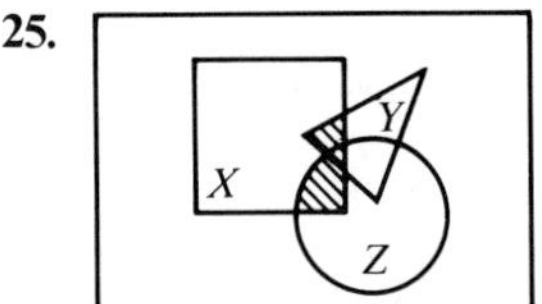

27. $X \cap (Y \cup Z) = (X \cap Y) \cup (X \cap Z)$

29.

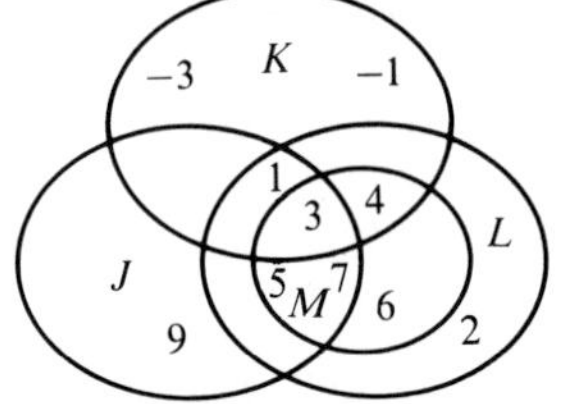

Challenge, page 467 Step 4: If you divide by $3 - a$, which is negative (because $a > 3$), the inequality must be reversed so that step 5 is $a < 3 + a$.

Written Exercises, pages 470-471

1.

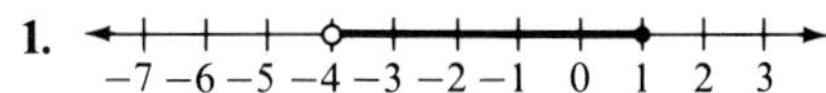

3.

−2 −1 0 1 2 3 4 5 6 7 8

5. {the real numbers between −3 and 2}

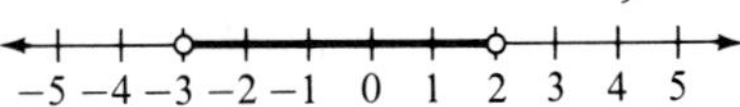

7. {8, and the real numbers between 0 and 8}

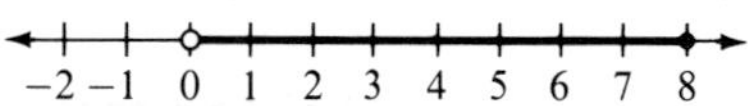

9. {−2, and the real numbers between −2 and 3}

−4 −3 −2 −1 0 1 2 3 4 5 6

11. {−2, and the real numbers between −2 and 1}

−6 −5 −4 −3 −2 −1 0 1 2 3 4

13. {4, and the real numbers less than −2 or greater than 4}

−4 −3 −2 −1 0 1 2 3 4 5 6

15. $\{-2, \frac{2}{3}$, and the real numbers greater than $\frac{2}{3}$ or less than $-2\}$

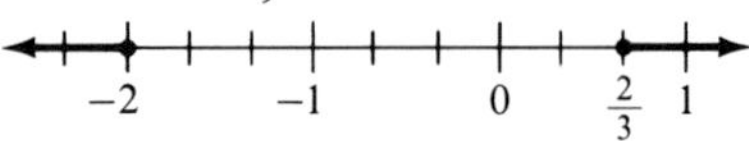

17. {−2, 3, and the real numbers greater than 3 or less than −2}

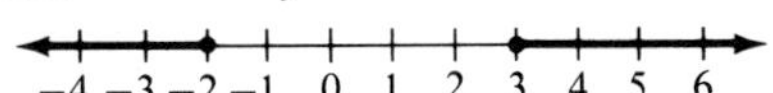

19. $\{-3, 5,$ and the real numbers between -3 and $5\}$

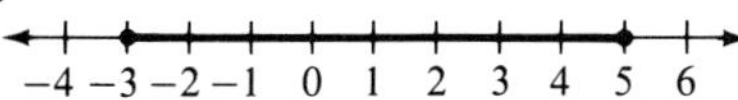

21. 4, and the real numbers between -3 and $4\}$

−4 −3 −2 −1 0 1 2 3 4 5 6

23. -3, and the real numbers between -3 and $5\}$

−4 −3 −2 −1 0 1 2 3 4 5 6

25. $\emptyset$

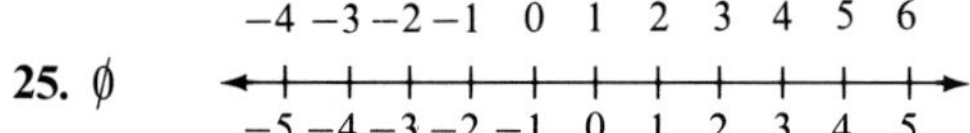

27. $\{5,$ and the real numbers between -2 and $5\}$

−5 −4 −3 −2 −1 0 1 2 3 4 5

29. {the real numbers greater than 15 or less than -1}

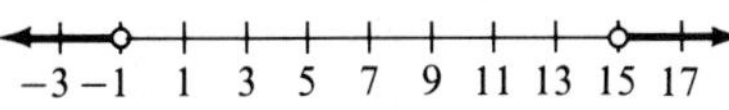

31. {the real numbers greater than 5 or less than -1}

−5 −4 −3 −2 −1 0 1 2 3 4 5

33. $\{-\frac{3}{2}, 2,$ and the real numbers between $-\frac{3}{2}$ and $2\}$

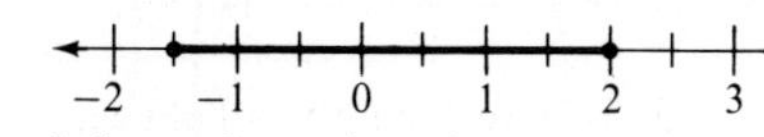

35. $\{4,$ and the real numbers between 1 and $4\}$

−5 −4 −3 −2 −1 0 1 2 3 4 5

37. $\{6,$ and the real numbers less than $6\}$

−3 −2 −1 0 1 2 3 4 5 6 7

39. $\{0, 2, 4, 6\}$, $\{-2, 0, 2, 4\}$, $\{-4, -2, 0, 2\}$

41. a. $a = 20$, $b = 3$, $c = 40$, $d = 5$
b. $a = 4$, $b = -3$, $c = 0$, $d = -2$

Written Exercises, page 475 **1.** $|x| < 1$
3. $|x + 2| = 3$ **5.** $|x - 1| \geq 3$

7. $\{7, 9\}$

3 4 5 6 7 8 9 10 11 12

9. $\{1, -13\}$

−17 −13 −9 −5 −1 1 3

11. {the real numbers between -2.5 and 2.5}

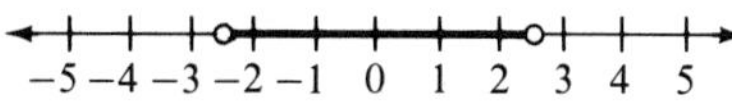

13. {the real numbers greater than -4 or less than -8}

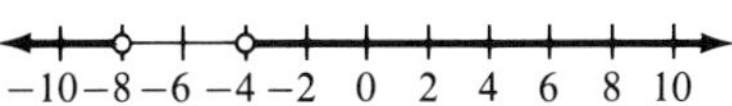

15. $\{2, 10,$ and the real numbers between 2 and $10\}$

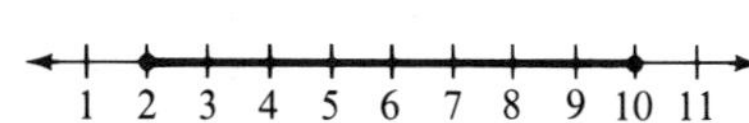

17. $\{-6, 2,$ and the real numbers greater than 2 or less than $-6\}$

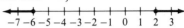

−7 −6 −5 −4 −3 −2 −1 0 1 2 3

19. $\{-3, 3,$ and the real numbers greater than 3 or less than $-3\}$

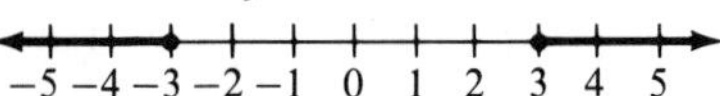

21. {the real numbers greater than 7 or less than -1}

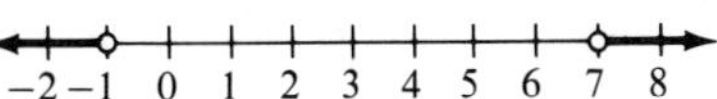

23. $\{-4, 4,$ and the real numbers between -4 and $4\}$

−5 −4 −3 −2 −1 0 1 2 3 4 5

25. $\{0, 4,$ and the real numbers greater than 4 or less than $0\}$

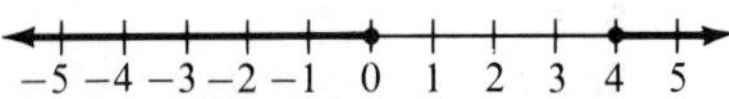

27. $\{-2, 2,$ and the real numbers between -2 and $2\}$

−5 −4 −3 −2 −1 0 1 2 3 4 5

29. $\{\frac{2}{3}, 2\}$

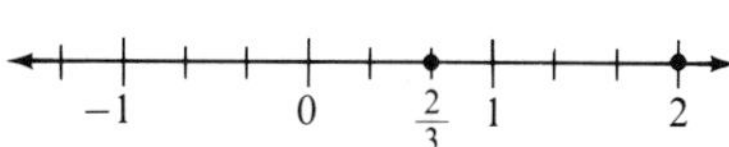

31. {the real numbers greater than or equal to 3}

−5 −4 −3 −2 −1 0 1 2 3 4 5

33. $\emptyset$

−5 −4 −3 −2 −1 0 1 2 3 4 5

Written Exercises, pages 477–478

1. $\{5, -5\}$

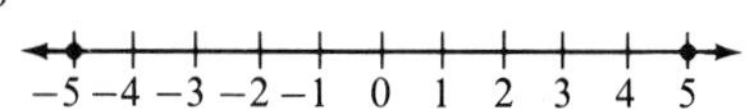

3. $\{-3, 3,$ and the real numbers greater than 3 or less than $-3\}$

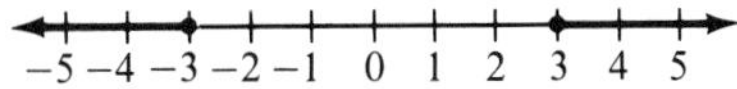

5. $\{-3, 4\}$

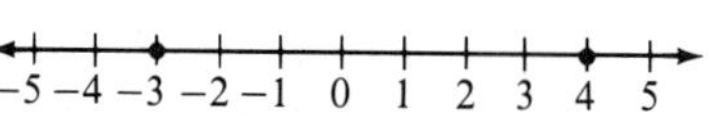

7. $\{\frac{3}{2}, 3$, and the real numbers between $\frac{3}{2}$ and $3\}$

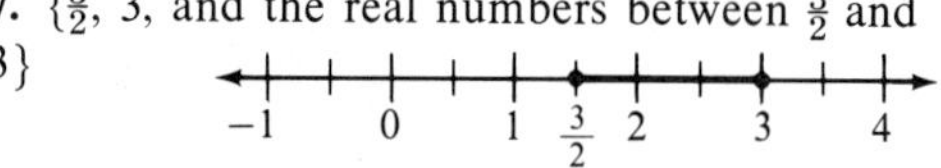

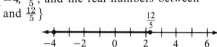

9. $\{-4, \frac{12}{5}$, and the real numbers between -4 and $\frac{12}{5}\}$

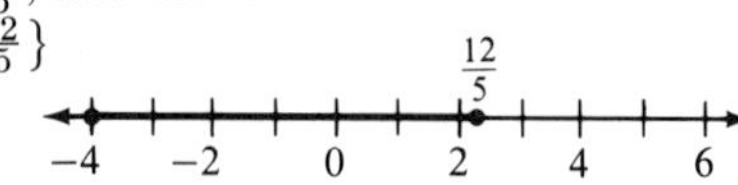

11. $\{15, -3$, and the real numbers greater than 15 or less than $-3\}$

13. {the real numbers between $-\frac{19}{3}$ and 7}

15. $\{-1, \frac{1}{2}\}$

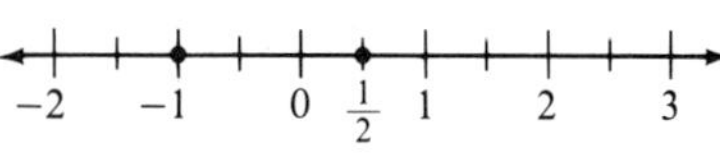

17. $\emptyset$

19. true **21.** false, $a = -2$ **23.** true

25. 50°C, 14°C

Written Exercises, pages 482–483

1.

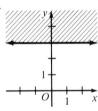

3.

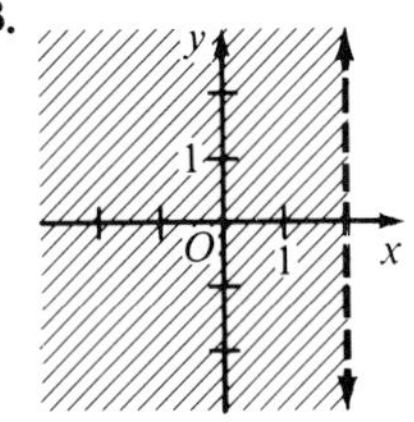

5.

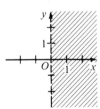

7.

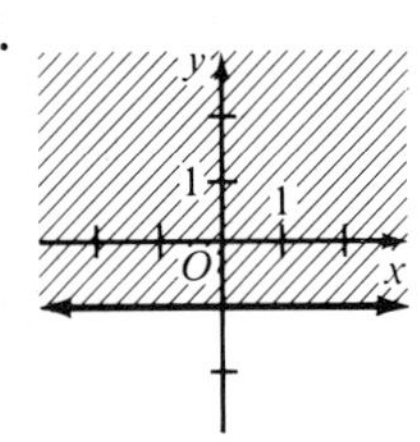

9.

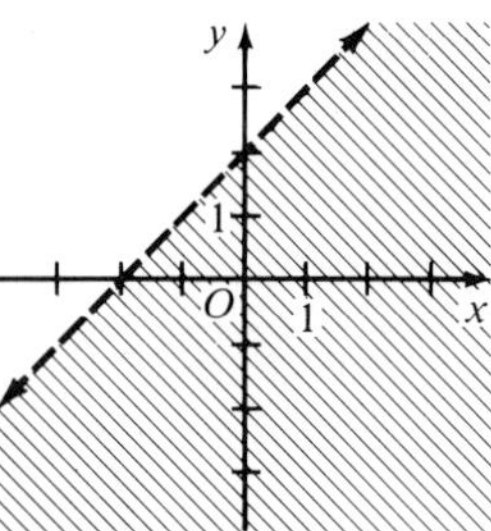

11.

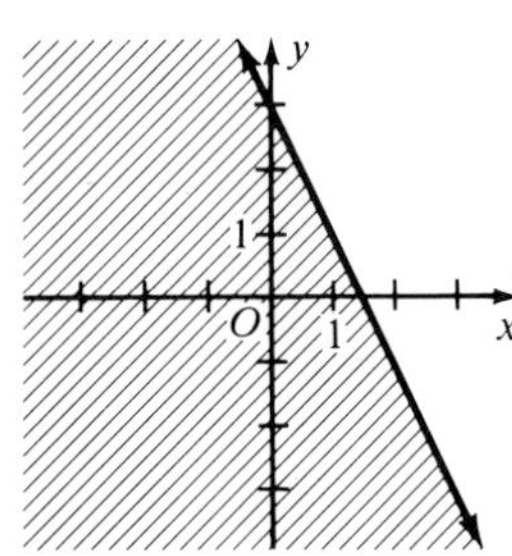

13. $y < -x + 2$

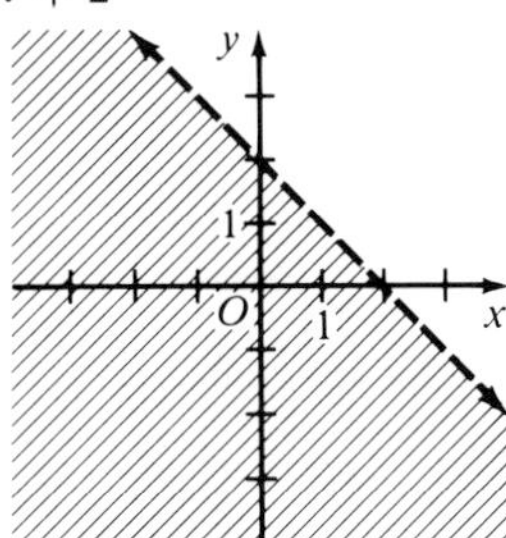

15. $y \geq \frac{1}{2}x + \frac{7}{2}$

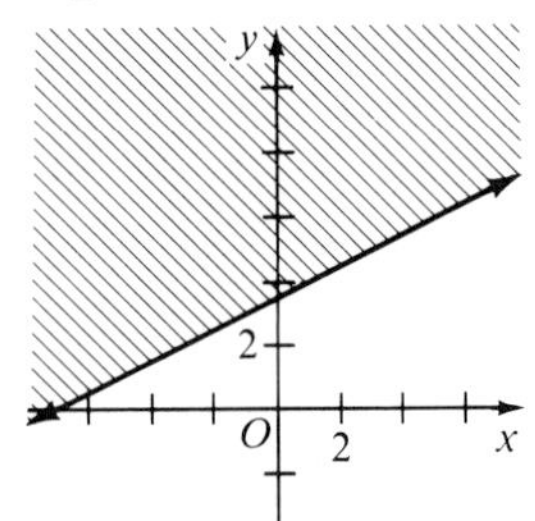

17. $y < 3x - 6$

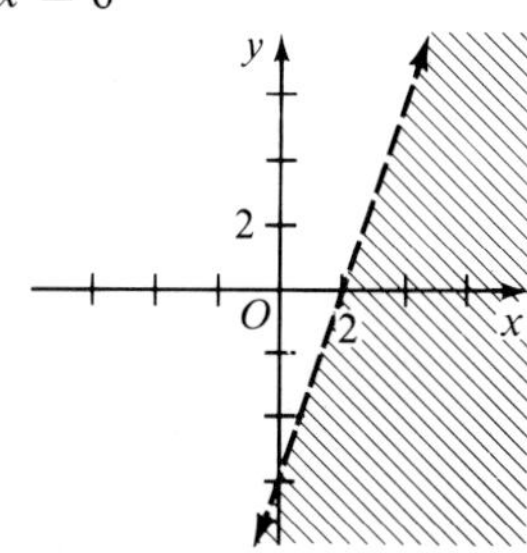

19. $y \leq \frac{3}{2}x - 5$

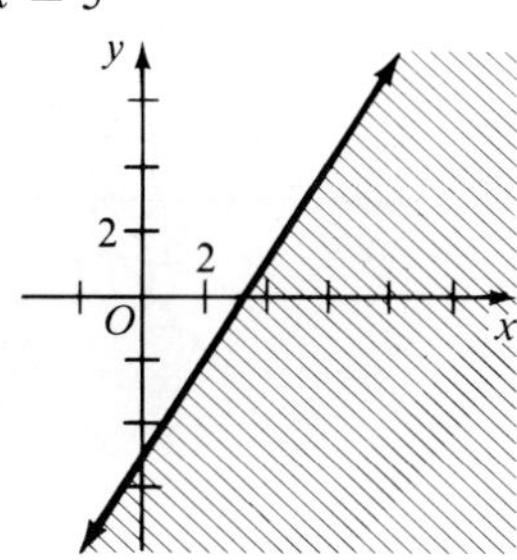

21. $y \leq -\frac{3}{2}x - 2$

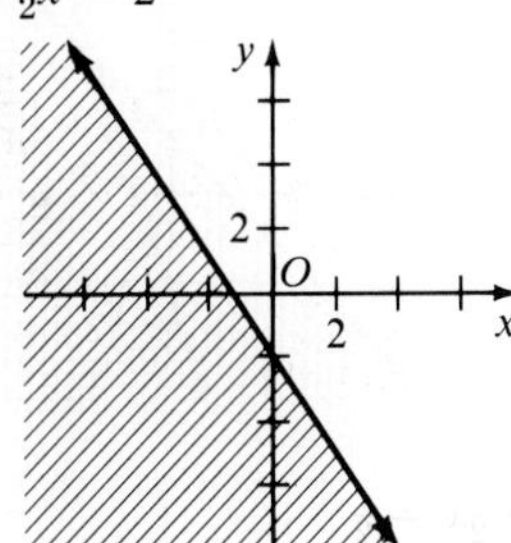

23. $y \leq -\frac{1}{3}x - \frac{7}{3}$

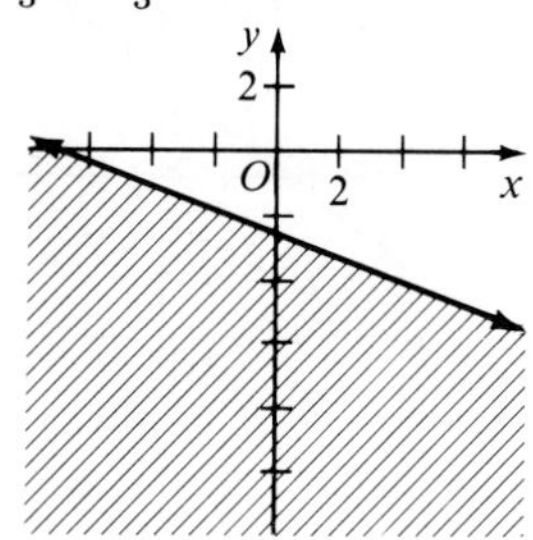

25. $y > -2$
27. $y \leq -\frac{2}{3}x + 2$
29. $y \geq \frac{5}{3}x + 5$ **31.** $y > \frac{1}{2}x - 2$
33. $y \leq -x + 4$

35.

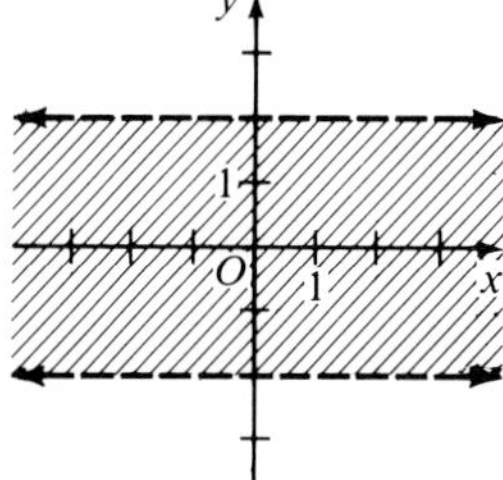

37.

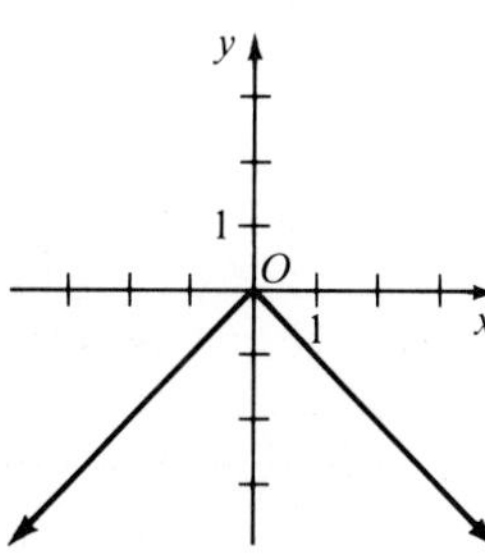

39.

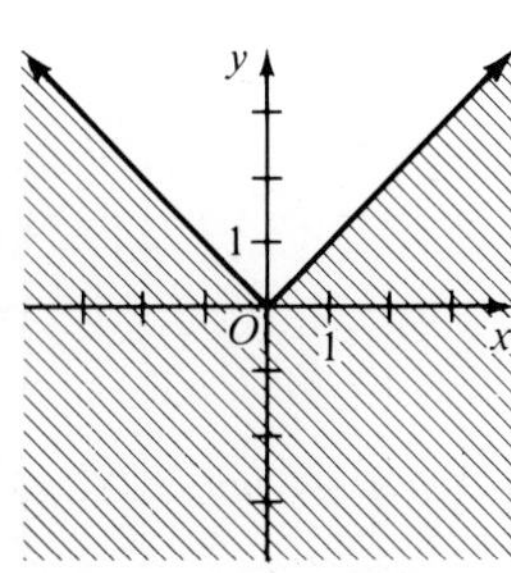

Written Exercises, pages 485–487

1.

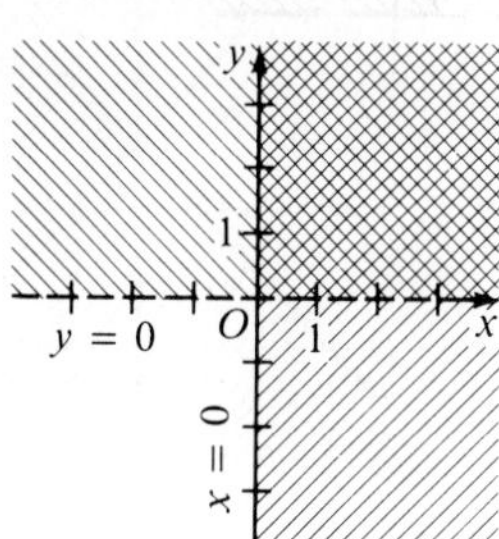

3.

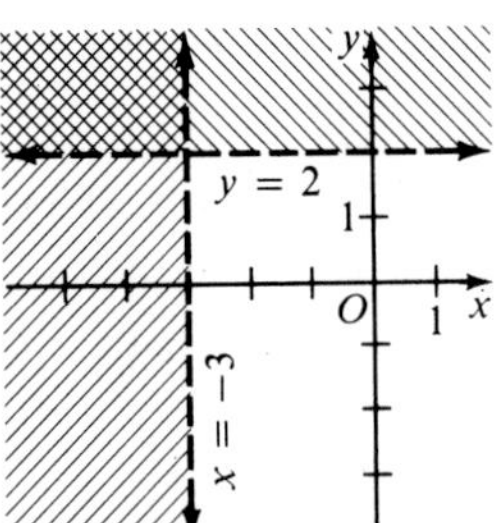

5.

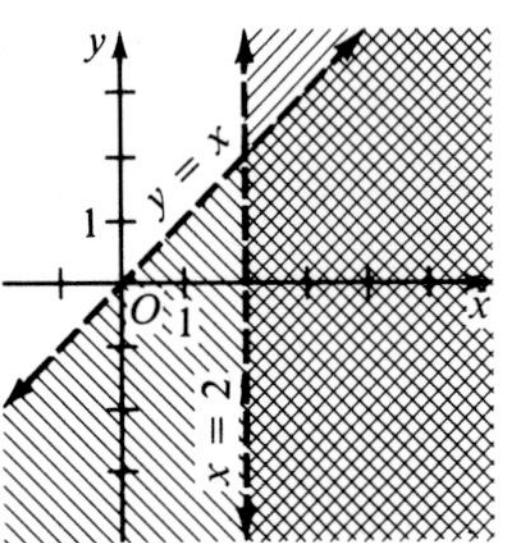

7.

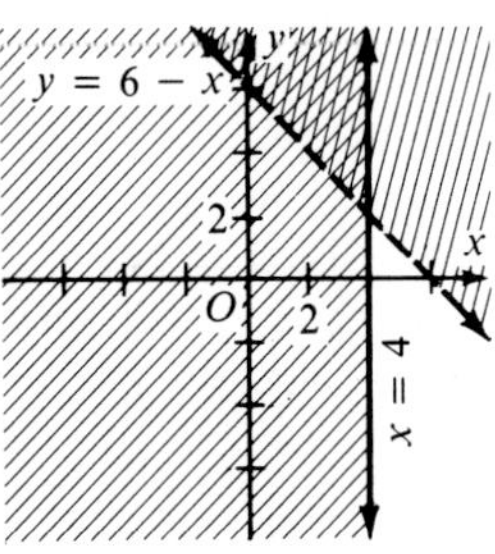

9.

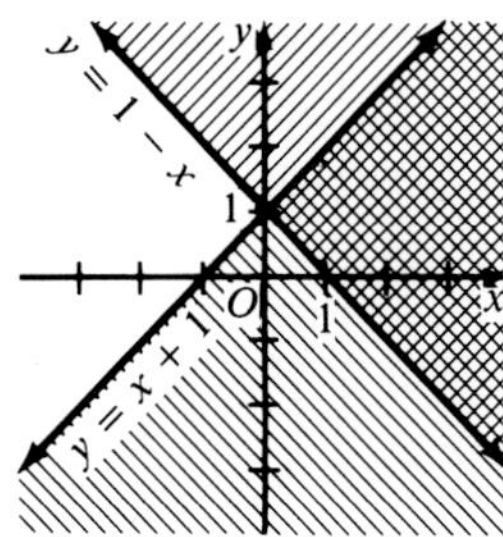

11.

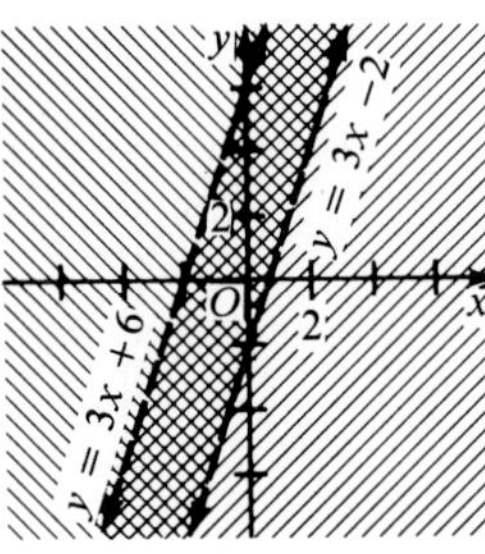

13.

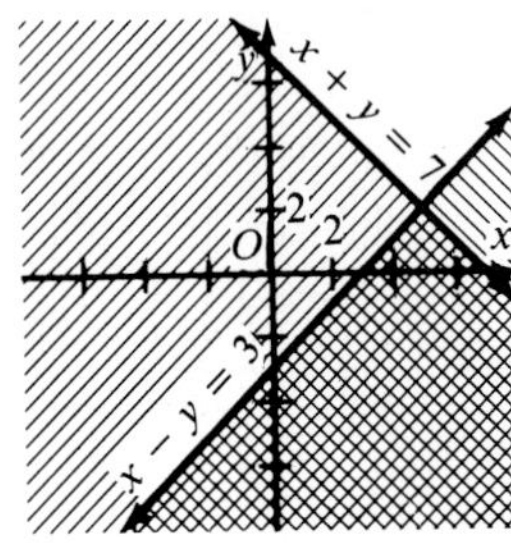

15.

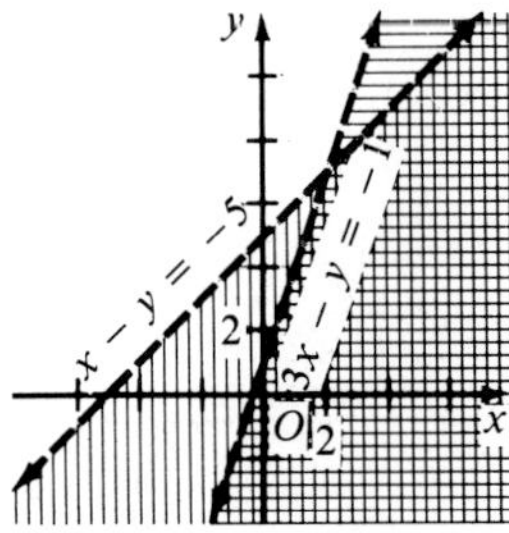

17.

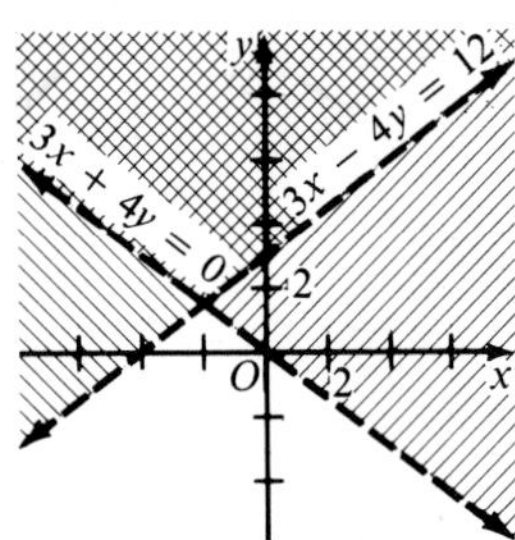

19. $y \geq -4$
$y < x - 4$

21. $y < -2x + 2$
$y < \frac{2}{3}x - \frac{10}{3}$

23. $x \geq 3$
$y \leq -x + 1$
$y \geq \frac{1}{7}x - \frac{25}{7}$

25.

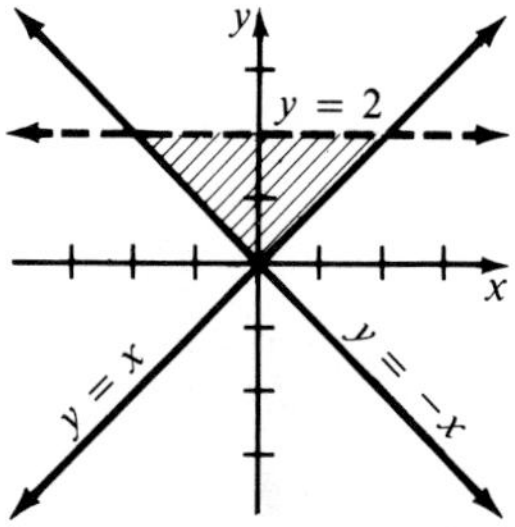

27.

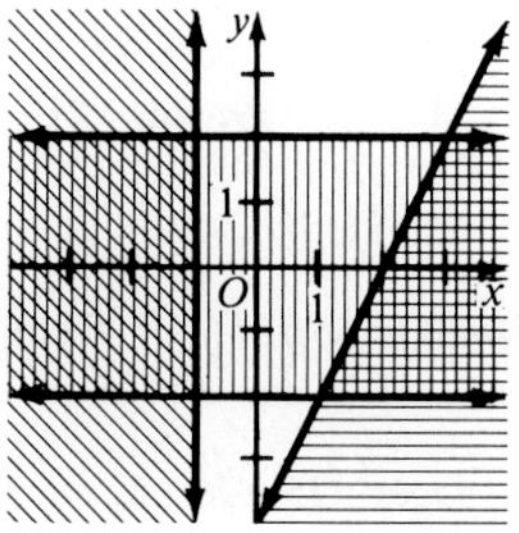

Calculator Key-In, page 487 **1.** false **3.** false

Extra, pages 487–490

1. a.

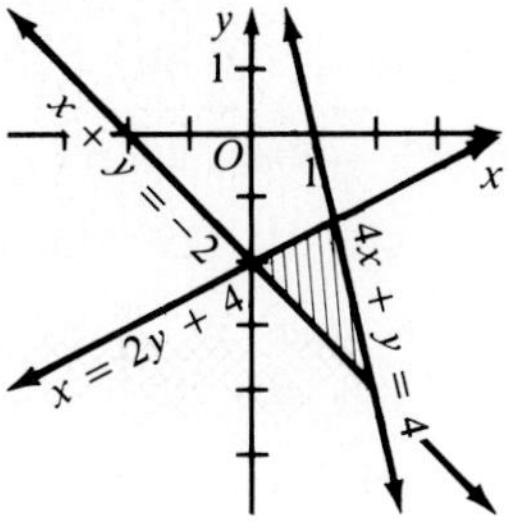

b. $(\frac{4}{3}, -\frac{4}{3})$, $(2, -4)$, $(0, -2)$ **c.** maximum: -4; minimum: -20 **3. a.** $6c + 12s \leq 2400$; $12c + 16s \leq 3600$; $c \geq 0$; $s \geq 0$

b.

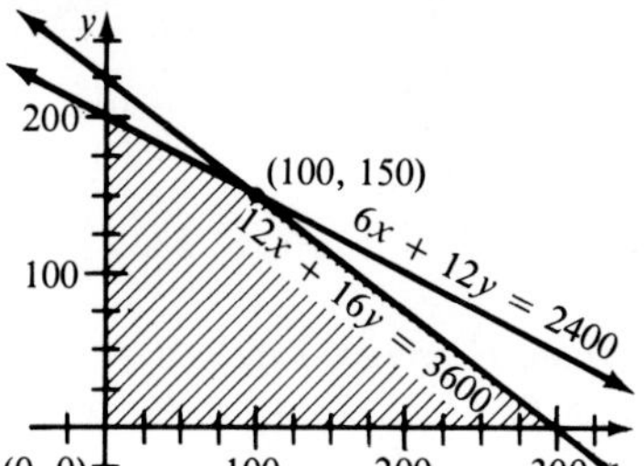

c. 100 acres of corn, 150 acres of soybeans; 0 acres of corn, 200 acres of soybeans

Challenge, page 490 one sphere and one cube

Chapter Review, pages 492–493 **1.** c **3.** c **5.** d **7.** b **9.** b **11.** b

Cumulative Review, page 494 **1.** $-4b - 4$ **3.** $27x^{14}y^{12}$ **5.** $15c^3 - 23c^2d + 44cd^2 - 8d^3$ **7.** $\frac{x-3}{3x+2}$ **9.** 2.4×10^6 **11.** y^2

13. $6(5z^2 + 40z + 16)$

15. $(4z - y - 5)(4z + y + 5)$

17. $x - 2y = -7$

19.

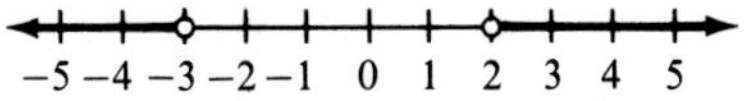

21. $\{7, -7\}$ **23.** 75 **25.** 0 **27.** $\{-1, -3\}$ **29.** $\{\frac{5}{3}, -1\}$ **31.** $-\frac{4}{3}$ **33.** $(1, 4)$ **35.** $(-1, 2)$ **37.** {the real numbers less than $-\frac{6}{5}$} **39.** $7\frac{1}{2}$ h

Maintaining Skills, page 495 **1.** $\{-4, 10\}$ **3.** -6 **5.** $\{\frac{1}{5}, -1\}$ **7.** $\{-\frac{2}{5}, \frac{4}{3}\}$ **9.** $\{-\frac{9}{16}, 1\}$ **11.** 2 **13.** $-\frac{2}{5}$ **15.** no solution **17.** 6 **19.** no solution **21.** no solution **23.** 2

Mixed Review, page 496

1. $(4b - 5)(5b + 3)$ **3.** prime **5.** 10 **7.** 140 **9.** {the real numbers greater than 2 or less than $\frac{2}{3}$} **11.** $\{5, -3\}$ **13.** -2 **15.** 63 L **17.** 12.05 km/h, 27.95 km/h **19.** 72 **21.** 15 m, 24 m, 33 m

23.

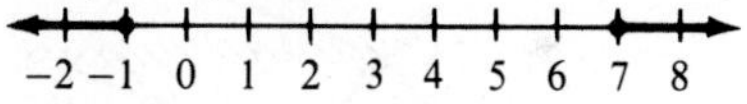

Preparing for College Entrance Exams, page 497 **1.** A **3.** D **5.** D

CHAPTER 11 RATIONAL AND IRRATIONAL NUMBERS

Written Exercises, pages 501–503 **1.** $>$ **3.** $<$ **5.** $<$ **7.** $>$ **9.** $<$ **11.** $-\frac{4}{9}, \frac{3}{8}, \frac{5}{6}$ **13.** $\frac{303}{56}$, 5.6, $\frac{107}{18}$ **15.** $-\frac{6}{7}, -\frac{3}{5}, -\frac{5}{9}, -\frac{3}{7}$ **17.** $\frac{61}{88}$ **19.** $-\frac{1497}{6720}$ **21.** $\frac{41}{21}$ **23.** increases **25.** decreases **27.** $\frac{27}{28}$ **29.** $-\frac{31}{75}$ **31.** for example, $\frac{13}{24}$ **33.** $\frac{29a}{126}$ **35. a.** yes **b.** $a + \frac{1}{2}(b - a) = \frac{a+b}{2}$ **37.** $w < z$

37. $z > w$

Challenge, page 503 yes; no

Written Exercises, pages 507–508 **1.** 0.375 **3.** $0.\overline{5}$ **5.** 1.24 **7.** $3.\overline{6}$ **9.** $-0.2\overline{7}$ **11.** -2.35 **13.** $0.\overline{82}$ **15.** $-0.\overline{48}$ **17.** $\frac{33}{50}$ **19.** $\frac{5}{9}$ **21.** $\frac{13}{40}$ **23.** $\frac{24}{5}$ **25.** $\frac{7}{99}$ **27.** $-\frac{37}{15}$ **29.** 0.753 **31.** $0.773\overline{8}$ **33.** $0.1\overline{453}$ **35.** $\frac{3}{8}$ **37.** $\frac{1}{3}$ **39.** $\frac{55}{486}$ **41. a.** $0.\overline{142857}$, $0.\overline{714285}$ **b.** $0.\overline{714285} = 5(0.\overline{142857})$ **c.** $0.\overline{285714}$, $0.\overline{428571}$, $0.\overline{857142}$ **43. a.** $0.\overline{05}$, $0.\overline{25}$, $0.\overline{74}$ **b.** $1 = \frac{99}{99} = 0.\overline{99} = 0.\overline{9}$

Computer Key-In, pages 508–509 **1.** $0.\overline{142857}$; $0.\overline{285714}$; $0.\overline{428571}$; $0.\overline{571428}$; $0.\overline{714285}$; $0.\overline{857142}$ **3.** $0.0\overline{714285}$; $0.2\overline{142857}$; $0.3\overline{571428}$; $0.6\overline{428571}$; $0.7\overline{857142}$; $0.9\overline{285714}$

Written Exercises, page 512 **1.** 5 **3.** 10 **5.** -21 **7.** -14 **9.** ± 17 **11.** 40 **13.** 42 **15.** 90 **17.** $\pm\frac{20}{9}$ **19.** $\frac{1}{16}$ **21.** $-\frac{27}{10}$ **23.** $\frac{32}{43}$ **25.** $\pm\frac{22}{23}$ **27.** -0.7 **29.** ± 1.5 **31.** 0.13 **33.** -0.48 **35.** 0.05 **37.** -8 **39.** -8 **41.** $-\frac{2}{5}$ **43.** $\pm\frac{5}{2}$ **45.** $\pm\frac{7}{8}$ **47.** $\frac{5}{12}$ **49.** $\frac{21}{100}$

Calculator Key-In, page 512 **1.** 2.632148 **3.** 1.8707313 **5.** 1.3753959

Challenge, page 513

1.

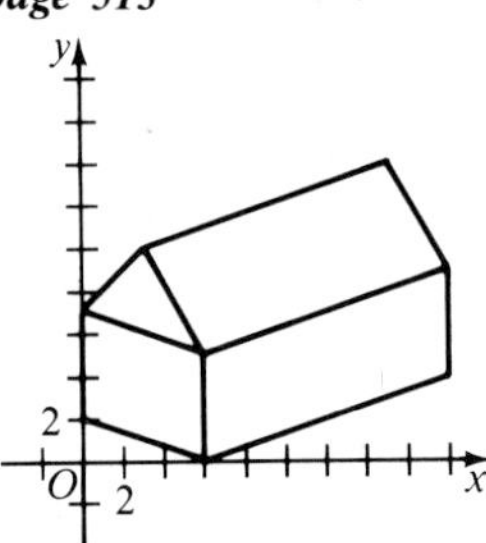

Written Exercises, page 516 **1.** 15 **3.** $2\sqrt{30}$ **5.** $30\sqrt{2}$ **7.** $27\sqrt{10}$ **9.** $60\sqrt{2}$ **11.** $50\sqrt{3}$ **13.** $8\sqrt{2}$ **15.** 85 **17.** -69.3 **19.** 95.9 **21.** 9.27 **23.** -0.55 **25.** -0.28 **27.** 346 **29.** 721

Written Exercises, page 518 **1.** $12|a|$ **3.** $5b^2\sqrt{3}$ **5.** $4|ab|\sqrt{5}$ **7.** $9|z|$ **9.** $-3c^2$ **11.** $9|x|y\sqrt{7y}$ **13.** $2|r^3|s^2\sqrt{14}$ **15.** $3\left|\frac{m}{n}\right|$ **17.** $21|a^3|b^2$ **19.** $-1.8x^2$ **21.** $\frac{2|e|}{25}$ **23.** $\frac{13}{20s^6}$ **25.** $\frac{13|r^{25}|}{5}$ **27.** $|m-5|$ **29.** $\{4, -4\}$ **31.** $\{1, -1\}$ **33.** $\{\frac{5}{2}, -\frac{5}{2}\}$ **35.** $\{4, -4\}$ **37.** $\{\frac{5}{3}, -\frac{5}{3}\}$ **39.** $\{12.8, -12.8\}$ **41.** $\{14.3, -14.3\}$ **43.** $\{3.3, -3.3\}$ **45.** $\{4.4, -4.4\}$ **47.** $\{7.6, -7.6\}$ **49.** $\{8.6, -8.6\}$

Problems, pages 518–519 **1.** 14.1 cm **3.** 18 m **5.** $\frac{20}{3}$ mm **7.** $\sqrt{2}:1$ **9.** 18 s **11.** 86.5 m^2

Written Exercises, page 523 **1.** 15 **3.** 8.06 **5.** 9.90 **7.** 8 **9.** 39.55 **11.** no **13.** yes **15.** no **17.** no **19.** yes **21.** 9.49 **23.** 13.42 **25.** 23.43 **27.** $a = 18.96$, $b = 6.32$ **29.** $a = 28.85$, $b = 43.27$

Problems, page 524 **1.** 25 cm **3.** 9 m **5.** 6, 8, 10 **7.** 51.96 cm **9.** 1.6 m

Extra, pages 525–526 **1.** 8 **3.** 6.3 **5.** 6.4 **7.** 9.8 **9.** 11.2 **11.** 8.5 **13.** The lengths of the sides are $\sqrt{17}$, $\sqrt{17}$, $3\sqrt{2}$. Since two sides have equal length, the triangle is isosceles.

Written Exercises, page 528 **1.** 6 **3.** $3\sqrt{10}$ **5.** $2\sqrt{35}$ **7.** 6 **9.** $72\sqrt{2}$ **11.** $\sqrt{2}$ **13.** $\frac{1}{4}\sqrt{10}$ **15.** $\frac{1}{3}\sqrt{2}$ **17.** $\frac{1}{10}\sqrt{3}$ **19.** $\frac{\sqrt{65}}{13}$ **21.** $4\sqrt{3}$ **23.** 56 **25.** $-10ab$ **27.** $4\sqrt{r} - r$ **29.** $-480\sqrt{2}$ **31.** $12x^2$ **33.** $112y$ **35.** $\frac{6x^2}{y}$ **37.** $4a - 6a\sqrt{6a}$ **39.** $24x^2 - 120x^3\sqrt{x}$ **41.** $135y^4\sqrt{5y}$ **43.** $50x^4y^2\sqrt{2} - 100x^2y^4$

Written Exercises, page 530 **1.** $4\sqrt{2}$ **3.** $-16\sqrt{23}$ **5.** $27\sqrt{2}$ **7.** $-11\sqrt{7}$ **9.** $16\sqrt{2} - 9\sqrt{3}$ **11.** $-22\sqrt{2} - 14\sqrt{3}$ **13.** $12\sqrt{19} - 7\sqrt{11}$ **15.** $12\sqrt{7} - \sqrt{14}$ **17.** $-14\sqrt{2}$ **19.** $\frac{2}{3}\sqrt{6}$ **21.** $\frac{46\sqrt{2}}{5}$ **23.** $\frac{1}{15}\sqrt{30}$ **25.** $9\sqrt{5} - \frac{9}{5}\sqrt{10}$ **27.** $2\sqrt{14} - \frac{7}{2}\sqrt{2}$ **29.** $18 - 18\sqrt{2}$ **31.** $18x\sqrt{x} - 15x^2\sqrt{x}$ **33.** $\frac{5x}{12}$ **35.** $\frac{x\sqrt{a^2 + b^2}}{ab}$

Written Exercises, pages 532–533 **1.** -1 **3.** 1 **5.** 12 **7.** $28 + 10\sqrt{3}$ **9.** $17 - 12\sqrt{2}$ **11.** $33 + 4\sqrt{65}$ **13.** $30\sqrt{2} - 40$ **15.** $-42\sqrt{2} + 70$ **17.** $9 + 2\sqrt{3}$ **19.** $54 - 21\sqrt{35}$ **21.** $208 + 25\sqrt{30}$ **23.** $-4 + 4\sqrt{2}$ **25.** $\frac{3 + \sqrt{3}}{6}$

27. $\frac{2 + \sqrt{5} + 2\sqrt{3} + \sqrt{15}}{-2}$ **29.** $\frac{21\sqrt{3} - 28}{11}$
31. $8 - 4\sqrt{7}$ **33.** 0
35. $[x - (1 + \sqrt{3})][x - (1 - \sqrt{3})] = x^2 - 2x - 2$
37. $\left[x - \left(\frac{1}{3} + \frac{\sqrt{7}}{3}\right)\right]\left[x - \left(\frac{1}{3} - \frac{\sqrt{7}}{3}\right)\right] = 3x^2 - 2x - 2$
39. $x - y^2$ **41.** $15r^2s - rq\sqrt{s} - 6q^2$

Written Exercises, page 535 **1.** 100 **3.** 32 **5.** $\frac{1}{36}$ **7.** 25 **9.** $\frac{25}{9}$ **11.** 180 **13.** -4 **15.** $\frac{3}{25}$ **17.** 27 **19.** 3 **21.** $\frac{5}{3}$ **23.** $\frac{245}{8}$ **25.** 21 **27.** 22 **29.** 63 **31.** $\pm 3\sqrt{7}$ **33.** $\{\sqrt{19}, -\sqrt{19}\}$ **35.** 6 **37.** 0 **39.** $\sqrt{7}$ **41.** 0 **43.** $\{1, -4\}$ **45.** 1 **47.** (8, 18)

Problems, page 536 **1.** 98 **3.** 900 **5.** 29 **7.** 225π cm^2 **9.** 10 m **11.** 50, 52 or -52, -50

Extra, pages 537–539 **1.** $5^{\frac{1}{2}}$ **3.** $3^{\frac{1}{4}}$ **5.** $6^{\frac{2}{3}}$ **7.** $2^{\frac{3}{2}}$ **9.** 7 **11.** -3 **13.** 8 **15.** 3 **17.** 125 **19.** 81

Application, page 540 **1.** 360 cm^3 **3.** 600 cm^3 **5.** 22.5 m^3 or 22,500,000 cm^3

Chapter Review, pages 542–543 **1.** b **3.** c **5.** c **7.** b **9.** a **11.** c **13.** b **15.** d **17.** a

Cumulative Review, page 544 **1.** -21
3. $16a^6b^2 + 72a^3bc^2 + 81c^4$ **5.** 1.024×10^{-7}
7. $\frac{7x + 1}{x + 3}$ **9.** $\frac{4t^2 + 3t - 16}{(t + 4)(t - 2)}$ **11.** $\sqrt{7}$
13. $\frac{5}{6}\sqrt{30}$ **15.** $\frac{2\sqrt{6} + \sqrt{30}}{6}$
17. $(2c - d - 3)(2c - d + 3)$
19.

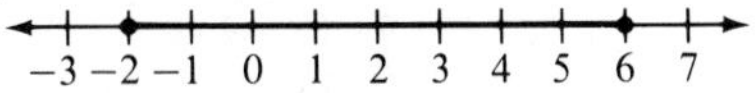

21.

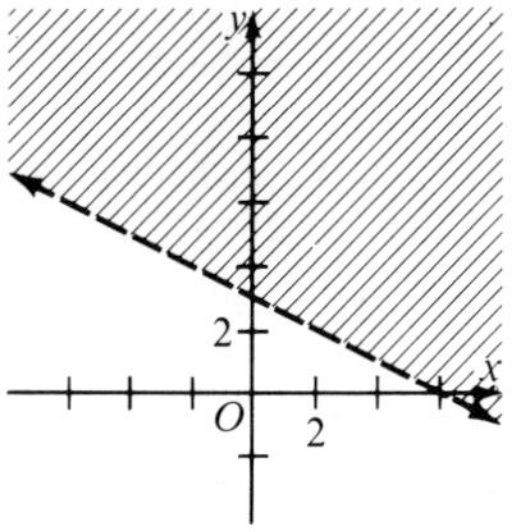

23. 0 **25.**

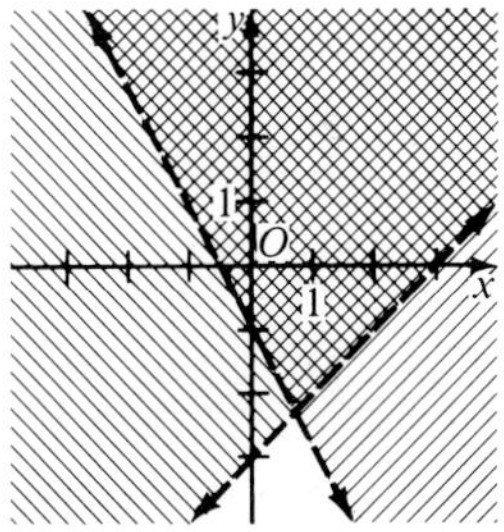

27. 15 **29.** $-\frac{5}{2}$ **31.** $\{3, -1\}$ **33.** $(-1, -\frac{1}{5})$ **35.** $\{\frac{7}{2}$, 6, and the real numbers between $\frac{7}{2}$ and 6$\}$ **37.** {the real numbers greater than $-\frac{2}{3}$} **39.** 5 **41.** 15.59 cm

Maintaining Skills, page 545 **1.** $(-1, 2)$ **3.** (5, 5) **5.** $(\frac{1}{2}, \frac{1}{3})$ **7.** $(-\frac{2}{3}, \frac{7}{3})$ **9.** (7, 3) **11.** $(12, -1)$ **13.** (0, 0) **15.** $(7, -1)$ **17.** $(-7, 12)$ **19.** (5, 6) **21.** (9, 4)

CHAPTER 12 QUADRATIC FUNCTIONS

Written Exercises, page 549 **1.** $\{7, -7\}$ **3.** $\{\frac{11}{12}, -\frac{11}{12}\}$ **5.** $\{6, -6\}$ **7.** $\{2, -2\}$ **9.** no solution **11.** $\{\sqrt{3}, -\sqrt{3}\}$ **13.** $\{\sqrt{3}, -\sqrt{3}\}$ **15.** $\{\sqrt{6}, -\sqrt{6}\}$ **17.** $\{\sqrt{11}, -\sqrt{11}\}$
19. $\{0, -6\}$ **21.** $\{-2 + 2\sqrt{3}, -2 - 2\sqrt{3}\}$
23. $\{3 + 4\sqrt{2}, 3 - 4\sqrt{2}\}$
25. $\{8 + \sqrt{5}, 8 - \sqrt{5}\}$
27. $\{-3 + \sqrt{6}, -3 - \sqrt{6}\}$ **29.** $\{\frac{5}{6}, -\frac{1}{2}\}$
31. $\{-5, 1\}$ **33.** $\{1, -21\}$ **35.** $\{\frac{3}{4}, -\frac{3}{4}\}$
37. $\{\sqrt{19}, -\sqrt{19}\}$ **39.** $\{\frac{8}{13}, -\frac{8}{13}\}$
41. $\{\frac{3}{4}, -\frac{3}{4}\}$ **43.** $\{\frac{37}{12}, \frac{35}{12}\}$
45. $\left\{\frac{16 + 9\sqrt{3}}{36}, \frac{16 - 9\sqrt{3}}{36}\right\}$ **47.** $\{0, 5, -5\}$
49. $\{0, \frac{1}{4}, -\frac{1}{4}\}$ **51.** $\{0, 8, -8\}$ **53.** $\{\frac{1}{3}, 0\}$
55. no solution **57.** $\{\sqrt{5} + \sqrt{3}, \sqrt{5} - \sqrt{3}\}$

Written Exercises, page 552
1. $\{1 + \sqrt{21}, 1 - \sqrt{21}\}$, $\{5.6, -3.6\}$
3. $\{-6 + \sqrt{34}, -6 - \sqrt{34}\}$, $\{-11.8, -0.2\}$
5. $\{2 + \sqrt{7}, 2 - \sqrt{7}\}$, $\{4.6, -0.6\}$
7. $\{-22, 6\}$ **9.** $\{3 + 4\sqrt{21}, 3 - 4\sqrt{21}\}$, $\{21.3, -15.3\}$ **11.** $\{-3 + 3\sqrt{2}, -3 - 3\sqrt{2}\}$, $\{-7.2, 1.2\}$ **13.** $\left\{\frac{-1 + \sqrt{21}}{2}, \frac{-1 - \sqrt{21}}{2}\right\}$, $\{1.8, -2.8\}$ **15.** $\left\{\frac{9 + \sqrt{109}}{2}, \frac{9 - \sqrt{109}}{2}\right\}$, $\{9.7, -0.7\}$ **17.** $\{31, -37\}$ **19.** $\{9, 5\}$
21. $\{-30, 2\}$ **23.** $\{1, -\frac{1}{5}\}$ **25.** $\{8, -2\}$

27. $\{-\frac{1}{2}, 4\}$ **29.** $\left\{\frac{3 + \sqrt{201}}{8}, \frac{3 - \sqrt{201}}{8}\right\}$

31. $\left\{\frac{-11 + \sqrt{193}}{12}, \frac{-11 - \sqrt{193}}{12}\right\}$

33. $\left\{\frac{13 + \sqrt{113}}{14}, \frac{13 - \sqrt{113}}{14}\right\}$

35. $\left\{\frac{-3 + \sqrt{29}}{4}, \frac{-3 - \sqrt{29}}{4}\right\}$

37. $\left\{\frac{-b \pm \sqrt{b^2 - 4}}{2}\right\}$, $b \geq 2$ or $b \leq -2$

39. $\left\{\frac{-b \pm \sqrt{b^2 - 4ac}}{2a}\right\}$, $b^2 - 4ac \geq 0$, $a \neq 0$

Written Exercises, pages 554-555

1. $\left\{\frac{-3 + \sqrt{5}}{2}, \frac{-3 - \sqrt{5}}{2}\right\}$, $\{-0.4, -2.6\}$

3. $\{-2 + \sqrt{10}, -2 - \sqrt{10}\}$, $\{1.2, -5.2\}$

5. $\{6, -1\}$ **7.** $\{-1, -\frac{1}{4}\}$ **9.** no solution

11. $\{\frac{4}{3}, 1\}$ **13.** $\left\{\frac{-9 + \sqrt{41}}{20}, \frac{-9 - \sqrt{41}}{20}\right\}$

15. $\left\{\frac{2 + \sqrt{29}}{10}, \frac{2 - \sqrt{29}}{10}\right\}$

17. $\left\{\frac{25 + 3\sqrt{105}}{8}, \frac{25 - 3\sqrt{105}}{8}\right\}$

19. $\left\{\frac{7 + \sqrt{65}}{2}, \frac{7 - \sqrt{65}}{2}\right\}$

21. $\left\{\frac{3 + 2\sqrt{3}}{2}, \frac{3 - 2\sqrt{3}}{2}\right\}$ **23.** $-\frac{b}{a}$

25. $x^2 - 6x + 7 = 0$

Computer Key-In, page 555 **3.** $\{0.75, 1\}$
5. $\{3.41, 0.59\}$ **7.** no solution

Extra, pages 555-556 **1.** i **3.** $-i$ **5.** i
7. $6i$ **9.** $4i\sqrt{5}$ **11.** $20i$ **13.** $24i$ **15.** $\frac{5i}{7}$

17. $-\frac{3i}{5}$ **19.** $\{11i, -11i\}$

21. $\{7i\sqrt{2}, -7i\sqrt{2}\}$

Written Exercises, page 559 **1.** 4; two **3.** 0; one **5.** 0; one **7.** 0; one **9.** 40; two **11.** 1.16; two **13.** two; below **15.** two; above **17.** none; below **19.** 4

Written Exercises, pages 563-564
1. $\{-1, -4\}$ **3.** $\{-4 + \sqrt{19}, -4 - \sqrt{19}\}$

5. $\{2, -2\}$ **7.** $\left\{\frac{-7 + \sqrt{41}}{2}, \frac{-7 - \sqrt{41}}{2}\right\}$

9. $\{-3 + \sqrt{14}, -3 - \sqrt{14}\}$ **11.** $\{0, 4\}$

13. $\{\frac{1}{4}, -2\}$ **15.** $\left\{\frac{-2 + \sqrt{19}}{5}, \frac{-2 - \sqrt{19}}{5}\right\}$

17. $\left\{\frac{-5 + \sqrt{115}}{6}, \frac{-5 - \sqrt{115}}{6}\right\}$

19. $\{-6 + \sqrt{39}, -6 - \sqrt{39}\}$

21. $\left\{\frac{3 + \sqrt{73}}{16}, \frac{3 - \sqrt{73}}{16}\right\}$

23. $\left\{\frac{-2 + 3\sqrt{6}}{5}, \frac{-2 - 3\sqrt{6}}{5}\right\}$ **25.** $\{5, \frac{37}{8}\}$

27. $\{\frac{1}{11}, -\frac{5}{3}\}$ **29.** $\left\{\frac{\sqrt{3}}{2}, -\frac{\sqrt{3}}{2}\right\}$

31. no solution

Problems, pages 566-567 **1.** 15 m by 9 m **3.** 8 or −9 **5.** 10 cm **7.** 7 cm **9.** 50 m by 36 m **11.** Sara, 31.0 h; Mary, 29.0 h **13.** 27 students **15.** 6 h

Extra, pages 567-568

1.

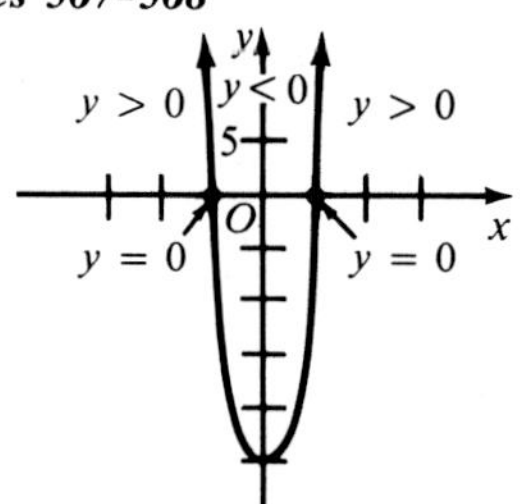

3.

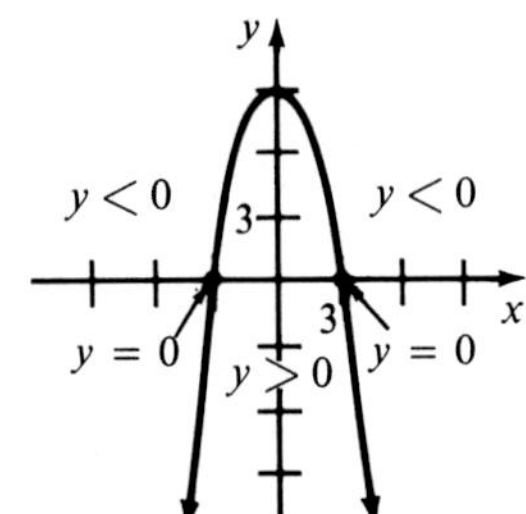

5.

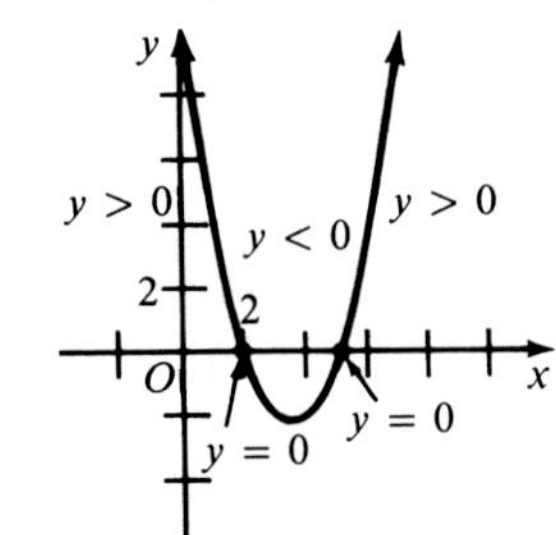

7. {all real numbers ≥ 5 or ≤ 0}
9. {all real numbers ≤ 3 or ≥ 7}

Chapter Review, pages 569–570 **1.** d **3.** d **5.** b **7.** b **9.** a

Cumulative Review, pages 571–572 **1.** $\frac{3}{2}$ **3.** 0 **5.** 1 **7.** -232 **9.** -133

11. $36c - 55$ **13.** $16a^4b^3 - 28a^3b^4$ **15.** $\frac{3wx}{4y^2}$

17. $8u^3 + 1$ **19.** $27z^2 + 21z - 20$

21. $64r^6t^2 - 9v^2$ **23.** $\frac{2c - 3d}{2(c - 3d)}$

25. $9x^2 - 12x + 16$ **27.** $\frac{3z + 4}{(z + 3)(z - 1)}$

29. $a - 2$ **31.** $\frac{5m + 21}{2(m - 3)(m + 3)}$

33. $60 - 24\sqrt{5}$ **35.** $12a$ **37.** $14\sqrt{5}$

39. $\frac{4\sqrt{2} + 9\sqrt{5} - 3\sqrt{10} - 12}{7}$

41. $t^3(2t - 3)(2t + 3)$

43. $-16z^2(z - 4)(z - 1)$ **45.** prime

47. $(c - 4)^2$ **49.** $\frac{44}{3}$ **51.** $\frac{52}{7}$ **53.** 200

55. $\{1, -5\}$ **57.** $\{\frac{1}{4}, -\frac{2}{3}\}$ **59.** $(-2, 2)$

61. -16 **63.** {the real numbers between -2 and 8} **65.** $\{-\frac{3}{2}$, 2, and the real numbers between $-\frac{3}{2}$ and 2} **67.** 8 **69.** 5

71. $\left\{\frac{-5 + \sqrt{17}}{4}, \frac{-5 - \sqrt{17}}{4}\right\}$

73. -5 -4 -3 -2 -1 0 1 2 3 4 5

75.

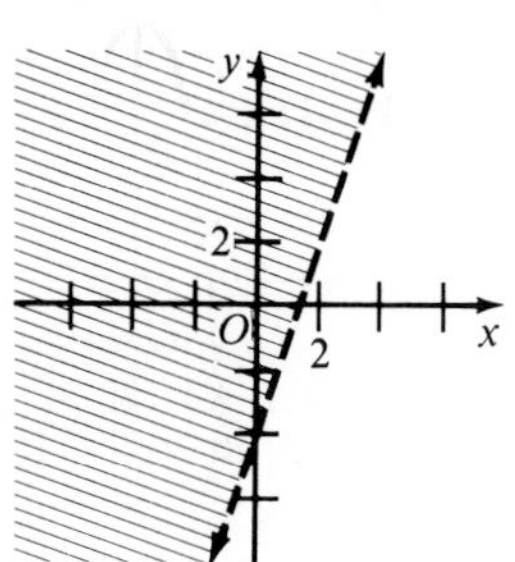

77.

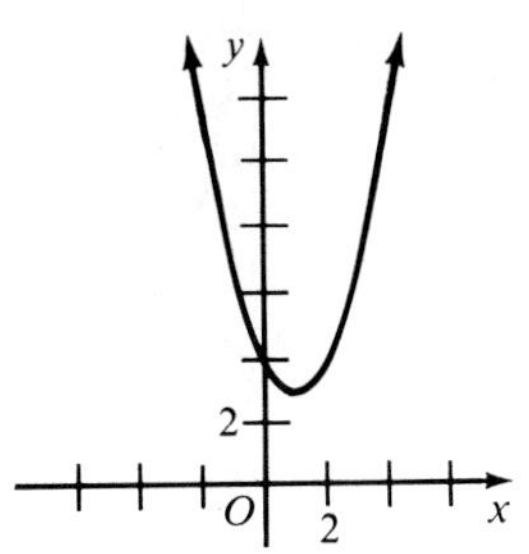

79.

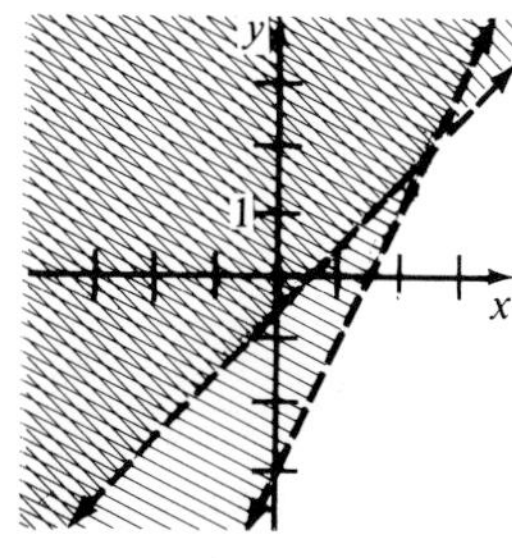

81. 12 h **83.** less than 6 h

Mixed Review, pages 573–574 **1.** (3, 5), $x = 3$ **3.** 48 L **5.** $\frac{\sqrt{30} - 2\sqrt{6} - \sqrt{5} + 2}{5}$

7. $\frac{ab^2}{12}$ **9.** $\frac{4b + 5}{4(b + 1)}$ **11.** 1.922×10^8

13. $16\sqrt{3} - 24\sqrt{6}$ **15.** $-9m^3n^3 + 6mn^5$

17. $\frac{2\sqrt{2} + 5\sqrt{3}}{4}$ **19.** $3c^2\sqrt{34}$ **21.** $2^3 \cdot 3^2 \cdot 5$

23. prime **25.** $2\pi r(2r - h)$

27. $3t(3t - 1)(2t + 5)$ **29.** $-\frac{4}{9}$, 4.0×10^{-2}, $\frac{2}{5}$, $\frac{43}{99}$, $0.\overline{4}$, $\frac{1}{2}$ **31.** \$1500

33.

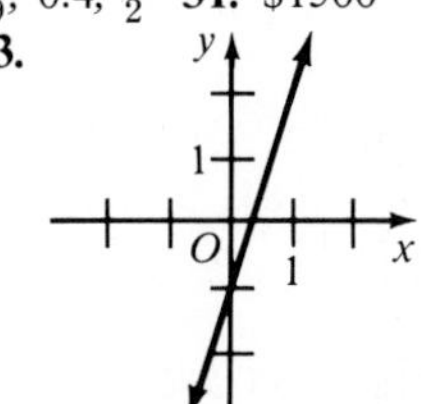

35. -1 0 1 2 3 4 5 6 7 8 9

37. -18 **39.** 3 **41.** $\{-\frac{1}{3}, 2\}$ **43.** -3

45. $(12, -2)$ **47.** $\{\sqrt{6}, -\sqrt{6}\}$ **49.** {1}

51. {the real numbers less than 10 or greater than 18} **53.** $(-5, 3)$ **55.** 1 h or 60 min

57. 11 **59.** 32 **61.** $2x - y = -1$ **63.** 10; 22 **65.** \$1500 at 9%, \$1300 at $9\frac{1}{2}$%

67. 4.94×10^9 km

Preparing for College Entrance Exams, page 575 **1.** D **3.** A **5.** C **7.** E

LOOKING AHEAD

Written Exercises, page 578 **1.** Any five of $\overline{LM}$, $\overline{MN}$, $\overline{NP}$, $\overline{LN}$, $\overline{LP}$, $\overline{MP}$ **3.** Any five of $\overline{XY}$, $\overline{YW}$, $\overline{WX}$, $\overline{SY}$, $\overline{YZ}$, $\overline{SZ}$, $\overline{XS}$, $\overline{WZ}$

5. acute **7.** acute **9.** obtuse **11.** obtuse
13. point

15. line segment

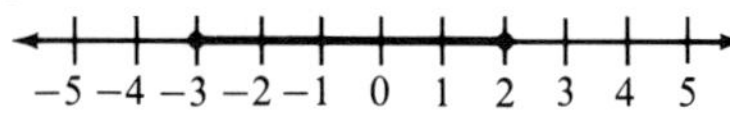

17. line segment

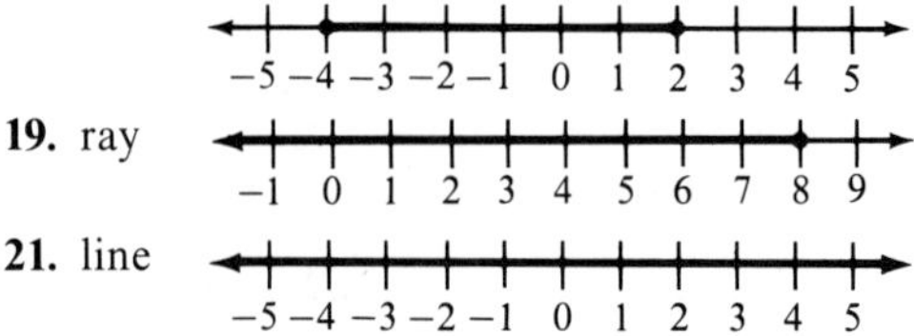

Written Exercises, page 580 **1.** $\angle BCJ$, $\angle KCA$, $\angle FIH$ **3.** 150° **5.** 70°, 110° **7.** 73° **9.** 82°

Written Exercises, page 582 **1.** 69° **3.** 48° **5.** 123° **7.** no **9.** yes **11.** yes **13.** 10 **15.** 9 **17.** 80 **19.** $4\sqrt{10}$ **21.** $3\sqrt{5}$ **23.** $x\sqrt{2}$

Problems, page 583 **1.** 15, 75 **3.** 15, 60, 105 **5.** 12, 24, 144 **7.** 48, 48, 84 **9.** 18, 58, 104 **11.** 24, 48, 108

Written Exercises, pages 585–586 **1.** $\angle A$, $\angle F$; $\angle B$, $\angle D$; $\angle C$, $\angle E$; $\overline{AB}$, $\overline{FD}$; $\overline{BC}$, $\overline{DE}$; $\overline{CA}$, $\overline{EF}$ **3.** false **5.** true **7.** $EF = 10$, $FD = 12$ **9.** $FE = 4$, $DF = 6$ **11.** $EF = 12$, $AC = 10$ **13.** $AB = 28$, $FD = 15$

Problems, page 586 **1.** 28 cm **3.** 12 m **5.** 225 m **7.** 3 m **9.** 11.25 m

Written Exercises, page 589 **1.** $\sin A = \frac{4}{5}$, $\cos A = \frac{3}{5}$, $\tan A = \frac{4}{3}$, $\sin B = \frac{3}{5}$, $\cos B = \frac{4}{5}$, $\tan B = \frac{3}{4}$ **3.** $\sin A = \frac{2\sqrt{29}}{29}$, $\cos A = \frac{5\sqrt{29}}{29}$, $\tan A = \frac{2}{5}$, $\sin B = \frac{5\sqrt{29}}{29}$, $\cos B = \frac{2\sqrt{29}}{29}$, $\tan B = \frac{5}{2}$ **5.** $\sin A = \frac{\sqrt{51}}{10}$, $\cos A = \frac{7}{10}$, $\tan A = \frac{\sqrt{51}}{7}$, $\sin B = \frac{7}{10}$, $\cos B = \frac{\sqrt{51}}{10}$, $\tan B = \frac{7\sqrt{51}}{51}$ **7.** $\sin A = \frac{\sqrt{2}}{2}$, $\cos A = \frac{\sqrt{2}}{2}$, $\tan A = 1$, $\sin B = \frac{\sqrt{2}}{2}$, $\cos B = \frac{\sqrt{2}}{2}$, $\tan B = 1$ **9.** $\sin A = \frac{4\sqrt{137}}{137}$, $\cos A = \frac{11\sqrt{137}}{137}$, $\tan A = \frac{4}{11}$, $\sin B = \frac{11\sqrt{137}}{137}$, $\cos B = \frac{4\sqrt{137}}{137}$, $\tan B = \frac{11}{4}$ **11.** $\cos A = \frac{b}{c}$, $\sin B = \frac{b}{c}$

13. $\frac{\sin A}{\cos A} = \frac{\frac{a}{c}}{\frac{b}{c}} = \frac{a}{b} = \tan B$ **15.** $\frac{\sqrt{39}}{8}$

Written Exercises, page 591 **1.** 0.1736, 0.9848, 0.1763 **3.** 0.9962, 0.0872, 11.4301 **5.** 0.7071, 0.7071, 1.0000 **7.** 0.3090, 0.9511, 0.3249 **9.** 0.5592, 0.8290, 0.6745 **11.** 0.1219, 0.9925, 0.1228 **13.** 85° **15.** 64° **17.** 43° **19.** 26° **21.** 77° **23.** 53° **25.** 76° **27.** 44°

Challenge, page 591 **1.** no; $\angle A$, $\angle R$, $\angle Z$ are necessarily angles of a triangle.

Written Exercises, pages 593–594 **1.** 20 **3.** 32 **5.** 59 **7.** $BC = 40$, $AC = 27$ **9.** $AC = 17$, $AB = 87$ **11.** $\angle D = 49°$, $\angle F = 41°$ **13.** $\angle D = 42°$, $\angle F = 48°$ **15.** $XZ = 75$, $YZ = 99$ **17.** $YZ = 55$, $YX = 49$

Problems, pages 594–595 **1.** 18 m **3.** 226 m **5.** 117 m **7.** 4° **9.** 185 m **11.** 2154 m **13.** 530 m **15.** 182 m

Written Exercises, pages 597–598
1. a. $\{A, B, C, D, E, F, G, H, I, J, K\}$ **b.** $\{A, E, I\}$ **c.** $\{C, F, G, I\}$ **d.** $\{A, C, D, F, H, I, K\}$ **3. a.** {(2, 1), (2, 4), (2, 9), (4, 1), (4, 4), (4, 9), (8, 1), (8, 4), (8, 9), (15, 1), (15, 4), (15, 9)} **b.** {(4, 4)} **c.** {(15, 1), (15, 9)} **d.** {(4, 9), (8, 9), (15, 1), (15, 4), (15, 9)} **e.** {(2, 1), (4, 1)}
5. a. {(on, on, on), (on, on, off), (on, off, off), (on, off, on), (off, on, on), (off, on, off), (off, off, off), (off, off, on)} **b.** {(on, on, on), (on, on, off), (on, off, on), (off, on, on)} **c.** {(on, on, off), (on, off, off), (on, off, on), (off, on, on), (off, on, off), (off, off, off), (off, off, on)} **d.** {(off, off, off)} **7.** {(1, 3), (2, 2), (3, 1)} **9.** {(1, 1), (1, 3), (2, 2), (3, 1), (3, 3), (4, 2)} **11.** {(1, 1), (1, 3), (2, 1), (2, 2), (2, 3), (3, 1), (3, 3), (4, 1), (4, 2), (4, 3)}

Written Exercises, pages 600–601 **1. a.** $\frac{1}{3}$ **b.** $\frac{1}{6}$ **c.** $\frac{1}{2}$ **d.** 0 **e.** $\frac{2}{3}$ **3. a.** $\frac{1}{25}$ **b.** $\frac{2}{5}$ **c.** $\frac{1}{5}$ **d.** $\frac{6}{25}$ **5. a.** $\frac{1}{8}$ **b.** $\frac{3}{8}$ **c.** $\frac{1}{2}$ **d.** $\frac{3}{4}$ **7. a.** $\frac{1}{12}$ **b.** $\frac{1}{4}$ **c.** $\frac{1}{12}$ **d.** $\frac{1}{4}$ **e.** $\frac{1}{6}$ **f.** $\frac{7}{12}$

Calculator Key-In, page 601 **1.** 37.95 cm^2 **3.** 71.55 m^2 **5.** 4.92 m^2 **7.** 51.51 cm^2

Written Exercises, page 604 **1.** 41, 39, none, 29 **3.** $64\frac{2}{3}$, $62\frac{1}{2}$, 62, 15 **5.** $27\frac{6}{7}$, 26, 25, and 33, 11 **7.** $27\frac{1}{3}$, 28, 28, 6 **9.** 13.1, 13.5, 15, 11 **11.** 182 **13. a.** 4 times greater **b.** 4 times greater **c.** 4 times greater **d.** 4 times greater **15.** 27

Review, pages 605–606 **1.** b **3.** c **5.** c **7.** c **9.** b **11.** d **13.** c

EXTRA PRACTICE: Skills

Chapter 1, pages 607–608 **1.** 37 **3.** 100 **5.** 198 **7.** 12 **9.** 23 **11.** 24 **13.** 6 **15.** 9 **17.** 8 **19.** 3 **21.** 23 **23.** {6} **25.** {0, 1, 2, 3, 4, 5, 6} **27.** {0} **29.** {6} **31.** {4} **33.** {0, 5} **35.** {2} **37.** {0} **39.** $\frac{1}{2}z - 4$ **41.** $5w - 1$ **43.** $7x$ **45.** $x - 4$ **47.** $n - 5$ **49.** $m(m + 4) = 140$ **51.** $12p = 1.39$ **53.** $g + 5 = 34$ **55.** $2x + x = 48$; 32 blue T-shirts, 16 red T-shirts **57.** 400 **59.** -10 **61.** -2

63.
−5 −4 −3 −2 −1 0 1 2 3 4 5

65. -3 **67.** 18 **69.** 11 **71.** 3 **73.** 0 **75.** 9.4 **77.** $>$ **79.** $<$ **81.** $<$ **83.** $<$ **85.** $<$

Chapter 2, pages 609–611 **1.** 350 **3.** 20 **5.** 16 **7.** $3m + 12$ **9.** $6w + 12$ **11.** $88n$ **13.** $60pqr$ **15.** $60hmw$ **17.** 0 **19.** -12 **21.** 20 **23.** -19 **25.** -5.6 **27.** -1 **29.** -153 **31.** -4 **33.** 19 **35.** 9 **37.** -1 **39.** 100 **41.** -83 **43.** 215 **45.** 17 **47.** -30 **49.** 4 **51.** 8 **53.** 34 **55.** 580 **57.** $7q$ **59.** $42a$ **61.** $7c + 27$ **63.** $8j - 15$ **65.** $8x + 20$ **67.** $2u + 5$ **69.** $2f + 10g$ **71.** 135 **73.** -180 **75.** -135 **77.** -480 **79.** 11 **81.** -270 **83.** $-7m + 42p$ **85.** $-24n + 36v$ **87.** $-4 - 8t$ **89.** $-29x + 16y$ **91.** $-3c - 17d$

Answers may vary for Exercises 93–97 **93.** $n + (n + 1) + (n + 2) = 75$ **95.** $n + (n + 2) + (n + 4) = 138$ **97.** $n + 2 = 3n + 8$ **99.** -5 **101.** 7 **103.** -4 **105.** $11xy$ **107.** $8g$ **109.** $9h - 6$ **111.** $-6x + 9y$ **113.** $5p + 10q$ **115.** -8 **117.** 0 **119.** -40 **121.** 0 **123.** $-31.5a$ **125.** 11 **127.** $-x$ **129.** $5h$

Chapter 3, pages 611–613 **1.** 30 **3.** 8 **5.** -15 **7.** 20 **9.** -3 **11.** -12 **13.** 2 **15.** 12 **17.** -18 **19.** -14 **21.** -64 **23.** 50 **25.** -128 **27.** 120 **29.** $\frac{1}{6}$ **31.** 7 **33.** 6 **35.** 8 **37.** -13 **39.** -27 **41.** 4 **43.** 6 **45.** -3 **47.** 10 **49.** 21 **51.** 4 m, 6 m, 8 m **53.** 7 **55.** -8 **57.** -6 **59.** -4 **61.** 15 **63.** $\frac{11}{8}$ **65.** -7 **67.** 3 **69.** 5 years old, 7 years old, 9 years old **71.** 16 cm by 10 cm, 14 cm by 13 cm **73.** 56 doz **75.** 4 h **77.** substitution principle; associative axiom of addition; axiom of opposites; identity axiom for addition

Chapter 4, pages 613–614 **1.** 343 **3.** -48 **5.** 32 **7.** -26 **9.** 5 **11.** 68 **13.** 49 **15.** -2744 **17.** 1 **19.** $\frac{81}{4}$ **21.** $b - 2$ **23.** $4t - 10$ **25.** $10x^2 - 3xy + 2y^2$ **27.** $3a^2 + 3ab - b^2$ **29.** $5b + 10$ **31.** $-8t - 4$ **33.** $2x^2 - xy + 4y^2$ **35.** $7a^2 - 15ab + b^2$ **37.** $8f^7$ **39.** $-10g^4h^3$ **41.** $60j^5k^3l^5$ **43.** $-a^6$ **45.** 3^6 or 729 **47.** 2^{11} or 2048 **49.** $4d^{10}$ **51.** x^{10} **53.** z^{2n} **55.** b^{3n} **57.** d^{3n} **59.** g^4h^4 **61.** $64m^3n^{15}$ **63.** $9a^{10}b^8$ **65.** $-512x^{15}$ **67.** $-200l^{13}$ **69.** $375x^7y^5$ **71.** $5y - 20$ **73.** $-8 - 32m$ **75.** $-12t + 8t^2$ **77.** $-40h^2 - 15h$ **79.** $-15b^4 + 10b^3 - 30b^2$ **81.** $5u^3v^2 - 2u^2v^3 + 4uv^4$ **83.** $n^2 + 2n - 15$ **85.** $5x^2 + 33x - 14$ **87.** $30b^2 + 38b + 12$ **89.** $3v^3 + v^2 + 3v - 7$ **91.** $21x^2 - 26xy + 8y^2$ **93.** $e^3 + 2e^2f + 2ef^2 + f^3$ **95.** $a = \frac{2A}{p}$, $p \neq 0$ **97.** $b_1 = \frac{2A - hb_2}{h}$, $h \neq 0$ **99.** $r = \sqrt{\frac{A}{\pi}}$, $A \geq 0$ **101.** $C = \frac{5}{9}(F - 32)$ **103.** $t = \frac{I}{Pr}$, $P \neq 0$, $r \neq 0$ **105.** $\frac{3}{2}$ h **107.** 13.25 in. by 39.75 in.

Chapter 5, pages 615–617 **1.** (1)(42), (2)(21), (3)(14), (6)(7), (−1)(−42), (−2)(−21), (−3)(−14), (−6)(−7) **3.** (1)(91), (7)(13), (−1)(−91), (−7)(−13) **5.** (1)(52), (2)(26), (4)(13), (−1)(−52), (−2)(−26), (−4)(−13) **7.** $2^4 \cdot 5$ **9.** $2^3 \cdot 3^2$ **11.** 42 **13.** 13 **15.** $3x^4$ **17.** $-\frac{1}{3b^4}$ **19.** $\frac{1}{w^{12}}$ **21.** $-\frac{27}{y^3}$ **23.** $3e + 2$ **25.** $2x^2 + 6x + 1$ **27.** $3 - 5m - m^2$ **29.** $5(3w^2 - 2w + 1)$ **31.** $7u^2(u + 2)$ **33.** $3c(5c + d)$ **35.** $x^2 + 8x + 15$ **37.** $n^2 + 4n - 21$ **39.** $6 + 5m + m^2$ **41.** $8y^2 - 10y + 3$ **43.** $20n^2 - 22n + 6$ **45.** $12h^3 + 55h^2 + 63h$ **47.** $k^2 - 25$ **49.** $16d^2 - 64$ **51.** $25m^4 - n^2$ **53.** $(4e - 3)(4e + 3)$ **55.** $(9 - f)(9 + f)$ **57.** $(7 - 10y)(7 + 10y)$ **59.** $(s^3 - 2)(s^3 + 2)$ **61.** $g^2 + 14g + 49$ **63.** $4x^2 + 24x + 36$ **65.** $4m^2 + 12mn + 9n^2$ **67.** $e^2f^2 - 16ef + 64$ **69.** $(x - 3)^2$ **71.** $(2 - 7h)^2$ **73.** $(2m - 9n)^2$ **75.** $(k + 7)(k + 1)$ **77.** $(a - 1)^2$ **79.** $(b - 12)(b - 4)$ **81.** $(x + 6y)(x + 7y)$ **83.** $(e - 4f)(e - 11f)$ **85.** $(x - 7)(x + 5)$ **87.** $(h - 9)(h + 2)$ **89.** $(t - 9)(t + 5)$ **91.** $(u + 4v)(u - v)$ **93.** $(2x + 3)(x + 4)$ **95.** $(5d + 3)(2d - 1)$ **97.** prime **99.** $(5x + y)(3x + 2y)$ **101.** $(7m + 3n)(2m - n)$ **103.** $2(a + 2)(3a + 2)$ **105.** $(b + 1)^2(b - 3)$ **107.** $(7w + 3)(c - w)$ **109.** $(1 - m)(1 + m)(64 + m^4)$ **111.** $6y(5y + 1)(2y - 1)$ **113.** $16a^2(a - 3)(a + 3)$ **115.** $2w^5(14w^2 - 51)$ **117.** $-12(c - d)^2$ **119.** $\{-13, -8\}$ **121.** $\{2, \frac{5}{3}\}$ **123.** $\{0, -\frac{3}{4}\}$ **125.** $\{-6, -1\}$ **127.** $\{5, 9\}$ **129.** $\{4, -9\}$ **131.** $\{\frac{1}{4}, -6\}$ **133.** $\{\frac{5}{2}, -2\}$ **135.** $\{\frac{2}{3}, -\frac{2}{3}\}$ **137.** 7 or −8 **139.** 11 cm by 8 cm

Chapter 6, pages 617–619 **1.** 5; $m \neq 3$ **3.** $\frac{c - d}{c + d}$; $c \neq -d$ **5.** $\frac{3}{u - v}$; $u \neq 0$, $v \neq 0$, $u \neq v$ **7.** $\frac{x + 8}{x + 7}$; $x \neq 8$, $x \neq -7$ **9.** $\frac{3}{5m - 2n}$; $m \neq \frac{2}{5}n$, $m \neq -\frac{2}{5}n$ **11.** −1; $k \neq 3$, $k \neq \frac{2}{7}$ **13.** $\frac{t - 7}{t + 2}$; $t \neq 2$, $t \neq -2$ **15.** $-\frac{1}{(5w - x)^2}$; $w \neq \frac{x}{5}$ **17.** $\frac{4}{5}$ **19.** $\frac{3}{20}$ **21.** $\frac{e}{h}$ **23.** 2 **25.** $\frac{2uw^2}{3v^3}$ **27.** $\frac{1}{4xy(4 + y)}$ **29.** $25k^6$ **31.** $\frac{9x^2}{16}$ **33.** $-\frac{x^6}{125}$ **35.** $\frac{8c^5}{d^3}$ **37.** $\frac{1}{12}$ **39.** $\frac{2}{n^2}$ **41.** 1 **43.** $\frac{1}{(n - 3)(n - 5)}$ **45.** $\frac{(x - y)(x + y)(x - 4)}{2x}$ **47.** $\frac{(2t - 3s)(m^2 + n^2)}{7(4s - 5t)(m + n)}$ **49.** $\frac{x^2}{y^3}$ **51.** $\frac{c^2}{3}$ **53.** −1 **55.** $2h - 8$ **57.** $30m - 5n$ **59.** $12s^2t$ **61.** $5e + 5$ **63.** $5z$ **65.** $3ab$ **67.** $\frac{3x - 6}{48}, \frac{4x + 12}{48}$ **69.** $\frac{d}{3cd^2}, \frac{12}{3cd^2}$ **71.** $\frac{2wx + 6w}{3(x - 3)(x + 3)}, \frac{3}{3(x - 3)(x + 3)}$ **73.** $\frac{4}{x}$ **75.** $\frac{-k - 4}{5}$ **77.** $\frac{7}{g - 3}$ **79.** $\frac{5 + 3t}{t^2}$ **81.** $\frac{2 - 3x}{10wx}$ **83.** $\frac{2 + 3x}{3(x + 2)}$ **85.** $\frac{3(h + 1)}{10}$ **87.** $\frac{2x + 1}{(x + 2)(x + 3)}$ **89.** $\frac{u - 3}{u - 4}$ **91.** $\frac{5n + 1}{n}$ **93.** $\frac{x + 3y}{y}$ **95.** $\frac{8z - 14}{z - 2}$ **97.** $\frac{8h^2 + 23h}{h + 3}$ **99.** $\frac{5e^2 - e - 8}{e^2 - 1}$ **101.** $\frac{2w^2 - 7w - 3}{w - 3}$ **103.** $\frac{2v^2}{(v + u)(v - u)}$ **105.** $x + 5$ **107.** $a - 7 + \frac{11}{a + 2}$ **109.** $k + 1 + \frac{12}{k - 5}$ **111.** $b^2 - b + 1 - \frac{2}{b + 1}$ **113.** $w^2 + 2w + 4$ **115.** $t - 4$ **117.** $v^2 + 3v + 7 + \frac{15}{v - 2}$

Chapter 7, pages 619–621 **1.** 1:3 **3.** 200:3 **5.** $18d$:5 **7.** 25:11 **9.** 9 **11.** $\frac{7}{6}$ **13.** 6 **15.** 18 **17.** 12 **19.** 72 **21.** −9 **23.** −7 **25.** 6 **27.** 2 **29.** −6 **31.** 202.5 **33.** 30 **35.** 25% **37.** 40 **39.** 800 **41.** 300 **43.** 8.4 kg **45.** \$127.50 **47.** 24 kg **49.** 30 min **51.** 1.47×10^8 **53.** 9.8×10^{-6} **55.** 1.0×10^{-11} **57.** $\frac{1}{125}$ **59.** $\frac{1}{729}$ **61.** 36 **63.** 64 **65.** $\frac{1}{729y^3}$ **67.** $\frac{1}{a^2b^3}$ **69.** $\frac{e^2}{d^4f^2}$ **71.** $\frac{x^{12}y^{15}}{z^9}$

Chapter 8, pages 621–622 **1.** no, yes **3.** no, no **5.** yes, yes **7.** $y = \frac{8 - x}{2}$ **9.** $y = \frac{6 - 3x}{4}$ **11.** $y = -\frac{4}{3}x$

13.

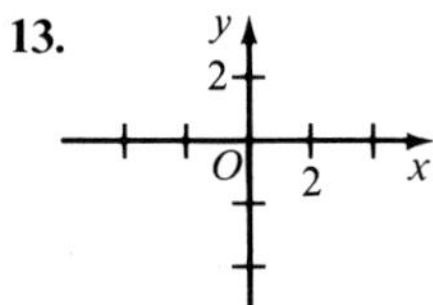

15.

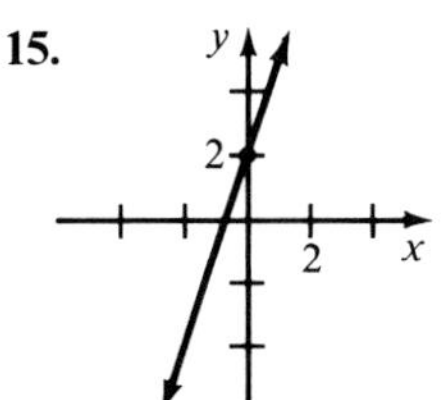

17.

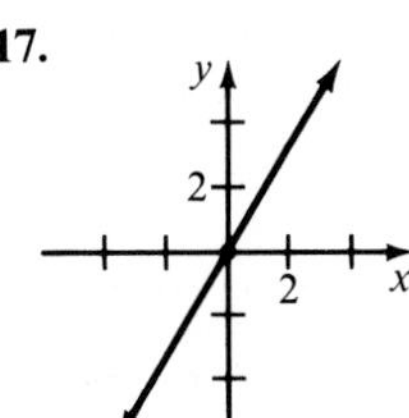

19.

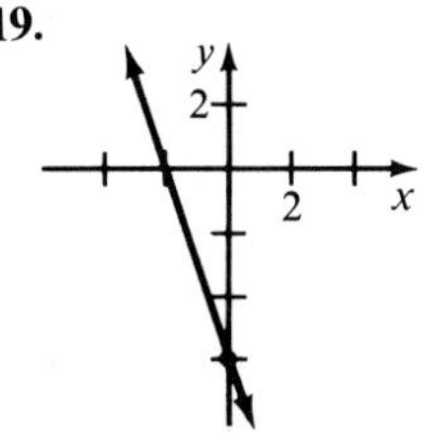

21.

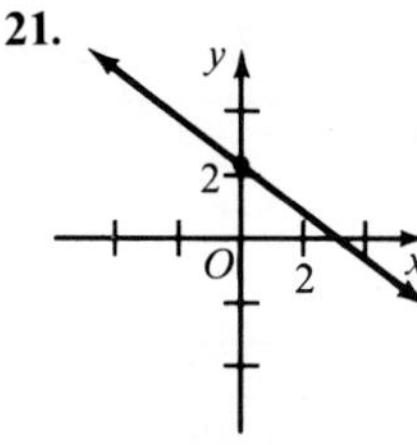

23. (3, 6)

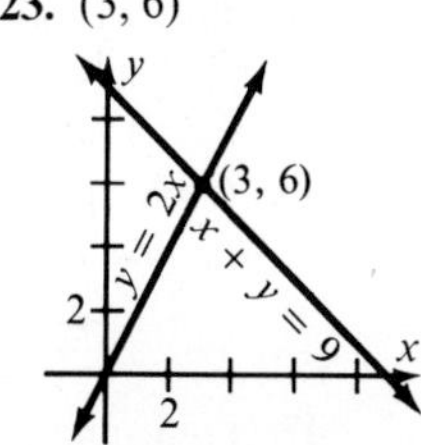

25. no solution

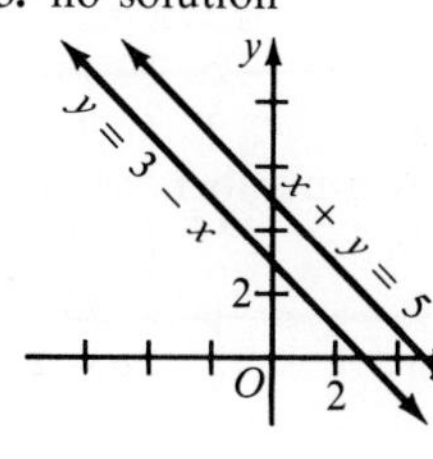

27. infinite number of solutions

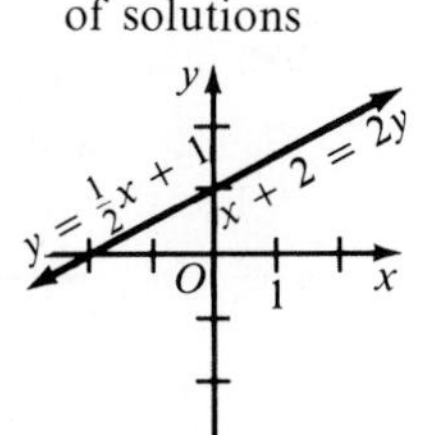

29. $(-\frac{3}{4}, \frac{13}{12})$ **31.** (3, 1) **33.** (5, 5) **35.** Janet, 3 mi; Lynn, 5 mi **37.** $(5, -\frac{25}{2})$ **39.** $(-3, 2)$ **41.** $(5, -2)$ **43.** (2, 3) **45.** $(-3, -4)$ **47.** (2, 5) **49.** 52 **51.** $\frac{7}{8}$

Chapter 9, pages 622-626 **1.** $\frac{4}{3}$ **3.** -6 **5.** $-\frac{1}{2}$ **7.** 7 **9.** $\frac{3}{2}$ **11.** $-\frac{5}{4}$ **13.** yes, 2 **15.** no

17.

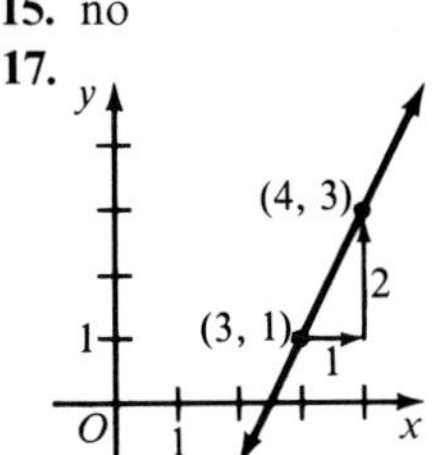

19.

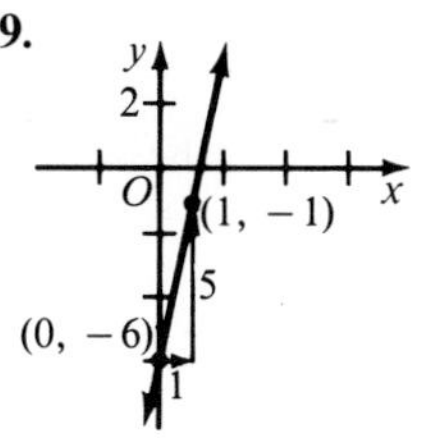

21.

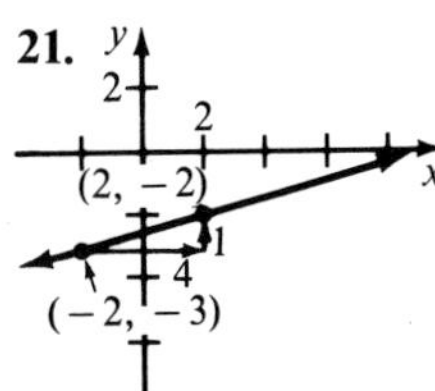

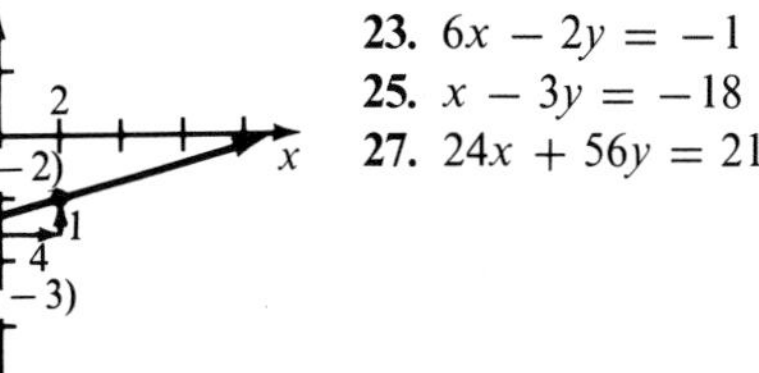

23. $6x - 2y = -1$
25. $x - 3y = -18$
27. $24x + 56y = 21$

29. $y = -x - 3$

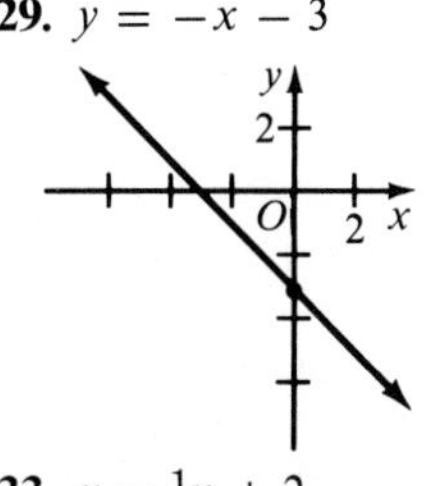

31. $y = 4x - 3$

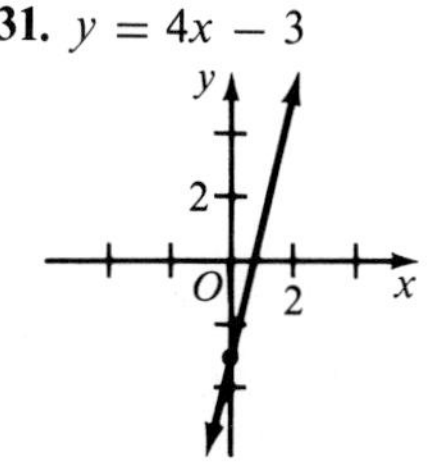

33. $y = \frac{1}{5}x + 2$

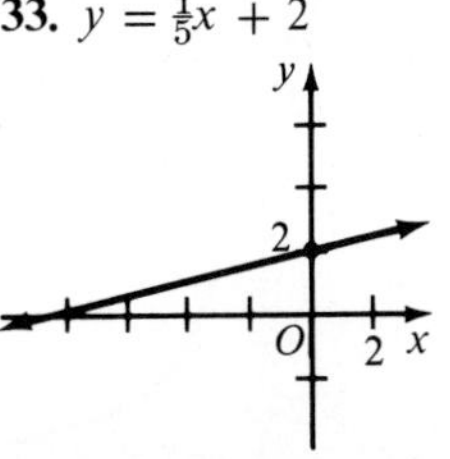

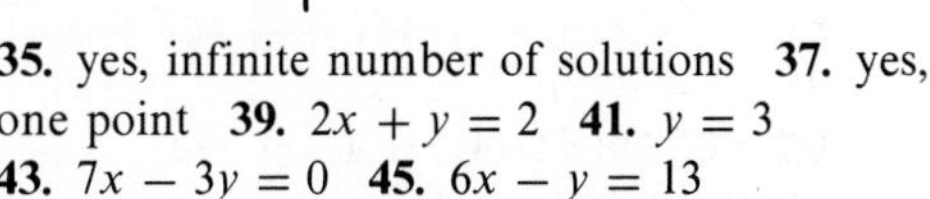

35. yes, infinite number of solutions **37.** yes, one point **39.** $2x + y = 2$ **41.** $y = 3$ **43.** $7x - 3y = 0$ **45.** $6x - y = 13$ **47.** $x = -3$ **49.** $3x - 13y = 70$ **51.** 6 **53.** 20 **55.** -12 **57.** 33 **59.** $\{-3, 3, 1\}$ **61.** $\{-10, 10, 2\}$ **63.** $\{-1, 2, 7\}$ **65.** $D = \{1930, 1940, 1950, 1960, 1970\}$, $R = \{1782, 2331, 6403, 6881, 11{,}261\}$

67.

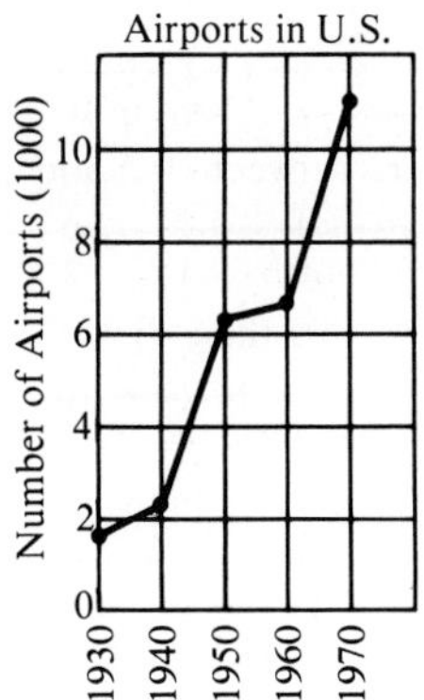

69. (0, 0), $x = 0$

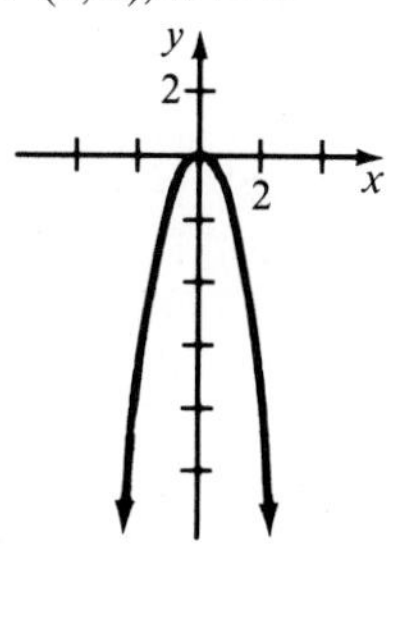

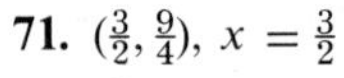

71. $(\frac{3}{2}, \frac{9}{4})$, $x = \frac{3}{2}$

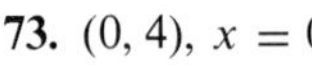

73. $(0, 4)$, $x = 0$

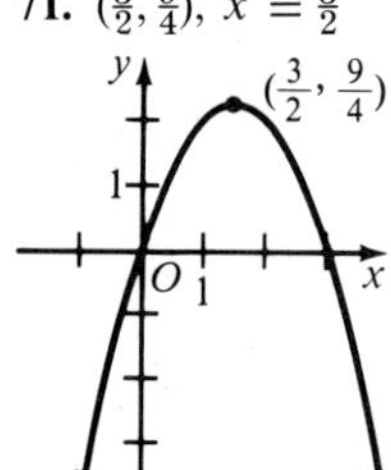

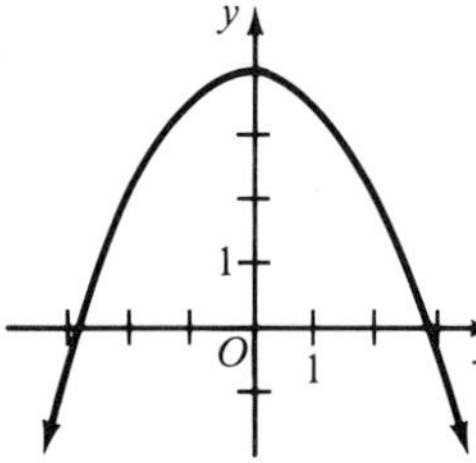

75. $-\frac{25}{4}$ **77.** $\frac{1}{12}$ **79.** $-\frac{3}{4}$ **81.** 6 **83.** 91 **85.** 1.04 **87. a.** $C = kd$ **b.** $\frac{C_1}{d_1} = \frac{C_2}{d_2}$ **89. a.** $l = kh$ **b.** $\frac{l_1}{h_1} = \frac{l_2}{h_2}$ **91. a.** $hb = k$ **b.** $h_1b_1 = h_2b_2$

93.

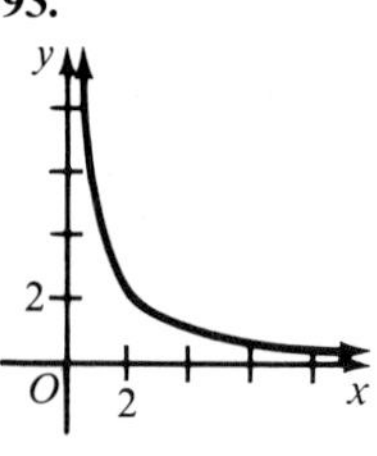

95.

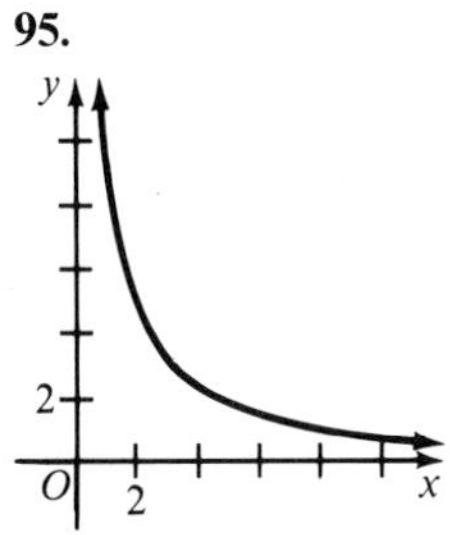

97. 10 **99.** $\frac{1}{3}$ **101.** $p = kv^2$ **103.** $V = khr^2$ **105.** $F = \frac{kv^2}{r}$

Chapter 10, pages 626–628 **1.** false **3.** true **5.** false **7.** false **9.** true **11.** $\{-4, -3\}$ **13.** $\{-3, -2, -1, 0, 1, 2, 3\}$ **15.** $\{-6, -5, -4, -3, -2, -1\}$

−7 −6 −5 −4 −3 −2 −1 0 1 2 3

17. {the real numbers between −2 and 2}

−2 −1 0 1 2 3

19. {the real numbers less than 4}

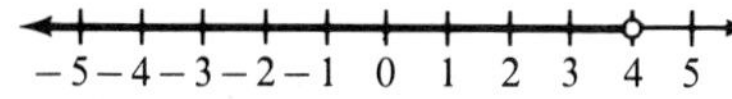

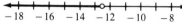

21. {the real numbers greater than −98}

−98 −96 −94 −92 −90 −88

23. {the real numbers less than $-\frac{25}{2}$}

−18 −16 −14 −12 −10 −8

25. {the real numbers greater than 8}

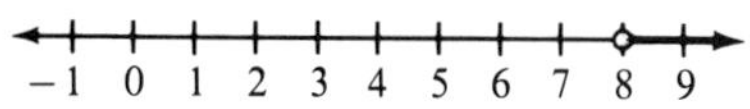

27. {the real numbers greater than 4}

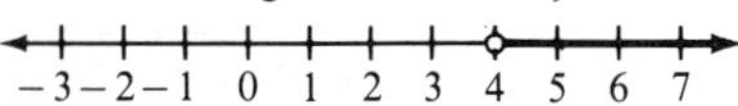

29. {the real numbers greater than −14}

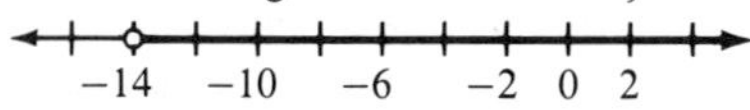

31. {the real numbers less than 4}

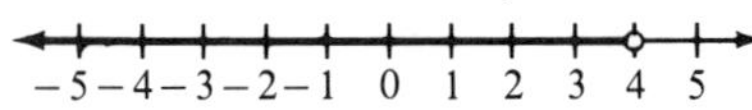

33. a. j **b.** $2j - 9 \leq 43$ **35. a.** r **b.** $\frac{1}{2}r - 10 \geq 25$ **37. a.** p **b.** $p - 6 < \frac{1}{2}p$

39. {8, and the real numbers between 0 and 8}

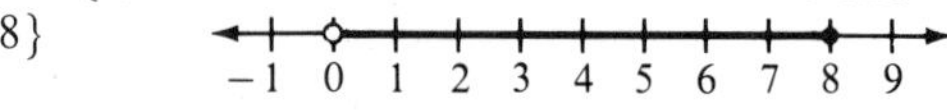

41. {−1, 2, and the real numbers between −1 and 2}

43. {−9, and the real numbers greater than −4 or less than −9}

−10 −9 −8 −7 −6 −5 −4 −3 −2 −1 0

45. {−3, and the real numbers greater than 5 or less than −3}

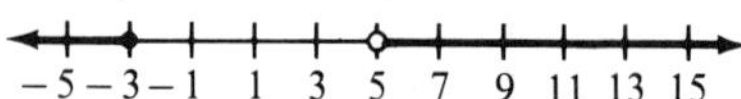

47. {2, 6, and the real numbers greater than 6 or less than 2}

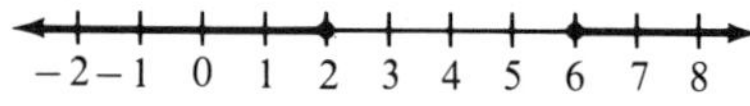

49. {3, 13}

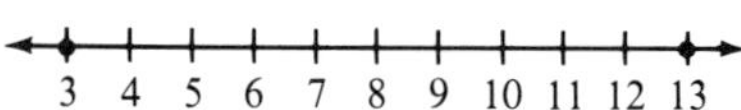

51. {−1.5, 1.5, and the real numbers between −1.5 and 1.5}

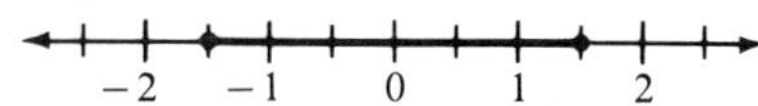

53. {−7, 1, and the real numbers between −7 and 1}

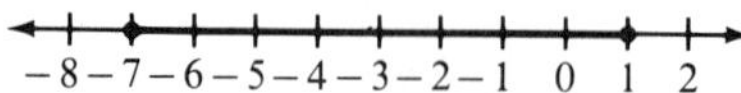

55. {the real numbers greater than 3 or less than −11}

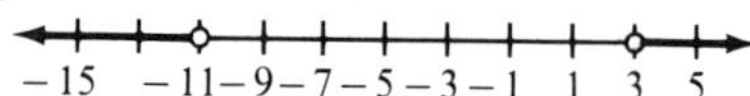

57. $\{-\frac{3}{2}, \frac{3}{2}$, and the real numbers between $-\frac{3}{2}$ and $\frac{3}{2}\}$

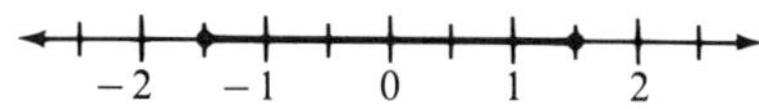

59. {the real numbers between -4 and 10}

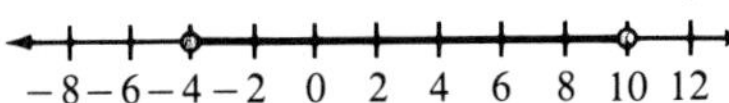

61. {-6, 6, and the real numbers greater than 6 or less than -6}

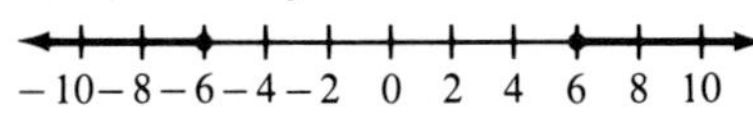

63. $\{4, -\frac{14}{5}\}$

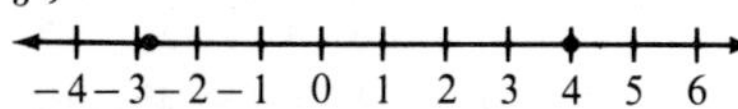

65. {the real numbers greater than 4 or less than -1}

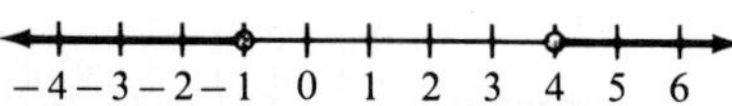

67. {-4, 8, and the real numbers between -4 and 8}

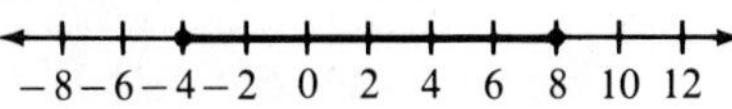

69. {the real numbers between -2 and 4}

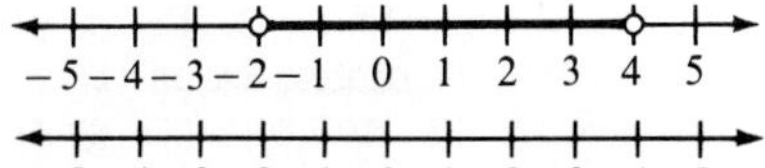

71. $\emptyset$

73.

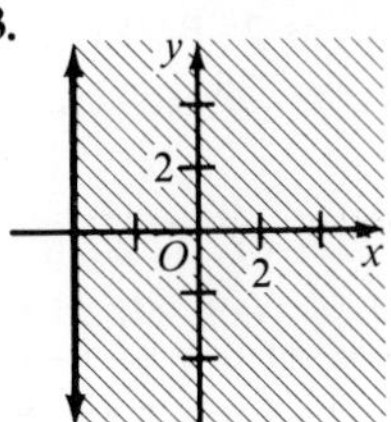

75.

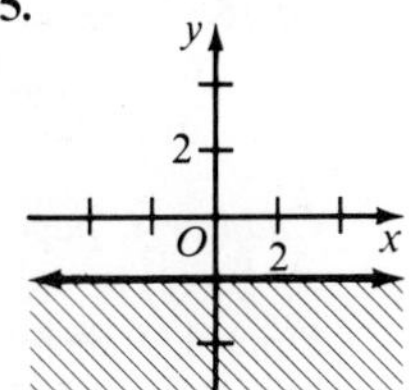

77.

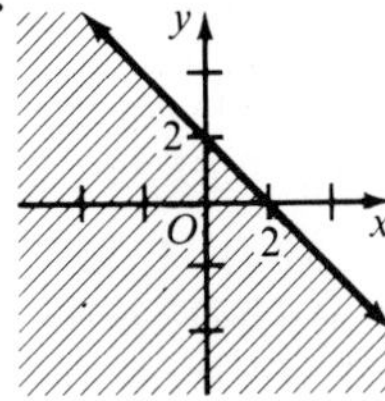

79.

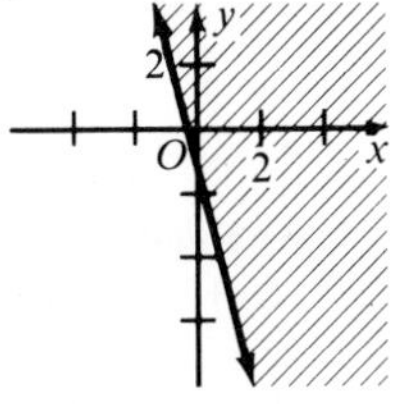

81. $y \leq -4x - 2$

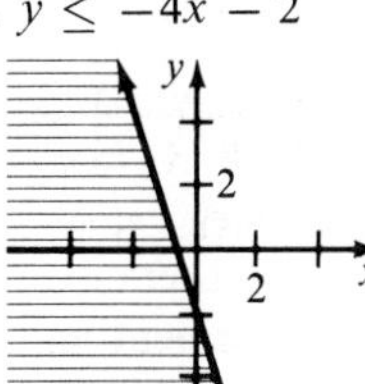

83. $y > 6x - 2$

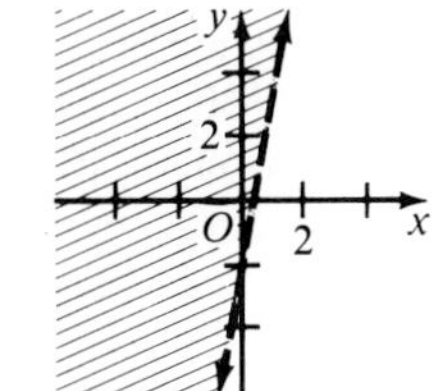

85. $y < \frac{5}{4}x$

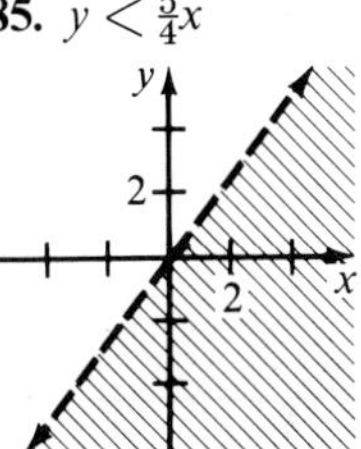

87. $y > 2x - \frac{2}{3}$

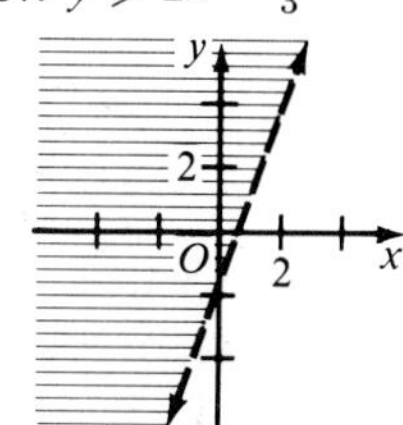

89.

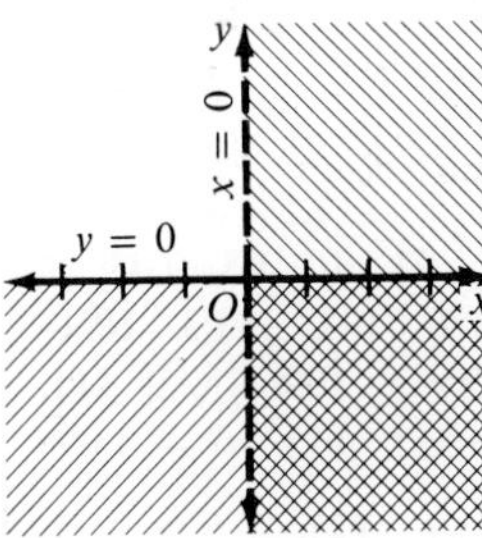

91.

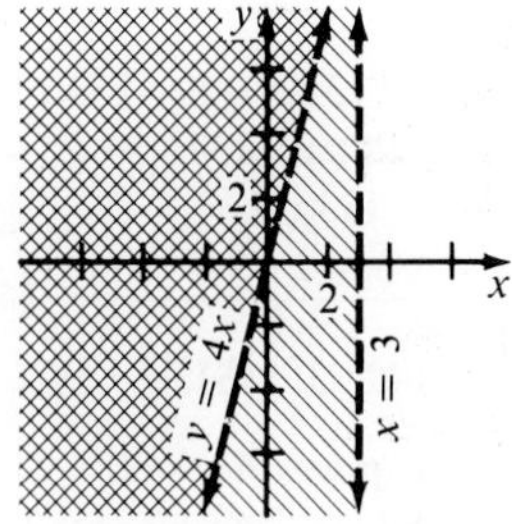

93.

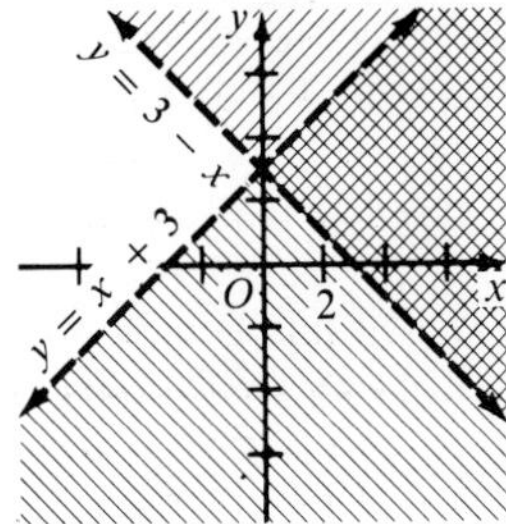

95.

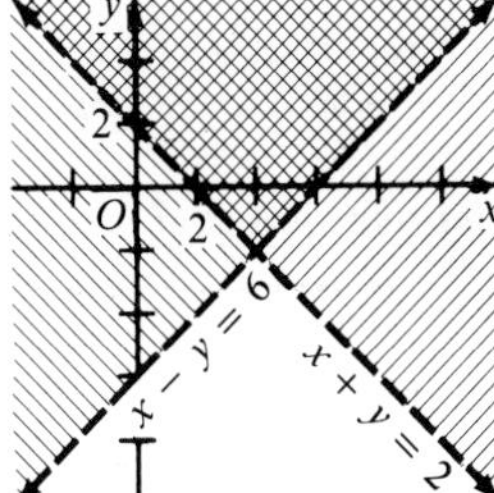

Chapter 11, pages 628-631 **1.** $<$ **3.** $<$ **5.** $\frac{2}{3}, \frac{12}{17}, \frac{5}{7}, \frac{11}{15}$ **7.** $\frac{1135}{1517}$ **9.** $\frac{111}{56}$ **11.** increases **13.** decreases **15.** $0.\overline{4}$ **17.** 3.55 **19.** $0.7\overline{45}$ **21.** $\frac{2}{3}$ **23.** $2\frac{37}{99}$ **25.** 0.6275 **27.** $0.6\overline{32}$ **29.** $\frac{8}{27}$ **31.** 21 **33.** 52 **35.** 104 **37.** 0.8 **39.** 0.12 **41.** $\frac{3}{5}$ **43.** $\frac{9}{22}$ **45.** $\frac{8}{9}$ **47.** $4\sqrt{11}$ **49.** $12\sqrt{11}$ **51.** $90\sqrt{2}$ **53.** $4\sqrt{42}$ **55.** $21\sqrt{6}$ **57.** -28.3 **59.** 91.7 **61.** $13|m|$ **63.** $5x^2\sqrt{5}$ **65.** $-6|t^3|$ **67.** $-12|xy|\sqrt{2x}$ **69.** $-2.2w^2$ **71.** $\frac{a^2|b^3|\sqrt{3}}{6|c|}$ **73.** $\frac{3k^4}{4}$ **75.** $\frac{15x^{20}}{4}$ **77.** $|a-2|$ **79.** $\{7, -7\}$ **81.** $\{\frac{4}{5}, -\frac{4}{5}\}$ **83.** $\{3, -3\}$ **85.** $\{11.5, -11.5\}$ **87.** $\{6.6, -6.6\}$ **89.** no **91.** no **93.** no **95.** 9.43 **97.** 11.18 **99.** 22.36 **101.** 18.03 **103.** 30 **105.** 14 **107.** $72\sqrt{2}$ **109.** $\frac{3}{2}\sqrt{2}$ **111.** $\frac{1}{4}\sqrt{2}$ **113.** $\frac{11}{7}\sqrt{3}$ **115.** $n^2 + 3\sqrt{n}$ **117.** $4\sqrt{3}$ **119.** $7\sqrt{6}$ **121.** $-50\sqrt{2}$ **123.** $\frac{12\sqrt{2} - \sqrt{30}}{6}$ **125.** $\frac{80\sqrt{7} + 21\sqrt{2}}{28}$ **127.** $10\sqrt{3} - \sqrt{30}$ **129.** $3\sqrt{15}$ **131.** -29 **133.** $18 + 8\sqrt{2}$ **135.** $34 - 24\sqrt{2}$ **137.** $20\sqrt{3} - 24\sqrt{2}$ **139.** $252 + 133\sqrt{2}$ **141.** $\frac{2 + \sqrt{3} + 2\sqrt{5} + \sqrt{15}}{-4}$ **143.** $\frac{3}{8}$ **145.** $\frac{16}{25}$ **147.** 83 **149.** 3 **151.** $\frac{2}{5}$ **153.** 45

Chapter 12, pages 631-632 **1.** $\{\frac{5}{7}, -\frac{5}{7}\}$ **3.** no solution **5.** $\{4, -4\}$ **7.** $\{\sqrt{3}, -\sqrt{3}\}$ **9.** $\{-1, -9\}$ **11.** $\{-4 + 3\sqrt{3}, -4 - 3\sqrt{3}\}$ **13.** $\{-7 + \sqrt{21}, -7 - \sqrt{21}\}$ **15.** $\left\{\frac{1 + 2\sqrt{6}}{3}, \frac{1 - 2\sqrt{6}}{3}\right\}$ **17.** $\{13, -1\}$ **19.** $\{-1, -15\}$ **21.** $\{6 + \sqrt{246}, 6 - \sqrt{246}\}$; $\{21.7, -9.7\}$ **23.** $\left\{\frac{3 + \sqrt{29}}{3}, \frac{3 - \sqrt{29}}{2}\right\}$; $\{4.2, -1.2\}$ **25.** $\{3, 7\}$ **27.** $\{-\frac{7}{2}, 2\}$ **29.** $\{-\frac{5}{2}, 2\}$ **31.** $\left\{\frac{-7 + \sqrt{37}}{2}, \frac{-7 - \sqrt{37}}{2}\right\}$; $\{-0.5, -6.6\}$ **33.** $\left\{\frac{5 + \sqrt{37}}{2}, \frac{5 - \sqrt{37}}{2}\right\}$; $\{5.6, -0.6\}$ **35.** $\{1, \frac{2}{3}\}$ **37.** $\left\{\frac{-3 + \sqrt{89}}{20}, \frac{-3 - \sqrt{89}}{20}\right\}$; $\{0.3, -0.6\}$ **39.** $\left\{\frac{7 + \sqrt{57}}{2}, \frac{7 - \sqrt{57}}{2}\right\}$; $\{7.3, -0.3\}$ **41.** no real roots **43.** no real roots **45.** 2 roots **47. a.** 0 points **b.** below **49.** $\{-3, -4\}$ **51.** $\{0, \frac{9}{5}\}$ **53.** $\{-4 + \sqrt{13}, -4 - \sqrt{13}\}$ **55.** $\left\{\frac{-2 + \sqrt{10}}{6}, \frac{-2 - \sqrt{10}}{6}\right\}$ **57.** $\left\{\frac{4 + 2\sqrt{31}}{9}, \frac{4 - 2\sqrt{31}}{9}\right\}$ **59.** $\left\{\frac{1 + \sqrt{7}}{6}, \frac{1 - \sqrt{7}}{6}\right\}$ **61.** $\left\{\frac{-5 + \sqrt{13}}{2}, \frac{-5 - \sqrt{13}}{2}\right\}$ **63.** 22.2 cm by 3.7 cm **65.** 14 m

EXTRA PRACTICE: Problem-Solving

Chapter 1, page 633 ***(1-7)*** **1.** 225 km **3.** 8 games **5.** 19

Chapter 2, page 633 ***(2-3)*** **1.** 38 yd **3.** $205 **5.** 10 A.M. ***(2-4)*** **1.** 2.52° **3.** 28 blocks **5.** 397 m below sea level

Chapter 3, page 634 ***(3-1)*** **1.** -18 **3.** 58 **5.** $747 ***(3-2)*** **1.** -34 **3.** 30¢/kg **5.** 12 cm ***(3-4)*** **1.** 12 **3.** $124 **5.** 16 nickels, 12 dimes, 8 quarters ***(3-5)*** **1.** -9, -8 **3.** 12 **5.** 7, 9, 11 ***(3-6)*** **1.** Kevin is 18; Karen is 6 **3.** Zachary is 15; father is 40 **5.** Ryan is 4; Amy is 2; Becky is 6 ***(3-7)*** **1.** 13 quarters, 35 dimes **3.** 7.5 h **5.** 36 quarters

Chapter 4, page 636 ***(4-8)*** **1.** 2.5 h **3.** 2400 km **5.** 7 P.M. ***(4-9)*** **1.** 11 m by 7 m **3.** 9 m by 5 m **5.** 60 cm by 50 cm ***(4-10)*** **1.** no solution **3.** no solution **5.** -5, -4, -3

Chapter 5, page 638 ***(5-13)*** **1.** -12 or 11 **3.** 20 cm by 12 cm **5.** 8 m by 4 m

Chapter 7, page 638 ***(7-1)*** **1.** 50, 75 **3.** 40, 60, 100 **5.** 180 coins ***(7-2)*** **1.** $7 **3.** $167.50 **5.** 180 lb ***(7-3)*** **1.** Juan is 16; Sylvia is 14 **3.** Bart is 14; mother is 42 **5.** 20 dimes ***(7-4)*** **1.** $\frac{3}{4}$ or $\frac{4}{3}$ **3.** $\frac{1}{3}$ **5.** 50 km/h ***(7-5)*** **1.** $10.50 **3.** $40 **5.** $630 ***(7-6)*** **1.** 35% **3.** 1475 people **5.** $9600 ***(7-7)*** **Chemistry** **1.** 80 L **3.** 25.6% **Grocery** **1.** 40 L cranberry, 80 L apple **3.** $1.75/lb **Investment and Wages** **1.** $12.50/h **3.** $15,000 ***(7-8)*** **1.** $\frac{11}{15}$ **3.** 13 h 20 min **5.** 54 min ***(7-9)*** **1.** 1.28 s **3.** 2.03×10^4 s **5.** 6×10^{-5} cm ***(7-10)*** **1. a.** 10,000 people **b.** 9709 people **c.** 10,300 people **3.** 61 bacteria **5.** 6701 people

Chapter 8, page 643 ***(8-5)*** **1.** 32 quarters **3.** 17 by 10 **5.** $\frac{5}{12}$ ***(8-6)*** **1.** 15, 21 **3.** 87 boys **5.** 20 dimes, 18 quarters ***(8-7)*** **1.** 19, 32 **3.** 150 ft **5.** 42 questions ***(8-8)*** **1.** boat, 23 km/h; current, 7 km/h **3.** current, 2 km/h; swimmer, 8 km/h **5.** 200 km/h

Chapter 9, page 644 ***(9-7)*** **1.** 3.1 cm **3.** 33 kg **5.** 226,800 km^2 ***(9-8)*** **1.** 7 h **3.** $1875 **5.** 55 cm ***(9-9)*** **1.** 85.75 m **3.** 1 unit **5.** $\frac{1}{9}$ as great ***(9-10)*** **1.** 6¢ **3.** 5.25 h

Chapter 10, page 646 ***(10-3)*** **1.** 40, 41 **3.** 260 **5.** 90 km/h

Chapter 11, page 647 ***(11-5)*** **1.** 13.6 cm **3.** 4.5 cm **5.** 3.3 m ***(11-6)*** **1.** 53.85 m **3.** 15 cm, 8 cm, 17 cm **5.** 9 cm, 12 cm, 15 cm ***(11-10)*** **1.** 784 **3.** 49 **5.** 30, 32

Chapter 12, page 648 ***(12-6)*** **1.** −6 or 5 **3.** 60 m by 9 m **5.** 90 h, 72 h

APPENDIX: Divide and Average Method

Written Exercises, page 652 **1.** 5.39 **3.** −6.86 **5.** 18.71 **7.** −12.92 **9.** 4.88 **11.** 3.8730 **13.** −6.2450 **15.** −16.5227 **17.** 20.1990 **19.** −6.3797

APPENDIX: Presenting Statistical Data

Written Exercises, page 666 **1.** 13, 15, 18, 20, 21, 22, 25, 27, 32, 33, 34, 34, 35, 36, 37, 40, 41, 42, 47

3.

2	7, 9
3	8, 9, 6, 9
4	2, 5, 4, 7, 0, 9
5	3, 0, 6

5.

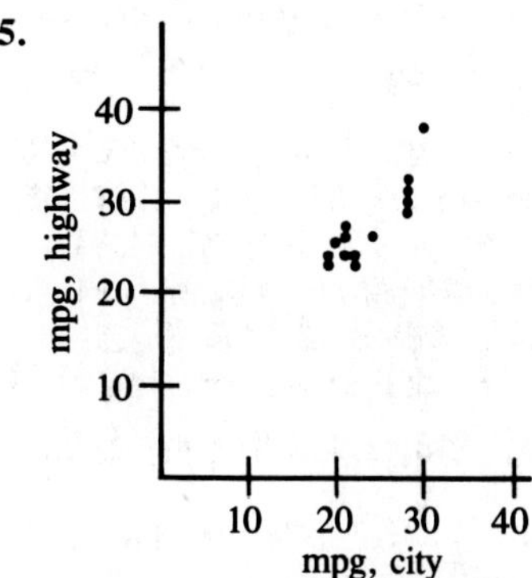

7. 26, 24, 30, 38, 23 **9.** Answers will vary.

APPENDIX: Measures of Variation

Written Exercises, pages 668–669 **1.** 6, 6, 2 **3.** 0, 4, 0 **5. a.** 1 **b.** −0.8 **c.** −1.8 **d.** 0.6 **e.** 0 **f.** 2.8 **7.** Class A **9.** 94